The Life of Bacteria

KENNETH V. THIMANN

Higgins Professor of Biology

Harvard University

The Life of Bacteria

THEIR GROWTH,

METABOLISM, AND RELATIONSHIPS

SECOND EDITION

The Macmillan Company, New York

Collier-Macmillan Limited, London

Fifth Printing, 1967

Library of Congress catalog card number: 63–15263

The Macmillan Company, New York
Collier-Macmillan Canada, Ltd., Toronto, Ontario

Printed in the United States of America

"Lieve God, wat zijnder al wonderen in soo een kleyn schepsel!"*

LEEUWENHOEK'S DRAUGHTSMAN
(Letter No. 76, Oct. 15, 1693)

"The most important discoveries of the laws, methods and progress of Nature have nearly always sprung from the examination of the smallest objects which she contains."

J. B. LAMARCK
Philosophie Zoologique, 1809

* "Dear God, what marvels there are in so small a creature!"

Preface to the Second Edition

Seven years is a long time in microbiology. When the first edition of this book was being completed seven years ago, the rate of progress was considered "stimulating," but since then it has become explosive. Journals which were no more than healthy infants at that time—some indeed which were not even born—are now bulging with solid and extensive research reports, a very large number of them dealing with microorganisms. The genetics of bacteria, which came to life only in the very late 1940's, is now one of the major divisions of our subject. But perhaps the greatest change is the swing of interest toward the synthetic processes in bacteria—the syntheses of all the large and small molecules of the cell—which have taken over much of the center of the stage, where formerly the destructive actions exerted by bacteria on their surroundings were dominant.

These changes have necessitated many alterations in the book. In the first place, all the topics have been brought up to date, and since there are very few indeed that have not undergone notable advance, not many pages have escaped some reworking. Next, a chapter on inheritance has been added, and genetical material elsewhere in the book, e.g., in sections on the nucleus, on conjugation, on viruses, and on mutagenic effects of dyes and radiations, has been expanded. Third, routes and mechanisms of syntheses have been treated in some detail. These have not been assembled into one chapter or section, for such a unit would have been impossibly heterogeneous; instead they have been integrated with the corresponding discussions of metabolism, amino acid syntheses being treated along with deamination, bacterial lipids and their formation along with the related butyric and caproic fermentations, syntheses of aromatic compounds along with their breakdown by Pseudomonads, and synthesis of carotenoids and pyrrole pigments along with the photosynthetic bacteria that carry them out. The synthesis of proteins and enzymes was felt important enough to be assigned most of a long chapter to itself, and indeed aspects of it appear in more than one place.

Among other topics needing completely new treatment may be mentioned: bacterial cell walls, bacterial pigments, the rhizosphere, pentose fermentations, the mechanisms of propionic fermentation, of nitrogen fixation, of solute uptake and permeation, of antibiotic action, and of autotrophy. The miscellaneous nature of these topics itself indicates something of the wholesale extent to which the text has had to be rewritten.

All these changes have inevitably expanded the book, even though a few topics could be condensed. To some extent the rapid accretion of scientific knowledge has the same effect on all our books, and five-volume treatises are now the order of the day. "Let me have men about me that are fat," said Julius Caesar, and the same is surely a sound criterion for scientific books, for a book that does not pass on a good share of the accumulated information of the last quarter century hardly merits shelf-room now, and corpulence is at least a *prima facie* guide to usefulness. It is earnestly hoped that its increased size will not make *The Life of Bacteria* less useful for teaching, at least at the advanced level.

Again, I must thank numerous friends and correspondents for valuable criticisms and for the loan of figures; I particularly thank my colleague Paul R. Levine for criticizing the chapter on genetics and Professor Donald D. Woods of Oxford for many constructive suggestions on a variety of topics.

KENNETH V. THIMANN

Preface to the First Edition

The accelerated pace of biological research is stimulating to those in it, but discouraging to those who are endeavoring to put together its glittering fragments into a balanced and satisfying picture. Because this book has been in preparation for more than fifteen years, with numerous breaks (including a complete one of over four years for the war), the subject matter has had to be continually changed. Samuel Johnson lamented in 1755 that "no dictionary of a living tongue can ever be perfect, since, while it is hastening to publication, some words are budding, and some falling away." The same is true for a book on a living science, whose ideas and conclusions are constantly being modified.

Furthermore, the emphasis and the perspective have shifted considerably during the book's preparation. In part this is due to a shift in biology itself, but in part also it represents a change in the conception of the book. Originally written largely to fill a gap (there was no full-length treatment of the physiology of microorganisms at that time), the book slowly came to be envisaged as a text for an advanced course. Meanwhile the gap was partially filled, first by the several editions of the late Marjorie Stephenson's *Bacterial Metabolism* and more recently by several other books, especially those of J. R. Porter (1946), E. F. Gale (1948), and Werkman and Wilson (1951).

There is reason to believe, however, that the gap has not been completely filled. Indeed, it has widened, for it has gradually become apparent that bacteriology as a science is being blurred out, and instead students are being taught such specialties as bacteriological chemistry, agricultural microbiology, dairy bacteriology, industrial fermentations, and medical bacteriology (arrogantly called "bacteriology" by many, mistaking the part for the whole). "The division of science into sciences," writes George Sarton, the historian of science, "is to a large extent artificial, and apparent only in concrete cases. It is clear that a collector of butterflies need not study thermodynamics, and that an observer of meteors can do very well without botany or palaeontology. It is also clear that the great mass of our scientists and technicians are so deeply specialized that they can no longer see the wood for the trees, or the tree for the twigs."

The development of the specialties has certainly made it next to impossible to see bacteriology as a whole, let alone the still broader topic of microbiology. In the special case of bacteriology, there is an additional unfortunate result, namely, that it is not thought of as a subject in itself but as an adjunct to other activities. To some biochemists, bacteria are merely something which grows on agar and which can be used for the preparation of enzymes or for the assay of vitamins. There are medical, industrial, and agricultural counterparts of this viewpoint. Thus the science by specialization has not only lost its unity (that happens to nearly all the sciences), but it has lost its self-consciousness.

Now while it is only within recent years that great progress has been made in understanding the life of bacteria, microbiology is not a particularly modern science. Its roots go deep into man's simple needs and activities—the yield of crops, the making of bread, the fermenting of wine and cheese, and the preservation of food. These ancient arts, the applied microbiology of the past, have made a profound impression on our culture, which needs to be borne in mind as background to the modern scientific development.

For these reasons the book has come to be an attempt not only to see bacteriology as a whole—that is, as a branch of biology—but also to see it in its perspective as a development from the past and as an active area of modern investigation. How far these dual aims may have been achieved it will be for the reader to determine. The original idea of including all of microbiology has been abandoned as too sweeping; a broader mind will be required to accomplish this very necessary synthesis. The book deals with the structure and activities of the bacteria, and with their influence on the surrounding world.

But even with limitations to the bacteria, the question of where to draw boundaries is a difficult one. No apology need be made for treating some aspects of the physiology of fungi along with that of the bacteria. The fermentations, for instance, can hardly be treated in a unitary manner without the alcoholic fermentation of yeast, the study of which has largely pioneered the unraveling of carbohydrate metabolism. This and certain other activities of yeasts, which are interwoven with similar activities of bacteria, have had to be treated in detail. There is a corresponding problem in presenting photosynthesis, though it is somewhat eased by the clear-cut differences between the process in bacteria and that in other plants; however, even here it was found necessary to draw on the behavior of the algae at some points. The field of the viruses and bacteriophages seemed too large to attempt to bring within the scope of the book, and accordingly these entities have been given brief treatment at the outset followed only by occasional consideration wherever they could not well be excluded.

The complexly interrelated state of modern biology makes the drawing of area-boundaries *within* the field of bacteriology almost as difficult as plotting its external limits. Once the general plan of the book is laid down, the problem of subdivision in large part resolves itself into choosing topics around which to group the facts. Thus some topics appear as chapter heads which might not be expected to do so, while others become divided up. Nutrition, for instance, is taken up not as a whole but in connection with amino acids and vitamins in one place, uptake of materials in another, and the synthesis of assimilates and of protoplasm in a third. In the same way genetics appears in several places, under cellular fusion, adaptation, transference of characters, and so forth. Such points of arrangement are to some extent arbitrary and every author might make a different choice. In this book the dominant theme of the second and third parts is the natural processes caused by bacteria, and many details of selection and arrangement stem from this plan.

The enormous and growing literature on the subject is very difficult to cover completely, and equally difficult to present selectively. Naturally, advantage has been taken of reviews in many cases, but not in all, for reviews, however competent, seldom give the "flavor" of the original research, and the writer has found as a matter of teaching practice that the detailed reading of one original paper often gives more insight into a subject than the coverage of twenty times as much literature through reviews. Recourse has therefore been had primarily to original papers, and students are urged to do the same. For this reason, rather large bibliographies are given with each chapter, and references rich in additional citations are marked with an asterisk. The long bibliography has the disadvantage that titles of papers cannot be quoted, but this is partly offset by giving first and last pages, to indicate length of papers, and by giving titles in the case of reviews and dissertations.

Although a very large number of facts has unavoidably been included, it is still hoped that the book will be found useful for teaching. Naturally, it can be used only where a course beyond the elementary is given. In spite of the widespread adoption of General Education, some biology courses are still given at a genuinely advanced level. The physiology of bacteria can be taught only as an advanced course, for several reasons. One is that no physiological subject can be presented adequately in these days without a good working knowledge of organic chemistry. This book assumes such a knowledge, and organic chemistry is used throughout without introduction or explanation. In the writer's experience, however, the average biology student's command of physical chemistry is considerably less fluent, and for this reason thermodynamics and other physiochemical matters have been introduced more gingerly and with what may seem to some readers excessive explanation.

Another reason for postponing the physiology of bacteria to the senior or even the first graduate year is the need for some knowledge of the other plant groups, especially the fungi and algae. An elementary acquaintance with these has also been taken for granted in the book, and a more than elementary one would be of great value in setting the subject into perspective and into relation with the rest of experimental biology.

In addition to teaching the subject, the author has had the advantage of many discussions with research workers, and in particular of critical reviews of some of the chapters by outstanding experts. The chapter on bacteria in relation to other organisms was reviewed by E. G. Pringsheim; that on deamination by Ernest Gale; that on oxidations by F. Lipmann; that on the butyric fermentation by H. A. Barker; that on the oxidative fermentations by R. Y. Stanier; that on fermentations using inorganic hydrogen acceptors by A. J. Kluyver; that on antibiotics by J. W. Foster; that on photosynthesis by C. S. Yocum; and the three chapters on the propionic fermentation, photosynthesis, and autotrophic life, as well as an early draft of Chapter I, by C. B. van Niel. The criticisms of these men were given without mercy, and many of them were extensive. Their suggestions have been adopted wherever possible. Nevertheless the book cannot claim the weight of their authority, and the responsibility for everything in it must be the author's.

Acknowledgment must be made to the many workers who have supplied me with original prints or negatives for the plates. Many of them have gone to considerable trouble to locate and sort out long-forgotten illustrations which seemed to me appropriate. Some of those printed before the war were unfortunately not available, but this loss has been offset in part by the advent of the electron microscope with its splendid contributions to our knowledge of the anatomy of bacteria. The author desires to thank also the many editors and publishers who have kindly permitted the reproduction of figures. The sources of these are acknowledged in the legends. In some cases figures have been redrawn, data replotted, or other liberties taken for which tolerance is earnestly requested.

Here I want to thank my tireless and extremely efficient secretary, Mrs. J. Lockwood Chamberlin, whose ability to read and type heavily "corrected" and well-nigh illegible manuscript has been invaluable. And lastly I owe a great deal to my wife, without whose patient understanding and encouragement the book would never have been brought to completion.

Kenneth V. Thimann

Note on Nomenclature

The naming of bacteria is a matter for endless discussion. Though a "rose by any other name" may be acceptable to the poet, it is rejected with horror by the systematist, because the name implies assignment to a definite genus and species. Agreement on classification of the bacteria is far from being reached, however, and for a good reason—namely, that it is not clear what constitutes a species. Among higher organisms the concept of species rests on the phenomena of sexuality; for example, the zoologist Ernst Mayr defines a species as a population which regularly interbreeds. The bacteria, in which sexuality is only one of several types of genetic interchange, are not subject to such clear-cut and practical definitions. "Species," as recorded in the literature, may differ from one another only in size, in the possession of a single enzyme, or in the hosts they parasitize. Modern geneticists recognize enough "strains" of *E. coli* to staff a whole family of the older taxonomic type, with subdivision into dozens of genera and species. Furthermore, the criteria of species are different in different groups, and in the hands of different taxonomists.

If the border line of a species is difficult to draw, that of a genus is equally so. Hence the names of bacteria are constantly changing. While these problems are taken up again in the closing chapter, they are mentioned here to justify a certain conservatism in the use of names. Some readers may be surprised to find that the author has chosen not to adhere to Bergey's classification slavishly, but the fact is that "Bergey" is not universally accepted, especially outside of America. For this reason, older names which seem more logical have often been retained. Generally, however, the Bergey synonymy has been given as well, so that there should be no difficulty in recognizing the organisms referred to. This is particularly to be noted in the treatment of the lactic and the coliform bacteria (Chaps. XII and XIV). It is hoped that lovers of Bergey will be no more shocked at finding their sacred text occasionally not followed than medical bacteriologists will be to find that some of their "Bacilli" have been assigned to quite other and varied groups.

A minor departure has been made also in the use of abbreviations. The common practice of using a single letter for the genus is quite unsatisfactory. The abbreviation *C.* may mean Corynebacterium, Clostridium, Chromatium, or Cytophaga (to offer only a few choices). This may be acceptable in scientific papers, which commonly deal only with the members of a single genus, but in a book like the present, where many genera may be discussed in juxtaposition, it would be much too confusing. Accordingly, two or more letters have been adopted for most genera. As far as possible these have been chosen for their immediate recognizability, and in some cases they are already in the older literature. One simple rule is that *B.* means Bacterium whether alone or in compound names, so that *Mycob.* (pronounced "myco-bee") naturally means Mycobacterium. *Bac.* similarly means Bacillus. Other abbreviations are equally obvious. A partial list of those adopted throughout the book follows.

Partial List of Abbreviations for Organisms Used in This Book

A.	Acetobacter	Ms.	Methanosarcina
Act.	Actinomyces	Mycob.	Mycobacterium
Aerob.	Aerobacter	Myxob.	Myxobacterium
Aerobac.	Aerobacillus		
Asp.	Aspergillus	N.	Neisseria
Azotob. or Az.	Azotobacter	Noc.	Nocardia
		P.	Proteus
B.	Bacterium	Pen.	Penicillium
Bac.	Bacillus	Pr.	Propionibacterium
Butyrib.	Butyribacterium	Ps.	Pseudomonas
C.	Corynebacterium	R.	Rhizobium
Chl.	Chlorobium	Rh.	Rhizopus
Chr.	Chromatium	Rhodo-ps.	Rhodo-pseudomonas
Cl.	Clostridium	Rhodo-sp.	Rhodo-spirillum
Cyt.	Cytophaga		
		S.	Salmonella
D.	Diplococcus	Sacch.	Saccharomyces
		Sc.	Streptococcus
E.	Escherichia	Sp.	Spirillum
		Sporocyt.	Sporocytophaga
F.	Fusarium	Sporov.	Sporovibrio
		Str.	Streptomyces
H.	Hemophilus		
		T.	Thiobacillus
L.	Lactobacillus		
Ln.	Leuconostoc	V.	Vibrio
M.	Micrococcus		
Mb.	Methanobacterium	Zygosacch.	Zygosaccharomyces
Mm.	Micromonospora	Zs.	Zymosarcina

Contents

Part Four. Growth and Synthesis

Part One

The Morphology and General
Physiology of Bacteria

CHAPTER I

How Microorganisms Have Been
Cultivated and Studied

The past, the infinite greatness of the past!
For what is the present, after all, but a growth out of the past?

WALT WHITMAN: *Passage to India*

The world of microorganisms is one of enormous numbers. A handful of soil contains as many microorganisms as there are human beings in the world. How, then, can we ever study a single kind separated from all others, and if we could separate it, what chance have we of preserving it free from the contamination of the surrounding multitudes of its fellows?

The development of a technique for studying these smallest members of creation is the result of the combined labors of many men, spread over a period of some 200 years. The methods by which it has been possible to separate microbes from their surroundings, to cultivate and to study them, can best be described in the order in which they were arrived at, because the problems that arise in the growth of an experimental science can only be understood in the light of the knowledge that was available at the time.

1. EARLIEST IDEAS

Belief in the existence of invisibly small microorganisms goes back to very early days. Varro in the second century B.C. discusses the possibility of contagion by such creatures, and the idea was familiar to many of the Roman and Arabic writers on medicine. Lucretius, famed for his atomic view of matter, believed that living things arose from a sort of atom, or seed. In *De Rerum Natura*, about 75 B.C., he suggests that even the plague must be caused by a kind of atom. For, "just as there are seeds helpful to our life, so, for sure, others fly about that cause disease and death" (Book VI). This view might be considered a statement of the microbial nature of infection, except that the "seeds" are not regarded as living organisms.

Furthermore, "because things are all produced from fixed seeds, each thing is born . . . out of that which has in it the substance and first bodies of each" (Book I). On the other hand, the "seeds" do not contain all the properties of the finished organism; sensory properties such as color and smell are considered to arise only from combinations of the seeds. Elsewhere he considers that life can also arise *de novo*, since even "seeds" have to come from something: "What we perceive to have feeling consists nevertheless of first beginnings [*principiis*] that have no feeling. Why, you may see worms arise all alive from stinking dung when the drenched earth becomes rotten from excessive rains."

It is clear that in this passage, so often misquoted and misunderstood, two different points are being introduced. The first deals with the rise of new properties in a system, i.e., the view that the combination of existing factors may give rise to a new property which is not present in any of the factors separately (cf. for instance Smuts' *Holism*). The second, which is evidently meant to be a specific instance of the general case, describes the spontaneous appearance of living from nonliving systems, and lays the basis for a view which was to persist for over 1500 years.

The ideas of Lucretius, particularly about the nature of the ultimate particles of matter, i.e., the atoms, were after a long eclipse brought back into prominence by Giordano Bruno at the end of the sixteenth century. They strongly influenced Robert Boyle and probably also Isaac Newton and John Dalton. However, mere reasoning that microorganisms exist cannot substitute for the proof of their actuality. It was the discovery of the magnifying power of a lens, described by Seneca about A.D. 63, studied by Alhazen (ibn al-Haitham) in the tenth century, and developed by Galileo in the seventeenth century, that made possible the demonstration of microorganisms.

2. THE FIRST OBSERVATIONS

The first man to make a lens powerful enough to see the unicellular organisms was Antonie van Leeuwenhoek, of Delft, Holland (1632–1723), who used a powerful convex lens with the object placed just inside the focal length (see Fig. I–1). This arrangement produces a greatly enlarged virtual image. With this simple microscope he was able to observe many "animalcules," including protozoa, both free-living and parasitic in the guts of animals, filamentous fungi, and globular bodies which we now know as yeasts. He made marvelous observations of the structure of plants, particularly of seeds and embryos, and discovered the spermatozoa of animals. His works were embellished with fine drawings made under his supervision by competent artists. In 1676 he observed still smaller animalcules, the bacteria, first in pepper infusion and later in scrapings from his teeth and elsewhere. The follow-

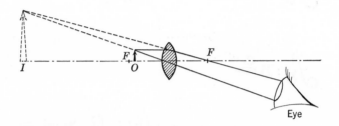

FIGURE I–1

Diagram of the simple microscope. The object O, placed within the focal length, F, is seen as the greatly enlarged virtual image, I. In this and Figure I–4 the Huygens construction is used; a ray parallel to the axis is bent to pass through F, and a ray through the lens center is unrefracted.

ing sentences (from letter No. 18, translated by C. Dobell, 1932) contain the gist of the discovery:

> The fourth sort of little animals which drifted among the three sorts aforesaid[1] were incredibly small, nay, so small in my sight that I judged that even if 100 of these very small animals lay stretched out one against another, they could not reach to the length of a grain of coarse sand;[2] and if this be true, then ten hundred thousand of these living creatures could scarce equal the bulk of a coarse sand grain.

Leeuwenhoek's discoveries were communicated by letter to the Royal Society, a particularly appropriate method of publication since (as Andrade points out) "it was insistence upon the value of experiment which was the particular service of the men who founded the Royal Society."

[1] These "aforesaid" were protozoa, tentatively identified by Dobell as Bodo (a flagellate), and Cyclidium and Vorticella (ciliates).

[2] Described elsewhere as $\frac{1}{30}$ of an inch in diameter, or 850 μ, so the bacteria were less than 8 μ long.

Figure I–2, which is a copy of one of the drawings from a later letter (1683), shows bacteria from his teeth, and includes his observation of the motility of bacteria.

He was also greatly impressed by their enormous numbers, calculating that more than 10,000 of them were present in a single drop of water. He even made the important discovery (1680) that bacteria may live and multiply in the almost complete absence of air, when

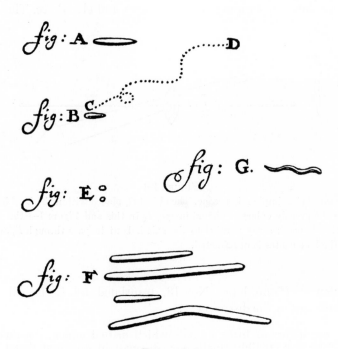

FIGURE I–2

The first drawings of bacteria. Preparations from the human mouth. From Leeuwenhoek's letter No. 39 of Sept. 17, 1683, enlarged 1.5 ×. (From C. Dobell, 1932, Plate XXIV.)

he sealed up pepper water in a glass tube and opened it after five days to discover many "animalcules" in it. The extent and excellence of his observations were made possible only by the good quality of his lenses. Leeuwenhoek's lens, in the microscope which is preserved at Utrecht, magnified 280 times and still resolves structures about 2 μ wide, even though it is now somewhat scratched (van Cittert, 1932). The focal length was less than 1 mm, and some device was therefore needed to bring the object into focus. This was achieved by mounting the drop of liquid or other object on a screw below the lens (see Fig. I–3). He made at least 150 of these little microscopes.[3] The compound microscope, which is capable of greater magnification and certainly more convenient to use, had been invented earlier, in 1590, by Zacharias Jansen[4] and was used in 1630 by F. Stelluti to study the

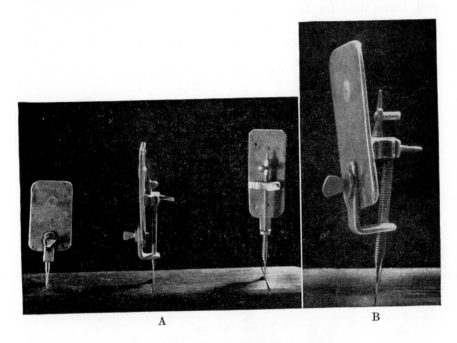

A   B

FIGURE I–3

A. The three Leeuwenhoek microscopes at the National Museum for History of Science, Leiden, Holland. Two are of brass and one of silver.

B. Close-up of the silver microscope showing the point on which the object (usually a drop of liquid) is placed and the screws for adjusting it with reference to the lens. The lens is contained in the depression between the two plates. (Courtesy National Museum for History of Science, Leiden.)

honey bee and the weevil, in what is probably the first work of scientific microscopy. However, the models produced before 1800 were not equal in resolving power to the best simple lenses. As Dobell says (1932, p. 52), "[Leeuwenhoek's] observations excited the greatest interest— but that was all. Nobody seriously attempted to repeat or extend them.

[3] A number were given to the Royal Society, but these have since disappeared.

[4] Jansen's and other early models used spectacle lenses, spectacles having been made in North Germany and in Italy since the early fourteenth century.

The superexcellence of his lenses, combined with the exceptional keenness of his eye, killed all competition."

In the compound microscope (Fig. I–4) the object is placed beyond the focal length of the object lens, L_1, and the enlarged (inverted) real image which results is used as an object for the eyepiece, L_2, giving a very much enlarged virtual image. With such an instrument, although with lenses doubtless far inferior to those of Leeuwenhoek, Hooke had observed filamentous fungi in 1667. His instrument is shown in Figure I–5. Hooke's descriptions include one of a Mucor which he considered to

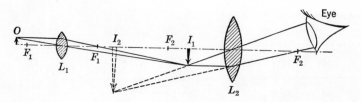

FIGURE I–4

Diagram of the compound microscope. The object O placed beyond the focal length F_1 of the object lens L_1 gives an enlarged real image I_1 which falls just within the focal length of the eyepiece L_2. This image is then viewed in the same manner as in the simple microscope, appearing as the large virtual image I_2.

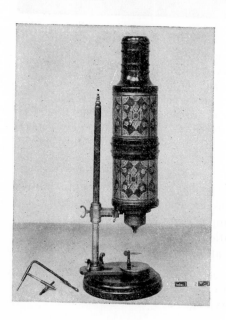

FIGURE I–5

Robert Hooke's own microscope, a compound instrument. (From an exhibit in the Science Museum, London. British Crown Copyright.)

have been "generated by tissues of higher plants." Of course the large fungi were known much earlier, and by 1623 Bauhin had described 100 kinds. Later, Micheli (in 1729) grew microfungi (Botrytis and Rhizopus) through the whole life cycle from "seed" to "seed." With a compound microscope, also, Müller, in Denmark, observed and described in 1786 a number of bacteria and other microorganisms. The modern compound microscope contains one improvement of great importance over Müller's instrument, namely, a device for illumination of the object with a wide cone of light. This "condenser," due to Ernst Abbé, is necessary when large magnifications are being used in order that the light intensity may be sufficient to see with. Other improvements consist in the use of achromatic lens combinations and dark-field illumination devices.

3. THE SPONTANEOUS GENERATION CONTROVERSY

An understanding of the true importance of microorganisms in the world only began as a result of the controversy on whether life could develop out of lifeless matter or not. In the beginnings of modern science two schools of thought were to be found—those who, taking Lucretius at his crudest, thought animals could develop from dead matter ("spontaneous generation") and those who believed that life comes only from life—"*omne vivum ex vivo.*" The ancients, believing in spontaneous generation, gave recipes for the preparation of worms from hairs or of mice from meal. Opposition to this view was expressed by Redi, who in 1668 showed that the apparent spontaneous generation of maggots from meat was in reality due to the visits of flies, which laid eggs on the meat. However, even as late as 1745, the celebrated experiments of Needham provided strong evidence in support of spontaneous generation.

Needham boiled meat extract in a flask, stoppered it, and found after some days that living and moving creatures swarmed in it. Since it was generally known that living things are killed by boiling, it followed that these creatures must have developed spontaneously from the meat. A similar argument was made for the appearance of mites in cheese. However, more careful experiments by Spallanzani in 1776 led to the opposite conclusion. He made an infusion in the same way as Needham, but used various kinds of seeds as the source of organic matter. These gave rise, on standing, to many organisms, but Spallanzani made a distinction between the larger ones, which were destroyed by boiling for one-half minute, and the "microbes of the lowest order," which survived boiling and developed even when the vials were hermetically sealed. He showed that the heat, which "completely devastated" the infusions so far as larger organisms were concerned, could not be acting merely by driving out the air; indeed, the growing microbes actually developed a positive pressure in the sealed tubes. Finally, after many trials, he found that if the infusions after being hermetically sealed were boiled for as much as 45 minutes, no microbes at all developed. Thereafter, if left sealed, the vials could be kept indefinitely without the development of any organisms. On the other hand, if unheated air were admitted, the infusion soon became putrid. The validity of his inference, that the seeds or "first beginnings" of the living creatures must be present in the air, was not generally accepted; rather was it supposed that the air in the flask had been impaired in quality by heating and so would not support the life of the microorganisms. Nevertheless, his experiments were repeated from a practical viewpoint by a Parisian cook, François Appert, who readily found that fruit and vegetables, by being placed in hermetically sealed jars and then in boiling water, could be preserved indefinitely. He thus not only became wealthy,[5] but also founded a major industry—canning.

The objection to Spallanzani's conclusion was virtually removed by an experiment of Schultze (1836), who attached two outlets to the flask of meat infusion, one connected to a vessel containing sulfuric acid and the other to a similar vessel with potassium hydroxide solution. The connections were made, after prolonged boiling, while steam was still vigorously escaping. Subsequently fresh air was very slowly drawn through the solutions into the flask twice daily for three months. The meat infusion remained uncontaminated throughout, all microorganisms being killed by the passage through sulfuric acid. In 1837, Theodor Schwann performed a similar experiment, but drew the air through a bath of fusible metal, and showed that both meat broth and sugary solutions could be kept indefinitely. Ordinary air at once caused the development of bacteria in the broth and of yeast in the sweet liquid. His conclusion shows complete understanding of the situation: ". . . . The germs of the fungi and infusoria, which according to this view *are present in the air*, are destroyed by glowing out the air. Hence putrefaction must be due to the fact that these germs, in developing and nourishing themselves at the cost of the organic substance, bring about such a decomposition of this that the phenomena of putrefaction arise."[6]

The technique of such experiments was greatly simplified by the discovery of Schröder and Dusch (1853) that, instead of sealing up the

---

[5] The French government in 1810 awarded him a prize of 12,000 francs for making the process public.

[6] Translation and italics mine.

flask after boiling, it was sufficient to close the open end with a plug of cotton. The air passing through the narrow tortuous spaces in the cotton is effectively filtered from all microorganisms in it.

These early experiments thus laid the foundation of the technique for cultivating microorganisms. The first step is to make a suitable medium and to free it from all microorganisms by heating; the second is to keep the medium sterile, i.e., to prevent microorganisms from entering.

Why did the scientific public not accept the conclusions of Spallanzani, Schultze, and Schwann? Partly because the experiments could not always be repeated. As we know now, some organisms resist heating at 100° C, even for several hours. It must be remembered that the opponents of spontaneous generation were endeavoring to prove a negative, i.e., to prove that it does *not* occur, and therefore a single positive experiment greatly damaged their case. Koch's study of anthrax bacilli, carried out later, made it clear that the spores of some bacteria are extremely resistant to heat and can only be killed by heating for 20 minutes at 120° C. At present, of course, media are almost invariably sterilized by heating under pressure to 120° C for 15 to 20 minutes. Occasionally, if the medium contains large numbers of spores, a few may even survive this treatment (cf. Chap. IV).

However, another and perhaps more important reason why the conclusions could not be accepted was undoubtedly the absence of any general theory underlying the whole question. The inference from the fact that spontaneous generation does not occur is that *all putrefaction is due to the action of microorganisms*. This great generalization, although clearly formulated by Schwann in 1837, was only made acceptable to scientific thought by the genius of Louis Pasteur, who combined scientific ability with persuasiveness and a sense of drama. Pasteur (1862) boiled infusions in an apparatus such that, when the vessel cooled, the entering air was first heated thoroughly in a furnace and then cooled in a tube surrounded by water (see Fig. I–6). Under these conditions the infusion remained clear. Further, adopting a suggestion of Balard, the chemist, he used flasks to which, after introduction of the infusion, a curved side tube was attached (Fig. I–7). In this case, providing the initial heating had been sufficient, the infusion remained clear indefinitely, but it decayed as soon as the swan neck was removed. The microbes in the entering air were evidently deposited on the wet glass surface of the long tube. He confirmed the experiments of Schröder and Dusch, boiled meat infusion remaining clear in flasks closed with cotton plugs. Further, he made the plugs of guncotton (cellulose nitrate), dissolved them afterward in alcohol, and thus set free the germs which they had caught from the air. On microscopic examination these particles were shown to include various sorts of globules resembling the spores of fungi and bacteria.

Pasteur's experiments, like earlier ones, could not always be repeated. Jeffries Wyman in America made many attempts, but got infections even when the vessels were hermetically sealed.[7] In France, Pouchet also failed and challenged Pasteur to repeat the result. This led to a lengthy controversy. The reason for the difficulty lay, as stated above, in the heat resistance of spores. From the historical viewpoint,

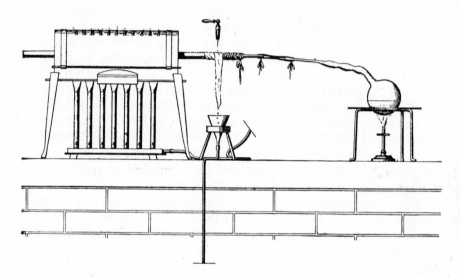

FIGURE I–6

Pasteur's experiment. The flask containing nutrient solution is boiled, and on cooling, air enters through the long heated tube and is cooled by the wet cloth wrapped around it. (From L. Pasteur, 1862.)

however, this appears only as a minor blemish on the broad picture. Pasteur's experiments, in principle, finally settled the spontaneous generation controversy. For this reason it is of some interest to see how he was led to carry out these experiments.

[7] The following experimental notes, which are typical of many, are taken from one of Wyman's (unpublished) notebooks.

"Mar. 29, 1865.

"10 flasks with beef juice boiled and filtered then sealed and boiled 15'.—30th no change. 31st no change.

"Ap. 15th. 5 flasks turbid.

"Ap. 17th. Nine flasks have a film, the 10th is turbid but has no film."

(I am indebted to Dr. G. E. Erickson for the opportunity of seeing these.)

Pasteur was primarily a chemist and in 1860 had made the discovery of the relation between stereoisomerism in crystals (potassium tartrate) and the optical rotation of their solutions. He found that the only substances that, when in solution, showed optical activity were those of natural origin, i.e., those derived from living creatures; crystalline salts synthesized in the laboratory had no effect on polarized light. Since in the fermentation of sugar by yeast, optically active amyl alcohol is sometimes produced, Pasteur quite logically came to think of fermentation as the action of a living creature. That yeasts were living organisms had been recognized by numerous observers since Leeuwenhoek, while Cagniard-Latour in 1835 had characterized them as "capable of reproducing themselves by budding, and probably acting on sugar only as a result of their growth." Schwann also showed that the yeast cells *grow* during the fermentation. In Pasteur's later studies

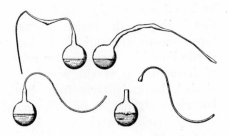

FIGURE I–7
Various forms of flasks with long tubes attached. At lower right a flask has been opened, and organisms are developing on the infusion. (From L. Pasteur, 1862.)

of the butyric fermentation and the production of vinegar he again found the processes to be due to the growth and development of specific living organisms, the *"vibrion butyrique"* (Chap. XIV) and *"Mycoderma aceti"* (Chap. XVI), respectively. It was natural, therefore, that he should enter the spontaneous generation controversy firmly convinced that all putrefaction is caused by the admission of microorganisms to the material.

The views of Liebig were opposed completely to this idea, although they also constituted an important generalization. Liebig considered putrefactions and fermentations to be initiated by "ferments" (Latin *fermentum*, from *fervere*, to boil, referring to the evolution of the gas). These ferments consisted of *decomposing* organic matter. The particle of old cheese that, when added to boiled milk, brings about the lactic fermentation, and the piece of bad meat that initiates putrefaction in a clear meat infusion, were considered to be ferments. That yeast was a living organism was in no sense a complication, since it must also die, and in dying decompose, and thus act as a ferment. In their death the yeast cells carried along with them in some way the complex molecules of the fermentable liquid, which were thus broken down. "The yeast of beer, and in general all animal and plant substances undergoing putrefaction, impart to other substances the state of decomposition in which they find themselves."[8]

Pasteur proved, as had Schwann earlier, that the yeast actually grows during the fermentation, and since it had been believed that the yeast arose out of the proteins of the beer and was thus a result rather than a cause, he demonstrated (1860) that fermentation may occur in complete absence of proteins. His additional finding, namely, that the fermentation products included glycerol and succinic acid, made worthless the attempts of Liebig to reduce the reaction to a simple chemical equation. Such an equation had been formulated by Gay-Lussac after his determination of the composition of cane sugar (see Chap. XI); not only is it quite inadequate, but Duclaux in his biography of Pasteur (1920) even claims that Gay-Lussac's results were "cooked" by 2 to 3 per cent. In fine, Pasteur's experiments proved that fermentation is due to the action of microorganisms in the solution, just as "spontaneous generation" is due to the infection of the previously sterile liquid by fermentative microorganisms. Further, a definite kind of fermentation is characteristic of each organism; yeasts produce alcohol, lactic bacteria form lactic acid, *"vibrion butyrique"* forms butyric acid, and so on. The purely chemical view of fermentation was too crude to explain the facts, yet not sufficiently clear in its conceptions to stimulate further research. At the same time it was very close to the truth, since the idea of nonliving ferments, or enzymes, which exert an action only by their presence, was afterward shown to be correct by the experiments of Eduard Buchner, who found that the expressed juice of yeast cells could carry out alcoholic fermentation (see Chap. XI). Furthermore, Pasteur's refusal to consider fermentation as a kind of chemical reaction would sound very peculiar if restated today, when every fermentation is considered to be a chain of catalyzed chemical reactions.

As we saw above, the basic idea needed for the understanding of spontaneous putrefaction is the universal distribution of microorganisms in the air. This idea was substantiated and developed from quite a new direction by the experiments of John Tyndall (1876, 1881).

[8] These views had been expressed before Liebig; apparently they were rather widespread among chemists. Stahl wrote, "Every substance in a state of putrefaction easily transmits this state to another body still free from decay. Thus it is that a body already animated by an internal movement may, with the greatest facility, involve in the same internal movement another body still in repose but disposed by nature to a similar movement." This was called at the time the "molecular-physiological theory of fermentation."

This physicist was much interested in the scattering of light by air and water (the phenomenon now called the "Tyndall effect"). A beam of light in an ordinary room can be seen from the side, and it becomes still more brightly visible if we blow smoke into it. This means that some of the light is being scattered laterally. Tyndall showed that air which has been stored in a clean glass globe for some weeks does not show up a beam of light when viewed from the side; it is "optically empty," the reason being that the scattering of light is in reality due to tiny particles or motes in the air, which settle out slowly when the air is still. In 1869 he showed that air can be made optically empty by

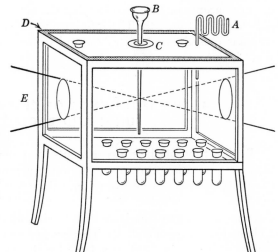

FIGURE I–8
The cabinet for the ex-
periment of John Tyndall
(see text).

passing it slowly through a tight cotton plug. The relation between these findings and those of Schwann and Pasteur was obvious to him; the tiny particles could be none other than the microorganisms. It followed that "optically empty" air ought not to initiate putrefaction, and Tyndall demonstrated this as follows (1876):

A cabinet was constructed with glass windows, a long vertical tube (Fig. I–8, *B*) supported by a piece of sheet rubber (*C*) and plugged, and two finer tubes (as *A*) with many bends, to allow equalization of pressure inside and out. All interior surfaces were spread with glycerin. In the bottom, 12 test tubes were inserted. On September 10, 1875, when the case was closed, a beam of light (*E*) passing through the two side windows was strongly visible from the front, showing that it was full of motes. By September 13 these had settled, and the air was optically empty. Through the central tube fresh urine was now introduced into the test tubes, and a bath of hot brine was brought up underneath so that the urine boiled for five minutes. Other test tubes containing similarly boiled urine stood on the laboratory bench, open to the air. By September 17, i.e., in four days, these open tubes were turbid with bacteria, but the tubes in the cabinet remained clear and transparent for four months. On opening the door all became infected in four days. Many repetitions were made, using meat and fish infusions, all with similar results. In one instance the cabinet was shifted during the experiment and at once one of the tubes became infected (doubtless by dislodgment of dust). On other occasions a drop of infected liquid from the control tubes outside was added to the tubes in the cabinet; they at once became turbid, showing that the air in the cabinet was perfectly able to support growth. The inference was clear: ordinary air normally contains quantities of microbes, and to these all "spontaneous generation" is due.

4. THE BEGINNINGS OF CLASSIFICATION:
FUNGI AND BACTERIA

By the time of these experiments, and the conclusion of the spontaneous generation controversy, immense progress had been made in the study of bacteria and fungi and their role in the world. Beginning in 1601, with Clusius' little *Fungorum historia*, botanists began to describe the larger fungi, and in 1735 Linnaeus established for them a class of *cryptogamic* plants. This became well filled, first by Bulliard's studies of fungi in 1791 and later by the extensive work of Persoon, whose three-volume *Mycologia Europaea* (1822–1828), together with the work of Fries (1821–1832), laid the foundations of our present system of classifying the fungi. The Tulasne brothers (1861–1865) developed the morphology of fungi, emphasizing microscopic structure and its relation to development, and finally in 1866 de Bary began his studies of life cycles which have dominated some parts of mycology ever since.

Less progress was made with the bacteria. Linnaeus first called the bacteria "specia dubia" (doubtful species) and classified them along with the worms! Ehrenberg (1838) continued the studies begun by Müller and recognized definite types, such as the Spirillum, but recognition of the bacteria as a botanical group had to await the patience and application of Ferdinand Cohn (1872–1876). It was Cohn who, after extensive observations, adopted *size* and *shape* as the primary basis for classifying bacteria. This was a logical extension of the system used for the higher plants, but it could only hold if the size and shape of bacteria were practically constant. On this point opinion differed. Bail and Pasteur (see below) had found that the submerged form of some fungi was different from the aerial form. Nägeli and Zopf believed that bacteria showed comparable variations. In studies of Beggiatoa and of "Cladothrix," both relatively elaborate forms, not true bacteria, Zopf found that the long threads could break up into small pieces of varying length and shape, some almost short enough to be cocci (cf. Chap. XXII). He thus concluded that in general one and the same organism could give rise to bacilli, cocci, or spirilla. This conclusion was partly due to confusion between *units* of a chain and the chain itself, and partly due to the atypical nature of these particular organisms. Cohn's observations on true bacteria supported the idea that size and shape of a given organism are constant within narrow limits ("monomorphism"). This view, of course, has been much modified through later growth studies (Chap. XIX, sec. 2).

5. SPECIFIC TYPES OF BACTERIA AND THEIR ACTIONS

Historically the first recognition of a specific microbial cause of a specific type of change was probably that of Bizio in 1823. Polenta which had been kept moist in unusually warm weather was found to have blood-red spots on it. Bizio showed that if such a piece was put under a bell jar with fresh polenta the latter also became bloody; in other words, this was an infection, a fungus, which spread in moist air. Similar infections of bread have been observed from time to time, and because the bread appears to be turned into blood the organism has been called *B. prodigiosum*, the "miracle" bacterium. Bizio did not recognize it as a bacterium, but seems to have considered each raised moist spot as a single mushroom-like organism instead of a mass of millions of bacteria. (The retention of his name for it, *Serratia marcescens*, in the present-day taxonomy by Bergey *et al.* is therefore unjustified.)

An important study of the microorganisms in milk was made by Fuchs (1841). At that time it was a frequently observed phenomenon that milk became blue on standing. (With modern improvements in dairying this has become rather rare.) Fuchs showed that the blue milk contained large numbers of bacteria, *Ps. syncyanea*,[9] and that these would develop if a little was transferred to an infusion of mallow plants. What is most important, however, was his observation that on introducing a little of the mallow infusion culture into fresh milk

[9] Fuchs called it *Vibrio cyanogenus*.

it rapidly turned blue. This was probably the first production of a desired change by an artificially introduced infection. Fuchs' observations were later greatly extended by Neelsen (1880).

Another field in which microbes are highly active, the breakdown of polysaccharides, was opened up by an observation of Mitscherlich (1850). Observing under a microscope a piece of potato, he found that numbers of bacteria were growing on it, and saw that where the organisms were thickest the cell walls were broken down (pectin hydrolysis; cf. Chap. XVII, sec. 3).

In 1861 Pasteur discovered the organism responsible for the butyric fermentation and was shocked to find that it was motile and thus apparently an animal. Motility was at that time still regarded as an animal characteristic, and the difficulty of differentiating between plants and animals was not yet appreciated. But what was more remarkable about the *"vibrion butyrique"*[10] was that it developed only in the absence of air. Actually, anaerobic growth of bacteria had been described by Leeuwenhoek in his observations on pepper water, in 1680, but Pasteur was not aware of this. Pasteur and Professor Chassang coined the term *anaerobic* for this mode of life, as opposed to the *aerobic* growth of the vinegar-producing organism. Later he made a study of the fermentation brought about by molds growing beneath the surface of a liquid. These organisms undergo a change of morphology from the normal hyphal form to a yeastlike form, on immersion in the liquid. This change had been described by Bail in 1856, but Bail believed then that what had taken place was the conversion of the Mucor into a yeast. Pasteur showed that the yeastlike cells were still Mucor (*M. racemosus* or *M. rouxii*)—for they gave rise only to normal hyphae on aerobic cultivation—but that they were Mucor in its fermentative form. There is thus a special *morphology* connected with growth beneath the surface, i.e., under anaerobic conditions, and there is also a special *physiology* connected with it, namely, the fermentation. These are the two complementary aspects of anaerobic life.[11] This work fitted perfectly with Pasteur's earlier work on fermentation, according to which *"la fermentation est la vie sans l'air."* As put by Fitz somewhat later (1873), a fermentative fungus needs oxygen for its development; if it finds any free oxygen it utilizes it, assimilating one part of the sugar and burning the other, while in the absence of oxygen the fungus appropriates what oxygen it requires

[10] It was not really a Vibrio; Cohn complained bitterly of Pasteur's looseness in morphological terms. (Vibrios are described on p. 42).

[11] As it turns out, the matter is a little more complex than Pasteur thought. If *Mucor rouxii* is grown in nitrogen it ferments glucose actively, but grows in the hyphal form. Only in nitrogen containing 25 per cent CO_2 is it converted to the yeastlike form (Bartnicki-Garcia and Nickerson, 1959).

from the sugar. This is not quite the true meaning of fermentation (see Chap. V).

In a study of wine (1866), undertaken at the request of some vintners, Pasteur found that the "disease" of overacidity in wine was due to too much access of air. This allowed the growth of the vinegar-producing bacteria, which formed acid. Such undesirable organisms could be completely eliminated by heating the bottled wine to about 50° C for a short time. This is the process of pasteurization, which has since been extended to beer and to milk with such entire success that it is now a universal practice.

The ideas of Pasteur, particularly those developed in the work on spontaneous generation, made a great impression on Joseph Lister, a Scottish surgeon, who reasoned that if microorganisms are responsible for organic decompositions, they must be the cause of the infection of surgical wounds. He therefore began to carry out his operations under a phenol spray and treated all wounds with concentrated solutions of phenol. (Phenol is highly toxic to bacteria; cf. Chap. XXIV.) At this time (1867–1869) it was usual for 25 to 50 per cent of surgical patients to die of so-called hospital gangrene, or from suppurations of their wounds which led to septicemia. A patient entering a hospital for surgery had small chance of coming out alive; often the operation had to be followed by more and more extensive amputations as infection spread (cf. Godlee's *Life of Lister* [1918]). There was no conception of the cause of these infections; no particular precautions as to cleanliness were taken, and the conditions under which the patients lived must have been appalling. During the first two years in which he practiced his new treatment, no less than 34 out of Lister's 40 patients recovered—an unprecedented proportion. It is tragic that his methods were not used in the Franco-Prussian War (1870–1871). His work revolutionized the treatment of wounds and initiated modern surgery. The *aseptic*, as opposed to the *antiseptic*, method was of later development and has of course completely displaced the use of antiseptics, but the primary advance was made by Lister.

Besides his work in surgery, Lister made an important contribution to the technique of bacteriology, the *dilution method* (1878).[12] In studying the souring of milk, he diluted a small quantity of the milk with sterile water, diluted some of the resulting mixture with sterile water again, and continued the dilution process until a sample of the mixture, when added to fresh sterile milk, caused no souring. The last dilution which still caused souring then obviously contained just

[12] This method was ascribed to Nägeli (1877) by Zopf, and to Buchner by Koch (see Koch, 1881, p. 19). It may well be, since the idea is a logical one, that all these men developed it independently.

the minimum number of the active organisms and was considered by Lister to be a *pure culture*, i.e., to contain organisms of one species only. This method will give pure cultures only if the organism studied is present in much greater numbers than any other, because then the highest dilutions will not contain any of the other types. It will only rarely give pure cultures of a given organism when another is present in comparable numbers. However, the dilution method is an essential auxiliary to pure culture methods and a regular part of modern bacteriological techniques. In this case it led to the isolation of *Streptococcus lactis*, one of the most widely distributed of the milk-souring organisms.

Up to this time the observation of bacteria had been limited to the organisms in the natural state; but since their refractive index is not very different from that of water, and their size is close to the limit of visibility, the discovery of a method by which they could be more easily seen was an important step forward. This discovery was made by Weigert when, in 1875, he followed up the work of Gerlach, who 13 years earlier had succeeded in staining animal tissues with dyes. Weigert found that killed bacteria would take up picrocarmine and become heavily stained. Later many other dyes were introduced, notably methylene blue, fuchsin in presence of phenol, and gentian or crystal violet. In 1884 Christian Gram discovered a simple procedure which divides all bacteria into two classes (see p. 42); other, more special stains have since been introduced, especially for the study of nuclei and of flagella.

6. MICROBES AND DISEASE

At this point there developed, within the space of a few years, some of the most far-reaching discoveries microbiology has made, and a revolutionary advance in medicine—the proof that many diseases are caused by microorganisms. Most of this work was done with animals, but plant diseases were not neglected. It seems to have been understood from early times, indeed, that the diseases of plants were due to living organisms, largely because fungi were much more prominent among plant pathogens than bacteria. Virgil, in the *Georgics* (Book I), refers to mildew of wheat as "feeding on the stems," and in more recent times Fontana in Italy (1767) examined wheat rust (*Puccinia graminis*) under the microscope and identified it as an independent plant "feeding at the expense of the green plant," and not an "exanthema" or excretion. The outbreak of late blight on potatoes in Ireland in 1845 also led to extensive work on the parasite causing this (*Botrytis infestans*), and Berkeley was protagonist of the idea that the fungus was itself the cause and not merely, as others thought, a secondary invader growing on already diseased tissues. In the case of rust- and smut-infected cereals, de Bary (1853) clearly showed these diseases to be *due to* the growth of the parasite in the host tissue, with changes in the physiology and also the structure of the host plant.

The work with animals can be considered to begin from 1850, although of course every experiment is founded on an earlier one. It was in 1850 that Davaine and Rayer observed, in the blood of cattle that had died from anthrax, tiny rods in very large numbers. They ascribed little significance to them at the time, but 10 years later it was shown by Delafond that these rods multiplied in number when the blood was kept in a laboratory; i.e., they were living creatures. After reading Pasteur's work on the butyric fermentation (1861), Davaine realized that anthrax might be the product of a fermentation analogous to the butyric, and he afterward showed that the tiny rods were always present in the disease, and that if blood containing them was inoculated into a healthy animal the animal thereupon contracted the disease. Although Davaine was convinced that these rods were the cause of anthrax, he was not able to make definite proof. Others ascribed the success of his inoculation experiments to the fact that the blood itself was diseased and therefore communicated the disease to the animal into which it was injected. This last objection was only countered much later by an experiment of Klebs and Tiegel, who passed blood from heavily infected animals through the porous porcelain filter invented by Chamberland. This filter held back the finest particles. The filtrate did not transfer the disease to a healthy animal, and therefore the cause must lie in the solids which were held back—the corpuscles or the bacteria.

Although the proof could thus not be given at the time, the idea that infectious diseases are due to microorganisms seems to have been accepted by a few medical workers. William Budd as early as 1862 put forward a scheme for the systematic study of epidemic diseases and spoke of their causes as something that can "breed and multiply." He concluded that "these poisons . . . like animals and plants, however they may have once originated, are only propagated now by the law of continuous succession." It is obvious that the "poisons" must be organisms. Budd had already discarded the current medical ideas which ascribed such diseases to foul airs or miasmas.

At about this time, 1865–1870, Pasteur was studying the "pébrine" disease of silkworms in the south of France, where it was a serious menace to the silk industry. He succeeded in showing that the diseased worms contained "corpuscles" (bacteria), and although these were often present in the eggs in numbers too small to be seen, they could always be seen in the moths. By using only the eggs laid by moths free of the corpuscles, he could raise healthy silkworms. In 1868 he showed that healthy worms, if fed on the debris of moths that had had the disease, developed it. He had considerable difficulty in getting the silkworm growers to adopt his ideas, but when in 1866 he correctly predicted the future behavior of 14 lots of eggs (after examining the moths that had laid them), this made a great impression. This research strongly influenced the work on anthrax, which followed soon after.

It was Robert Koch (1876) who found that the anthrax organisms produce spores, or resting forms. These spores, when transferred to fresh blood serum, regenerated the original rod-shaped forms observed by Davaine. The formation and germination of such spores in other bacilli had been described by Cohn in 1873 and were studied further by Brefeld (1878) (see Chap. II, sec. 2B; Chap. III, sec. 4). In the spores of anthrax, Koch recognized the mechanism of dissemination of the disease, since the spores could be shed in great numbers from the carcasses of dead cattle, could be distributed widely in infected areas, and could remain alive under very unfavorable conditions of temperature and moisture. Food infected with them caused anthrax in mice. The etiology of anthrax was thus satisfactorily explained, provided only that clear proof of the carriage of it by the bacterium and not by the blood could be given. Such proof was given by Koch when he infected blood serum with a drop of blood from an anthrax victim, allowed the organism to grow, and transferred a drop of the culture to fresh serum. After eight such transfers the last was still capable of giving anthrax to a healthy animal. The original blood had thus been diluted very extensively; the virulence remained. In the following year, Pasteur used urine as a medium and obtained better growth and still more extensive dilution of the original blood.

The proof that anthrax is actually caused by a bacterium was followed by demonstration of the bacterial nature of many important diseases. Klebs (1883) and Löffler (1884) obtained the organism of diphtheria in culture, and although at first Löffler believed it was not the causal agent, later its virulence was proved by injecting it into healthy animals, with subsequent appearance of the typical disease. In 1882 Koch did the same for tuberculosis, but this time obtained the bacteria in pure cultures, owing to a new method of culturing which he had invented in 1881. Kitasato with tetanus and Eberth and Gaffky with typhoid fever carried out similar and equally conclusive experiments; finally the same was done for plague by Kitasato and by Yersin in 1894 during an outbreak at Hong Kong.

The evidence required to prove that an organism causes a disease was defined by Koch in his celebrated "postulates" as follows:[13] (1) The organism must always be present in the lesions of the disease; (2) it must be possible to grow the organism in pure culture outside of the body; (3) on introducing the culture of the organism into a healthy animal, the typical disease must follow (providing, of course, that the animal is of a kind susceptible to this disease); (4) in the disease so caused by inoculation, the same organism must invariably be present. In the case of anthrax, postulate No. 2 was not strictly carried out, since methods for attaining an absolutely pure culture were not then (1876) available. In the diseases of bacterial origin, both of animals and plants, which have been studied since that time, the postulates were all fulfilled. On the other hand, in diseases caused by viruses, cultivation outside a living host is not possible, so that the second postulate is frequently fulfilled by chemical purification of the virus outside the host, while observations of characteristic crystalline forms have been substituted for observations of living organisms. The third postulate is also more difficult than it looks, because the "typical" disease is often elusive, and an experimental animal may not show the same symptoms as man (cf. King, 1952).

Koch made another most important contribution to bacteriology: a simple method for obtaining a pure culture (1881). It consisted of adding to the medium—broth, serum, or whatever else was suitable— some gelatin. The medium was sterilized by heat, cooled to body temperature, and some of the culture added. Finally it was further cooled until the gelatin solidified. The bacteria, which had been mixed in with the medium, were now isolated from one another, and when they subsequently grew, each organism gave rise to a separate *colony*. (This technique was, Koch says, suggested by seeing such separate colonies on a piece of potato.) Since several bacteria may come to rest close to one another, the resulting colonies are not necessarily each a pure culture, but by repeating the process two or three times pure cultures may usually be obtained, especially if the Lister dilution method is first used to eliminate all bacteria except those that are present in relatively large numbers. The Koch procedure is also applicable to fungi, using spores for inoculation. It was further improved in 1883 by Frau Hesse, in Koch's laboratory. Since gelatin is liquefied by some bacteria, she substituted agar, which is liquefied by very few microorganisms (see Chap. IV, sec. 4). Furthermore, gelatin, being a protein, contributes to the nutrient matter of the medium, while agar is not readily available as a food. In this way the nutrients in the medium can be controlled quite independently of the solidifying

[13] First stated by Jacob Henle, a contemporary of Koch's.

agent. In later work silica gel, instead of agar, has sometimes been used as a solidifying agent so as to avoid all contamination with organic compounds.

A modification of the dilution method was developed by Hansen (1896) in the course of his extensive studies on yeasts. A series of small drops of water or broth is placed on a cover slip; to the first one is added a droplet of a yeast culture and, after mixing, a droplet is transferred to the second drop, a droplet of this to the third, and so on. The drops are examined under the microscope, and with relatively large cells like the yeasts one can soon find the drop that contains just one cell; this is then transferred to a fresh medium.

In 1880, the year before the discovery of the gelatin plate method, it was shown by Burrill that a bacterium was responsible for the disease of fire blight in pears. Burrill used the methods of Koch, cultivated the organism outside the plant, and was able to produce the disease when the bacterial culture was injected into healthy trees. The phenomena of bacterial disease in plants, with the exception of immunity, which plants do not acquire, are thus parallel to those in animals.

7. LATER DEVELOPMENTS

The last fundamental advance in technique was the so-called enrichment culture, introduced by Beijerinck and by Winogradsky from 1890 to 1900. This consists simply in the selection of a medium that will favor the development of one particular kind of organism and not of another. If it is believed that an organism capable of attacking a given substrate exists, it can be induced to multiply by using that substrate, with appropriate inorganic salts, as the medium, and inoculating with soil or other natural material. Of all the different organisms in the soil only those that can attack the given substance will grow profusely; the others will be dependent on the products of action of the first type, or on impurities in the medium, and hence will grow poorly. After several transfers the desired kind will be strongly enriched. Organisms attacking every conceivable substrate have been isolated in this way, and the method was the basis for Beijerinck's studies of "microbial ecology," i.e., the relation between environmental conditions and the special forms of life corresponding to them (see van Niel, 1949). As a special case, organisms capable of fixing CO_2 from the air were favored by the use of a medium free from organic carbon compounds, so that, by combining the methods of enrichment culture, dilution, and use of solid medium, Winogradsky could obtain CO_2-fixing organisms in pure culture from soil and water.

Methods in which a substance, toxic to some but harmless to other organisms, is added to the medium have also been used, particularly in the enrichment of pathogenic bacteria among soil and feces organisms. The bodies of bacteria themselves have been used as substrate in enrichment cultures designed to develop organisms producing antibiotics (see Chap. XXV).

The developments of the twentieth century have been biochemical and physiological. Few new strictly microbiological methods have been introduced. The methods are essentially those dealing with enzymes. Probably the three most important are:

A. The Measurement of Gas Exchange

Respiring organisms consume oxygen and generally produce H_2O and CO_2; in the presence of alkali, therefore, the gas volume decreases. The decrease is a measure of oxygen consumption. By measuring both the CO_2 production and the oxygen consumption, the ratio between them, CO_2/O_2, called the respiratory quotient (RQ) can be found. In 1900 Puriewitsch measured the RQ of Aspergillus and showed that it was about 1 for dextrose and sucrose, but 1.6 for tartaric acid (cf. Chap. V). Convenient methods for measuring gas exchange by following the pressure change in a closed vessel were developed by Barcroft and Warburg in the 1920's and now are used almost universally. The same procedures can be applied to fermentation (CO_2 evolution), nitrogen fixation (gas absorption corrected for oxygen), decarboxylation, acid production, and other processes. Details of the various methods have been summarized by Umbreit, Burris, and Stauffer (1949).

B. The Direct Measurement of Hydrogen Transfer

This was introduced by Thunberg and applied to bacteria by Harden and Zilva in 1915. Here a substance is added to the living organisms, or extracts, whose color changes when it is reduced or hydrogenated. Methylene blue, for instance, is blue in the oxidized form and colorless when hydrogenated, and many dyes behave in the same way (cf. Chap. V):

$$AH_2 + \underset{\text{(blue)}}{MB} \xrightarrow{\text{enzyme}} A + \underset{\text{(white)}}{MBH_2}$$

where AH_2 is some substrate which the microorganism can dehydrogenate. Some of the natural substrates, such as coenzymes, are colorless whether reduced or oxidized, but their absorption changes in the ultraviolet, and thus their reduction can be followed, using a spectro-photometer.

C. The Disruption of Bacterial Cells

The small size of bacteria makes them hard to break up. Only in recent years has the technique developed far enough to allow general study of their intracellular enzymes. The cells can be disrupted by repeated freezing and thawing, by prolonged grinding, by shaking vigorously with fine glass beads, or by exposing to supersonic vibrations. Subsequent purification using the methods of protein chemistry has made it possible to separate and study the individual enzymatic reactions. For example, in fermenting glucose to lactic acid 11 enzymes take part; all have been separated, at least partially purified, and their actions worked out in detail. Vast numbers of other bacterial enzymes have been extracted and a few even crystallized. Their activities will be encountered throughout the book.

Among other methods that have played important parts in the study of microorganisms should be mentioned the control of hydrogen-ion concentration; the isolation and culture of mutated forms; the measurement of growth by turbidity of liquid cultures; and, of course, the application of all the methods of analytical and organic chemistry.

In the "Diary" which follows, some other modern developments are included.

8. DIARY OF THE PRINCIPAL DATES IN THE DEVELOPMENT OF MODERN MICROBIOLOGY

1667	Hooke first observes filamentous microfungi.
1676	Leeuwenhoek first observes bacteria.
1680	Leeuwenhoek discovers anaerobic growth of bacteria.
1765	Müller's observations of bacteria, using compound microscope.
1776	Spallanzani's experiments on spontaneous generation.
1796	Jenner first vaccinates man, with cowpox vaccine.
1810	Gay-Lussac formulates equation of alcoholic fermentation.
1811	Appert makes preserves by hermetical sealing after boiling.
1822–32	Persoon and Fries describe and classify the fungi of Europe.
1826	Wöhler synthesizes urea from inorganic compounds only, thus breaking barrier between organic and inorganic worlds.
1835–37	Cagnaird-Latour, Schwann, and Kützing (independently)

recognize yeasts as living organisms, multiplying by budding; ascribe fermentation to their growth, the alcohol being an excretion.

1837   Schwann proves that fermentation and putrefaction are due to microorganisms present in the air.

1838   Ehrenberg's observations of bacteria, including Spirilla.

1838   Boussingault shows that clover increases the nitrogen of soil, but not if grown from seed in calcined sand.

1841   Fuchs identifies cause of blue milk with a bacterium.

1850   Mitscherlich observes breakdown of potato cell walls by bacteria.

1850   Davaine observes *Bacillus anthracis* in blood of cattle suffering from anthrax.

1853   Schröder and Dusch introduce cotton plugs to keep media sterile.

1853   De Bary shows rust and smut of cereals to be caused by parasitic fungi.

1858   Pasteur proves lactic fermentation to be exclusively due to living bacteria.

1860   Lister begins antiseptic surgery.

1861   Pasteur discovers the "*vibrion butyrique*" and elucidates its anaerobic nature.

1866   Pasteur studies "diseases" of wine and invents pasteurization.

1872   Cohn classifies the known bacteria.

1875   Weigert introduces staining of bacteria by aniline dyes.

1876   Tyndall proves the universal presence of microorganisms in unfiltered air.

1876   Koch provides final proof that anthrax is a bacterial disease.

1878   Lister isolates a milk-souring organism (*Sc. lactis*) by dilution method.

1879   Hansen begins studies on yeasts of fermentation.

1881   Pasteur and Roux make successful public inoculation of 25 sheep against anthrax.

1882   Koch invents poured-plate technique with gelatin.

1882   Schloesing and Müntz prove that nitrification in soil is a biological process.

1882   Eberth and Gaffky isolate the organism of typhoid fever.

1883   Metchnikoff discovers phagocytosis.

1883   Frau Hesse introduces agar in the poured-plate method.

1883–84   Klebs and Löffler prove diphtheria bacterial and isolate the organism.

1884   Koch isolates the organism of tuberculosis in pure culture.

1884   Chamberland invents unglazed porcelain filter.

1884   Gram discovers differential staining for bacteria.

1885–86   Hellriegel and Willfarth prove that nitrogen fixation in legumes is inseparable from nodule formation, which is due to action of special bacteria.

1888   Beijerinck isolates nodule-forming bacteria from root nodules of legumes in pure culture.

1889   Kitasato isolates anaerobic bacterium causative of tetanus, and elucidates the etiology of the disease.

1890   Von Behring and Kitasato discover diphtheria antitoxin.

1890–91   Winogradsky shows nitrifying organisms to be autotrophic, and isolates both species in pure culture.

1892   Ivanowsky discovers a filterable virus causing tobacco mosaic disease.

1894   Kitasato and (independently) Yersin isolate the organism of plague, *Pasteurella pestis*.

1895   Winogradsky isolates anaerobic free-living nitrogen-fixing bacteria (*Clostridium pastorianum*).

1895   Beijerinck proves sulfate reduction to be a bacterial process, and isolates the organisms responsible.

1896   Lehmann and Neumann issue their *Atlas und Grundriss der Bakteriologie*.

1897   Frosch and Löffler discover the first filterable virus of animal disease (foot-and-mouth disease).

1897   Buchner obtains fermentation by yeast press-juice, without living cells.

1897   Migula publishes a new classification of bacteria.

1900   Erwin Smith begins studies on plant pathogens.

1901   Beijerinck isolates aerobic free-living nitrogen-fixing bacteria (*Azotobacter chroöcoccum*).

1905   Harden and Young discover effect of phosphates on alcoholic fermentation.

1909   Sörensen discovers importance of hydrogen-ion concentration in enzyme systems, and introduces buffers and term pH.

1909   Orla-Jensen introduces biochemical characters into classification of bacteria.

1911   Neuberg begins studies on alcoholic fermentation.

1915   Twort discovers transmissible lysis in bacteria.

1917   D'Herelle independently rediscovers transmissible lysis and ascribes it to be a submicroorganism, *Bacteriophagum intestinale* (bacteriophage).

1926   Kluyver and Donker systematize the chemistry of fermentations by application of hydrogen-transfer conceptions.

1928	Quastel and Wooldridge discover the inhibition of succinate dehydrogenation by malonate.
1929	Fleming discovers penicillin.
1930	Karström introduces the concept of adaptive enzymes.
1931	Van Niel explains the mode of life of the purple bacteria as anaerobic photosynthesis.
1935	Warburg discovers the first yellow enzyme system and also purifies its coenzyme.
1936	Stanley crystallizes the first virus, that of tobacco mosaic.
1940	Woods and Fildes establish antagonism between sulfonamides and p-aminobenzoic acid.
1941	Lipmann introduces concept of high-energy phosphate bonds.
1943	Waksman isolates streptomycin.
1947	Tatum and Lederberg discover sexuality in bacteria.

The increasing number of workers in microbiology has greatly increased the tempo of research, and this in turn makes it difficult to judge the importance of the individual steps forward. The list therefore stops at a point where at least a little perspective can be introduced. Doubtless if it were recompiled a generation hence, many of the twentieth-century entries would be changed.

REFERENCES

Bartnicki-Garcia, S. and Nickerson, W. 1959, 1962. Proc. IXth. Int. Bot. Congress, Montreal, p. 22; cf. *J. Bact.*, **84**:829–840 (1962).

de Bary, A. 1853. Untersuchungen über die Brandpilze und die durch sie verursachten. Krankheiten der Pflanzen. 144 pp.

de Bary, A. 1866. Morphologie und Physiologie der Pilze, Flechten u. Myxomyceten. Leipzig, W. Engelmann.

Brefeld, O. 1878. Untersuchungen über Schimmelpilze. Vol. 4. Berlin.

van Cittert, P. 1932. *Proc. Kon. Akad. Wetensch. Amsterdam*, **35**, 1062–1066.

Cohn, Ferdinand. 1872–1876. Untersuchungen über Bacterien. Pts. 1, 2, and 4. *Beitr. Biol. Pflanzen*, **I** (Heft 2):127–224 (1872); **I** (Heft 3):141–207 (1875); **II** (Heft 2): 249–276 (1876).

Cohn, Ferdinand. 1873. *Ber. d. Schles. Ges.*, pp. 42–45. Cited by Cohn, 1875, q.v.

Dobell, C. 1932. Antonie van Leeuwenhoek and His "Little Animals." London, Staples Press.

Duclaux, E. 1920. Pasteur, the History of a Mind. Philadelphia. W. B. Saunders. (Trans. E. F. Smith and F. Hedges.)

Ehrenberg, A. 1838. Abhandl. Berlin Akad. 38. Die Infusionsthierchen als vollendete Organismen. Leipzig.

Fitz, A. 1873. *Ber. deut. chem. Ges.*, **6**:48–57, 57–58.

Fontana, F. 1767. Osservazioni sopra la Ruggine del grano. Cf. R. A. Micheli, 1729, Nova plantarum genera, Florence.

Fries, Elias. 1821–1832. Systema mycologicum. Vols. I–III. Greifswald, Ernest Mauritius.

Fuchs, C. J. 1841. Cited by Neelsen, q.v.

Gale, E. F. 1948. Chemical Activities of Bacteria. London, University Tutorial Press; New York, Academic Press.

Godlee, Sir R. 1918. Lord Lister. London, Macmillan. Chap. 10, Hospital Diseases; see also C. R. Dukes, 1924. Lord Lister 1827–1912. London, Roadmaker Series.

Hansen, E. Chr. 1896. Practical Studies in Fermentation. London. (Trans. A. K. Miller.)

King, L. S. 1952. *J. History of Med.*, **7**:350–361.

Klebs, G. 1883. Verhandl. Congresse für innere Medizin, Wiesbaden, **II**:143.

Koch, Robert. 1876. *Beitr. Biol. Pflanzen*, **II** (Heft 2):277–308.

Koch, Robert. 1881. *Mitth. a. d. Kaiserl. Gesundheitsamt.*, **1**:49–79.

Lister, J. 1878. *Trans. Pathol. Soc. (London)*, **29**:425–467; also in The Lancet, **ii**:918, (1877).

Löffler, E. 1884. *Mitth. a. d. Kaiserl. Gesundheitsamt.*, **2**:421–499.

Mitscherlich, E. 1850. *Monatschr. Kais. Akad. Wiss. Berlin*, pp. 102–110.

Neelsen, F. 1880. *Beitr. Biol. Pflanzen*, **III** (Heft 2):187–246.

van Niel, C. B. 1949. The "Delft School" and the Rise of General Microbiology. *Bact. Revs.*, **13**:161–174.

Pasteur, L. 1860. *Ann. chim. phys. 3 sér.*, **58**:323–426.

Pasteur, L. 1861. *Compt. rend.*, **52**:344–347.

Pasteur, L. 1862. *Ann. chim. phys. 3 sér.*, **64**:5–110.

Pasteur, L. 1866. Etudes sur le vin, ses maladies, causes qui les provoquent, procédés nouveaux pour le conserver, et pour le vieillir, 2nd ed. Paris, F. Savy. 1873.

Pasteur, L. 1870. Etude sur la maladie des vers a soie. Paris, Gauthier-Villars, 2 vols.

Pasteur, L. 1876. Etudes sur la bière. Paris, Gauthier-Villars. English trans: Studies on Fermentation; the Diseases of Beer, Their Causes and the Means of Preventing Them. F. Faulkner and D. C. Robb. London, Macmillan, 1879.

Persoon, C. H. 1822–1828. Mycologia Europaea, etc. Erlangen, J. J. Palm.

Porter, J. R. 1946. Bacterial Chemistry and Physiology. New York, John Wiley and Sons.

Prazmowski, A. 1880. Untersuchungen über die Entwicklungsgeschichte und Ferment-wirkung einiger Bacterien Arten. Leipzig, Hugo Voigt.

Schroeder, H., and Dusch, T. von. 1854. *Ann. Chem. Pharm.*, **89**:232; Schroeder, H. 1859. Cited by Pasteur, 1862.

Schultze, F. 1836. *Ann. Chem. Pharm.*, **39**:487; see *New Philos. J.*, Edinburgh, Oct., 1837.

Schwann, Theodor. 1837. *Poggendorf's Ann.*, **41** (or II, Ser. **11**):184–193.

Spallanzani, Lazzaro. 1776. Opuscoli di Fisica Animale, e Vegetabile. Modena (especially Chap. 3).

Stephenson, M. 1949. Bacterial Metabolism, 3rd ed. London, Longmans, Green and Co.

Tulasne, L. R., and Tulasne, C. 1861–1865. Selecta fungorum Carpologia. Vols. 1–3. 782 pp.

Tyndall, J. 1876. *Phil. Trans. Roy. Soc.*, **166**:27–74.

Tyndall, J. 1881. Essays on the Floating Matter of the Air. London, Longmans, Green and Co.

Umbreit, W. W.; Burris, R. H.; and Stauffer, J. F. 1949. Manometric Techniques and Tissue Metabolism. Minneapolis, Burgess Pub. Co.

Werkman, C. H., and Wilson, P. W., editors. 1951. Bacterial Physiology. New York, Academic Press.

CHAPTER II

The Bacterial Cell and Its Relationship to Other Organisms

Könnte man einen Menschen unter einem solchen Linsensystem ganz
überschauen, er würde so gross erscheinen, wie der Mont Blanc oder gar
Chimborasso. Aber selbst unter diesen kolossalen Vergrösserungen sehen
die kleinsten Bacterien nicht viel grösser aus als die Punkte und Kommas
eines guten Drucks; von ihren inneren Theilen ist wenig oder gar
nichts zu unterscheiden, und selbst die Existenz würde von den meisten
verborgen bleiben, wenn sie nicht in unendlichen Mengen gesellig lebten.

FERDINAND COHN (1872)[1]

The bacteria are a group of organisms of very varied activities, but
their morphology is, superficially at least, rather simple and well defined. The definition of the group given by Cohn, upon whose careful
and painstaking work all subsequent recognition of species and classification have been based, was as follows (1872): "The bacteria are
chlorophyll-free cells of spherical, oblong or cylindrical shape, the
latter sometimes twisted or curved, multiplying exclusively by transverse fission and growing either isolated or in cell-families." The term
chlorophyll-free can no longer be retained (see sec. 3), but the rest
remains adequate. Because the bacteria can be properly appreciated only
in their relationship to other microorganisms, it will be convenient to
consider first the whole group of the lower plants.

1. THE THALLOPHYTA

The lowermost group of plants, those without woody vascular tissue
and with only limited differentiation into definite vegetative organs,
is called the *Thallophyta*. This comprises two great groups, the algae,

[1] If one could inspect a man under a similar lens system, he would appear as big as
Mont Blanc or even as Mt. Chimborazo. But even under these colossal magnifications
the smallest bacteria look no larger than the periods and commas of good print; little
or nothing can be distinguished of their inner parts, and of most of them their very
existence would have remained unsuspected if it had not been for their countless
numbers.

containing chlorophyll, and the fungi, without chlorophyll. The bacteria have something in common with both these, and in general may be thought of as lying between and below them, although completely distinct from either.

The algae are classified in the first instance by their "accessory" pigments, which often mask the green color of the chlorophyll. These pigments are now known to participate actively in photosynthesis, so that they are by no means merely accessory in function, but are of great physiological importance. Furthermore, many other properties, such as motility and type of flagella, chemical nature of the stored products, cell-wall material, and the type of plant body or colony are more or less correlated with the differences in pigments. The principal characters are summarized for reference in Table II–1. The most primitive are the *Myxophyceae*, or blue-green algae, which have their photosynthetic pigments distributed throughout the outer part of the cell (instead of in plastids); they reproduce vegetatively and have the simplest organization in single nonmotile cells or in filaments. It is important, too, to note that generally these are among the smallest of the algal cells. The various divisions of the bacteria according to shape also have their counterparts among the *Myxophyceae*.

Some algologists (e.g., Smith, 1950) prefer the terminology given in parentheses in the first column of the table.

The algae possess many colorless relatives. In general all groups that have flagella, as well as some others of simple morphology, have colorless members. The *Chlorophyceae* or "grass-green algae" have a strong tendency to produce colorless forms, and one of these, *Prototheca zopfii*, was known long before it was recognized as an alga. Even the diatoms have one known colorless form (Pringsheim, 1951). The colorless members of the *Myxophyceae* are especially close to the bacteria and some of them, like Beggiatoa, have been considered as "higher bacteria."

The fungi consist of four large groups, classified by their structure and mode of spore formation. One group (not necessarily the most primitive) consists of naked ameba-like cells (Myxamebae), some of which are flagellated; these germinate from spores and after a time fuse in pairs to form zygotes which coalesce, either partly or completely, in enormous numbers. The result is a mass or a network of protoplasm (termed a plasmodium or, when coalescence is incomplete, a pseudoplasmodium). Finally the mass heaps itself up into a stalked fruiting body and many of the cells round up into spores (cf. sec. 6B). These are the *Myxomycetes*, or slime fungi. Not all workers regard these as true fungi. The other three groups have definite cell walls and consist mainly of threadlike structures (hyphae); these are sometimes reduced

TABLE II–1

Groups	Pigment Color	Food Products	Flagellation
1. *Chlorophyceae* (*Chlorophyta*)	Green (chloro-phylls)	Starch (often with fat)	2 or 4; equal, anterior
2. *Euglenineae* (*Euglenophyta*)	Green (chloro-phylls)	"Paramylum" (glucose-β-1,3-glucoside)	2, unequal, one generally not locomotory
3. *Chloromonadineae*	Yellow-green	Fat	2; unequal, anterior
4. *Cryptophyceae* (may be combined with 6 as *Pyrrophyta*)	Almost any, often brown, reddish, or blue-green	Starch (often with fat)	2; slightly unequal
5. *Xanthophyceae*	Green (or yellow-green)	Fat	2; unequal, anterior
6. *Dinophyceae*	Golden-brown or greenish-brown; occasionally blue-green	Fat or starch	2; inserted laterally; 1 directed transversely, 1 directed posteriorly
7. *Chrysophyceae* (may be combined with 3, 5, and 8 as *Chrysophyta*)	Golden-brown	Fat and/or "leucosin"	1 or 2; anterior
8. *Bacillariophyceae* (diatoms)	Brown	Fats	Rare, only in reproductive cells
9. *Phaeophyceae* (*Phaeophyta*)	Brown (fucoxanthin)	Fat, mannitol, and "Laminarin" (glucose-β-1,3-glucoside)	(only in reproductive cells) 2 anterior; 1 posterior
10. *Rhodophyceae* (*Rhodophyta*)	Red or purple (phycoerythrin)	Floridean starch (glucose-α-1,4-glucoside)	None
11. *Myxophyceae* (*Cyanophyta*)	Blue-green or reddish (phycocyanin, phycoerythrin)	Amylopectin in some	None

TABLE II-1 (Continued)

Cell Wall: Material and Form	Plant Body or Colony Type	Sexuality
1. Cellulose with other poly-saccharides; semirigid	Many types, or unicellular; not parenchymatous or massive	Simple to advanced
2. Flexible	Unicellular only; all flagellated cells, except in palmella stage	None
3. Flexible	Unicellular	None known
4. Flexible or cellulose	Unicellular; flagellate or coccoid	None known
5. Two overlapping halves; resting stages silicified	Many types, or unicellular	Simple; rare
6. Flexible or cellulose; in 2 laterally disposed halves (some heavily sculptured)	Unicellular or small colonies	Simple; rare, if any
7. ? Pectin; cysts heavily silicified	Unicellular, flagellate, filamentous, or palmelloid	Not certain
8. Two overlapping halves, silicified	Unicellular; forming colonies, however	Special type
9. Thick; gelatinous (algin)	Mostly large, massive, parenchymatous; a few filamentous	Simple to advanced
10. Thick; gelatinous	Mostly large, massive, parenchymatous; a few filamentous	Advanced and complex
11. Pectin wall, gummy capsule	Unicellular or composed of filaments	None

to single cells, but more commonly are united in a mycelium. In the *Phycomycetes*, the hyphae, if formed, are nonseptate, i.e., not divided into separate cells; many nuclei are scattered through the mycelium, as they are also in the plasmodium of *Myxomycetes*. Some are unicellular (order *Chytridiales*), although they may form rhizoids or other outgrowths for attachment.

In the other two large groups, the *Ascomycetes* and *Basidiomycetes*, the hyphae are septate, forming separate cells; a few important forms, including the yeasts (cf. Chap. XI), are reduced to single cells. These two groups have relatively complete methods of sexual reproduction, generally by the fusion of two hyphae, followed by the fusion of nuclei. This takes place at different stages in the life cycle of the different groups, and sometimes individual genera within a family show quite large differences. In the *Ascomycetes*, spores are formed "endogenously," i.e., within the cell, and in fact within a sac or ascus usually containing eight; in the *Basidiomycetes* they are formed "exogenously" on small protuberances, in groups of four. There are also many mycelial fungi in which sexuality has not yet been observed; these are classed as *Fungi imperfecti*—most of them probably belong to the *Ascomycetes*.

Asexual or vegetative reproduction also occurs in all groups; in the water forms (which belong to the *Phycomycetes*) by motile zöospores, and in most aerial forms by the cutting off of small spherical "conidia" which are scattered by air currents. In the *Myxomycetes* a large part of the plasmodium may be converted, after growth has ceased, into small uninucleate spores.

Lastly the protozoa should be mentioned, if only because of possible relationships between: (1) the amebae (class *Rhizopoda*) and the Myxamebae, (2) some of the flagellates and the flagellate algae, and (3) the *Trypanosoma* (of the flagellates) and the *Spirochaetales* (of the bacteria).

It is probable that the bacteria are a heterogeneous group, because some members show similarities with the *Myxophyceae* (although this has been seriously disputed by Pringsheim, 1949), and others with some of the fungi or protozoa.

The broad general relations among the main groups are shown in Fig. II–1. In this diagram the solid lines indicate accepted relationships, while dotted lines indicate similarities, which *may* be due to true phylogenetic relationships, or perhaps only to parallel lines of evolution. Arrows indicate a one-way direction of evolution, since colorless forms are never known to give rise to chlorophyllous forms, although presumably this happened some time in evolutionary history (cf. Chap 26).

This chapter will be limited to a description of the bacteria. The morphology and cytology of the algae and fungi have been treated *in*

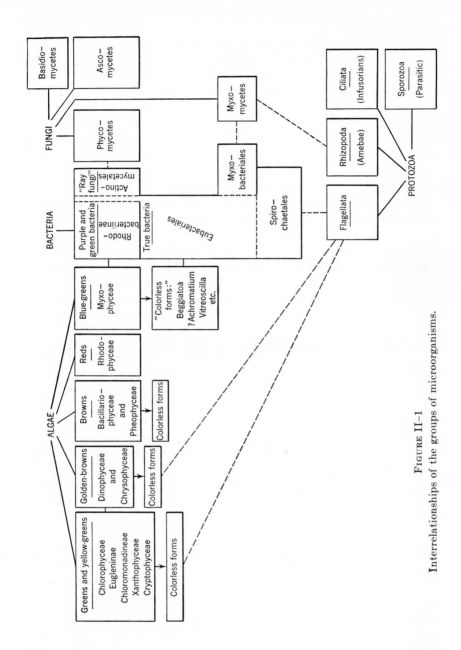

FIGURE II-1

Interrelationships of the groups of microorganisms.

extenso in books on these groups, for example, Fritsch (1935 and 1945) or Smith (1950) on the algae, and Bessey (1950) or Gäumann (1949) on the fungi, while physiology of the fungi is treated by Foster (1949) and Cochrane (1958). No attempt will be made, therefore, to describe these groups here. The student of microbiology, however, must have a working knowledge of the algae and fungi as well as of the bacteria, and the study of a given process in one organism is continually shedding light on the corresponding process in others.

The current publication of a five-volume treatise on the bacteria, with all chapters written by experts (Stanier and Gunsalus, 1960–1964), will provide a general source of more detailed information and bibliography on most of the matters treated in this book.

2. THE EUBACTERIA

A. Size of Bacteria

The Eubacteria, or true bacteria, which are the simplest group (nonfilamentous, nonphotosynthetic, with rigid cell walls) include the smallest of living organisms, and most of them consist of only a single cell, although in a few cases they intergrade with filamentous forms in which the unit seems to be multicellular. The single cell, if a sphere, may have a diameter as small as 0.5 μ or less (1 μ = 0.001 mm). In order to make them visible, they must be magnified to an extent difficult to realize, as the quotation from Cohn at the head of this chapter points out. With a magnification of 1000 diameters, the image is still only $\frac{1}{2}$ mm across.

This small size has two rather important consequences. The first is that the ratio of surface to volume in bacteria is enormously greater than in other creatures. In the small sphere mentioned above, the ratio, surface/volume, is 120,000. An ameba, regarded for simplicity as a sphere of radius 150 μ, has a surface/volume ratio of only 400 (the actual value would be a little higher on account of its irregular shape); the ratio for a hen's egg is about 1.5 and for a 200-lb man, 0.3. Since in general the rate of metabolism increases with the surface/volume ratio, it follows that the bacteria would be expected to be, weight for weight, immensely more active physiologically than the higher creatures. This deduction is borne out by many observations, e.g., a lactose-fermenting bacterium breaks down from 1000 to 10,000 times its own weight of lactose in an hour. For a man to metabolize even 1000 times his own weight of sugar would take about 250,000 hours, or almost half a lifetime.

The second consequence of the small size of bacteria is best seen from some simple calculations. The volume of a sphere of 0.5 μ diameter —the size mentioned above—is 6.10^{-14} ml. The volume of an average protein molecule is about 5.10^{-20} ml. Assuming 10 per cent of the cell volume is dry matter, it could contain only 100,000 protein molecules, and since it is (of course) not all protein, there is clearly room for only a limited number of molecules of the all-important enzyme proteins. Thus the number of different enzymatic activities of which a bacterium is capable is limited by sheer size.

Yet one culture of bacteria may carry out many different chemical reactions, each one of which is dependent on the presence of a specific enzyme. Evidently, therefore, the number of enzyme molecules needed for each specific reaction cannot be very great.

One bacterial enzyme, catalase, turns out to constitute 1 to 2 per cent of the dry weight of the cells (of *Micrococcus lysodeikticus*) from which it was obtained (Herbert and Pinsent, 1948). On this basis our coccus of volume 6.10^{-14} ml would contain some 2000 catalase molecules. This organism has a particularly high catalase activity, but its other enzymes must surely be present in smaller amounts, since the number of enzymes needed to synthesize the different amino acids, fats, nucleoproteins, and polysaccharides of a living cell amounts to a thousand or more.

The case of hydrogen ions is even more interesting. Most bacteria can live at a hydrogen-ion concentration of not far from 10^{-7} gm ions per liter (shortened to pH 7, where pH indicates — $\log_{10}$ of the hydrogen-ion concentration). If we assume that the pH inside the cells is the same as that outside, then in a bacterial cell of volume 6.10^{-14} ml there would be 6.10^{-24} gm ions. Since the Avogadro number, i.e., the number of ions in a gram ion, is only 6.10^{23}, it follows that such an organism will contain on an average $6.10^{-24} \times 6.10^{23} = 3.6$ hydrogen ions. At an internal pH of 8, the figure would be 0.36, i.e., the chances would be about 3 to 1 against its containing a hydrogen ion at all at any given moment. In this case the addition or loss of only one, especially one so active as the hydrogen ion, might cause profound changes in the nature of the organism. Its ability to carry out a given reaction, its response to a stimulus, and perhaps even its structure may very well be altered by the chance acquisition of a hydrogen ion. What applies to hydrogen ions applies equally well to the ions of those metals that must be present in very small concentrations in order for bacteria to grow (see Chap. IV).

B. Shape

In general as we go down the scale from large to small organisms the morphology becomes progressively simpler. Bacteria, the smallest

of creatures, have the simplest of morphology. Some of the organisms
lying on the border line of the bacteria present special features, which
will be considered under the sulfur and iron bacteria (Chap. XXII),
while the Myxobacteria (sec. 6 below) form complex fruiting structures.
At this point discussion will be limited to the simple organisms, the
Eubacteria.

On a favorable medium, a bacterium will increase somewhat in
size, and then develop a cross wall and break apart into two (Chap.
III, sec. 5). This method of multiplication is called *fission*. The typical
yeasts and some fungi related to them, on the other hand, multiply by
forming a tiny outgrowth which increases in size until it separates
completely from the mother cell. This is multiplication by *budding*.
Multiplication by "simple" fission is mainly limited to the bacteria
and the blue-green algae. These were therefore grouped together by

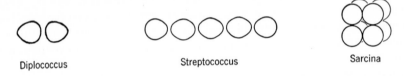

Diplococcus   Streptococcus   Sarcina

Figure II–2
Types of Coccus.

Cohn as *Schizophyta*, or fission plants, the bacteria being called
Schizomycetes—fission fungi—and the fission algae *Schizophyceae*.
The term *Schizomycetes* (*Spaltpilze*), which was coined by Nägeli,
has survived better than this classification. Protozoa multiply by fission,
but this involves very complex reorganization of the parts of the cell,
and in addition is accompanied by true mitosis, i.e., splitting of the
chromosomes and their orderly separation by means of a spindle
mechanism. This does not differ in principle from cell division in higher
plants and animals and is to be distinguished from *simple* fission. The
same is true for the fission of certain yeasts (*Schizosaccharomyces*);
although mitosis in these is difficult to observe, there can be no doubt
that it occurs. The nuclear phenomena of cell division in bacteria,
while admittedly hard to observe in detail, are apparently simpler
and at present it is far from certain that true mitosis occurs at all (see
Figs. III–10 and III–12).

The shapes of the Eubacteria are limited to the sphere, the straight
rod, and the curved rod.

1. SPHERE. A spherical bacterium is called a *coccus* (Gr. *kokkos*, a berry). The diameter of cocci may be from 0.2 μ, which is close to the limit of resolution of the optical microscope, up to about 4 μ.

The cocci may be grouped according to their spatial arrangement, which results from the method of division (Fig. II–2):

(*a*) An organism that remains in pairs after dividing has been termed a *Diplococcus*. Generally the organisms are slightly flattened toward one another. The organism of pneumonia, *Diplococcus pneumoniae* Weichselbaum, often called simply *Pneumococcus*, is an example.

(*b*) If, however, the organism continues to divide in the same plane, a chain will result. Such an organism is termed a *Streptococcus* (Gr. *streptos*, twisted, in the sense of string, necklace, or chain). The commonest of these are *Sc.* (= *Streptococcus*) *lactis*, the organism of sour milk, and *Sc. pyogenes*, a common cause of local and systemic infections. Diplococci are usually included among the short-chain streptococci (cf. Chap. XII); however, streptococci are somewhat elongated in the direction of the chain, while diplococci are often flattened and pointed at the opposite end (Fig. III–4). The length of the chain is often very characteristic (see Fig. XII–1), *Sc. lactis* giving only two to three organisms in a chain, while *Sc. agalactiae* produces long filaments. The streptococci are paralleled in the blue-green algae by Nostoc and Anabaena, both of which form filaments of indefinite length, but, as the name *Myxophyceae* (= slime algae) implies, these filaments are usually covered with a thick sheath of slimy or gelatinous (polysaccharide or pectin) material. Indeed, a group of Streptococci particularly active in forming gelatinous slime is called *Leuconostoc* (= colorless Nostoc).

(*c*) When division takes place in two dimensions a sheet or plate of bacteria results. Such organisms have been sometimes termed *Staphylococcus* (Greek *staphylos*, bunch of grapes); "*Staph.*" *aureus* is responsible for boils and similar localized skin infections. This type, if indeed it is real [cf. (*e*) below], is paralleled by such organisms as *Merismopedia* among the blue-green algae, but again the extracellular jelly-like sheath is much more in evidence than with the bacteria. A few cocci form planar tetrads only and not larger groups; these have been called *Tetracoccus*, *Pediococcus*, and *Gaffkya*, and their division in two planes is characteristic (Gunther, 1959).

(*d*) Lastly, division may take place in three dimensions, giving rise to characteristic packets of eight (Fig. II–2). This group is known as *Sarcina* (Latin *sarcina*, a packet or bundle) and includes some common air-borne saprophytes, such as *Sarcina lutea*, some motile sporeformers, *Sporosarcina*, and a few anaerobic fermenting organisms, the *Zymo-*

sarcinae (Fig. XVIII-3). The Sarcina type is paralleled by *Eucapsa* among the blue-green algae.

(*e*) Those cocci that show no special division form are grouped together as *Micrococcus*. This group has been subdivided on the basis of the reaction to Gram's stain, a very widely used method of staining which divides all microorganisms into two classes—those that take the stain (gram-positive) and those that do not (gram-negative).[2] The gram-negative micrococci are mostly parasites or pathogens, and include the *Meningococcus*, causative of meningitis, and the *Gonococcus*, causative of gonorrhea. Other members inhabit the mouth of man and the rumen of herbivorous animals. The gram-positive members are probably a somewhat heterogeneous group. Since there is little real distinction between Staphylococcus and Micrococcus, groups (*c*) and (*e*) are often classed under one head (Shaw *et al.*, 1951). All the cocci of classes (*a*) to (*d*) are also gram-positive.

2. CURVED ROD

(*a*) The rod may have a single curve, the organism being more or less C-shaped. This group is known, following Müller, as *Vibrio*. It includes, among others, the pathogen of Asiatic cholera, *Vibrio comma*, and also the bacteria (called *Desulfovibrio*) that reduce sulfate to sulfide at the expense of organic material (see Chap. XVIII).

(*b*) The more tortuous rods, shaped like a screw or a spiral, are called *Spirillum*. These are mostly found in water and were considered difficult to culture on artificial media until the work of Giesberger (1936). Several spirilla, including *Sp. undula*, were described by Müller in 1783 from stagnant water, and even Leeuwenhoek in 1676 described "aeltgens of wormtgens" (little eels or worms) in pepper infusion which from their size must have been spirilla (see Dobell, p. 144). They are thus among the first bacteria to have been recognized. They were also the first bacteria in which flagella were seen (Cohn, 1872) (see Fig. II-5, p. 50).

The two types, Vibrio and Spirillum, have little, morphologically, to distinguish them from each other, except for differences in their organs of movement, the *flagella:* the vibrios have their flagella (a single one or a bunch) at *one* pole, the spirilla at *both* poles. Both types

---

[2] The method is as follows: The organisms are spread thinly on a clean slide, dried and "fixed" by being passed through the flame two or three times. The smear is stained with very weakly alkaline crystal violet, i.e., 2 per cent crystal violet containing 0.8 per cent ammonium oxalate. After one minute in this it is "mordanted" with 0.5 per cent iodine in 2 per cent KI for another minute. It is then rinsed by pouring on absolute alcohol dropwise till no more color comes away. Gram-negative cells are colorless at this point, gram-positive ones, deep purple. The film is lightly stained with safranin, neutral red, or Bismarck brown to color the gram-negative cells. The significance of the Gram stain is discussed in Chap. III, sec. 3.

are gram-negative. Since some of the gram-negative members of the rod group, the *Pseudomonads* (below), are often very slightly curved or bean-shaped, the relationship between these and vibrios is probably rather close. All are placed in the family *Pseudomonadaceae*.

A point of importance is that both these types are more or less rigid, although curved, and thus to be clearly distinguished from the *Spirochaetales*, which are flexuous (sec. 7).

3. STRAIGHT ROD. The rod shape has given the name *Bacterium* to the whole group of organisms (Gr. *bakterion*, diminutive of *baktron*, a rod). Some of the rod-shaped bacteria can undergo a reversible change into a heat-resistant stage, the *spore*, and these form the genera *Bacillus* and *Clostridium* (see below); the nonsporeformers comprise the class of *Bacterium* proper, with its many families.

a) BACTERIUM. The nonsporeforming rods may be subdivided by their reaction to Gram's stain. The larger and the nonmotile forms are mostly gram-positive. The gram-negative forms, however, are the more numerous, and include seven "families" and a very large number of "species," many of which are imperfectly described.

Within these two categories, especially within the gram-negative group, distinction is made on the basis of the flagella. These will be described below. At this point it is only necessary to note that some bacteria have the flagella only at one end or pole of the cell (*monotrichous* or *cephalotrichous*); these are called *Pseudomonas*. Others have them only at the side of the cell (*peritrichous*), and still others are without flagella altogether. Many of those that possess flagella do not have them under all conditions, old cultures being often deficient in them. Furthermore, some of the motile groups with flagella inserted at the sides contain also nonmotile species; these are clearly related to the group in other respects and hence belong with them. It seems as if in these laterally flagellated forms the possession of flagella is not so important and characteristic as in the polarly flagellated forms.

Differentiation into groups is also made on grounds of physiology. For example, the bacteria producing lactic acid from sugar form a rather homogeneous group, all of which are gram-positive and practically all nonmotile (Chap. XII), although morphologically they are varied, including both cocci and rods. Those producing formic acid constitute another group, the *Enterobacteriaceae* (Chap. XIV), all of which are gram-negative, although on account of differences in habitat, oxygen requirement, and so on, this group is extensively further subdivided. The strictly anaerobic mode of life separates certain other groups and subgroups. An outline of the main divisions of the straight rods is given in Table II–2.

b) BACILLUS. The great majority of the bacteria which form spores

TABLE II-2. The Major Subdivisions among the Straight Rods

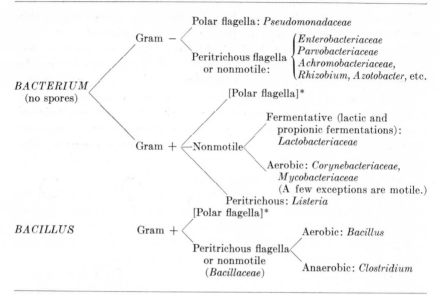

* Forms in brackets are not known as yet.

are straight rods, though spores are formed by isolated members of the groups Vibrio and Sarcina. The group that includes *Bac.* (= *Bacillus*) *subtilis* and *Bac. megatherium*, the celebrated pathogen *Bac. anthracis* (see p. 22), and many others, are all primarily aerobic and are termed *Bacillus*. Those sporeformers that only develop under strictly anaerobic conditions are classed as *Clostridium*. The distinction was first clearly made by Prazmowski (1880) who showed that Cohn's view that *Bac. subtilis* was identical with Pasteur's "vibrion butyrique" (*Clostridium butyricum*) was completely wrong, not only because the former was aerobic and the latter anaerobic, but on morphological grounds as well. Pasteur noticed how the organisms at the edge of his preparation, i.e., those to which air first penetrated, quickly lost the power of motion, while those in the center, and thus still under anaerobic conditions, continued to move. This led him to recognize the existence of anaerobic organisms.

Among the clostridia are included the bacteria responsible for butyric acid (*Cl. butyricum*), butyl alcohol and acetone (*Cl. aceto-butylicum*) fermentations (Chap. XV), and also the pathogens of gas gangrene (*Cl. welchii*), tetanus (*Cl. tetani*), and botulism (*Cl. botu-linum*). In addition there is a small group, sometimes called *Aerobact.*

lus, which have some of the fermentative powers of clostridia but are able to develop both aerobically and anaerobically like the bacilli.

Spore formation was discovered by Cohn in 1873, although spores were actually seen much earlier by Trécul; spores were also seen and recognized as "cysts" resistant to drying out by Pasteur (1876), who was apparently unaware of Cohn's work. The process was studied by Brefeld and in more detail by Prazmowski (1880) in *Bac. subtilis* and *Cl. butyricum,* and by de Bary (1887) in *Bac. megatherium.* The change begins with the formation of a small area of denser material at one end of the cell. After two to three hours this becomes more refractile, and the rod frequently shows a swelling at this position. The

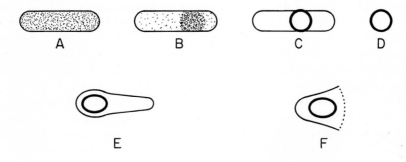

FIGURE II–3

Formation of spores (diagrammatic).

A–D. Bacillus sp. *A.* Vegetative cell; *B.* growing agglomeration of matter in one part of the cell; *C.* sporangium and spore; *D.* mature spore.

E and *F.* Stages corresponding to *C* and *D* in Clostridium.

high refractility was ascribed by Cohn to a high-fat content, but is more likely due to great increase in concentration of solid matter, for although the resulting spore occupies only a fraction of the volume of the original cell (in *Bac. megatherium* only about one-tenth), it contains most of the solid material. In some species the remains of the mother cell quickly disappear (Fig. II–3A to *D*); in others it persists as a faint sporangium. The spore may arise in the center or at one end of the cell; in bacilli it is usually of about the same diameter as the cell, and in clostridia very much broader (Fig. II–3E to *F*). It is clear and highly refractile, and in ordinary stained preparations takes dyes very poorly. However, it can be stained with a powerful dye, such as warm fuchsin in phenol, and the dye, once in, will stay in the cell even when washed with alcohol or 1 N acetic acid; the difficulty in staining is therefore due to the nature of the spore membrane. Details of spore formation and germination, as well as of the spore wall and nucleus, are discussed in the next chapter (sec. 4 and 5).

C. Motility

The flagella are very fine whips by means of which the organisms swim about. Some rods, e.g., the milk-souring group, *Lactobacillus*, are entirely without them at all times and therefore nonmotile; others are motile only in young cultures and later lose their flagella.

Some of the so-called "higher" bacteria, which are considered to be colorless members of the *Myxophyceae*, possess a kind of motility without having flagella. It is very slow, not exceeding 2 to 5 μ per second, compared to figures up to 200 μ per second for bacteria with flagella. *Beggiatoa*, which consists of a number of disc-shaped cells forming a filament (Chap. XXII), shows a very characteristic gentle swaying to and fro in water. This is in part a rotary movement of the tip of the filament; the appearance of swaying "is due to the optical projection of a conical circulation, complicated by the friction between slide and cover slip which forces the tip to describe a narrow ellipse instead of a circle"(Pringsheim, 1949). The movement is apparently very much the same as that of *Oscillatoria*, a filamentous blue-green alga, and indeed it is one of the reasons for considering Beggiatoa as a colorless blue-green alga (cf. Fig. II–1). In addition there is a true translatory movement, the whole filament, in the case of Oscillatoria, going backward and forward at about 4 μ per second. Ullrich (1929) has made motion-picture records of the movement of Beggiatoa and of Oscillatoria and ascribes its mechanism to longitudinal waves of contraction and swelling, but it would be hard to explain actual translocation in this way.

The slow creeping movement of the diatoms (*Bacillariophyceae*) over solid media is also achieved without flagella and is thought to be caused by a film of slime which is constantly being secreted through the pores of the organism and flows down over its whole length. The very rapid sliding movements of a group of pennate diatoms one against another, as seen in the genus *Bacillaria*, represent a magnification of this type of movement. The Myxobacteria (sec. 6) show a slow gliding movement which is probably connected in some way with the secretion of the slime or mucilage characteristic of this group. Thus, all these gliding movements in a variety of organisms have much in common, although doubtless the mechanism has numerous variants. Jarosch (1959), in reviewing the extensive literature, concludes that the motive force is located at the surface, in the form of individual protoplasmic fibrils which act directly or indirectly upon the slime film.

The motile Eubacteria are, however, all dependent on flagella. These may occur in two types of arrangement, as mentioned above, namely, polar and nonpolar. The polar flagellation may consist either of a single flagellum (*monotrichous*) or a number of flagella in a bunch at the same pole (*cephalotrichous*) (see Fig. II–4). All rod-shaped organisms with polar flagella are classed in the Pseudomonas family, *Pseudomonadaceae*. The *Rhizobium* group, which infect the roots of legumes, giving rise to nodules, seem to have polar flagella at first, changing to a "subpolar" arrangement in the long rods during their motile stage of existence (Chap. IX). The spirilla have flagella at both poles (*lophotrichous;* see Fig. II–5), usually in bunches, although they are apparently used all together as a single organ (see below). The vibrios are apparently monotrichous.

Those rods that have flagella distributed along the sides and not at the poles (*peritrichous*) include the Gram-negative organisms of the intestine, called the *Enterobacteriaceae*, and many other fermenting bacteria of various types. A few cocci have been observed to be motile, with peritrichous flagella. Those sporeforming rods that are motile are also invariably peritrichous. Some weakly motile bacteria have one to four flagella inserted laterally or subpolarly; these are regarded as "degenerately peritrichous" (cf. Clark and Carr, 1951).

Some short peritrichous rods, like *S. typhosa*, have only two or four flagella each, one or two on each side. Others, like *Proteus mirabilis*, have large numbers of flagella on either side (Fig. II–6), and when these bacteria are united into a chain, the result is most impressive. Electron micrographs confirm that a single peritrichous rod can have a very large number of flagella (Fig. II–7). In some cases flagella are wound up into bundles, which can unwind into finer threads (Pijper, 1931; Hofer, 1944) when the bacteria are dying.

The flagella are only 0.12 μ thick (Astbury and Weibull, 1949), which means that they cannot individually be seen by direct illumination under the microscope. They can be observed under the following conditions: (1) with dark-field illumination, which shows objects just below the range of visibility, and in which flagella can be seen if they are stuck together in bundles, or under special optical conditions; (2) after subjection to a special treatment which swells and thickens them to visible size; and (3) with the electron microscope, which gives magnifications up to 100 times greater than the optical microscope. The second procedure, as developed by Löffler and Zettnow, consists of depositing antimony tannate on the flagella, and then letting the swollen, tanned flagella react with ammoniacal (or ethylamine) silver nitrate, so that they are blackened by silver. Figure II–6 was prepared in this way. Other methods use different mordants and tanning agents,

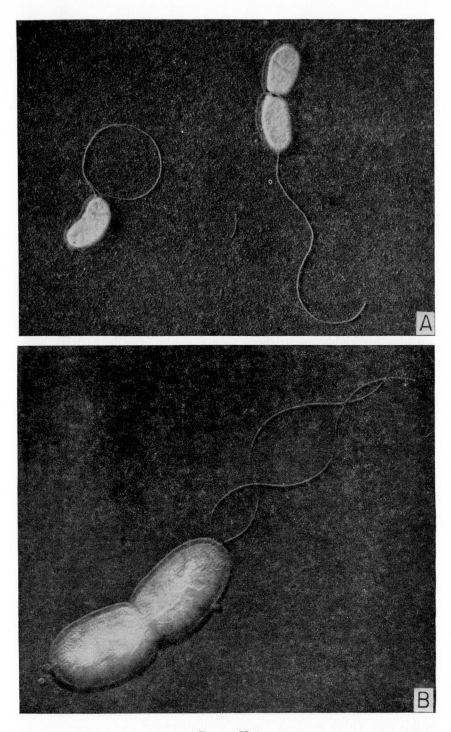

FIGURE II–4
For descriptive legend see page 49.

and deposit dyes instead of silver. The critical point in the procedure, however, lies not in the chemical used but in the preparation of the film, since the violent fluctuations and currents that occur when the film dries up often tear all flagella off the cells, and sometimes they appear as a background to the whole preparation. In addition, Proteus can "shoot off" its flagella while the cell remains intact (Kingma-Boltjes, 1948).

Figure II–8 shows that the flagella in stained preparations take up very different configurations. In normal flagella there is a regular "wavelength," which is from 1.5 to 2.5 μ, while in "curly" flagella it is from one-half to one-fourth this length. In some organisms the curly type appears mainly in acid cultures, the normal in neutral or alkaline media, but in others curliness is simply a character of particular strains. The very fine small amplitude wavelength as in c is characteristic of the small rod *Listeria*, and the coiled form as in d of *Serratia marcescens* (Chap. XIV, sec. 1). Types c and f are associated with very low motility. Occasionally two types may be seen on the same cell or (rarely) on the same flagellum (Leifson, 1960). The significance of these flagellar forms is not understood.

Most of the finer details of the flagella remained unknown until the advent of the electron microscope in the last few years. Photographs like Fig. II–5 and II–7 establish that: (1) the bases of the flagella lie just within the cell wall, probably ending in a basal granule; (2) if there is a capsule surrounding the cell, the flagella pass right through it; (3) flagella may be of different thicknesses, and some may consist of finer threads wound together; (4) flagella are uniform and free from lumps or thick portions; (5) the lengths of flagella, and the number per cell, are more or less characteristic for a given species.

Since they are so fine, the exact movement of flagella has been difficult to make out. In Euglena and Monas, flagellate protozoa many times larger than a bacterium, the single flagellum is at the front, and pulls the organism along by a characteristic whiplike movement (Krijgsman, 1925). In the spermatozoa of animals, on the other hand, the flagellum is used to lash the water from behind. The very much shorter *cilia* of the ciliate protozoa, which are situated all around the

---

FIGURE II–4

Polar flagella, as seen in the electron microscope.

A. *Vibrio metschnikovii*, monotrichous. 4100 ✕. (Photo W. van Iterson; E. M., Delft. From *Biochim. Biophys. Acta*, 1:527.)

B. *Ps. fluorescens*, cephalotrichous. 18,000 ✕. (Photo A. L. Houwink and W. van Iterson; E. M., Delft. From *Biochim. Biophys. Acta*, 5:10–44. Copyright 1947 and 1950, respectively, by Elsevier Publishing Co., Amsterdam, The Netherlands.)

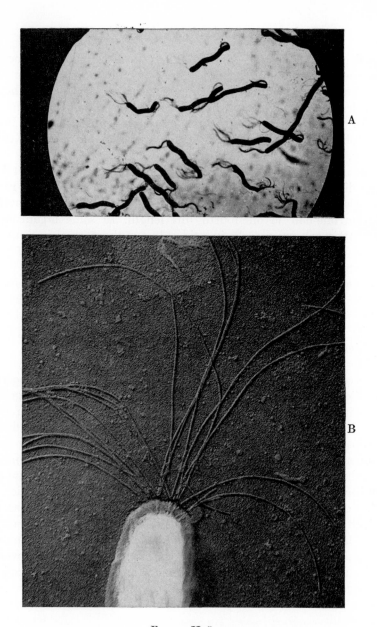

FIGURE II-5

Two views of the flagella of the same organism, *Spirillum serpens*.

A. Optical microscope, flagella stain. 1000 ×. (From Kingma-Boltjes, 1948, *J. Path. Bact.*, **60**:257–287.)

B. Electron microscope. 12,000 ×. (Photo W. van Iterson; E. M., Delft. From *Biochim. Biophys. Acta*, 1:527–548. Copyright by Elsevier Publishing Co., Amsterdam, The Netherlands.)

Note that the flagella pass through the outer envelope of the cell.

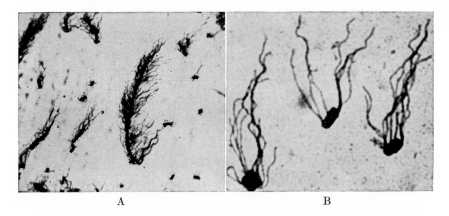

A   B

FIGURE II–6

A. *Proteus mirabilis*. Flagella stain, showing a long filament containing many cells. 1000 ×.

B. Same organism at higher magnification; single cells. Note how the flagella have been oriented by currents of fluid on the slide. 3000 ×. (From Kingma-Boltjes, 1948. *J. Path. Bact.*, **60**:257–287.)

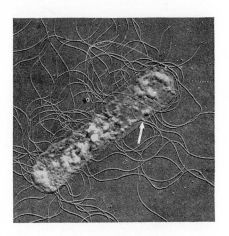

FIGURE II–7

Proteus vulgaris. An autolyzed cell in which nothing remains of the protoplast but the granules, such as those at the base of the flagella (*arrow*). Preparation by C. F. Robinow. 8000 × (Photo A. L. Houwink and W. van Iterson. From *Biochim. Biophys. Acta*, **5**:10–44. R.C.A. Laboratories. Copyright 1950 by Elsevier Publishing Co., Amsterdam, The Netherlands.)

side of the organism, are comparatively stiff and simply move to and fro like oars—"a modern example of the old-fashioned galley-boat" (van Niel, 1926). This can readily be seen at low temperatures. There is no evidence that the movements of bacterial flagella comprise any of these types.

The large lophotrichous spirilla, which have been observed in dark-field illumination, move with circular rotation of semirigid flagella, the group in front being curved back toward the body, the group

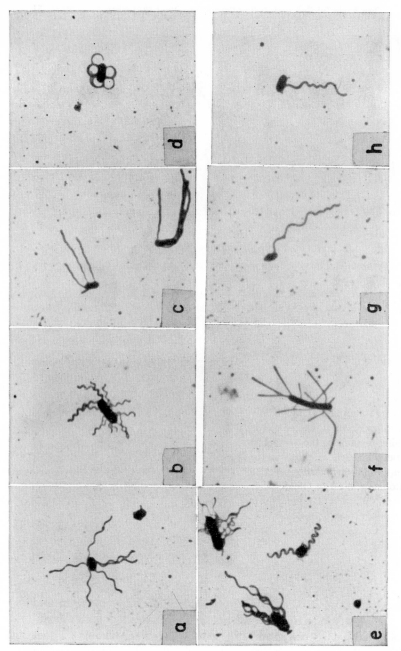

FIGURE II-8

Fixed and stained flagella showing different types of curling. *a.* Normal (Salmonella typhi); *b.* curly (Alcaligenes); *c.* small amplitude (Listeria); *d.* coiled (Serratia); *e.* semicoiled (Proteus); *f.* straight (Listeria); *g* and *h.* two types on same flagellum (Proteus and Cellulomonas, respectively). (All from Leifson, Atlas of Bacterial Flagellation, New York, Academic Press, 1961.)

behind curved out behind it like a propeller (see Fig. II–9). In some cases, however, the group in front is stretched out straight forward (Kingma-Boltjes, 1948). The flagella all swing together, creating a single cone of revolution. At the same time the body of the organism itself rotates, although at about one-third the speed of rotation of the flagella. Thus the spirillum "screws" itself into the water. Apparently the arrangement can be reversed at will, and the spirilla can reverse

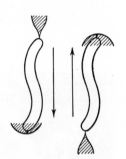

FIGURE II–9

Diagram of movement of the flagella of a Spirillum. (Modified from P. Metzner, 1920, *Jahrb. wiss. Bot.*, **59**:325–412; Berlin, Gebrüder Borntraeger.)

FIGURE II–10

Motility of a large Chromatium showing movement of the fluid through the flagellar vortex. (From P. Metzner, 1920, *Jahrb. wiss. Bot.*, **59**:325–412; Berlin, Gebrüder Borntraeger.)

direction without having to turn around. Those spirilla that are purple, i.e., those in the *Rhodobacteriinae*, are phototactic and swim toward an area of brighter light (Chap. XXIII, sec. 5).

In a few spirilla, Metzner noticed that the front and rear flagella were both operating in the same way; as a result the organism remained stationary (see Fig. II–12).

The same principle, with flagellum astern only, is used in the large sulfur bacterium, Chromatium, shown in Fig. II–10. The diagram indicates the movement of the liquid through the cone of rotating flagella, as interpreted from watching small particles (Metzner, 1920). A model working along similar lines has been constructed, and its movement compared with that calculated on hydrodynamical principles (Taylor, 1952). As with the spirilla, it was found that the body of the model rotated about its axis.

The movement of peritrichous organisms has been studied by focusing intense light into bacterial suspensions thickened by gelatin or gum arabic, and viewing by dark-field illumination (Neumann, 1925; Pijper, 1940; Kingma-Boltjes, 1948). In very young cells the

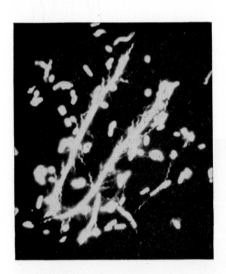

FIGURE II–11

A filament of *Proteus mirabilis*. Photographed in actual movement through viscous medium. Dark-field, 720 ×, exposure ⅕ second. (From Kingma-Boltjes, 1948, *J. Path. Bact.*, **60**:275–287.)

flagella, being too fine, cannot be made visible in this way, but in later stages they become thicker and apparently fewer. Neumann (1925) distinguishes three stages: in the first they are close and fine, in the second they are well separated from one another, and in the third probably combined into thick tufts which act each as a single flagellum. In gum arabic preparations of short rods like *S. typhosa*, a bundle of flagella is held out as a "tail" astern. This is probably a thickly combined tuft; the motion may be due to other flagella further forward retaining their individuality and being thus too fine, or moving too fast, to be seen. With a long train of *Proteus mirabilis* cells in the second or third stage (Fig. II–11) it can be seen that the flagella are held close to the body, and the driving force is very probably achieved by propagation of a spiral wave motion along each flagellum. The waves are of rather constant amplitude, and the wavelength is around 2 μ (Leifson and Hugh, 1954; cf. Fig. II–7 and 8).

This idea of the propagation of a wave of contraction receives support from the chemistry of the flagellum. Isolated flagella of Proteus, collected by ammonium sulfate precipitation, consist of an elastic fibrous protein of constant composition (Weibull, 1948–1951). It is closely allied to keratin of skin and myosin of muscle (Astbury and Weibull, 1949), although its amino acid composition is not identical with either. It is thus probably a special kind of muscle. Its thickness would not allow of many protein molecules in cross section, and it is suggested that the protein is laid down in the form of a few "monomolecular" chains. Such chains could presumably undergo contraction and relaxation like muscle, and if there were two chains per flagellum, alternate contractions on the two sides would cause propagation of a wave of motion along the flagellum.

The speed of movement of flagella is very great. Buder (1915) used flashing light to photograph Chromatium in course of movement, and with an exposure of $\frac{1}{25}$ second the complete conical or hemispherical path of the flagellum was still visible. Metzner (1920), by increasing the speed of the flash, determined the rate with spirilla at about 40 revolutions per second. Both front and rear flagella turn at the same speed. At about 13 flashes per second the rotation of the spirillum itself appeared to vanish, i.e., one rotation was made between each flash, so that in this organism the flagella turn at just three times the speed of the body (Fig. II–12). The flagellar speed of 40 revolutions per second, or 2400 rpm, is equal to that of an electric motor.

The rate of forward movement is also very high. Figures from 27 μ per second for *Bac. megatherium* up to 200 μ per second for *Vibrio comma* have been recorded. This last figure means that the cell moves 50 times its own length in a second. If a 6-ft man could do the same, he would swim at 100 yards per second; the Olympic record for swimming 100 yards, however, is 57 seconds! Nevertheless the motility uses only a fraction, perhaps 0.1 per cent, of the total metabolic energy of a bacterium.

It was mentioned above that some bacteria can move over the surface of solid media. This ability is limited to a few peritrichs, including *Bac. rotans*, *Bac. circulans*, *Bac. alvei*, and some Proteus species. Usually they travel spirally outward from the center of a colony, "marching" with several in line abreast. Occasionally, however, the marching column swings off across the medium to curl inward and start a new colony elsewhere. Very small colonies of *Bac. alvei* will move en masse across the agar, leaving a faint trail of nonmotile cells to mark the edge of the track. The surface of the medium must be moist for these movements to occur. They can be prevented by mild antiseptics like borate or dilute phenol. The speeds do not exceed 14 μ per second (Shinn, 1940) which is well below the rates of movement in liquid media; so that it seems likely that the flagella are the cause of movement and the cells are probably "wading" in the film of moisture on the surface of the medium.

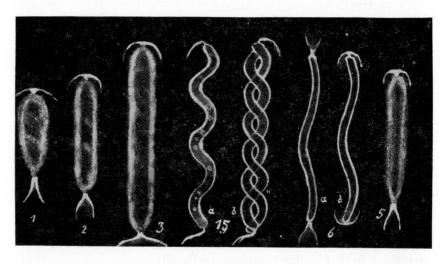

FIGURE II–12

Motile Spirilla in dark-field.

1 and *2*. *Sp. undula; 3. Sp. volutans; 5* and *6. Sp. serpens*. In *6* the organisms have oppositely rotating flagella and are therefore stationary; in *1, 2, 3*, and *5* the body is rotating, and only its envelope is seen. *15* (center). *Sp. volutans* viewed in flashing light. Left 13, right 26 flashes per second. All ca. 720 ×. (All from P. Metzner, 1920, *Jahrb. wiss. Bot.*, **59**:325–412; Berlin, Gebrüder Borntraeger.)

Considerations such as those of the great rate of metabolism, mentioned above, and the extreme rapidity of motion of the flagella, combine to give an impressive picture of the life and behavior of a bacterium. It is an organism of tremendous activity, capable, if motile, of moving through the water at (relatively) high speed, surrounded by flagella many times its own length, each whirring with the velocity of an electric motor. Correspondingly it eats voraciously, matter equivalent to its own weight pouring through it every five seconds. It also grows with great rapidity, fast enough to cover the earth with the progeny of one individual in less than 48 hours.

The varied activities of the Eubacteria comprise the bulk of this book and cannot usefully be summarized here. Before proceeding to their detailed consideration it is necessary to consider briefly the morphology and interrelationships of other types of bacteria.

3. THE PURPLE, BROWN, AND GREEN BACTERIA

A large number of organisms are known which morphologically are clearly bacteria, but which live by photosynthesis, as do the algae and the higher plants. The photosynthesis differs from that of the green plants, however, in not producing oxygen; instead, it leads to the production of sulfur or various dehydrogenated organic compounds. The majority of the organisms are in fact anaerobic or microaerophilic. Because of their wide variety and characteristic physiology, they are either considered as a separate suborder, the *Rhodobacteriineae*, or an order, the *Rhodobacteriales*.

These bacteria are from 1 to over 20 μ in length; until lately only the smaller forms had been successfully cultivated (van Niel, 1931, 1944), but now the very large forms can be successfully grown too (Schlegel and Pfennig, 1961). They include all the shapes characteristic of the Eubacteria, i.e., vibrio, spirillum, rod, and various types of coccus. The only exceptions are that spore formation does not occur, and that when there are flagella, they are always polar. There are also a few purple forms which appear to be motile though without flagella, apparently by means of a gliding movement; these have been inadequately studied but may possibly represent purple forms of the *Myxophyceae* or the Myxobacteria (see below). Some of the forms described as green bacteria may really belong in the *Myxophyceae* (see Fritsch, 1945, p. 860).

Physiologically the *Rhodobacteriineae* are a moderately well-unified group. All contain a pigment similar to chlorophyll, which is responsible for the photosynthesis. In addition, the purple and brown forms contain various "accessory" pigments which, as in the algae, more or less mask the green color; these are carotenoids. They differ from the carotenoids of algae or higher plants in being more unsaturated and redder in color.

Because some of these bacteria contain globules of sulfur, they have been at one time confused with other forms that contain sulfur but that are highly *aerobic* and colorless, i.e., the so-called "sulfur bacteria." Some of these are relatively complex in structure, and are probably colorless *Myxophyceae;* in any event they have an entirely different physiology from that of the *Rhodobacteriineae* (see Chaps. XXII and XXIII). It is characteristic of the purple, brown, and green bacteria that they will grow in light in strictly anaerobic conditions; on the other hand, a few members of the group can also grow aerobically, and these can also be cultured in the dark, i.e., they are *facultatively* photosynthetic.

There are two main types of purple bacteria; one group (*Thiorhodaceae*) requires H_2S or other sulfur compounds as well as CO_2, while the other (*Athiorhodaceae*) requires organic compounds, including one or more vitamins. It is in the *Athiorhodaceae* that the facultatively photosynthetic forms are found. The green bacteria (*Chlorobacteriaceae*) have a "sulfur" type of photosynthetic metabolism. All of these organisms are taken up in detail in Chapter XXIII.

4. THE MYCOBACTERIA

Somewhat different from the Eubacteria are the Mycobacteria, a group of organisms which, although they possess the rod shape, are morphologically a little more variable. The outlines of stained Mycobacteria are characteristically rather irregular, and there may also be a tendency to branch. Many form long filaments, in this respect resembling some of the lactic bacteria (Chap. XII).

None forms spores, and truly motile forms are rare. The group comprises two different types—the Mycobacteria proper and the Corynebacteria. Both react positively to Gram's stain.

A. Mycobacteria

These are long rods, often of lumpy outline in heat-fixed preparations, in some cases forming filaments. When stained with fuchsin in phenol,[3] the Mycobacteria subsequently retain the stain against washing with acid, in the same way as spores do against washing with alcohol. This "acid-fastness" is a property typical, to varying degrees, of the whole group. The most acid-fast are the pathogens of tuberculosis—human, bovine, and avian. Besides these and the pathogen of leprosy (*Mycob. leprae*) the group comprises a large number of important saprophytes. These are strongly aerobic and can oxidize such relatively inert substances as paraffins, benzene, and aromatic amines.

---

[3] The Ziehl-Neelsen technique. The dried and fixed smear is treated five minutes at steaming heat with 1.5 per cent basic fuchsin in 2.5 per cent phenol (or 0.2 per cent basic fuchsin in 20 per cent aqueous propylene glycol + 4 per cent phenol), rinsed, and then washed with cold 1 per cent H_2SO_4, or 3 per cent HCl in alcohol. A light counterstain with methylene blue enables other organisms, tissue cells, and so on, to be seen. When used on spores, a preliminary washing of the film with chloroform and with chromic acid improves the results.

Among the parasites, *M. leprae* (but not *M. tuberculosis*) also attacks hydrocarbons. On account of this property, some Mycobacteria may be isolated from soil by using media containing no source of carbon, and exposing the plates to the vapors of paraffins or other volatile compounds (Söhngen, 1913; Wagner, 1914; ZoBell, 1946). *M. salmonicolor* and *M. opacum* (de Jong, 1926) attack the lower fatty acids up as far as caproic and also many other organic compounds (cf. Table VIII–4, p. 352). *M. leprae* has not been successfully grown in culture.

The composition of Mycobacteria is unlike that of the Eubacteria, the cells being very rich in fats and waxes. *M. tuberculosis* may contain up to 40 per cent of its dry weight in the form of ether- or acetone-soluble material (Anderson, 1940), and *M. leprae* may contain almost as much. The amount of these lipids depends on the medium, especially on its glycerol content; for example, raising the glycerol content from 0.5 per cent to 12.5 per cent increased the lipid content of *M. tuberculosis* from 10.4 per cent to 27.6 per cent (Long and Finner, 1927).

One of the lipid constituents, "mycolic acid," is weakly acid-fast when extracted from the cell, and it has been suggested that this substance accounts for the staining properties of Mycobacteria (Anderson, 1929, 1940). However, the whole group of lipids contribute to the acid-fastness, by virtue of the much greater solubility of the phenol-dye complex in them than in dilute acid (Lamanna, 1946). The dye can be washed out with hot water (75° to 90° C), and if the cells are ground or crushed, they can even be decolorized with acid (Wells *et al.*, 1932). It is possible, therefore, that the bulk of the lipid layer which retains the dye is oriented on or near the cell wall, perhaps in connection with the Gram-staining complex (see Chap. III, sec. 3; Chap. XV, sec. 5; and the discussion by Dubos, 1947).

B. Corynebacteria

These commonly appear club-shaped or "lumpy" in preparations, but this is probably an artifact. When the cell walls are stained with tannic acid and crystal violet, it is seen that the characteristically "lumpy" rod in reality consists of three to six very short or elliptical cells (Bisset, 1949). Slight differences in the thickness or orientation of these cause the apparent lumpiness (Fig. II–13). The phenomenon is accentuated by the shrinkage which accompanies heat-fixation. There is nothing lumpy or of irregular outline about the individual short rods.

Most Corynebacteria are nonmotile and, unlike the Mycobacteria, do not form chains. The few weakly motile forms are "degenerately peritrichous" (cf. p. 47). They are not acid-fast. Some, like the Mycobacteria, are highly aerobic, oxidizing many organic compounds, but so far only five have been found to attack hydrocarbons, thus differing, as a general rule, from the Mycobacteria (Bushnell and Haas, 1941). A very few species, including the best-known member, *C. diphtheriae* (the pathogen of diphtheria), and *C. acnes,* can ferment simple carbohydrates to formic, acetic, propionic, lactic, and succinic acids (de Wolff, 1927). The formation of propionic acid is especially significant, since it establishes a link with the propionic acid bacteria (Chap. XIII). *C. diphtheriae* is not a typical Corynebacterium, however, since it is not highly aerobic and attacks only very few

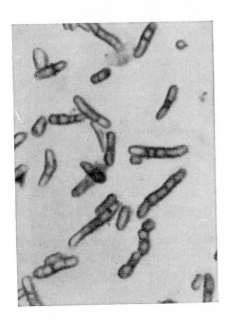

FIGURE II–13

Dividing Corynebacteria stained to show cell walls. The large lumpy "cells" are in reality multiple. (Photographed by K. A. Bisset.)

amino acids (Schmidt, 1933). Its DNA composition (cf. Chap. XXVI) places it nearer the Lactobacilli than the Actinomycetes.

Some of the nonpathogenic Corynebacteria have been placed in a new genus, Arthrobacter, by Conn and Dimmick (1947), on the ground that the cells are gram-negative when young, and that they can grow on ammonium nitrogen, while the Corynebacteria require amino acids. Chemical analyses of the cell walls (Cummins and Harris, 1959) support some separation of this group, for while *C. diphtheriae* has arabinose and DL-diaminopimelic acid in its cell wall, all the seven Arthrobacters tested had no arabinose, two of them had LL-diaminopimelic acid, and five did not contain this acid but had lysine instead.

Both the morphology and physiology of the Corynebacteria place them close to the propionic acid bacteria (Chap. XIII), and *C. acnes* actually carries out a propionic fermentation. Bergey's classification (1957) places these two families next to one another in the order Eubacteriales but includes Mycobacteria as the first family in the order Actinomycetales (below).

5. THE ACTINOMYCETES

A. General

There is a large group of organisms which, though closely related to the bacteria, is more complex in morphology, having the characteristic form of a branched *mycelium*. The threads or hyphae, though often extremely long, are without transverse walls at first and show true branching; they therefore resemble superficially the hyphae of Phycomycetes, which also form mycelium without cross walls (p. 36). However, the important difference is that the mycelia of Actinomycetes are thin, like bacteria, not exceeding 1.5 μ in thickness, while Phycomycete hyphae are 5 μ or more in diameter.

After a day or two's growth, the mycelium of some forms (*Actinomyces* proper and *Proactinomyces* or *Nocardia*) breaks up into single rod-shaped or spheroidal cells; others (*Streptomyces* and *Micromonospora*) continue as a true mycelium. The colonies in agar tend to embed themselves, and typically have a hard, dry, chalky consistency, while in many of them the mycelium is partly raised into the air like that of a true fungus.

The first organism of this type was described by Cohn in 1872 under the name of *Streptothrix*, and shortly afterward (1877) the most important animal pathogen in the group was identified by Harz as *Actinomyces* (= "ray-fungus"), the name being based on the radiating structure of the mycelial granule in animal tissue (Fig. II–14B). The resulting disease is called "lumpy jaw" or actinomycosis of cattle. Since that time many names have been applied to the Actinomycetes, especially words ending with "-thrix," which designates the threadlike or hyphal form. The actinomycosis organism is not typical, since it is anaerobic while virtually all the others are strongly aerobic. It was made clear by Jensen (1931) that the group contains two main types: those whose mycelium readily breaks up into bacteria-like cells and which do not form "spores" (Actinomyces and Proactinomyces [now called Nocardia]), and those whose mycelium remains more or less intact but cuts off conidia or spores (now called the

Streptomycetaceae). Some Nocardiae are acid-fast and thus related to the Mycobacteria. Many students have, indeed, classed the Myco-bacteria together with the Actinomycetes, but there seems little reason for this since the formation of a mycelium is a major point of difference. The basis of Jensen's subdivision has been generally ac-cepted and extended and is summarized below. The earlier systems are discussed in the books by Waksman (1950 and 1960).

B. Systematics

The description is essentially as follows:

They are elongated, usually filamentous cells, not exceeding 1.5 μ in diameter, usually producing a branched mycelium. They multiply (1) by fragmentation of the hyphae, followed by more or less rounding up of the resulting spore; (2) by simple segmentation into oidia; or (3) by cutting off conidia singly or in chains at the end of special hyphae. Growing readily on artificial media, they form well-developed colonies whose surface may become covered with an aerial mycelium. They are saprophytes or parasites, aerobic or anaerobic, pigmented or colorless, mesophilic or thermophilic, and are gram-positive.

The genera can be separated as follows (Lechevalier *et al.*, 1961):

Anaerobic or microaerophilic, forming no conidia	1. *Actinomyces*
Aerobic:	
A. Conidia formed singly	
a. No aerial mycelium	2. *Micromonospora*
b. Aerial mycelium formed	3. *Thermoactinomyces*
B. Conidia formed in longitudinal pairs on the aerial mycelium	4. *Waksmania*
C. Conidia formed both singly and in chains on the aerial mycelium and on the substrate	5. *Micropolyspora*
D. Conidia, when formed, in chains on the aerial mycelium only	
a. Mycelium fragmenting, conidia often absent	6. *Nocardia*
b. Mycelium nonfragmenting, conidia always formed	7. *Streptomyces*
E. Spores produced within sporangia, as well as conidia (family Actinoplanaceae)	
a. Spores nonmotile	8. *Streptosporangium*
b. Spores actively motile	9. *Actinoplanes*

The Nocardias are the simplest; they form aerial mycelium only slowly if at all, and usually no conidia. Their cell walls, like those of the Mycobacteria, are not dissolved by lysozyme, while those of Streptomyces are. Those that are acid-fast can generally grow on paraffin or phenols as a carbon source, and usually do not hydrolyze starch or proteins, although *N. brasiliensis*, which is partially acid-fast, does hydrolyze casein and gelatin (Gordon and Mihm, 1959). The degree of acid-fastness depends on nutrition, and is increased by adding milk or 12 per cent glycerol to the medium (Erikson, 1949). The growth type grades all the way from bacteria-like, forming diffuse growth in liquid media, to Actinomyces-like, forming microcolonies in liquid media and hard, mycelial colonies on agar. An old colony which has fragmented into rods looks very much like a colony of Mycobacteria, both macroscopically (wrinkled, mealy consistency, often brightly colored) and microscopically. The pathogenic forms, however, show characteristic club-shaped hyphae in animal tissue, which suggests relationship with the diphtheroids and other Corynebacteria.

Actinomyces proper is really only a single form, *Act. bovis*, although the human pathogen is often regarded as a distinct species, *Act. israeli* (after J. Israel who, with Wolf, first obtained it in pure culture [1891]). In animals infected with lumpy jaw, it occurs as compact yellowish granules either in the tissue or in exudates. Cross sections of the granules show the radiating structure from which the name derives (Fig. II–14*A*, *B*) and also, round the periphery, thick club-shaped structures. These are bigger and more characteristic than those of pathogenic Nocardiae; they probably consist of two cells joined together, one swollen and rounded, the other rod-shaped. Different isolates vary in one or more characters; some produce rough-surfaced colonies in which real branched filaments are seen, while others produce smooth-surfaced colonies consisting mostly of shortish, irregular, diphtheroid cells which often stain irregularly (Fig. II–14*A*). In culture, the young mycelia at first show no cross walls, but these appear later, and when the colony becomes old, it may break up completely into separate short rods. The anaerobic growth is promoted by 5 per cent CO_2 (Rosebury *et al.*, 1944).

Streptomyces is the biggest group, comprising 149 "species" accepted by Bergey. These are mainly soil organisms and have recently come into prominence for their production of powerful antibiotics—streptothricin from *Str. lavendulae*, chloroamphenicol from *Str. venezuelae*, chlorotetracycline from *Str. aureofaciens*, oxytetracycline from *Str. rimosus*, and streptomycin from *Str. griseus* (see Chap. XXV). Vitamin B_{12} is also produced from cultures of *Str. griseus* after extraction of the antibiotic. The pathogen of potato scab disease, *Str. scabies*, is also in the group. Most of them are proteolytic and some can attack cellulose. All are aerobic and produce aerial mycelium.

In many Streptomyces species the breaking up of the terminal parts into conidia is preceded by a curious coiling of the hyphae into spirals (Fig. II–14C); when this happens, the spiral hyphae are the only ones that break up and are therefore to be considered as specialized conidiophores. In others the hyphae that are to produce conidia are borne in broom-shaped clusters, or in little whorls. All these structures can be considered, from the evolutionary viewpoint, as the beginning

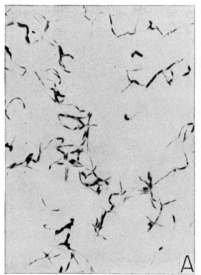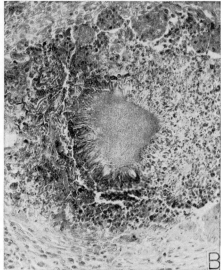

FIGURE II–14

Three types of Actinomycetes.

A. *Act. bovis*, Gram stain of a rough culture. 940 ✕.

B. The same, sectioned through a granule in rabbit lung. 240 ✕.

(A and B from T. Rosebury, L. J. Epps, and A. R. Clark, *J. Infectious Diseases*, 74:131–149. Copyright 1944 by the Univ. of Chicago Press.)

C. Streptomyces sp. Gram stain. 760 ✕. (Prepared by M. L. Littman.)

D. Micromonospora. Two types showing (*left*) spore-bearing hyphae, single or branched; (*right*) spore-bearing hyphae clustered. Contact preparations (see p. 278) made from compost.

(C and D from S. A. Waksman, 1950; The Actinomycetes. Waltham, Mass., The Chronica Botanica Co. Courtesy of Dr. Waksman and the Chronica Botanica Co.)

of specialization, and as an indication of how much less primitive these organisms are than the bacteria.

A characteristic of many Streptomyces species is the production of an "earthy" smell in cultures; the smell of freshly dug soil probably derives from this, since direct microscopy shows that these organisms are among the most numerous of all in soil (see Chap. VI, sec. 4). The

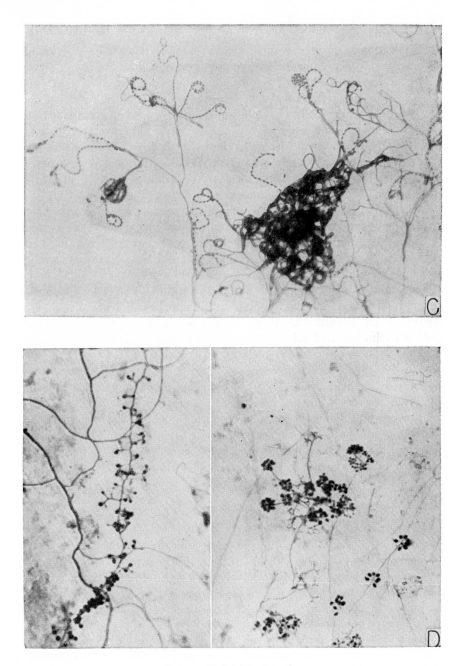

FIGURE II–14 (*Continued*)

smell is mainly produced by the round-spored forms (Lieske, 1921) and is due to an ether-soluble volatile compound which may be an amine (Thaysen, 1936).

The *Micromonosporas* are a small group, originally described by Ørskov (1923), which bear single conidia on the end of a short hyphal branch, 5 to 10 μ long (Fig. II–14D). The mycelium does not grow in the air at all but tends to burrow into the medium, at least in agar. They are somewhat tough organisms, because the spores can resist eight months' desiccation and one to five minutes heating at 80° C (Waksman, 1950). At least one member is thermophilic.

Somewhat like Micromonospora is an organism isolated from a case of pleuritis and pneumonia and possibly the cause of it, and subsequently found in several patients suspected of tuberculosis. This organism, *Waksmania rosea*, also called Microbispora, forms its conidia or spores in pairs (Louria and Gordon, 1960).

Micropolyspora brevicatena and a few similar species form conidia in short chains (three to five) on little branches (Lechevalier *et al.*, 1961). Like Waksmania they were isolated from the sputum of patients who had had tuberculosis. There is also a related thermophilic species.

Lastly, the *Actinoplanaceae* are noteworthy for their fungus-like sporangia (Couch, 1950, 1955). When newly formed, the interior of these seems to consist of a tightly coiled hypha, but later this breaks up into minute sub-globose or angular spores, which in some species swim actively like pseudomonads. The sporangia are formed best on floating grass-leaves in water. Some 30 species have been isolated, and the family appears to be world-wide.

C. Spores

The spores (conidia) of the Actinomycetes are very small—less than 1.5 μ in their maximum dimension—and therefore similar to those of the Eubacteria. They differ from these, however, in not being stable to heat; even those of the relatively heat-resistant *Mm. chalcea* can hardly be compared with those of, say, *Bac. subtilis*, which withstand actual boiling for many minutes. A number of Streptomyces species form spores whose outer wall has grown out into numerous long spines. These arise from the wall of the aerial mycelium from which the spores were formed by subdivision (Mach, 1960). Like the wall, they are soluble in lysozyme. The motile spores of Actinoplanes bear a tuft of flagella, but the exact way they move is not known.

Germination of a spore is by protrusion of one or more "germ tubes" which develop into ordinary hyphae. Sometimes cylindrical spores give rise to four germ tubes, one at each corner. Lieske (1921) was inclined to attribute special significance to this "Vier-Hyphen-Spore," and it is tempting to speculate on some relation with a nuclear reduction-division, but there is no direct evidence for this as yet.

6. THE MYXOBACTERIA

A. General Properties

A number of rod-shaped bacteria of peculiar properties, a few of which had previously been imperfectly described and placed in various families of fungi, were brought together by Thaxter (1892) as "a new

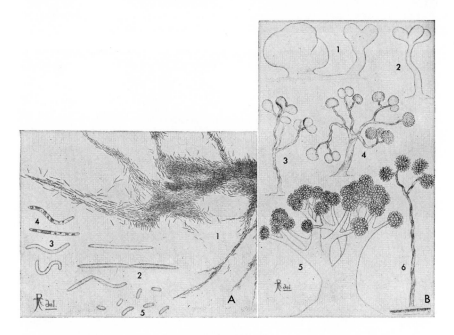

FIGURE II–15

Thaxter's original drawings of Myxobacteria.

A. Chondromyces aurantiacus. 1. Rod mass in fluid agar; *2* and *3.* living rods; *4.* stained with borax-carmine; *5.* rods from crushed cysts.

B. Chondromyces crocatus. 1, 2, 3, 4, and *6.* stages (reconstructed) in the development of the cystophore; *5.* another individual with thicker base, perhaps because grown on moister agar.

(Both from R. Thaxter, *The Botanical Gazette*, **17**:389–406, 1892. By courtesy of the Univ. of Chicago Press.)

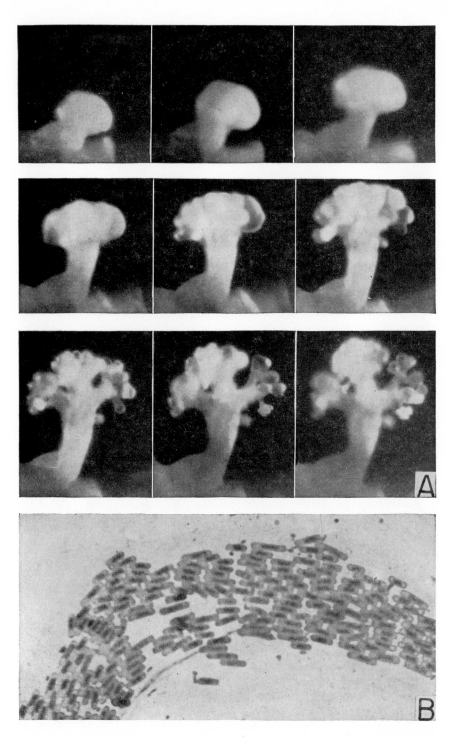

FIGURE II–16
For descriptive legend see page 69.

order of Schizomycetes," the *Myxobacteriaceae*.[4] The rods are long and slender and differ from other bacteria in being *flexible*, so that they often assume a slightly curved appearance. There is no evidence of any rigid or elastic cell wall, and when squeezed the organisms readily break up into a disorganized mass. In some forms (*Myxococcus*, *Polyangium*) the rods have pointed ends, which is unusual in the bacteria. Highly characteristic is the formation of a gelatinous gum, which is not sticky, like the gum of Azotobacter or Aerobacter, but firm and coherent so that whole colonies may be lifted intact from the surface of the medium. Most of the Myxobacteria are red, a few orange, yellow, or green.

The most remarkable character of these organisms is the tendency of the colonies to heap up into raised masses which may subsequently branch to produce very elaborate treelike forms. The colonies are at first quite thin and filmy, and the growth is hard to see, but the heaped-up mass makes a very characteristic colored spot. The heaping-up comes about through a slow movement of the individuals, first toward one another and then en masse. There is no "motility" in the usual sense and no flagella are known; the movement seems to have more in common with that of the blue-green algae or the diatoms than with that of the true bacteria. It may be connected with the excretion of the layer of slime on which the cells lie (Jahn, 1924). The lower parts of the raised masses often thin out into stalks; the upper parts either remain as rounded masses (in the case of Myxococcus) or else separate further into a number of globes, which may in turn each be covered with pointed papillae (as in *Chondromyces*) (see Figs. II–15B and II–16A). In these upper parts the rods are massed together and held in the gum, which by then has hardened into a gelatinous envelope. In Myxococcus and related forms, the rods shorten and round up into spheres ("microcysts"), while in the other forms, although they shorten and round up somewhat, they remain clearly rod-shaped (Fig. II–15A). The rod-masses or cysts after-

---

[4] We should nowadays use the term *Myxobacteriales* for an order, the ending *aceae* being restricted to families.

FIGURE II–16

Chondromyces.

A. Stages in formation of the fruiting body photographed at intervals of about an hour.

B. The individual rods streaming toward a center of aggregation. Stained with Giemsa stain to show nuclear granules.

(Both from J. T. Bonner, *An Essay of Development*. Copyright 1952 by Princeton Univ. Press.)

ward dry out and break up, releasing the individual cells into the air or on to a nutrient medium. The whole raised structure is referred to as a "fruiting body." The movement is ascribed to the excretion by some cells of a substance to which other cells are attracted, i.e., a chemotaxis. Fruiting bodies in contact with a cellophane membrane cause cells on the other side of the membrane to aggregate (McVittie and Zahler, 1962).

Closely related to Myxococcus, although not forming the raised structures or cysts, is a group of organisms which vigorously attacks paper, textiles, and other forms of cellulose and is known as Cytophaga (cf. Chap. XVII). These organisms quickly form colored stains on paper or cotton if this is impregnated with nutrient salts (including NH_4^+, but no soluble carbon compound) and inoculated with soil. The peculiar cultures, in which at first only long, slightly curved rods are seen but later contain mainly large "cocci," were for a long time difficult to understand. Both forms are produced by a pure *clone*, i.e., a culture derived from a single cell. The fact that the rods are not rigid gave the key to the problem; the coccus form is a *microcyst* and can germinate again into a long rod (Krzemieniewska, 1933); the organism is a simplified form of Myxococcus. It differs from Myxococcus in not forming the fruiting body. Other closely related forms have not yet been seen to round up into a microcyst at all and are therefore to be regarded as the simplest or most "imperfect" members of the *Myxobacteriales*. The names *Sporocytophaga* for those forming microcysts and *Cytophaga* for the "imperfect" forms (Stanier, 1940) have been adopted. It is clear that these represent modifications of the normal myxobacterial cycle; conversion from rod to sphere takes place in raised cysts in Myxococcus, in each individual cell in Sporocytophaga, and is absent altogether in Cytophaga.

Similar modifications can be induced in true Myxococci (*M. rubescens* and *M. virescens*) by simply adding about 1 per cent peptone to the medium; the organisms then appear only as long rods (Quehl, 1906), although they grow in a very characteristic radiating fashion (Finck, 1951). Such a ready loss of the cyst-forming ability supports the view that the Cytophagas are derived, or imperfect, forms of Myxococcus. Also in some of the more complex Myxobacteria, like *Polyangium fuscum*, the addition of peptone greatly simplifies the normally elaborate cysts.

Like *Cytophaga*, *Myxococcus* and several species of *Sorangium* and *Polyangium* have been shown to attack paper, while *Chondromyces* will grow on straw or wood; thus the ability to attack cellulose is probably widespread in the order. One of the Cytophagas, *Cyt. johnsonae*, decomposes chitin, and two of the marine forms decompose

agar (Stanier, 1942, 1947). The attack on chitin and related substances may be the basis for the frequent growth of Myxobacteria on
fungi and lichens and even on living Eubacteria (Snieszko *et al.*,
1941–1942). Several Myxobacteria indeed can lyse living or dead
bacterial cells; *Myxococcus virescens* even produces a diffusible antibiotic which kills the bacteria, and the lytic enzyme then breaks up
the cells so that they can be ingested (Singh, 1947). This organism
can also oxidize the separated lipids and proteins of *E. coli* (Loebeck
and Klein, 1956).

The one pathogen, *Chondrococcus columnaris*, which causes a
disease of fish, does not attack polysaccharides but readily hydrolyzes
proteins (Ordal and Rucker, 1944). In general, therefore, the group is
strongly endowed with the ability to attack insoluble polymers. It
should be mentioned, however, that the older view that Cytophagas
are *restricted* to polysaccharides is incorrect; they can also grow on
simple sugars—*Sporocytophaga* and *Cyt. hutchinsonii* on glucose and
cellobiose, *Cyt. rubra* on glucose, cellobiose, and xylose (Chap. XVII).

The Myxobacteria are widely distributed in soils, especially low-
land agricultural soils (S. and H., Krzemieniewski, 1927). They grow
readily on nutrient agar, soil cultures or dung, and have often been
isolated from dung in the first instance, perhaps because they can
attack Eubacteria, since a large fraction of the dung of most animals
is bacteria.

B. Interrelationships

An interesting relationship of the Myxobacteria was brought out
in Thaxter's original description (1892). It concerns the Myxomycetes,
which, although classed with the fungi, are like the Myxobacteria
in forming relatively large stalked spore masses or fructifications, by
the coming together of a large number of separate vegetative cells
(cf. p. 33). The Myxomycete cells are small flagellate amebae
(Myxamebae), not bacteria. Furthermore, when they come together
they fuse with one another, first in pairs to form zygotes and then in
large numbers to produce the plasmodium, which continues vegetative
life as a unit, often for weeks, before forming the fruiting bodies. Also
the structure of the fruiting bodies or sporangia is quite elaborate,
with an outer membrane, a network of fine tubes (called *elaters*),
and a mass of rounded spores embedded in them. The relationship with
the Myxobacteria is thus not really very close. However, there is a
special small group of Myxomycetes called the *Acrasiales*, in which
the separate amebae are not flagellated, and, when they agglomerate,
join together as individuals. The resulting mass, called a pseudoplasmo-

dium, does not feed, but merely moves off across the medium as a unit and at once forms a simple fruiting body, consisting only of a base, a stalk, and a mass of rounded spores (see Raper, 1940–1941, and Bonner, 1952, 1959, for descriptions). Thus it is to the *Acrasiales* that the Myxobacteria really have resemblance. When it is further noted that the slow creeping movement of Myxobacteria might be compared with the slow movement of Myxamebae, and the flexibility of the rods with the lack of rigid cell walls in Myxamebae, the resemblance is seen to be really very suggestive. The Myxococci can, in fact, enlarge and take on *ameboid* forms when grown on yeast extract (Finck, 1951). It is of interest, too, that the *Acrasiales* are like the Myxobacteria in being readily able to feed on Eubacteria.

In 1892 Thaxter found it hard to believe that normal-looking amebae, even though small, could be related to the far smaller and rod-shaped myxobacterial cells. In this misgiving (shared by Stanier and van Niel, 1941) he gave some emphasis to the presence of a nucleus in the Myxamebae and its supposed absence in bacteria. Now that the bacterial nucleus has been definitely identified (see Chap. III), this objection is no longer valid.

C. Systematics

The most recent classification of the Myxobacteria (Bergey, 1957) when reduced to its simplest terms is essentially as follows:

1. Microcysts elongate; fruiting bodies produced
   A. Fruiting bodies of indefinite shape, mesenteric
      or columnar   *Archangium* and
                                                     Stelangium
   B. Fruiting bodies of definite shape:
      (a) Angular; vegetative cells thick and short   *Sorangium*
      (b) Rounded; vegetative cells long and thin
              Family *Polyangiaceae* with five genera:
                                                     Polyangium,
                                                     Synangium,
                                                     Melittangium,
                                                     Podangium, and
                                                     Chondromyces
         These are distinguished by shape and structure of fruiting bodies
2. Microcysts spherical or ellipsoidal; fruiting bodies
   may or may not be produced
           Family *Myxococcaceae*, with four genera, of which three:
                                                     $\left\{ \begin{array}{l} \textit{Myxococcus,} \\ \textit{Chondrococcus,} \\ \text{and } \textit{Angiococcus} \end{array} \right.$

         form fruiting bodies, and one: *Sporocytophaga*
         forms none.

3. Neither microcysts nor fruiting bodies produced;
flexible rods, sometimes pointed

Cytophaga

Some of these organisms will be further discussed in connection with the breakdown of polysaccharides (Chap. XVII).

7. THE SPIROCHAETALES

This last group of bacteria occupies a somewhat isolated position and has received little really fundamental study. They are elongated cells ranging from 4 μ all the way up to 500 μ in length, but so thin that the smaller members can only be seen by using dark-field illumination, or after a treatment with tannic acid and silver, which thickens them in the same way as it does flagella. Some possess a long flagellum or filament at one or both ends of the cell. Like the Myxobacteria, they are without a rigid cell wall and are therefore quite flexible.

The basic structure appears to consist of a long central undulating cylinder, the "axile filament," surrounded by cytoplasm several times its thickness. A bundle of fine fibrils is wound spirally around the body either inside or outside the thin flexible outer membrane (Bradfield and Cater, 1952). Figures II–17 *A*, *B*, and *C* show two of the smaller forms, *Treponema* and *Leptospira* respectively, while *D* and *E* show *Cristispira*, one of the biggest. In *C* the Treponema (along with mouse erythrocytes) has been partly digested with trypsin; the central body, outer membrane, and spirally wound fiber bundle are clearly seen. In *B* the Leptospira has so fine a fiber bundle that it does not show, although again it can be seen on partial digestion (van Thiel and van Iterson, 1947). The axile filament of Leptospira is only 200 to 300 AU wide—about one-tenth that of the cytoplasmic body. In *D* and *E* the bundle of fibrils is seen unwound, and the individual fibrils can be compared with bacterial flagella. The spiral bundle viewed in the optical microscope has been in the past recorded as a ribbon or "crista," or as "cross striations." The mode of swimming is not clear, although it involves flexure of the whole body; perhaps the fibrils are contractile, causing the body alternately to undulate and straighten, the axile filament acting as a spring. Like flagella, the fibrils appear to be of muscle-like material (Bradfield and Cater, 1952). Some Leptospiras form peculiar large discs, 2 to 10 μ in diameter, linked to the spiral body by a fine thread. These have several times been recorded and may be some kind of reproductive bodies (Varpholomeeva and Stanislavsky, 1958).

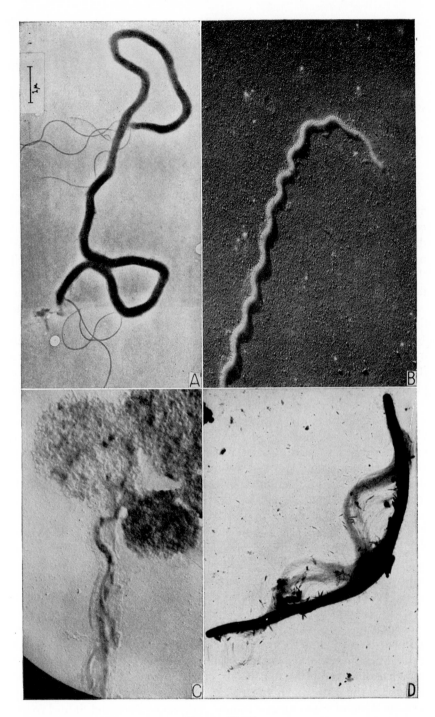

FIGURE II–17

74

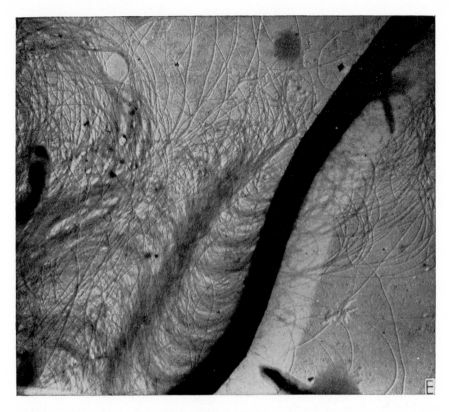

FIGURE II–17 (*Continued*)

Spirochaetes.

A. Treponema pallidum. (From S. Mudd and T. F. Anderson, 1944. Courtesy Soc. of Am. Bacteriologists.)

B. Leptospira biflexa. 7500 ×. (From P. H. van Thiel and W. van Iterson, 1947; *Proc. Kon. Akad. Wetensch. Amsterdam,* **50**:3–6. E. M., Delft.)

C. Treponema duttoni, after partial digestion with trypsin, showing the membrane, the body, and the spirally wound bundle of flagella. The circular objects are erythrocytes. 7400 ×.

D. Cristispira balbiani, showing the spiral bundle of flagella partially unwound. 2000 ×.

E. Critispira balbiani at higher magnification. Note that the individual flagella are comparable with those of Eubacteria. 7000 ×.

(*C, D,* and *E* from J. R. G. Bradfield and D. B. Cater, *Nature,* **169**:944, 1952.)

The first subdivision is made simply on the basis of size, the small forms being called Treponemas and the large ones, Spirochaetes. The classification given by Bergey (1957) is essentially as follows:

1. Cells 4 to 20 μ long. Family *Treponemataceae*
   A. Anaerobic; mostly parasites   *Treponema*
   B. More or less aerobic:
      (a) Coarse shallow coils; stained easily; parasites   *Borrelia*
      (b) Fine coils; stained with difficulty; one or both
          ends bent into a semicircular hook; parasites and
          saprophytes   *Leptospira*
2. Cells 30 to 500 μ long. Family *Spirochaetaceae*
   A. Cells without membrane;[5] saprophytes   *Spirochaeta*
   B. Cells with clearly visible membrane and "cross
      striations"[6]
      (a) Saprophytes   *Saprospira*
      (b) Commensal in, or parasitic on, mollusks   *Cristispira*

By far the most studied physiologically is *Treponema pallida*, the pathogen of syphilis. As the disease is difficult to cure, this organism has been the target of chemotherapeutic research for some 40 years, since Ehrlich introduced organic arsenicals to combat it in the human tissues (see Chap. XXIV, sec. 1). A related organism, *T. Zuelzerae*, is free-living in anaerobic mud; it ferments glucose to lactic and acetic acids (Veldkamp, 1960).

Leptospira buccalis is a common organism in the mouth and can readily be seen in fresh tooth-scrapings, although it has never been grown in culture. *Leptospira icterohemorrhagicae* is the cause of infectious jaundice. There are many related strains and disease types, as well as leptospiral diseases of dogs and cattle (see Schlossberger and Brandis, 1954). The large Cristispiras are parasites in shellfish, and nothing is known of their mode of life. Saprospira is multicellular (Lewin, 1962) and hence does not belong here at all.

8. OUTLINE OF BACTERIAL CLASSIFICATION

In order that the reader may keep the various types in mind, an outline classification is appended here. This differs here and there from existing classifications such as that of Bergey, particularly in the direction of simplification; for instance, the gram-negative peritrichous rods have been "lumped" rather than "split," because the differentiation between them seems scarcely to justify setting up all the genera used by Bergey (cf. Chap. XIV). Furthermore, a number of organisms about which our physiological knowledge is incomplete, such as the

---

[5] Probably incorrect.

[6] I.e., spirally wound bundle of fibrils.

Flavobacterium and Bacteroides groups, have been omitted; no doubt many of the gram-negative rods listed in these groups would be placed elsewhere if they were more completely known. Because of the uncertainty about their status, "families" have been avoided as far as possible, and the emphasis placed on genera.

OUTLINE TAXONOMY OF THE BACTERIA

I. *Cells unicellular, with rigid cell walls. Motility, when present, by flagella.*

THE EUBACTERIALES

1. *Cells roughly spherical*

A. Gram −   Genus:
    1. About 1 μ in diameter. Animal pathogens or commensals.
        a. Aerobic. Ex: *Gonococcus, Meningococcus.*   *Neisseria*
        b. Anaerobic.   *Veillonella*
    2. Large, 2 to 6 μ in diameter, often elliptical. Commonly forming pairs or short chains. Can fix N_2. Generally motile. Aerobic.   *Azotobacter*

B. Gram +
    3. Small, about 1 μ in diameter. Aerobic. A few are motile. Often subdivided into *Staphylococcus* (animal pathogens), *Rhodococcus* (pink or red organisms) etc.; such divisions uncertain. Ex: *M. (Staph.) aureus.*   *Micrococcus*
    4. Similar to 3 but dividing in one direction to form chains. Microaerophilic. Form lactic acid. Ex: *Pneumococcus,*   *Streptococcus*
       Sc. lactis, Sc. pyogenes.   (and *Leuconostoc*)
    5. Large or small; dividing in three directions to form packets.
        a. Aerobic. Nonmotile. Usually colored. Ex: *Sarcina lutea.*   *Sarcina*
        b. Anaerobic. Cells up to 3 μ in diameter. Fermenting carbohydrates. Ex: *Zs. ventriculi.*   *Zymosarcina*
        c. Aerobic. Motile and sporeforming. Ex: *Sporos. ureae.*   *Sporosarcina*

2. *Cells curved rods*

    6. S-shaped or spiral. Motile by polar flagella at both ends. Gram −. Aerobic, oxidizing organic acids best. Ex: *Sp. undula.*   *Spirillum*

7. S-shaped or C-shaped. Motile by polar
flagella at one end. Gram —. Aerobic
or anaerobic. Ex: *V. comma* (Asiatic
cholera), *V. desulfuricans* (or *Desulfo-
vibrio*).   *Vibrio*

3. *Cells straight rods*

A. Gram —
  8. Motile by polar flagella (mono- or
     cephalotrichous). Aerobic and highly
     oxidative (some can oxidize alcohol).
     Produce greenish pigments. Ex: *Ps.
     fluorescens.*   *Pseudomonas*
     a. The autotrophic pseudomonads, not
        secreting pigment, growing in ab-
        sence of organic carbon as ordinar-
        ily understood, may be included
        here. Ex: *Nitrosomonas, Nitrobacter,
        Thiobacillus, "Methanomonas."*
  9. Motile in young cultures by polar or
     "pseudopolar" flagella. May produce
     branched and swollen forms. Plant
     parasites ("symbionts"). Aerobic. Fix
     N_2 only in symbiosis with legumes.
     Ex: *Rh. phaseoli.*   *Rhizobium*
 10. With very brief motile phase; peri-   *Acetobacter*
     trichous or polar flagella. Highly pleo-   (peritrich) or
     morphic in old cultures. Aerobic. Can   *Acetomonas*
     grow on alcohol as sole carbon source.   (cephalotrich)
     Ex: *A. xylinum.*
     a. The amine-oxidizing *Protaminobac-
        ter* probably are related here.
 11. Nonmotile, or when motile peritri-   *Enterobacteriaceae*
     chous. Aerobic or facultative.   includes
     Includes many nondescript organ-   *Escherichia,*
     isms as well as the whole formic-   *Salmonella,*
     fermenting ("coliform") group.   *Shigella,*
     Water and soil organisms, animal   *Erwinia,*
     and plant parasites included. Ex: *B.   Proteus,* etc.
     coli, B. typhosum, B. prodigiosum,
     B. carotovorum* (old names).
B. Gram +
 12. Nonmotile or peritrichous. Strictly
     anaerobic. Large rods, forming heat-
     resistant *spores.*
     May be subdivided into: *Clostridium*
     a. *Clostridium* proper, carrying out
        butyric or related fermentations,
        able to fix N_2. Ex: *Cl. pasteurianum,
        Cl. acetobutylicum.*

b. *Peptoclostridium*, growing well in absence of carbohydrates (some animal pathogens). Ex: *Cl. welchii, Cl. histolyticum, Cl. tetani.*

13. Similar to 12 but facultatively anaerobic. Ex: *Aerobac. macerans.* — *Aerobacillus*

14. Nonmotile or (more generally) peritrichous. Aerobic. Mostly smaller than 12. Commonly form well-defined surface pellicle. Ex: *Bac. megatherium.* Sometimes subdivided according to whether spores are formed terminally or centrally. — *Bacillus* (also *Denitrobacillus*)

15. Nonmotile. *Not* forming spores. Cells unite into long filaments, and whole colony produces feathery growth in agar. Aerobic. Not attacking sugars. Ex: *K. Zopfii.* — *Kurthia*

16. Nonmotile. *Not* forming spores. Microaerophilic. Producing lactic acid from sugars. Catalase negative. Some produce long chains. Ex: *L. casei, L. bulgaricus.* — *Lactobacillus*

17. Similar to 16. Slightly irregular in outline. Producing propionic acid from lactic acid or from sugars. Some catalase-negative. Microaerophilic. — *Propionibacterium*

18. Similar to 17. Rods appearing of irregular shape when stained, with forms like those of *Rhizobia* (but see Fig. II–13); showing barred or granular staining. Aerobic or facultative. Ex: *C. diphtheriae.* — *Corynebacterium*

19. Long rods with tendency to form filaments. Acid-fast. Aerobic. Rich in waxy materials. Ex: *Mycob. tuberculosis, Mycob. opacum.* — *Mycobacterium*

II. *Cells as in the Eubacteriales, but organisms photosynthetic, although not producing oxygen. Cells colored green, purple, red, or brown.*

THE RHODOBACTERIALES
(or RHODOBACTERIINAE)

20. Similar to 6, but with many turns per cell. Anaerobic, photosynthetic, requiring H_2S and CO_2; not evolving oxygen. Green chlorophyll-like nondiffusible pigment. — *Chlorobium*

21. Cells of types 3, 6, 7, and 8. Anaerobic,

photosynthetic. Contain both a green
and a red or purple pigment. Grow
only in light, in presence of CO_2 and
also H_2S, sulfur, thiosulfate, or organic
acids.   Family
                                    Thiorhodaceae

22. Similar to 21 but anaerobic or facultative, photosynthetic in light, some also
heterotrophic in the dark, growing in
presence of various organic acids and
alcohols together with biotin. At least   Family
one forms motile colonies.   *Athiorhodaceae*

III. *Organisms multicellular or mycelial in character, with rigid cell
walls, nonmotile.*

THE ACTINOMYCETALES

23. Cells branching filaments of indefinite
length, dividing by segmentation into
rods. Gram-positive. Anaerobic, patho-
genic.   *Actinomyces*
24. Similar but aerobic. Conidia, when
formed, singly or in chains (see sec. 5).
*Nocardia, Micromonospora, Thermo-
actinomyces, Waksmania, Micropolyspora,* and *Streptomyces*
25. As 24 but conidia formed inside
sporangia.
a. Spores motile.   *Actinoplanes*
b. Spores (formed usually in coils)
nonmotile.   *Streptosporangium*

IV. *Organisms unicellular, at least in young cultures, but without rigid
cell walls. Length 3 to 10 μ. Motility, when present, by creeping.*

All except *Cytophaga* and *Sporocytophaga* form characteristic fruiting
bodies.

THE MYXOBACTERIALES

(see p. 67)

V. *Organisms unicellular, but without rigid cell walls. Length 4 to
500 μ. Motility by flexuous movement of a spirillum-like body.*

THE SPIROCHAETALES

(see p. 73)

This outline is to be regarded simply as a condensed listing and a
guide, for consultation while reading the remainder of the book. The
whole question of evolutionary development and of probable "natural"
classification will be taken up in Chapter XXVI.

9. SOME ORGANISMS HARD TO CLASSIFY

Here, first of all, come several groups of very large bacteria.

The family *Achromatiaceae* comprises large, usually motile, single cells, varying from 5-μ spheres up to ovoids 35 $\times$ 100 μ in size—the largest bacterium known. If it were not for the absence of organelles (cytostome, cilia, and so on) they would be considered more nearly related to the protozoa than the bacteria. Some accumulate droplets of sulfur, with or without crystalline masses of $CaCO_3$.

Caryophanon (two species) has rods consisting of a small number of thick cylindrical cells, about 3 $\times$ 10 to 30 μ (Pringsheim and Robinow, 1947). Each cell contains several partly completed cross walls, and when these are dissolved by lysozyme (Chap. III, sec. 1), the contents of more than one section may give only one protoplast (Provost and Doetsch, 1962). The growth of Caryophanon is favored by acetate. It is gram-positive and, like Beggiatoa, may possibly be a colorless member of the Myxophyceae.

Lineola (two species) has very long peritrichously flagellated rods, 1.5 $\times$ 20 to 50 μ, forming threads up to several hundred microns in length (Pringsheim, 1950). The threads may be branched. It is gram-negative and does not form spores. The mode of division (by constriction and fission) is clearly that of a bacterium. Perhaps these are to be considered as giant forms of *Proteus vulgaris*, which (see Fig. II–6A) has a marked tendency to form long motile chains. None of these large cells has been cultured in synthetic media, and their physiology remains unknown. *Lineola* appears to require acetate for growth.

Fasciculus consists of extremely long, thin cells, 2 $\times$ 50 to 100 μ, tapering and often slightly curved, united into spindle-shaped colonial bundles, which are motile (Pringsheim, 1959). The moving colony looks like a flagellate.

Along with these may be mentioned the sheathed filamentous types, of which the sulfur bacterium Beggiatoa has been mentioned. While its special physiology is discussed in Chapter XXII, there are similar forms, called Vitreoscilla, which grow on organic matter (Pringsheim, 1949). The filaments tend to break up into short lengths ("hormogonia"), as does the alga Oscillatoria; these have gliding motion and characteristically when grown on agar they start up new colonies at a distance from the old. Unlike Beggiatoa they do not deposit sulfur and require complex media. Shorter filaments composed of discoid cells, named *Oscillospira*, occur in the digestive tracts of animals and may be related to *Caryophanon*. Saprospira (p. 76) may be related here too.

Secondly there are the stalked bacteria, considered as an order,

Caulobacteriales, by Henrici and Johnson (1935). Some of these (*Gallionella*), which precipitate iron hydroxide, are described in Chapter XXII, section 4; they are curved rods, which grow crosswise on the stalk. Others, including *Caulobacter*, grow lengthwise on the stalk, which is attached to a submerged object or sometimes to the organic film at the water surface (see Fig. II–18). The stalk grows out at the same "sub-polar" location as the flagellum, so that two types of cell, stalked or flagellated, are found in the same culture (Stove and Stanier, 1962). It is not certain that they are at all related to the iron bacteria.

The oddest member of the group is *Hyphomicrobium* (Chap. XXII, sec. 3), of which each cell develops as an elliptical bud on the end of a long, thin, unattached stalk (Kingma-Boltjes, 1936; see Fig. II–19.) The other end of the cell has a flagellum, and the new cell when fully grown may break away and be motile for a time, settling down again and growing a new stalk on a suitable substratum. The new stalk appears to grow out from the old point of attachment. From the end of this new stalk, new daughter cells may again be produced, one after the other, in succession. Simple fission was not seen, although it apparently does take place in Caulobacter (Fig. II–18*A*). This point is important, because if it does not divide by fission, Hyphomicrobium is scarcely a bacterium, by definition. Its motility separates it from the Actinomycetes, and Kingma-Boltjes suggests that it may be intermediate between the bacteria and the Phycomycetes. A purple bacterium, *Rhodomicrobium vanniellii*, which also produces a new cell at the end of a stalk, may be related to it, although the serial production of new cells was not observed in Rhodomicrobium (Duchow and Douglas, 1949). Its motile cells are peritrichous while those of *Hyphomicrobium* are polar (Douglas and Wolfe, 1959). In both forms the stalk is used for reproduction rather than for attachment. It seems clear that the stalked bacteria are a highly heterogeneous group.

Third, there is the Pleuropneumonia group, originally isolated from cattle suffering from pleuropneumonia and believed to cause a number of diseases of farm animals (see Hayflick and Stinebring, 1960); under some conditions these resemble ordinary, but small, bacteria, but they pass through an exceedingly minute stage like viruses. In this state they penetrate bacteria-retaining filters, as well as the membranes of animal cells, but unlike the viruses they can be grown on cell-free media, usually doing best in the presence of blood serum. The minute forms give rise to large globules or masses, up to 10 μ in diameter, which may be of almost any shape, and which break up again into granules, small normal-looking rods, or minute forms (Dienes, 1946). The cells do not take up any stains readily and are gram-

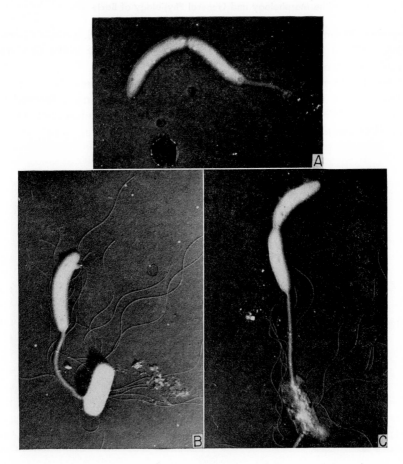

FIGURE II–18

Caulobacter species.

A. Dividing cell showing terminal flagellum at one end and stalk at the other. 7500 ×. (Photo by A. L. Houwink and W. van Iterson, E. M., Delft. From *Biochim. Biophys. Acta,* **5**:10–44. Copyright 1950 by Elsevier Publishing Co., Amsterdam, The Netherlands.)

B. Caulobacter with stalk attached to a cell of *Bac. subtilis.* The area of attachment is clearly seen. 7500 ×.

C. A similar cell interpreted as a later stage. The bacillus appears plasmolyzed or empty. 7500 ×.

(Both *B* and *C* photographed by A. L. Houwink, E. M., Delft. *Nature,* **168**:154, 1951.)

negative. When they form colonies on agar media, these are always minute. They are mainly animal parasites. In many ways they resemble very small Myxobacteria.

Similar forms derived from ordinary bacteria, especially from the gram-negative rods, have been described under the name L-forms (see Dienes and Weinberger, 1951). An actinomycete-like organism, *Streptobacillus moniliformis*, behaves similarly (Klieneberger-Nobel, 1951).

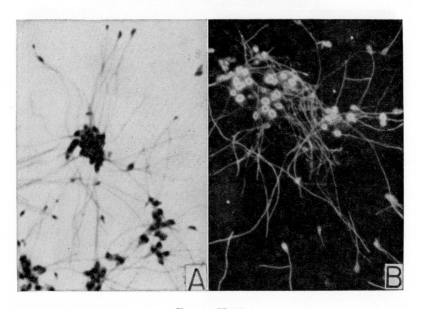

FIGURE II–19

Hyphomycrobium vulgare.
    A. Stained with carbol-fuchsin. 1700 ×.
    B. In dark-field. 1400 ×.
Note the small cells developing at the ends of the filaments.
    (Both *A* and *B* from Kingma-Boltjes, 1936.)

They tend to arise in very old cultures or after exposure to penicillin, immune sera, refrigeration, or other growth-inhibiting conditions. Most probably they are bacterial cells that have failed to form normal cell walls, i.e., "protoplasts." Such protoplasts can be produced by dissolving the bacterial wall with lysozyme (Chap. III, sec. 1) or by growing bacteria in the presence of penicillin, which inhibits cell-wall formation (Chap. XXV); they are delicate and easily burst, but can be maintained intact in sugar solutions and show the enzymatic and genetic behavior of normal bacteria. The L-forms reported are much less delicate but otherwise so similar that it seems likely they are protoplasts which have produced a membrane somewhat tougher than normal, though still flexible. L-forms have more complex growth requirements than the bacteria from which they were derived, which indicates major changes in synthetic abilities (see Edward, 1954). The pleuropneumonia organisms are just as demanding, and in addition require cholesterol for their growth, so that there is perhaps a wide spectrum of these curious forms.

10. THE MICROMICROORGANISMS

Nowhere is the importance of size more evident in the world of organisms than when we approach the limits of the visible. Our knowledge of the bacteria may be imperfect,[7] but it is rather extensive. By comparison, the life and functions of the smaller organisms are shrouded in ignorance. Indeed, in most cases it is not even certain that they are organisms at all.

A. The Rickettsiales

The *Rickettsiales* are a group of objects frequently on the borders of visibility, i.e., 0.2 to 0.5 μ in diameter, but sometimes up to 2 μ long; varied in shape, gram-negative in staining, and parasitic in mode of life. Not only are they parasitic but (with one or two exceptions) they are obligately so, i.e., they can grow only in a living host. This is probably not a matter of nutrition, since if it were, the Rickettsias could be grown in blood serum or tissue extracts, which can be made to contain all known vitamins and accessory factors. It probably means that some metabolic process essential for life, or at any rate for growth, is missing from the Rickettsias and has to be supplied by the host.

The *Rickettsiales* were named for Ricketts, who discovered the first of them, the cause of Rocky Mountain spotted fever, in 1909. He also discovered a second, the cause of typhus fever, which afterwards killed him. Typhus[8] is a disease of rats which is transmitted to man either by lice (epidemic typhus) or by fleas (endemic typhus, a milder form). The louse, which carries the typhus agent in its saliva, itself dies of the disease, but this is an exception, because as a rule the Rickettsias are not pathogenic to their insect hosts. Wood ticks carry Rocky Mountain spotted fever indefinitely, transmitting it from generation to generation

---

[7] R. Y. Stanier is reported to have commented, after attending a bacteriologists' meeting, that it is evident that no one really knows what a bacterium is.

[8] See Zinsser (1935) for an entertaining account of this disease.

through the eggs (cf. Rivers, 1948). Other important diseases caused by this group are Q fever, common in southeast Asia; tsutsugamushi, a mainly Japanese disease of swamplands; psittacosis, a disease of man and parrots; conjunctivitis; and the venereal disease, lymphogranuloma venereum.

The Rickettsias have been subdivided into three families: one—*Rickettsiaceae*—transmitted by insects or other arthropods; one—*Chlamydozoaceae*—not so transmitted, and often considered as viruses; and a third—*Bartonellaceae*—of which some are transmitted by insects and some are not. In this third group are found the only forms that can multiply in cell-free media. The existence of the whole order as a genuine biological division is really quite doubtful. Bergey's classification is based on the diameter; the *Rickettsiales* are stated to be more than 0.1 μ in diameter, and the viruses mainly less than this. However, since at least 10 major viruses exceed 0.1 μ in diameter, and a number of others, that are long and thin, exceed 0.1 μ in one dimension, it seems that both the size distinction itself and the use of the term "diameter" are almost meaningless. It is quite possible that with the exception of those few Bartonellas that can grow outside of host cells, the whole group of Rickettsias should be considered as viruses, or akin to L-forms. The *Bartonellaceae* are themselves heterogeneous, for the genus Bartonella has flagella and is probably a small bacterium, while the genera Hemobartonella and Eperythrozoon have their closest affinities with the Pleuropneumonia group. As to Rickettsia, it contains ATP and can reduce cytochrome; its growth is inhibited by antibiotics, and it can mutate (see Weiss *et al.*, 1959). Thus, it is certainly an organism.

B. The Viruses

Pasteur's work on rabies was really the first study of a virus, although he did not so recognize it. He did find that spinal cord tissue of rabid animals, though highly infective, showed no traces of living bacteria, and he wondered whether organisms too small to be visible might still carry infection. It was in 1892, after the great outburst of medical bacteriology described in Chapter I, that the first positive demonstration was made. Ivanovski was studying a disease of tobacco in which the leaves showed a "mosaic" of dark- and light-green patches. The sap of diseased plants, even if passed through a Berkefeld filter, carried the disease to healthy plants. In confirming and extending the work, Beijerinck in 1898 suggested that the infection was due to a *contagium fluidum vivum*, i.e., a liquid infective agent. If this were to be interpreted to mean something in solution, Beijerinck was very close to the truth. A few months afterward Frosch and Löffler showed that the cause of foot-and-mouth disease of cattle could also pass through the Berkefeld filter, and since then a very large number of diseases has been shown to be due to "filterable viruses." These include: smallpox, measles, mumps, influenza, atypical pneumonia, yellow fever, and infantile paralysis of man; rabies, foot-and-mouth disease, and distemper of animals; diseases of insects and birds; mosaic, yellows, and wilt diseases of plants, as well as many striped conditions in plants which are not ordinarily considered as diseases (e.g., "break" in tulips). Finally, even the diseases of bacteria are caused by a special group of viruses termed *bacteriophage*.

The fact that viruses multiply only in a living host means that the cultivation of viruses is quite different from that of bacteria. Instead of cultivating the organisms, one has to cultivate *living infected hosts*. In plants this is not difficult, since the virus diseases seldom kill the plants but only weaken them, but in animals special methods are required. These are:

(1) TISSUE CULTURES. Fragments of tissue are obtained aseptically and transferred to sterile, glucose-salt mixtures with added blood serum or embryo juice. The infected material is added and the cultures incubated. Transfers are usually made very frequently. The same procedure has been used for typhus rickettsia. The recent successful vaccines against poliomyelitis were made possible by this method.

(2) EMBRYO CULTURES. Mature chicks may not be susceptible to many viruses, but eggs are quite nonspecific and will support the growth of most viruses and rickettsias. The usual procedure is to break the shell aseptically, pierce the shell membrane, and inoculate either onto the chorioallantoic membrane or in the yolk-sac.

The enumeration of viruses also involves special methods, of which three are mainly used:

(1) DILUTION TO THE MINIMUM INFECTIVE DOSE. This requires many plants or animals, but with carefully standardized techniques gives good results. It is closely comparable to Lister's dilution method described in Chapter I, except that infection, rather than growth, is the criterion.

(2) COUNTING OF LOCAL LESIONS. Plants infected with a virus that does not produce systemic symptoms, or generalized infection, often respond with small localized lesions, like bacterial colonies on a plate. For instance, tobacco mosaic virus, which on ordinary tobacco (*Nicotiana tabacum*) causes an all-over mosaic, forms lesions when rubbed on the leaves of another species, *N. glutinosa*, or on the kidney bean (Fig. II–22). Bushy stunt virus of tomato does the same on *N*.

glutinosa, and so does cucumber virus on the cowpea. Since the number of lesions formed by a given sample of virus varies with the plant, the age of the leaf, and the details of the method, the best results are obtained when the samples to be compared are applied to opposite halves of the same leaf (see Bawden, 1950). By washing the virus off the leaf after the infection, it has been determined that only about one in a million of the virus particles produces a lesion. Nevertheless, curiously enough, the number of lesions is proportional to the concentration. In some cases animal viruses will produce local lesions on the egg membrane in a similar way. The determination of bacteriophage (see below) is a comparable method.

(3) THE METHODS OF IMMUNOLOGY. These have been used with most of the animal viruses (see Chap. III, sec. 2). They allow the assay of virus concentrations by precipitation with serial dilutions of specific antibodies. These antibodies appear in the blood of animals that have been injected with the virus. The minimum virus concentration that will cause a just visible precipitate can be used as a unit.

Viruses can be prepared pure by chemical methods, utilizing their nucleoprotein nature. Beginning with the virus of tobacco mosaic (Stanley, 1936), a great many have been crystallized, although those animal viruses that grow mainly in nervous tissue are difficult to separate from the host material. Elaborate procedures of differential centrifuging, however, have led to the crystallization of poliomyelitis virus (Schwerdt, 1957). Viruses have particle sizes corresponding to "molecular weights" of many millions. Alfalfa mosaic, for instance, has a molecular weight of 2,100,000 and a particle diameter of 16.5 mμ; poliomyelitis, 6,800,000 and 24 mμ; tomato bushy stunt, which forms beautiful 12-sided crystals, 7,400,000 and 26 mμ. Much larger are the rod-shaped particles of potato and tobacco mosaic diseases, the latter being 15 $\times$ 280 mμ and of a molecular weight about 40 millions. The spherical particles of fowl plague correspond to a molecular weight of 200 to 400 millions. At the uppermost end of the scale, vaccinia virus has a diameter of about 0.25 μ and intergrades in size with the rickettsias. A group of virus crystals is shown in Fig. II–20.

Some of the large viruses often form crystal-like structures, which are not true crystals; for example, tobacco mosaic virus on treatment with ammonium sulfate forms large needles, while in infected cells it forms "crystalline inclusions"—of quite different shape, in or near the nucleus. Some viruses of insect larvae similarly appear crystalline in the tissue and are referred to as "polyhedral viruses" on that account, but the apparent crystals are really packets of rod-shaped virus particles enclosed within a membrane.

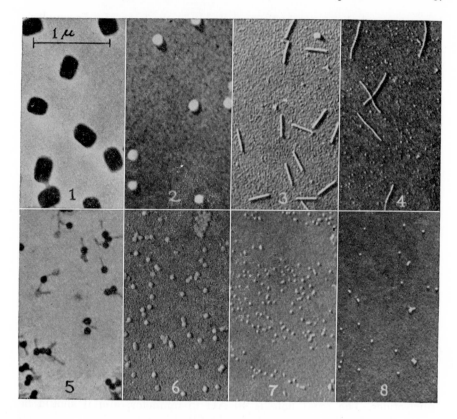

FIGURE II–20

Electron micrographs of eight highly purified viruses.

1. Vaccinia; *2.* influenza (Lee strain); *3.* tobacco mosaic; *4.* potato-X (latent) mosaic; *5.* bacteriophage T2; *6.* Shope papilloma; *7.* southern bean mosaic; *8.* tomato bushy stunt.

(*1* from Green, Anderson, and Smadel, 1942. The remainder photographed by Oster, Sigurgeirsson, Knight, and Stanley. All from C. A. Knight, *Cold Spring Harbor Symp.*, **12:**115–121, 1947, and photographed to same scale.)

As to composition, the smaller viruses consist of nucleic acid and protein only. Those of plants contain ribose nucleic acid, RNA, i.e., the acid characteristic of cytoplasm, rather than the 2-deoxyribose derivative, DNA, which is present in nuclei (see p. 127). The viruses of animals are about equally divided, some containing RNA and some DNA. The procedures of immunology show tobacco mosaic virus to contain only a single "antigen," i.e., one protein (see p. 120). The larger viruses contain other compounds; equine encephalomyelitis and human encephalitis contain lipid, probably in the form of a liponucleo-protein; influenza and mumps viruses contain 25 per cent of lipid and large amounts of carbohydrate, consequently their RNA content is only 2 per cent; vaccinia (5.6 per cent DNA) contains a little copper and has been claimed to have enzymes also, but this is probably because of adsorption of enzymes from the surrounding medium.

The larger animal viruses and many of the plant viruses are inactivated by exposure to 56° C for 10 to 30 minutes. Indeed, sugar cane pieces, for planting new fields, can be freed from viruses by brief immersion in water at 52° C. On the other hand, viruses resist low temperatures better than bacteria; rabies virus can be kept at least two years in the frozen state. Most of them are inactivated by ultra-violet light, especially of wavelength 2650 AU. Some are made non-infective by bactericidal chemicals, but poliomyelitis resists a wide variety of bactericides, and tobacco mosaic is resistant to heat, hy-drolytic enzymes, phenol, and ultraviolet light.

Recently the structure of tobacco mosaic virus has been elucidated by x-ray analysis of the crystals; it is shown in Figure II–21. The virus protein is in the form of a large number (about 2100) of equivalent protein molecules of molecular weight 17,400, spiraled around the particle axis. Each "turn of the screw" takes 23 AU, and 49 of the protein subunits occupy three turns. The RNA is a single chain coiled compactly between turns of the protein, as shown at the top where part of the protein is cut away. Each turn of the RNA spiral contains 49 nucleotides. The axial hole is 40 AU in diameter, and it should be noted that the RNA does not simply fill this hole as has often been thought, although it is clearly quite surrounded by the protein.

A remarkable characteristic of viruses is their ability to mutate. "Attenuation," or loss of virulence, is one of the commonest of such mutations. Pasteur, as far back as 1885, found that after several passages through rabbits' brains, the virulence of rabies for rabbits was constant but that for man had become very low. Similarly, when the "curly top" virus of sugar beet is passed through the related *Chenopodium murale*, it loses its virulence for sugar beet. A remarkable example is that of tobacco mosaic. If this virus is cultivated first in tomato plants at 35° C and then in *Nicotiana glutinosa*, it still causes local lesions (cf. Fig. II–22) in *N. glutinosa* leaves, but no symptoms at all in tobacco (*N. tabacum*); nevertheless, it remains able to grow in tobacco. This so-called "masked" strain has been kept for over four years without mutating back to pathogenicity for tobacco. Numerous other mutants causing modified disease symptoms in tobacco are known, e.g., *flavus* causes yellow leaves; *luridum*, very large pale areas (see Markham, 1959). Insect-borne viruses can sometimes be

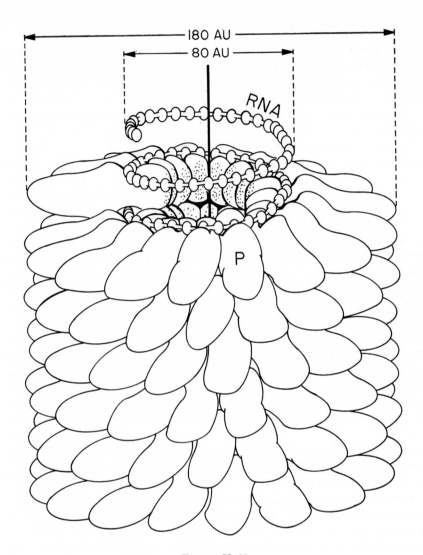

FIGURE II–21

Drawing of the structure of tobacco mosaic virus (TMV), based mainly on the x-ray diffraction studies of Rosalind Franklin. About one-twentieth of the total length of the rod-shaped particle (3000 AU long) is shown. Three turns of the major helix (of pitch 23 AU) contain 49 of the protein sub-units, *P*, of molecular weight, 17,000, and the RNA chain is coiled between them. (From A. Klug and D. L. D. Caspar, *Advances in Virus Research*, VII, 1960.)

attenuated within the insect host; thus the Aster yellows virus (causing yellowing but not death of Asters) loses most of its pathogenicity if the leaf hopper, which carries it, is kept at 32° C for 12 days. Mutation can also result in increased virulence.

Mutations are commonly accompanied by slight changes in amino-acid composition. In tobacco mosaic, two wild strains, *vulgare* and *dahlemense*, and the mutant *flavus* which probably arose from *vulgare*, have the following content of four important amino acids (Aach, 1958):

	vulgare	*dahlemense*	*flavus*
Aspartic acid	19	17	17
Glutamic acid	15	18	15
Alanine	14	14	15
Valine	12	12	13

Thus, in *flavus* an extra molecule each of alanine and valine substitute for two of aspartic acid. Many other small amino acid differences between mutants are known. There are amino acid differences also between the A and B strains of influenza virus, but these are less closely related.

However, the important fact is that it is the nucleic acid which is the critical part of the virus, not the protein fraction. In 1956 it was shown simultaneously in Germany and the United States that by treating with phenol or detergents the protein of tobacco mosaic can be separated from the RNA, and if the RNA alone is applied to plants, it can cause typical mosaic symptoms (Gierer and Schramm, 1956; Fraenkel-Conrat *et al.*, 1957). The infectivity is only a few per cent of that of the intact virus, but it is real and not due to traces of con-taminating virus. Intact virus can be recovered from plants infected with the RNA alone. It is also possible to recombine the RNA with the protein and obtain greatly increased infectivity as a result. Mengo encephalitis virus can be similarly broken up, and its RNA also is infec-tive alone (Colter *et al.*, 1958). Evidently, therefore, the ability to infect and grow is a function of the RNA, while the protein acts as a modifying and stabilizing agent. The slight changes in protein composi-tion in the different mutants therefore must be the *result* of changes in the RNA. Now the RNA is a large molecule, but it contains only the four bases, adenine, guanine, cytosine, and uracil (all present as ribosephosphates), in constant amounts. It follows that unless there are very small changes in the ratios of these nucleotides, too small for the analytical methods to indicate, the specificity must depend on changes in their *arrangement*. This has given rise to the current idea that the order of arrangement of nucleotides is a system of *coding* the structure of proteins. With many hundred nucleotides to be arranged, there are certainly plenty of possibilities.

It is now known (see Chap. XX) that protein synthesis is controlled by a group of RNA's. The free amino acids become linked to specific soluble forms of RNA and thence are carried to the insoluble RNA of intracellular particles, where they are combined together into proteins. Thus the virus RNA no doubt behaves somewhat as does the normal cellular RNA. Gamow and Ycas (1955) pointed out that if the four different nucleotides in RNA are combined three at a time, they yield 20 combinations, which is probably the number of different free amino acids that have to be taken up to form proteins; thus specific groupings of three adjacent nucleotides could participate in picking up each amino acid. It follows that chemical changes in the RNA of virus must alter the virus protein, so that if mutations are due to changes in the RNA, they must be reflected in small changes in the protein composition. In turn, of course, they will be reflected in differences in the disease symptoms.

This prediction was verified when Gierer and Mundry (1958) obtained mutations in tobacco mosaic by treating the virus, or its RNA, with nitrous acid. This attacks the amino groups of adenine, guanine, or cytosine, converting them to hydroxyl groups (cf. Chap. VIII, sec. 8):

$$RNH_2 + HONO = ROH + N_2 + H_2O$$

The rate of appearance of mutants led these workers to the calculation that the chemical change of one nucleotide was enough to produce one mutant. Each also contained a slightly changed protein.

The occurrence of natural mutations (see Chap. XXI, sec. 1) is a random process, and no doubt many occur that are not detected. In Drosophila the frequency of mutations is of the order of one in a million individuals, and in bacteria about one in 10^8 cell divisions; an infected plant may form 10^{12} virus particles from a small inoculum, so that on the same basis 10,000 or more mutants might be expected. Even granting that the parallel is a hazardous one to draw, it seems likely that most mutants "grow" more slowly than the parent form and thus are selected against. Nevertheless, it is a common observation that plants that have been infected a long time yield mutant viruses.

This raises the question of what "growth" means in the case of viruses. Superficially it may be likened to crystallization, the inoculum being the seed crystal and the host cytoplasm providing the material which can crystallize out. However, viruses do not increase in amount in blood, or in sap expressed from the infected plant, or even in whole chloroplasts. In order for them to grow, the living host must cooperate. Thus the virus is not strictly self-reproducing, but it *specifically modifies the behavior of host cells to produce more virus*. It organizes the enzymes of the host, enslaving them to its own service. In tobacco mosaic, at least, the virus protein is not formed by modifying the plant's own protein, but is produced *de novo* from the pool of amino acids and ammonia (Commoner *et al.*, 1952), under the control of the virus RNA. Superficially the behavior of viruses is like that of the genes, carriers of heredity; genes are self-reproducing only in the sense that they direct the enzymes of nucleic acid synthesis to produce more of their own material. In the case of genes, however, the nucleic acid is DNA, which not only reproduces *itself* but also controls the formation of specific forms of RNA which then specifically determine the proteins synthesized in the cell (Chap. XXI).

A characteristic feature of virus multiplication is the following: when the virus has infected the host cell, it "disappears" for a while, i.e., ground-up infected cells no longer yield infective particles. This "eclipse period" for the Rous sarcoma virus in chick embryos is one to two days. Thereafter infectious particles can again be obtained, and indeed in increased numbers. In other words, the virus breaks up in order to multiply; presumably it is the RNA that first multiplies, then causes the synthesis of protein that reconstitutes the intact virus (see Wildman, 1959). The same phenomenon occurs with bacteriophage (see below).

No virus preparation, however concentrated, has been shown to have any respiration of its own, although some contain a few enzymes. The bacteriophages have an enzyme to attack the host cell wall (see below); influenza virus contains a mucoproteinase which perhaps, by attacking the host mucoprotein, helps the virus to multiply in the cell (Gottschalk, 1957). If the virus is to be regarded as a kind of organism, then it is a very incomplete one, dependent on the host to supply not only its food but also its enzymes.

There are other particles that are self-reproducing in the same limited sense as viruses; these are the "transforming factors" described in section 6 of Chapter XXI. These too are nucleic acids and can be purified from protein without losing their ability to act.

C. Bacteriophage

A group of viruses of special interest are those that multiply in bacteria. These were first detected by Twort and by d'Herelle, both of whom observed that within bacterial colonies cleared areas or "plaques" appeared, where the cells were being lysed. The lytic principle could be transferred to fresh cultures and multiplied therein. The name *bacteriophage* (see d'Herelle, 1926) means bacteria-eater.

Phages can be obtained readily from river water, feces, or sewage, and sometimes from old cultures. They will parasitize many kinds of bacteria, producing "moth-eaten" colonies on solid media, or clearing the turbidity in liquid cultures. The phage particles can be counted, like those of virus, by (1) dilution to the minimum dose that will clear a liquid bacterial culture, presumably therefore a single particle;

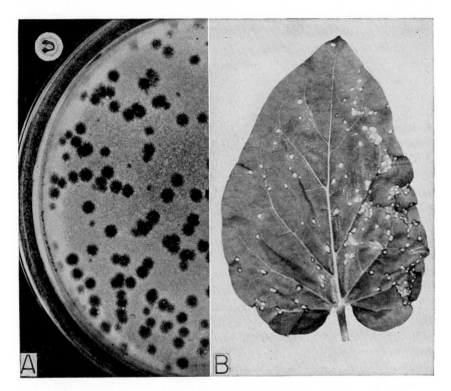

FIGURE II–22

Two types of virus colonies.

A. Plaques of bacteriophage in a plate of Rhizobium sp. (From J. Kleczkowska, 1945. Courtesy Soc. Am. Bacteriologists.)

B. Leaf of *Nicotiana glutinosa* after inoculation with virus. *Left*, virus 1 mg per liter; *right*, 10 mg per liter. The leaf had been shaded before inoculation to increase the number of lesions. (From Bawden, *Plant Viruses and Virus Diseases*, 1950. Waltham, Mass., Chronica Botanica Co.)

(2) counting the plaques formed in a uniform, heavily seeded plate culture (Fig. II–22). In both cases, after the phage has completed its work, resistant bacteria may begin to multiply, giving rise in (1) to renewed turbidity, or in (2) to secondary small colonies within the cleared plaques. These resistant forms represent normal mutations which

are regularly occurring and are not an adaptation to the presence of phage (Newcombe, 1949). Phage-resistant mutants have been found very convenient for genetic studies (see Chap. III, sec. 5C). The majority of bacteria, and perhaps all, can be parasitized by phages.

By centrifuging off any unattacked bacteria from a cleared culture, concentrated phage suspensions can be obtained and these have been carefully analyzed. The purified phage T2 (grown upon *E. coli* strain B) proved to contain 5.2 per cent P and 16.2 per cent N, no lipid, and only a trace of RNA, doubtless an impurity (Herriott and Barlow, 1952). Of the N, 6 per cent was in amino acids, 40 per cent in protein, and 53 per cent in nucleic acids; the P was almost wholly (97 per cent) in nucleic acid, which was DNA. A peculiarity of the DNA is that it contains, instead of cytosine, 5-hydroxymethylcytosine, at least in phages T2, T4, and T6 (Wyatt and Cohen, 1953). This base, which is not known to occur in the nucleic acids of other organisms, is largely combined with glucose. It was found that if the particles are transferred suddenly from strong (3 M) salt solution to water ("osmotic shock"), they burst, the DNA going into solution while the protein remains as insoluble "ghosts" which can be centrifuged off. Thus the phage particle is almost nothing but DNA and protein, and can be separated into its constituents. Other phages have similar composition.

Understanding of the peculiar nature of the relationship between phage and the host cell came from the demonstration by Hershey and Chase (1952) that the DNA of phage particles is not hydrolyzed by the enzyme DNA-ase, although this enzyme acts rapidly on free DNA. But if the host bacteria have been heated, the enzyme now hydrolyzes the DNA (detected by using phage labeled with P^{32}, obtained by growing bacteria in $KH_2P^{32}O_4$). A similar result was obtained by repeatedly freezing and thawing the infected cells (see p. 188), but it was also noted that if the freezing and thawing broke up the bacteria, the DNA was not released into solution but could be centrifuged with the cell debris. Thus the DNA in the phage is protected from DNA-ase in some way, but when it is in the bacteria, it is protected only by the host cell membrane, and if this is destroyed by heat or cold treatment, the DNA is exposed. Yet the DNA within the host is still in an organized structure. They deduced, therefore, that in the phage the protein surrounds the DNA, while on infection the DNA passes en bloc into the host, leaving the protein behind. This conclusion was confirmed by using phage labeled with both P^{32} and S^{35}, because nucleic acid contains no sulfur and hence the S must be in the protein. It was found that if the bacteria were violently agitated five minutes after the phage had been added, the S^{35} (and therefore the protein) broke off in a form that could only be centrifuged out at high speed, while the P^{32} (i.e., the DNA) mostly remained within the bacteria. Thus the process of infection (at least with phages T2, T4, and T6) is as follows:

(1) The phage becomes attached or adsorbed to the host cell. It can be calculated that there are more than 100 receptor sites for each cell, and the relative sizes of phage and host are seen graphically in Figure II–23A. Phages of the T and P series, as well as λ which is similar, consist of a hexagonal head and a rigid tail, and they attach to the host cell by the tail (Fig. II–24). The attachment is a chemical process and occurs only in appropriate media; two of the phages of *E. coli* require tryptophan for attachment, and indole inhibits the adsorption (Anderson, 1945); since the bacteria can produce indole from tryptophan, this means that they have a means of self-protection. Other phages require calcium for attachment, and in general the salt composition of the medium is important. Hydrogen peroxide and some other agents prevent attachment, and phages thus treated show that the base of the tail has been modified (see Cohen, 1957). Attached phages are shown in Figure III–3, p. 118.

(2) Almost at once, an enzyme in the base of the tail softens or opens the cell wall; if phage is adsorbed onto broken bacteria, the cell-wall fragments may show holes under the electron microscope, and some of their nitrogen leaks out into solution. Cells can also have "ghosts" (i.e., the isolated protein coats of phage, prepared by osmotic shock), attached to them, and this in some cases lyses them very rapidly—in other cases it prevents the cell from multiplying (Herriott and Barlow, 1957). Evidently, therefore, the integrity of the cell is seriously damaged by the attachment process, quite apart from the effects of the DNA. Phages attacking many organisms have essentially similar structures, as shown by comparing the phage for Streptomyces in Figure II–25 with that for *E. coli* in Figure II–24.

(3) There is a time lapse, which in the case of *E. coli* is about 20 minutes. During this time the DNA of the phage (about 2.10^{-16}) passes bodily into the bacteria. A recent careful study of the sensitivity of DNA to mechanical treatment shows that the molecule breaks very easily, so that most of the previous molecular weight values are too small; unstirred natural DNA of phage T2 has physical properties that suggest a true molecular weight near 60 millions (Hershey and Burgi, 1960). This would mean the whole amount of DNA in the phage particle is in two molecules. Probably it all enters in one piece.

If the cells are broken mechanically at this stage and applied to other sensitive bacteria, no infective phage can be detected (Doermann, 1953), which means that the DNA without its protein cannot attack and infect new cells. However, after 15 minutes or more, phage

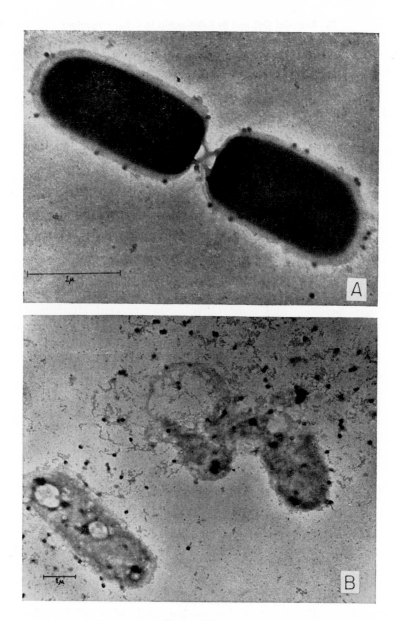

FIGURE II–23

A. Dividing cells of *E. coli* with particles of bacteriophage (α) adsorbed; photographed after 15 minutes' contact. (For more detail, see Figure III–3.)

B. Cells of *E. coli* and bacteriophage particles (γ) photographed after 23 minutes' contact. The cells are lysed and the phage particles set free. (Both from S. E. Luria, M. Delbrück, and T. F. Anderson, 1943. Courtesy Soc. Am. Bacteriologists.)

particles can be detected when the host cells are broken up. Most of them appear to be grouped together in one or more foci in the cell (Takeya *et al.*, 1959). Intact phage is thus now being formed.

(4) A sudden increase in the number of phage particles can now be detected; some of the bacteria can be seen to burst, liberating the phage particles (Fig. II–23*B*). The number of particles liberated per

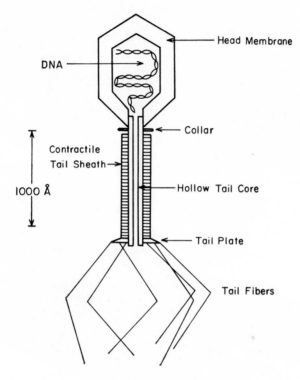

F<small>IGURE</small> II–24

Diagram of a T2 bacteriophage. Original. By Dr. Lloyd M. Kozloff.

cell destroyed, the "burst size," is fairly constant for a given host and phage, and frequently is around 100. Evidently, then, the lapse of time was used not only for entry and for resynthesis of the protein sheaths, but also for multiplication of the DNA.

D. Phage Genetics

If the cells are simultaneously infected with two phages, then on release not only the original types of particles but also a few new

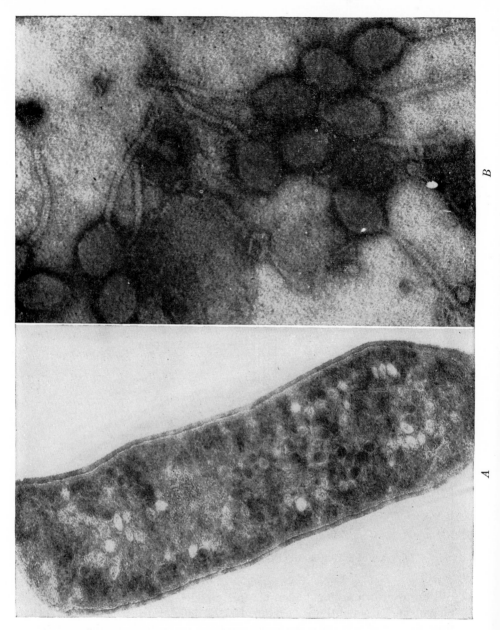

B

A

FIGURE II–25
For descriptive legend see page 101.

ones may appear. These can be detected by using phages having characteristic effects. For example, a T2 phage forming small dark plaques and another forming large light ones, on dual infection, give rise to a few phages causing large dark and small light plaques, respectively (Benzer, 1955). This means the genetic material of the two phages has "recombined." Phage λ has several hundred such genetic characters, T4 several thousand, and the experiment has been done many times with different characters, yielding a whole new subject of phage genetics. Analysis of the frequency with which the hybrids occur shows that the characters must be in a linear order as on a chromosome (see the reviews of Hershey, 1957; Levinthal, 1959). If the DNA of one of the parent phages contains isotope, then the recombinant phage when first formed may contain up to 50 per cent of this isotope, from which it follows that the hybrid is a result of true crossing over between the two linear strands of DNA, followed by its duplication (Meselson and Weigle, 1961).

A revealing fact, observed with the *E. coli* phages, is that they fall into two groups as regards their sensitivity to ultraviolet light. Bacteria treated with ultraviolet are damaged or killed (the phenomenon is described in Chap. XXIV), and the survivors contain many mutant forms. But ultraviolet dosages that do not greatly reduce the growth of the bacteria very greatly reduce the ability of certain phages to grow in them. This is true of phages T1, T7, λ, and P22, while phages T2, T4, and T6 are relatively insensitive to ultraviolet. The difference probably means (see Stent, 1958) that when phages replicate themselves, they mate as they do so; some types mate with each other, but other types can mate *with the host's chromosomes*. Those that mate with each other would be insensitive to ultraviolet, but the second type would be unable to replicate when the host's genes are damaged. This view is supported by the observation (Kellenberger and Weigle, 1958) that when *E. coli* has been so irradiated that it no longer allows multiplication of a single phage strain, it can still allow (though weakly) multiplication of several strains applied simultaneously. Thus the phage-host mating can be replaced by phage-phage mating.

The idea of mating between phage and host arose first in another connection, namely, the phenomenon of *transduction* (Chap. XXI, sec. 4). By this means, in the Salmonellae (and some other related

---

FIGURE II–25

Bacteriophage ("actinophage") infecting *Streptomyces olivaceus*. *A*. Cell of *Str. olivaceus* showing the many phage particles filling the cytoplasm. × 40,000. *B*. Individual particles. The transverse striations in the tail and the tail fibers (top) compare closely with those in Figure II–24. Photos by F. Mach, courtesy of Prof. Dr. H. Borriss.

organisms), heritable characters can be interchanged one at a time by infection with special phages, which transfer characters to the actual genetic material of the host.

There is another type of bacteriophage that becomes even more intimately associated with the host cell. These phages, P1, P2, P22, and λ, do not destroy the host cells but lyse only a small number of them. The cells that are not lysed carry the phage, however, and when they are irradiated with x-rays or ultraviolet light, they do lyse (in most cases) and liberate active phage (see the reviews of Lwoff, 1953; Jacob et al., 1959). Fairly high concentrations of certain chemicals, including H_2O_2, will also induce lysis. To some extent the cells lyse naturally when the culture becomes old. The phage-carrying bacteria are called *lysogenic* and the phages *temperate*.

Lysogenic strains seem more or less normal in culture, because spontaneous lysis is usually too slight to affect the growth rate. They can be carried on agar for years without losing their lysogeny. Yet the phage must be present in most of the cells, since it can be induced to appear by the proper treatment. Nevertheless, all attempts to prepare phage from lysogenic cells by mechanical or other means have failed. Thus the phage "has no continuous existence" (Northrop, 1958) and must be present in partial form, as a so-called *prophage*. Genetic evidence from crosses has now established that a heritable character or gene controls lysogeny and also controls the specificity of the temperate phage to which the cell responds. The factor controlling lysogeny is closely linked, in *E. coli*, to the gene giving the ability to ferment galactose. It is deduced, therefore, that the heritable factor (carried in the host's own chromosome) is *itself* the prophage (see Bertani, 1958, and Chap. XXI).

The way in which the DNA of the phage somehow enters the host's own chromosome is not clear; the same question occurs when the temperate phage *transduces* host characters. The prophage is not physiologically inert when it has entered the genetic material, since its presence often reduces the sensitivity of the host to other phages. The effect is specific for both host and phage, and is not exerted on the process of adsorption or attachment. Nor is it clear what change occurs when the cells are induced to lyse and liberate phage. The phage produced is the same as that liberated by ordinarily sensitive cells, so that the last stages of phage formation must be the same in both types. Northrop (1958) has shown that low concentrations of H_2O_2 increase the proportion of phage-forming cells to exactly the same extent as they induce mutations, and he considers therefore that reversion to phage formation is a kind of mutation; radiation also causes mutations (Chap. XXIV) and so do most of the other chemicals that induce phage formation. Apparently the host's chromosome breaks apart at a specific point to let the phage DNA in, and then, when made unstable by mutagenic forces, it squeezes the phage out again into the cytoplasm.

Finally, the importance of phages in nature must be mentioned. Since the balance between host and parasite is a common means of population control in higher organisms, it is likely that phages serve to control bacterial populations everywhere. Their close relationship to the host's genetic material makes them a peculiarly intimate type of parasite. As far as we know, ordinary viruses in higher animals and plants have no such close relationship. It is a curious fact that the bacteriophage particle is about the largest of the viruses (almost 0.2 μ in length), yet it attacks the smallest of organisms. Could it be that it is because of its relatively large size compared to its host that its effects are so special? It might be interesting to study the effects of phage on the very smallest bacteria such as Dialister or Bartonella. The importance of size, as was stated at the outset of this section, may be even more fundamental than it appears.

REFERENCES

Aach, H. G. 1958. *Z. f. Naturforschung*, **13b**:425–433.
Anderson, R. J. 1929. *J. Biol. Chem.*, **83**:505–522.
Anderson, R. J. 1940. The Chemistry of the Lipids of Tubercle Bacilli. *Harvey Lect.*, **35**:271–313.
Anderson, T. F. 1945. *J. Cell. Comp. Physiol.*, **25**:17–26; cf. also Delbruck, M. 1948. *J. Bact.*, **56**:1–16.
Astbury, W. T., and Weibull, C. 1949. *Nature*, **163**:280–282.
de Bary, A. 1887. Lectures on Bacteria. P. 16. Oxford, Clarendon Press.
*Bawden, F. C. 1950. Plant Viruses and Virus Diseases, 3rd ed. Waltham, Mass., Chronica Botanica Co.
Benzer, S. 1955. *Proc. Nat. Acad. Sci.*, **41**:344–354.
Bergey's Manual of Determinative Bacteriology, 7th ed. 1957. Ed. by R. S. Breed, E. G. D. Murray, and A. P. Hitchens. Baltimore, Williams and Wilkins Co.
Bertani, G. 1958. Lysogeny. *Advances in Virus Research*, **5**:151–193.
*Bessey, E. A. 1950. Morphology and Taxonomy of Fungi. Philadelphia, Blakiston Co
Bissett, K. A. 1949. *J. Gen. Microbiol.*, **3**:93–96.
Bissett, K. A. 1957. *J. Gen. Microbiol.*, **17**:562–566.
Bonner, J. T. 1952. Morphogenesis: An Essay on Development. Princeton Univ. Press.
Bonner, J. T. 1959. The Cellular Slime Molds. Princeton University Press.

Bradfield, J. R. G., and Cater, D. B. 1952. *Nature*, **169**:944–950.

Buder, J. 1915. *Jahrb. wiss. Botanik*, **56**:529–584.

Bushnell, L. D., and Haas, H. F. 1941. *J. Bact.*, **41**:653–673; cf. also *Chem. Abstr.*, **36**:1978 (1942).

Chapman, G. B. 1959. *J. Bact.*, **78**:96–104.

Clark, F. E., and Carr, P. H. 1951. *J. Bact.*, **62**:1–6.

Cochrane, V. W. 1958. Physiology of Fungi. New York, John Wiley.

Cohen, S. S. 1957. In, The Chemical Basis of Heredity. Baltimore, Johns Hopkins Press, pp. 651–685.

Cohn, F. 1872. Die Bakterien. *Sammlung gemeinverständlicher wiss. Vorträge*, **7**:Heft 165. Berlin.

Colter, J. S.; Bird, H. H.; Moyer, A. W.; and Brown, R. A. 1958. *Virology*, **4**:522–529.

Commoner, B.; Newmark, P.; and Rodenberg, S. D. 1952. *Arch. Biochem. Biophys.*, **37**:15–36.

Conn, H. J., and Dimmick, I. 1947. *J. Bact.*, **54**:291–303.

Couch, J. N. 1950, 1955. *J. Elisha Mitchell Sci. Soc.*, **66**:87–92; **71**:148–155.

Cummins, C. S., and Harris, H. 1959. *Nature*, **184**:831–832.

Davern, C. I., and Meselson, M. 1960. *J. Mol. Biol.*, **2**:153–160.

Dienes, L. 1946. *Proc. Soc. Exp. Biol. Med.*, **63**:265–270; *Cold Spring Harbor Symp. Quant. Biol.*, **11**:51–59.

Dienes, L., and Weinberger, H. I. 1951. The L-Forms of Bacteria. *Bact. Revs.*, **15**:245–288.

Doermann, A. H. 1953. The Vegetative State in the Life Cycle of Bacteriophage. *Cold Spring Harbor Symp. Quant. Biol.*, **18**:3–11.

Donker, H. J. L. 1926. Bijdrage tot de Kennis der boterzuur, butylalcohol en acetongistingen. Dissertation, Delft.

Douglas, H. C., and Wolfe, R. S. 1959. *J. Bact.*, **78**:597.

*Dubos, R. J. 1947. The Bacterial Cell. Cambridge, Mass., Harvard Univ. Press.

Duchow, E., and Douglas, H. C. 1949. *J. Bact.*, **58**:409–416.

Edward, D. G. ff. 1954. The Pleuropneumonia Group of Organisms: A Review, Together with Some New Observations. *J. Gen. Microbiol.*, **10**:27–64.

Erikson, D. 1949. *J. Gen. Microbiol.* **3**:361–368.

Finck, G. 1951. *Arch. Mikrobiol.*, **15**:358–388.

Foster, J. W. 1949. Chemical Activities of the Fungi. New York, Academic Press.

Fraenkel-Conrat, H.; Singer, B.; and Williams, R. C. 1957. *Biochim. Biophys. Acta*, **25**:87–96.

*Fritsch, F. E. 1935, 1945. The Structure and Reproduction of the Algae. Vols. I and II. New York, Cambridge Univ. Press.

Gamow, G., and Ycas, M. 1955. *Proc. Nat. Acad. Sci.* **41**:1011–1019.

*Gäumann, E. 1949. Die Pilze. Basel, Birkhäuser Verlag.

Gierer, A., and Mundry K. W. 1958. *Nature*, **182**:1457; Schuster, H., and Schramm, G. *Z. f. Naturforschung*, **13b**:697–704.

Gierer, A., and Schramm, G. 1956. *Z. f. Naturforschung*, **11b**:138–142.

Giesberger, G. 1936. Beiträge zur Kenntniss der Gattung Spirillum Ehbg. Dissertation, Utrecht.

Gordon, R. E., and Mihm, J. M. 1959. *J. Gen. Microbiol.*, **21**:736–748.

*Gottschalk, A. 1957. *Physiol. Revs.*, **37**:66–83.

Gunther, H. L. 1959. *Nature*, **183**:903–904.

Hayflick, L., and Stinebring, W. R. 1960. *Annals New York Acad. Sci.*, **79**:443–449.

Henrici, A. T., and Johnson, D. E. 1935. *J. Bact.*, **29**:3–4; **30**:61–86.

Herbert, D., and Pinsent, J. 1948. *Biochem. J.*, **43**:193–202.

d'Herelle, F. 1926. The Bacteriophage and Its Behavior. Baltimore, Williams and Wilkins Co. (Trans. G. H. Smith.)

Herriott, R. M., and Barlow, J. L. 1952. *J. Gen. Physiol.*, **36**:17–28.

Herriott, R. M., and Barlow, J. L. 1957. *J. Gen. Physiol.*, **41**:307–331.

Hershey, A. D. 1957. Bacteriophages as Genetic and Biochemical Systems. *Advances in Virus Research*, **4**:25–61.

Hershey, A. D., and Burgi, E. 1960. *J. Molec. Biol.*, **2**:143–152.

Hershey, A. D., and Chase, M. 1952. *J. Gen. Physiol.*, **36**:39–56.

Hofer, A. W. 1944. *J. Bact.*, **47**:415–416.

Houwink, A. L. 1951. *Nature*, **168**:654.

Houwink, A. L., and van Iterson, W. 1950. *Biochim. biophys. Acta*, **5**:10-44.

van Iterson, W. 1947. *Biochim. Biophys. Acta*, **1**:527–548.

Jacob, F.; Schaeffer, P.; and Wellman, E. L. 1959. Episomic Elements in Bacteria. In, *Symp. Soc. Exp. Biol.*, Cambridge Univ. Press, No. 10, pp. 67–91.

Jahn, B. 1924. Beitr. zur botanischen Protistologie. I. Die Polyangiden. Leipzig, Borntraeger.

Jarosch, R. 1959. *Protoplasma*, **50**:277–289.

Jensen, H. L. 1931. *Proc. Linnaean Soc. N. S. Wales* (Australia), **56**:79–98; 345–370.

de Jong, L. E. den Dooren. 1926. Bijdrage tot de kennis van het mineralisatieproces. Rotterdam, Nijgh and Van Ditmar.

Kellenberger, G., and Weigle, J. J. 1958. *Biochim. Biophys. Acta*, **30**:112–124.

Kingma-Boltjes, T. Y. 1936. *Arch. Mikrobiol.*, **7**:188–205.

Kingma-Boltjes, T. Y. 1948. *J. Path. and Bact.*, **60**:275–287.

*Klieneberger-Nobel, E. 1951. Filterable Forms of Bacteria. *Bact. Revs.*, **15**:77–103.

Krijgsman, B. J. 1925. *Arch. Protistenkunde*, **52**:478–488.

Krzemieniewska, H. 1933. *Arch. Mikrobiol.*, **4**:394–408.

Krzemieniewski, S., and Krzemieniewska, H. 1927–1928. *Acta Soc. Botan. Poloniae*, **5**: 46–90; 102–131.

Lamanna, C. 1946 *J. Bact.*, **52**:99–103.

Lechevalier, H. A.; Solotorovsky, M.; and McDurmont, C. I. 1961. *J. Gen. Microbiol.*, **26**:11–18.

Leifson, E. 1960. Atlas of Bacterial Flagellation. New York, Academic Press.

Leifson, E., and Hugh, R. 1954. *J. Gen. Microbiol.*, **10**:68–70.

Levinthal, C. 1959. Bacteriophage Genetics. In, The Viruses; ed. F. M. Barret and W. M. Stanley, New York, Academic Press, **2**:281–317.

Lewin, R. A. 1962. *Canad. J. Microbiol.*, **8**:555–563.

Lieske, R. 1921. Morphologie und Biologie der Strahlenpilze. Leipzig, Gebrüde. Borntraeger.

Loebeck, M. E., and Klein, H. P. 1956. *J. Gen Microbiol.*, **14**:281–289

Long, E. R., and Finner, L. L. 1927. *Am. Rev. Tuberculosis*, **16**:523–529.

Louria, D. B., and Gordon, R. E. 1960. *Amer. Rev. Resp. Diseases*, **81**:83–88.

*Lwoff, A. 1953. Lysogeny. *Bact. Revs.*, **17**:269–337.

Mach, F. 1960. *Experientia*, **16**:142–143.

McVittie, A., and Zahler, S. A. 1962. *Nature*, **194**:1299–1300.

*Markham, R. 1959. Biochemistry of Plant Viruses. In, The Viruses, ed. F. M. Barret and W. M Stanley, New York, Academic Press, **2**:33–125

Meselson, M., and Weigle, J. J. 1961. *Proc. Nat. Acad. Sci.*, **47**:857–868.

Metzner, P. 1920. *Jahrb. wiss. Bot.*, **59**:325–412.

Neumann, F. 1925. *Zentr. Bakt. I orig.*, **96**:250–262.

Newcombe, H. B. 1949. *Nature*, **164**:150.

van Niel, C. B. 1926–1927. *Ned. Tijdschr. Hyg. Microbiol. Serol.*, pp. 305–326 (1926); 93–112 (1937).

*van Niel, C. B. 1931. *Arch. Mikrobiol.*, **3**:2–112.

*van Niel, C. B. 1944. The Culture, General Physiology, Morphology and Classification of the Non-sulfur Purple and Brown Bacteria. *Bact. Revs.*, **8**:1–118.

Northrop, J. H. 1958. *J. Gen. Physiol.*, **42**:109–136.

Ordal, E. J., and Rucker, R. R. 1944. *Proc. Soc. Expt. Biol. Med.*, **56**:15–18.

Ørskov, J. 1923. Investigations into the Morphology of the Ray Fungi. Copenhagen, Levin and Munksgaard.

Pijper, A. 1930–1931. *Zentr. Bakt. I orig.*, **118**:113–121; **123**:195–201.

Pijper, A. 1940. Cited in Dubos, 1947.

Prazmowski, A. 1880. Untersuchungen über Entwicklungsgeschichte und Fermentwirkung einiger Bakterien Arten. Dissertation, Leipzig, Hugo Voigt.

*Pringsheim, E. G. 1949. The Relationship between Bacteria and Myxophyceae. *Bacteriol. Revs.*, **13**:47–98.

Pringsheim, E. G. 1950. *J. Gen. Microbiol.*, **4**:198–209.

Pringsheim, E. G. 1951. *Arch. Mikrobiol.*, **16**:18–27.

Pringsheim, E. G. 1959. *Nature*, **184**:1098–1100.

Pringsheim, E. G., and Robinow, C. F. 1947. *J. Gen. Microbiol.*, **1**:267–278.

Provost, P., and Doetsch, R. N. 1962. *J. Gen. Microbiol.*, **28**:547–557.

Quehl, A. 1906. *Zentr. Bakt. II*, **16**:9–34.

Raper, K. B. 1940. *Am. J. Bot.*, **27**:436–448; cf. also *Growth* (Suppl.), **5**:41–76 (1941).

Rivers, T. M. 1948. Viral and Rickettsial Infections of Man. Philadelphia, Lippincott Co.

Rosebury, T.; Epps, L. J.; and Clark, A. R. 1944. *J. Inf. Dis.*, **74**:131–149.

Schlegel, H. G., and Pfennig, N. 1961. *Arch. Mikrobiol.*, **38**:1–39.

*Schlossberger, H., and Brandis, H. 1954. Leptospira. *Ann. Revs. Microbiol.*, **8**:133–152.

Schmidt, H. 1933. *Zentr. Bakt. I*, **130**:391–400.

Schwerdt, C. E. 1957. Physical and Chemical Characters of Purified Polio Virus. In, Cellular Biology, Nucleic Acids and Viruses, ed. T. M. Rivers. N. Y. Acad. Sci., Special Publications, **5**:1–414.

Shaw, C.; Stitt, J. M.; and Cowan, S. T. 1951. *J. Gen. Microbiol.*, **5**:1010–1023.

Shinn, L. E. 1940. *J. Bact.*, **39**:22 (abstr.).

Singh, B. N. 1947. *J. Gen. Microbiol.*, **1**:1–10.

Smith, G. M. 1950. The Fresh-Water Algae of the United States. New York, McGraw-Hill Book Co.

Snieszko, S. F.; McAllister, J.; and Hitchner, E. R. 1941–1942. *J. Bact.*, **41**:26–27; **43**:28–29.

Söhngen, N. L. 1913. *Zentr. Bakt. II*, **37**:595–609.

Stanier, R. Y. 1940. *J. Bact.*, **40**:619–635.

*Stanier, R. Y. 1942. The Cytophaga Group: a Contribution to the Biology of Myxobacteria. *Bact. Revs.*, **6**:143–196.

Stanier, R. Y. 1947. *J. Bact.*, **53**:297–315.

Stanier, R. Y., and van Niel, C. B. 1941. *J. Bact.*, **42**:437–466.

*Stanier, R. Y., and Gunsalus, I. C. (eds.) 1960–1964. The Bacteria. 5 vols. New York, Academic Press.

Stanley, W. M. 1936. *Phytopathol.*, **26**:305–320.

Stent, G. S. 1958. Mating in the Reproduction of Bacterial Viruses. *Advances in Virus Research*, **5**:95–149.

Stove, J. L., and Stanier, R. Y. 1962. *Nature*, **196**:1189–1192.

Takeya, K.: Koike, M.; Mori, R.; Yuda, Y.; and Toda, T. 1959. *J. Bact.*, **78**:313–319.

Taylor, Sir G. 1952. *Proc. Roy. Soc.*, A **211**:225–239.

Thaxter, R. 1892. *Bot. Gaz.*, **17**:389–406.

Thaysen, A. C. 1936. *Ann. Applied Biol.*, **23**:99–104.

van Thiel, P. H., and van Iterson, W. 1947. *Proc. Kon. Akad. Wetenschap. Amsterdam*, **50**:3–6.

Varpholomeeva, A. A., and Stanislavsky, E. S. 1958. *Ann. Inst. Pasteur,* **94**:361–366.

Veldkamp, H. 1960. *Ant. v. Leeuwenhock,* **26**:103–125.

Wagner, R. 1914. *Z. Gärungsphysiol.,* **4**:289–319; cf. *Zentr. Bakt. II,* **44**:175–176.

*Waksman, S. A. 1950. The Actinomycetes. Waltham, Mass., Chronica Botanica Co.

*Waksman, S. A. 1960. The Actinomycetes, Vol. 2. New York, Ronald Press.

Weibull, C. 1948–1951. *Biochim. Biophys. Acta,* **2**:351–353; **3**:378–382; *Acta chem. Scand.,* **4**:268 (1950); **5**:529–534 (1951).

Weiss, E., Dressler, H. R., and Suitor, E. C. 1959. *J. Bact.,* **78**:432–440.

Wells, H. G.; Dewitt, L. M.; and Long, E. R. 1932. The Chemistry of Tuberculosis, 2nd ed. Baltimore, Williams and Wilkins Co.

*Wildman, S. G. 1959. The Process of Infection and Virus Synthesis. In, The Viruses, ed. F. M. Barret and W. M. Stanley, New York, Academic Press, **2**:1–31.

Wolf, M., and Israel, J. 1891. *Arch. path. anat.,* **126**:11–59.

de Wolff, H. H. 1927. Biochemische Eigenschappen van de Diphtherie- en van de Pseudodiphtherie-bacterie. Thesis, Utrecht.

Wyatt, G. R., and Cohen, S. S. 1953. *Biochem. J.,* **55**:774–782.

Zinsser, H. 1935. Rats, Lice and History. Boston, Little, Brown and Co.

ZoBell, C. 1946. Marine Microbiology. Waltham, Mass., Chronica Botanica Co.

CHAPTER III

The Internal Structure of Bacteria

The Microbe is so very small
You cannot make him out at all,
But many sanguine people hope
To see him through a microscope.
His jointed tongue that lies beneath
A hundred curious rows of teeth,
His seven tufted tails with lots
Of lovely pink and purple spots
On each of which a pattern stands,
Composed of forty separate bands;
His eyebrows of a tender green—
All these have never yet been seen.
But scientists who ought to know,
Assure us that they must be so,—
Oh, let us never, never doubt
What nobody is sure about.

HILAIRE BELLOC

1. THE WALL

The bacterial cell has an outer wall and an inner membrane. The outer wall can be made visible by placing the cells in a strong sugar solution, when the cytoplasm loses water and thus shrinks away from the smooth, apparently structureless wall (plasmolysis). It was even detected with the optical microscope as long ago as 1895 by Alfred Fischer, and it can be stained with tannic acid and crystal violet (Robinow, 1944) or with a detergent and Congo red (Dyar, 1947). Preparations for chemical analysis can be made by breaking up the cells so that the contents are extruded, when the walls remain nearly intact (Fig. III–1). In sections cut through the cell the thickness of the wall can be determined (Fig. III–12, p. 142); it varies from 0.01 to 0.06 μ and may be layered in two or even three zones of varying density, like the cell walls of higher plants. In old cultures it sometimes appears wrinkled. In one Spirillum it appears overlaid with, or formed from, small spheres in a hexagonal pattern (Houwink, 1953), but this is unusual. The more delicate membrane within the wall is not more than 0.008 μ thick, and it is this that first divides the cytoplasm in two at cell division (Chapman, 1959). Only after the cell wall has also grown across does the constriction occur that separates the walls (Fig. III–12, p. 142).

The functions of the wall are dramatically illustrated by what happens when it is taken away. Following the discovery of Salton that isolated cell walls of *M. lysodeikticus* can be dissolved by the enzyme, lysozyme, which hydrolyzes mucopolysaccharides, Weibull (1953) treated intact bacterial cells with this enzyme. The results were striking; within a few minutes cultures of *Bac. megaterium* lost their turbidity, and under the microscope the cells had disappeared,

FIGURE III–1

Electron micrograph of cell walls of *Micrococcus* (*"Staph."*) *aureus* after shaking for one hour with 200-mesh glass beads and centrifuging. Palladium shadow-cast. 11,000 ✕. (Photo, I. M. Dawson and Harold Stem, Univ. Glasgow. From *British J. of Exp. Path.*, **33**:177, 1952.)

leaving a viscous solution containing a few granules and some thin, empty spheres. However, if the cells were suspended in strong sucrose solution before the enzyme was added, they did not lyse, but instead formed little chains of spheres or "protoplasts"—one to four per original rod. Since the visible rods commonly have already divided and thus contain ready-formed cross walls, this means that each true cell is rounded up into a sphere. Sometimes the spheres are seen to have flagella attached, which confirms that they really are the cell contents; however, they are nonmotile. Thus, because the lysozyme has dissolved away the wall, the rod has changed to a sphere. It follows that the wall *must have been rigid* and must have determined the rod shape of the normal cell. The wall also gives necessary mechanical support, since in its absence the cell at once goes to pieces unless in a strong sugar solution. If the protoplast suspension in sucrose is diluted, the cells lyse as before, leaving granules and empty spheres; these latter are evidently the inner membranes and contain pigments. The protoplasts have normal respiration and can synthesize several enzymes; they do not, however, multiply to form colonies on agar. Bacteriophage can grow in them and produces about one-third as many particles as in whole cells; however, if the protoplasts are lysed by dilution, the growth of phage is slight or zero (Salton and McQuillen, 1955). Similar protoplasts can be made from *Sarcina lutea*.

Gram-negative cells are generally resistant to lysozyme, but in alkaline buffer in the presence of a metal-chelating agent, *E. coli* and several related bacteria, as well as *Ps. aeruginosa* and *Azotobacter vinelandii*, yield apparently wall-free forms. Bodies that look similar can be prepared by adding penicillin to a growing culture of *E. coli* in a strong sugar solution (Lederberg, 1956); the penicillin inhibits synthesis of cell-wall material (see Chap. XXV). These bodies persist because the osmotic pressure of the sugary medium saves them from bursting. From their initially spherical shape they may change to ameboid forms with lobes and outgrowths—further evidence that the typical, regular cell form is due to the rigidity of the wall. However, after several hours a number of them revert to normal cells, i.e., they resynthesize the cell wall. According to McQuillen (1960), there is some doubt whether *all* the cell wall is removed from gram-negative forms, either by lysozyme or by penicillin, and the term "spheroplast" has been suggested for these spherical bodies.

The *inner membrane* appears to consist largely of lipoprotein (i.e., a protein-fat or protein-phosphatide complex) perhaps in the form of uniform macromolecular layers. It has to be mainly non-aqueous since it is the barrier between the aqueous medium and the aqueous cell contents. Preparations of the membrane made by osmotic bursting and centrifuging indicate that it makes up 10 to 20 per cent of the dry weight of the wall (Mitchell and Moyle, 1956–1959); it contains RNA and also the cytochrome pigments (see Chap. V). Probably it is this membrane that synthesizes the cell wall, because when protein synthesis in *Bac. megaterium* is stopped (by adding the antibiotic chloramphenicol), C^{14}-labeled amino acids can still be incorporated *both* into the membrane *and* into the wall. It is deduced that the membrane is probably the site of synthesis of the peptide in the wall (Brookes *et al.*, 1959; see below). It is also the "osmotic barrier" of the cell, limiting the entry of small molecules into the cytoplasm (Mitchell and Moyle, 1956–1959).

The chemical nature of the wall is under active investigation. Bacterial walls can be prepared free of cytoplasm either mechanically

TABLE III–1. Composition of Cell Walls of Two Gram-positive Bacteria
(The numbers in heavy type give the relative numbers of molecules present; otherwise, the percentage of the wall dry weight is given.)

Micrococcus lysodeikticus (Perkins and Rogers, 1959)	*Bacillus subtilis* (vegetative cells) (Salton and Marshall, 1959)
Amino Acids	
Alanine **2** Glutamic acid **1** Glycine **1.4** Lysine **1**	Alanine **4** Glutamic acid **2** (traces of four others) Diaminopimelic **1**
Amino Sugars	
N-acetyl-glucosamine (14% =) **0.7** N-acetyl-muramic acid (24% =) **0.9**	N-acetyl-glucosamine (7.9%) N-acetyl-muramic acid (4.1%)
Sugar	
Glucose (4% =) **0.3**	Glucose
Other	
	Total P 4.2% (mainly as ribitol phosphate polymer, "teichoic acid") Lipid 9.7%

as in Figure III–1, or in the case of gram-positive cells by treating with trypsin, ribonuclease, and pepsin (Cummins and Harris, 1956). The insoluble product can be hydrolyzed with lysozyme or with acid. Although different bacteria give somewhat different results, there is a general similarity or basal structure, especially among gram-positive cells, which is exemplified in Table III–I. There are four parts: (1) a peptide consisting of three to eight amino acids; (2) the amino sugars N-acetyl-glucosamine (VII below) and its 3-carboxyethyl derivative, N-acetyl-muramic acid, IV, generally linked together in alternating β-1-6 and β-1-4 configurations, sometimes along with some galactosamine; (3) varying amounts of polysaccharide; and (4) polymers of ribitol or glycerol phosphate, called "teichoic acids." There may also be a small account of lipid. It is the β-1-4 bonds that are attacked by lysozyme (Salton and Ghuysen, 1960). In *Bac. anthracis* the polysaccharide is a large fraction and contains galactose, while the peptide is smaller in amount, although its principal components, alanine, glycine, glutamic and aspartic acids, resemble those in Table III–1.

The teichoic acids are a varied group of polymers of 5-phosphoribitol or 3-phosphoglycerol, linked 1:5 or 1:3, respectively. Sugars and/or alanine are substituted in the 2 and 4 positions of the ribitol or the 2 position of the glycerol. In *L. arabinosus* and *Bac. subtilis*, the sugar is glucose; in the Staphylococci (*M. aureus* and *M. albus*), it is both glucose and N-acetyl-galactosamine (Baddiley *et al.*, 1961). The chains are 6 to 16 units long, and similar, though not identical, compounds have also been found free in the cell contents; thus the teichoic acids are probably polymerized *in situ* rather than being simply deposited from solution. A representative teichoic acid, that from *Bac. subtilis* walls (Armstrong *et al.*, 1961) is:

$$HO\left[-HPO_2\cdot O\cdot CH_2-\overset{H}{\underset{\underset{\beta\,gluc.}{O}}{C}}-\overset{H}{\underset{OH}{C}}-\overset{H}{\underset{\underset{\underset{CH_3\overset{\cdot}{C}HNH_2}{CO}}{O}}{C}}-CH_2O-\right]_9 H$$

(The alanyl group may also be on the adjacent position.) For comparison, one of the phosphoglycerol compounds, that found intracellularly in *L. casei* (Kelemen and Baddiley, 1961) is:

$$HO\left[-HPO_3-CH_2-\overset{H}{\underset{\underset{\underset{CH_3\overset{\cdot}{C}HNH_2}{CO}}{O}}{C}}-CH_2O\right]_n H$$

In the wall peptide, alanine and glutamic acid occur mainly as the D-isomers, i.e., the forms that do *not* occur in protein (see Strange, 1959). In addition there is present *either* lysine, I, *or* diaminopimelic acid, II, but not both.

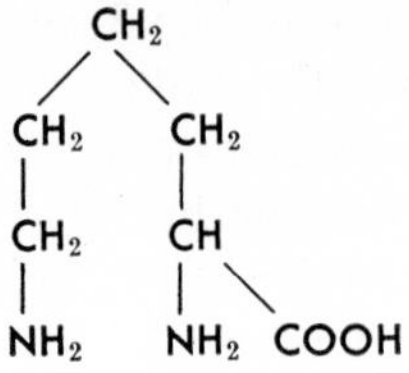

I

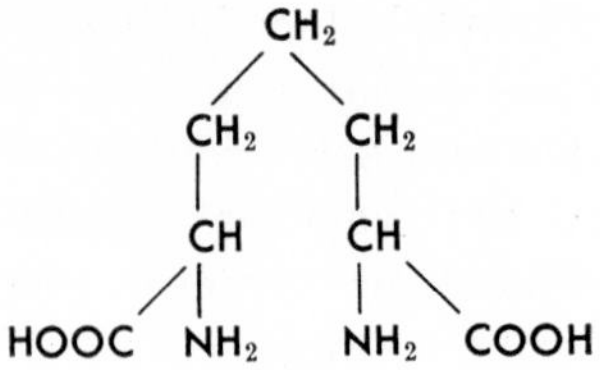

II

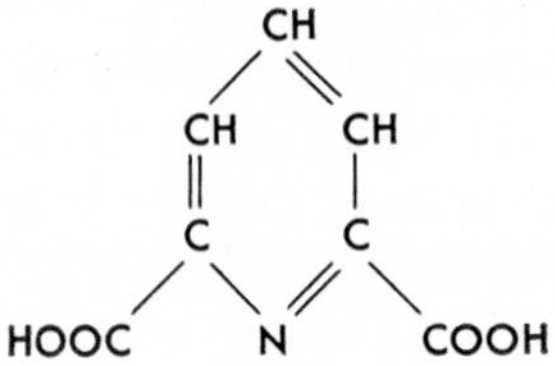

III

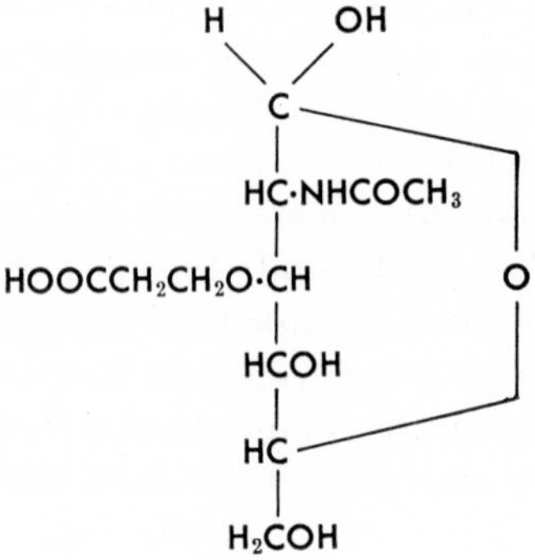

IV

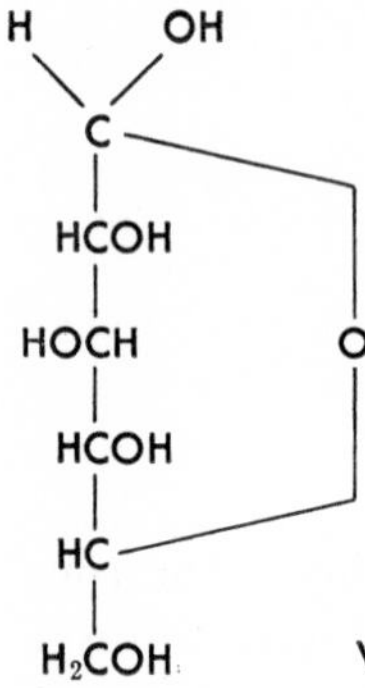

V

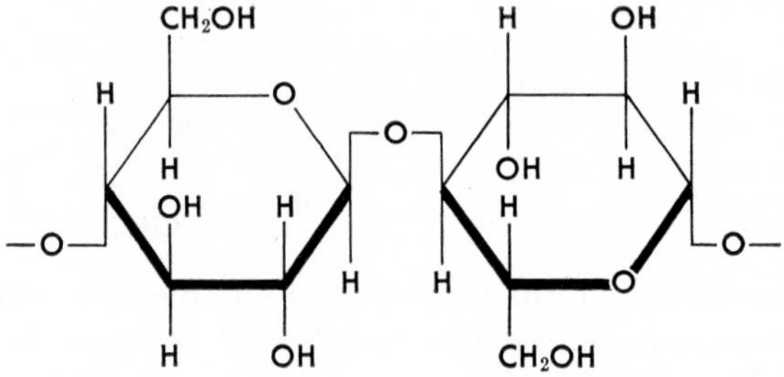

VI

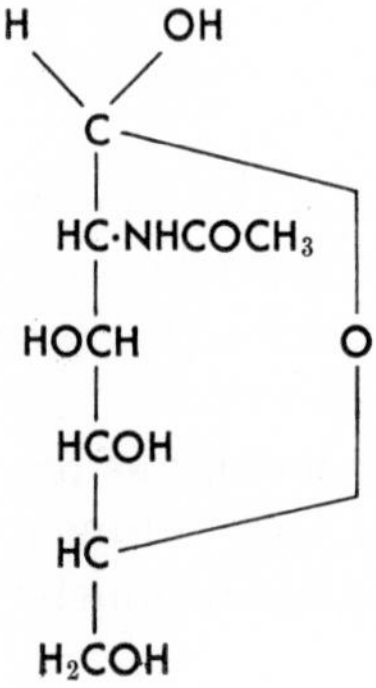

VII

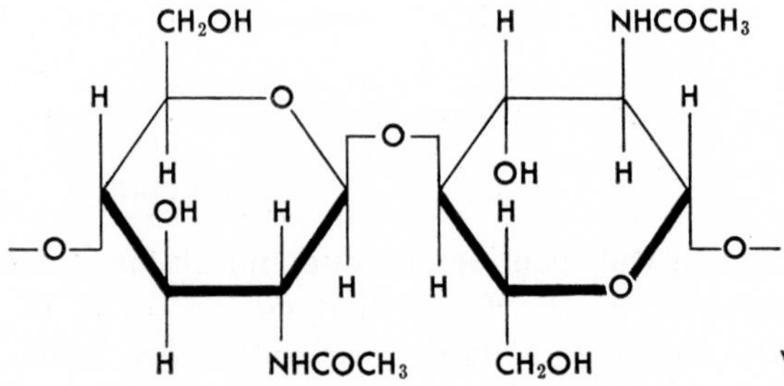

VIII

The latter compound is not known as a natural product in other organisms; it is closely related to lysine and also to *pyridine-dicarboxylic acid*, III, which occurs in spores (see below). *Muramic acid* is also not known elsewhere and was first identified from bacterial walls by Strange and Dark in 1956; both it and glucosamine occur as the N-acetyl derivatives (IV and VII, respectively).

In gram-negative cells, such as *E. coli*, the same "basal structure" occurs, but is a much smaller fraction of the total; a good deal of the weight is made up of lipoprotein, which is apparently present as a second layer, because electron micrographs indicate that these cells have a two-layered wall (Kellenberger and Ryter, 1958). The lipid may make up 10 to 20 per cent of the wall. Correspondingly *E. coli* is converted to protoplasts with lysozyme much less readily than the gram-positive organisms. It contains also an unusual 7-carbon sugar, L-Gala-D-manno-heptose (Weidel, 1955).

A group of recent analyses of the peptides of cell walls is summarized in Table III–2, in which the number of moles of each amino

TABLE III–2. Relative Composition of the Peptide of Bacterial Walls

(from data of Kandler and Hund, 1959)

Amino Acid	18 spp. of Lactobacilli	15 spp. of Lactic Cocci	11 spp. of Propionic Acid Bacteria and Micro-bacteria	15 spp. of Bacilli	4 spp. of Gram-negative Rods
Diaminopimelic	—*	—	0.64	0.55	0.51
Aspartic	0.22	0.16	0.05	0.06	0.08
Glutamic	0.56	0.53	0.65	0.66	0.60
Lysine	1.02	1.03	0.25	0.24	0.21
Glycine	0.17	0.23	0.51	0.16	0.21
Serine	0.03	0.09	0.02	0.03	0.06
Valine	0.10	0.10	0.12	0.12	0.14
Leucine	0.23	0.22	0.25	0.25	0.27
(Alanine)	(1.0)	(1.0)	(1.0)	(1.0)	(1.0)

* One was found to have 0.50 mols DAP, this one had only 0.07 lysine.

acid is given relative to the number of moles of alanine. In another series of analyses (Salton and Pavlik, 1960) on 23 gram-positive organisms, a total of 6 Bacilli, *M. varians*, and *Lactob. arabinosus* were found to have diaminopimelic acid, while the other 15 had lysine. The results can be grouped and recalculated for alanine 1.00 as follows:

	DAP	Lysine	Glutamine	Glycine	Serine
8 species:	—	0.35	0.45	0.59	0.10
15 species:	0.32	—	0.65	0.07	—

Only in a few cases was any amino acid present in higher concentration than alanine. Thus the agreement with the data in the table is very good.

The fact that so much acetyl amino sugar and so little simple sugar are present in bacterial walls is of interest for the interrelations of the bacteria with other groups. The cell walls of the green algae and of higher plants consist almost wholly of polysaccharides, especially polymers of glucose, V, and xylose, and the most insoluble and characteristic material is cellulose, a 1–4 β-linked polyglucoside (VI) which forms fibrillar molecules of indefinite length. This characterizes the wall of all higher plants, and the majority of red, brown, and green algae, although a 1–3 β-linked xylan takes its place in the red Porphyra and in the green order Siphonales (Irika and Miwa, 1960; Frei and Preston, 1961). In the fungi, polysaccharides only make up part of the wall, and acetyl amino sugars appear; a prominent constituent is *chitin*, a 1–4 β-linked polymer of N-acetyl-2-glucosamine (VIII). This material, like cellulose, forms insoluble fibrils. It makes up almost entirely the cell walls of the Dermatophyte fungi (Blank, 1953) and is a major constituent in most other fungi, but the walls of yeast contain only a little chitin, together with two polysaccharides, one of which comprises chains of mannose combined with protein and the other glucose linked in the 1-3-β position (Roelofsen and Hoette, 1951; Northcote and Horne, 1952). Softening of the rigidity of the polysaccharide-protein, by hydrogenation of an S—S link, is believed to be the first stage in the budding of yeasts (Nickerson and Falcone, 1959). In addition to polysaccharides and amino sugars, fungal walls, including those of Phycomyces (Castle, 1945) and of yeasts (Northcote and Horne, 1952) also contain lipids. We can conclude that the bacterial walls are much more closely related to those of the fungi than to those of green plants. On the other hand, the peculiar peptide, the presence of muramic acid, and the lack of any of the fibrillar structure so typical of both green plants and fungi (see Fig. III–1), all indicate that the bacterial wall is characteristic and individual.

Outside of the Eubacteria not so much is known. The fact that the walls of the Streptomycetes are solubilized by lysozyme shows that they also have N-acetyl-glucosamine as a major constituent, since this unit linked β-1-4 in a polymer provides the point of attack for lysozyme (Meyer and Hahnel, 1946; Salton and Ghuysen, 1960); the material is probably not chitin itself. The resistance of Gram-negative cells to lysozyme is probably (as stated above) due to their large content of lipoprotein, while the resistance of the Mycobacteria and Nocardias is believed due to the presence of a polymer of arabinose. *Actinomyces bovis* walls are rich in 6-deoxy sugars (MacLennan, 1961). As more analyses are made, these differences in cell-wall composition will probably prove valuable as aids to taxonomy (Cummins and Harris, 1956, 1958).

There are three species of bacteria that do form cellulose, but it is not a part of the cell wall, being excreted outside it. One of these, *Acetobacter xylinum*, often can be seen in old vinegar as a floating, paper-like pellicle. When grown on media containing sugar, this organism may convert up to 19 per cent of the sugar to cellulose. The cellulose is excreted in fine fibrils, which, with a gummy polysaccharide, become matted together into a sort of textile (see Fig. III–2).

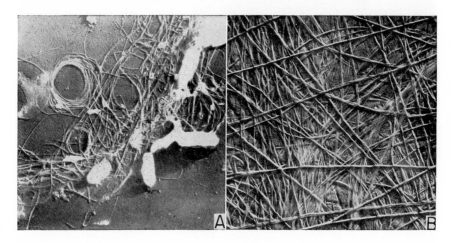

FIGURE III–2

A. Acetobacter xylinum cells and the tangled cellulose fibrils which it has excreted. Shadow-cast. 4000 ×.

B. The network of cellulose fibrils. 8100 ×.

(Both from K. Mühlethaler, *Biochim. Biophys. Acta*, **3**:15–25, 1949. Copyright Elsevier Publishing Co., Amsterdam, The Netherlands.)

The x-ray diffraction pattern of the bacterial cellulose is identical with that of cotton and shows changes on mercerization and on nitration parallel to those undergone by cotton cellulose (Khouvine *et al.*, 1932). The fibrils themselves look much like those of plant celluloses. How an insoluble polymer comes to be deposited outside the cell wall is discussed in Chapter XVI. Both the enzyme and the glucose-carrying precursor, which appears to contain a fatty acid moiety, have to be excreted into the medium and react there.

When bacteriophages become attached, the cell wall is the site of attachment, as described on page 97 and shown in Figure III–3. Phage can also be attached to isolated cell walls. The attachment is followed by the release of wall material into solution, and in the case of *E. coli*, alanine, glutamic acid, diaminopimelic acid, and muramic acid have been identified (Weidel and Primosigh, 1957). A wall-hydrolyzing enzyme must, therefore, be present in the tail of the *coli* phage, and

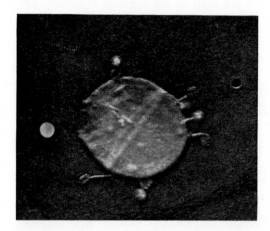

FIGURE III–3
Electron micrograph of cell wall of *Micrococcus aureus* obtained in the same manner as Figure III–1 but after treatment of the culture with bacteriophage. The protein membranes of the phage are seen adhering to the cell wall. (The white body is a polystyrene granule.) 35,400 ×. (Photo I. M. Dawson and J. E. Hotchin. From *British J. of Exp. Path.*, 33:177, 1952.)

no doubt similar enzymes occur in the phages for gram-positive organisms.

2. THE CAPSULE

Many bacteria produce from sugar media a thick, transparent, gelatinous or slimy capsule; this does not stain readily but is most easily seen in stained preparations of crowded organisms, when the cells appear to be surrounded by a clear space. It can be more easily seen (with the phase microscope) by precipitating proteins within the capsular substance (Tomcsik, 1956).[1] In liquid media much of the capsule diffuses off into the solution; clearly, therefore, it is outside the cell wall. In most instances the capsule is largely composed of polysaccharide, but in one or two cases the characteristic constituents are polypeptides. In some streptococci it is a polymer of N-acetyl-glucosamine and glucuronic acid; this material, "hyaluronic acid," is similar

[1] Capsules can sometimes be stained pink with Giemsa's solution, or with 5 per cent tannic acid followed after one-half hour with 0.01 per cent crystal violet (Klieneberger-Nobel 1948).

to the intercellular substance of animal tissues. In *B. dysenteriae* (= *Shigella shiga*) it contains polysaccharide, phospholipid, and protein (Morgan, 1950), while in the sporeformers, *Bac. subtilis*, *Bac. mesentericus*, and *Bac. anthracis*, it consists almost wholly of a polypeptide of D-glutamic acid, the isomer *not* present in protein (Ivanovics and co-workers, 1937; Hanby and Rydon, 1946). This polypeptide is excreted into the medium and thus has been prepared in quantity for analysis. Its molecular weight is about 53,000, meaning that (if pure) it consists of about 400 D-glutamic acid residues. These are linked in long chains of about 50 to 100 α-peptides joined by short chains of γ-peptides:

$$
\begin{array}{cccccc}
\text{COOH} & \text{COOH} & & \text{CO} & & \text{CO} \\
| & | & & | & & | \\
\text{CH}_2 & \text{CH}_2 & & \text{CH}_2 & & \text{CH}_2 \\
| & | & & | & & | \\
\text{CH}_2 & \text{CH}_2 & & \text{CH}_2 & & \text{CH}_2 \\
| & | & & | & & | \\
\text{CH—NH} & \text{CH—NH} & & \text{CH—NH} & & \text{CH—NH—} \\
| & | & & | & & | \\
\text{—CO} & \text{CO} & & \text{COOH} & & \text{COOH}
\end{array}
$$

| α-Peptide | γ-Peptide |

The commonest capsular materials, however, are polysaccharides of dextrose, levulose, or galactose, which in most cases contain carboxylic acid groups as well; they have molecular weights around a million.

Capsular material is not formed during the whole life of a bacterium, but at different growth stages, depending on the organism. The pneumococci form a capsule mainly when growth is slowing down, while streptococci produce it in the early stages of growth and lose it later. Aerobacter forms it both during and after growth, though the *rate* of formation is highest during the logarithmic growth phase (Duguid and Wilkinson, 1953). *Bac. anthracis* forms its capsule only in presence of CO_2, while in other species excess of carbohydrates and low concentrations of P and N favor the formation (Duguid, 1948). Addition of blood serum to the medium strongly favors capsule formation by many pathogens.

Typically the polysaccharides are produced best on sucrose media and not from hexoses. *Leuconostoc dextranicus*, for instance, forms little or no capsular material on dextrose or levulose media, while on sucrose it makes so much polysaccharide that the whole medium becomes ropy and gelatinous, like frog's eggs (hence the German term *Froschlaich-*, or frog's spawn, *bacterium*). In sugar refineries, where large tanks of impure sucrose solutions sometimes have to be kept for a day or two, *Leuconostoc* is a serious menace, since it grows very rapidly in the warm solution. Van Tieghem, who named this bacterium in 1878, mentions the conversion of 5000 liters of molasses to useless jelly in 12 hours! The effectiveness of sucrose as precursor is due to the fact that the glucosidic linkage is already formed and can thus be transferred to other sugar units with little or no expenditure of energy. For example:

$$n \text{ Glucose-levuloside} \rightleftharpoons (\text{Glucose})_n + n \text{ Levulose, or}$$
$$\rightleftharpoons (\text{Levulose})_n + n \text{ Glucose}$$

i.e., either a *dextran* or a *levan* can be formed (cf. Chap. XX).

Presence of a capsule has a striking effect on the appearance of the culture. Encapsulated bacteria (S-forms) produce smooth, glistening colonies on solid media and stable suspensions in broth; unencapsulated ones (R-forms) produce rough, wrinkled colonies on solid media, often with "medusa-head" structure of twisted coils, and a deposit in broth. Intermediate forms, Rs, producing only a little polysaccharide, and also "extremely rough" types, ER, are known. The smooth appearance of the S colony is of course due to the thick polysaccharide, which fills the spaces between the cells and smooths off the outer surface (see Fig. III–4).

When bacteria producing smooth colonies are grown in any quantity, it is common to find a few rough colonies appearing from time to time. These are mutants. The "smooth-to-rough" (S → R) transformation takes place in all smooth organisms, so that rough mutants of smooth forms are almost always to be found. Comparative study of the two groups has brought out an important generalization: when the smooth form is a pathogen, its rough variant is usually nonpathogenic. This was first shown for Streptococcus by Bordet in 1897, and virulent streptococci are now known to be always encapsulated. In other words, virulence is associated with the capsular substance.

The reverse change, R → S, is relatively rare, but can be favored, in Brucella or Pneumococcus, by conditions which selectively promote the growth of the occasional mutant S cell. Addition of DNA together with the enzyme DNA-ase, so that the cells are exposed to a mixture of nucleic acid breakdown products, brings about the change very effectively (Firshein and Braun, 1960). Manganese further promotes it slightly (see Fig. III–5). The whole phenomenon is discussed in Chapter XXI, section 5.

In Pneumococcus there are a great many types of the smooth form, and each of these has a characteristic polysaccharide. The polysaccharides are thus *type-specific substances*, and the different types of lobar pneumonia are due to different polysaccharides. The importance of this fact is seen in the phenomena of *immunity*. When whole bacteria, or bacterial extracts, or indeed almost any protein, is injected into the blood of an animal, the lymphatic cells secrete a compound that corresponds in structure to the injected compound and reacts with it

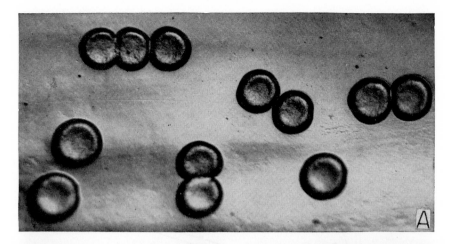

FIGURE III-4

Photographs of Pneumococcus colonies on solid medium.

    A. Rough form, without capsule.

    B. Smooth form with type III polysaccharide capsule. Ca. 28 ✕. (Photos H. Taylor Ephrussi. From *Sta. Zool. Napoli,* **22,** Suppl. 1–14, 1950.)

specifically, producing a precipitate or other evidence of combination. In the case of whole bacteria the cells are agglutinated. Compounds having this effect on the animal are *antigens,* and the specific reactants produced by the animal are *antibodies.* Most antigens of bacteria are proteins, but the pneumococcus polysaccharides are also antigenic; when injected into rabbits they give rise to type-specific antibodies. If whole pneumococci of the same type are injected afterward, the antibodies cause their capsules to swell up to five or ten times the normal thickness.

The swelling phenomenon was worked up by Neufeld (1902) into a

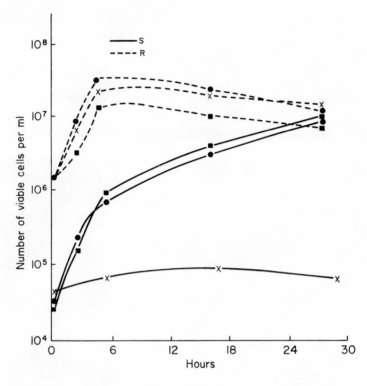

FIGURE III–5

Viable counts of smooth (*solid lines*) and rough (*dashed lines*) pneumococci in presence of:

● DNA-ase and its hydrolytic products from DNA.

■ The same plus 55 mg Mn++ per liter.

X Control.

Note how the DNA-breakdown products increase the number of S cells, partly at the expense of R cells. (From W. Firshein and W. Braun, *J. Bact.*, **79**:246–260, 1960.)

routine for determining pneumococcal types; rabbits are injected each with a different type-specific polysaccharide (or with whole bacteria), and into their sera, which now contain antibodies, are introduced the bacteria from a patient with pneumonia. Only one serum, containing the type-specific antibody, will cause the capsules to swell (Fig. III–6).

The rough form also contains antigens, but they are not type-specific, being the proteins of the cell contents; the antibodies formed in response to them will therefore react with extracts of any of the pneumococcus types. Furthermore, such antibodies will not precipitate intact S cells because their polysaccharide is on the outside of the cell, while the antigenic protein is inside.

Much effort has been devoted to working out the structure of the polysaccharides, mainly by Heidelberger and his associates (see Heidelberger, 1956). Type III produces the largest amount of polysaccharide

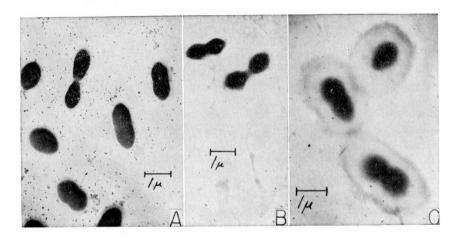

FIGURE III–6

Electron micrographs of *Diplococcus pneumoniae*.

A. Type 3. *B.* Type 3 in type 1 serum. *C.* Type 1 in type 1 serum. (Courtesy, Soc. Am. Bacteriologists.)

(1 per cent of the volume of liquid medium); the bulk of it is a chain of units of 4-β-glucuronosido-glucose, the glucuronic acid being linked by its 3-position to the 1-position of glucose:

4-β-glucuronosido-3 glucosido-

This basic disaccharide is the uronic acid related to cellobiose, i.e., cellobiuronic acid.

Type VIII substance contains a pair of glucose molecules (gl) between each of the above units, thus:

Glucuronic-gl-gl-gl-glucuronic-gl-gl-gl-

Correspondingly, types III and VIII cross-precipitate with oxidized cotton, which contains up to 13 per cent of cellobiuronic acid, but in which the molecules are linked by the 4 position only.

Type II substance contains three constituents, glucuronic acid, rhamnose, and glucose; the glucose and glucuronic acid units are linked by the 1 and 6 position into a branched structure of the same configuration as in glycogen and starch (Chap. XVII). For this reason type II antibody is partly precipitated by glycogen from oysters or liver, and by cornstarch. Cross-precipitation with antibodies of types IX, XII, XX, and XXII indicates that the same structure is present there also. Since the glucuronic acid groups are in part at the ends of the molecules, a number of plant gums and cell-wall materials, containing glucuronic acid as end-groups, also cross-precipitate with antibodies of type II (Heidelberger, 1960). Type VI contains galactose, glucose, rhamnose, and ribitol-5-phosphate; since the glucose and rhamnose are linked together in the 1,3 position in both types II and VI, their antibodies show some cross-precipitation. Thus, in general, the specificities of these capsular substances are due to the presence of specific sugar linkages. It is noteworthy too that ribitol-phosphate, which occurs in the cell walls (cf. above), is also found in the capsule.

Knowledge of the structure of these polysaccharides has made possible the production of synthetic antigens. By linking cellobiuronic acid glucoside with a serum globulin by diazotization, Goebel (1939) prepared an antigen that protected mice against type III pneumococcus.

In several cases antibodies prepared against pneumococci will precipitate the polysaccharide formed by *Leuconostoc mesenteroides*, the structure of which is well understood (long chains of 1:6-linked D-glucose, with the chains cross-linked to one another at every fifth glucose residue). These precipitation reactions have therefore helped to establish the structure of the pneumococcus substances.

The streptococci produce several different capsular materials; some of these are type-specific polysaccharides like those above. *Sc. bovis* forms a dextran like that of Leuconostoc, and *Sc. salivarius* a levan, while a number of others form *hyaluronic acid*, a polymer of N-acetyl-glucosamine and glucuronic acid. Some have extracellular protein instead of polysaccharide, and these so-called M and T proteins, though small in amount, are important as antigens (see Lancefield, 1954).

The polysaccharides of smooth cultures of *Vibrio comma* contain galactose instead of glucose, linked in glucuronosido-galactose units similar to the above; they also contain either additional galactose (in the case of most cholera pathogens) or arabinose (in nonpathogenic strains).

The carboxyl group gives the type III pneumococcus polysaccharide a high degree of polarity, making it water-soluble and viscous; the viscosity is very high. Small colonies flow together (Fig. III–4). The same physical properties are characteristic of the mucopolysaccharides and of amino-polysaccharides like hyaluronic acid.

Using the purified polysaccharides as sole nutrients in enrichment cultures, bacteria have been obtained from soil that hydrolyze them to reducing sugars (Dubos and Avery, 1931; Sickles and Shaw, 1934). This they do by means of specific enzymes, which are in the class of polysaccharidases (Chap. XVII). Injection of the enzyme along with virulent pneumococci greatly increases the rate at which the bacteria are destroyed in the animal's blood.

In *Bac. anthracis* the polyglutamate capsule also confers virulence; rough forms are avirulent and do not appreciably differ from the harmless soil bacillus, *Bac. cereus*. In *Brucella melitensis*, the gram-negative rod which causes Malta fever, the capsule contains fatty substances and may actually be a lipopolysaccharide; like that of *Shigella*, it is too thin to show, though detectable by chemical methods.

3. THE CYTOPLASM

In addition to a finely granular cytoplasm, the bacterial cell may contain at least seven types of granules:

(1) Relatively large fat bodies or globules are sometimes present and appear as clear spaces, giving an irregular or banded appearance to the cell. They can be stained with naphthol blue or Sudan black (Burdon, 1944). Apparently such fat bodies have in the past been mistaken for tiny reproductive forms or *gonidia*, especially in Rhizobia, where they are particularly prominent (see sec. 1C of Chap. IX). In addition to globules, there is sometimes a layer of fatty material close to the cell wall (Burdon, 1944). In many cells the "fat" is really a polymer of β-hydroxybutyric acid [see (3) below].

(2) After bacteria have assimilated nutrients vigorously, granules appear that stain violet in methylene blue. These *metachromatic granules* or volutin appear to consist of nucleoprotein (Delaporte, 1939). They disappear again on starvation and are therefore perhaps a substrate for endogenous respiration.

(3) A number of stored carbohydrates form granules. The Clostridia contain a starchlike polysaccharide that stains blue with iodine and has been called granulose. This material has not yet been studied by modern methods. Some of the bacilli contain glycogen, staining red-brown with iodine. Many bacteria convert their substrates temporarily to a polymer of β-hydroxybutyric acid. First discovered in Bacilli by Lemoigne in 1927, this compound has since been found as an assimilation product in Pseudomonads and in chemosynthetic and photosynthetic forms (Forsyth et al., 1958; Chaps. XX, XXII, and XXIII).

(4) Electron micrographs indicate that at the base of each flagellum is a granule or a hook (cf. Fig. II–7). These may be homologous with the *blepharoplasts* or basal granules of flagellate algae and ciliate protozoa, and they probably control flagellar movement.

(5) The purple bacteria contain chromatophores (see Chap. XXIII), usually set close to the membrane.

(6) From numerous bacteria, grinding sets free uniform particles, of "molecular weight" about a million and with a diameter about 0.015 μ (Schachman et al., 1952). These particles, called ribosomes, are rich in ribonucleic acid, RNA, and account for more than 80 per cent of the total RNA of the cells. They correspond to the "microsomes" of higher plant and animal cells, which are the seat of protein synthesis (Hunter et al., 1959), and they have the same function in bacteria (Chap. XX, sec. 5). Purification of these particles from *E. coli* indicates that there are four types, having "molecular weights" 0.7, 1.8, 2.6, and 5.2 millions, respectively; the last two are made up of combinations of the first two, the combination being controlled by Mg^{++} (Tissières et al., 1959). All four have the same composition, about 63 per cent RNA and 37 per cent protein. These granules constitute a major part of the cytoplasm and are often visible in electron micrographs. It is calculated that one *E. coli* cell in rapid growth contains some 90,000 of them.

(7) Most members of the Enterobacteriaceae have on the outside short, stiff fibers, called *fimbriae*, superficially similar to flagella but apparently quite different in function (Duguid et al., 1955–1959, see Fig. III–15). Fimbriae are of several types, and some types cause the cells to stick together into a pellicle, or to stick to other types of cells, or to make red blood cells agglutinate; this may give them a role in parasitism. They are proteinaceous and act as antigens. Fimbriate and nonfimbriate strains of Shigella can mutate back and forth.

(8) In addition there are sometimes in dividing cells a pair of very dense spheres which may be related to the cell-division process, as well as several granules of unknown function which have been noted from time to time (e.g., by Chapman, 1956). It was at one time thought also that bacteria contain oxidative granules corresponding to mitochondria in higher organisms, but these granules are now known to be pieces of

the disintegrated inner membrane, in which the cytochromes and other oxidation enzymes are located (Mitchell and Moyle, 1956; de Ley and Dochy, 1960).

An important differentiating characteristic of bacteria is the ability to take Gram's stain. The stain consists of crystal violet in weakly alkaline solution, followed by iodine and rinsing with alcohol (see footnote, p. 42). The gram-positive forms include the Actinomycetes and Mycobacteria, most of the sporeformers, the lactic bacteria, and the majority of the cocci. A few unusual sporeformers, especially from the rumen of sheep or cattle, may be truly gram-negative (Hobson and Purdon, 1959). Yeasts and most fungi are gram-positive.

The intensity of the gram(-positive) stain depends on the physiological state of the cells. Maximum staining occurs at an age of 24 to 48 hours, or earlier in the case of thermophiles, and old cultures often stain quite weakly (Lasseur and Schmitt, 1927). The staining can be destroyed by breaking up the cells, by careful acid or alkaline hydrolysis, or by autolysis, as, for instance, when pneumococci, suspended in water, are attacked by their own enzymes. Treatment with sodium cholate or with lysozyme has the same effect. Evidently, therefore, the staining is due to a specific, hydrolyzable, cell constituent.

A clue to the nature of this material was first given by the observation that when gram-positive cells were gently hydrolyzed or autolyzed to make them gram-negative, nucleoprotein was released from the cells (Deussen, 1918–1921; Thompson and Dubos, 1938; see Bartholomew and Mittwer, 1952). By careful extraction of heat-killed, gram-positive bacteria with bile salts, so that the cells became gram-negative, Henry and Stacy (1943, 1946) found the extract to contain carbohydrates, protein, and the magnesium salt of ribonucleic acid, RNA. It seems, then, that a complex of these substances is the specific cause of the Gram stain. RNA typically occurs outside the nucleus; it contains the phosphate of ribose, whereas the compound typical of the nucleus contains the phosphate of deoxyribose:

D-Ribose   2-Deoxy D-ribose

The two nucleic acids differ also in their nonsugar constituents. Both compounds contain adenine, guanine, and cytosine, but the ribose compound contains uracil as a fourth base, while the deoxyribose compound contains thymine (which is 5-methyluracil) and a small amount of 5-methylcytosine.

The ribonucleate, combined with protein, is deposited just inside and close to the cell wall, both in the bacteria and in yeast (Lamanna and Mallette, 1950). As a matter of fact, it was shown long ago that gram-positive bacteria have an outer layer of protoplasm which differs from the inner material (Gutstein, 1924–1926). This "ectoplasm" retains a basic dye after treatment with tannic acid, while the endoplasm does not. Many bacteria appear smaller after becoming gram-negative, owing to the loss of the outer layer (see Bartholomew and Mittwer, 1952).

Some remarkable evidence supports the above ideas. After being made gram-negative by extraction with bile salt, the bacterial residues can be made gram-positive again by soaking in a solution of magnesium ribonucleate from yeast (Henry and Stacey, 1946). In other words, the gram-positive material is "replated" on the cells. Truly gram-negative cells cannot be made gram-positive in this way, although some positivity has been conferred on Neisseriae. The ribonucleoprotein has been separated intact from *Cl. perfringens*, and this too can be "replated" on extracted cells (Parsons, 1953). Here, however, there is strict specificity, and the protein cannot be replated on extracted cells of another species, *Cl. septicum*. In addition, killed cells of many gram-positive organisms and also of yeasts can be rendered gram-negative by treatment with the specific enzyme ribonuclease, which hydrolyzes only ribonucleic acid (Bartholomew and Umbreit, 1944).

Benzimidazole, which structurally resembles adenine and so probably inhibits nucleic acid metabolism, is found to make some bacteria gram-negative when incorporated in the medium. When Mycobacteria are grown on a benzimidazole medium (0.1 to 1.0 gm per liter) they become not only gram-negative but also nonacid-fast, at least for a few days (Knaysi *et al.*, 1950). The acid-fast layer may therefore be connected with the gram-staining complex in some way.

4. SPORES

A. Nature of Spore Formation

The observable changes in the cell when spores are formed were described in Chapter II. Examples are shown in detail in Figure III–7.

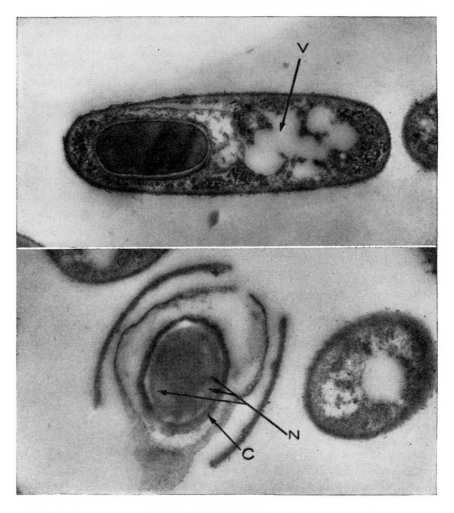

FIGURE III–7

Sporulation in *Bac. cereus*. (*Top*) Spore almost fully formed, note three spore-coats
(*Bac. megaterium* shows only two). (*V*) Sporangium developing vacuole.

(*Below*) Mature spore; the layers beyond the outermost spore-coat (*C*) are remains
of the sporangium. The nuclear material (*N*) is arranged peripherally. Magnification,
40,000 ✕. (From G. B. Chapman, *J. Bact.*, **71**:348–355, 1956.)

(The arrangement of nucleic material will be discussed in sec. 5A).
The dense spore cytoplasm becomes surrounded by a series of walls,
of which the outermost one, which appears light in the electron microscope, comprises at least 30 per cent of the thickness. The great increase
in wall thickness obviously explains the difficulty of staining. Chemical

analysis of spore walls of *Bac. subtilis* (Salton and Marshall, 1959) shows the presence of glucosamine, diaminopimelic and muramic acids, and ribitol-phosphate, as in the vegetative cells (Table III–1), although in much smaller amounts. To compensate, almost three times as much of the weight is amino acids, of which 17 can be detected—a composition quite unlike that of the "wall peptide." Probably, therefore, a true protein is a major constituent of the spore wall.

These chemical differences, as well as the mass of wall produced, must mean that major changes are involved in spore formation. What causes these changes is only beginning to be understood. The old idea that the process is a reaction to "unfavorable conditions" is negated by the fact that simple drying does not promote sporulation, nor will aerobes sporulate in the absence of oxygen. In part it is a function of nutrition and age, yet some bacilli, e.g., *Bac. subtilis*, seem to have at least a few spores present at all times. The general conclusion has been summed up in the curious statement that spores are formed "by healthy cells faced with starvation in presence of oxygen" (Knaysi, 1945). That starvation is a factor is supported by the fact that several nutrients do prevent sporulation. These include alanine, glucose, and fatty acids with 10 to 14 carbon atoms (Hardwick *et al.*, 1951). However, their effect is not one of general nutrition, but is much more specific, since ammonium, a *nutrient* for many bacteria, often *promotes* sporulation. Some salts promote the process too, particularly KNO_3 and $NaNO_2$. An orderly series of metabolic changes (see Williams *et al.*, 1952) is evidently involved.

It has been shown that *Bac. mycoides* will not only form spores in the growth medium, but will also sporulate in distilled water about 11 hours after transfer from the growth medium; the process takes place rather suddenly, about 90 per cent of the organisms having formed spores between the tenth and thirteenth hour (Hardwick and Foster, 1952). Under these conditions sporulation is completely prevented by glucose, provided it is added before the fifth hour; if ammonia is added along with the glucose, however, some sporulation can be reinstated. It is evident, therefore, that the spore formation that begins after 10 hours depends on the production of some materials in the cell during the previous hours. Hardwick and Foster envisage sporulation as due to the gradual breaking down of "vegetative proteins" and their conversion to spore substances. Glucose would oppose this through its action in "sparing" proteins from breakdown (cf. Chap. VII); ammonia, on the other hand, would promote it by acting as a nitrogen source. Sporulation is also prevented by compounds that inhibit amino acid metabolism, and in the presence of these inhibitors it is reinstated by adding amino acids. As an example, norleucine, which inhibits the metabolism of leucine and methionine, inhibits sporulation, while methionine completely reverses the inhibition, probably due to its spatial similarity:

$$CH_3CH_2CH_2CH_2CHNH_2COOH \qquad \text{Norleucine}$$
$$CH_3-S-CH_2CH_2CHNH_2COOH \qquad \text{Methionine}$$

In addition, it was shown that when the cells have been suspended in distilled water for seven hours, i.e., when they are irreversibly committed to spore formation, they can no longer form new enzyme proteins.

The attractive feature of this concept is that among the vegetative proteins broken down would presumably be some of the enzymes, and this could go a long way toward explaining the drastically reduced metabolism of spores, since the most careful measurements show that the respiration of mature spores is essentially zero. Catalase, transaminases, many deaminases, and the enzymes of organic acid oxidation —17 enzymes in all that were tested for—are all essentially absent from simple spore extracts (Hardwick and Foster, 1953). Among the few active enzymes are alanine racemase, which converts D- or L-alanine to the DL-form, and the enzymes that eliminate ammonia and ribose from adenosine (Powell and Strange, 1956–57). However, if the spores are abraded by grinding with powdered glass, they rapidly become heat-sensitive, and develop considerable enzyme activity, even oxidizing glucose (Rode and Foster, 1960). Thus, the inactivity of the enzymes is dependent on the integrity of the spore, and when the wall is broken so that water can enter, the enzymes become active. This result suggests that it is the dryness of the spore contents that causes their metabolic inactivity and their heat resistance (see Chap. IV, sec. 5D).

Elucidation of the differences between spores and vegetative cells does not, unfortunately, tell us anything about how the change occurs. The initiating factor is evidently *time after transfer*, either to water as above, or to a new medium in the case of *Bac. cereus* (Young and Fitz-James, 1959). A clue to the nature of the change is given by the observation that analogues of the bases in RNA, i.e., 8-azaguanine and 5-fluorouracil, inhibit sporulation of *Bac. cereus* completely if added before eight hours, but not at a later time. Actinomycin D, which prevents RNA synthesis altogether, has the same effect (del Valle and Aronson, 1962). Hence it seems that a changed RNA has to be synthesized, and this causes the changes in protein synthesis. That a reverse change in RNA precedes germination would explain the action of adenosine and inosine noted below.

B. Spore Germination

If transplanted to a fresh suitable medium, most spores at once germinate. The first visible change is swelling, so that the spore loses its characteristic high refractility and is presumably taking up water. At this stage it can be stained with methylene blue. The next step may take place in one of two ways, as described first by Brefeld in 1878 and Prazmowski in 1880, and later by Knaysi in 1938:

(1) The spore wall is split equatorially, and the rapidly elongating vegetative cell inside bends it backward hingewise until it can pop out. Sometimes the emergence is delayed until the new cell has grown to

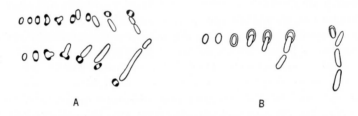

A   B

FIGURE III–8

Prazmowski's drawings of spore germination.
   A. Equatorial (*Bac. subtilis*).
   B. Polar (*Cl. butyricum*).
(From A. Prazmowski, 1880.)

full length (Fig. III–8*A*). This "equatorial emergence" is characteristic of *Bac. subtilitis* and *Bac. mesentericus*.

(2) The spore wall swells and is broken open at one end; through the opening the vegetative cell emerges like a chick from its shell (Fig. III–8*B*). This "polar emergence" is characteristic of clostridia (cf. also Fig. XV–1, p. 528).

In both types the empty spore cases or *sporangia* may be seen afterward as faintly staining residues. The type of germination is not absolutely characteristic of a given organism, since some may germinate in different ways in different parts of the culture.

The kinetics of germination have been studied with *Cl. botulinum* (Wynne and Foster, 1948). After the spores are transferred to a suitable germination medium, the number that have germinated can be determined by heating to 75° C or 80° C to kill the vegetative cells and by counting the survivors. Once germination has begun, it is found that the log of the number of survivors goes down linearly with time, i.e., germination behaves like a first-order reaction. If there are I spores at the beginning, and if germination starts at time t_o, and G spores have germinated at the time t, then:

$$K = \frac{1}{(t - t_o)} \ln \frac{I}{I - G}$$

or

$$.434K = \frac{1}{(t - t_o)} \log \frac{I}{R}$$

where R is the number of residual spores. The time to the beginning of germination, t_o, depends on the conditions; exposure to air, even briefly, makes it longer, but it can be shortened by increasing the number of spores in the inoculum. This may perhaps be due to the establishment of reducing conditions, since other clostridia will only germinate below a certain oxygen tension (cf. Chap. V, sec. 7E).

The processes that go on in germination are complex. Long before visible emergence takes place, the spore becomes physiologically active. Its nuclear granule and central cytoplasmic body change their appearance in a few minutes at 37° C (Robinow, 1942). Spores of *Bac. anthracis* put into broth at 37° C are not visibly germinated for two hours, but they begin to consume oxygen after five minutes, and after 10 minutes they have become heat-sensitive (Jensen, 1950). The same changes take about an hour at 18° C. Spores of *Bac. danicus* do not germinate on simple media, but require the addition of some alcohol-insoluble constituent of yeast extract; in the presence of very dilute yeast extract they become heat-sensitive in about 30 minutes at 25° C (Thimann, 1934). *Bac. anthracis* shows a similar activation, and in this case the agent has been identified as adenosine (Hills, 1949); as little as 0.2 mg per liter suffices to cause germination. Some strains of *Bac. megaterium* also respond to adenosine, while other strains, and *Bac. subtilis*, will germinate in simple glucose or alanine solution (Powell, 1950–1951). *Cl. botulinum* requires CO_2, oxalacetate, or a mixture of organic acids (Wynne and Foster, 1948; cf. the symposium of Williams *et al.*, 1952). Manganese plays a role in the first stages, increasing the percentage of *Bac. megaterium* spores that swell and become stainable in glucose solution, but it does not allow emergence or subsequent division; these processes specifically require sulfate or sulfur compounds (Levinson and Hyatt, 1956–57, 1961). Chloride is also important. The relation between the organic material and the metal ions is complex, because in *Bac. cereus*, where alanine and inosine promote germination, this occurs only in the presence of a variety of inorganic salts. Rode and Foster (1962) believe the salts are the primary stimulus, the organic compounds merely "facilitating" their effect.

During germination the spores lose 25 to 30 per cent of their dry weight. This material is excreted into the medium and is evidently hydrolyzed wall substance, since it comprises amino acids, simple peptides, and glucosamine. But it also contains the calcium salt of pyridine-2:6-dicarboxylic acid or dipicolinic acid (Powell and Strange, 1953; Powell, 1953; see formula III, p. 114) in large amount; indeed, it makes up 12 per cent of the dry weight in *Bac. megaterium*, or 5 per cent in *Bac. cereus*. (The aromatic structure of this compound, which makes it absorb in the ultraviolet, is believed to be the cause of the dark appearance of spores in ultraviolet light.) Evidently it is a major constituent of the wall. Spore walls mechanically broken by shaking with powdered glass lose their dipicolinate on repeated washing (Salton and Marshall, 1959; Rode and Foster, 1960); hence it cannot be combined into a polymer. The formation in spore walls of so much of this acid, which is not found in the walls of vegetative cells, appears to be one of the chief biochemical changes in sporulation. Surprisingly, calcium dipicolinate causes germination of *Bac. megaterium* spores (Riemann and Ordal, 1961), but again it may be only "facilitating" the action of inorganic ions.

When *Bac. cereus* is grown with C^{14}-labeled diaminopimelic acid, from 4 to 9 per cent of it is converted to C^{14} dipicolinic acid (Perry and Foster, 1955), but more efficient conversion is obtained from 2:6-diketopimelic acid, in the presence of NH_3 (Powell and Strange, 1959). This keto acid may therefore be an intermediate. Other labeling experiments show that aspartate, pyruvate, and succinate function as precursors, being condensed to N-succinyldiaminopimelic acid. This yields the L-form of diaminopimelic acid, which is then racemized to the *meso*-form (see Gilvarg, 1960). Labeled diaminopimelic acid supplied to *vegetative* cells does not, of course, form pyridine-dicarboxylic acid but instead is decarboxylated to *lysine*. This latter reaction requires as coenzyme pyridoxal phosphate (cf. p. 340), which is present in much larger amounts in vegetative cells than in spores (Powell, 1958). The *E. coli* mutant 26-26, which requires lysine for growth, lacks the decarboxylating enzyme and excretes both L- and meso-forms of diaminopimelic acid.

These processes can be summarized thus:

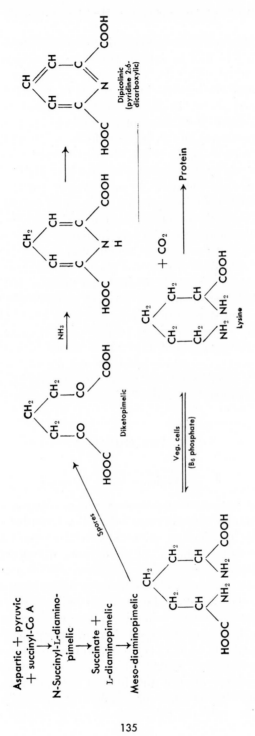

With vegetative cells, the process shown may be reversible, but for spores it is not, and thus represents from the cell's viewpoint a waste of valuable material. Why this extravagant process has not been supplanted by a more efficient one in the course of evolution is a mystery.

As mentioned above, if *Bac. megaterium* spores are abraded by shaking with ground glass, some of the dipicolinate is liberated; they then become heat-sensitive (75 per cent killed in 20 minutes as 65° C) and stainable with dyes. They also become sensitive to freezing and thawing and to the toxic action of alcohol and of H_2O_2. They can even germinate to normal cells (Rode and Foster, 1960). In sum, this "mechanical germination" duplicates the normal germination process, from which it could be concluded that breaking of the heavy impermeable wall is the main process in germination.

Perhaps this is the reason for the effect of preheating. The conidia of Neurospora (Goddard, 1939) and the spores of most bacilli (Tarr, 1933; Curran and Evans, 1945; Powell and Strange, 1953) are greatly promoted in their germination by heating to 80°or 85° C for 8 to 10 minutes. Prolonged storage may have a similar effect (Powell, 1950–1951). These treatments perhaps make the wall crack or otherwise become more permeable and thus allow water to enter and hence metabolism to begin. Enzymatic breakdown of the wall materials would then follow. But whether the key process in germination is water entry or some more obscure "activation" phenomenon is not clear.

5. THE NUCLEUS

A. The Evidence for Its Existence

Whether or not bacteria possess a nucleus was a subject of discussion and argument for 40 years before it was settled (in the affirmative). Granules regarded as nuclei were often reported by the early microbiologists, but at that time no definite microchemical test for chromatin existed.

An attack on the subject was made possible by the discovery of Feulgen and co-workers that the nuclei of animals and higher plants, after partial hydrolysis with acid, give a deep violet color with fuchsin-sulfite (i.e., fuchsin that has been decolorized by acid sulfite). This reaction (Feulgen and Voit, 1924) is due to the presence of deoxyribose nucleic acid (abbreviated DNA) which on partial hydrolysis sets free aldehydes or related groups; the fuchsin coloration is probably the Schiff reaction, characteristic of aldehydes. Should free aldehydes be present in the cell, the color will be given without hydrolysis, so that the true Feulgen reaction can only be ascertained by comparing results on hydrolyzed cells with those obtained before hydrolysis. About four minutes' heating in 1 N HCl at 60° C is sufficient to hydrolyze the material. Only DNA gives the reaction; the other type of nucleic acid, RNA, which is not characteristic of nuclei, gives no color. The reaction can therefore be used as a test for the constituents of a true nucleus. Using the Feulgen method, Voit (1925, 1927) first showed that thick streaks of various bacteria give a definite purple color. His results were confirmed by de Cunha and Muniz (1939) on *Bac. anthracis*, by Neumann (1930) on Azotobacter, and by Pietschmann and Rippel (1932) on *Bac. mycoides*. In this work the Feulgen-staining material was diffusely spread through the cell, owing to too vigorous hydrolysis. Some workers concluded that bacteria have a diffuse nucleus. However, Stille (1937) showed that if yeasts, which certainly have discrete nuclei, are hydrolyzed at 70° C or higher, the Feulgen-reacting material becomes spread diffusely through the cell. Even onion epidermis gives only a diffuse reaction if hydrolyzed at 95° C. Using 60 minutes' hydrolysis at 40° C, Stille demonstrated two to four Feulgen granules in bacterial cells; these could not be due to plasmolysis, were not dependent on culture conditions, and were not the first stages of spore formation. They are generally dumbbell-shaped. In bacilli two such granules are normally present, but the cells are generally in pairs; the very youngest cells show only a single granule (Robinow, 1942, 1947; Fig. III–9). In Sarcina each coccus appears to have but *one* granule, probably dumbbell-shaped and thus sometimes appearing as two (Stille, 1937). Similarly in the spores of *Bac. subtilis, megaterium, mycoides*, and *anthracoides*, a single crescent-shaped or dumbbell-shaped Feulgen-staining body is present.

When spores are formed, it seems clear that if two granules are present, one disappears with the cell residue, while the other enters the spore. In ultrathin sections of spores this nuclear material is seen to lie in a thin ring or shell within the outermost zone, but close to the surface (Robinow, 1956, cf. Fig. III–7). However, if the cells are treated with hot acid, the nuclear material is extruded and appears as a Feulgen-staining excrescence on the side.

The Feulgen staining is weakened by the enzyme deoxyribonuclease, and the nuclear granule disappears altogether after treatment with trypsin at pH 8 (Robinow, 1956). These points confirm the nuclear nature of the Feulgen-staining material. In some of the observations, Giemsa's stain, often used for animal nuclei, has been found to give almost identical results (see especially Delaporte, 1950).

The work with the Feulgen stain fits well with other observations made by various staining methods in earlier times, although these were

generally very variable. Methyl green, acetocarmine, and even hema-
toxylin (the classic nuclear stain) scarcely stain the bacterial nuclei
at all.

The formation and germination of spores of *Bac. subtilis* and *Bac.
mycoides* were followed with an eosin-differentiated method, by making
a series of drop-cultures and fixing one or two every half hour (Badian,

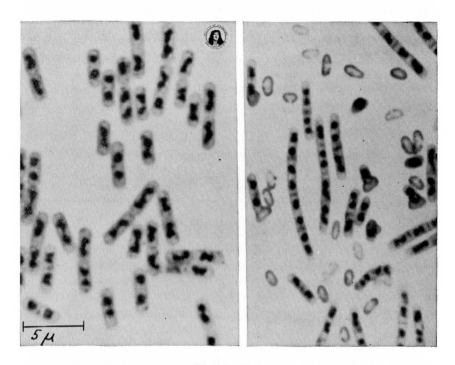

FIGURE III–9

"Chromatinic bodies" or nuclei in two bacilli.

Left. Bac. cereus. Right. Bac. mesentericus.

In many cells the nucleus can be seen dividing. In the top left a cell is dividing in
two and separating while the nucleus is beginning its next division. At the right may
be noted examples of equatorial emergence from the spores as well as many empty
spore cases. (Prepared by C. F. Robinow. Courtesy, Soc. Amer. Bacteriologists.)

1933). Badian's interpretation of the series of changes is summarized in
Figure III–10. The chromatin divides, and the parts fuse again (*autogamy*); it then divides into four, of which three parts go to the poles.
These three parts disappear during the spore formation, while the odd
one, at right angles to the rest, is absorbed into the spore, where it
can no longer be stained by the method used. On germination of the

spore the particle reappears, and there is rapid division, first of the chromatin and then of the cell itself; four cells, each with one bar of chromatin, are the result. The whole process is remarkably suggestive of the phenomena occurring in ascus formation in fungi. Somewhat similar changes are seen in the Myxobacteria belonging to the Cytophaga group (see Chap. XVII), where there is a deeply staining substance which centers in one or two bands across the middle of the cell (Krzemieniewska, 1930). When these organisms produce the microcyst (which differs from a spore in that it is not heat-resistant), the chromatic material contracts as the sphere form is reached and then again finally expands to fill the sphere. Similar chromatic bodies were

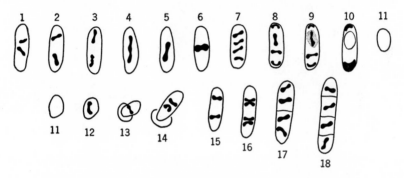

FIGURE III–10

Nuclear changes in *Bac. subtilis* (interpretation). *1* to *6*. Autogamy. *6* to *11*. Spore formation. *11* to *18*. Vegetative multiplication. (From J. Badian, 1933.) Series 11 to 18 correspond exactly with Fig. III–9, but series 1 to 11 have not been confirmed.

observed in other Myxobacteria (1928); in this case there were regularly two such bodies in each cell, and each of these divided again into two at the time of formation of the microcyst. Of the resulting four, two afterward disappeared, a process resembling the reduction division of chromosomes in mitosis. In migrating myxobacteria of Chondromyces, on the other hand, the two bodies appear combined into a long central granule (Fig. II–16). It was reported that *S. typhosa*, in young cultures, appears to contain two or four granules per cell (Piekarski, 1937, 1939), but it seems now that such "cells" may have really divided (see below). However, *Shigella dysenteriae* and *Sarcina ventriculi* show even more granules, united in a complex network (Murray, 1960).

One outstanding gap in all the preceding observations is the absence of any visible spindle apparatus during divisions. The occurrence of a very faintly staining spindle has been claimed in *Bac. megaterium* and *M. cryophilus* (Delamater and Hunter, 1951; Delamater and Woodburn, 1952; Fig. III–11), though most workers doubt this (cf. Bisset, 1954), and careful observations of dividing bacteria under the phase microscope, which shows up the chromatin bodies in the *living* state, do not suggest any such structure (Mason and Powelson,

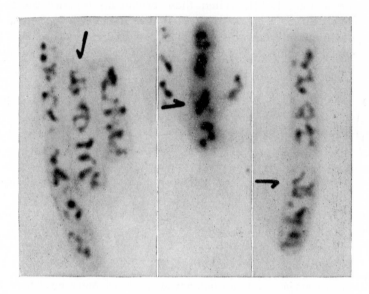

FIGURE III–11

Nuclear granules in *Bacillus megaterium*. Fixed with osmic acid while still in agar, then treated with 1 N HCl at 60° C., rinsed and stained with thionine + thionyl chloride. The *arrow* on the center cell points to an apparent "spindle" with the chromosomes on a "metaphase plate" and "centrioles" visible. The *arrow* on the right-hand cell shows clearly three rod-shaped chromosomes (interpreted as prophase). All ca. 5000 ×. (Photo, E. D. Delamater and M. E. Hunter, 1951. From *Am. J. of Botany*, **38**:659–662.)

1956). Quite clearly the nuclei shown by Delamater's technique, as well as some of those shown by Murray, are much more extended than the rodlike forms described above, and there appear to be not less than three chromosomes per cell (Fig. III–11). These differences are due to changes in the external conditions, especially in the ionic constituents. Sodium chloride, or high osmotic concentration of the medium, promotes aggregation into granules, and Murray (1960) has shown that the apparent form of the chromatin bodies can be drastically changed by five minutes in a salt medium.

Observations of the nucleus with the electron microscope support the idea that its form is readily varied. Unfortunately, it is not dense and appears either as a shapeless light area near the middle of the cell (see, e.g., Chapman, 1956), or, if the cells are exposed to osmic acid for 16 hours in presence of the ions Ca^{++} or La^{+++}, as large well-defined granules filled with fine fibrils (Kellenberger et al., 1958).

An interesting comparison with the nuclei of higher organisms is given by observations on cells having double the normal complement of genes. From genetic evidence, Lederberg et al. (1951; Lederberg and Tatum, 1953) concluded that a strain of E. coli is heterozygous for lactose fermentation, some cells reacting positively, some negatively, and some evidently containing both the + and − genes. These last would be considered diploid, the other two types haploid. The nuclei of the diploids do appear clearly different from those of the haploids, although whether they actually have two chromosomes instead of one (or four instead of two) is not clear.

Taking the observations as a whole, there can be no doubt that bacteria possess one or two nuclear granules or chromosomes. The behavior of these granules in sporulation, and in microcyst formation of Myxobacteria, is about what would be expected of a nucleus. The weak staining, variability of form and absence of mitotic figures show that it is nevertheless very different from the nuclei of higher plants and animals. To complete the picture we must consider the behavior of the nucleus during cell division and the evidence for cellular or sexual fusion.

B. Cell Division

As far as has been observed, it appears that the separation of the cell into two is only the last phase in a series of processes (Robinow, 1944, 1947; Chapman, 1959). The initial process is some sort of nuclear division which is as yet not clear; the second is formation of a septum which really divides the cell into two; and the third is the externally visible fission (see Fig. III–12). This only occurs after the septum has become double and is continuous with the outer wall. By the time it takes place, the cytoplasm of the two daughter cells may be again dividing. Peripheral bodies appear near the place of division and may be connected with the wall formation (Chapman, 1959). In the case of young, growing bacilli, such as Bac. anthracis and Bac. mesentericus, the apparently single rod is usually composed of four cells, because if the walls are now dissolved by lysozyme, each rod gives rise to a short chain of spheres. Bisset (1950) states that in "smooth" rod-shaped bacteria the apparently single rod is indeed single. The "cells" of Corynebacteria are often multiple (see Fig. II–13, p. 60).

If we compare these observations with those on the nuclear granules, we see that the bacillus containing four granules may be in reality two cells or even four. The bacterium with two granules may be one or two cells. Thus, the apparent variation in number of nuclear

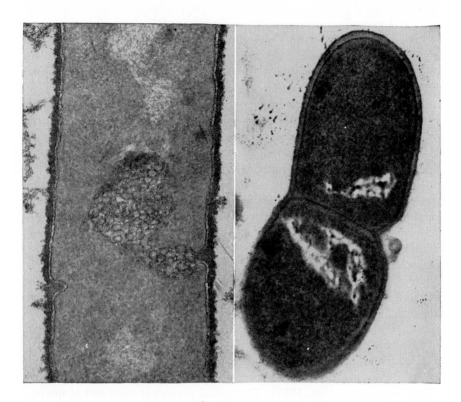

FIGURE III–12

Two stages in cell division. (*Left*) The beginning of septum formation in *Bac. subtilis;* note that both membrane (light) and wall (dark) are involved. (From van Iterson, *LKB Instrument Journal*, 7:17, 1960.) (*Right*) The beginning of cell separation in an unknown bacterium. The light material in the center of each cell is the nuclear apparatus. Note the double nature of the septum as revealed by the triangle at left. 42,000 ×. (From G. B. Chapman, *J. Bact.*, 78:96–104, 1959.)

granules is reduced; each rod contains one, or, if it is about to divide, two; in other words, the nuclear granule divides before the cell divides.

Cell division proceeds in about the same way in cocci, and perhaps also in the blue-green alga Gleocapsa, studied long ago by Olive (1904).

The streptococcus which appears elliptical, i.e., elongated in the direction of the chain, shows two granules and is probably already divided by a septum. Larger cocci often show two septa at right angles, i.e., the "cell" has already divided into four to form a tetrad (Bisset, 1954; see Fig. III–13). Such tetrads show an even partition of the Feulgen-staining material into all four cells (Murray, 1960).

Whether streptococci remain together in a chain or not, after successive divisions, depends on the activity of a chain-breaking enzyme, secreted into the medium (Lominski *et al.*, 1958). The medium in which a short-chained strain of *Sc. fecalis* has grown can break up the long chains formed by another strain. Since some of

FIGURE III–13

Cell division in a large coccus, showing two septa at different stages of development. Cell wall staining (cf. p. 109). Note that many of the cells would resemble a single coccus when stained conventionally. Ca. 4000 ×. (From K. A. Bisset, 1954.)

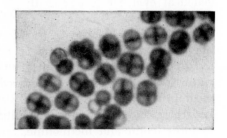

the cells become gram-negative in the process, the cementing material may be related to the gram-staining nucleoprotein.

C. Conjugation

That bacterial nuclei under some circumstances can fuse has been suspected for a long time. A speculative intracellular fusion was shown above (Fig. III–10). Similarly it was claimed that in Myxobacteria, before formation of the microcyst, the nuclear granules first fuse, then divide again, then become separated by a septum, and then fuse again (Krzemieniewska, 1930). If true, this would be fusion between two separated cells. Bisset (1950) has made a comparable observation with bacilli. In both cases, however, although the cytological preparations are beautiful, the interpretation depends on placing the forms observed in a chronological order, which may not be justified.

It has often been suggested that the star-shaped aggregations of four to six cells seen in such organisms as Radiobacter or Phytomonas represent some sort of fusion process. Angular pairs of *Ps. malvacearum* also look very much as though they were undergoing fusion (Stoughton, 1932). In the case of *Phytomonas tumefaciens*, careful Feulgen staining shows the nuclear material to be all assembled at the center of the star (Stapp, 1942). The cells elongate greatly while in the star form (see Fig. III–14) and are so firmly attached that they can be washed and prodded with the micromanipulator without separating them. After several days, however, they separate spontaneously. The attraction is not due to flagella, since these are at the outer ends of the star only (Braun and Elrod, 1946). All these observations point strongly to fusion, although they do not prove it. The electron micrographs do not actually show extrusion of protoplasm, and the center of the star looks far from dense.

Proof that conjugation takes place is genetical, and only with this evidence has cytological confirmation become possible. The genetical evidence is essentially as follows: *E. coli* does not need to have vitamins or amino acids added to the medium because it can synthesize these. However, occasionally mutant cells occur in which the ability to synthesize one or other of these substances has been lost. The number of mutants can be increased by irradiation of a culture, and they can be discovered by plating from a fully enriched medium into media with various deficiencies. In this way Tatum and Lederberg (1947) obtained a culture of *E. coli*, strain K12, unable to form biotin and methionine, and another culture unable to form proline and threonine. The first could, of course, form proline and threonine; the second could equally form biotin and methionine; i.e., they were "B—M—P+T+" and "B+M+P—T—," respectively. These two types were then grown together in a liquid medium. From the resulting culture, cells were isolated that could form biotin, methionine, proline, and threonine, i.e., they were B+M+P+T+. Now in any one of the two original cultures, reversion to the ability to synthesize one of the substances (back-mutation) happens about once in 10^7 divisions; reversion to the synthesis of both substances would therefore occur only once in 10^{14}. Yet the new fully synthetic type, or *prototroph*, happened 100 times in 10^9 cells inoculated. It was deduced that back-mutation could not explain the formation of so many prototrophs; hence, *recombination* of the factors must have occurred. By far the most probable mechanism for this is that the nuclear material must have been transferred from one cell to another.

Such a deduction requires rigid controls of several sorts. A number of these were carried out successfully. Two require special mention. (1) The characters could not have been carried from cell to cell by soluble factors like those discussed in Chapter XXI, section 5, because cultures in close contact but separated by a sintered glass filter do not show recombination (Davis, 1950). Besides, such soluble "transforming factors" transfer characters one at a time only. (2) Recom-

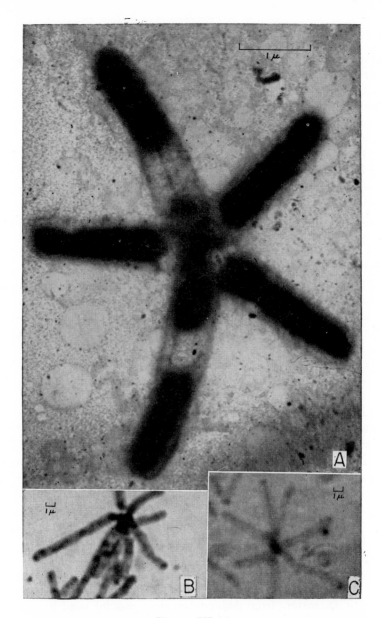

FIGURE III–14

A. Electron micrograph of star-shaped aggregation of *Ps.* ("*Agrobact.*") *tume-faciens.* The cells appear separated by their outer membranes. 14,200 ×.

B and *C.* Optical micrographs of similar stars. 2500 ×. *B* stained by Feulgeu method to show the nuclei assembled at the point of contact.

(Photos by A. C. Braun and R. P. Elrod. From *J. Bact.*, 1946.)

145

bination would require that the number of prototrophs formed be proportional to the product of the concentrations of the two types of parental cells, and also to the time during which they remained in contact. Both these expectations were found, over a considerable range of "concentrations" (i.e., cell numbers per milliliter) and times (Nelson, 1951).

Other strains of *E. coli*, in which the factors present and missing comprised resistance to various bacteriophages (Lederberg, 1947), to streptomycin, and to toxic extracts called "colicines" (Fredericq and Betz-Bareau, 1951), ability to form specific enzymes, and even the carrying of the lysogenic prophage λ (p. 102), have all given similar results. In other words, the phenomenon of recombination is independent of the exact nature of the factors that recombine. At first, attempts to find similar results in other strains of *E. coli* were unsuccessful, but later many other recombining strains were found (Lederberg and Tatum, 1953; Hayes, 1953). The ability to recombine is governed by a gene pair, termed F+ and F—, which some strains do not possess. Further, some strains of Salmonella and Shigella, members of the Bacterium group along with *E. coli*, can also recombine with *E. coli*, although at relatively low frequency (Miyake and Demerec, 1959). Good evidence for recombination among certain strains of *Ps. aeruginosa* and also in *Str. coelicolor* has been obtained, while in Serratia a kind of incomplete recombination, perhaps involving transfer only of fragments of the nuclear material, occurs (see Cavalli-Sforza, 1957).[2] An important step forward was the recognition, also due to Hayes, that the two individuals recombining play different roles. If one of the two partners is prevented from multiplying by adding streptomycin, there is no effect if it is the F+ which is thus inhibited, but if the F— is inhibited, no recombination occurs. Thus the F+ is the *donor* (and does not need to multiply), while the F— is the *receiver*, and after having received the genetic material from the donor it must multiply in order to yield the recombinant colonies.

This information has been used and developed in elegant experiments by Jacob and Wollman (1958) in which the rate of transfer of genetic characters from donor to receiver was followed by sampling

---

[2] There are other methods of genetic recombination not requiring conjugation (see Chap. XXI).

FIGURE III–15.
Conjugating cells of *E. coli*. The lower (donor) cell is Hfr and has adsorbed on it four particles of bacteriophage whose heads can be seen at about 0.1μ from the cell; the upper (receptor) cell is F— and bears fimbriae. The conjugation tube is less than 0.1μ thick. (From Anderson, Wollman, and Jacob, *Ann. de l'Inst. Pasteur.* Courtesy, Dr. T. F. Anderson.)

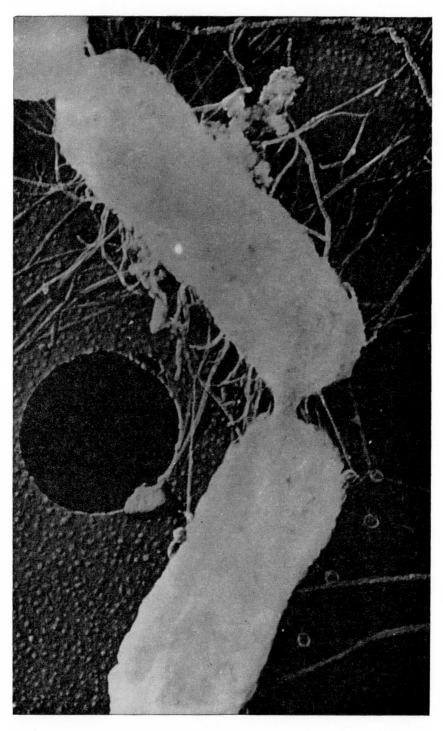

FIGURE III–15
For descriptive legend see page 146.

and plating every few minutes; it appeared that a maximum is reached in a little over an hour. However, if the conjugation were interrupted by mechanical stirring, certain recombinations could be more easily prevented from taking place than others. For example, if the receptor F— was unable to synthesize threonine and leucine (thre⁻ leu⁻) or to use galactose (Gal⁻), but was resistant to streptomycin (S^r), then the recombinants having thre$^+$ and leu$^+$ with S^r appear when the mixture is stirred after only 10 minutes of contact, while the recombinant fermenting galactose (Gal$^+$) together with . S^r does not appear unless 25 minutes of contact have been allowed. It is deduced that the characters are transferred *in a definite linear order*. The chromosome penetrates the receiver cell at a constant speed for the first half of its length, and those characters that are transferred more rarely are those near the tail end of the chromosome, the conjugation being usually not complete. In this way one can *map the linear order of the genes*, in terms of time required from contact until transfer, in exactly the same way as they can be mapped in higher organisms by frequency of crossing over. This phenomenon is taken up again in Chapter XXI (see also the review of Hayes, 1962).

Taking advantage of the high frequency of conjugation in these strains and the relatively long time it lasts, Anderson, Wollman, and Jacob (1957) have been able to photograph the cells undergoing conjugation (Fig. III–15). The thin narrow tube carrying hereditary material suggests the conjugation tubes of such yeasts as Zygosaccharomyces; it is evident that no complete fusion of cells takes place, and there is no evidence that anything but genetic material is transferred. It is not clear yet how the nonlinear and shapeless nuclei shown by the electron microscope resolve themselves into a linear strand for transfer.

In conclusion it should be said that the discovery of an important phenomenon like conjugation, coming after more than half a century's fairly intensive study of bacteria, shows how fluid is the state of our knowledge of these remarkable cells.*

---

* Since the closing paragraphs were written, J. Cairns (*J. Mol. Biol.*, 6:208–213, 1963) has shown by incorporating tritium into the thymidylic acid of the *E. coli* nucleus, and then lysing the cells and making autoradiographs, that the nuclear material or chromosome is a single piece of two-stranded DNA 700 to 900 μ long. It must be folded or wound hundreds of times within the cell. Probably it exists in the cells as a circle, which explains very well the genetical findings above.

REFERENCES

Anderson, T. F.; Wollman, E. L.; and Jacob, F. 1957. *Ann. Inst. Pasteur*, **93**:450–455.

Armstrong, J. J.; Baddiley, J.; and Buchanan, J. G. 1961. *Biochem. J.*, **80**:254–261.

Baddiley, J.; Buchanan, J. G.; Rajbhandary, V. L.; and Sanderson, A. R. 1962. *Biochem. J.*, **82**:439–448.

Badian, J. 1933. *Arch. Mikrobiol.*, **4**:409–418.

Bartholomew, J. W., and Mittwer, T. 1952. The Gram Stain. *Bact. Revs.*, **16**:1–29; *J. Gen. Microbiol.*, **5**:39–45 (1951).

Bartholomew, J. W., and Umbreit, W. W. 1944. *J. Bact.*, **48**:567–578.

*Bisset, K. A. 1950. The Cytology and Life History of Bacteria. Chap. IV. Edinburgh, E. and S. Livingstone.

Bisset, K. A. 1954. *J. Bact.*, **67**:41–44.

Blank, F. 1953. *Biochim. Biophys. Acta*, **10**:110–113.

Braun, A. C., and Elrod, R. P. 1946. *J. Bact.*, **52**:695–702.

Brookes, P.; Crathorn, A. R.; and Hunter, G. D. 1959. *Biochem. J.*, **73**:396–401.

Burdon, K. L. 1944. *J. Bact.*, **47**:414–415.

Castle, E. S. 1945. *Am. J. Bot.*, **36**:148–151.

Cavalli-Sforza, L. L. 1957. Bacterial Genetics. *Ann. Rev. Microbiol.*, **11**:391–418.

Chapman, G. B. 1956. *J. Bact.*, **71**:348–355.

Chapman, G. B. 1959. *Ibid.*, **78**:96–104.

Cummins, C. S., and Harris, H. 1956. *J. Gen. Microbiol.*, **14**:583–600.

Cummins, C. S., and Harris, H. 1958. *Ibid.*, **18**:173–189.

de Cunha, A., and Muniz, J. 1929. *Compt. rend. Soc. biol.*, **100**:951–958.

Curran, H. R., and Evans, F. R. 1945. *J. Bact.*, **49**:335–346.

Davis, B. D. 1950. *J. Bact.*, **60**:507–508.

Delamater, E. D., and Hunter, M. E. 1951. *Am. J. Bot.*, **38**:656–692.

Delamater, E. D., and Woodburn, M. 1952. *J. Bact.*, **64**:793–803.

Delaporte, B. 1939. *Rev. Gén. de Bot.*, **51**:449–482.

Delaporte, B. 1950. *Adv. in Genetics*, **3**:1–32.

De Ley, J., and Dochy, R. 1960. *Biochim. Biophys. Acta*, **40**:277–289; **42**:538–541.

Del Valle, M. R., and Aronson, A. I. 1962. *Biochem. Biophys. Res. Comms.*, **9**:421–425.

Deussen, E. 1918–1921. *Z. Hyg. Infektionskrankh*, **85**:235–322 (1918); **93**:512–522 (1921); *Biochem. Z.*, **103**:123–141 (1920).

*Dubos, R. J. 1947. The Bacterial Cell. Cambridge, Mass., Harvard Univ. Press.

Dubos, R. J., and Avery, O. T. 1931. *J. Exp. Med.*, **54**:51–71.

Duguid, J. P. 1948. *J. Path. and Bact.*, **58**:114; **60**:265–274.

Duguid, J. P., and Wilkinson, J. F. 1953. *J. Gen. Microbiol.*, **9**:174–189.

Duguid et al., 1955–59. Duguid, J. P.; Smith, I. W.; Dempster, G.; and Edmunds, P. N. 1955. *J. Path. and Bact.*, **70**:335–348; Duguid, J. P., and Gillies, R. R. 1957. *Ibid.*, **74**:397–411; Duguid, J. P., and Gillies, R. R. 1958. *Ibid.*, **75**:519–529; Duguid, J. P. 1959. *J. Gen. Microbiol.*, **21**:271–286. (Note fine plates.)

Dyar, M. T. 1947. *J. Bact.*, **53**:498.

Feulgen, R., and Voit, K. 1924. *Z. Physiol. Chem.*, **135**:249–252; **136**:57–61; **137**: 272–286; Feulgen, R., and Rossenbeck, H. *Ibid.*, **135**:203–248.

Firshein, W., and Braun, W. 1960. *J. Bact.*, **79**:246–260.

Fischer, A. 1895. *Jahrb. f. wiss. Botanik*, **27**:1–163.

Forsyth, W. G. C.; Hayward, A. C.; and Roberts, J. B. 1958. *Nature*, **182**:800–801.

Fredericq, P., and Betz-Bareau, M. 1951. *Compt. rend. Soc. biol.*, **145**:1436–1439.

Frei, E., and Preston, R. D. 1961. *Nature*, **192**:939–943.

Giesberger, G. 1936. Beiträge zur Kenntnis der Gattung Spirillum Ehbg. Dissertation, Delft. 136 pp.

Gilvarg, C. 1960. *Fed. Proc.*, **19**:948–952.

Goddard, D. R. 1939. The Reversible Heat Activation of Respiration in Neurospora. *Cold Spring Harbor Symp. Quant. Biol.*, **7**:362–376.

Goebel, W. F. 1939. *J. Exp. Med.*, **69**:353–364.

Gutstein, M. 1924–1926. *Zentr. Bakt. I. orig.*, **93**:233–239, 393–402; **94**:145–151; ·**95**:1–20; **100**:1–9.

Hanby, W. E., and Rydon, H. N. 1946. *Biochem. J.*, **40**:297–307 (with an appendix by B. P. White).

Hardwick, W. A.. and Foster, J. W. 1952. *J. Gen. Physiol.*, **35**:907–927.
Hardwick, W. A., and Foster, J. W. 1953. *J. Bact.*, **65**:355–360.

Hardwick, W. A.; Guirard, D. B.; and Foster, J. W. 1951. *J. Bact.*, **61**:145–151.

Hayes, W. 1953. *Cold Spring Harbor Symp. Quant. Biol.*, **18**:75–93.

Hayes, W. 1962. *British Med. Bull.*, **18**:36–40.

*Heidelberger, M. 1956. Lectures in Immunochemistry. New York, Academic Press.

Heidelberger, M. 1960. *J. Exp. Med.*, **111**:33–43; *Heidelberger, M., and Rebers, P. A. 1960. *J. Bact.*, **80**:145–153.

Henry, H., and Stacey, M. 1943. *Nature*, **151**:671. 1946. *Proc. Roy. Soc.*, **B133**:391–406 (note fine figs).

Hills, G. M. 1949. *Biochem. J.*, **45**:353–362.

Hobson, P. N., and Purdom, M. R. 1959. *Nature*, **183**:904–905.

Houwink, A. L. 1953. *Biochim. Biophys. Acta*, **10**:360–366.

Hunter, G. D.; Brookes, P.; Crathorn, A. R.; and Butler, J. A. 1959. *Biochem. J.*, **73**:369–376.

Iriki, V., and Miwa, T. 1960. *Nature*, **185**:178.

Ivanovics, G., and Erdös, L. 1937. *Z. Immunitätsforsch*, **90**:5–19; Bruckner, V., and Ivanovics, G. 1937. *Z. Physiol. Chem.*, **247**:281–284.

Jacob, F., and Wollman, E. L. 1956. *Ann. Inst. Pasteur*, **91**:486–510.

Jacob, F., and Wollman, E. L. 1958. *Ibid.*, **95**:497–519, 641–666.

Jensen, J. 1950. *Zentr. Bakt., I orig.*, **156**:118–128.

Kandler, O., and Hund, A. 1959. *Zentralbl. f. Bakt.*, II Abt., **113**:63–70.

Kelemen, M. V., and Baddiley, J. 1961. *Biochem. J.*, **80**:246–254.

Kellenberger, E., and Ryter, A. 1958. *J. Biophys.·Biochem. Cytol.*, **4**:323–325; Kellenberger, E.; Ryter, A.; and Séchaud, J. *Ibid.*, **4**:671–676.

Khouvine, Y.; Champetier, G.; and Sutra, R. 1932. *Compt. rend. Acad. sci.*, **194**:208–210.

Knaysi, G. 1938, 1949. Bacterial Cytology. *Botan. Revs.*, **4**:83–112; **15**:106–151.

Knaysi, G. 1945. *J. Bact.*, **49**:473–493.

Knaysi, G.; Hillier, J.; and Fabricant, C. 1950. *J. Bact.*, **60**:423–447.

Krzemieniewska, H. 1930. *Acta Soc. Bot. Poloniae*, **7**:507–519.

Krzemieniewska, H., and Krzemieniewski, S. 1927–1928. *Acta Soc. Bot. Poloniae*, **5**:16–90; see also Milovidov, 1935.

Lamanna, C., and Mallette, M. F. 1950. *J. Bact.*, **60**:499–505.

Lancefield, R. 1954. Chap. I. In, Streptococcal Infections, ed. M. McCarty. New York, Columbia Univ. Press.

Lasseur, P., and Schmitt, F. 1927. *Ann. Inst. Pasteur*, **41**:554–575.

Lederberg, J. 1947. *Genetics*, **32**:505–525.

Lederberg, J. 1956. *Proc. Nat. Acad. Sci.*, **42**:574–577.

Lederberg, J.; Lederberg, E. M.; Zinder, N. D.; and Lively, E. R. 1951. Recombination Analysis of Bacterial Heredity. *Cold Spring Harbor Symp. Quant. Biol.*, **16**:413–443.

Lederberg, J., and Tatum, E. L. 1953. *Science*, **118**:169–175.

Levinson, H. S., and Hyatt, M. T. 1956–1957, 1961. *J. Bact.*, **72**:176–183; **74**:87–93; **81**:204–211 (1961).

*Lewis, I. M. 1941. The Cytology of Bacteria, *Bact. Revs.*, 5:181–230.

Lominski, I.; Cameron, J.; and Wyllie, G. 1958. *Nature*, 181:1477.

MacLennan, A. P. 1961. *Biochim. Biophys. Acta*, 48:600–604.

*McQuillen, K. 1960. Bacterial Protoplasts. In, The Bacteria, ed. I. C. Gunsalus and R. Y. Stanier. New York, Academic Press, pp. 250–359.

Mason, D. J., and Powelson, D. M. 1956. *J. Bact.*, 71:474–479.

Meyer, K., and Hahnel, E. 1946. *J. Biol. Chem.*, 163:723–732.

Mitchell, P., and Moyle, J. 1956–1959. Osmotic Function and Structure in Bacteria. In, Bacterial Anatomy, VIth Symp. Soc. Gen. Microbiol. pp. 150–180 (1956); *J. Gen. Microbiol.*, 16:184–190 (1957); 20:434–441 (1959).

Miyake, T., and Demerec, M. 1959. *Nature*, 183:1586.

Morgan, W. T. J. 1937. *Biochem. J.*, 31:2003–2021.

Morgan, W. T. J. 1950. In, Nature of the Bacterial Surface. *Symp. Soc. Gen. Microbiol.*, 1:9–28.

Mühlethaler, K. 1949. *Biochim. Biophys. Acta*, 3:15–25.

Murray, R. G. E. 1960. The Internal Structure of the Cell. In, The Bacteria, ed. I. C. Gunsalus and R. Y. Stanier. New York, Academic Press, Vol. I.

Nelson, T. C. 1951. *Genetics*, 36:162–175.

Neufeld, F. 1902. *Z. Hyg.*, 40:54–72.

Neumann, F. 1930. *Berliner tier. Wochenschr.*, 46:101.

Nickerson, W. J., and Falcone, G. 1959. In, Symp. on Sulfur in Proteins, ed. R. Benesch. New York, Academic Press.

Northcote, D. H., and Horne, B. W. 1952. *Biochem. J.*, 51:233–236.

Olive, E. W. 1904. *Beih. Bot. Centralbl.*, 18:9–44 (103 figs.).

Parsons, C. H., Jr. 1953. *Arch. Biochem. Biophys.*, 47:76–87.

Perkins, H. R., and Rogers, H. J. 1959. *Biochem. J.*, 72:647–654.

Perry, J. J., and Foster, J. W. 1955. *J. Bact.*, 69:337–346.

Piekarski, G. 1937, 1939. *Arch. Mikrobiol.*, 8:428–439 (1937); *Zentr. Bakt., I orig.*, 144:140 (1939).

Pietschmann, K., and Rippel, A. 1932. *Arch. Mikrobiol.*, 3:422–452.

Powell, J. F. 1950–1951. *J. Gen. Microbiol.*, 4:330–338; 5:993–1000.

Powell, J. F. 1953. *Biochem. J.*, 54:210–211.

Powell, J. F. 1958. *Ibid.*, 70:91–96.

Powell, J. F., and Strange, R. E. 1953. *Ibid.*, 54:205–209.

Powell, J. F., and Strange, R. E. 1956–1957. *Ibid.*, 63:661–668; 65:700–708.

Powell, J. F., and Strange, R. E. 1959. *Nature*, 184:878–880.

Prazmowski, A. 1880. Untersuchungen über Entwicklungsgescheite und Fermentwirtkung einiger Bakterien. Dissertation, Leipzig.

Riemann, H., and Ordal, Z. G. 1961. *Science*, 133:1703.

Robinow, C. F. 1942. *Proc. Roy. Soc.*, B130:299–324.

Robinow, C. F. 1944. *J. Hyg.*, 43:413–423.

*Robinow, C. F. 1947. Addendum to R. J. Dubos: The Bacterial Cell, pp. 355–377, and literature cited therein.

*Robinow, C. F. 1956. The Chromatin Bodies of Bacteria. *Bact. Revs.*, 20:207–242.

Rode, L. J., and Foster, J. W. 1960. *Proc. Nat. Acad. Sci.*, 46:118–128; *J. Bact.*, 79: 650–656.

Rode, L. J., and Foster, J. W. 1962. *Arch. Mikrobiol.*, 43:183–200, 201–212.

Roelofsen, P. A., and Hoette, I. 1951. *Ant. v. Leeuwenhoek*, 17:297–313.

Salton, M. R. J. 1952. *Nature*, 170:746–747; cf. Tomcsik, J., and Guex-Holzer, S. 1952. *Schweiz. Zeit. allgem. Path. Bakt.*, 15:517–525.

Salton, M. R. J., and Ghuysen, J. M. 1960. *Biochim. Biophys. Acta*, 45:355–363.

Salton, M. R. J., and Horne, R. W. 1951. *Biochim. Biophys. Acta*, 7:177–187.

Salton, M. R. J., and McQuillen, K. 1955. *Biochim. Biophys. Acta,* **17**:465–472; cf. Brenner, S., and Stent, G. S. *Ibid.,* **17**:473–736.

Salton, M. R. J., and Marshall, B. 1959. *J. Gen. Microbiol.,* **21**:415–420.

Salton, M. R. J., and Pavlik, J. G. 1960. *Biochim. Biophys. Acta,* **39**:398–407.

Schachman, H. K.; Pardee, A. B.; and Stanier, R. Y. 1952. *Arch. Biochem. Biophys.,* **38**:245–260.

Sickles, G. M., and Shaw, M. 1934. *J. Bact.,* **28**:415–431.

Stapp, C. 1942. *Zentr. Bakt., II orig.,* **105**:1–18.

Stille, B. 1937. *Arch. Mikrobiol.,* **8**:125–148.

Stoughton, R. H. 1929, 1932. *Proc. Roy. Soc.,* **B105**:469–484; **111**:46–52.

*Strange, R. E. 1959. Cell-wall Lysis and the Release of Peptides in Bacteria. *Bact. Revs.,* **23**:1–9.

Strange, R. E., and Dark, F. A. 1956. *Nature,* **177**:186–188.

Tatum, E. L., and Lederberg, J. 1947. *J. Bact.,* **53**:673–684.

Thimann, K. V. 1934. Unpublished observations.

Thompson, R. H. S., and Dubos, R. J. 1938. *J. Biol. Chem.,* **125**:65–74.

Tissières, A.; Watson, J. D.; Schlessinger, D.; and Hollingsworth, B. R. 1959. *J. Mol. Biol.,* **1**:221–233.

*Tomcsik, J. 1956. Antibodies as Indicators of Bacterial Surface Structures. *Ann. Rev. Microbiol.,* **10**:213–236.

Voit, K. 1925, 1927. *Z. exp. Med.,* **47**:183; **55**:564.

Weibull, C. 1953. *J. Bact.,* **66**:688–695, 696–702.

Weidel, W. 1955. *Zeit. Physiol. Chem.,* **299**:253–257.

Weidel, W., and Primosigh, J. 1957. *Zeit. Naturf.,* **12b**:421–427.

Williams, O. B., *et al.,* and nine contributors. 1952. Symposium on the Biology of Bacterial Spores. *Bact. Revs.,* **16**:89–143.

Wynne, E. S., and Foster, J. W. 1948. *J. Bact.,* **55**:61–68, 69–73, 331–339.

Young, I. E., and Fitz-James, P. C. 1959. *J. Biophys. Biochem. Cytol.,* **6**:467–498.

CHAPTER IV

Conditions of Culture: Media, Ions, and Temperature

Look what thy memory cannot contain,
Commit to these waste blanks, and thou shalt find
Those children nurs'd, deliver'd from thy brain,
To take a new acquaintance of thy mind.
  These offices, so oft as thou wilt look,
  Shall profit thee, and much enrich thy book.

SHAKESPEARE

. . . wherewith shall it be salted?

MATTHEW 5:13

1. THE CHOICE OF A SUBSTRATE

Microorganisms multiply in nature under three different sets of conditions: (1) as saprophytes, i.e., on organic matter derived from dead bodies and excreta of other organisms;[1] (2) as parasites, growing in living organisms, with or without harm to the host; or (3) in the absence of organic nutrient, their organic matter being formed by the reduction of carbon dioxide. This last method of nutrition is termed *autotrophic* (Greek *autos*, self; *trophe*, nourishment) (see Chaps. XXII and XXIII). To some extent the choice of a culture medium will be different for each of these three groups. For *saprophytes* (which include the fungi and most of the bacteria) some knowledge of the natural substrate is the obvious guide. Organisms found growing on plant detritus, much of which is cellulose, would hardly be cultured on a protein medium, while bacteria from the sea obviously thrive in the presence of about 3 per cent NaCl. A still better guide is a knowledge of the physiology of the organism; e.g., bacteria that cause the souring of milk by converting lactose to lactic acid obviously must be cultured (at least at first) on a medium containing sugar and phosphate.

---

[1] Those organisms that live habitually on the *outside* of other organisms, as *B. herbicola* does on leaves, or yeasts on sweet fruits, are probably to be regarded as saprophytes growing on substances diffusing through the epidermis of the host.

Simple as these principles are, they have often been neglected. Sometimes also the state of knowledge about an organism is simply inadequate, and "shotgun" media containing yeast autolyzate, meat extract, or commercial peptones are adopted. These substrates provide amino acids, peptides, and vitamins to varying extents. Since the vitamin requirements of many bacteria and fungi have now been elucidated, synthetic media can be more widely used (see e.g., Chap. XII, sec. 3).

Parasites have often, in the course of evolution, become adapted to the special conditions of the host. Animal pathogens, for instance, commonly need a *p*H near neutrality and a temperature near 37° C. Sometimes their synthetic abilities are severely limited, and a host of vitamins and special substances must be supplied. For example, the Hemophilus group of bacteria requires the presence of hemoglobin (one part in a million) or of hematin for the synthesis of a hemin-containing respiratory enzyme (Lwoff, 1934); they also need DPN, which they cannot synthesize. The requirements for some parasites— e.g., *Mycobacterium leprae*, and many spirochetes—are so elusive that they never have been successfully cultured (cf. Hanks, 1951). The extreme case is that of the viruses, which cannot grow on any medium, since they depend on the host to supply the enzymes with which to synthesize virus material.

Autotrophic organisms are of two types, using the energy of light and of chemical "dark" reactions. The former group, which includes the algae and the *Rhodobacteriinae* (p. 57 and Chap. XXIII) generally grow on simple media, sometimes with the addition of a few vitamins. For blue-green algae, tap water plus KH_2PO_4 was successfully used by Beijerinck for many years; ammonium or nitrate was added for grass-green algae. Modern media are essentially the same as those for solution culture of higher plants (see Pringsheim, 1948), i.e., they contain KNO_3, KH_2PO_4, $MgSO_4$, $Ca(NO_3)_2$, and smaller amounts of Fe, Zn, Mn, B, Cu, and Mo. The colorless autotrophic bacteria, i.e., the second type, are generally hard to obtain in pure culture, and a knowledge of their particular type of physiology, e.g., oxidation of ammonia and the like, is essential. Enrichment cultures can usually be made from an inorganic salt mixture with the addition of the single substance known to be oxidized (see Chaps. X and XXII).

The major considerations in making up media, other than the actual nutrients, are salts, hydrogen-ion concentration, solidifying agents, temperature, and the access of oxygen. Some of the effects of these external agents on the life and growth of bacteria will be taken up systematically in this and the following chapter.

2. THE INFLUENCE OF SALTS ON GROWTH

A. General

When bacteria are suspended in distilled water, the addition of simple salts generally has a dual effect. Most salts act toxically if their concentration is high enough, but in lower concentrations they promote

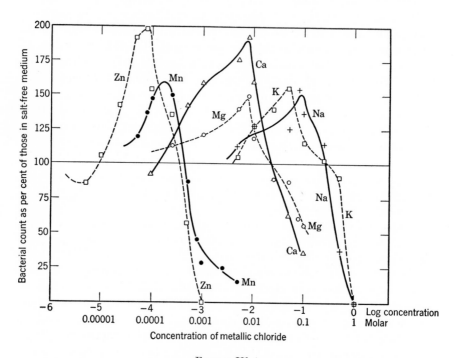

FIGURE IV–1

Growth of *E. coli* in different salt solutions. For simplicity, the growth is expressed as percentage of that of controls in distilled water. Each salt shows a clear optimum and depresses growth at high concentrations. (Plotted from data of C.-E. A. Winslow and E. T. Haywood, *J. Bact.*, **22**:49–69, 1931.)

survival and growth; these effects are individual, being different for different ions of the same valency. The stimulating and depressing concentrations for different cations, in a series of metallic chlorides, are summarized in Fig. IV–1 (Winslow and Haywood, 1931; Winslow, 1934). The population of the controls increased about 10 times in the 48 hours at 37° C, and all the salts had a region of concentration in which they produced an increase greater than in the controls, while higher concentrations inhibited. The figures for Zn and Cd may be compared with others on Hg, of which 10^{-6} M was found stimulating and 10^{-5} M highly toxic (Hotchkiss, 1923; cf. Chap. XXIV). The stimulating concentrations of Zn, in turn, appear to be about one-tenth those of Mn (Colley, 1931). Scattered data in the literature suggest that the order of magnitude of the concentrations in Figure IV–1 applies to most bacteria; e.g., *Treponema pallida* in salt solutions survives optimally with K and Na at 0.03 to 0.06 M, which agrees well with the figure. Rubidium or Cs would partly replace K, and Li or NH₄ would replace Na, but the optimal concentrations of these ions were higher (Doak *et al.*, 1959).

Neutral salts have many nonspecific effects. They promote the combination of some bacteriophages with bacteria (Cherry and Watson, 1949). They promote respiration; in the case of NaCl, 0.05 N was optimal for a number of bacilli and micrococci (Ingram, 1936), and organisms tolerating high salt concentrations behaved in about the same way as others. In moderate concentrations they retard motility (Tschermak and Garbosky, 1951), and the order of effectiveness Al > Ca > Na in slowing down Azotobacter is suggestive of Figure IV–1. In high concentrations they act as osmotica, allowing the survival of isolated protoplasts; however, most workers prefer to use organic solutes such as sugar for this purpose. The role of salts in spore germination was discussed on p. 133; although spores tend to be high in calcium and to germinate well in presence of sodium, the effects appear rather nonspecific.

B. Individual Ions

Magnesium is present around the periphery of gram-positive bacteria as a complex ribonucleate (Chap. III, sec. 3), but it is needed also by gram-negative forms, both for survival (Fig. IV–1) and for growth (Lodge and Hinshelwood, 1943). There are, however, considerable differences in the absolute levels needed; *Serratia marcescens* (gram-negative) has its optimum at 4 to 6 parts of Mg per million, while for *Bac. subtilis* and *Bac. mycoides* (gram-positive), the optima are at 25 and 40 parts per million, respectively, which would be high enough to inhibit the growth of many gram-negative forms (Webb, 1949). Sporeformers grown in dialyzed peptone become filamentous with cells 50 to 200 μ long, and the addition of Mg maintains the normal cellular form, though it will not cause filaments already formed to divide (Webb, 1948, 1953). Other metals will not substitute for Mg. Magnesium-deficient Mycobacteria show branching, which is probably an analogous response (Spitznagel and Sharp, 1959) and indicates that Mg specifically controls cell division. This may be brought about through influencing phosphorus metabolism, as shown in Figure IV–2; Mg-deficient cells also show marked reduction in the formation of volutin, which is rich in nucleic acid (Smith *et al.*, 1954; Spitznagel and Sharp, 1959). Even the total protein is lowered in some cases. In the purple and green bacteria, one Mg atom is present in each molecule of chlorophyll. The properties of ribosomes, too, are dependent on Mg, the smallest sizes being agglomerated by Mg into larger ones which centrifuge down more rapidly (see Chap. III, sec. 3).

Magnesium antagonizes the toxic action of heavy metals like Co and Ni. A nickel concentration of 0.2 parts per million, which almost completely inhibited growth of Aerobacter in a low-Mg medium, had very little effect when the Mg was raised to 20 parts per million (Abelson and Aldous, 1950). At this high-Mg concentration the uptake of Ni was largely prevented. Correspondingly the promotion of P uptake by Mg is prevented by Co (Fig. IV–2). The incorporation of Ca into *Bac. megaterium* spores is also decreased by Mg.

Many enzymes are known to require Mg. In most cases Mn can be substituted in the isolated systems, but Mn usually cannot substitute for Mg in the growth medium. Through these enzymes (cf. Chap. XI) the Mg ion exerts a controlling influence on carbohydrate metabolism at several points. For example, the Mg-deficient filamentous forms of *Bac. cereus* oxidize added substrates only 15 to 30 per cent as fast as normal cells (Nickerson and Sherman, 1952).

Calcium plays a minor role in the growth of microorganisms. Essential for algae, it is deposited in large quantities as $CaCO_3$ by certain calcareous forms. However, it is seldom required by fungi, except perhaps in traces, and a careful study with *E. coli* revealed no requirement for Ca even on a medium made with thoroughly purified salts (Young, Begg, and Rentz, 1944). It is needed for protein hydrolysis by Proteus (Chap. VII), in which it causes formation of a proteinase. It is needed for attachment of certain bacteriophages of *E. coli* (but not all) to their host cells (Beumer and Beumer-Jochmans, 1951), and even for the adsorption of the phage by cell-free extracts of the bacteria. Another special case is the necessity of calcium for growth of the autotrophic bacterium, Nitrosomonas (cf. Chap. X). Calcium appears to play an important role in spores, where it may constitute up to 3 per cent of the dry weight; in Ca deficiency, sporulation is impaired, and in some species, though not in all, the spores are less heat-resistant (Grelet, 1952; Slepecky and Foster, 1959). Much of the Ca is lost as dipicolinate when the spores germinate (Chap. III, sec. 4B).

Potassium doubtless has many effects. It acts particularly in phosphate transfer. When yeast ferments dextrose, two phosphate radicals are transferred to the sugar to make hexosediphosphate (Chap. XI, sec. 8). Since yeast juice that has been thoroughly freed from potassium can ferment hexosediphosphate, but not hexosemonophosphate, it ap-

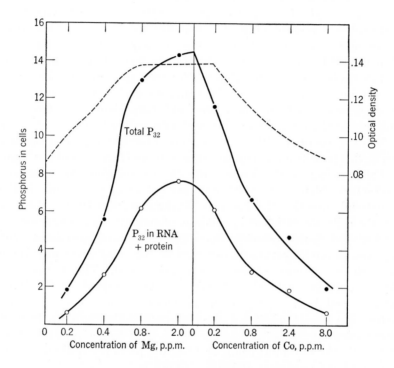

FIGURE IV–2

Left. The effect of Mg in promoting the uptake of phosphate and its conversion to protein and nucleic acid.

Right. The effect of Co, in presence of optimum Mg, in opposing these processes.

Dotted curve. Growth measured as optical density; the maximum increase is to about double the initial.

E. coli. Duration of experiment, 1 hour.

(Data selected from P. H. Abelson and E. Aldous, *J. Bact.,* 401–413, 1950.)

pears that the K+ ion is needed for the transfer of the second phosphate radical (Muntz, 1947). The hydrolysis of ATP to yield free phosphate also requires K+ ions. In both cases NH₄+ will substitute. Because of these reactions K+ promotes many types of sugar breakdown. Its effects in promoting growth (cf. Chap. XIX) and in promoting the uptake of Mg (Quastel and Webley, 1942) very likely stem from this basic control. Perhaps even its strong promotion of ascus formation in yeasts, especially in presence of sodium acetate (McClary *et al.*, 1959) may have the same basis. Another reaction dependent on K^+ is the decarboxylation of malic acid, either oxidatively to pyruvic acid, as in Moraxella (Lwoff and Ionesco, 1947), or directly to lactic acid as in *Lactobacillus casei* (Korkes and Ochoa, 1948; Nossal, 1952).

Recently a mutant of *E. coli* was isolated that has a lowered K uptake and a correspondingly lower K requirement (Schultz and Solomon, 1961–1962). On a medium only 10^{-5} M in K, the original (K 12) strain accumulated K to an internal concentration of 10^{-1} M, but the mutant only to one-fifth this level. Yet the mutant grew better on the low-K medium than did the original, so that its K requirement must have been appropriately reduced.

Iron is concerned with the formation of hemins and hemin-proteins such as the cytochromes. The function of these is considered in Chapter V, and here we need consider only their formation. An example is Aerobacter, which needs 0.025 parts per million of iron in the medium for optimal growth (Waring and Werkman, 1943–1944). With less iron, the cells are deficient in catalase, peroxidase, and cytochrome, all of which are hemin-proteins. Some cytochrome still persisted in the cells even in the lowest iron concentrations, provided there was growth, but complete absence of iron prevented growth. The formation of other compounds, related to hemin, is also sensitive to Fe. Purple bacteria need it for chlorophyll formation (Chap. XXIII), and *B. prodigiosum* for its bright red pigment, prodigiosin (p. 334). Even the nonoxidizing anaerobes such as *Cl. tetani* and *Cl. sporogenes* need iron for growth, the optimum being at 0.5 to 0.6 parts per million (Lerner, 1951; Bard and Gunsalus, 1950).

A curious group of iron-containing growth factors has recently been brought to light: (1) The fungus Pilobolus (like several others) requires dung or dung extracts for growth, and this was traced by Hesseltine and co-workers (1952–1953) to the brick-red, hemin-like substance, *coprogen*. (2) The soil organism *Arthrobacter terregens* requires a growth factor from soil extract which is also formed by its relative, *Arthrob. pascens* (both Corynebacteria); this "terregens factor" or TF turns out to be a peptide with the ability to combine strongly with iron to form red-brown complexes (Burton *et al.*, 1954). Because hemin or coprogen can be substituted for TF, it seems that its Fe-combining ability is its important property. (3) The smut fungus, *Ustilago sphaerogena*, contains a red pigment of the approximate composition $C_{28}H_{44}O_{12}N_9Fe$; this compound, *ferrichrome*, resembles a hemin derivative but is chemically different (Neilands, 1952, 1957).

To some extent these three materials are interchangeable; coprogen or ferrichrome can substitute for TF, and ferrichrome for coprogen. Then, too, the lactic rod, *Microbacterium lacticum* (Chap. XII), or a near relative, requires a growth factor in liver extract, replaceable not only by coprogen or TF, but also by several hemes, as well as N-glucosyl-glycine, which might be a heme precursor (Demain and Hendlin, 1959). There is some interaction, too, with growth factors for other lactic bacteria. The effective concentrations of all these

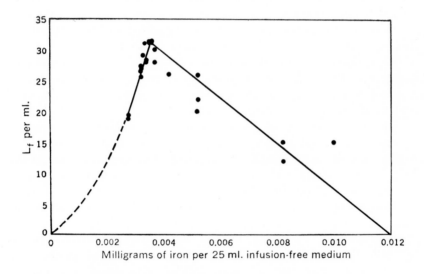

FIGURE IV–3

Formation of diphtheria toxin as a function of iron content of the medium. Ordinate: units of toxin per ml. Abscissa: Fe in medium. (From A. M. Pappenheimer and S. J. Johnson, *Brit. J. of Exp. Path.*, 1936.)

materials are around 0.001 to 0.01 parts per million. They apparently constitute a closely related group of heme-like growth substances effective on several organisms and are believed to act as "internal iron-transporting factors" (Neilands, 1957).

A striking action of Fe is in the production of bacterial toxins, which takes place only within a narrow range of Fe concentrations. With *C. diphtheriae* (the diphtheria pathogen) the formation of toxin passes through a sharp optimum at 0.14 mg of Fe per liter, and at 0.6 mg per liter reaches zero again (Fig. IV–3). At these high levels of Fe, where no toxin is formed, growth remains quite normal, in rate and duration, and both Fe++ and Fe+++ are taken up rapidly and quantitatively from the medium (Edwards and Seamer, 1960). When the Fe is in the toxin-producing range, a red porphyrin is excreted into the medium as well. Pappenheimer therefore suggested (1947) that iron enables the Corynebacteria to combine this porphyrin with protein, making a normal hemoprotein enzyme; without iron the porphyrin cannot be used and is excreted. The toxin would then be a normal enzymatic protein deprived of its porphyrin prosthetic group. This conclusion may be of general validity, since Fe inhibits toxin production by the organisms of dysentery (Dubos and Geiger, 1946) and of tetanus (Lerner, 1951). Also, in the preparation of diphtheria toxin other proteins besides toxin are excreted into the medium, and this excretion also is under the control of iron. The total protein in the medium has its peak at 0.1 to 0.2 mg Fe per liter (Tasman and Ramshorst, 1951). Hence as a practical matter the purest toxin is obtained with suboptimal Fe concentrations, because not too much contaminating protein is being excreted.

Iron also modifies the carbohydrate fermentations of *Cl. welchii* (Pappenheimer and Shaskan, 1944), *Cl. tetani* (Lerner and Mueller, 1949), and the formic acid decomposing enzymes of *E. coli* (Chap. XIV, sec. 4). Along with Ca, Fe increases the heat stability of spores of some bacilli (Sugiyama, 1951).

Manganese acts in many of the enzymes of carbohydrate metabolism like magnesium. Manganese is present in xanthine oxidase and is also necessary for carboxylations (see Ochoa, 1951). It is needed for both the anaerobic and aerobic decomposition of pyruvate by *Lactobacillus arabinosus* (Nossal, 1952). Manganese also plays a role in spore germination (p. 133).

Molybdenum and *vanadium* function in nitrogen metabolism, Mo being essential for nitrogen fixation (Chap. IX, sec. E) and for nitrate reduction (Chap. X, sec. B). Tungsten, next above molybdenum in the periodic table, inhibits these processes (Aurich, 1959).

Cobalt enters into the composition of vitamin B_{12}, which is required by some bacteria and synthesized by many others (see Marston, 1952). The vitamin is obtained commercially from cultures of *Streptomyces griseus* after separation of the antibiotic for which the organism is primarily grown, as well as from thermophilic bacilli and propionic bacteria (Perlman, 1959). A peculiar result of the ability of bacteria to convert Co to organic complexes is that, in cattle, vitamin B_{12} is synthesized only in the rumen; as a result, cobalt-deficient animals cannot be cured by injection of Co++ into the blood, but only by eating the cobalt. The vitamin, however, is fully effective on injection (Marston, 1952). When legume plants are grown symbiotically with

Rhizobia, cobalt greatly stimulates their growth (cf. Chap. IX), and it appears to be an essential growth factor for several *Rhizobia* (Lowe *et al.*, 1960). On the other hand, cobalt added to growth media inhibits many bacterial processes, especially enzyme formation and the uptake of NH_3 and phosphate (cf. Fig. IV–2). From the fact that inhibitions by Co can be reversed *either* by the chelating agent, EDTA (which combines with several metals), *or* by ferrous iron, de Turk and Bernheim (1960) concluded that Co inhibits by displacing Fe, probably from the cell membrane, where it is presumed to control the entry of numerous substrates. Cells that had grown with the isotopic $Fe^{59}Cl_3$ were directly shown to release radioactivity (i.e., Fe^{59}) to the medium on addition of $CoCl_2$.

Another action of added Co is to establish reducing conditions in the medium. This effect is so strong that 4 mg of Co^{++} per liter of medium is claimed to allow *Cl. tetani* (a strict anaerobe) to grow aerobically (Dedic and Koch, 1956).

Copper is needed in the formation of the brownish-black pigment of *Azotobacter chroöcoccum* and of the spores of *Aspergillus niger* (Mulder, 1938). These pigments are melanins, formed from tyrosine or certain phenols by the enzyme, tyrosinase, which contains Cu. Copper also promotes the oxidation of alcohol to acetic acid by Acetobacter, in concentrations around 2.10^{-7} M (Mulder, 1950).

Zinc is needed for formation of several enzymes, of which alcohol dehydrogenase is the best known. The enzyme contains four atoms of Zn per protein molecule (Vallee and Hoch, 1955). Among other actions not so well understood is the peculiar one on *Mycob. tuberculosis*, which forms a floating film on liquid synthetic media, so long as the Zn supply is adequate. But at 2 mg Zn per liter, or below, the film sinks to the bottom, and subsequently its protein formation is decreased (Dekker and Huittema, 1958).

C. NaCl

Sodium is not required by most microorganisms. It is essential, however (along with potassium), for marine bacteria (McLeod and Onofrey, 1957). Of six species tested, only one needed the Cl^- ion, but all had an absolute requirement for Na. These organisms are best cultivated in media containing 2 per cent NaCl ($= 0.35$ M); this, as will be seen in Figure IV–1, would inhibit fresh-water bacteria like *E. coli*. In the case of the sulfate-reducing anaerobe, *Desulfovibrio desulfuricans*, two forms can be isolated. The fresh-water form will not grow in 3 per cent NaCl (Fig. IV–4), while the marine form will not grow in the absence of NaCl. However, the response can be altered by selection, the organisms being cultivated from fresh water into gradually increasing salt concentrations (Table IV–1). After a series of such transfers the bacteria were now "adapted" to the presence of the NaCl, and on transference back into the salt-free medium they did

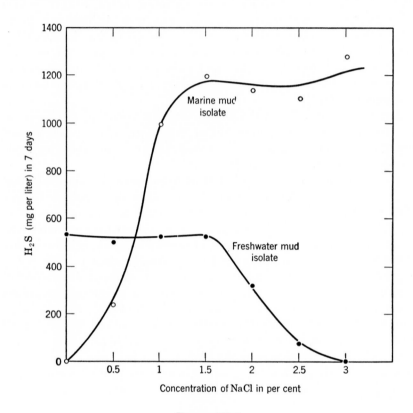

FIGURE IV–4

The activity of fresh-water and marine strains of Desulfovibrio in media of varying NaCl content. Note that the organism from fresh water is inhibited by NaCl concentrations optimal for the organisms from sea water. Activity measured as H_2S production. (Plotted from data of J. K. Baars, 1930.)

not grow well. The salt-loving form had now become a definite race, or even a species, since the form isolated from salt-water mud had formerly been regarded as a different species and named *Vibrio aestuarii*. This organism in fresh culture grows poorly in the absence of NaCl, but again it can be adapted (Table IV–1). In the light of Baars' work, therefore, the marine form is not a separate species, but only a salt-acclimatized form, selected out from the mass population by the successive transfers.

Similarly the other naturally occurring marine bacteria are most likely *salt-adapted forms* or *races* of fresh-water types. In the ocean are to be found types that correspond physiologically and morpholog-

TABLE IV–1

(From Baars, 1930)
(Adaptation of Desulfovibrio to NaCl. Figures are H_2S produced in milligrams per liter after 2 days.)

Grown in:	0%	1%	2%	3% NaCl
Original Culture (*a*) from Fresh-water Mud, Kept in 0% NaCl				
First transfer from *a*	405 = *b*	340	169	84
Inoculated from *b*		425 = *c*		
Inoculated from *c*			460 = *d*	
Inoculated from *d*				410
Original Culture (*a'*) from Marine Mud (*Desulfovibrio aestuarii*), Kept in 3% NaCl				
First transfer from *a'*	112	312 = *b'*	460	450
Inoculated from *b'*	237 = *c'*			
Inoculated from *c'*	472			

ically with the known fresh-water and soil organisms; there are proteolytic, urea-hydrolyzing, nitrogen-fixing, ammonia-oxidizing, sulfur-oxidizing, sulfate-reducing, and many other bacteria (see ZoBell, 1946, and Ferguson Wood, 1958). There are also quite a number of marine Actinomycetes, including representatives of *Nocardia, Micromonospora,* and *Streptomyces* (Grein and Myers, 1958). Most marine organisms abound in the sea bottom rather than the water itself; i.e., they correspond in their habitat to soil organisms. Some of the purple bacteria are also found in marine environments, so that it is of interest that one of them, *Rhodo-ps. spheroides* (Table XXIII–1, p. 724), was recently found to have a specific requirement for Na (Sistrom, 1960); about 10 mg NaCl per liter is optimal for growth. Perhaps this indicates a marine origin.

The *halophilic bacteria* comprise organisms isolated at different times from salted fish or other media of exceptionally high-salt content and cultivated in media containing 10 to 15 per cent NaCl. Like the marine bacteria, many types of organisms occur in halophilic modifications. These include bacilli, pseudomonads, organisms able to reduce sulfate to sulfide, some that oxidize cellulose, and a representative of the green *Thiorhodaceae*. Some of those found may be salt-tolerant rather than salt-requiring (Hof, 1935). Many soil organisms can be grown in enrichment cultures in the presence of 1 to 3 M NaCl, and Hof even obtained bacterial nitrate reduction in 30 per cent NaCl. Such halophiles may burst without NaCl (Abram and Gibbons, 1961).

One of the characteristics of halophilic organisms is the presence of red and yellow carotenoid pigments (Petter, 1931). It is remarkable, too, that, of the isolations of marine micrococci from estuarine mud or sea fish, about two-thirds are yellow or orange forms (Ferguson Wood, 1951). *Bac. mycoides*, an ordinary colorless soil organism, when cultivated in media containing up to 32 per cent NaCl, produces similar yellow and red pigments (Haag *et al.*, 1929), while *Str. griseus*, a colorless actinomycete, turns yellow when grown on a sea-water medium (Grein and Meyers, 1958). Such pigmentation apparently involves no fundamental changes, because the metabolism of three red marine bacteria showed no major difference from that of a related colorless form (Katznelson and Robinson, 1956). All four were highly oxidative. In another case, *Ps. Beijerinckii*, the characteristic purple pigment is formed only in alkaline brine, i.e., 12 to 18 per cent NaCl and pH 8.4 (Hof, 1935), but here the pigment is not a carotenoid but a hydroxyquinone (Kluyver *et al.*, 1939). In view of the argument developed above, it seems probable that the "halophilic" bacteria, like the marine bacteria, are to be regarded as salt-adapted races of common organisms, modified by the pigments which arise in some way in response to the saline substrate. It is to be noted, too, that the most prominent algae of salt-evaporating pools, where the solution is saturated with NaCl, are bright red (*Dunaliella salina*).

An interesting result of treatment with high-salt concentrations is the appearance of exceedingly irregular "involution" forms, sometimes resembling those growing in the presence of antibiotics (Chap. XXV). With *Bac. mycoides*, 0.05 M $MgSO_4$ or 0.5 M Li_2SO_4 had a most striking effect, giving rise in a few days to large spheres up to

20 μ in diameter (Stapp and Zycka, 1931; Pietschmann and Rippel, 1932). Although none of these salt-induced forms grew further, similar large spheres produced by LiCl in *E. coli* have been shown to grow slowly into visible colonies on agar, while on transfer back to salt-free medium they grew as normal rods (Pitzurra *et al.*, 1957, 1959). Other salt treatments have given rise to minute coccoid forms which grew back to normal rods (Haag *et al.*, 1929). All these findings suggest that salts, especially of Li, modify the formation of the cell wall.

3. HYDROGEN-ION CONCENTRATION

The small size and great mobility of the hydrogen ion undoubtedly render it of supreme importance in many chemical processes; in biological processes its importance is still greater because so many of these processes consist of a transfer of hydrogen from one molecule to another. The tendency of the hydrogen to dissociate from its organic combination thus determines the probability of the reaction (Chap. V).

The concentration of hydrogen ion is practically always low in the natural habitats of microorganisms, but, on the other hand, no organisms can grow in its complete absence. In general, the effects are essentially similar to those of the metallic ions discussed above, i.e., high concentrations are toxic, and moderately low concentrations permit growth, but very low concentrations are again unfavorable. In other words, strong acids and strong alkalis alike inhibit the development of bacteria, and most organisms thrive best not too far from "neutrality," i.e., a hydrogen-ion concentration near 10^{-7} molar. If this concentration is equal to that inside the bacterial cell, then each cell would contain only a few hydrogen ions (Chap. II, sec. 2A).

Table IV–2 summarizes the minimum, maximum, and optimum concentrations of H^+ for many bacteria and for some fungi. The expression of hydrogen-ion concentration in logarithmic form as pH ($= -\log(H^+)$) tends to make the differences between organisms look smaller than they are. Reference to the table brings out the following points:

(1) A pH between 4 and 6 on the acid side and a pH between 8 and 9 on the alkaline side represent the limits between which growth of most bacteria occurs, the optimum being usually close to pH 7.

(2) On the acid side, with a few interesting exceptions, the bacteria cannot tolerate pH less than 4, while the yeasts and fungi are markedly acid-loving. Five of the fungal species listed can grow in acid stronger than $N/100$ (pH 2). Bottles of reagent acids kept

TABLE IV–2. The pH Ranges for Growth of Bacteria and Fungi

(P) indicates animal pathogens.

	Organism	Min.	Max.	Optimum
Cocci	*Dipl. pneumoniae* (P)	7.0	8.3	7.8
	Sc. pyogenes (P)	4.5	9.2	7.8
	Sc. viridans	4.5	8.0	6.8–7.8
	Sc. liquefaciens	5.5	8.0	6.2–7.0
	N. meningiditis (P)	6.1	7.8	7.4
	N. gonorrhoeae (P)	5.8	8.3	7.3
Rods	*Escherichia coli*	4.3	9.5	6.0–7.0
	Aerobacter aerogenes	4.4	9.0	6.0
	Salmonella paratyphosa A (P)	4.0	9.6	6.2–7.2
	Salmonella typhosa (P)	4.0	9.6	6.8–7.2
	Shigella dysenteriae (P)	4.5	9.6	ca 7.0
	B. alcaligenes	4.6	9.7	8.5
	Brucella melitensis (P)	6.3	8.4	6.6–8.2
	Erwinia carotovorum	4.6	9.3	
	Proteus vulgaris	4.4	9.2	6.5
	B. prodigiosum (*Serratia marcescens*)	4.6	8.0	6.0–7.0
	Pasteurella pestis (P)	5.0	8.2	6.2–7 0
	Ps. pyocyanea	4.4	8.8	6.6–7.0
	Ps. (Agrobact.) tumefaciens	5.7	9.2	
	Bac. subtilis	4.5	8.5	6.0–7.5
	Bac. anthracis (P)	6.0	8.5	7.0–7.4
	Cl. sporogenes	5.0	9.0	6.5–7.5
	Cl. tetani (P)	5.5	8.3	7.0–7.6
	Vibrio comma (*cholerae*) (P)	5.6	9.6	7.0–7.4
	Nitrobacter	5.7	10.2	8.4–9.2
	Nitrosomonas	7.6	9.4	8.5–8.8
	Thiob. thioöxidans	1.0	9.8	2.0–5.0
	Thiob. denitrificans	5.0	10.7	7.0–9.0
	Azotob. chroöcoccum	5.8		7.4–7.6
	Rhizobium leguminosarum (5 strains)	3.2–5.0	10–11	
	C. diphtheriae (P)	6.0	8.3	7.3–7.5
	Mycob. tuberculosis (P)	5.0	8.4	6.8–7.7
	Mycob. phlei	5.0	8.4	
	Streptomyces scabies	5.4	9	8.5
Fungi	*Sacch. cereviseae*	2.4		4.0–5.0
	Mucor glomerula	3.2	9.2	
	Asp. oryzae	1.6	9.3	
	Asp. terricola	1.6	9.3	
	Pen. italicum	1.9	9.3	
	Pen. variabile	1.6	11.1	
	Fusarium bullatum	2.0	11.2	
	Fusarium oxysporium	1.8	11.1	
	Marasmius graminum	3.5	9.0	6.9
	Marasmius foetidus	2	6.8	3.1
	Phycomyces blakesleeanus	3.0	7.5	3.6–4.1

All bacteria, except Nitrobacter and Nitrosomonas, collected by Buchanan and Fulmer (1930).
Nitrobacter and Nitrosomonas: Meyerhof, 1916–1917.
Fungi: Lindeberg (1939) and Johnson (1923).

in the laboratory, at concentrations up to decinormal, often become infected with imperfect fungi. Among the bacteria, marked acidity is tolerated by Acetobacter (the vinegar-producing bacteria), *Zymosarcina ventriculi* (which may infect the mammalian stomach, where the *p*H often approaches 1), and *Thiobacillus thio-oxidans,* one of the sulfur-oxidizing bacteria.

(3) Animal pathogens (marked P in table), have in general a narrower range than nonpathogens; the optimum range almost invariably centers about *p*H 7.2–7.4.

(4) Of the pathogens, those infecting the intestinal tract, i.e., the *coli-typhosum-dysenteriae* group, tolerate a more acid *p*H than those growing in blood or tissue, such as the pathogenic cocci, Brucella, or *Bac. anthracis.*

(5) Tolerance on the alkaline side is greatest in the organisms whose typical habitat is the soil. The optimum for the nitrifying bacteria is on the alkaline side. Strong alkalinity is also tolerated by Rhizobium (the root-nodule organisms), the urea-hydrolyzers, and some strains of *Sc. fecalis* and *Bac. circulans,* which have been reported to grow down to *p*H 11.0. In a strain of *Bac. cereus,* resistance to alkali could be increased by a series of 66 transfers into media of increasing alkalinity (like Baars' experiment with increasing salinity). Finally the organism would grow, and its spores would germinate, at *p*H 10.3, while growth at *p*H 7.4 was undiminished (Kushner and Lisson, 1959; Chislett and Kushner, 1960–1961). The nature of the metabolic change that confers alkali-resistance has not been elucidated.

(6) Actinomyetes are somewhat acid-intolerant, and some have their optimum *p*H at about 8.5.

The production of acid or alkali from the substrate by the growth of bacteria frequently limits their growth or brings it to a standstill. For acid-forming organisms, an insoluble alkali like $CaCO_3$ or $MgCO_3$ can often be added. For alkali-forming organisms, e.g., sulfate-reducers, nitrate-reducers, and active ammonifiers, no such procedure is possible.

The effects of *p*H are so many and varied that they will be considered with the discussion on the separate bacterial types and processes.

4. SOLIDIFYING AGENTS

For solidification, gelatin, agar, and occasionally silica gel have been used. Since these substances are so universally used in culture media, a few words about their nature may be useful.

GELATIN. When bones are treated with HCl, the $CaCO_3$ is decomposed and the $Ca_3(PO_4)_2$ is dissolved. The remaining stiff spongy material consists largely of the precursor of gelatin, collagen. When collagen is treated with boiling water, it is converted into gelatin, which goes into solution. The hot solution is cooled, and the resulting gel cut up and dried in a current of cold air. Manufacturers extract the bones directly with boiling water, the decalcification not being a necessary preliminary. Skin may also be substituted for bone. Gelatin is a protein; it consists of amino acids in peptide linkage (see Chap. VII), but cysteine and tryptophan being absent, it is a poor nutrient when unsupplemented.

Gelatin is not a single substance; even after extensive purification by washing, electrodialysis, and flocculation, its composition still varies indefinitely according to the treatment to which it is subjected, and fractions soluble and insoluble in cold water are present (see Schryver *et al.*, 1921–1927). The centrifugal experiments of Krishnamurti and Svedberg (1930) also show that highly purified gelatin still consists of a number of components of different molecular weight. Gelatin is thus a group of substances of similar properties and related composition. Casein has a similar nature. Gelatin solutions of concentration greater than 2 per cent set to a gel on cooling (although this is not true if the gelatin has been extensively purified). Dilute gels have little rigidity, and gelatin is, therefore, used for media in a concentration of 10 to 12 per cent. At 25 to 30° C the gel melts more or less reversibly, but some irreversible change takes place every time a gelatin gel is warmed to bring it into solution. It follows that when making bacterial media, gelatin should not be heated any longer than is necessary for sterilization. Since the irreversible change takes place rapidly at above 100° C, gelatin media are often sterilized by three successive steamings, although 16 per cent gelatin will set to a gel after 15 minutes at 120° C. (The use of sterile glassware and boiled water minimizes infections.) Since gelatin is readily hydrolyzed by hot acid or alkali, the final medium must be close to pH 7 when sterilized.

AGAR. This is a carbohydrate. It is obtained from marine algae, of whose structure it forms an important component. Almost any of the red algae (*Rhodophyceae*) will yield some agar, but members of the Gelidium genus, particularly *G. amansii* and *G. carneum*, are the best commercial sources. These grow profusely off the coast of Japan. They are extracted for 12 hours at about 80° C with $N/300$ H_2SO_4, filtered, and the solution allowed to set to a gel. The gel is cut up and frozen; on thawing, most of the water drains away, and the concentrated gel is dried down in a current of air. The crude product contains 12 to 100 parts per million of free iodine (Itano and Tsuji, 1933) as well as many organic impurities. These can largely be removed by washing the dried agar for 10 to 15 days, changing the water daily. Such washed agar will barely support the growth of bacteria, and it is excellent for cultures of algae or even, in some cases, for autotrophic bacteria.

Unfortunately a few Eubacteria, Myxobacteria, and Myxomycetes can hydrolyze agar, liquifying the gel (though not as extensively as gelatin) and presumably metabolizing the resulting galactose.

On hydrolysis, agar yields D-galactose, a small amount of L-galactose, and sulfuric acid. It has therefore been assigned the structure:

$$\text{D-galactose} \xrightarrow{\text{1-3}'} (\text{D-galactose})_7 \xrightarrow{\text{1-3}} \text{D-galactose} \xrightarrow{\text{1-4}'} \text{L-galactose-6-sulfate}$$

About 14 of these 10-sugar units make up the chain-molecule that constitutes agar; the sulfate ester would account for its acidic properties, and ordinary agar would be the Ca or Mg salt. However, Araki (1956) believes the L-galactose to be present in its 3-6-anhydro form and linked to the D-galactose as a recurring biose unit; the sulfate esterification would be incomplete and variable in amount, since there is less than one sulfate for 10 galactose units. In any case, the chains are relatively short, and some sulfate is always present (see Araki and Hirose, 1960–1961).

Most agar gels, unlike gelatin, do not undergo an irreversible change on heating (except at pH <2 or >9). Media containing agar can therefore be freely autoclaved at $120°$ C. Two per cent agar is generally used in microbiological media, but in a very few cases liquid media with about 0.1 per cent agar to give viscosity have been found to promote growth, perhaps by preventing inoculum from falling to the bottom (Pringsheim, 1950). Very weak agar, generally 0.2 per cent, is also used to detect motility in feebly motile forms that show no motility on 2 per cent agar media (Clark and Carr, 1951). Agar gels of 1.5 to 3 per cent do not melt until about $95°$ C is reached, but they can be cooled to $48°$ C before solidifying. The cooled liquid can then be inoculated just before it reaches the setting temperature and quickly poured into Petri dishes, to give separate colonies.

SILICA. When sodium silicate solution ("water glass") is acidified with HCl, or, better, with phosphoric acid, the resulting silicic acid sets slowly to a gel at room temperature. The sodium salts have to be removed by prolonged washing. Since the gel, once set, cannot be liquified, it must be made in the Petri dish or other vessel where it will be used. After washing, the surface is sterilized by flaming, and sterile nutrients added in the form of small volumes of concentrated solution which will sink into the gel (see Winogradsky, 1932; Kingsbury and Barghoorn, 1954). Since the silica is totally nonnutrient, it is used for autotrophic organisms, to minimize the growth of heterotrophs and to avoid the growth inhibition by organic compounds to which some autotrophs are subject (cf. Chap. X).

5. THE TEMPERATURE

A. Influence of Temperature on Reaction Rates

The majority of known chemical reactions are increased in rate by increase in temperature. In biological systems this increase in rate is limited by the fact that at higher temperatures the enzymes begin to be denatured. We therefore find an increase of reaction rate up to a certain "optimum" temperature, and then generally a rapid decrease due to destruction or denaturation.

The effect of temperature upon a homogenous chemical reaction can be expressed by its effect on the velocity constant, K, of the react:on. The simplest case is that of a monomolecular or "first-order" reaction, i.e., one whose rate depends only on the concentration of a single molecular species. Classical examples are the decomposition of N_2O_5, or the hydrolysis of esters or of sucrose, catalyzed by H^+ ions. The acid is a "perfect" catalyst and not used up: the solution is dilute enough so that the concentration of water is constant and the rate of the reverse reaction is negligible. Hence the rate at which sucrose is hydrolyzed depends only on its concentration. Thus if we start with a molecules of sucrose, and x of these molecules have been hydrolyzed after time t, the rate depends on the remaining unhydrolyzed molecules, i.e., the rate of change of x with time depends on $(a - x)$, or:

$$\frac{dx}{dt} = K(a - x)$$

(where K = velocity constant of the reaction). By integration:

$$K = \frac{1}{t} \ln \frac{a}{a - x} \tag{1}$$

For a second-order reaction, i.e., one involving two reactants, whose initial concentrations are a and b:

$$\frac{dx}{dt} = K(a - x)(b - x)$$

again integrating,

$$K = \frac{1}{t(a - b)} \ln \frac{b(a - x)}{a(b - x)} \tag{2}$$

In the case where a and b are equal,

$$K = \frac{1}{t} \frac{x}{a(a - x)}$$

These reaction constants, which measure the readiness with which the reaction occurs, depend on the amount of free energy liberated (or absorbed) in the reaction, the relation being:

$$-\Delta F = RT \ln K \tag{3}$$

where R is the gas constant, and ΔF the difference between the free energy of the reactants and of the products (both measured under standard conditions). Conventionally, if a reaction goes spontaneously, $-\Delta F$ is positive.

For any two temperatures T_1 and T_2, the corresponding velocity constants K_1 and K_2 are therefore given by:

$$\ln \frac{K_2}{K_1} = \frac{-\Delta F}{R} \times \left(\frac{1}{T_1} - \frac{1}{T_2} \right) = \frac{-\Delta F}{R} \times \left(\frac{T_2 - T_1}{T_1 T_2} \right)$$

or by:

$$\log \frac{K_2}{K_1} = \mu \frac{T_2 - T_1}{T_1 T_2} \tag{4}$$

where $-\Delta F / 2.303\ R$ is replaced by the more noncommittal μ, the "temperature characteristic" or Arrhenius constant. It can also be considered as including the *energy of activation*, i.e., the amount of energy a mole of the substrate must have to bring it "over the hump" of its inertia into the activated state where it can react.[2]

Now if $T_2 - T_1$ be fixed at, say, 10° C, it is clear that the higher the temperature range considered, i.e., the *larger* the product $T_1 T_2$, the *smaller* is the ratio $\frac{K_2}{K_1}$. The quotient of the reaction rate at T and that at $T - 10°$ C, i.e., the quotient for 10° C, may be written Q_{10}; it is a convenient measure of the rate at which reaction rate changes with temperature. The K values at any two temperatures will yield Q_{10} via the expression:

$$\log Q_{10} = \frac{10}{T_2 - T_1} \log \frac{K_2}{K_1} \tag{5}$$

Evidently Q_{10} decreases with increasing temperature.

Table IV–3 shows the variation of Q_{10} with temperature for various chemical reactions and for the growth of some bacteria. Some important generalizations may be noted. As a rule both simple chemical reactions and complex biological processes show a Q_{10} which is between 2 and 3 at room temperature and steadily increases as the temperature is lowered. However, protein coagulation has an exceptionally high Q_{10}, often between 10 and 20, and so does the destruction of microorganisms by heat. At the other extreme, the hydrolysis of esters by alkalies or by enzymes has a low Q_{10}, while a purely physical process such as diffu-

[2] A good discussion of the activation concept is given by Blum (1955).

sion will have a reaction rate proportional to absolute temperature and hence a Q_{10} of about 1.03.

The effect on growth is also illustrated by the data of Barber (1908) on *E. coli* (Fig. IV–5); in this the time plotted is the actual time re-

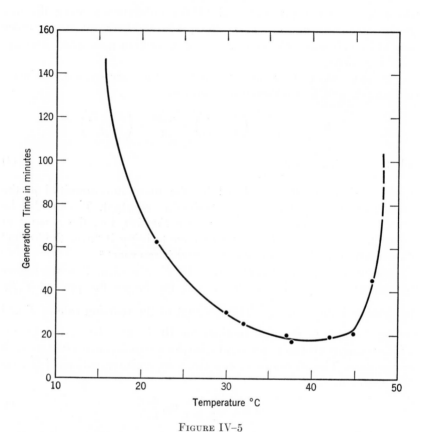

FIGURE IV–5
The generation time of *E. coli* as a function of temperature. (Data of M. A. Barber, *J. of Infectious Diseases*, **5**:379–400, 1908. By courtesy of The Univ. of Chicago Press.)

quired for an organism to divide once, i.e., the "generation time." This time is infinitely great at low temperatures and goes back again to infinity when the temperature is so high that the bacteria are destroyed faster than they can grow. Similar data on *Lactobacillus delbrückii* were given by Slator (1916; see Table IV–3) and for a number of bacteria at four fixed temperatures by Jennison (1935). Ingraham's measurements on a Pseudomonas (1958) show a curve similar to that of Fig. IV–5, but with a maximum temperature at 32° C. The Q_{10} for growth

TABLE IV-3. Examples of Velocity Constants and Q_{10} Values

A. DECOMPOSITION:

Temp. °C	The Classic Monomolecular Reaction $N_2O_5 \rightarrow N_2O_4 + \frac{1}{2}O_2$		H_2O_2 (cat. by NaOH) $H_2O_2 \rightarrow H_2O + \frac{1}{2}O_2$	
	$K \times 10^3$	Q_{10}	$K \times 10^3$	Q_{10}
0	0.047			
10	.....	4.99		
20	1.17		1.06	
25	2.03	3.98		2.9
30	.....		3.08	
35	8.08	3.70	5.16	
40	.....		7.90	2.6
45	29.9		13.4	
50	.....	3.01	17.3	2.2
55	90		.....	

B. COAGULATION:

Temp. °C	Milk by Rennet		Hemoglobin (3% aq.) by Heat	
	v	Q_{10}	K	Q_{10}
25	1			
30	1.69	2.86		
35	3.15	3.32		
40	5.40	2.94		
50				
60			0.0093	15.6
62.6			0.019	16.5
65.6			0.044	13.4
67.6			0.074	11.0
70.4			0.15	

C. HYDROLYSIS:

Temp. °C	Propyl Acetate by KOH		Sucrose by Invertase	
	Ka	Q_{10}	$K \times 10^5$	Q_{10}
0	1.03		18	
10	2.15	2.09	.....	2.47
20	4.23	1.97	120*	1.40
30	8.10	1.91	163	1.34
40	14.95	1.85	216	1.39
50			302	

D. GROWTH:

Temp. °C	Lactobacillus		Bac. ramosus	E. coli
	$K \times .434$	Q_{10}	Q_{10}	Q_{10}
15	0.084			
25	0.184	4.3	3.4	4.2
30	0.365			
35	0.62	3.3	1.2	1.9
40	0.84	2.3	...	1.04
45	0.98	1.4		
50				

* For 21° C.

between 20° and 30° C comes to 1.7, that between 10° and 20° C to 2.5, and that between 0° and 10° C is 6.3. For the range 0° to 4° C, it is 9.8.

In contrast with Q_{10}, the value of μ, the Arrhenius constant, should not alter with temperature because μ expresses merely the energy of activation of the reaction. Equation (4) above indicates that log K varies inversely with the (absolute) temperature, and hence that a plot

TABLE IV-4. Temperature Characteristics for Some Biological Processes

Reaction	Temperature Range in °C	Value of μ (cals. per mole)
Respiration of yeast*	0–15	19,500
	15–30	12,400
	above 30	8,300
Respiration of *Chlorella* on glucose†	0–18	19,000
	above 18	12,000+
Dehydrogenation of acetate, glycine, glutamate, lactate, succinate, glucose, mannitol, galactose, xylose, and sucrose by *E. coli*‡	up to 37	19,000
Dehydrogenation of formate by *E. coli*‡	up to 37	15,000
Dehydrogenation of maltose by *E. coli*‡	up to 37	21,000
Movement of *Oscillatoria* sp.§	6–36	9,240
Luminescence of "*B. phosphorescens*"‖	2–8	22,440
	8–22	16,590
Hydrolysis of 2-phosphoglycerol		7,400
Inversion of sucrose	20–40	4,400
Coagulation of hemoglobin	60–70	63,500
Inactivation of *Sc. lactis* bacteriophage#	30–55	11,000
	above 55	ca. 76,000

* Slator, 1906; Stier, 1933.
† Tang and French, 1933.
‡ Gould and Sizer, 1938.
§ Crozier and Federighi, 1924.
‖ Morrison, 1925.
Cherry and Watson, 1949.

of log K against reciprocal temperature should give a straight line. The slope of this line is μ. Many biological processes, however, do not give a straight line, but give either a curve, or a series of two or more straight lines of different slopes (for examples, see Crozier and Hoagland, 1934). This means that with increasing temperature in biological systems the value of μ for the over-all process often does decrease. It has been suggested that μ is determined by the slowest reaction of a whole chain, rather than by a single reaction, and since each reaction has a different temperature coefficient, the slowest reactions, by which the process is limited, will not be the same at different temperatures.

Values of μ for biochemical reactions vary between 4400 for sucrose inversion and 60,000 to 130,000 for protein coagulation; for biological processes such as heartbeats, movements, growth, and fermentations, the commonest values are 18,000, 12,000, and 8000 (see Table IV–4). A Q_{10} of 2 at 25° C corresponds to a value of μ of 12,000; 2.5 corresponds to 16,500.

The high value of Q_{10} at low temperatures is of practical importance, since in cold storage of food, a small change in temperature greatly influences bacterial attack. For example, the rate of bacterial hydrolysis of fish muscle is twice as great at +2.2° C as it is at −1.1° C (Hess, 1932). This would correspond to a Q_{10}, in this range, of about 8. A small further improvement in cooling machinery is therefore a good investment (see Elliott and Michener, 1961).

B. Optimum Temperature

Bacteria are often divided into three classes on the basis of the temperatures at which they grow best. Those growing at high temperatures (above 40° C), are classed as *thermophiles*, as opposed to *mesophiles* living at medium temperatures (20° to 37° C) and *psychrophiles* which can grow at temperatures down to 0° or even sometimes to −10° C. The *optimum* temperature of psychrophilic forms (which are mainly gram-negative rods) usually lies above 20° C, however (Ingraham and Stokes, 1959). Thermophiles, whose optimum may lie as high as 65° C, occur in nature in hot springs, tropical soil, manure heaps, and the like. Thiobacillus grows at temperatures up to 76° C in hot springs, and blue-green algae are even found at above 80° C; *Mastigocladus laminosus* has been recorded at 82° C, 83° C, and 89° C (Emoto and Hirose, 1942). The spontaneous heating of stacked hay, which sometimes causes it to burst into flame, is partly caused by the presence of active thermophiles; *Bac. calfactor* takes hay from 30° C up to 75° C, and when growing on bread in the incubator it could warm the bread up to 74° C (Miehe, 1907). The warming up of germinating seeds is also due to the associated bacteria, sterile seeds remaining quite cool while germinating (Miehe, 1930).

Although from the point of view of culturing the organism the idea of an optimum temperature seems clear enough, from a kinetic point of view it is far from definite. It was shown above that increase in temperature increases the rate of all the reactions involved in growth, i.e., it accelerates not only those reactions that constitute normal metabolism, but also those reactions, like enzyme inactivation and protein denaturation, that are damaging to the cell. Protein denaturation can be fully reversible, and hence heated cultures sometimes revert at once to normal on cooling. In any event, the *optimum* temperature for growth must be defined loosely as that temperature above which the damaging reactions just produce a discernible effect. Correspondingly, the *maximum* temperature is that at which the rates of damaging reactions become just equal to those of the metabolic processes so that no growth takes place.

The value of the optimum temperature depends to some extent on the time taken in the observations. This was first recognized by Tammann in his well-known study of the enzymatic hydrolysis of salicin. The Q_{10} for the hydrolysis at 25° to 45° C is 1.26, but the Q_{10} for deterioration of the enzyme (emulsin) is 6 to 8, so that the longer the experiment, the more emulsin will have been destroyed. Buchner in 1903 showed the same thing for yeast press-juice; for an experiment lasting one day the optimum fermentation temperature was 28° to 30° C, for two to four days it was 22° C, for six to ten days it was 12° to 14° C. Similarly, many bacteria grow very rapidly at a high temperature, but only for a short time, while at lower temperatures, although the initial growth rate is slower, the final yield may be greater (cf. Chap. XIX).

In culturing organisms, one must note also that different processes may react differently to temperature. For example, Pasteurella grown at 22° C is motile, but when transferred to 37° C it loses its flagella. The transition point is about 30° C, which is maximum for motility but not for growth (Preston and Maitland, 1952). Similarly, *E. coli* type I grown at 15° to 25° C has flagella and is motile; at 25° to 40° C it has flagella which are not functional and is therefore immotile, while at 44° C most cells have no flagella (Morrison and McCapra, 1961). There are parallel changes in pigments; many strains of *B. prodigiosum* have a lower optimum for formation of the red pigment than for growth. Some thermophiles have different nutrient requirements at different temperatures too (Campbell and Williams, 1953); indeed, several genetic strains of Neurospora are known that require a certain vitamin at high temperatures but not at low temperatures. One genetic strain also has an enzyme (glutamic dehydrogenase) which only becomes active at above 35° C (Chap. VIII, sec. 2). Enzymes do not usually change in this way; e.g., catalase from Oscillatoria grown at 35° C is no different in temperature sensitivity (or in energy of activation) than that from seaweeds growing at about 20° C or from beef liver (Kubin, 1959). Its μ for heat denaturation is 59,000, compared to 51,000 for beef catalase.

In any event it is evident that optimum temperature, though useful for practical purposes, is an ill-defined property.

C. Thermal Disinfection and Pasteurization

From the early researches (Chap. I) the important fact emerged that mere boiling of an aqueous solution is not usually sufficient to kill all the bacteria in it. Nevertheless, Pasteur showed that vinegar-producing and milk-souring bacteria could be completely destroyed by heating 10 to 20 minutes at about 70° C. Neither of these groups forms spores; this treatment suffices to kill the *vegetative* forms. Besides a few thermophiles and other heat-resisting bacteria, the main survivors of heating to 70° C are the spores, and it is their subsequent germination that repopulates the boiled medium. The process of heating to about 70° C, or pasteurization, is extensively used in the fermentation and dairy industries.

The original "flash" method of pasteurizing milk consisted in heating for 10 minutes at 80° C; it gives a slightly cooked taste to the milk and was until recently generally replaced by the "holder" method, in which the milk is held for 30 minutes at 62° C (143.6° F) and then rapidly cooled. This gives no taste and does not greatly affect the separation of cream, nor cause appreciable amounts of protein coagulation (Barthel, 1918). With modern equipment most dairies have returned to a flash method, using 16 seconds at 71.7° C. Naturally any sporeformers in milk will not be killed by pasteurization, whichever type is used, but these are usually present in small numbers, and mainly derive from water. A few "thermoduric" nonsporeformers also survive.

Considerable discussion has centered around the destruction of pathogens by pasteurization. The times and temperatures used in the holder method in the USA are founded largely on the resistance of *Mycob. tuberculosis* (North and Park, 1927), which is killed by 15 minutes at 60° C. For the organisms of typhoid, diphtheria, and cholera, 10 minutes suffice. Streptococci are among the most heat-sensitive. The few heat-resisting streptococci are not pathogens, and truly hemolytic streptococci added to milk are readily killed on pasteurization (Hucker, 1928). Hence there is no reason to fear the survival of nonsporeforming pathogens in pasteurized milk.

Food products such as canned meat, fruits, and vegetables, whose flora consists to a considerable extent of sporeformers, cannot, of course, be usefully pasteurized, but must be heated under pressure. The bacterial flora of sugar itself largely consists of sporeformers; some samples of sucrose contain spores that resist 20 minutes at 120° C. The time and temperature required for "processing" vary with the material, but for small volumes of liquid 10 to 15 minutes at 120° C usually suffice. One of the most important factors commercially is the time taken for the contents to heat through. If the sporeformers are not killed by heat, they may subsequently develop under anaerobic conditions in the can, to produce either acid only ("flat sours") or acid and gas ("blown cans" or "swells").

The *rate of killing* of spores or of nonsporeforming bacteria by heat appears to be described by the following simple considerations: If there are a cells at the start, and at any time t there are b survivors, then the rate at which the number of survivors decreases depends simply on the number present, or:

$$\frac{db}{dt} \propto b$$

whence

$$\frac{db}{dt} = Kb \quad \text{or} \quad \frac{1}{b} db = Kdt$$

By integration, $\ln b = Kt + c$ (where c is the integration constant). Hence a plot of *log* (*survivors*) against *time* gives a straight line. At time zero, the number is equal to that at the start, i.e.,

$$c = \ln a$$

Hence

$$\ln b - \ln a = Kt$$

This is sometimes expressed by saying the "order of death" is logarithmic.[3]

In some cases this is not true. These are explained on the basis of a difference in the sensitivity of different individual cells; i.e., on raising the temperature, the most sensitive organisms succumb first, while the most resistant ones survive after the bulk of the population has been killed. The sensitivity is considered to be distributed statistically. Hence the larger the population, the greater is the chance of having a few individuals of extreme resistance present. This has the practical result that in order to kill every individual, i.e., to sterilize, a large seeding of bacteria will require more heating than a small one. This deduction is borne out by numerous early studies of canning processes (e.g., Williams, 1929). Fortunately the data show that even with large seedings of resistant organisms, about 20 minutes at 120°C —the usual procedure for sterilization of bacteriological media—kills all the organisms. Williams' data show that with 10^5 spores per milliliter, sterilization by boiling was achieved in 6 minutes; with 10^6, it took 8 minutes, and with 10^8, 19 minutes. More recently Amaha (1953) has shown both for bacilli and clostridia that the survival time, t, at

---

[3] An excellent discussion of all matters concerned with the killing of bacteria by heat is to be found in Rahn's book (1932); cf. also Williams *et al.* (1952).

$100°$ C is related to the concentration of spores, N, by the equation $\log t = a + b \log N$. The constant a depends on the temperature.

Instead of autoclaving, media can also be sterilized by heating at $100°$ C on three successive days, commonly for 30 minutes the first day, 20 the second, and 10 on the third. The underlying theory is that after destruction of the vegetative cells by the first boiling, the spores will germinate and thus be killed by the second boiling. Those few that did not germinate after the first boiling will develop after the second and so be killed by the third. Not much advantage appears to

TABLE IV–5. Resistance of Clostridia to Boiling

(Data Collected by Hampill, 1932)

Organism	Medium	Death Time (minutes at 100° C)	
Cl. welchii	Brain broth	8–90	
Cl. novyii	"	60	
"Vibrion septique"	"	2–20	
Cl. chauvoei	"	2–12	
Cl. histolyticum	"	60–90	
Cl. tetani	"	60–180	
Cl. oedematis maligni Type I	"	2–6	
Type II	"	120–180	
Cl. sporogenes	"	60–120	
Cl. bifermentans	"	40–150	
Cl. tertium	"	2–10	
Cl. sphenoides	"	2–10	
Cl. cochlearium	"	60–180	
Cl. botulinum Type A	Broth or buffer	240–360	41 min at 105° C 4 min at 121° C
Type B	"	125–360	24–70 min at 105° C 4 min at 121° C

be gained by this method. It has been used with media containing sugar on the assumption that the three treatments at $100°$ C will cause less breakdown of the sugars than one exposure at $120°$ C, but direct determinations of sugar decomposition have not borne this out. Furthermore, some synthetic media are not favorable for spore germination, so that in the periods between the heatings germination may actually be slight.

The principal resistant forms are clostridia. Some of these can survive more than two hours' boiling, as shown in Table IV–5. It will be noted that the record goes to *Cl. botulinum;* unfortunately this organism produces a highly potent toxin, and hence it has been responsible for numbers of deaths from eating canned food. While aerobes are usually much less resistant, it is worth noting that *Bac. larvae* spores, in honey at *p*H 3, resist 160 minutes at 100° C (Calesnick and White, 1952). Several Actinomycetes show moderate heat-resistance. Thus the spores of *Micromonospora vulgaris* germinate well at 60° C, and the germination is improved by preheating three minutes at 100° C; *Streptomyces albus* can stand one minute at 90° C, and *Nocardia sebivorans*, 10 minutes at 90° C or even, in dense suspensions, three minutes at 100° C (Erickson, 1955).

D. Mechanism of Heat-Resistance of Spores and Thermophiles

The resistance of spores to heat is somewhat difficult to understand. No insulating properties of the wall, however great, could prevent the cell from reaching the temperature applied to it, for it is not more than 0.2 μ thick at most. Yet almost all enzymes are destroyed when their solutions are heated to temperatures well below 100° C, and proteins of the albumin and globulin groups are coagulated rapidly at 75° C. However, proteins are quite resistant when heated in the dry state. Thoroughly dried ovalbumin may be heated to 170° C without losing its solubility in cold water, and partially dry preparations, or very concentrated solutions, withstand intermediate temperatures. Barker (1933) found that the temperature of denaturation, which is defined as the temperature at which half of the ovalbumin becomes insoluble in distilled water, is a linear function of the moisture content. Albumin in equilibrium with a relative humidity of 40 per cent (containing about 9 per cent water) only becomes half denatured on heating 10 minutes at 120° C, i.e., under the conditions necessary to kill spores.

Enzymes show a corresponding behavior when dry. It has, therefore, been suggested that it is the extensive dehydration of the spore which renders it insensitive to temperature. This apparently reasonable suggestion has never been proved; when the composition of spores was compared directly with that of vegetative cells (Virtanen and Pulkki, 1933), they had *both* been dried beforehand so that the water contents were not very different. The volume of the spores of most bacilli is from one-fourth to one-tenth of the volume of the vegetative cells, and much of this represents wall, so that the volume of water in the cytoplasm must decrease greatly, and hence the solute concentration must increase correspondingly, when the spore is formed. Judging by Figure III–7, a tenfold increase might be possible. As noted above, in order for ovalbumin to be one-half denatured in 10 minutes at 120° C it must contain only about 9 per cent water; i.e., it must be in a 91 per cent solution. Now if the spore is to contain a 91 per cent solution, the solution in the original cell would be ten times more dilute, or 9.1 per cent protein. This is indeed possible since most bacterial cells contain 10 to 15 per cent dry weight.

A second factor in heat-resistance is the protective action exerted by the presence of colloids. For example, the temperature required to kill lactic acid bacteria is much greater in cream or milk than in peptone water. The heat stability of *Cl. botulinum* spores is markedly increased by growth in media containing long-chain fatty acids, perhaps due to an increase in their fat content (Sugiyama, 1951; Williams *et al.*, 1952). Protective phenomena are shown in vitro by the proteinase prepared from *Ps. fluorescens* (Virtanen and Tarnanen, 1932); in 10 minutes at 80° C it was 80 per cent destroyed in water, but only 27 per cent destroyed in the presence of casein.

A third, though somewhat mystifying, factor, is the calcium dipicolinate which constitutes so large a fraction of the spore (Chap. III, sec. 4). The fact that heat-resistance of spores is decreased when they are formed on media very low in calcium was mentioned on page 158. This is true even if the Ca content is artificially lowered by high concentrations of Cu, Co, Mn, or Zn (Slepecky and Foster, 1959). In such cultures some spores seem to be sensitive and some resistant, suggesting that those that are formed first "corner" all the available Ca, while the rest, being Ca-deficient, remain heat-sensitive. There is a striking parallel between the heat-resistance of *Bac. cereus* spores and their dipicolinate content (Church and Halvorson, 1959). Since this can be varied by changing the amount of yeast extract or of B vitamins in the medium, the heat-resistance can be experimentally controlled, both through this acid and through the Ca content (see Fig. IV–6). On the other hand, the heat resistance of spores can also be controlled by allowing bacilli to sporulate at different temperatures; the higher the sporulation temperature, the greater the heat resistance (Lechowich and Ordal, 1962). The correlation with dipicolinate content now does not hold, for in *Bac. subtilis* both the dipicolinate and the calcium content vary parallel to the heat resistance, while in *Bac. coagulans* they vary inversely. Thus the view that the dipicolinate is *itself* the source of heat resistance is too simple.

The picture is complicated by the fact that in spores and thermophiles some of the *enzymes themselves* are heat-resistant. A malic acid oxidase from a thermophilic bacillus (Militzer *et al.*, 1949–1950; Marsh and Militzer, 1952) was only 50 per cent destroyed after an hour at 65° C, while the corresponding oxidase from heart muscle was destroyed in five minutes at this temperature. The malic dehydrogenase from the same bacillus actually has its optimum temperature at 60° C, in experiments of an hour's duration. Similarly, the amylase extracted from a thermophilic strain of *Bac. coagulans* resisted 24 hours' heating at 90° C, while the amylase from a normal strain was almost destroyed in one hour at 90° C. The enzyme alanine racemase, which converts D-alanine to L-alanine, has been compared

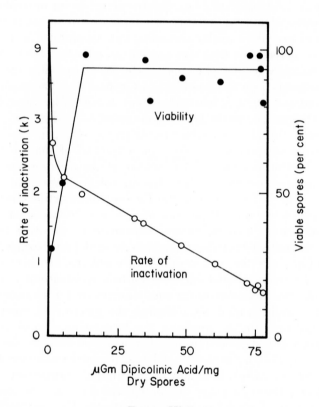

FIGURE IV–6

Relation between the dipicolinic acid content of spores of *Bac. cereus*, var. *terminalis* (as controlled by the vitamins and amino acids of the medium) and their heat resistance. Viability and heat inactivation rate determined by heating at 80° C. (From B. D. Church and H. Halvorson, *Nature*, **183**:125, 1959.)

in spores and vegetative cells of *Bac. terminalis;* that from the spores, which was contained in particles, resisted two hours at 80° C, while that from the vegetative cells was destroyed in 15 minutes at this temperature (Stewart and Halvorson, 1954). The force of these observations is somewhat reduced by the recent findings that *Azotobacter agilis*, which is neither a sporeformer nor a thermophile, possesses a pyrophosphatase which resists two hours at 75° C (Johnson and Johnson, 1959), while the pyrophosphatase extracted from spores of *Bac. cereus* is quite heat-labile (Levinson *et al.*, 1958). At least it is clear that some enzymes exist that are inherently resistant to high temperatures. Perhaps all four factors—inherent resistance, protective action of peptones and fats, specific effect of calcium dipicolinate, and dehydration—participate in causing the extreme thermostability of spores.

The temperature coefficient for killing is high. Q_{10} for death of *Bac. anthracis* spores is between 9 and 11, and higher values have been reported. Since the only process with such a high Q_{10} is heat coagulation of proteins (see Table IV–3), it seems fair to deduce that the destruction of bacteria by moist heat is essentially a protein coagulation.

E. Thermal Death Point

The exact sensitivity of the vegetative cells of bacteria to killing by heat is not easily determined. Different organisms can be compared by adopting a standard time of heating; for this purpose 10 minutes is generally used. The temperature at which a culture of bacteria is completely killed in 10 minutes is known as the *thermal death point*. For mesophilic bacteria it lies between 40° and 60° C, for thermophilic bacteria it is considerably higher. As the above discussion shows, the thermal death point will vary somewhat with the thickness of the bacterial suspension used, since it measures the most resistant individual cell.

In determining thermal death points it is necessary to take care that the organisms are exposed to the stated temperature for the whole period; in addition, the thermal death point varies to some extent with the medium in which it is determined. Thermal death points, to have any absolute value, should therefore be determined in water. For this purpose, tubes containing a known amount of water are brought to the temperatures to be studied, inoculated with a small volume of the suspension, and after exactly 10 minutes a sample is withdrawn and inoculated into fresh nutrient medium. This procedure is essential in order to avoid the loss of part of the 10 minutes in warming up, and to ensure immediate cooling at the end of the time.

F. The Effect of Low Temperatures

As stated above, the general increase of Q_{10} with decreasing temperature means that metabolic activities fall off very rapidly around freezing point. They do not entirely stop, however, since molds grow on meat in cold storage at about $-10°$ C, and urea-hydrolyzing bacilli continue to grow and hydrolyze urea at $2°$ to $4°$ C below zero (ZoBell and Feltham, 1935), while proteolytic bacteria growing at $0°$ C are ubiquitous. Growth of *Ps. fluorescens* has been recorded down to $-10°$ C, and motility to $-6°$ C (see Ingraham and Stokes, 1959; Elliott and Michener, 1961).

Simple exposure to low temperatures does not kill bacteria effectively. The majority die off, but the rest survive almost indefinitely. In cream stored a year at $-20°$ C the total count per milliliter fell from two and a half millions only to 680,000 (Fabian and Trout, 1943). Even the "delicate" spirochetes survive well; *Treponema pallidum* and *T. pertenue* survived a year at $-78°$ C with undiminished virulence (Turner, 1938). From a practical viewpoint the survival of bacteria in the cold is important, since frozen foods may thus carry pathogens for an indefinite time. Typhoid bacteria have been isolated from ice cream kept for over two years at $-20°$ C (see Hampill, 1932).

Lower temperatures are less damaging than those near freezing; many bacteria survive better at $-20°$ than at $-2°$ or even $-10°$ C (Borgstrom, 1955), and some remarkable survivals are on record. The milk-souring organism, *Sc. lactis*, in gelatin or in water, survived 111 days' immersion in liquid air ($-191°$ C) or 45 minutes in liquid hydrogen ($-253°$ C) and subsequently grew at the same speed as controls (Beijerinck and Jacobsen, 1908). The luminous bacterium, *Photob. phosphoreum*, behaved in the same way. However, the blue-green algae Nostoc and Anabaena were killed in 15 minutes at $-191°$ C. The yeasts were about 99 per cent killed in three days at $-191°$ C, but the spores of the ascogenous yeasts and of other fungi were more resistant. The most remarkable studies of this sort are those of Becquerel (1935), who exposed seeds of higher plants, pollen grains, and spores of bacteria and molds in sealed tubes *in vacuo* (pressure of 10^{-7} mm of Hg) successively to the temperatures of liquid nitrogen, liquid hydrogen, and finally liquid helium at $-269°$ to $-271°$ C. There was no loss of germinating power on the part of the spores. Becquerel points out that under these conditions the organisms show a true suspension of life; there is no growth or metabolism of any kind, but both begin again when conditions are once more favorable.

However, it must be said that mere observations of survival give no indication of *how many* of the organisms survived. There can be no doubt that on exposure to such low temperatures the majority of the population is indeed killed. Counts show that the percentage of survivors of *Pasteurella tularensis* after brief exposure to $-60°$ C may be as low as 0.1 per cent (Mazur *et al.*, 1957). The value is, for temperatures below $-25°$ C, dependent on the conditions, espe-

cially on the rates of cooling and warming. Rapid warming from
$-75°$ C to room temperature resulted in 30 per cent survivors, while
slow warming over the same range allowed only 0.01 per cent to
survive. Almost equally striking is the effect of the cooling rate; for
a given rate of warming, slowing of the cooling rate could increase
the per cent surviving from 1 to 20 per cent. *Aspergillus flavus* spores
behaved very similarly. In both organisms these effects were not
observed with temperatures above about $-25°$ C (Mazur, 1960). The
minimum temperature reached seems not to be a determining factor
unless the warming rate is slow; in Haines' experiments on *Ps.
fluorescens* (1938), where the warming was very rapid, the low point
in temperature had almost no influence.

The favorable effect of slow cooling is believed due to the gradual
loss of water from the cells; when the external water freezes, the
intracellular liquid water has a higher vapor pressure than the external
ice and it therefore distills out of the cell, leaving the contents highly
concentrated. The result is that the slowly cooled cells freeze much
less readily. Slowly cooled yeast cells were in fact shown to be shrunken
and unfrozen under conditions where rapidly cooled ones were completely frozen (Nei, 1954). Thus the determining factor in death
from cold is probably the occurrence of freezing *within* the cells.
Slow warming may also promote cellular freezing through the migrating of ice crystals from outside across the membrane (Mazur, 1960).
That killing by cold could be due to intracellular freezing is supported
also by observations on cells of animals and higher plants.

A valuable application of these principles is *freeze-drying*, or
lyophilizing, in which bacteria are dried by rapid evacuation and
frozen at the same time. It is much less damaging than freezing in
solution, and the method is now widely used for long-term preservation
of cultures.

In the discussions during the last century of the origin of life on
the earth, it was suggested that the earth was first populated by spores
of microorganisms that were carried here from other planets. Although
these views are no longer held, it is interesting to reassess them in
the light of our present knowledge. Interplanetary space is at approximately absolute zero; yet bacteria and mold spores, but apparently
not yeasts or blue-green algae, could have survived the journey.
However, the atmospheres of the other planets appear to be so low
in oxygen and water that the organisms there (if any) would have to
be of very specialized types, and when transplanted from there to
the earth they could hope to find only extremely limited conditions
suitable for growth.

As opposed to really low temperatures, simple chilling to $0°$ C has
a destructive effect on some bacteria when in the logarithmic growth

phase (Chap. XIX, sec. 4). The effect is less marked in complex than in simple media and is accompanied by leakage of amino acids and other constituents out of the cells (Strange and Dark, 1962; Strange and Ness, 1963). Adding back the leakage products protected Aerobacter cultures against the chilling. Thus the effect is mainly exerted on the cell membrane.

Exposure to repeated freezing and thawing is much more lethal than simple freezing. Table IV–6 compares the number of bacteria

TABLE IV–6. Comparison of Lethal Effectiveness of Simple Freezing and of Alternate Freezing and Thawing

(Data of Hilliard and Davis, 1918)

FROZEN SOLID	*S. typhosa*	*B. pro- digiosum*	ALTERNATE FREEZING AND THAWING	*S. typhosa*	*B. pro- digiosum*
Original inoculum	40,900	339,500	Original inoculum	40,900	339,500
Frozen for 24 hours	29,800	36,400	Frozen once	—	2,570
" " 48 "	—	14,400	" 2 times	—	275
" " 72 "	1,800	—	" 3 times	90	15
" " 96 "	950	4,850	" 4 times	—	0
" " 120 "	2,490	—	" 5 times	0	—

surviving from pure cultures subjected to the two treatments. The autolysis resulting from repeated freezing and thawing provided for many years the best way of making extracts of the bacterial cell, although nowadays grinding or supersonic vibration is more often used. Bacteria can be protected against the effects of freezing and thawing by adding glycerol (Howard, 1956); the optimum concentration is about 10 per cent (= 1 M). In this solution cells of Shigella frozen and thawed five times decreased in number from 57 millions (initial) only to 0.7 million per milliliter, while the same inoculum in ordinary medium decreased to 770 per milliliter—a protection factor of 1000 times (Nakamura *et al.*, 1962). The effect is perhaps due to preventing the growth of ice crystals.

REFERENCES

Abelson, P. H., and Aldous, E. 1950. *J. Bact.*, **60**:401–413.
Abram, D., and Gibbons, N. E. 1961. *Canad. J. Microbiol.*, **7**:741–750.
Amaha, M. 1953. *Food Res.*, **18**:411–420.
Araki, C. 1956. *Bull. Chem. Soc. Japan*, **9**:543–550.

Araki, C., and Hirose, S. 1960–1961. *Bull. Chem. Soc. Japan*, **33**:291–295, 597–600; **34**:1048.

Aurich, H. 1959. *Arch. Mikrobiol.*, **33**:46–49.

Baars, J. K., 1930. Over Sulfaatreductie Door Bacterien. Dissertation, Delft; cf. Kluyver, A. J., and Baars, J. K. *Proc. Kon. Akad. Wetensch., Amsterdam*, **35**: 370–378.

Barber, M. A. 1908. *J. Inf. Dis.*, **5**:379–400.

Bard, R. C., and Gunsalus, I. C. 1950. *J. Bact.*, **59**:387–400.

Barker, H. A. 1933. *J. Gen. Physiol.*, **17**:21–34.

Barthel, C. 1918. *Z. Gärungsphysiol.*, **6**:65–109; Barthel, C., and Stenstrøm, O. 1918. *Ibid.*, **6**:110–124.

Becquerel, P. 1935. *Proc. 6th Int. Bot. Congr.*, **II**:279–281.

Beijerinck, M. W., and Jacobsen, M. H. 1908. Proc. 1er Congrès Int. du Froid, Paris. 9 pp.

Beumer, J., and Beumer-Jochmans, M. P. 1951. *Ann. Inst. Pasteur*, **81**:489–506.

Blum, H. F. 1955. Time's Arrow and Evolution, 2nd ed. Chap. III. Princeton Univ. Press.

Borgstrom, G. A. 1955. Microbiological Problems of Frozen Food Products. *Adv. in Food Res.*, **6**:163–230.

Buchanan, R. E., and Fulmer, E. I. 1930. Physiology and Biochemistry of the Bacteria, Bk. II, pp. 315–317. Baltimore, Williams and Wilkins.

Burton, M. O.; Sowden, F. J.; and Lochhead, A. G. 1954. *Canad. J. Biochem. Phys.*, **32**:400–406.

Calesnick, E. J., and White, J. W. 1952. *J. Bact.*, **64**:9–15.

Campbell, L. L., and Williams, O. B. 1953. *J. Bact.*, **65**:141–145, 146–147.

Cherry, W. B., and Watson, D. W. 1949. *J. Bact.*, **58**:601–610, 611–620.

Chislett, M. E., and Kushner, D. J. 1960–1961, *J. Gen. Microbiol.*, **24**:187–191; **25**: 151–156.

Church, B. D., and Halvorson, H. 1959. *Nature*, **183**:124–125.

Clark, F. E., and Carr, P. M. 1951. *J. Bact.*, **62**:1–6.

Colley, M. W. 1931. *Am. J. Bot.*, **18**:266–287.

Crozier, W. J., and Federighi, H. 1924. *J. Gen. Physiol.*, **7**:137–150.

*Crozier, W. J., and Hoagland, H. 1934. The Study of Living Organisms. Chap. I. Handbook of General Experimental Psychology. Worcester, Clark University Press.

Curran, H. R.; Brunstetter, B. C.; and Myers, A. T. 1943. *J. Bact.*, **45**:485–494.

Dedic, G. A., and Koch, O. G. 1955, 1956. *Arch. Mikrobiol.*, **23**:130–141; *J. Bact.*, **71**:126.

Dekker, T., and Huittema, H. 1958. *Nature*, **182**:1387–1388.

Demain, A. L., and Hendlin, D. 1959. *J. Gen. Microbiol.*, **21**:72–79.

Doak, G. O.; Freedman, L. D.; and Clark, J. W. 1959. *J. Bact.*, **79**:703–708.

Doi, R.; Halvorson, H.; and Church, B. 1959. *J. Bact.*, **77**:43–53.

Dubos, R. J., and Geiger, J. W. 1946. *J. Exp. Med.*, **84**:143–156.

Edwards, D. C., and Seamer, P. A. 1960. *J. Gen. Microbiol.*, **22**:705–712.

Elliott, R. P. and Michener, H. D. 1961. *Applied Microbiol.*, **9**:452–468.

Emoto, Y., and Hirose, H. 1942. *Bot. Mag.* (Tokyo), **56**:25–42.

Erickson, D. 1955. *J. Gen. Microbiol.*, **13**:119–126, 127–135.

Fabian, F. W., and Trout, J. 1943. *J. Dairy Sci.*, **26**:959.

Ferguson Wood, E. J. 1951. *J. Gen. Microbiol.*, **6**:205–210.

*Ferguson Wood, E. J. 1958. The Significance of Marine Microbiology. *Bact. Revs.*, **22**:1–19.

*Flannery, W. L. 1956. Current Status of Knowledge of Halophilic Bacteria. *Bact. Revs.*, **20**:49–66 (153 refs.).

Gould, B. S., and Sizer, I. W. 1938. *J. Biol. Chem.*, **124**:269–279.

Grein, A., and Myers, S. P. 1958. *J. Bact.*, **76**:457–463.

Grelet, N. 1952. *Ann. Inst. Pasteur*, **83**:71–79.

Haag, F. E.; Oesterle, P.; and Stahle, C. A. 1929. *Zentr. Bakt. II*, **79**:1–25.

Haines, R. B. 1938. *Proc. Roy. Soc.*, **B124**:451–463.

*Hamphill, B. 1932. The Influence of Temperature on the Life Processes and Death of Bacteria. *Quart. Rev. Biol.*, **7**:172–196.

Hanks, J. H. 1951. The Bacteriology of Leprosy. *Ann. N. Y. Acad. Sci.*, **54**:12–19.

Hess, E. 1932. *Contrib. Canad. Biol. Fisheries*, **7**:149–163.

Hesseltine, C. W.; Pidacks, C.; Whitehill, A. R.; Bohonos, N.; Hutchings, B. L.; and Williams, J. H. 1952–1953. *J. Am. Chem. Soc.*, **74**:1362; *Mycologia*, **45**:7–19.

Hilliard, C. M., and Davis, M. A. 1918. *J. Bact.*, **3**:423–431.

*Hof, T. 1935. *Rec. trav. bot. néerl.*, **32**:92–173.

Howard, D. H. 1956. *J. Bact.*, **71**:625.

Hucker, G. J. 1928. *Zentr. Bakt.*, **II 76**:17–37.

Ingraham, J. L. 1958. *J. Bact.*, **76**:75–80.

*Ingraham, J. L., and Stokes, J. L. 1959. Psychrophilic Bacteria. *Bact. Revs.*, **23**: 97–108.

Ingram, M. 1936. Report of Food Inv. Board for 1935 (D.S.I.R., London), pp. 53–57.

Itano, A., and Tsuji, Y. 1933. *Ber. Ohara Inst. landw. Japan*, **6**:No. 1, 59–72.

Jennison, M. W. 1935. *J. Bact.*, **30**:603–623.

Johnson, E. J., and Johnson, M. K. 1959. *J. Bact.*, **79**:792–795.

Johnson, H. W. 1923. *Iowa Agric. Expt. Sta. Res. Bull.*, **76**:307–344.

Katznelson, H., and Robinson, J. 1956. *J. Bact.*, **71**:244–249.

Kingsbury, J. M., and Barghoorn, E. S. 1954. *Applied Microbiol.*, **2**:5–8.

Kluyver, A. J.; Hof, T.; and Boezaardt, A. G. J. 1939. *Enzymologia*, **7**:257–272.

Korkes, S., and Ochoa, S. 1948. *J. Biol. Chem.*, **176**:463–464.

Krishnamurti, F., and Svedberg, T. 1930. *J. Amer. Chem. Soc.*, **52**:2897–2906.

Kubin, S. 1959. *Biol. Plant., Acad. Sci. Bohemoslov.*, **1**:3–8.

Kushner, D. J., and Lisson, T. A. 1959. *J. Gen. Microbiol.*, **21**:96–108.

Lechowich, R. V., and Ordal, Z. J. 1962. *Can. J. Microbiol.*, **8**:287–295.

Lerner, E. 1951. Private communication.

Lerner, E. M., and Mueller, J. H. 1949. *J. Biol. Chem.*, **181**:43–45.

Levinson, H. S.; Sloan, J. D.; and Hyatt, M. D. 1958. *J. Bact.*, **75**:291–299.

Lindeberg, G. 1939. *Svensk, Bot. Tidskr.*, **33**:341–346.

Lodge, R. M., and Hinshelwood, C. N. 1943. *Trans. Faraday Soc.*, **39**:420–423.

Lowe, R. H.; Evans, H. J.; and Ahmad, S. 1960. *Biochem. Biophys. Res. Comms.*, **3**:675–678.

Lwoff, A. 1934. *Zentr. Bakt., I orig.*, **130**:498–518.

Lwoff, A., and Ionesco, H. 1947. *Compt. rend. Acad. sci.*, **225**:77–79.

McClary, D. O.; Nulty, W. L.; and Miller, G. R. 1959. *J. Bact.*, **79**:362–368.

McLeod, R. A., and Onofrey, E. 1957. *J. Comp. Cell. Physiol.*, **50**:389–401; *J. Bact.*, **71**:661–667.

Marsh, C., and Militzer, W. 1952. *Arch. Biochem. Biophys.*, **36**:269–275.

Marston, H. R. 1952. Cu, Co, and Mo in the Nutrition of Animals and Plants. *Physiol. Revs.*, **32**:66–121.

*Mazur, P. 1960. *Annals New York Acad. Sci.*, **85**:610–629.

Mazur, P.; Rhian, M. A.; and Mahlandt, B. G. 1957. *Arch. Biochem. Biophys.*, **71**: 31–51; *J. Bact.*, **73**:394–397.

Meyerhof, O. 1916–1917. *Arch. ges. Physiol. (Pflüger's)*, **164**:353–427; **166**:240–280.

Miehe, H. 1907. Die Selbsterhitzung des Heus. Jena, G. Fischer. 127 pp.

Miehe, H. 1930. *Arch. Mikrobiol.*, **1**:78–118.

Militzer, W.; Sonderegger, J. B.; Tuttle, L. C.; and Georgi, C. E. 1949–1950. *Arch. Biochem.*, **24**:75–82; **26**:299–306.

Morrison, R. B., and McCapra, J. 1961. *Nature*, **192**:774–776.

Morrison, T. F. 1925. *J. Gen. Physiol.*, **7**:741–753.

Mulder, E. G. 1938. Over de beteekenis van koper voor de groei van planten en micro-organismen. Thesis, Wageningen.

Mulder, E. G. 1950. In, Trace Elements in Plant Physiology (p. 45). Waltham, Mass., Chronica Botanica Co.

Muntz, J. A. 1947. *J. Biol. Chem.*, **171**:653–665.

Nakamura, M.; Farnum, J. L.; and Oke, M. A. 1962. *Nature*, **194**:405.

Nei, T. 1954. *J. Agric. Chem. Soc. Japan*, **28**:91–94.

Neilands, J. B. 1952. *J. Am. Chem. Soc.*, **74**:4846–4847.

Neilands, J. B. 1957. Some Aspects of Iron Metabolism. *Bact. Revs.*, **21**:101–111.

Nickerson, W. J., and Sherman, F. G. 1952. *J. Bact.*, **64**:667–678.

North, C. E., and Park, W. H. 1927. *Am. J. Hyg.*, **7**:147–173.

Nossal, P. M. 1952. *Biochem. J.*, **50**:591–595.

*Ochoa, S. 1951. Biological Mechanisms of Carboxylation and Decarboxylation. *Physiol. Revs.*, **31**:56–106.

Pappenheimer, A. M., and Johnson, S. J. 1936. *Brit. J. Exp. Path.*, **17**:335–344.

Pappenheimer, A. M., and Shaskan, E. 1944. *J. Biol. Chem.*, **155**:265–275; Pappenheimer, A. M. 1947. *J. Biol. Chem.*, **167**:251–259.

Perlman, D. 1959. *Adv. Applied Microbiol.*, **1**:87–122.

Petter, H. F. M. 1931. *Proc. Kon. Akad. Wetensch. Amsterdam*, **34**:1417–1421.

Pietschmann, K., and Rippel, A. 1932. *Arch. Mikrobiol.*, **3**:422–452.

*Pigman, W. W. 1957. The Carbohydrates; Chemistry, Biochemistry, Physiology. New York, Academic Press.

Pitzurra, M., and Mori, N. 1957. *Boll. Inst. Sieroterap, Milan*, **36**:74–79; Pitzurra, M., and Szybalski, W. 1959. *J. Bact.*, **77**:614–620.

Preston, N. W., and Maitland, H. B. 1952. *J. Gen. Microbiol.*, **7**:117–128.

Pringsheim, E. G. 1948. The Culture of Algae. Boston, Cambridge Univ. Press.

Pringsheim, E. G. 1950. *J. Gen. Microbiol.*, **4**:198–209.

Quastel, J. H., and Webley, D. M. 1942. *Biochem. J.*, **36**:8–33.

*Rahn, O. 1932. Physiology of Bacteria. Philadelphia, Blakiston.

Rode, L. J., and Foster, J. W. 1960. *Proc. Nat. Acad. Sci.*, **46**:118–127.

Roseman, M. C. 1908. *U. S. Publ. Health Bull.*, No. 42.

Schryver, S. B., and co-workers, 1921–1927. *Biochem. J.*, **15**:523–529; **17**:473–487; **18**:1070–1078, 1079–1084, 1085–1094, 1095–1101, 1102–1106; **21**:1284–1301.

Schultz, S. G., and Solomon, A. K. 1961–1962. *J. Gen. Physiol.*, **45**:355–361; **46**:159–166.

Sistrom, W. R. 1960. *J. Gen. Microbiol.*, **22**:778–785.

Slator, A. 1906, 1908. *Trans. Chem. Soc.*, **89**:128–142; **93**:217–242.

Slator, A. 1916. *Trans. Chem. Soc.*, **109**:2–10.

Slepecky, R., and Foster, J. W. 1959. *J. Bact.*, **78**:117–123.

Smith, I. W.; Wilkinson, J. F.; and Duguid, J. P. 1954. *J. Bact.*, **68**:450–463.

Spitznagel, J. K., and Sharp, D. G. 1959. *J. Bact.*, **79**:453–462.

Stapp, C., and Zycka, H. 1931. *Arch. Mikrobiol.*, **2**:493–536.

Stewart, B. T., and Halvorson, H. O. 1954. *Arch. Biochem. Biophys.*, **49**:168–178.

Stier, T. J. B. 1933. *J. Gen. Physiol.*, **16**:815–840.

Strange, R. E., and Dark, F. A. 1962. *J. Gen. Microbiol.*, **29**:719–730.

Strange, R. E., and Ness, A. G. 1963. *Nature*, **197**:819.

Sugiyama, H. 1951. *J. Bact.*, **62**:81–96.

Talmadge, M. B., and Herriott, R. M. 1960. *Biochem. Biophys. Res. Comm.*, **2**:203–206.

Tang, P. S., and French, C. S. 1933. *Chinese J. Physiol.*, **7**:353–378.

Tasman, A., and Ramshorst, J. V. 1951. *Ant. v. Leeuwenhoek*, **17**:153–158.

Tschermak, M., and Garbosky, A. J. 1951. *Revista Inv. Agricolas* (Buenos Aires), **5**: 541–553.

Turk, W. E. de, and Bernheim, F. 1960. *Arch. Biochem. Biophys.*, **90**:218–223.

Turner, T. B. 1938. *J. Exp. Med.*, **67**:61–78.

Vallee, B. L., and Hoch, F. L. 1955. *J. Am. Chem. Soc.*, **77**:821; *Proc. Nat. Acad. Sci.*, **41**:327–337.

Virtanen, A. I., and Pulkki, L. 1933. *Arch. Mikrobiol.*, **4**:99–122; cf. Virtanen, A. I., *Ann. Acad. Sci. Fennicae*, **A36**: No. 11, 28 pp.

Virtanen, A. I., and Tarnanen, J. 1932. *Z. Physiol. Chem.*, **204**:247–258.

Ward, H. Marshall. 1895. *Proc. Roy. Soc.*, **B58**:265–468.

Waring, W. S., and Werkman, C. H. 1943–1944. *Arch. Biochem.*, **3**:425–433; **4**:75–87.

Webb, M. 1948. *J. Gen. Microbiol.*, **2**:275–287.

Webb, M. 1949. *J. Gen. Microbiol.*, **3**:410–418.

Webb, M. 1953. *Science*, **118**:607–611.

Williams, O. B. 1929. *J. Inf. Dis.*, **44**:421–465.

*Williams, O. B., and nine contributors. 1952. Symposium on the Biology of Bacterial Spores. *Bact. Revs.*, **16**:89–143.

Winogradsky, S. 1932. *Ann. Inst. Pasteur*, **48**:89–134.

Winslow, C.-E. A., and Haywood, E. T. 1931. *J. Bact.*, **22**:49–69; cf. Winslow, C.-E. A 1934. *Quart. Rev. Biol.*, **9**:259–274.

Young, E. G.; Begg, R. W.; and Rentz, E. 1944. *Arch. Biochem.*, **5**:121–136.

ZoBell, C. E. 1946. Marine Microbiology. Waltham, Mass., Chronica Botanica Co.

ZoBell, C. E , and Feltham, C. B. 1935. *Science*, **81**(2096): 234–236.

CHAPTER V

Conditions of Culture: Oxygen and Oxidations

The cell knows but one fuel:—hydrogen.

A. von Szent-Györgyi (1938)

1. GENERAL CONSIDERATIONS

The accessibility of air is one of the most important of the conditions affecting growth and metabolism of microorganisms. In order to understand the full significance of this factor, it will be necessary to consider the nature of oxidations in general. Almost all higher plants and animals require a continuous supply of oxygen in order to keep alive. It is true that some insects can do without oxygen for a short time, and certain animals, notably some parasitic worms, can live and develop without oxygen (see von Brand, 1946). The great bulk of higher organisms, however, are dependent on oxygen. With microorganisms, access to oxygen may or may not be desirable. Four groups can be distinguished. First, many of the bacteria are strictly *aerobic*, i.e., develop only in oxygen—the nonpathogenic micrococci and mycobacteria provide good examples. Second, some develop only in the absence of oxygen and are killed as soon as air is admitted to the culture. This group, the strict *anaerobes*, includes the sporeforming clostridia and some nonsporeforming rods (Bacteroides) about which little is known. Third, the lactic bacteria provide an intermediate group, since they develop best in the presence of low oxygen tensions; these organisms have been called *microaerophilic*. Fourth, those bacteria and fungi that, like yeast, are capable of activity under both aerobic and anaerobic conditions are termed *facultative*.

194

2. METABOLISM, RESPIRATION, AND FERMENTATION

As shown in Chapter I, it was Pasteur's great contribution to microbiology that he recognized that fermentation is the result of anaerobic development. He viewed it as a type of respiration in which, instead of the oxygen of the air, the oxygen combined in organic molecules was used to support life. His famous definition, *"La fermentation est la vie sans l'air,"* is still valid, though often extended (see below). His concepts are made clear in the following (from *Etudes sur la Bière,* 1876):

In the experiments which we have described, fermentation by yeast is seen to be the direct consequence of the processes of nutrition, assimilation and life, when these are carried on without the agency of free oxygen. The heat required in the accomplishment of that work must necessarily have been borrowed from the decomposition of the fermentation matter. . . . Fermentation by yeast appears, therefore, to be essentially connected with the property possessed by this minute cellular plant of performing its respiratory functions, somehow or other, with the oxygen existing combined in sugar.

The same idea had been stated in an earlier paper (1861):

When yeast functions as a ferment by living apart from the influence of air, it derives oxygen from the sugar, and that is the origin of its fermentative character.

In Pasteur's day oxygen was considered an essential participant in metabolism, and therefore he thought of the yeast as using the oxygen in the sugar. Present-day conceptions are very different, being essentially as follows:

Metabolism is the transfer of groups of atoms, single atoms, or electrons from combination with one substance to combination with another. In respiration, hydrogen atoms and electrons removed from organic compounds are brought into combination with oxygen; in fermentation they are combined only with other organic compounds.

The enormous number of metabolic reactions can be classified (with a few exceptions) into about five clearly marked types, each of which is catalyzed by a different group of enzymes.

A. Hydrogen Transfer

This reaction is the transfer of two H atoms from one compound to another and is catalyzed by a group of enzymes called dehydrogenases. Many organic substances can serve as donors or acceptors

of the hydrogen atoms, but the reaction can be formulated in general
(Kluyver, 1931) as:

$$AH_2 + B \rightleftharpoons BH_2 + A \tag{1}$$

Among the examples important in microbiology may be specially
mentioned the dehydrogenation of succinic to fumaric acid, and of
lactic to pyruvic acid:

$$\begin{array}{ccc}
CH_2\text{---}COOH & \xrightarrow[\text{dehydrogenase}]{\text{succinic}} & CH\cdot COOH^1 \\
| & \rightleftharpoons & \| \\
CH_2\text{---}COOH & & CH\cdot COOH
\end{array} + 2(H) \tag{2}$$

$$CH_3CHOHCOOH \xrightarrow[\rule{2cm}{0.4pt}]{\substack{\text{lactic} \\ \text{dehydrogenase}}} CH_3CO\cdot COOH + 2(H) \tag{3}$$

If the 2(H) is used to "reduce" another metabolite (e.g., the 2[H]
from succinic dehydrogenase might, in certain conditions, reduce
pyruvic to lactic acid), the process requires no air and is therefore
fermentative.

   A characteristic of many dehydrogenases is their absolute requirement for a specific hydrogen acceptor. The most important acceptors
are the nucleotides called DPN (Chap. XI) and TPN (or NAD and
NADP). As a rule these are not exchangeable, "DPN-linked" dehydrogenases being unable to reduce TPN. The enzyme commonly
combines with one of these nucleotides, transferring 2(H). However,
alcohol dehydrogenase, which contains 4 Zn atoms, requires 4 molecules
of DPN. Succinic and lactic dehydrogenases are linked to cytochrome
B as acceptor.

   If the 2(H) is made, by means of an oxidase, to combine with
oxygen:

$$2(H) + \tfrac{1}{2} O_2 \rightarrow H_2O^2$$

then the process as a whole becomes:

$$AH_2 + \tfrac{1}{2} O_2 \rightarrow A + H_2O$$

and is an oxidation. This leads to a second definition:

   *Respiration is that part of metabolism (or that type of metabolism)
which involves the uptake of oxygen.*

---

   [1] The structural formula for fumaric acid is correctly written as:

$$\begin{array}{c}
HOOC\cdot C\cdot H \\
\| \\
H\cdot C\cdot COOH
\end{array}$$

—i.e., it is the *trans*-isomer, the corresponding *cis*-acid being maleic acid. Since we
shall have no need here to differentiate between these two substances, the formula
for fumaric acid will in general be written as above.

   [2] In some cases the combination produces hydrogen peroxide, which is then decomposed by a second reaction, but the over-all result is the same.

The terms *respiration* and *fermentation* have been terribly abused. *Respiration* was originally used to denote breathing, i.e., the process of *oxygen consumption*, but later the metabolism of strict anaerobes was called respiration, and Stephenson (1949) even used the term "respiration" to denote "any chemical reaction, aerobic or anaerobic, by which energy is liberated by the cell." In a similarly loose way, the term *fermentation* is used by industrial chemists and manufacturers to denote any microbiological process, and it is not uncommon to read of the importance of aerating the medium during a "fermentation."[3] It is evident that such use renders these terms virtually meaningless and makes both of them almost synonymous with metabolism. The definitions given above are at least consistent and have the merit of simplicity.

B. Electron Transfer

The formation of water in respiration can be viewed as the combination of hydrogen and oxygen ions:

$$2 \text{ H}^+ + \text{O}^= \rightarrow \text{H}_2\text{O}$$

The dehydrogenation, which precedes it (equations 2 and 3), really produces hydrogen ions and electrons rather than neutral (H), i.e.:

$$\text{AH}_2 \rightarrow \text{A} + 2 \text{ H}^+ + 2 \text{ e} \tag{4}$$

The role of the oxidase is therefore essentially to transfer electrons to oxygen:

$$\text{H}^+ + \tfrac{1}{2} \text{ O}_2 + 2 \text{ e} \rightarrow \text{HO}^-$$

The manner of accomplishing this, described in the next section, entails the temporary acceptance of electrons by the constituents of the oxidase, which passes them on to other constituents and finally to oxygen itself. When two electrons are transferred, the acceptor passes through an unstable state in which it has accepted one electron and is present as a free radical which can then accept a second electron (Michaelis, 1940, 1951).

Thus all oxidations, and in fact all dehydrogenations, are really electron transfers. Oxidation is often *defined* as loss of electrons.

C. Group Transfers

(1) *Transamination* is the transfer of an amino group, e.g., from aspartic acid to pyruvic acid to form alanine (cf. Chap. VIII, sec. 1):

[3] There is, however, some justification for the special use of the term *oxidative fermentation* discussed in Chapter XVI.

$$
\begin{array}{c}
\underset{\displaystyle \text{COOH}}{|} \quad \underset{\displaystyle \text{CH}_3}{|} \\
\text{CHNH}_2 \quad \text{CO} \quad \xrightleftharpoons{\text{transaminase}} \quad \text{CO} \quad \text{CHNH}_2 \\
\text{CH}_2 \; + \; \text{COOH} \qquad \text{CH}_2 \; + \; \text{COOH} \\
\text{COOH} \qquad \qquad \text{COOH}
\end{array}
\qquad (5)
$$

(2) *Transpeptidation* is the similar reversible transfer of a whole peptide unit, as the γ-glutamyl group in glutathione (Hanes *et al.*, 1952):

$$
\text{Glutamyl-cysteylglycine} + \text{Leucine} \;\underset{\text{peptidase}}{\overset{\text{trans-}}{\rightleftharpoons}}\; \text{Glutamyl-leucine} + \text{Cysteylglycine}
$$

(3) *Transphosphorylation*, one of the most important of all these transfers of radicals, is exemplified by the conversion of glucose to glucose-6-phosphate with the aid of a phosphate radical from adenosine-triphosphate (von Euler and Adler, 1935; Meyerhof and Kiessling, (1935):

$$
\text{Glucose} + \text{Adenosine-triphosphate (ATP)} \underset{}{\overset{\text{hexokinase}}{\rightleftharpoons}} \text{Glucose-6-phosphate}
$$
$$
+ \text{ Adenosine-diphosphate (ADP)}
$$

(4) *Transmethylation* and *transformylation* are transfers of "one-carbon" groups; the best example in bacteria is the formation of methionine by transfer of a methyl group (with reduction) from serine to homocysteine (Cross and Woods, 1954):

$$
\text{HOCH}_2\text{CHNH}_2\text{COOH} + \text{HS(CH}_2)_2\text{CHNH}_2\text{COOH} + 2\text{(H)} \rightleftharpoons
$$
$$
\text{CH}_3\text{S(CH}_2)_2\text{CHNH}_2\text{COOH} + \text{CH}_2\text{NH}_2\text{COOH} + \text{H}_2\text{O}
$$

Vitamin B_{12} (cyanocobalamin) catalyzes the reaction.

(5) *Transglycosidation* is the transfer of a whole glycoside unit from one sugar molecule to another, involving the interconversion of di- or polysaccharides (cf. Chap. XX). Generally, uridine-diphos-phoglucose (Chap. XII, sec. 2B) acts as coenzyme.

(6) *Transacetylation* specifically requires coenzyme A (p. 244) which accepts and releases acetyl, or other acyl groups, to form acetoacetic acid, acetyl phosphate, acetoin, etc.; e.g.:

$$
\text{CH}_3\text{CO·CoA} + \text{CH}_3\text{COOH} \rightleftharpoons \text{CH}_3\text{COCH}_2\text{COOH} + \text{CoA·H.}
$$

D. Carboxylation and Decarboxylation

These reactions establish relationship between CO_2 and the carboxyl groups of organic acids. The three outstanding examples in micro-biology (see Ochoa, 1951) are:

decarboxylation of pyruvic acid to acetaldehyde (Chap. XI):

$$CH_3COCOOH \rightarrow CH_3CHO + CO_2$$

decarboxylation of amino acids to amines (Chap. VIII):

$$RCHNH_2COOH \rightarrow RCH_2NH_2 + CO_2$$

carboxylation of pyruvic acid to oxalacetic acid (Chap. XIII):

$$CH_3COCOOH + CO_2 \rightleftharpoons HOOCCH_2COCOOH$$

This last reaction is not really a simple carboxylation but requires phosphorylation as a prerequisite; it is phosphopyruvic acid rather than pyruvic acid which is carboxylated (Utter *et al.*, 1954). In the absence of phosphorylation the equilibrium lies strongly toward the left. Alternatively, however, the reaction can be made to go from left to right by reduction of the product to malic acid, so that carboxylation and reduction occur as a single process.

$$CH_3COCOOH + CO_2 + 2(H) \rightleftharpoons HOOCCH_2CHOHCOOH$$

A still more complex process is the *oxidative decarboxylation* of pyruvic acid to produce acetic acid; this involves many steps (Chap. XII, XIV) and requires thiamine, or in some cases biotin, as coenzyme. The over-all reaction is:

$$CH_3COCOOH + \tfrac{1}{2} O_2 \rightarrow CH_3COOH + CO_2$$

The key reaction in photosynthesis is the carboxylation of ribulose-diphosphate, which results in its cleaving into two molecules of phosphoglyceric acid (Chap. XXIII, sec. 8).

E. Hydrolysis

This process is the insertion of the elements of water in the place of a chemical bond, resulting in splitting of the receptor compound. Insofar as hydrolysis can be considered as a transfer of H^+ and ^-OH, it has something in common with the group transfers, but the universal presence of water in all living systems gives hydrolysis many special qualities. Of the many examples may be mentioned:

(1) *Peptide-splitting* (Chap. VII):

$$\underset{\underset{NH_2}{|}}{RCHCO} \cdot \underset{\underset{R'}{|}}{NHCHCOOH} + H_2O \overset{peptidase}{\rightleftharpoons} \underset{\underset{NH_2}{|}}{RCHCOOH} + \underset{\underset{R'}{|}}{NH_2CHCOOH}$$

Hydrolysis of proteins is of the same type.

(2) *Ester-splitting:*

$$RCOOCH_3 + H_2O \overset{esterase}{\rightleftharpoons} RCOOH + CH_3OH$$

The lipases, hydrolyzing fats, are also to be classed as esterases.

(3) *Di- and polysaccharide-splitting:*

$$C_6H_{11}O_5\text{—O—}C_6H_{11}O_5 + H_2O \underset{\text{disaccharidase}}{\rightleftharpoons} 2\ C_6H_{12}O_6$$

Many of these enzymes are discussed in Chapter XVII.

(4) *Phosphatases:*

$$\text{Glucose-6-phosphate} + H_2O \xrightarrow[\leftarrow]{\text{hexosemono-phosphatase}} \text{Glucose} + H_3PO_4$$

Many phosphatases are not specific for the substrate but hydrolyze any compound having a certain type of bond, such as the monoesters of orthophosphoric acid. There are large numbers of phosphatases, sometimes several in the same tissue or organism.

To these five reaction types must be added the photochemical reactions which, as in photosynthesis, photo-oxidation, or luminescence, involve the uptake or emission of light energy. Chemical energy, which is always exchanged in the above reactions, will be considered next.

3. PRODUCTION AND TRANSFER OF ENERGY

A. General

The most important difference between respiration and fermentation is that in the former case the large amount of energy set free in the formation of water is made available to the process. For example, compare the energy set free in the oxidation of glucose with that set free in its fermentation:

$$C_6H_{12}O_6 + 6\ O_2 \rightarrow 6\ CO_2 + 6\ H_2O + 688,000\ cal.^{[4]}$$
$$C_6H_{12}O_6 \qquad\ \rightarrow 2\ CH_3CHOHCOOH + 58,000\ cal.^{[4]}$$
$$C_6H_{12}O_6 \qquad\ \rightarrow 2\ C_2H_5OH + 2\ CO_2 + ca.\ 57,000^{[4]}\ cal.$$

The fermentations set free only about 8 per cent of the energy of oxidation of glucose. Since the energy set free is not wasted as heat, but is in good part converted to the chemical energy of other substances, it becomes of great importance to the cell how much energy its metabolic reactions produce. The implications of this can best be appreciated after seeing how the energy is transferred.

The mechanism of energy transfer appears to be centered in a few thioesters and in a larger number of organic phosphates. The

[4] These figures are the approximate free-energy changes under biological conditions. They vary slightly according to the data used for calculation (see Kaplan, 1951).

thioesters are formed in metabolism by combination of an organic acid radical with the S atom of an enzyme mercaptan complex:

$$CH_3CO \cdot R + (E) \cdot SR' \rightleftharpoons CH_3CO \sim SR' + (E) \cdot R \tag{6}$$

Only two compounds, coenzyme A and lipoic acid, as far as is known now, form these thioesters. They are discussed in section 8 and Chapter XII.

The organic phosphates are of two kinds: (1) those that are essentially esters, like the glucose phosphates, in which the phosphate group is esterified with an alcoholic hydroxyl, e.g., $C_6H_{11}O_5$—O—H_2PO_3; in these compounds the energy of the phosphate linkage is about 3000 calories per mole, and the linkage is relatively stable; (2) those in which the phosphorus is linked with either a double-bonded carbon atom or with a second phosphorus atom (which is of course double-bonded to O). In this group the energy of the phosphate linkage is 7,000 to 14,000 calories per mole, and the linkage is unstable; these "energy-rich" bonds (Lipmann, 1941) are denoted $\sim$P. Eleven of these compounds are known so far, six of which are shown in Table V–1; the other five are the triphosphates of guanosine, uridine, inosine, thymidine, and cytidine (abbreviated GTP, UTP, ITP, TTP, and CTP) analogous to that of adenosine.

B. Substrate-level Phosphorylation

High-energy phosphate bonds are formed in two ways, namely, in fermentation reactions (see Chaps. XI and XII) and in oxidations. In the former, or "substrate-level phosphorylations," the energy of a thioester bond, formed as in equation (6) above, can be transferred to that of phosphate. Acetylphosphate is formed in this way from acetyl coenzyme A by the action of the enzyme trans-acetylase:

$$CH_3CO \sim S \cdot CoA + {}^-HPO_3 \cdot OH \rightleftharpoons CH_3COO \sim PO_3H^- + HS \cdot CoA \tag{7}$$

In another fermentative reaction type, a bond of low energy is increased to one of high energy by loss of saturation. For example, 2-phosphoglyceric acid, containing an ordinary ester bond, loses a molecule of water to become phosphoenolpyruvic acid, in which the unsaturation adjacent to the bond makes it of higher energy:

$$
\begin{array}{ccc}
CH_2OH & & CH_2 \\
| & & \parallel \\
HC\!-\!O \cdot HPO_3^- & \xrightarrow{-H_2O} & C \sim O \cdot HPO_3^- \\
| & & | \\
COO^- & & COO^-
\end{array}
\tag{8}
$$

TABLE V–1. The High-Energy Phosphate Compounds

Type	Name	Formula

In this case the energy of the dehydration reaction becomes concentrated in the phosphate bond. Many energy-rich phosphate bonds ultimately become transferred to GTP, UTP, CTP, or especially ATP which is used as a "currency" for exchange (see "transphosphorylation" above).

The energy of the phosphate bond is finally transferred to a carbon-

carbon bond and thus brings about synthesis. Biological syntheses making use of phosphate-bond energy include the synthesis of protein, of nucleic acids, of polysaccharides, of glutathione, glutamine, and arginine; phosphate also energizes the reduction of carboxyl to aldehyde. The energy of the sulfur bond is utilized in the transfer of acetyl groups, as in the synthesis of citric acid (Fig. V–14) and the formation and breakdown of fats.

C. Oxidative Phosphorylation

In facultative organisms, growth is always far more vigorous under aerobic than anaerobic conditions, and this is doubtless because of the phosphate-bond energy made available by respiration. The equations above show that the energy yield of lactic or alcoholic fermentation of glucose is only enough to produce four high-energy phosphate bonds, whereas its complete oxidation can produce 30 to 40. It was Pasteur who first noted with yeast that aerobic conditions favored growth, while anaerobic conditions led to faster utilization of sugar. The increased sugar metabolism in the absence of oxygen is still called the Pasteur effect (see Chap. XI, sec. 11).

The mechanism whereby oxidation energy is converted to phosphate-bond energy is centered in the cytochrome system and in the oxidation and reduction of a group of quinones, interrelated with it (see the next section).

In contrast to the high energy yielded by oxidations, and the moderate energy of fermentations, very little energy is set free in hydrolytic reactions. Hence few organisms can *grow* by the energy of hydrolysis alone.

In considering the energy set free or absorbed in chemical reactions, it is important to distinguish the total heat of reaction $(-\Delta H)$ from the free energy of reaction $(-\Delta F)$, which is the maximum amount of work obtainable from the reaction and is in general less. Only $-\Delta F$ measures the chemical energy available. The free energy yielded by any given reaction depends on the temperature, pressure of gases, and concentration of solutes reacting. For many biological reactions it is within 20 per cent of the heat of reaction. Some examples are:

$$CH_{4(gas)} + 2\ O_{2(gas)} \rightarrow CO_{2(gas)} + 2\ H_2O_{(liquid)}$$
$$-\Delta H = 212,600\ \text{cal.}$$
$$-\Delta F = 194,600\ \text{cal.}$$

$$C_6H_{12}O_{6(solid)} + 6\ O_{2(gas,\ 0.2\ atm.)} \rightarrow 6\ CO_{2(gas\ 0.0003\ atm)} + 6\ H_2O_{(liquid)}$$
$$-\Delta H = 674,000\ \text{cal.}$$
$$-\Delta F = 688,000\ \text{cal.}$$

4. THE CYTOCHROME SYSTEM

A. Discovery

The materials causing oxidation are of three types, namely, (1) enzymes combining with oxygen, i.e., oxidases; (2) enzymes combining with hydrogen, i.e., dehydrogenases; and (3) linking substances. Of the oxidases, the cytochrome oxidase, which together with cytochrome comprises the cytochrome system, is the most important.

The action of the cytochrome system was discovered by Warburg through a study of the resemblance between biological oxidations and

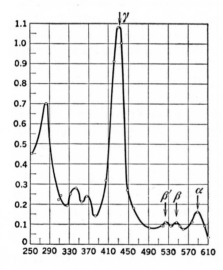

Figure V–1

Action spectrum of the reversal of CO inhibition of respiration by light. Abscissa: wave length in mμ. Ordinate: relative absorption, determined from the respiration in CO and O_2. *Acetobacter rancens*, var. *pasteurianum*. (From F. Kubowitz and E. Haas, *Biochem. Z.*, **255**:247–277, 1932. By courtesy of O. Warburg.)

the oxidations catalyzed by blood charcoal. These latter are dependent on the iron in the charcoal, which comes from the hemin in the blood, and because of this they are inhibited by cyanide (which forms stable ferro- and ferricyanides) and by CO (which forms stable carbonyls). The same is true of biological oxidations. Because the carbonyls are decomposed by light, Warburg and his coworkers tested the effect of light on bacterial respiration that had been inhibited by CO; the inhibition could be completely prevented. By comparing the effectiveness of different wavelengths of light, they could determine the extent to which each was absorbed and thus plot the absorption spectrum of the oxidation enzyme, although it is present only in virtually invisible traces (Fig. V–1). The resulting spectrum is closely similar to those of the hemin derivatives. Similar results for several aerobic organisms have shown that oxygen consumption is almost universally catalyzed by an enzyme of the hemin type, present only in traces and inhibitable by iron-combining reagents. The significance

TABLE V–2. Absorption Bands of Reduced Cytochrome Components

COMPONENT	OCCURRENCE	WAVELENGTH IN Mμ		
Cytochromes		α-Band	β-Band	γ-Band
a	Muscle, yeast	604	530	445
a_1	E. coli, etc.	590	522–530	442
a_1CO cpd.		590	540	427
b	Muscle, yeast	564	530	432
b_1	E. coli, C. diptheriae, Ps. denitrificans	559	528	426
b_2	Yeast	556	528	424
b_5	Insects, microsomes	557	527	426
c	Heart muscle	550	521	416*
c_1	Heart muscle, Ps. denitrificans, yeast	553	523	418*
$c_{(553)}$	Ps. aeruginosa†	553	520	416
c_4	} Azotob. vinelandii {	551	522	416
c_5		555	526	420
f	Green leaves	555		
h	Snails	556	526.5	422
Oxidases				
a_2	E. coli	630‡		§
a_2CO cpd.		635		
a_2CN cpd.		636		
a_3	Heart muscle	600		445
a_3CO cpd.		590		426
a_3CN cpd.		590		432
c_3	Desulfovibrio	553	525	419
"Bacterial cytochrome oxidase"	M. albus, Proteus vulgaris			440
CO cpd.		567	535	418

* 408 in oxidized form.

† Bands correspond to those of c_1, but this cytochrome does not interact with the mammalian system (Kamen and Takeda, 1956).

‡ 645 in oxidized form.

§ a_2 has no γ-band.

of the iron is that it can change valency from ferric to ferrous; since ferrous salts are easily oxidized by air, it is deduced that the ferric iron of the hemin is reduced to ferrous by the organic matter of the cell and reoxidized by oxygen.

A group of spectral bands, like those of the oxidizing enzyme but multiple in nature, can be directly seen when actively metabolizing cells are temporarily deprived of oxygen. Keilin (1925) saw them in the muscles of the bee and the moth when the insect was active, but they disappeared on resting. Because they appeared also when the insect was surrounded by nitrogen or hydrogen, Keilin deduced that the bands are due to the substances in the reduced form, and that their disappearance may be due to a change into an oxidized form that has no marked absorption bands. There are five absorption bands visible, three spaced (α-bands) and a pair very close together (β-bands). During rest the three main (or α) bands disappeared separately; they must therefore belong to three separate substances, each of which has one α band. Keilin named them cytochromes a, b, c. In addition, each has a γ-band in the violet which absorbs much more strongly than the others (see Table V–2). The bands ascribed to cytochrome c have subsequently been found to be due to two components, c and c_1, which interact. When c is extracted with salt solutions, c_1 is left behind, and its spectrum can be observed directly.

Microorganisms often contain modified forms of cytochromes a, b, and c (a_1, a_2, etc.) with absorption peaks at varied wavelengths (see below). Chemically they are all closely related, being hemin proteins.

The essential property of the cytochromes is that cell metabolism readily reduces them to the ferrous form, while in air they are rapidly reoxidized. Thus they play an important part in cellular oxidations, and Keilin deduced that the system acts as a respiratory catalyst, conducting metabolic hydrogen to oxygen of the air.

B. Distinction between Cytochromes and Cytochrome Oxidase

When KCN is added to a tissue in which the cytochromes are in the oxidized state, the reduced bands at once appear; KCN, therefore, inhibits the oxidation of the cytochromes but does not prevent their being reduced. Even if air is bubbled through the cell suspension, the cytochromes are not oxidized. Carbon monoxide (in the dark) behaves like KCN.

Opposite to the behavior of CO and KCN is that of alcohol, formalin, or ethyl urethane, $NH_2COOC_2H_5$; these Keilin and Hartree (1939) found to prevent the appearance of the bands. Cautious heating to 52° C had the same effect. It follows that the mechanism for *reducing* the cytochromes, though unaffected by CO and KCN, is inhibited by alcohol, etc. Correspondingly the CO and KCN must be *inhibiting the mechanism for oxidizing the cytochromes*. Since the oxidizing enzyme (oxidase) was seen above to be also a hemin protein, it follows that the visible cytochromes are not themselves oxidases, but are intermediates, and that the oxidase is *another* hemin protein very similar to the cytochromes.

Visual evidence for the difference between the cytochromes and the oxidase comes from studying the absorption bands. Figure V–1 shows the α-band of the CO-oxidase compound to be at 592 mμ. Thick suspensions of the bacteria show at this point a weak visible band, which goes back in air to a position where it is overlapped by that of cytochrome a (Warburg, 1934, and later). In CO a new visible γ-band appears also, at about 430 mμ (Fig. V–1). Thus the oxidase bands are normally overlapped by those of cytochrome a, but shift slightly on combining with CO. Recent measurements of the band intensities under different conditions show that 50 per cent of the band at 445 mμ and 25 per cent of that at 605 mμ are due to the oxidase, the remainder to cytochrome a (Yonetani, 1960). Because its bands are so close to those of a, the oxidase is referred to as cytochrome a_3.

Although the bands of a_3 also shift in cyanide, they still disappear on aeration, but they now no longer reappear in reducing conditions; thus cyanide must have "stabilized this component in the oxidized state" (Keilin and Hartree, 1939). In other words, it is in the ferric form that the cyanide compound is stable. Conversely, the CO compound is the ferrous form.

The function of the oxidase a_3 is specifically to catalyze the oxidation of the cytochromes. It reacts with no other substrate and hence is termed *cytochrome oxidase*. In addition to iron, it contains an atom of copper per molecule (Wainio *et al.*, 1959, and earlier work there cited). It may be that it is the presence of the *two* metals that makes it oxidizable by O_2, while the other cytochromes are only oxidized (rapidly) by the ferric form of the oxidase.[5]

The oxidized cytochromes are in turn reduced by a group of *cytochrome reductases* (and also by the specific dehydrogenases of formic, lactic, and succinic acids). Only one cytochrome is directly reduced, usually b or c_1, and only one is oxidized by the oxidase; the others are reduced or oxidized indirectly, so that the cytochromes are a chain of compounds passing electrons from one to the other. In each step an iron compound becomes reduced from the ferric to the ferrous state:

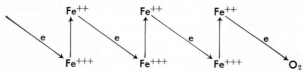

[5] The copper of cytochrome oxidase does not itself change valency, however, during oxidation.

C. The Pathway of Oxidation

The ultimate source of the electrons is, of course, the substrate. For most substrates the dehydrogenases reduce DPN or TPN, and the reduced forms of these in turn reduce a special dehydrogenase, *cytochrome reductase* or *diaphorase*, a flavoprotein (see Table V–5). This reduces the cytochromes. An additional substance which may be an intermediate here is *coenzyme Q* or *ubiquinone*. This material is a benzoquinone derivative with the structure:

$$CH_3O\quad CH_3\quad CH_3$$
$$CH_3O \qquad (CH_2CH{=}C{\cdot}CH_2)_nH$$

The number of C_5 (isoprene) units, n, in the side chain varies, being 10 in heart muscle, Neurospora, and *Ps. denitrificans* (Page *et al.*, 1960), 9 in some other pseudomonads, 7 or 8 in various bacteria, and 6 in yeast. Basidiomycetes do not contain CoQ but have a related compound instead, and aerobic gram-positive bacteria use vitamin K, a naphthoquinone, in its place (Bishop *et al.*, 1962). The yeast compound has been synthesized (Gloor *et al.*, 1958). Like other quinones, it is readily reduced to the quinol, QH_2. However, CoQ's position and function in the chain are both unclear as yet.

In the animal cell the cytochromes occur in a special body, the mitochondrion, and in bacteria they are also in a special structure, namely, the membrane. In this they are apparently bound up with phospholipids. In intact mitochondria direct observations of the time sequence of oxidations (Chance and Williams, 1956) show that the electrons from DPNH and cytochrome reductase reduce the *b* component first, making the sequence:

$$DPNH \rightarrow reductase \rightarrow b \rightarrow c_1 \rightarrow c \rightarrow a \rightarrow a_3 \rightarrow O_2$$

However, in the case of succinic, lactic, and (probably) formic dehydrogenases, DPNH does not participate since the dehydrogenase itself contains a flavin which directly acts upon a cytochrome of the *b* group attached to it. Isolated lactic, succinic, and formic dehydrogenases consist of complexes with cytochromes—succinic with *b*, from Propionibacterium (Lara, 1959); lactic with b_2, from yeast (Boeri and Tosi, 1956; Appleby and Morton, 1959; Morton, 1961); and formic with a b_1 which can be directly oxidized by air (Wrigley and Linnane, 1961; Itagaki *et al.*, 1961).

A complication noted above is that cytochrome c is dual; its two constituents, c_1 and c, are very similar (see Table V–2). Particles can be prepared that contain c_1 but not c and in which the c_1 is reduced by CoQ (Rabinowitz and de Bernard, 1957), by succinate, or by DPNH, in presence of suitable enzymes (Bomstein *et al.*, 1960). Since coenzyme Q can itself be reduced both by succinate (via succinic dehydrogenase) and by other substrates (*via* the cytochrome reductases), it follows that CoQ may lie on the pathway from both types of substrate to cytochrome c_1 (Green *et al.*, 1959; Hatefi *et al.*, 1961). Thus the whole system, in intact phosphorylating mitochondria, would be:

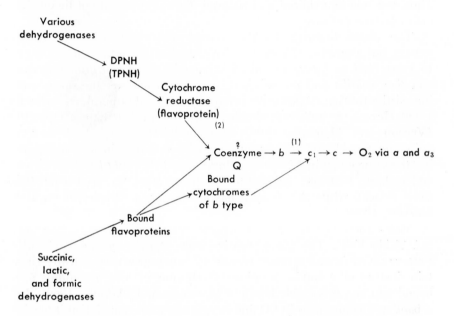

(In some conditions one or more of the steps may perhaps be by-passed.)

The reducing (left-hand) end of the scheme receives support from inhibitor studies. An antibiotic, *antimycin a*, prevents the oxidation of b but not of c or c_1 and is therefore thought to act at (1) in the diagram above (Chance and Williams, 1956); it also inhibits the oxidation of CoQ but not its reduction, which fits this site of action (Ramasarma and Lester, 1960). The drug amobarbital inhibits the reduction of CoQ by DPN-linked dehydrogenases ("CoQ reductase" of Hatefi *et al.*, 1961) but not by succinate, which places its site of action at (2) and confirms the branched pathway. The oxidizing (right-hand) end is still uncertain, however. The straight line sequence has usually been accepted, although Okunuki in 1940 had evidence against it; however,

Yonetani (1960), using purified preparations of the separate constituents, and ascorbic acid as a reducing agent, has found that the ascorbate can reduce a and a_3; but in order for them to be reoxidized rapidly, c must be added, i.e., c must mediate between a and a_3. Sekuzu *et al.* (1960) also find that purified a is only oxidized when c is added. These data point to the sequence:

$$\rightarrow c_1 \rightarrow c \rightarrow a_3 \rightarrow O_2$$
$$\text{\textuparrow\textdownarrow}$$
$$a$$

Thus, a would be oxidized and reduced like c, yet would not lie on the main electron pathway.

The above findings mainly concern the cytochromes of heart muscle, but a number of aerobic microorganisms have the same system. In yeast, *Sarcina lutea*, several Mycobacteria, *Rhodospirillum rubrum*, and *Bac. subtilis* and *megaterium*, the system appears the same, and indeed the two bacilli, after disruption by sonic vibration, have yielded a cytochrome c indistinguishable from the mammalian compound (Vernon and Mangum, 1960). The inhibitor 2 heptyl-4-hydroxy-quinoline-N-oxide, which prevents the oxidation of b in muscle tissue, has the same effect in *M. aureus*, *Proteus*, and *Bac. subtilis* (Lightbown and Jackson, 1956–58). Among the streptomycetes, *Str. griseus* has the same system, while *Str. fradiae* has a different a (Niederpruem and Hackett, 1959).

Many bacteria have quite divergent cytochrome systems, however (cf. Table V–2). The gram-negative cells, *Aerob. aerogenes*, *E. coli*, *Proteus vulgaris*, and *Azotob. vinelandii*, when grown aerobically contain, instead of a and a_3, another cytochrome, a_2, which contains one bound and one dissociable hemin (Yamanaka and Okunuki, 1962). Its α band at 630 mμ shifts in CO and in cyanide, and on oxidation it moves to 645 mμ. For these reasons it is evidently an oxidase (Keilin and Harpley, 1941; Tissières, 1951). Most of these bacteria contain a small amount of another a, called a_1 with its α band at 590 mμ, and also of another of b type called b_1 at 650 mμ, usually in amount some four times as much as the a_2. *Azotob. vinelandii* has two c type cytochromes, c_4 and c_5, with bands at 551 and 555 mμ (Tissières and Burris, 1956), and these may perhaps function like c and c_1 in the heart muscle system; *Ps. aeruginosa* may also contain c_1. In *E. coli* no c is present, if grown aerobically, and added c is not oxidized by either intact or crushed bacteria; its system is thus:

$$\text{DPNH} \rightarrow \text{Reductase} \rightarrow b_1 \rightarrow (a_1 \rightarrow)a_2 \rightarrow O_2$$

The a_2–b_1 system, with or without members of the c group, is widely distributed in bacteria (see Smith, 1954).

M. *"Staph." albus, Str. fradiae*, and some others have a third type of oxidase, combining with CO and cyanide, with the α band at about 570 mμ (Smith, 1954). Two further cytochromes, f and h, are acidic, but these have not yet been identified in bacteria.

A complicating factor is that the cytochrome complement of an organism often changes with the growth conditions. Yeast grown in air has a, b and c; anaerobically it has a_1 and b_1 (Chap. XX, sec. 5). *Bac. cereus* grown anaerobically loses its a and c and much of its b, and excretes a porphyrin (perhaps a cytochrome precursor) into the medium (Schaeffer, 1952). *E. coli* and related forms, when grown anaerobically, form a c type cytochrome which is not in the membrane, but soluble (Gray *et al.*, 1963). Mutations in the system occur, too; a mutant of *Coryneb. diphtheriae* has a cytochrome b (with peak at 558 mμ) which is reduced by succinate and directly oxidized by O_2 without intervention of the oxidase (Pappenheimer *et al.*, 1962).

One of the most unexpected findings is the presence of a cytochrome which reacts with oxygen in the strict anaerobe *Desulfovibrio* (Postgate, 1956). This substance, cytochrome c_3, is reduced by lactate and malate and can be reoxidized not only by O_2, but also by sulfite or thiosulfate (Chap. XVIII); the latter reoxidants are important in its normal physiology. Other cytochromes operate with nitrite and nitrate (Chap. X). One of the cytochromes participates in the photosynthetic process in purple and green bacteria (Chap. XXIII). We may conclude that the cytochrome system is a flexible means of electron transfer, subject to a number of variations and adapted in the course of evolution to many modes of life.

It was mentioned that in muscle cells the cytochromes are located in mitochondria; these are about the size of bacteria. In bacteria the role of mitochondria is taken instead by the cell membrane, which in *Bac. megaterium* contains the whole cytochrome system (Weibull *et al.*, 1959). More than 90 per cent of the cytochromes of *M. aureus* are located in the membrane, as well as the dehydrogenases for succinic, lactic and several other acids (Mitchell, 1959). The remaining 10 per cent, at least in Pseudomonas and Azotobacter, remains in true solution (Eagan and Williams, 1959); it contains cytochromes a_2 and c_1.

It has been suggested that both mitochondrion and bacterial membrane are composed of the same ultimate particles; mitochondria may indeed be broken up into minute "electron transfer particles," each of which contains the whole cytochrome system (Crane *et al.*, 1956). The bacterial membrane particles are like mitochondria in being rich in fatty material (about 40 per cent lipid and 20 per cent protein) and correspondingly their cytochromes are set free by lipase. The similarity is certainly suggestive. Perhaps bacteria and mitochondria are common evolutionary descendants of a primitive oxidizing complex.

Little has yet been said thus far as to how these oxidations generate ATP to provide energy for syntheses. This problem is still unsolved even in muscle tissue, whose cytochromes have been far more studied than those of bacteria (see Lehninger and Wadkins, 1962). Many electron transfer particles not only convert phosphate ions to ATP, they also exchange phosphate between ADP and ATP, and hydrolyze ATP. These effects seems to be interwoven. Fragments of membranes of *M. lysodeikticus* can perform all of these reactions, and while they are oxidizing DPNH, they make ATP in equimolar amounts (Ishikawa and Lehninger, 1962). If now put in distilled water they lose the ability to phosphorylate (though they can still oxidize), and instead they release a soluble protein. This protein has all the above phosphate-metabolizing reactions, and, when added back to the water-treated particles, restores their phosphorylating power; it is thus a "coupling factor." Several such coupling factors occur in muscle. *Alcaligenes fecalis* extracts also contain one, and here its action is better understood, since it is bound to the oxidase particles (Ox) by a nucleotide plus Mg^{++} (Shibko and Pinchot, 1961). When C^{14}-DPNH is used, the C^{14} is transferred to the soluble coupling factor (F), and this DPN binding is probably of high energy (Pinchot and Hormanski, 1962). Phosphate ions (P_i) replace the DPN with a high-energy phosphate bond; this forms ATP, and the liberated factor, F, can then, with the help of Mg, recombine with the oxidase, Ox, to reconstitute the intact oxidase (Ox·Mg·F), thus:

$$Ox \cdot Mg \cdot F + DPNH + H^+ + \tfrac{1}{2}\, O_2 \rightarrow DPN \sim F + H_2O + Ox \cdot Mg$$
$$DPN \sim F + P_i \rightleftharpoons P \sim F + DPN$$
$$P \sim F + ADP \rightleftharpoons F + ATP$$
$$F + Ox \cdot Mg \rightleftharpoons Ox \cdot Mg \cdot F$$

Pinchot's scheme explains well the phosphorylation that is linked to DPNH oxidation, but there are at least two other phosphorylating steps, probably lying between cytochromes b and c, and between C and O_2 (cf. Table V–7). What goes on there remains unknown.

5. THE DEHYDROGENASES OF BACTERIA

Early studies of the oxidation of succinic to fumaric acid by washed muscle showed that the reaction can proceed in the absence of oxygen if methylene blue is added, the methylene blue being rapidly reduced to the colorless leuco-compound (Thunberg, 1916). This experiment was afterward extended to a general method for the study of dehydrogenations, the procedure being to determine the time for the blue mixture to become colorless under given conditions and in the absence of oxygen. Alternatively, the actual rate of decolorization can be determined by putting the tube from time to time in a colorimeter. The more active the enzyme, the more rapidly will decolorization ensue.

By simply watching the rate of reduction of the dye, Thunberg with washed muscle, and later Harden, Quastel, and others with washed bacteria as source of enzyme were able to study the dehydrogenation of a number of organic compounds. In particular a washed and aerated suspension of *E. coli* could reduce methylene blue with many different substrates (Quastel and Whetham, 1924–1925). In the case of succinic acid, the hydrogen transfer was shown to be strictly reversible, because if fumarate is added from the side-arm of the evacuated tube, after the methylene blue has been reduced, the color returns:

$$\begin{matrix} CH_2COOH \\ | \\ CH_2COOH \end{matrix} + MB \underset{\text{dehydrogenase}}{\overset{\text{succinic}}{\rightleftharpoons}} \begin{matrix} CHCOOH \\ || \\ CHCOOH \end{matrix} + MBH_2$$

The extent to which the reaction will go depends on the dissociation constant:

$$K = \frac{[fum][MBH_2]}{[succ][MB]} = ca.\ 3.0\ at\ 45°\ C\ and\ pH\ 7.2$$

where the brackets indicate concentrations, and changes in dissociation of H^+ from carboxyl groups have been neglected.

TABLE V–3. Reduction Times of Methylene Blue by Washed *E. coli* after Various Treatments

(From Quastel and Wooldridge, 1927)

	Normal	After 5 Min in Toluene	After 1 Hr at pH 3.8	After 1 Hr at 67° C
Succinic	9	10	83	∞
Lactic	6	7	24	∞
Formic	3	3	5	18
Acetic	4	5	16	26
α-hydroxybutyric	8	24	66	∞
Fructose	4	107	16	∞
Glucose	4	∞	16	∞

The fact that there are many separate, specific enzymes can be shown by exposing the bacteria to unfavorable conditions, such as high temperatures, extreme pH, or various organic liquids. These treatments inactivate some but not all of the enzymes, as shown in Table V–3; it is clear that the enzymes for the simple organic acids are not affected by toluene, while those for the carbohydrates are almost completely destroyed. The enzymes for succinic, lactic, and hydroxybutyric acids are more sensitive to acidity and heat than those for formic and acetic acids; the enzyme(s) for glucose and fructose are relatively resistant to acidity but sensitive to toluene and so on. There must therefore be a large number of individual dehydrogenases, each of which is capable of reacting with one or only a very few substrates.

TABLE V–4. Inhibition of Lactic Dehydrogenase of _E. coli_ by Structurally Related Compounds

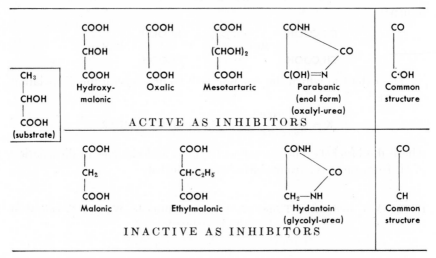

The specificity was also shown by experiments with inhibitors (Quastel and Wooldridge, 1928). For example, using toluene-treated _E. coli_ as a source of succinic dehydrogenase, malonic, phenylpropionic, and methyl succinic acids retard the reduction of methylene blue. Similarly, oxalic, hydroxymalonic, and mesotartaric acids retard the dye reduction when lactic acid is the substrate. The obvious interpretation is that these substances are adsorbed at the enzyme, but, since they are not activated there, they prevent it from acting upon its normal substrate. There is a strong structural relationship between the compounds that are adsorbed at a given enzyme; for the lactic dehydrogenase these are shown in Table V–4. It can be seen that hydroxymalonic and oxalic acids are inhibitory, i.e., strongly adsorbed at the enzyme, while malonic and ethylmalonic acids have no effect. The oxalic acid derivative, parabanic acid, also actively inhibits, while the corresponding reduced compound, hydantoin, has no effect. Consideration of the formulas of the inhibitors shows that, in order to be adsorbed at the lactic acid enzyme, a molecule must have the structure—CO·C(OH) shown at the end. Similar experiments with succinic dehydrogenase indicate that the adsorbable structure for this enzyme is —C—CH—COOH. In accordance with this, the purified succinic dehydrogenase from muscle attacks only methyl and ethyl succinic acids in addition to its substrate, and these but slowly (Franke and Siewerdt, 1944). Malonic, maleic and oxalacetic acids inhibit.

Most of these inhibitions are competitive, i.e., the substrate, if its concentration is high enough, can displace the inhibitor.

The algebraic treatment of these inhibitions, by Michaelis and Menten (1913), is helpful. It is based on the idea that an enzyme E combines reversibly with its substrate S to produce a compound ES which then breaks down to produce the product(s) P. The rate constants for the three reactions are k_1, k_2, and k_3;

$$E + S \underset{k_1}{\overset{k_2}{\rightleftharpoons}} ES \overset{k_3}{\rightarrow} E + P$$

The rate at which P is formed is proportional to the concentration of ES, which in turn depends on the concentrations of E and S;

$$k_2[E][S] - k_1[ES] = k_3[ES]$$

where the bracketed terms are concentrations.

If the total enzyme is E_T then the concentration of *free* enzyme is $[E_T - ES]$, hence

$$k_2[E_T - ES][S] = [k_1 + k_3][ES]$$

This gives three useful expressions, (9), (10) and (11):

$$\frac{[E_T - ES][S]}{[ES]} = \frac{k_1 + k_3}{k_2} \text{ which is termed } K_m \qquad (9)$$

(m for Michaelis).

Hence
$$\frac{[E_T - ES]}{[ES]} = \frac{K_m}{[S]} \qquad (10)$$

and
$$\frac{[E_T]}{[ES]} - 1 = \frac{K_m}{[S]} \quad \text{whence} \quad \frac{[E_T]}{[ES]} = \frac{[S] + K_m}{[S]} \qquad (11)$$

or
$$\frac{[ES]}{[E_T]} = \frac{[S]}{[S] + K_m} \qquad (11a)$$

Now since the rate depends on $[ES]$, it becomes maximal when $[ES]$ approaches $[E_T]$, i.e., the enzyme has *maximal affinity* for its substrate. The ratio in (11a) is then the ratio of the observed rate, V, to the maximum possible, V_{max}, or:

$$\frac{V}{V_{max}} = \frac{[S]}{[S] + K_m} \tag{12}$$

When $V = \frac{1}{2} V_{max}$, then $K_m = [S]$.

Thus *the affinity constant K_m is the concentration of substrate needed for half maximum velocity.*

Inverting (12) and rearranging:

$$V_{max} \cdot \frac{1}{V} = 1 + \frac{1}{[S]} K_m$$

Since V_{max} is a constant:

$$\frac{1}{V} \propto \frac{1}{[S]} \tag{13}$$

Hence, a plot of $\frac{1}{V}$ against $\frac{1}{[S]}$ gives a straight line (Lineweaver and Burk, 1934). The intercept of this line on the ordinate is $\frac{1}{V_{max}}$ and the slope is $K_m \cdot \frac{1}{V_{max}}$; the intercept on the base line is $-\frac{1}{K_m}$ (see Fig. V–2).

Now if an inhibitor, *I*, is present, then the enzyme participates in a new reaction

$$E + I \rightleftharpoons EI$$

and equation (10) is modified to:

$$\frac{[E_T - ES - EI]}{[ES]} = \frac{K_i}{[S]}$$

where K_i is the rate constant for the inhibited reaction. Since V is now decreased, $\frac{1}{V}$ is now greater than before. But if the inhibition is "competitive," S displaces I at the enzyme, so that if $[S]$ be made high enough, the reaction rate becomes as great as without the inhibitor. Thus a plot of $\frac{1}{V}$ against $\frac{1}{S}$ in the presence of an inhibitor yields a second straight line, *above* the first, but intersecting it at the same value of $\frac{1}{V_{max}}$ (Fig. V–2).

That the lines intersect at the same $\frac{1}{V_{max}}$ is then *a test for competitive inhibition.*

In the case of succinic dehydrogenase, the situation is envisaged in Figure V–3; the distance between the two points that combine with the carboxyl fits the structure of succinate, but can also accommodate malonate. The enzyme, which contains both cytochrome and flavoprotein, is also inactivated by reagents that combine with —SH groups, such as organic mercury compounds, etc. (see Chap. XXIV, sec. 1). If, however, the enzyme be treated with these reagents in the presence of either succinate or malonate, it is protected against inactivation (Hopkins *et al.*, 1938). This means that the —SH group has been covered up (Fig. V–3). Thus, when the succinate combines at the two carboxyl points, it passes its 2H to the SH group, which somehow passes them on to the acceptor (cytochrome *b*). Malonate is con-

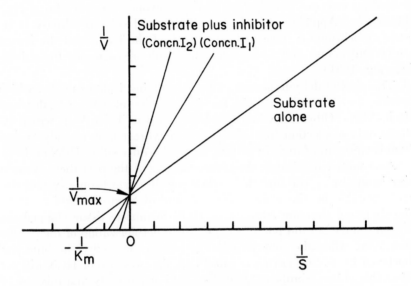

FIGURE V–2

Lineweaver-Burk plot of reciprocal of reaction rate (V) against reciprocal of substrate concentration (S). The two upper lines show the effects of a competitive inhibitor at concentrations I_1, and I_2; at infinitely high substrate concentration $\left(\frac{1}{S} \to 0\right)$, their inhibiting effects disappear.

FIGURE V–3

Structure of succinic dehydrogenase as envisaged by V. R. Potter and K. P. Dubois (*J. Gen. Physiol.*, **26**:391–404, 1942; modified).

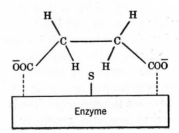

sidered to combine at the same points, and although it cannot yield 2H, it covers up the SH group just as well as succinate. This diagram does not, however, explain why the product is fumarate rather than maleate.

The formic acid enzyme, which, it will be noted (Table V–3), is one of the least affected by adverse treatment, is of special interest because of its complex relations with hydrogen gas (see Chap. XIV, sec. 4).

The lactic dehydrogenase has been prepared from several bacteria and crystallized from yeast; besides L-lactate, it acts on glycollate, β-hydroxybutyrate, and less actively on glycerate. As noted above, the crystalline enzyme contains not only a flavoprotein, but also a cytochrome, b_2 (Appleby and Morton, 1959), and correspondingly it reduces cytochrome c. Two molecules each of the flavin and the hemin are present in one enzyme molecule, and both are necessary for activity (Morton, 1961).

The alcohol dehydrogenase of yeast contains 4 atoms of Zn, which provide the combining points for 4 molecules of DPN (Vallee and Hoch, 1955). Other dehydrogenases are listed in Table V–5, which includes only a selection from the 80-odd dehydrogenases already known from bacteria and fungi. In general they all reduce either DPN or TPN.

As a matter of history, the understanding of the part these systems play in the living cell and their relation to the cytochrome system was made possible by the work of Fleisch and of Szent-Györgyi in 1924. Fleisch found that the addition of HCN to muscle tissue stopped the oxygen uptake but did not affect the rate of decolorization of methylene blue. Also, when the time required to reduce the methylene blue was shortened by adding citrate or succinate, the presence of HCN did not affect this either. Similarly, Szent-Györgyi added KCN to a mixture of tissue and succinate. The oxygen uptake, which had been vigorous, at once stopped. When methylene blue was added, the oxygen uptake started again (Fig. V–4). The methylene blue was now evidently being reduced by the tissue and reoxidized by the air. Since there was no stoichiometric relationship between the number of moles of cyanide and of methylene blue, the dye cannot act by combining chemically with the cyanide, so that there must be two distinct systems—one, involving oxygen and inhibited by KCN (i.e., the cytochromes and their oxidase), and the other independent of oxygen and unaffected by KCN. The latter is the dehydrogenase.

The carriers of electrons between the reduced DPN or TPN and the cytochrome system are the *cytochrome reductases* or diaphorases. These are flavoproteins (see below) and are specific for their substrates. Carriers are also generally needed between the dehydrogenases and methylene blue, but they can be demonstrated only when the enzymes are carefully purified. They are generally also flavoproteins.

In addition to the "straight" dehydrogenases listed in Table V–5, there are three dehydrogenase systems of a peculiar type, which simultaneously cause loss of CO_2. They act on pyruvic, α-ketoglutaric, and malic acids, doubtless in the form of their anions.

The *pyruvate* oxidizing system, which is present in many bacteria, catalyzes the over-all reaction:

$$CH_3COCOO^- + \tfrac{1}{2}\ O_2 \rightarrow CH_3COO^- + CO_2$$

The complete system requires for its action (1) inorganic phosphate; (2) Mg, Mn, or Co; (3) an oxidase to react with O_2—this is flavin-adenine-dinucleotide-protein; (4) the coenzymes, lipoic acid, coenzyme A, thiamine-pyrophosphate, and DPN. The system is detailed in

FIGURE V–4

Respiration of muscle tissue. On addition of cyanide, respiration virtually ceases; on addition of methylene blue, it returns almost to original rate. Abscissa: minutes; ordinate: O_2 consumed. (From Szent-Györgyi, *Biochem. Z.,* **150**:195–210, 1924.)

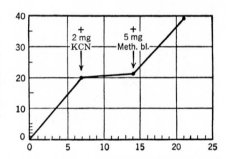

Chapter XII. The α-*ketoglutarate* enzyme acts in a similar way, and the products are succinate and CO_2.

The *"malic enzyme,"* which has been extensively purified from *L. arabinosus* (strain 17-5) (Korkes *et al.,* 1950), converts malate to pyruvate, 2(H), and CO_2, or vice versa. The acceptor or donor for the 2H is DPN. Moreover, the enzyme preparation contains L-lactate dehydrogenase; thus, the over-all reaction is the conversion of malate to lactate and CO_2:

$$\begin{array}{ccc} \mathrm{CHOH\cdot COOH} & \mathrm{CO\cdot COO^- + 2(H)} & \mathrm{CHOH\cdot COO^-} \\ | & \rightarrow\ | & \rightarrow\ | \\ \mathrm{CH_2\cdot COO^-} & \mathrm{CH_3\quad + CO_2} & \mathrm{CH_3\qquad + CO_2} \end{array}$$

The two enzymes appear to be bound together in one complex, so that the pyruvate is not set free but is reduced immediately to lactate (Kaufman *et al.,* 1951). Curiously enough, the incompletely purified preparation also contains a D-lactic dehydrogenase, so that a mixture of D- and L-lactic acids can be formed.

TABLE V-5. Some Dehydrogenases of Microbes

No.	H Donor (substrate)	Organism	H Acceptor	Properties	Inhibited by
			1. "ORDINARY" DEHYDROGENASES		
1	Formic	Coliform bacteria	Cytochrome b	Insoluble	O₂
2	Alcohol (also glycerol and some other alcohols)	Yeast, Acetobacter, E. coli	DPN (yeast); TPN (bacteria)	Sol., cryst.* Contains 4 Zn atoms and —SH groups	Iodoacetate, chelating agents
3	D-Lactic	Several bacteria	DPN	Soluble	See Table V-4
4	L-Malic	E. coli	DPN	Sol. (does not attack citric). Requires Mn	Oxalacetate
5	L-Isocitric	Fungi, bacteria	DPN or TPN		Iodoacetate
6	L(+)Glutamic	Yeast, E. coli, Neurospora	TPN†	Soluble; exists in several different forms	Temp. below 35° C in one strain of Neurospora
7	Glucose-6-phosphate (= 6-phosphoglucose)	Yeast	TPN	Soluble. Makes 6-phosphogluconic acid (Warburg's Zwischenferment)	Phosphate
8	6-phosphogluconic	Yeast, E. coli	TPN, also DPN	Decarboxylates‡	Phosphate
9	D-3-Phosphoglyceraldehyde	Yeast, E. coli	DPN	Uses H₃PO₄, forming diphosphoglycerate	Iodoacetate, lack of phosphate
10	L-β-Hydroxybutyric acid	Bac. megaterium, Mycob. tuberculosis, Clostridia	DPN	Forms acetoacetate	
11	Proline	Clostridia	DPN	See Chap. VIII, sec. 4. Requires Pyridoxal phosphate	
12	DPNH or TPNH (transhydrogenase)	Ps. fluorescens	TPN or DPN resp.§	Transfers H atoms, not merely charges	Mercuric salts, pyrophosphate
13	DPNH or TPNH	E. coli, Aerobacter, Azotobacter, yeast	Oxidized ascorbic acid; quinones	Several related enzymes	Dinitrophenol (quinone enzyme)
			2. YELLOW ENZYMES		
14	Succinic	Almost all	Cytochrome b	Particulate. Contains both flavin and iron	Malonate, oxalacetate, fluoride
15	L-Amino acids (and L-hydroxy acids)	Proteus	O₂ (an enzyme from Clostridia uses DPN)	Soluble; FMN‖	Octyl alcohol, HCN

No.	Substrate	Source	Acceptor	Properties	Inhibitors
16	d-Amino acids	Neurospora crassa and many bacteria	O_2	Soluble; FAD#	Salts; *not* by chelating agents
17	L-Lactic acid (and other α-hydroxy acids)	Yeast	Cytochrome c, also quinones or methylene blue	Contains both FMN and cytochrome b_2, + 8 extra Fe atoms, MW 230,000. Cryst.	
18	Glucose	Fusarium, Penicillium Aspergillus	O_2; accumulates H_2O_2	Soluble. (Notatin.) Contains FAD	Resistant to H_2O_2
19	Xanthine, aldehydes	Anaerobic micrococci	O_2. Converts xanthine to uric acid; aldehydes to acids	Soluble; contains 2 FAD, 8 Fe^{++} and 1–2 Mo atoms per molecule	2-Amino 4-OH-6-pteridyl aldehyde; H_2O_2
20	Diamine oxidase	Ps. aeruginosa, several Mycobacteria	Cytochrome c or methylene blue	? FMN or FAD, see Chap. VIII. Requires pyridoxal phosphate	Cyanide, semicarbazide
21	DPNH	(a) Almost all	Cytochrome c (O_2 slowly)	Insol.: FAD ("diaphorase," "coenzyme factor," etc.)	
		(b) Yeast	1,4-Naphthoquinone, coenzyme Q, vitamin K, etc.	Soluble	
22	DPNH or TPNH	(a) Yeast and several Bac.	Nitrite, NH_2OH, NO		(DPN usually acts also)
		(b) Ps. aeruginosa and other bacteria	O_2 (at high O_2 tension) or cytochrome c (slowly)	Several enzymes; at least one contains Cu	
23	TPNH	(a) (Bottom) Yeast, Lactobacilli	Methylene blue (O_2 very slowly)	Soluble.; "old" yellow enzyme; FMN. DPNH also acts	
		(b) (Bottom) Yeast	Cytochrome c	Soluble; FAD; "Haas yellow enzyme"	
		(c) (Top) Yeast (probably all aerobes)		FMN; "cytochrome reductase"	Atabrine

* This was the first isolation in pure form of a coenzyme-linked dehydrogenase (Negelein and Wulff, 1937).
† The corresponding enzyme in heart and muscle tissue reduces DPN.
‡ Produces 3-keto derivative, which then decarboxylates and at the same time rearranges to 5-phospho-D-ribulose.
§ Catalyzes reaction $TPNH + DPN^+ \rightleftharpoons DPNH + TPN^+$
|| FMN means that the flavin moiety is flavin mononucleotide.
FAD means that the flavin moiety is flavin adenine dinucleotide.

221

6. THE "YELLOW" OR FLAVOPROTEIN ENZYME SYSTEMS

When, as happens with most dehydrogenases, the product is reduced DPN or TPN,[6] this can be dehydrogenated in one of two ways. In fermentation it transfers its hydrogen to other organic compounds; in respiration it transfers it to *flavoproteins* or "yellow enzymes." These in turn are reoxidized, either slowly by oxygen, or (more rapidly) by the cytochrome system.

The role of the flavoproteins came to light through study of the respiration of the lactic bacteria. These organisms, which are considered more fully in Chapter XII, are typically microaerophilic; their respiration is very slow, is not inhibited by KCN or CO, and is accompanied by the *formation of H_2O_2*. They do not contain catalase, and addition of catalase to the medium sometimes promotes their growth (see sec. 7).

One consequence of the production of H_2O_2 is the formation of a green pigment when grown on blood-agar medium. This is shown by some of the lactic streptococci (called for that reason the "viridans" group) and two Lactobacilli, *L. bulgaricus* and *L. acidophilus*. The green pigment is an oxidation product of hemoglobin formed by the action of H_2O_2. Some bacteria with this type of metabolism actually require the addition of blood to the medium, in order to be able to grow under aerobic conditions. Examples are the plague bacterium, *Pasteurella pestis*, and its relative, *P. septicum*. The blood can be replaced by charcoal or reducing agents, by hematin, or, better still, by catalase. Added H_2O_2 inhibits growth, and hematin protects against it (Jordan, 1952). Hence the function of hematin, blood, or catalase is to destroy the H_2O_2 which is formed in respiration and inhibits growth. On a synthetic medium the H_2O_2 is formed only when glucose, galactose, or maltose is added, indicating that it may be produced by glucose dehydrogenase (No. 18 in Table V–5).

When respiring with sugar as substrate, *Lactob. delbrückii* and *L. acidophilus* evolve CO_2 equivalent to only half the oxygen taken up; the rest of the oxygen forms H_2O_2 thus:

$$C_6H_{12}O_6 + 6 \ H_2O + 12 \ O_2 \rightarrow 6 \ CO_2 + 12 \ H_2O_2$$

The respiratory quotient, CO_2/O_2, is 0.5 (Bertho and Gluck, 1932). In later stages more CO_2 appears, and the H_2O_2 formation is decreased due to the very rapid reaction with pyruvic acid which is formed in the fermentation:

$$CH_3COCOOH + H_2O_2 \rightarrow CH_3COOH + H_2O + CO_2 \tag{14}$$

This reaction needs no enzyme and is almost instantaneous at 38° C.

[6] Better names for these coenzymes are respectively nicotinamide-adenine-dinucleotide (NAD) and nicotinamide-adenine-dinucleotide phosphate (NADP).

When a suspension of the bacteria is saturated with oxygen, it appears yellow, and when the oxygen stream is stopped, it turns white. The yellow color is due to absorption bands at 465 and 496 mμ, which appear and disappear reversibly like those of cytochrome (Warburg and Christian, 1933). From partially purified preparations (from yeast) it was seen that the change is due to oxidation and reduction, and that when the reduced (colorless) form is reoxidized in air, it forms H_2O_2. After starving the bacteria, to use up substrate, the pigment became less readily reduced, and the effect of various added substrates could then be studied. The most effective was 6-phosphoglucose. The dehydrogenase for this substance (No. 7 in Table V–5) is present in the bacteria. The reactions are:

$$6\text{-Phospho-glucose} + FP \rightarrow FPH_2 + 6\text{-Phosphogluconic acid}$$
$$FPH_2 + O_2 \rightarrow FP + H_2O_2$$

where FP is the yellow pigment (flavoprotein). Methylene blue competes with oxygen:

$$FPH_2 + MB \rightarrow FP + MBH_2$$

Since the yellow pigment is reduced by a natural substrate (in presence of its dehydrogenase) and reoxidized by oxygen, it must be classed as an *oxidase*. It is one of a series of related compounds, not all of which react directly with O_2, but all of which contain yellow pigments of the same type, linked to colorless proteins.

The yellow moiety is riboflavin, or 6,7-dimethyl-9-D-ribityl-isoalloxazine (Chap. XI). In one flavoprotein it is linked to phosphate at C atom 5 of the ribitol (Theorell, 1934–1937) to form flavin-ribitol-phosphate or flavin mononucleotide, FMN. In others this nucleotide grouping is linked to a second nucleotide, adenosine-5-phosphate, to form:

$$\text{Isoalloxazine-ribityl-phosphoric acid}$$
$$|$$
$$\text{Adenine-ribose-phosphoric acid}$$

This compound is flavin adenine dinucleotide, or FAD.

Of the dozen or more known yellow enzymes, three contain FMN and the others FAD. The two are interrelated by an enzyme present in yeast that catalyzes the reaction between FMN and adenosine triphosphoric acid (ATP):

$$FMN + ATP \overset{Mg}{\rightleftharpoons} FAD + H_4P_2O_7$$

The reaction goes to the right in presence of Mg ions (Schrecker and Kornberg, 1950).

By purifying the flavoprotein from yeast, and adding substrate, dehydrogenase, and various ions, Warburg *et al.* (1935) found that a *coenzyme* was also an indispensable part of the system. A brilliant piece of chemical work led to the isolation of this coenzyme and its identification as a compound of purine and pentose with nicotinamide:

with the composition (finally established by Kornberg and Pricer, 1950):

Adenine-2-phospho-D-ribose-(HPO$_3$)$_2$-D-ribose-nicotinamide

Parallel work on cozymase, the coenzyme of alcoholic fermentation (Chap. XI), established it as having one less phosphate group:

Adenine-D-ribose-(HPO$_3$)$_2$-D-ribose-nicotinamide

Warburg's coenzyme is known as TPN (triphosphopyridine nucleotide), NADP, or Co II, while cozymase is DPN, NAD, or Co I. Both coenzymes act as hydrogen carriers, being readily reduced either by dehydrogenase systems or chemically with Na$_2$S$_2$O$_4$.

The mode of action of the yellow enzyme system of *Lactobacillus acidophilus* is therefore as shown in Fig. V–5; 6-phosphoglucose and its specific dehydrogenase, a colorless protein, combine with the coenzyme. This combination is shown by the reduced mobilities of the ions in each other's presence (Theorell, 1934). As a result the electrons of the carbon atom in position 1 of the glucose become activated, and one goes to the strongly positive N atom of the nicotinamide, while one hydrogen atom transfers to the para C atom of the nicotinamide, this atom having become essentially unsaturated and nucleophilic. The two molecules are held close to each other through combination with the (apo-) dehydrogenase at many points of attachment. These points of attachment make it specific for 6-phosphoglucose (as opposed to glucose), the pyridine ring (as opposed to any other), and the triphospho- (as opposed to the diphospho-) nucleotide structure.

The dehydrogenated phosphoglucose molecule next attracts to itself the molecule of water, which presumably is always associated with the reducing (aldehydic) group of a sugar, and rearranges to the carboxylic acid. The remaining hydrogen ion of the water, now showing as an extra titratable acidity, is neutralized by a dissociated phosphate radical in the coenzyme.

In the second step the coenzyme transfers its hydrogen to the flavoprotein, reducing the two doubly bonded nitrogen atoms. The third step is the reoxidation of reduced flavoprotein, forming H$_2$O$_2$.

The system just described reacts only with reduced coenzyme. Since it was discovered, many other yellow enzyme systems have been brought to light, and they embody two important variations from the above: (1) some can react directly with the substrate (in the presence of its dehydrogenase), dispensing with the coenzyme, and (2) some are not reoxidized by oxygen at an appreciable rate but require the

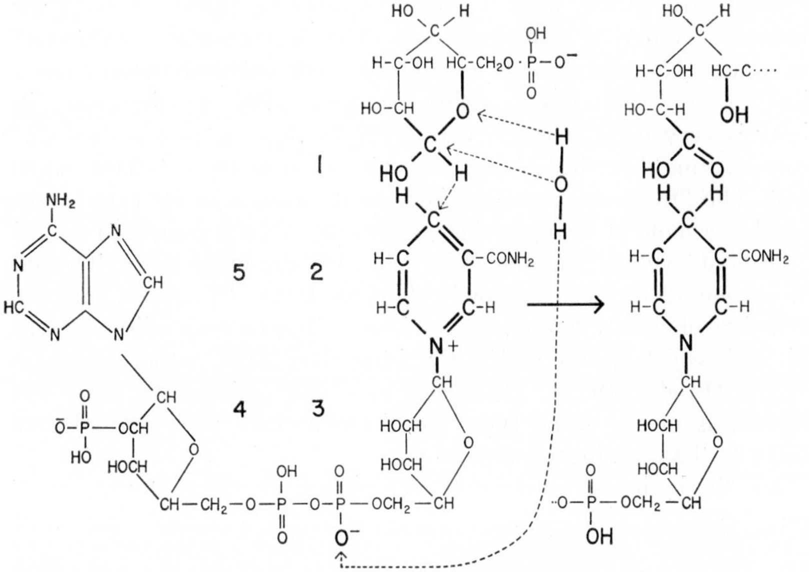

FIGURE V–5

Working detail of the transfer of hydrogen from 6-phosphoglucose (1) to the nicotinamide residue (2) of TPN, to produce 6-phosphogluconic acid (1a) and the reduced nicotinamide (2a). The new terminology for TPN is Nicotinic (2) Adenine (5) Dinucleotide (3, 4) Phosphate (4), or NADP.

cytochrome system or other oxidizing agents, such as quinones or fumarate or oxidized ascorbic acid, for electron and hydrogen acceptor.

The two flavoproteins reacting directly with protein-forming (L-) and nonprotein-forming (D-) amino acids, respectively (Nos. 15 and 16), are discussed in Chapter VIII. The reaction is:

$$\text{R—CH—COOH} \longrightarrow \text{R—C—COOH} + 2\ \text{H}^+ + 2\ \text{e}$$
$$\underset{\text{NH}_2}{|} \qquad\qquad \underset{\text{NH}}{\|}$$

The resulting imino acid is rapidly hydrolyzed to the keto acid. In the case of No. 18, the reaction glucose $\rightleftharpoons$ gluconic acid parallels that described above with 6-phosphoglucose (No. 7). It proceeds so rapidly that the resulting H_2O_2 accumulates fast enough to inhibit growth (see Chap. XXV, sec. 2). The lactic oxidase (No. 17) is quite different from the dehydrogenase, No. 3, since it contains cytochrome and reacts with oxygen.

Among the enzymes listed as Nos. 21 to 23, three belong to the type (2) mentioned above, namely, they require the intervention of the cytochrome system to reoxidize them. The "cytochrome c reductase" from yeast (No. 23c) reacts vigorously with oxidized cytochrome c (Haas *et al.*, 1940–1942), using reduced TPN. Furthermore, its activity is very high; it reacts with TPN 14 times as fast as the "old" yellow enzyme described above, and with cytochrome c 150,000 times as fast. The "turnover number," i.e., the number of moles cytochrome reduced per mole of flavoprotein per minute, is 1300 compared to < 1 for the "old" yellow enzyme (No. 23a). On the other hand, it reacts with oxygen 12 times more slowly than the latter. Its natural function is therefore obviously *to reduce cytochrome*. The corresponding enzyme of *E. coli*, which reacts with DPN instead of TPN, is not nearly so powerful (Brodie, 1952). These enzymes, and perhaps the other two flavoproteins of the same type, constitute a main path of hydrogen transfer to the cytochrome system.

Thus the hydrogen or electron path may have different numbers of steps:

(1) In the shortest systems (Nos. 15, 16, and 18), it goes from amino acid or glucose to the nitrogen of flavoprotein, thence to oxygen:

$$C \rightarrow N_{FP} \rightarrow O_2$$

(2) In the next type it goes from the carbon of substrate to the nitrogen of DPN or TPN, thence to the nitrogen of flavoprotein, thence to O_2:

$$C \rightarrow N_{DPN} \rightarrow N_{FP} \rightarrow O_2$$

This system was first realized with all pure components in the case of alcohol dehydrogenase of yeast (No. 2 of Table V–5), using crystalline dehydrogenase, pure flavoprotein, and pure DPN, with alcohol, pyrophosphate buffer, and the addition of semicarbazide to fix the aldehyde as fast as formed (Negelein and Wulff, 1937).

(3) In succinic and lactic oxidases (Nos. 14 and 17) the flavo-

protein and cytochrome are combined, so that the path is from substrate carbon to flavoprotein nitrogen to cytochrome iron:

$$C \rightarrow N_{FP} \rightarrow Fe_{Cyt} \dashrightarrow Fe_{Cyt\ ox} \rightarrow O_2$$

(4) Finally, in the cytochrome reductases (Nos. 21 and 23C) all the steps intervene:

$$C \rightarrow N_{DPN\ or\ TPN} \rightarrow N_{FP} \rightarrow Fe_{Cyt} \dashrightarrow Fe_{Cyt\ ox} \rightarrow O_2$$

There is much evidence that the carbon of coenzyme Q may also intervene within the cytochrome chain, as shown on page 209. Although all the details are still far from worked out, it is clear that the series comprises an elaborate set of variations on the theme of the accomplishment of large energy changes by small steps.

7. OXIDATION-REDUCTION POTENTIALS

A. Nature of the Potentials

The concept of *degree* in oxidation, or *intensity of oxidizing power*, is similar to that of pH. Sörensen made it clear that the total, or titratable, acid is quite different from the intensity of acidity, the latter being determined by the hydrogen-ion concentration, or more strictly by the hydrogen-ion activity. For example, 1 N acetic acid has more titratable acidity than the same volume of 0.1 N hydrochloric acid, but it is not so acid as the HCl, because acetic acid produces less hydrogen ions per unit volume. In the same way 1 N hypoiodite has more total available oxygen than 0.1 N permanganate, but it is not so oxidizing as the permanganate. The permanganate has a higher oxidizing *intensity* or *oxidation-reduction potential* (hereafter shortened to redox potential).

We have seen above that oxidation is essentially a *loss of electrons*. The oxidation of a ferrous salt, represented by:

$$2\ Fe(OH)_2 + \tfrac{1}{2}\ O_2 + H_2O \rightarrow 2\ Fe(OH)_3$$

consists of the two reactions:

$$2\ Fe^{++} \rightarrow 2\ Fe^{+++} + 2\ e$$

$$\tfrac{1}{2}\ O_2 + 2\ e + H_2O \rightarrow 2\ OH^-$$

Thus, a solution of ferrous ions has a tendency to give off electrons. A piece of metal introduced into the solution will then have a tendency to pick up the electrons, i.e., to attain a negative charge. If it is an inert metal like platinum, this negative charge can be measured against a reference electrode, which has a fixed tendency to pick up or lose charges. For this reference electrode a calomel or hydrogen electrode is generally adopted. The platinized platinum electrode, surrounded by 1 atmosphere of H_2 gas and dipped in 1 M hydrogen-ion solution, is the standard of zero potential. With reference to this zero, solutions that are more oxidizing tend to take electrons from the electrode and thus leave it *positive;* solutions that are more reducing correspondingly make the electrode *negative.*

B. Relation between State of Oxidation and the Potential

Since a solution of ferrous ions has a tendency to give up electrons, while a solution of ferric ions has a tendency to take on electrons, there must exist some mixture of ferrous and ferric ions which will be just in equilibrium; at this point we can put the relative concentrations

$$[Fe_0^{++}]/[Fe_0^{+++}] = K \tag{15}$$

Let us put such a solution into two vessels connected by a siphon (Fig. V–6) and insert platinum electrodes into each vessel. On passing a current through the system (from the battery B), electrons are supplied at the cathode, so that the Fe^{+++} becomes reduced to Fe^{++}; correspondingly at the anode Fe^{++} is oxidized to Fe^{+++}. If we now pass, under conditions designated as reversible, one coulomb through the system, we have created a concentration cell, and the work done, which is the same as the work we could get reversibly out of it, at the absolute temperature T, is given by the Nernst relation:

$$\text{work done} = -\Delta F = RT \ln \frac{[Fe_1^{++}]}{[Fe_0^{++}]} - RT \ln \frac{[Fe_1^{+++}]}{[Fe_0^{+++}]} \tag{16}$$

where Fe_0^{++} is the original concentration of ferrous ions and Fe_1^{++} the final; the same terminology holds for the ferric ions. Since the work was done reversibly, it can be recovered as electric energy, i.e., it is equal to the emf $(E) \times$ the value of one faraday $(F) \times$ the number of equivalents passed, n (in this case 1); i.e.,

$$-\Delta F = EnF$$

By rearranging and substituting from equation (15), E, the emf given by a ferrous-ferric solution at an inert electrode, is

$$E = K' - \frac{RT}{F} \ln \frac{[Fe^{++}]}{[Fe^{+++}]} \tag{17}$$

When the concentrations of ferrous and ferric ions are equal, the right-hand term disappears and the emf is determined by the constant

K'. This constant depends on the *tendency* of the system to take up or give out electrons ("electron fugacity"). Its dimensions are obviously that of a potential, and it is accordingly written E_o.

To make the above equations apply to all systems, in which more than one electron may be involved in the change from reduced to

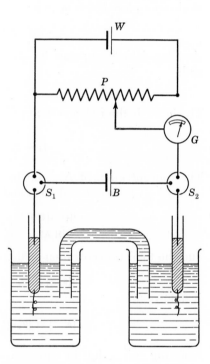

FIGURE V–6

Apparatus for redox measurements. *B*. Battery. *G*. Galvanometer. *P*. Potentiometer. S_1, S_2. Switches. *W*. Weston standard cell.

oxidized form, the number of electrons, n, involved in the change must be inserted, giving, as a general expression:

$$E_h = E_o - \frac{RT}{nF} \ln \frac{[Red]}{[Ox]} \tag{18}$$

where [Red] and [Ox] indicate the concentrations of the reduced and oxidized forms, respectively. The use of E_h instead of E indicates merely that the emf is determined against the standard hydrogen electrode. (As a practical matter, for the right-hand beaker of Fig. V–6 is substituted a standard half-cell such as a calomel electrode. The emf of this cell against the hydrogen electrode is known. The emf of the system is then measured against that of the standard cell W by means of the potentiometer and galvanometer.)

C. The Effect of pH

In organic reducing systems the relation is in general more complex, because the reduced form of most organic molecules differs also in hydrogen content (cf. eqs. [2] and [3], p. 196). The equilibrium is therefore governed by the tendency to lose H ions as well as by the tendency to lose electrons, i.e.:

$$AH_2 \rightleftharpoons A^{--} + 2\ H^+$$

the dissociation constants for these two hydrogen ions being k_1 and k_2, and:

$$A^{--} \rightleftharpoons A + 2\ e^7$$

The latter is the redox system proper, and its emf, by equation (18), is:

$$E_h = E_o - \frac{RT}{nF} \ln \frac{[A^{--}]}{[A]} \tag{19}$$

The concentration of A^{--} can be evaluated from the known total concentration of the reduced form and k_1 and k_2. For since:

$$\frac{[H^+][HA^-]}{[H_2A]} = k_1 \text{ and } \frac{[H^+][A^=]}{[HA^-]} = k_2$$

and the total concentration of the reduced form [Red] is given by:

$$[Red] = [A^{--}] + [HA^-] + [H_2A]$$

it follows that:

$$[A^{--}] = [Red] \frac{k_1k_2}{k_1k_2 + k_1[H] + [H]^2}$$

Inserting this value in equation (19), and calling [A] the total concentration of the oxidant, [Ox], we have:

$$E_h = E_o - \frac{RT}{2F} \ln \frac{[Red]}{[Ox]} + \frac{RT}{2F} \ln (k_1k_2 + k_1[H] + [H]^2) - \frac{RT}{2F} \ln k_1k_2 \tag{20}$$

By some writers the fourth term, which consists only of constants, is combined with E_o to give a new constant, which depends not only on the tendency of the system to lose or gain electrons, but also on its tendency to lose or gain hydrogen ions.

According to Michaelis (1951), the two electrons are usually lost separately with formation of an unstable intermediate. The above equations therefore hold only for the over-all process.

[7] The form of this reaction varies. In the case of methylene blue (Clark, Cohen, and Gibbs, 1925) it is:

$$MB^- \rightleftharpoons MB^+ + 2\ e$$

The significance of the various terms of the equation can best be seen from experiment. Suppose first that we titrate the oxidized form of a substance with a reducing agent, working in buffer solution to keep the pH constant. Then the third term, which deals only with hydrogen-ion concentrations, will be constant, and the observed emf will vary only with the ratio [Red]/[Ox]. Figure V–7 shows such a titration, titanous chloride being added to a solution of 1-naphthol-2-sulphonic acid-indophenol at pH 6.98. It is evident that the curve has the same form as that for an acid-alkali titration, in which pH is plotted against percentage neutralization. At the mid-point of the curve the concentrations of oxidized and reduced forms are equal, i.e., [Red] = [Ox]. Equation (20) shows that at this point the potential measured, E_h, is equal to E_o plus a function of the pH. The value of

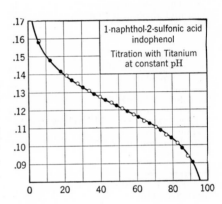

FIGURE V–7

The redox titration of 1-naphthol-2-sulfonic acid indophenol. The first redox system to be completely worked out. Abscissa: per cent reduction. Ordinate: redox potential. (From W. M. Clark and B. Cohen, U.S. *Public Health Reports*, 1923.)

E_o at a fixed pH (other than $pH = 0$) is for convenience written E_o'. At a fixed pH, say that of neutrality, we can arrange oxidizing-reducing systems in order of their E_o' values and thus have a scale of oxidizing intensities, just as we can have a scale of acid strengths. A selection of such values for systems of bacteriological importance is collected for reference in Table V–6.

Second, if the ratio [Red]/[Ox] is held constant and the pH varied, the second term of equation (20) is now zero and the potential varies (in the case of a substance yielding two hydrogen atoms) with the third term. There are three regions of hydrogen-ion concentration to be considered:

(1) At high acidities the value of the bracketed term is determined only by $[H]^2$. Calculation shows that then the potential changes by 0.060 volts (at 30° C) for an increase of one pH unit; i.e., the potential:

TABLE V–6. Oxidation-Reduction Potentials of Biologically Important Systems

(From Lardy, 1950, and Burton and Wilson, 1953)

(All data for pH 7.0 and room temperature unless otherwise indicated.)

System	Temp.	E_o' (Volts)	pH Range	Slope $\left(\dfrac{\Delta E_o'}{\Delta p\mathrm{H}}\right)$ 30° C
Pyruvate/acetate-bicarbonate	—	−0.630 (calc.)*	—	—
α-Ketoglutarate/succinate	—	−0.600 (calc.)*	—	—
Acetaldehyde/acetate	—	−0.468 (calc.)*	—	—
Glucose-6-phosphate/6-phospho- gluconate	—	−0.43	—	—
Formate/carbon dioxide	30	−0.420	—	—
Hydrogen/hydrogen ion	30	−0.4200*	—	—
Reduced DPN/oxidized DPN (co- enzyme 1)	25	−0.320	—	−.03
Glyceraldehyde-3-phosphate$^=$/ 1,3-Diphosphoglycerate^{4-}	25	−0.286†	—	—
Isopropyl alcohol/acetone	35	−0.251	—	—
Riboflavin	20	−0.186	0.4–6.5	−.06
			6.5–9.0	−.03
			10.0–12.8	−.06
Lactate/pyruvate	25	−0.190†	—	—
Ethanol/acetaldehyde	25	−0.200	—	—
Malate$^=$/oxalacetate	25	−0.166†	—	—
Cysteine/cystine	25	−0.14	0–7.0	−.06
Cytochrome b_1, pH 7.4	15	−0.13		
Malate/oxalacetate	38	−0.102	7.47–9.15	−.06
Yellow enzyme (="old" yellow en- zyme of Warburg)	38	−0.060	—	—
Cytochrome b, pH 7.4‡	20	−0.04	—	—
Pyocyanine	30	−0.034	5.0–9.0	−.06
			10.0–11.5	−.03
Butyrate/crotonate	—	−0.025	—	—
Succinate/fumarate	—	0.000	—	—
Methylene blue	—	+0.01	<5.0	−.09
			>6.0	−.03
1,4-Naphthoquinone	—	+0.036	—	—
Glutathione	25	+0.04	0–7.0	−.06
Resazurin	—	+0.051	—	—
Ascorbic acid/dehydroascorbic acid				
pH 3.30	35.5	+0.020	2.04–4.2	−.06
pH 6.43 (extrap.)		+0.080	4.2–6.4	−.03
2,6-Dichlorophenolindophenol	—	+0.217	4.0–9.0	−.06
			>11.0	−.03
Cytochrome c	—	+0.262	4.0–8.0	0
Cytochrome a, pH 7.4	20	+0.29	—	—
o-Quinone, pH 7.66	30	+0.333	—	—
Ferrous ion/ferric ion, pH 0.0	25	+0.771	acid	0
Water/oxygen	25	+0.815	—	−.06

* From thermodynamic considerations.

† From Burton and Wilson, 1953.

‡ Boonstra and Holton (1959) find 0.077.

pH curve has a slope of -0.06. Note that the potential due to the hydrogen electrode has the same slope, for

$$E_h = \frac{RT}{nF} \ln [H] = - \frac{RT}{nF} pH = -.06 \times pH.$$

Thus, the normal hydrogen electrode, which has $E_h = 0$ at pH 0, has $E_h = -0.42$ volt at pH 7.0.

(2) At acidities where [H] is comparable to k_1 and the term in [H]^2 can be neglected, the same reasoning gives us a slope of -0.03 volt per pH unit.

(3) Where [H] is so small in comparison to the dissociation constants that both terms in [H] can be neglected, the potential is independent of pH.

Examples of all three types of variation are included in Figure V–8; the ferrocyanide-ferricyanide system shows independence of pH over a wide range, while the indigo-sulfonates and indophenols show both a 0.06 and a 0.03 slope. Methylene blue in the acid range shows a 0.09 slope. As a practical matter, if one can determine the slope experimentally, one can deduce whether one or two electrons are involved. Some values for the slopes are included in Table V–6. The positions of the theoretically limiting hydrogen and oxygen electrode are shown at the bottom left and top right of the figure. Potentials beyond these can only occur if the hydrogen or oxygen fails to be evolved; this is termed *overvoltage*.

D. Redox Potentials and Energy Exchange

The above equations give directly the relation between the free-energy change (= reversible work) of an oxidation and the emf it registers at an electrode. Since a coulomb in calories is 23,068, the relation:

$$-\Delta F = EnF$$

means that the free-energy change of an oxidation in calories is $23,068 \times n$ (usually 2) $\times$ the voltage difference between the E_o of the system and that of oxygen. In the case of hydrogen itself, its oxidation corresponds to the whole voltage difference between the hydrogen electrode and the oxygen electrode, i.e., 1.23 volts (cf. Fig. V–8), or $2 \times 23,068 \times 1.23 = 58,000$ calories. This free energy is made available enzymatically in small steps. The energy exchange of these steps has been calculated partly from measurements of emf in presence of the appropriate enzyme and partly from thermodynamic data. The agreement is not always good. As an example, the redox potential of

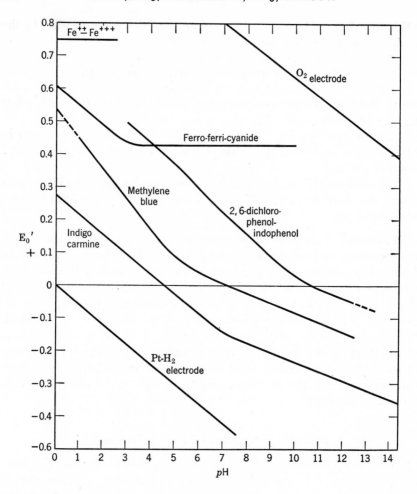

FIGURE V–8
Relation between redox potential (E_0') and pH for a series of dyes. The potentials of the hydrogen and oxygen electrodes are shown at top right and bottom left, respectively. Note slopes of 0.03 (dyes in alkaline range), 0.06 (most curves), and 0.09 (methylene blue in acid range). (Modified from W. M. Clark, B. Cohen, and H. D. Gibbs, *U.S. Public Health Reports*, 1925.)

DPNH/DPN, when determined by using xanthine oxidase to bring it into equilibrium with a reversibly oxidized and reduced dye, was found to be $E_o' = -0.278$ volt at pH 7 and 30° C (Rodkey and Ball, 1952). By measuring the equilibrium constant between isopropanol and acetone in presence of DPN as carrier and alcohol dehydrogenase as enzyme, the value of $E_o' = -0.320$ volt at pH 7 and 25° C was calculated (Burton and Wilson, 1953). Whichever value is right,[8] we must conclude that, since the hydrogen electrode at pH 7 is -0.42 volt, most of the energy between this and $+0.81$ volt, i.e., the energy made available by oxidation, must come in the stages *after* the coenzyme.

The way in which it may be distributed is summarized in Table V–7. Much of the energy liberated is transferred to high-energy phos-

TABLE V–7. E_0' and $-\Delta F$ for the Interaction of the Oxidative Enzymes at pH 7.0 and 30° C

(From Ball, 1944)

	E_0'		$-\Delta F$ per Electron
O_2	$+0.81$ v		
		0.52 v	12,000
Cytochrome oxidase	?		
Cytochrome a	$+0.29$ v		
		0.02 v	460
Cytochrome c	$+0.27$ v		
		0.31 v	7,150
Cytochrome b	-0.04 v*		
		0.04 v	920
Flavoprotein	-0.08 v		
		0.20 v	4,600 ($\times$ 2 = 9,200)
Pyridine nucleotide	-0.28 v†		
			25,130 cal.
H_2	-0.42 v		

$\Delta F = nFE = -1 \times 23,068 \times \text{voltage difference}$

* A later value (Boonstra and Holton, 1959) is $+0.077$ v.
† A later value (Burton and Wilson, 1953) is -0.32 v.

phate bonds, each of which carries from 8000 to 14,000 calories. The third column shows that there are probably only three sites at which such bonds can be made—between DPN or TPN and the flavoprotein, at the oxidation of cytochrome b, and between cytochrome a and O_2. Note that the value in Table V–6 for naphthoquinone (which would be near that of Co-Q) agrees with the position for Co-Q proposed above.

E. Redox Measurements in Bacterial Cultures[9]

When platinum electrodes are inserted into growing cultures of facultative organisms, protected from access of air, the potentials gen-

[8] Note also the two values for malate/oxalacetate in Table V–6.
[9] See Hewitt's book (1950) for a thorough treatment of the earlier work in this field.

erally become steadily negative. Figure V–9 shows such an experiment with yeast; the added succinate, which can be dehydrogenated and is thus a source of electrons, makes the potential still more negative. Methylene blue, however, raises the potential to the range in which it becomes reduced; the potential then changes only slowly while the dye is being reduced, but afterward falls again rapidly toward the succinate level. These changes closely resemble those produced by buffers in the pH of solutions; to complete the parallel we must imagine the organisms to be steadily producing alkali instead of electrons. Even when aerated, cell suspensions do not give a potential equal to that theoretically given by the oxygen electrode. They usually show E_h between 0.1 and 0.2 volt.

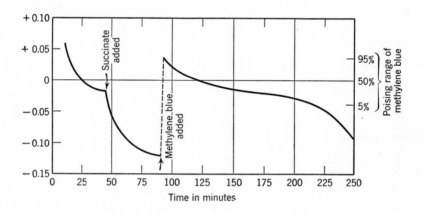

FIGURE V–9

Changes in potential in yeast culture (pH 7.4). (From R. K. Cannan, B. Cohen, and W. M. Clark, *U.S. Public Health Reports*, 1926.)

The production of peroxide by lactic bacteria and pneumococci (cf. p. 222), however, constitutes an exception to this rule. Cultures of hemolytic streptococci or pneumococci (which contain no catalase) go gradually negative if the vessel is closed, but if the culture is aerated, the potentials become very positive and remain there, poised evidently by a very oxidizing system. If now a preparation of catalase be added, oxygen gas comes off and the potential falls to a negative level (see Fig. V–10). The highly positive system is therefore H_2O_2, formed on aeration. In 18 hours the H_2O_2 has killed all the pneumococci, but in presence of catalase they survive. Similar measurements of *Corynebacterium diphtheriae* shows a potential much less affected by aeration, since the organisms are catalase-positive. The opposite behavior is shown by *M. lysodeikticus;* this shows when aerated a more *negative* potential than when simply left open to the air (Hewitt, 1931). The explanation for this apparent contradiction is that the organisms are catalase-positive, so that aeration does not produce H_2O_2, but because they are strict aerobes, the effect of aeration is to stimulate their growth which thus increases the reducing potential.

An essential difficulty in the application of redox measurements to bacterial systems is that the bacteria themselves cannot register a potential at the electrode, since the electrode cannot respond to suspended particles, but only to a system in true solution. The addition of

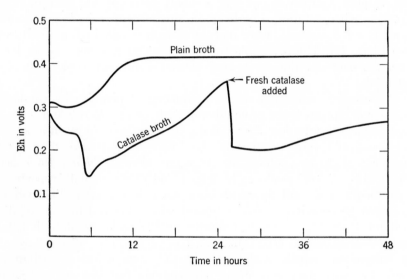

FIGURE V–10

Redox potentials in Pneumococcus cultures with and without catalase. When the potential of the broth culture reached +0.4 volt (12 hr.), peroxide could be detected chemically in the culture. (From L. F. Hewitt, *Biochem. J.*, **25**:169–176, 1931. Courtesy of Cambridge Univ. Press and the Biochemical Society.)

a trace of a reversible dye, as in Figure V–9, has the disadvantage that then the *capacity* factor of the dye comes into consideration, and if the equilibrium of the dye is not in the range being measured, the potential will be altered to the range at which the dye poises it and be held there until all the dye is reduced (or oxidized). In Lehmann's classic work on the succinic-fumaric equilibrium, methylene blue was added to the medium in order to give a potential at the electrode. Since the oxidation and reduction of methylene blue are right in the range of the succinic-fumaric equilibrium (see Table V–6), the dye is brought first to equilibrium with the enzyme system and then registers its equilibrium at the electrode. Thus, two factors are necessary for a dye to act as an intermediary; it must be oxidized and reduced in the right potential range, and it must react with the bacteria or enzyme system; the latter is a matter of affinity and varies from dye to dye.

It follows from the above that the potentials measured in bacterial cultures must be produced at the electrode by a reversible system that is in solution in the medium. Small amounts of such reversibly oxidized and reduced substances are usually present in broth, and bacteria may excrete such materials also. For example, Elema (1932), in studying the potentials observed during nitrate reduction by bacteria, found that without addition of any dye a steady potential was set up at the electrode when solutions of nitrate or nitrite, with a hydrogen donor (usually ethyl alcohol), were inoculated with the denitrifying cultures (see Chap. X). The reversible substance in this case must be set free from the bacteria; the nitrite and alcohol alone registered no steady potential.

An example analogous to the production of peroxide by catalase-negative organisms is the production of hydrogen by *E. coli* and related organisms. Not only do cultures of the coliform bacteria reach a potential practically equal to that of the hydrogen electrode, they even register a slight overvoltage of hydrogen (Cannan *et al.*, 1926; see Fig. V–11). *E. coli* produces hydrogen and CO_2 in equal proportions from formic acid, and therefore from sugar, but usually slightly less hydrogen because it becomes combined with other constituents of the medium. From his potentials, Gillespie (1920) could calculate that the pressure of hydrogen established must be of the order of one-third of an atmosphere, which, if the ratio $H_2:CO_2$ were a little less than 1, would be satisfactory agreement. The enzyme that leads to hydrogen evolution, *hydrogenlyase*, is a reversible system; the degree of reduction of the dye (methyl-viologen) in presence of hydrogen gas is the same whether *E. coli* or colloidal palladium is used as catalyst (Green and Stickland, 1934). The potentials agree with the theoretical for the hydrogen electrode:

$$H_2 \rightleftharpoons 2\ H^+ + 2\ e$$

A strain of *Proteus vulgaris*, which is in many ways similar to *E. coli* but did not set free hydrogen, did not reach anywhere near such a negative potential as *E. coli* (Fig. V–11) (cf. Chap. XIV, sec. 4).

There is some evidence that the redox potential may limit growth. Bredemann, in 1909, showed that clostridia germinate from their spores only if the oxygen content of the atmosphere is from 0 to 20 mg per liter; at 33 mg per liter no germination occurred. Knight and Fildes (1930) studied the phenomenon from the viewpoint of redox potentials and found that *Cl. tetani* spores germinate, at *p*H 7, only at E_h below

0.01 volt (colorimetrically). When the redox potential was kept at different levels by nitrogen-oxygen mixtures, the spores would germinate after short times at $E_h = +0.12$ volt, providing the potential was lowered thereafter. In general the different times required for germination in different media simply reflected the times required for the media to come down to 0.01 volt. Some animal tissues are poised at potentials above this and hence do not allow germination. The E_h:time limits for

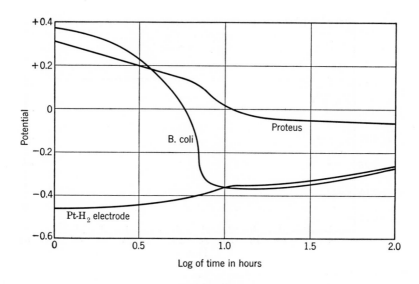

FIGURE V–11

Changes in redox potential of *E. coli* and *Proteus vulgaris* in glucose-peptone medium for four days. The hydrogen electrode shows the gradual formation of acid from the initial *p*H of 7.5. Although its hydrogen pressure is 1 atmos., and the E. coli produces only $\frac{1}{3}$ to $\frac{1}{2}$ atmos. hydrogen, yet the two curves coincide or even cross, due to slight overvoltage. Proteus, however, never becomes sufficiently negative to liberate H_2. (From R. K. Cannan, B. Cohen, and W. M. Clark, *U.S. Public Health Reports*, 1926.)

germination are shown in Figure V–12. At potentials below that of the hydrogen electrode, obtained by adding hydrosulfite, *Cl. tetani* does not grow; only when the potential comes up to about that of the hydrogen electrode does growth begin. The growth region for this organism is thus between E_h (at *p*H 7) −0.42 and −0.1. However, the addition of cobalt salts is reported to lower the redox potential sufficiently to allow *Cl. tetani* to grow aerobically (Dedic and Koch, 1956).

The fact that some organisms will only grow in ordinary media when a large inoculum is used has also been ascribed to the redox potential. Addition of cysteine, which makes the potential more negative, allows growth from smaller inocula. In a corresponding way, the growth-inhibiting effect of oxidized indophenols and methylene blue has been ascribed to their poising of the redox potential at too positive a value for growth.

It is unfortunate that the redox potentials of cultures have not made a more important contribution to the study of bacterial metabolism.

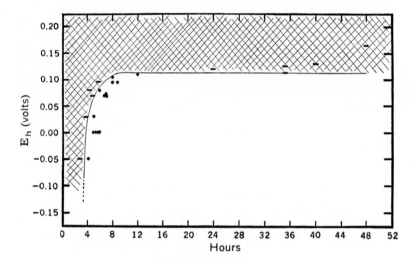

FIGURE V–12

Variation of time of germination of *Cl. tetani* spores with redox potential. ▬ No germination observed. • Germination first observed. In the shaded region conditions are too oxidizing for germination to occur. (From B. C. J. G. Knight and P. Fildes, *Biochem. J.*, **24**:1496–1502, 1930. Courtesy of Cambridge Univ. Press and the Biochemical Society.)

However, the practical difficulty due to the need of a soluble intermediary and the theoretical difficulty of ascribing an observed potential to a known enzyme system have delayed progress.

8. THE PATH OF SUGAR OXIDATION AND THE TRICARBOXYLIC ACID CYCLE

A. Hexose to Pyruvic Acid

The preceding sections have been mainly concerned with the general principles of oxidation and the enzyme systems' functioning. It remains to consider the substrate. There is reason to believe that in spite of the enormous number of aerobic organisms, the oxidation of carbohydrate proceeds along only a few standard paths. Two of these use hexose monophosphate, the other the diphosphate; all lead to pyruvic acid.

The first has been mentioned in section 6. Glucose-6-phosphate is oxidized to phosphogluconic acid; TPN is hydrogen acceptor (Warburg and Christian, 1938). Alternatively, gluconic acid can be formed from glucose (by glucose dehydrogenase) and then phosphorylated. This is carried out by ATP in presence of the enzyme gluconokinase, which is present in cultures of *E. coli* that have been grown on gluconic acid (Cohen, 1951):

$$HOOC(CHOH)_4CH_2OH + ATP \rightarrow HOOC(CHOH)_4CH_2O \cdot H_2PO_3 + ADP$$

The subsequent metabolism of 6-phosphogluconic acid, formed in these two ways, can give rise to triose by two different routes.

(1) In the more important route, the phosphogluconic acid is dehydrogenated at the 3 position by TPN, and then decarboxylated to 5-phospho-D-ribulose (Horecker and Smyrniotis, 1951):

COOH	COOH	(+CO₂)	
HCOH	HCOH	CH₂OH	CHO
HOCH	CO (+2 H)	CO	HCOH
HCOH	HCOH	HCOH	HCOH
HCOH	HCOH	HCOH	HCOH
H₂CO·H₂PO₃	H₂CO·H₂PO₃	H₂CO·H₂PO₃	H₂CO·H₂PO₃
6-Phospho-gluconic acid	6-Phospho-3-keto-gluconic acid	5-Phospho-ribulose	5-Phospho-ribose

The interconversion of 5-phosphoribulose and the corresponding aldose, 5-phosphoribose, probably explains why this latter phospho-sugar occurs so widely, in coenzymes, nucleotides, and nucleic acids. In other words, ribose lies on the direct path from glucose.

In the second step, 5-phosphoribulose is isomerized to 5-phospho-xylulose by an enzyme (ribulose-xylulose phosphate isomerase) which has been found in yeast, muscle, and spinach (Srere *et al.*, 1955); this compound is then split by the enzyme *transketolase* (which has been crystallized from yeast by Racker *et al.*, 1953), to yield the triose, D-3-phosphoglyceraldehyde. The remaining 2-carbon fragment is not set free, but carried by the enzyme to an acceptor; this can be glyceraldehyde, in which case a pentose is synthesized, but more gen-erally it is 5-phosphoribose, in which case the 7-carbon sugar sedoheptulose is formed. This ketose sugar is so named because it was first obtained from Sedum ("stonecrop") leaves.

```
  CH₂OH         CH₂OH        ⎛CH₂OH⎞                              CH₂OH
   |             |           ⎜  |   ⎟        HCO                   CO
   CO            CO          ⎝ CHO ⎠          |                    |
   |             |                           HCOH                 HOCH
   HCOH   ⇌     HOCH   ⇌      +               |                    |
   |             |            HCO             HCOH·                HCOH
   HCOH          HCOH          |               |                    |
   |             |            HCOH            HCOH                 HCOH
   H₂CO·H₂PO₃   H₂CO·H₂PO₃     |               |                    |
                             HCOH            HCOH                 HCOH
  5-Phospho-   5-Phospho-     |               |                    |
  ribulose     xylulose      H₂CO·H₂PO₃      H₂CO·H₂PO₃           H₂CO·H₂PO₃
                            "Fragment" +    5-Phospho-           7-Phospho-
                            3-phospho-      ribose               sedoheptulose
                            glyceraldehyde
```

Next, the heptose transfers its C atoms 1-3 (which are in the form of dihydroxyacetone) to the triose, 3-phosphoglyceraldehyde, thus forming fructose-6-phosphate and the phosphorylated 4-carbon sugar 4 phospho-erythrose. This latter combines with a second molecule of the 5 phospho-xylulose to produce fructose-6-phosphate again and to liberate the triose, 3 phosphoglyceraldehyde:

```
  CH₂OH ⎤                              CH₂OH
   |    ⎥
   CO   ⎥                               CO
   |    ⎥                                |
   HOCH ⎦          CH₂OH                 HOCH            HCO
   |                |                     |               |
   HCOH             CO                    HCOH           HCOH
   |        →        |            →        |        +      |               HCO
   HCOH            HOCH                    HCOH            HCOH             |
   |                |                       |              |               HCOH
   HCOH    +        HCO                     HCOH            HCOH             |
   |                |                        |              |              H₂CO·H₂PO₃
   H₂CO·H₂PO₃      HCOH                     H₂CO·H₂PO₃     H₂CO·H₂PO₃ →       +
                    |                                                       CH₂OH
                   H₂CO·H₂PO₃                              CH₂OH            |
                                                            |              C=O
                                                            C=O            |
                                                            |             HOCH
                                                           HOCH            |
                                                            |             HCOH
                                                           HCOH            |
                                                            |             HCOH
                                                           H₂CO·H₂PO₃      |
                                                                          H₂CO·H₂PO₃
```

This last reaction is somewhat obscure and may be complex.

The net result is that three hexose molecules are converted to two hexoses, three CO_2, and a triose:

$$2\ C_6 \rightarrow 2\ CO_2 + 2\ C_5 \rightarrow \begin{array}{l} C_3 \\ + \\ C_7 \end{array} \rightarrow \begin{array}{l} C_6 \\ + \\ C_4 \end{array} \Bigg] \rightarrow \begin{array}{l} C_3 \\ + \\ C_6 \end{array}$$

$$C_6 \rightarrow \quad CO_2 + \quad C_5$$

Total: $3\ C_6 \rightarrow 3\ CO_2 \qquad\qquad + 2\ C_6 \ + \ C_3$

(2) The second route is probably limited to a few Pseudomonads. Although relatively direct, there is little evidence for its wider occurrence. An intramolecular elimination of H_2O converts 6-phosphogluconic acid to its 2-keto, 3-deoxy derivative, and this splits at the position α to the keto group, just as the sedoheptulose above, to give pyruvic acid and phosphoglyceraldehyde (MacGee and Doudoroff, 1954; Kovachevich and Wood, 1955).

COOH	COOH	COOH
HCOH	CO	CO
HOCH	CH₂	CH₃
HCOH	HCOH	HCO
HCOH	HCOH	HCOH
H₂CO·H₂PO₃	H₂CO·H₂PO₃	H₂CO·H₂PO₃
6-Phospho-gluconic acid	2-Keto, 3-deoxy-6 phospho-gluconic acid	Pyruvic acid + 3-phospho-glyceraldehyde

Between the first and second structures: $\xrightarrow{-H_2O}$; between the second and third: $\rightarrow$

Both routes are commonly referred to as the "pentose pathway" and are equally important as synthetic pathways in photosynthesis (Chap. XXIII).

The alternative to these two oxidative routes is a strictly anaerobic one. In this process the hexose is *diphosphorylated*, and the resulting fructose-1,6-diphosphate is split by the enzyme *aldolase* into two molecules of phosphotriose. This process is described in Chapter XI.

All three routes yield *phosphotriose*. Another oxidation is required to convert this to pyruvic acid ($C_3H_6O_3 \rightarrow C_3H_4O_3 + 2\ H$), a deceptively simple-looking process which actually requires five enzymatic reactions. These also are described in Chapter XI and summarized in Figures XI–3 and XII–2.

B. Pyruvic Acid to CO₂

The subsequent oxidation of pyruvic acid involves a marvelously interdependent cycle of reactions. In the first step the pyruvate is combined with thiamine pyrophosphate or cocarboxylase, as described in Chapter XII, section 2D. The carboxyl is lost as CO_2, and the acetaldehyde residue temporarily is attached to the thiazole part of the thiamine. This unstable complex at once reacts with a second coenzyme, 6,8-dithiooctanoic acid or lipoic acid, to which the acetaldehyde residue is transferred:

$$
\begin{array}{ccc}
CH_2CH_2CH(CH_2)_4COOH & & CH_2CH_2CH(CH_2)_4COOH \\
| \quad\quad | & & | \quad\quad | \\
S\!-\!\!-\!\!-\!S & \rightarrow & S \quad\quad S \\
+ & & | \quad\quad | \\
(CH_3CHO) & & COCH_3 H
\end{array}
$$

In *E. coli* the lipoic acid and cocarboxylase are linked together in a single complex, lipothiamide pyrophosphate (Reed and de Busk, 1952–1953), but this may not be general.

The acetyl lipoic acid now transfers its acetyl group to the S atom of a third sulfur compound, coenzyme A, which has the structure (Baddiley *et al.*, 1953; Novelli *et al.*, 1954):

$$
\text{(adenine-3-phosphoribose)}
$$

$$
\begin{array}{c}
| \quad\quad\quad O \quad\quad O \quad\quad\quad\quad CH_3 \\
| \quad\quad\quad \| \quad\quad \| \quad\quad\quad\quad | \\
\!-\!OP\!-\!OP\!-\!OCH_2C\!-\!\!-\!\!-\!CHCONH(CH_2)_2CONH(CH_2)_2SH \\
| \quad\quad | \quad\quad\quad | \quad\quad\quad | \\
OH \quad OH \quad\quad CH_3 \quad OH
\end{array}
$$

For these reactions pyruvic dehydrogenase or "apo-oxidase" as well as cysteine, K^+, NH_4^+, and Mg^{++} are needed. Acetyl-Co A results.

Next, the reduced lipoic acid hydrogenates DPN and thus becomes able to react with another molecule of pyruvic acid. The hydrogenation of DPN, which is not reversible, is due to a special flavoprotein enzyme containing FAD and two —SH groups (Searls and Sanadi, 1959–1960). The sequence is thus:

$$
\left.
\begin{array}{l}
\quad\quad\quad\quad \text{lipoic} \quad\quad\quad \text{lipoic} \\
\quad\quad\quad\quad | \;\; | \quad\quad\quad\quad | \;\; | \\
\text{1. } CH_3COCOOH + S\!-\!S \rightleftharpoons CH_3COS \quad SH + CO_2 \\
\quad\quad\quad\quad\quad\quad\quad\quad\quad\quad\quad\quad\quad\quad \text{lipoic} \\
\quad\quad\quad\quad\quad\quad\quad\quad\quad\quad\quad\quad\quad\quad | \;\; | \\
\text{2. } CH_3COS\!\cdot\!SH \text{ lipoic} + HSCo A \rightleftharpoons CH_3CO\!\cdot\!SCo A + HS \quad SH \\
\text{3. } HS\!\cdot\!SH \text{ lipoic} + DPN^+ \rightarrow S\!-\!S \text{ lipoic} + DPNH + H^+
\end{array}
\right\} \quad (21)
$$

The first reaction can be made to go from right to left by adding lactic dehydrogenase, which reduces the pyruvate and thus shifts the equilibrium. In this way lipoic acid, in presence of both the enzymes, synthesizes lactate from acetyl-coenzyme A and CO_2.

The essence of these changes is that the acetyl group has been made available for chemical reactions. These reactions can be considered as "acetyl transfers," and are of several kinds:

In one, acetyl-coenzyme A comes to equilibrium with inorganic phosphate to form acetylphosphate (Stadtman *et al.*, 1952), providing the enzyme transacetylase is present:

$$\left.\begin{matrix} CH_3CO\cdot SCoA \\ enzyme \end{matrix}\right\} + HO\cdot H_2PO_3 \rightleftharpoons CH_3CO\cdot O\cdot H_2PO_3 + \left.\begin{matrix} HSCoA \\ enzyme \end{matrix}\right\}$$

The resulting acetylphosphate, having an energy-rich phosphate bond, can phosphorylate ADP, liberating acetic acid.

In the second place, in the presence of another enzyme, acetyl-coenzyme A can establish equilibrium with pyruvate and formate. This leads to a series of relationships described in Chapter XIV and is the mechanism whereby formic acid appears in some bacterial fermentations.

In the third place, an equilibrium can be established with acetic acid itself. This reaction enables acetic acid to be converted to acetyl-Co A and thus to become metabolically active. This reaction is complex and requires that the enzyme first be converted to a kind of nucleotide by reacting with ATP (Jones *et al.*, 1953):

$$E + Ad\cdot PPP \rightarrow E\cdot PAd + PP$$

Thus the utilization of free acetate requires high-energy phosphate (see Chap. XIV, sec. 2B); pyrophosphate (PP or $H_4P_2O_7$) is liberated.

Two other reactions of acetyl-coenzyme A will not be taken up here. They involve: (1) its participation in the acetylation of amines, as has been shown with sulfanilamide (it was this study that led to the discovery of coenzyme A by Lipmann *et al.*, 1947); (2) its role as a fundamental intermediate in fat metabolism, where acetyl-Co A condenses with malonyl-Co A to form acetoacetyl-Co A, which leads to aceto-acetic acid and thence to long-chain fatty acids (Chap. XV).

In the fourth place (and this is the reaction of main concern here), acetyl-coenzyme A can react with oxalacetic acid in the presence of a "condensing enzyme," called *citrogenase*, to form a 6-carbon compound, citric acid. This is the beginning of the main path of oxidation:

$$
\begin{array}{c}
\text{(Co A)} \\
\diagup \\
\underset{\displaystyle \underset{+}{\overset{|}{CO}}}{CH_3} \\
\end{array}
\quad
\begin{array}{c}
CO \\
| \\
CH_3 \\
\end{array}
\quad
\underset{\text{enzyme}}{\overset{\text{condensing}}{\rightleftharpoons}}
\quad
\begin{array}{c}
COOH \\
| \\
CH_2 \\
| \\
C(OH)COOH \\
| \\
CH_2 \\
| \\
COOH
\end{array}
\quad + \text{ Co A}
\qquad (22)
$$

(Co A)
 /
CO   COOH   + Co A
| |
CH₃   CH₂
  +   condensing
           enzyme
CO·COOH   ⇌   C(OH)COOH   (22)
| |
CH₂   CH₂
| |
COOH   COOH

The equilibrium is strongly to the right (Stern *et al.*, 1952; Korkes *et al.*, 1952).

The result of this step, following the reactions above, is that pyruvic acid is smoothly condensed with oxalacetic acid to form citric acid and CO_2. The various interactions of coenzyme A are summarized in Figure V–13.

Citric acid is brought into equilibrium with its isomers, *cis*-aconitic acid and isocitric acid, through the agency of the enzyme aconitase, which establishes equilibrium between all three:

COOH   COOH   COOH
| | |
CH₂   CH   HCOH
| −H₂O   ‖   +H₂O |
C(OH)·COOH ⇌   C·COOH   ⇌   CH·COOH   (23)
| | |
CH₂   CH₂   CH₂
| | |
COOH   COOH   COOH
Citric   cis-Aconitic   Isocitric

This reaction is the site of the inhibition of respiration (and there-fore the killing of animals) by fluoroacetate, FCH_2COONa. Reacting like acetate, this substance is converted to fluoroacetyl-CoA, and thence to fluorocitric acid, which powerfully inhibits the action of aconitase and thus stops further reactions (see Peters, 1957).

Isocitric acid is next dehydrogenated to the unstable intermediate oxalosuccinic acid (enzyme No. 5 in Table V–5), which is at once decarboxylated to α-ketoglutaric acid. This then undergoes a complex reaction similar to the conversion of pyruvate to acetyl-CoA (reaction No. 21 above) in which thiamine pyrophosphate and lipoic acid partici-pate, DPN is reduced, and the product is succinyl-coenzyme A (Kauf-man *et al.*, 1953). This then liberates CoA to produce succinic acid:

$$
\begin{array}{ccccc}
\text{COOH} & \text{COOH} & \text{COOH} & \text{CO}_2+ & \\
| & | & | & & \\
\text{HCOH} & \text{CO} & \text{CO} & \text{COCoA} & \text{COOH} \\
| & | \quad -2\,H & | \quad -2\,H & | & | \\
\text{CHCOOH} \xrightarrow{-2\,H} & \text{CHCOOH} \rightarrow \text{CO}_2+ & \text{CH}_2 \xrightarrow{\text{CoA}} & \text{CH}_2 \rightarrow & \text{CH}_2 \quad (24)\\
| & | & | & | & | \\
\text{CH}_2 & \text{CH}_2 & \text{CH}_2 & \text{CH}_2 & \text{CH}_2 \\
| & | & | & | & | \\
\text{COOH} & \text{COOH} & \text{COOH} & \text{COOH} & \text{COOH} \\
\text{Isocitric} & \text{Oxalosuccinic} & \text{Ketoglutaric} & \text{Succinyl-CoA} & \text{Succinic}
\end{array}
$$

Finally succinic acid is dehydrogenated to fumaric, and this, by means of fumarase, converted to malic, which is dehydrogenated to oxalacetic:

$$
\begin{array}{cccc}
\text{COOH} & \text{COOH} & \text{COOH} & \text{COOH} \\
| & | & | & | \\
\text{CH}_2 \xrightleftharpoons[\substack{\text{succinic}\\\text{dehydro-}\\\text{genase}}]{-2\,H} & \text{CH} \xrightleftharpoons[\text{fumarase}]{+H_2O} & \text{CHOH} \xrightleftharpoons[\substack{\text{malic}\\\text{dehydro-}\\\text{genase}}]{-2\,H} & \text{CO} \\
| & \| & | & | \\
\text{CH}_2 & \text{CH} & \text{CH}_2 & \text{CH}_2 \quad (25)\\
| & | & | & | \\
\text{COOH} & \text{COOH} & \text{COOH} & \text{COOH} \\
\text{Succinic} & \text{Fumaric} & \text{Malic} & \text{Oxalacetic}
\end{array}
$$

Thus, oxalacetic acid is regenerated and can again undergo reaction (22). The net result is that the pyruvic acid has been completely oxidized:

$$CH_3COCOOH + 2\tfrac{1}{2}\,O_2\,(=\,-10\ H)\ \rightarrow 2\ CO_2 + 2\ H_2O \qquad (26)$$

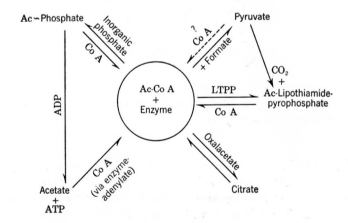

FIGURE V–13

Acetyl Co A reactions. (Modified from F. Lipmann, *Bact. Revs.*, **17**:1–16, 1953. Courtesy of the Williams and Wilkins Co., Baltimore, Md.)

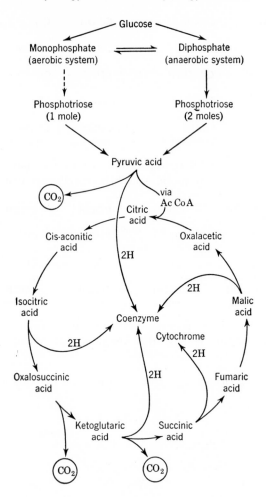

FIGURE V–14

Summary of the conversion of glucose to pyruvic acid and the oxidation of pyruvic acid via the tricarboxylic acid cycle.

Equations 22 through 25 constitute the cycle discovered by Krebs and others and sometimes called the Krebs cycle (Fig. V–14).

The energy set free by each of the five dehydrogenation stages is summarized in Table V–8. It will be seen that if the metabolic energy were completely transferred to high-energy phosphate bonds, each of 16.000 calories, 17 could be formed, which means 34 for a mole of hexose. For each pair of electrons (= 2 H), the average is 3.5 (cf. p. 233). With animal enzymes Krebs et al. (1953) found that ketoglutarate oxidation to succinate yields about four, and succinate to fumarate and malate yields two. This is very good agreement.

TABLE V-8. Redox Potentials and Free Energies of the Reactions of the Krebs Cycle

(From N. O. Kaplan, 1951)

Equation	Hydrogen Donor	Redox Potential (volts)	Difference from Oxygen Potential (volts)	$-\Delta F°$ per Electron Pair (calories)	Maximum Number of ($\sim$P) Generated
(18) + (19)	Pyruvate	−0.78	1.58	72,500	4.5
(21)	Isocitrate	−0.30	1.10	51,000	3.2
(21)	Ketoglutarate	−0.78	1.58	72,500	4.5
(22)	Succinate	−0.00	0.80	36,500	2.3
(22)	Malate	−0.18	0.98	45,000	2.8
(23)	Complete oxidation of pyruvate			277,500	17.3

Fats and proteins can also be oxidized through this cycle. Fats are hydrolyzed by lipases to glycerol and the fatty acids, and these acids are converted to their coenzyme A derivatives and then oxidized in a series of stages as follows (Lynen, 1954):

$$R(CH_2)_n—CH_2CH_2—COOH$$

$$ATP \downarrow CoA$$

$$R(CH_2)_n—CH_2CH_2—COCoA + AMP + Pyrophosphate$$

$$\downarrow$$

$$R(CH_2)_n—CH:CH—COCoA + 2(H)$$

$$H_2O \downarrow$$

$$R(CH_2)_n—HCOHCH_2·COCoA$$

$$\downarrow$$

$$R(CH_2)_n—CO—CH_2·COCoA + 2(H)$$

$$CoA \downarrow$$

$$R(CH_2)_n—COCoA \qquad + CH_3COCoA$$

$$\downarrow$$

$$R(CH_2)_{n-2}—CH:CH—COCoA \qquad + 2(H) \qquad etc.$$

Thus, two carbon atoms are split off at a time in the form of acetyl-Co A. Amino acids can be converted (via reactions described in Chap. VIII) to alanine or aspartic acid, and thence to pyruvic or oxalacetic acids, respectively; these are directly on the cycle.

The evidence that the Krebs cycle is the main path of oxidation in bacteria has swung from positive to negative and back; after much confusion, mainly due to the poor entry of the cycle intermediates into intact bacterial cells, it is now clear that virtually all aerobes oxidize pyruvate and acetate by way of the cycle. Kornberg's list of organisms in which the cycle occurs (1959) includes: four Acetobacters, two Azotobacters, two Bacilli, two Corynebacteria, four of the Entero-bacteriaceae, two Micrococci, two Mycobacteria, three Pseudomonads, three purple bacteria, three Streptomycetes, three yeasts and eight other fungi; surely a representative list. Furthermore, (1) inter-mediates of the cycle provide the carbon skeleton for the formation of amino acids, and (2) a modification of the cycle via glyoxylic acid allows for the continuous *accumulation* of such intermediates and accounts for the formation of citric and other acids in quantity from sugar.

The lines of evidence are essentially of four main types, although there are many supporting experiments (see Kornberg, 1959):

(1) Cell-free extracts from many organisms contain all the enzymes needed for operation of the cycle in its entirety.

(2) Mutants of *E. coli* and *Aerobacter* that lack the condensing enzyme for reaction 22 cannot oxidize acetate, although they can oxidize succinate. Also, they oxidize glucose only slowly. They require glutamic or α-ketoglutaric acid as a nutrient (since this would normally arise via the accumulative function of the cycle) (Gilvarg and Davis, 1956). Similarly *Acetomonas oxydans* (Chap. XVI), which cannot oxidize acetate, does not contain all the cycle enzymes.

(3) Large cultures of *E. coli* or *M. lysodeikticus*, metabolizing C^{14}-labeled acetate, were extracted and the various cycle intermediates purified; the specific radioactivities of all intermediates, and of the expired CO_2, were of the same order of magnitude and matched that of the recovered acetate (Swim and Krampitz, 1954; Saz and Krampitz, 1954–1955; Ajl and Wong, 1955). In yeast also the specific radio-activity of the CO_2 matched that of the two carboxyls of citrate, from which CO_2 should come in reaction 24 (de Moss and Swim, 1957).

(4) From yeast metabolizing C^{14} acetate, samples were taken every few minutes for analysis and for determination of the radioactivity of the cycle acids. After 10 minutes C^{14} was found only in citrate, succinate, and malate, and the activities indicated that nearly equal amounts of these three acids had been formed. Isotope also entered glutamate very early. Calculations from the rates of incorporation of C^{14} show that *all* of the acetate oxidized must pass through citrate, succinate, and malate (Kornberg, 1959). Similarly *Mycob. butyricum* oxidizing C^{14}-glycerol converts it to pyruvate and thence to oxalacetate, ketoglutarate, and CO_2; it also incorporates acetate into these products (Edson *et al.*, 1959). This shows that pyruvate must be oxidized *via* the cycle.

The accumulative function of the cycle is due to two additional reactions (Kornberg and Krebs, 1957):

Isocitric acid, in addition to reaction 24, can split into a C_4 and a C_2 compound under the action of *isocitritase:*

$$
\begin{array}{ll}
\text{COOH} & \text{COOH} \\
| & | \\
\text{HCOH} & \text{CHO} \\
| & + \\
\text{CHCOOH} \rightarrow & \text{CH}_2\text{COOH} \\
| & | \\
\text{CH}_2 & \text{CH}_2 \\
| & | \\
\text{COOH} & \text{COOH}
\end{array}
$$

The resulting glyoxylic acid can condense with acetyl-coenzyme A to form malic acid, under the action of *malate synthetase:*

$$
\begin{array}{lll}
\text{COOH} & & \text{COOH} \\
| & & | \\
\text{CHO} & & \text{HCOH} \\
+ & \rightarrow & | \\
\text{CH}_3 & & \text{CH}_2 \\
| & & | \\
\text{CO·CoA} & & \text{COOH}
\end{array}
$$

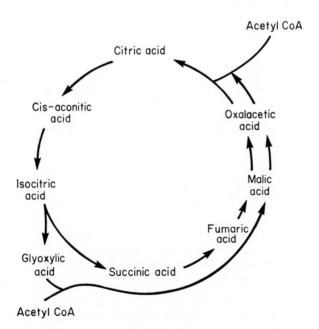

FIGURE V–15

Modification of the cycle in Figure V–14 by addition of isocitritase and malic synthetase (work of Ajl, Kornberg and Krebs, and others).

Since the succinic acid formed in (24) can also be oxidized to malic (reaction 25), citric acid in this system gives rise to *two* molecules of malic acid without loss of CO_2 (see Fig. V–15).

The enzyme isocitritase, which is the key enzyme for this "glyoxylic cycle," is formed in *Ps. ovalis* and *E. coli* only when these organisms are grown on acetate (Kornberg and Lund, 1959). Both it and malate synthetase have been demonstrated in a representative group of bacteria and fungi.

It is evident that this reaction, by taking up acetyl-coenzyme A and not giving off CO_2, steadily accumulates citric acid and other intermediates; the oxalacetate can be aminated to aspartic acid. Fungi like *Rhizopus nigricans*, which form large amounts of fumaric acid, or *Aspergillus niger*, which accumulates citric acid, doubtless operate through this cycle (Kornberg and Collins, 1958–1960). The introduction of two molecules of acetyl-coenzyme A makes it also a favorable system for the conversion of fats to succinate and thence to many other compounds.

The elucidation of these cycles is a major contribution to microbial biochemistry, and the exploration of all their side reactions should mean that the oxidative aspects of bacterial metabolism will come to be almost completely understood.

REFERENCES

Ajl, S. J., and Wong, D. T. O. 1955. *Arch. Biochem. Biophys.*, **54**:474–485.
Appleby, C. A., and Morton, R. K. 1959. *Biochem. J.*, **73**:539–550.
Baddiley, J.; Thain, E. M.; Novelli, G. D.; and Lipmann, F. 1953. *Nature*, **171**:76.
Ball, E. 1944. *Ann. N. Y. Acad. Sci.*, **45**:363–375.
Bartsch, R. G., and Kamen, M. D. 1960. *J. Biol. Chem.*, **235**:825–831.
Battelli, F., and Stern, L. 1910–1912. *Biochem. Z.*, **30**:172–194; **46**:317–342, 343–366.
Bertho, A., and Gluck, H. 1932. *Ann.*, **494**:159–191.
Bishop, D. H. L.; Pandya, H. P.; and King, H. K. 1962. *Biochem. J.*, **83**:606–614.
Boeri, E., and Tosi, L. 1956. *Arch. Biochem. Biophys.*, **60**:463–475.
Bomstein, R.; Goldberger, R.; and Tisdale, H. 1960. *Biochem. Biophys. Res. Comm.*, **3**:479–483.
Boonstra, J. Colpa-, and Holton, F. A. 1959. *Biochem. J.*, **72**: 4P.
Borsook, H., and Dubnoff, J. W. 1947. *J. Biol. Chem.*, **169**:247–258.
Brand, Th. Freiherr, von. 1946. Anaerobiosis in Invertebrates. Biodynamica Monographs, No. 4., Normandy, Missouri, USA, 328 pp.
Bredemann, G. 1909. *Zentr. Bakt. II*, **23**:385–568.
Brodie, A. F. 1952. *J. Biol. Chem.*, **199**:835–842.
Burton, K., and Wilson, T. H. 1953. *Biochem. J.*, **54**:86–94.
Cannan, R. K.; Cohen, B.; and Clark, W. M. 1926. *U. S. Publ. Health Repts., Suppl.*, **55**:34 pp.
*Chance, B., and Williams, G. R. 1956. The Respiratory Chain and Oxidative Phosphorylation. *Adv. in Enzymol.*, **17**:65–130.

Clark, W. M., and Cohen, B. 1923. *U. S. Publ. Health Repts.*, **38**:933–958.

*Clark, W. M.; Cohen, B. and Gibbs, H. D. 1925. *U. S. Publ. Health Repts.*, **40**:1131–1201.

Cohen, S. S. 1951. *J. Biol. Chem.*, **188**:501–508; **189**:617–628.

Crane, F. L.; Glenn, J. L.; and Green, D. E. 1956. *Biochim. Biophys. Acta*, **22**:475–487.

Cross, M. J., and Woods, D. D. 1954. *Biochem. J.*, **58**:xvi; Helleiner, C. W., and Woods, D. D. 1956. *Ibid.*, 26P.

Dedic, G. A., and Koch, O. G. 1956. *J. Bact.*, **71**:126.

Dickens, F. 1938. *Biochem. J.*, **32**:1626–1644, 1645–1653.

Eagon, R. G., and Williams, A. K. 1959. *Arch. Biochem. Biophys.*, **79**:401–402.

Edson, N. L. 1947. *Biochem. J.*, **41**:145–151.

Edson, H. L.; Hunter, G. J. E.; Kulka, R. G.; and Wright, D. E. 1959. *Biochem. J.*, **72**:249–261.

Einbeck, H. 1914. *Z. physiol. Chem.*, **90**:301–308.

Elema, B. 1932. See refs. to Chap. X.

Entner, N., and Stanier, R. Y. 1951. *J. Bact.*, **62**:181–186.

von Euler, H., and Adler, E. 1935. *Z. physiol. Chem.*, **235**:122–153.

Fischer, F. G.; Roedig, A.; and Rauch, K. 1942. *Ann.*, **552**:203–242.

Foster, J. W., and Carson, S. F. 1950. *Proc. Nat. Acad. Sci.*, **36**:219–229.

Franke, W., and Siewerdt, D. 1944. *Z. physiol. Chem.*, **280**:76–87.

Gillespie, L. J. 1920. *Soil Sci.*, **9**:199–216.

Gilvarg, C., and Davis, B. D. 1956. *J. Biol. Chem.*, **222**:307–319.

Gloor, V.; Isler, O.; Morton, R. A.; Rüegg, R.; and Wiss, O. 1958. *Helv. Chim. Acta*, **41**:2357–2362.

Gray, C. T.; Wimpenny, J. W. T.; Hughes, D. E.; and Ranlett, M. 1963. *Biochim. Biophys. Acta*, **67**:157–160.

Green, D. E., and Stickland, L. H. 1934. *Biochem. J.*, **28**:898–900.

Green, D. E.; Stickland, L. H.; and Tarr, H. L. A. 1934. *Biochem. J.*, **28**:1812–1824.

Green, D. E.; Ziegler, D. M.; and Doeg, K. A. 1959. *Arch. Biochem. Biophys.*, **84**:280–282.

Haas, E.; Horecker, B. L.; and Hogness, T. R. 1940, 1942. *J. Biol. Chem.*, **136**:747–774 (1940); Haas, E.; Harrer, C. J.; and Hogness, T. R. *J. Biol. Chem.*, **143**:341–349 (1942).

*Hanes, C. S.; Bird, F. J. R.; and Isherwood, F. A. 1952. *Biochem. J.*, **51**:25–35.

Hatefi, Y.; Haavik, A. G.; and Griffiths, D. E. 1961. *Biochem. Biophys. Res. Comms.*, **4**:441–446, 447–453.

Hewitt, L. F. 1931. *Biochem. J.*, **25**:169–176. 1452–1457.

*Hewitt, L. F. 1950. Oxidation Reduction Potentials in Bacteriology and Biochemistry, 6th ed. Edinburgh, E. S. Livingstone.

Hopkins, F. G.; Morgan, E. J.; and Lutwak-Mann, C. 1938. *Biochem. J.*, **32**:1829–1848.

Horecker, B. L., and Smyrniotis, P. Z. 1951. *J. Biol. Chem.*, **193**:371–381; Horecker, B. L.; Smyrniotis, P. Z.; and Seegmiller, J. E. *Ibid.*, 383–396.

Huennekens, F. M.; Osborn, M. J.; and Whiteley, H. R. 1958. *Science*, **128**:120–124.

Ishikawa, S., and Lehninger, A. L. 1962. *J. Biol. Chem.*, **237**:2401–2408.

Itagaki, E.; Fujita, T.; and Sato, R. 1961. *Biochem. Biophys. Res. Comms.*, **5**:30–34.

Jones, M. E.; Lipmann, F.; Hilz, H.; and Lynen, F. 1953. *J. Amer. Chem. Soc.*, **75**:3285–3286.

Jordan, R. M. M. 1952. *Brit. J. Exp. Path.*, **33**:27–35, 36–45.

Kamen, M. D., and Takeda, Y. 1956. *Biochim. Biophys. Acta*, **21**:518–523.

*Kaplan, N. O. 1951. Thermodynamics and Mechanism of the Phosphate Bond. In, The Enzymes, **2**(pt. 1): 55–113. New York, Academic Press.

Kaufman, S.; Gilvarg, C.; Cori, O.; and Ochoa, S. 1953. *J. Biol. Chem.*, **203**:869–888.

Kaufman, S.; Korkes, S.; and del Campillo, A. 1951. *J. Biol. Chem.*, **92**:301–312.

Keilin, D. 1925. *Proc. Roy. Soc.*, **B98**:312–339.

Keilin, D. 1929. *Ibid.*, **B104**:206–252.

Keilin, D. 1930. *Ibid.*, **B106**:418–444.

Keilin, D., and Harpley, C. H. 1941. *Biochem. J.*, **35**:688–692.

Keilin, D., and Hartree, R. 1939. *Proc. Roy. Soc.*, **B127**:167–191.

Kluyver, A. J. 1931. The Chemical Actions of Micro-organisms. Univ. London Press.

Knight, B. C. J. G., and Fildes, P. 1930. *Biochem. J.*, **24**:1496–1502; cf. Fildes, P. 1929. *Brit. J. Exp. Path.*, **10**:151–175, 197–204.

Korkes, S.; del Campillo, A.; Gunsalus, I. C.; and Ochoa, S. 1952. *J. Biol. Chem.*, **193**: 721–735.

Korkes, S.; del Campillo, A.; and Ochoa, S. 1950. *J. Biol. Chem.*, **187**:891–905.

Kornberg, A., and Pricer, W. E., Jr. 1950. *J. Biol. Chem.*, **186**:557–567.

*Kornberg, H. L. 1959. Aspects of Terminal Respiration in Microorganisms. *Ann. Rev. Microbiol.*, **13**:49–78; cf. Kornberg *et al.*, *Biochem. J.*, **68**:535–542, 542–548, 549–556 (1958); **77**:438–445 (1960); **81**:503–513 (1961).

Kornberg, H. L., and Collins, J. F. 1958–1960. *Biochem. J.*, **68**:3P; Collins, J. F., and Kornberg, H. L. 1960. *Ibid.* **77**:430–438.

Kornberg, H. L., and Krebs, H. A. 1957. *Nature*, **179**:988–991.

Kornberg, H. L., and Lund, P. 1959. *Biochem. J.*, **72**:33P.

Kovachevich, R., and Wood, W. A. 1955. *J. Biol. Chem.*, **213**:745–756.

Krebs, H. A.; Gurin, S.; and Eggleston, L. V. 1952. *Biochem. J.*, **51**:614–627.

Krebs, H. A.; Ruffo, A.; Johnson, M.; Eggleston, L. V.; and Hems, R. 1953. *Biochem. J.*, **54**:107–116.

Kubowitz, F., and Haas, E. 1932. *Biochem. Z.*, **255**:247–277.

Lara, F. J. S. 1959. *Biochim. Biophys. Acta*, **33**:565–567.

Lardy, H. A. (ed.). 1950. Respiratory Enzymes. Chap. IV, by L. Anderson and G. W. E. Plant. Minneapolis, Burgess Pub. Co.

*Lehninger, A. L., and Wadkins, C. L. 1962. Oxidative Phosphorylation. *Ann. Rev. Biochem.*, **31**:47–78.

*Lemberg, R.; Legge, J. W.; and Lockwood, W. H. 1941. *Biochem. J.*, **35**:328–352.

Lepper, E., and Martin, C. J. 1930. *Brit. J. Exp. Path.*, **11**:137–139, 140–145.

Lightbrown, J. W., and Jackson, F. L. 1956–1958. *Biochem. J.*, **63**:130–137; **69**:63–67 (1958).

Lineweaver, H., and Burk, D. 1934. *J. Am. Chem. Soc.*, **56**:658–666.

*Lipmann, F. 1941. Metabolic Generation and Utilization of Phosphate Bond Energy. *Adv. in Enzymol.*, **1**:99–162.

Lipmann, F. 1946. In, Currents in Biochemical Research. D. E. Green, ed. New York, Interscience Press.

*Lipmann, F. 1953. On the Chemistry and Function of Coenzyme A. *Bact. Revs.*, **17**: 1–16.

Lipmann, F.; Jones, M. E.; Black, S.; and Flynn, R. M. 1952. *J. Amer. Chem. Soc.*, **74**:2384.

Lipmann, F.; Kaplan, N. O.; Novelli, G. D.; Tuttle, L. C.; and Guirard, B. M. 1947. *J. Biol. Chem.*, **167**:869–870.

Lynen, F. 1954. Acetyl Coenzyme A and the Fatty Acid Cycle. *Harvey Lect.*, ser. 48, 210–244. New York, Academic Press.

MacGee, J., and Doudoroff, M. 1954. *J. Biol. Chem.*, **210**:617–626.

McLeod, J. W., and Gordon, J. 1923. *J. Path. and Bact.*, **26**:326–331, 332–340.

Massey, V. 1958. *Biochim. Biophys. Acta.*, **30**:500–509.

Meyerhof, O., and Kiessling, W. 1935. *Biochem. Z.*, **283**:83–113.

Michaelis, L. 1940. *Ann. N. Y. Acad. Sci.*, **40**:39–76.
*Michaelis, L. 1951. Theory of Oxidation-Reduction. In, The Enzymes, **2**(pt. 1): 1–54. New York, Academic Press.
Michaelis, L., and Menten, M. L. 1913. *Biochem. Zeit.*, **49**:333–369.
Mitchell, P. 1959. In, Structure and Function of Sub-cellular Components. *Biochem. Soc. Symposia*, **16**:73–93.
Morton, R. K. 1961. *Nature*, **192**:727–731.
Moss, J. A. de, and Swim, H. E. 1957. *J. Bact.*, **74**:445–451.
Negelein, E., and Wulff, H. J. 1937. *Biochem. Zeit.*, **289**:436–437; **290**:445–446.
Niederpruem, D. J., and Hackett, D. P. 1959. *Nature*, **184**:1954–1955.
Novelli, G. D.; Schmetz, F. J. Jr.; and Kaplan, N. O. 1954. *J. Biol. Chem.*, **206**: 533–545.
*Ochoa, S. 1951. Biological Mechanisms of Carboxylation and Decarboxylation. *Physiol. Revs.*, **31**:56–106.
Page, A. C.; Gale, P.; Wallick, H.; Walton, R. B.; McDaniel, L. E.; Woodruff, H. B.; and Folkers, K. 1960. *Arch. Biochem. Biophys.*, **87**:318–321.
Pappenheimer, A. M., Jr.; Howland, J. L.; and Miller, P. A. 1962. *Biochem. Biophys. Acta*, **64**:229–242.
Pappenheimer, A. M., Jr., and Williams, C. M. 1953–1954. *Anat. Rec.*, **117**:543; *J. Biol. Chem.*, **209**:915–929.
Pasteur, L. 1861. *Compt. rend. Acad. sci.*, **52**:1260.
Pasteur, L. 1876. Etudes sur la Bière. Paris (see Chap. I).
Peters, R. A. 1957. Mechanism of the Toxicity of *Dichapetalum cymosum*. *Adv. in Enzymol.*, **18**:113–159.
Pinchot, G. B., and Hormanski, M. 1962. *Proc. Nat. Acad. Sci.*, **48**:1970–1977.
Postgate, J. R. 1956. *J. Gen. Microbiol.*, **14**:545–572.
Potter, V. R., and duBois, K. P. 1942. *J. Gen. Physiol.*, **26**:391–404.
Quastel, J. H., and Whetham, M. D., 1924–1925. *Biochem. J.*, **18**:519–534; **19**:520–531, 645–651.
Quastel, J. H., and Wooldridge, W. R. 1927, 1928. *Biochem. J.*, **21**:148–168, 1224–1251; **22**:689–702 (1928).
Rabinowitz, M., and Bernard, G. de, 1957. *Biochim. Biophys. Acta*, **26**:22–29.
Racker, E. 1948. *Federation Proc.*, **7**:180.
Racker, E.; de la Haba, G.; and Leder, I. G. 1953. *J. Amer. Chem. Soc.*, **75**:1010–1011.
Ramasarma, T., and Lester, R. L. 1960. *J. Biol. Chem.*, **235**:3309–3314.
Reed, L. J., and de Busk, B. G. 1952–1953. *J. Amer. Chem. Soc.*, **74**:3457, 3964–3965; 75:1261–1262; *J. Biol. Chem.*, **199**:872–880, 881–888 (1952).
Rodkey, F. L., and Ball, E. G. 1952. *Proc. Nat. Acad. Sci.*, **38**:396–399.
Saz, H. J., and Krampitz, L. O. 1954–1955. *J. Bact.*, **67**:409–418; **69**:288–292.
Schachman, H. K.; Pardee, A. B.; and Stanier, R. Y. 1952. *Arch. Biochem. Biophys.*, **38**:245–260.
Schaeffer, P. 1952. *Biochim. Biophys. Acta*, **9**:261–270, 362–368.
*Schlenk, F. 1951. Codehydrogenases I and II and Apoenzymes. In, The Enzymes, **2** (pt. 1): 250–315. New York, Academic Press.
Schrecker, A. W., and Kornberg, A. 1950. *J. Biol. Chem.*, **182**:795–803.
Searls, R. L., and Sanadi, D. R. 1959, 1960. *Proc. Nat. Acad. Sci.*, **45**:697–701 (1959); *Biochem. Biophys. Res. Comm.*, **2**:189–192 (1960).
Sekuru, I.; Takemori, S.; Orii, Y.; and Okunuki, K. 1960. *Biochim. Biophys. Acta*, **37**:64–71.
Shibko, S., and Pinchot, G. B. 1961. *Arch. Biochem. Biophys.*, **93**:140–146.
Slater, E. C. 1950. *Biochem. J.*, **46**:484–498, 499–503.
Smith, L. 1954. Bacterial Cytochromes. *Bact. Revs.*, **18**:106–130.

Srere, P. A.; Cooper, J. R.; Klybas, V.; and Racker, E. 1955. *Arch. Biochem. Biophys.*, **59**:535-538.

Stadtman, E. R.; Novelli, G. D.; and Lipmann, F. 1952. *J. Biol. Chem.*, **191**:365.

Stephenson, M. 1928. *Biochem. J.*, **22**:605-614.

*Stephenson, M. 1949. Bacterial Metabolism, 3rd ed., Chap. 2. London, Longmans, Green and Co.

Stern, J. R.; Coon, M. J.; and del Campillo, A. 1953. *J. Amer. Chem. Soc.*, **57**:1517-1518.

Stern, J. R.; Shapiro, B.; Stadtman, E. R.; and Ochoa, S. 1952. *J. Biol. Chem.*, **193**:703-720.

Swim, H. E., and Krampitz, L. O. 1954. *J. Bact.*, **67**:419-425, 426-434.

Szent-Györgyi, A. 1924. *Biochem. Z.*, **150**:195-210.

Theorell, H. 1934-1937. *Biochem. Z.*, **272**:155-156 (1934); **278**:263-290 (1935); **290**:293-303 (1937).

Thunberg, T. 1916. *Zentr. Physiol.*, **31**:91-93; *Chem. Abstr.*, **11**:457 (1917).

Tissières, A. 1951. *Biochem. J.*, **50**:279-288.

Tissières, A., and Burris, R. H. 1956. *Biochim. Biophys. Acta*, **20**:436-437.

Todd, Sir A. 1959. *Proc. Nat. Acad. Sci.*, **45**:1389-1397.

Utter, M. F.; Kurahashi, K.; and Rose, I. A. 1954. *J. Biol. Chem.*, **207**:787-802, 821-841.

Vallee, B. L., and Hoch, F. L. 1955. *Proc. Nat. Acad. Sci.*, **41**:327-338.

Vernon, L. P. 1956. *J. Biol. Chem.*, **222**:1035-1044, 1045-1049.

Vernon, L. P., and Mangum, J. H. 1960. *Arch. Biochem. Biophys.*, **90**:103-104.

Wainio, W. W.; Person, P.; Eichel, B.; and Cooperstein, S. J. 1951. *J. Biol. Chem.*, **192**:349-360.

Wainio, W. W.; Vander Wende, C.; and Shimp, N. F. 1959. *J. Biol. Chem.*, **234**:2433, 2436.

Warburg, O. 1934. *Naturwiss.*, **22**:207, 441-449.

Warburg, O., and Christian, W. 1933. *Biochem. Z.*, **266**:377-411.

Warburg, O., and Christian, W. 1938. *Biochem. Z.*, **298**:150-168.

Warburg, O.; Christian, W.; and Griese, A. 1935. *Biochem. Z.*, **279**:143-144; **282**:157-205.

Warburg, O., and Negelein, E. 1933. *Biochem. Z.*, **262**:237-238.

Weibull, C.; Beckman, H.; and Bergstrom, L. 1959. *J. Gen. Microbiol.*, **20**:519-531.

Whiteley, H. A. 1953. *J. Amer. Chem. Soc.*, **75**:1518-1519.

Wrigley, C. W., and Linnane, A. W. 1961. *Biochem. Biophys. Res. Comms.*, **4**:66-70.

Yakushizi, E., and Okunuki, K. 1940. *Proc. Imp. Acad. Tokyo*, **16**:299-302.

Yamaguchi, S. 1935. *Acta Phytochim.* (Japan), **8**:263-284.

Yamanaka, T., and Okunuki, K. 1962. *Biochim. Biophys. Acta.*, **59**:755-756.

Yonetani, T. 1960. *J. Biol. Chem.*, **235**:3138-3142.

Yoshikawa, H. 1951. *J. Biochem.* (Japan), **38**:1-5.

CHAPTER VI

Bacteria and the Soil

Myriads of the minutest organisms populate this loosely-packed substratum, so extraordinarily well adapted to the life of microorganisms. Here they feed, respire, grow, multiply and die in the battle for existence. . . . The results of these intensive life processes in the soil are those manifold and wonderful changes both of organic and inorganic substances which are of such great significance not only for the economy of mankind but above all in the organisation of nature.

N. G. Cholodny (1930)

1. CONDITIONS IN THE SOIL

Before going further into the physiology of the bacteria, it will be necessary to consider briefly their natural habitat. The entire life of animals and men is not merely "rounded with a sleep" but rounded with a return to the soil. Not only is the matter of their bodies placed in the soil at death, but it is added to the soil constantly during life, in the form of excreta. Using the term *soil* in its most general sense to include also natural waters, all dead animal and vegetable matter finds its way there. In the soil the nitrogen of proteins and of animal excreta is converted to ammonia and nitrate, the carbon of organic material is mostly oxidized to carbonate, and organically bound minerals are set free as ions. These final products constitute the nutrient material for the plant world, since plants grow by the intake of nitrate (or ammonia), CO_2, and H_2O with metallic and acidic ions. Animals (except some protozoa) grow by consuming plants or by consuming other animals which have fed on plants, and so the cycle is completed. The animal kingdom is "parasitic" upon the cycle, and since its presence is not necessary, its complete disappearance would have little effect on the working of the cycle.

The essential breakdown processes, without which life would speedily come to a complete standstill, are brought about by bacteria and fungi. These saprophytic organisms are therefore of paramount importance in the world's economy. Their growth depends on the conditions in the soil, that is, on the water, air, minerals, pH, and temperature, as well as on the organic matter, and all these to varying extents are dependent on the type of soil and the vegetation growing in it.

A. Types of Soil

In order of increasing water and decreasing particle size, soils may be roughly classified thus:

TYPE	DIAMETER
Gravel	2 mm upward
Coarse sand	2 to 0.6 mm
Fine sand	0.6 to 0.2 mm
"Flour" sand	0.06 to 0.02 mm
Coarse silt	0.02 to 0.006 mm
Dust	0.006 to 0.002 mm
Clay	Below 0.002 mm

The clay thus defined has particles no larger than bacteria. In addition, soil contains organic matter or humus in varying amounts.

Soil types are characterized not only by their particle size and water content, but also by the vegetation they support. A good deal of this work has been done by Glinka, Dokuchaev, and others in Russia. The types and their dependence on climate are summarized in the following diagram (from Muckenhirn *et al.*, 1949; cf. Thorp and Smith, 1949):

COLD

Perpetual snow and ice				
Tundra soils				
Podzols (Taiga)				
Arid	*Semiarid*	*Subhumid*	*Humid to Wet*	
Sierozems and desert soils	Chestnut and brown soils	Chernozems and prairie soils	Podzols	
(desert grasses and shrubs)	(steppe vegetation)	(grassland)	(forest, rain forests)	
			Lateritic soils (tropical plains)	

DRY — WET

Increasing temperature

HOT

Increasing humidity ⟶

The temperate zone soils in the center of the diagram grade rather smoothly in their properties from left to right. The sierozems are weakly alkaline soils, poor in humus, high in carbonates, and with a relatively low clay content. They are not sharply differentiated into "horizons" or layers. At the other end the podzols have clear-cut horizons (see sec. F), high humus content, and acid reaction, at any rate in the upper layers.

The three principal groups of "horizons" are A, the upper or eluvial layers, from which material is being (or has been) leached; B, the middle or illuvial layers which are being (or have been) enriched; and C, the unenriched mineral layers beneath (Glinka, 1927). These are extensively subdivided according to soil type and vegetation.

B. Pore Space

The space between the particles may be filled with liquid (water or salt solution), or with gas (air or other gases).

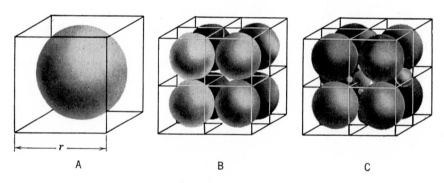

A   B   C

FIGURE VI–1
Pore space in soil particles (original).

In a soil consisting of spherical particles all of the same size, the space between the particles is independent of their size. This is clear from consideration of the three equal cubes of soil in Fig. VI–1. The first cube contains only one sphere, the second eight small spheres of equal size. If the side of the cube be r then the volume of the cube is r^3. The radius of the sphere in Figure VI–1A is $\frac{r}{2}$ and its volume therefore $\frac{4}{3}\pi\left(\frac{r}{2}\right)^3 = \frac{\pi r^3}{6}$. Now consider the eight small spheres, Figure

VI–1B. The radius of each is $\dfrac{r}{4}$ and the volume of each therefore $\dfrac{4}{3}\pi\left(\dfrac{r}{4}\right)^3$: the total volume of eight spheres is therefore $8\cdot\dfrac{4}{3}\pi\left(\dfrac{r}{4}\right)^3$ or $\dfrac{\pi r^3}{6}$, i.e., the same as the one sphere. The space between the spheres is hence $r^3-\dfrac{\pi r^3}{6}$ or $r^3\left(1-\dfrac{\pi}{6}\right)$ in each case. It is thus approximately 50 per cent of the total volume.

Soils are, of course, not packed so geometrically as in the above figures, because the particles are not all the same size and thus pack more closely. In actual soils, therefore, the pore space is usually smaller, generally from 30 to 45 per cent. This can be seen, without mathematical proof, from Figure VI–1C, in which the tiny spheres fill up part of the space between the large ones. Russell *et al*. (1923) give the following analyses of three Rothamsted soils (Table VI–1). The figures are in percentages of the volume.

TABLE VI–1

Soil Type	SOLIDS		Total Pore Space	OF THE PORE SPACE:	
	Mineral	Organic		Water Occupies	Air Occupies
Arable unmanured	62	4	34	23	11
Arable dunged	51	11	38	30	8
Pasture	41	12	47	40	7

The effect of the manure, or of the cover of grass, shows itself in an increase in the organic matter, moisture content, and pore space.

C. Soil Water and Its Effects

The space between the particles is filled partly with air and partly with water. The ratio between these two largely determines the conditions for bacterial development.

Water clings to the surface of each particle to an extent varying with the nature of the soil. Other things being equal, the amount of water will increase with decreasing particle size, simply because decreasing particle size means more surfaces for the capillary water to be held on. Hence, although the total pore space is independent of absolute particle size, and depends only on the heterogeneity, as shown above, the amount of space that is available for air will decrease with decreasing particle size. Clays are thus the wettest and also the least aerated of soils. The humus content is also a determining factor, because one of the properties of humus is that it increases the water content of soil (cf. Table VI–1).

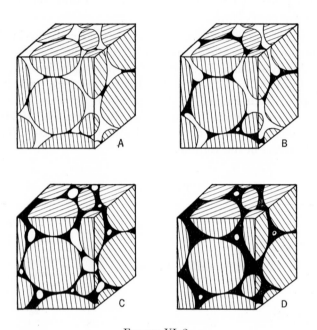

FIGURE VI–2

Air and water in soil particles.
   A. Pendulous state; water films completely disconnected.
   B. Funicular state; water films continuous, air spaces continuous.
   C. Replete state; water films continuous, air spaces discontinuous.
   D. Water-logged state; pore space almost completely filled with water.
   (After the scheme proposed by H. Gradmann, 1928.)

When the soil is dry, the continuous capillary film breaks up, as in Figure VI–2A. This has been called the *pendulous* state (Gradmann, 1928). The air spaces are interconnected and are continuous. In the partly wet state which will precede this, termed the *funicular* state, the capillary film is a continuous network, but the air spaces are still connected, as shown in Figure VI–2B. In the *replete* state, Figure VI–2C, the air spaces are isolated from one another, while in "waterlogged" soil there are practically no air spaces (Figure VI–2D, cf. also Baver, 1956).

Microorganisms cannot develop in the absence of water, but their types and development are also controlled by the presence or absence of air, so that, all in all, their activities depend largely on the thickness of the water film. With *Bac. mycoides*, Rahn (1913) found the optimum film thickness to be 20 to 40 μ; in sand with particles of 1-mm diameter, this would correspond to a water content of about 10 per cent. In average arable soil the corresponding water content would be much higher. Using a light sandy soil, Winogradsky (1924) determined the depths at which aerobic Azotobacter and anaerobic Clostridium were to be found, with increasing water content. Soil mixed with 1 per cent mannitol was filled into tubes of varying length, which could be opened at top and bottom for examination. After three days' incubation at 28° C he found the following:

WATER CONTENT	DEPTH TO WHICH AZOTOBACTER WAS FOUND	DEPTH TO WHICH CLOSTRIDIUM WAS FOUND
15.5%	23 cm	Very few, only below this level
18%	18 cm	" " " " " "
20.4%	4–5 cm	Many, below this level
23%	Only at extreme surface	Throughout; marked gas evolution after 12 hours' incubation

48% = total water-holding capacity of the light soil used

High water content thus encourages anaerobes, while oxidative processes, which destroy organic matter, do best in relatively dry soils. An example of this generalization is shown by the soils of Colombia, in which the organic matter content decreases steadily with decreasing rainfall (Jenny *et al.*, 1948). At high annual temperatures the organic matter also increases with increasing altitude, presumably due to increasing humidity.

The amount of soil water also affects temperature, since water has a higher specific heat than most solids. Cold soils tend to be richer in organic matter, because their rate of decomposition is slower. Extremes are exemplified by our northern forest soils with their high content of humus, and the subtropical soils of citrus orchards or pineapple fields where the organic matter is almost completely mineralized each season. In the southern United States well-drained soils have less than 0.05 per cent organic nitrogen, while in the northern states the values will be above 0.2 per cent (Jenny, 1930).

The "water" is of course not pure water, but *soil solution*. It can be obtained by forcing water through a column of soil under pressure, or by mixing soil with paraffin and separating the aqueous layer. It is a mixture of salts, having a total osmotic pressure of about one-half to one atmosphere (or a molarity of about M/50) in normal soils. Its content of each salt may vary within wide limits. The following table relates to cropped agricultural soils from California; it shows a general decrease in nutrient ions (but not in bicarbonate) as a result of the plant growth. The low values for phosphate reflect the fact that most

TABLE VI–2. Composition of Typical Soil Solutions

(From Russell, 1942)

(Soil from field sown to barley. Data recalculated to uniform moisture content.)

	PARTS PER MILLION							
	NO_3	HCO_3	SO_4	PO_4	Ca	Mg	Na	K
Spring	150–260	80–260	560–780	0.6–3.3	222–336	76–97	42–87	12–41
Fall	16–60	150–230	430–600	0.6–1.2	190	47–64	40	9–22

of this is in insoluble form (soil pH 7.4 to 8.2), and the figures essentially represent saturated solutions of calcium phosphate. In addition some phosphate, sometimes as much as half, is bound in organic complexes (cf. Dean, 1949). With this exception the composition of the soil solution is not far from that of a dilute culture solution (Chap. IV, sec. 2), but the addition of salts often improves the culture conditions further. The addition of potassium, phosphate, or ammonium usually stimulates the conversion of organic matter in soil to CO_2, which indicates increased bacterial and fungal activity.

D. The Gases in the Soil

That part of the pore space that does not contain water contains a mixture of gases, more or less modified from the atmosphere. A number of analyses of soil gases, made at Rothamsted[1] on arable soil, show an average of 0.25 per cent CO_2, as against 0.03 per cent in air (Russell and Appleyard, 1915). Grassland showed higher CO_2 and lower O_2 values, due to its higher organic matter and lower air space (cf. Table VI–1). In general, the CO_2 content indicates (1) the amount of organic matter available for bacterial decomposition; (2) the rate of bacterial

[1] The first of all agricultural experiment stations, near Harpenden, England.

activity; and (3) the efficiency of communication with the air, and therefore the degree of anaerobiosis in the soil. The interpretation of CO_2 content is, however, complicated by interaction with bicarbonate.

Carbon dioxide is only absorbed to a limited extent by roots, and this cannot substitute for the uptake by leaves, so that soil CO_2 is not beneficial (Stolwijk and Thimann, 1957). High soil CO_2 may even inhibit root growth.

In the presence of organic matter and under conditions of poor aeration, not only CO_2 but also hydrogen and sometimes methane are produced by the bacterial fermentations. The highly anaerobic soil under rice, which is kept flooded, contains almost no oxygen, but con-

TABLE VI–3. Analyses of Soil Gases (in %)

(Data Assembled by Waksman, 1932)

Gas	Fallow Land		Cornfield (near roots of corn)	Green Manured Land	Swamp Rice Land
	Before Rainfall	After Rainfall			
Nitrogen	78.05	78.83	80.15	79.18	85.59
Oxygen	20.40	19.26	9.00	7.71	0.54
Carbon dioxide	0.58	0.95	9.11	12.03	4.42
Hydrogen	—	—	0.73	0.07	6.42
Methane	—	—	—	—	2.81

siderable amounts of CH_4 and H_2 (see Table VI–3). The presence of H_2 can also be detected in the humus-rich parts of pasture land, as the table shows. The combustible gases bubbling up from marshes and swamps are, of course, well known; they are usually rich in CH_4 (Chap. XVIII). Nitrous oxide, doubtless formed by reduction of nitrate, is also sometimes found.

E. Hydrogen-Ion Concentration

Frequently the hydrogen-ion concentration is the principal factor controlling microbial development. Well-aerated garden soils usually are close to neutrality, i.e., pH 6.0 to 7.5. Soils rich in organic matter become acid through the fermentative production of organic acids; since fermentation is an anaerobic process, waterlogged soils reach the greatest acidities. Peat may thus attain a pH of 3.2, while the dark-brown soil under forest humus will be about pH 4.5. The acidity is reduced by aeration, the organic acids being oxidized to CO_2. In arid soils, where aeration is intense and temperature high, organic matter is completely oxidized away; as a result such soils frequently become highly alkaline, as in the deserts of Arizona, Nevada, and California, where the soil pH may reach 10.0.

The pH has many more direct effects on the soil than those exerted on the microbial flora. High acidity may lead to binding of organic phosphorus compounds, especially nucleic acids, by adsorption on the clay particles (Bower, 1949). This makes the phosphorus less available to bacteria and to plants. However, organic acid anions, such as citrate, powerfully oppose the adsorption (Goring and Bartholomew, 1952), thus perhaps facilitating the liberation of phosphate to plants, since roots generally excrete some organic acids in the *rhizosphere*. High alkalinity, on the other hand, leads to binding of heavy metals by precipitation as basic carbonates or phosphates. Soils of arid or tropical climates may thus show deficiency of Fe or Mn, although these may be present in normal amounts.

Fertilizers often have a marked effect on the pH, owing to the removal of one ion by the plants; for example, when $Ca(NO_3)_2$ is added, the nitrate ion is absorbed preferentially and the soil becomes alkaline, while when $(NH_4)_2SO_4$ is added, the reverse is true and the soil becomes acid. Urea, owing to its rapid hydrolysis, first turns the soil alkaline, but after a few days the oxidation and absorption of the ammonium result in acidity. These changes are reduced in magnitude by the buffering action of the phosphates, carbonates, and other weak acids in the soil. Calcium carbonate is of prime importance in the soil, as in artificial culture media, in holding the pH weakly alkaline. In addition, it flocculates the colloidal particles of clay and therefore reduces its stickiness and improves the texture. Dressings of $CaCO_3$ or dolomite, up to 1 per cent of the topsoil, are therefore desirable for acid or clay soils, or if organic manure is being used.

F. Humus

Common in varying amounts to all soils are the partly decayed plant residues known as humus. As seen in section A, the humus is most prominent in the wetter and colder soils, particularly those of swamps and forests. Breakdown takes place in the upper layers, is both aerobic and anaerobic, and is carried out by bacteria, actinomycetes, and fungi. The soluble products are leached out into the B horizon of the soil below. The organic acids increase the leaching process, leading sometimes, as in podzol soils, to the formation of a clearly defined leached zone above the enriched B horizons.

Humus greatly affects the workability (*tilth*) and structure of soil, since its essentially fibrous nature introduces friability and prevents hardening into a mass, i.e., it increases the amount of pore space. In addition, it increases the water-holding capacity, probably by chemical combination with the soil colloids, to produce a new and more hydrophilic surface (Quastel and Webley, 1947).

The compounds principally entering into humus formation are those parts of plants and animals that are most resistant to microbes, namely, lignin, some of the hemicelluloses, chitin, tannin, and waxes; to a lesser extent, because more readily broken down, cellulose. There is also some nitrogenous material, because, although part of the protein

TABLE VI–4. Composition of Pine Needles and the Humus Formed from Them

Fraction	Pine Needles	Rotting Layer	Mull
Water-soluble material	13.02	5.80	2.73
Hemicellulose	14.68	15.28	12.39
Cellulose	18.26	9.44	2.56
Lignin	27.63	39.30	50.39
Crude protein	8.53	8.29	7.51
Ether-soluble (waxes, fats)	7.65	4.41	2.99
Ash	3.08	9.20	11.61
Totals	92.85	91.72	90.18
pH		5.6	4.9

is broken down, part is converted to stable aromatic compounds and melanins. However, since plant structures are generally low in nitrogen, the nitrogen content of humus is low (1 to 2 per cent). The chemical nature of humus constituents, apart from that of the plant and animal materials initially added, is somewhat obscure. The so-called humic acids are an ill-defined group of phenolic acids of little-known structure and probably too high molecular weight to be absorbed by roots (Prat, 1962).

The analysis (Table VI–4) of the second and third layers ("mull") of the humus in a northern coniferous forest, compared with the composition of the pine needles themselves, is due to Waksman, Tenney, and Stevens (1928). It shows clearly the breakdown of the cellulose, of part of the hemicellulose, and of the water-soluble material, in contrast to the slight changes in hemicellulose and protein, and the marked resistance of the lignin. Leaves of deciduous trees decay more rapidly than pine needles in general, and the bacterial count in deciduous forest soils is higher than under conifers (Meyer, 1959–1960); hence the A horizon is commonly thinner there. In both forest types the microbial population of the raw humus is much less than in the decaying layers beneath.

If the organic matter decays in or under water, the decay process is slowed down more for some constituents than for others, with the result that the soluble carbohydrates, the pectins, proteins, and often cellulose are largely broken down, and the lignins, hemicelluloses, and waxes accumulate. This constitutes *peat*. Peat may therefore be considered as *anaerobic humus*. Two main types of peat are distinguishable: (1) those formed in low moors, where the water level is maintained by drainage from higher ground, and hence where the water is rich in salts; these have an active flora of cellulose-decomposing and nitrifying bacteria, and many actinomycetes; (2) those formed in high moors, where the water level is maintained by rain and snow, and therefore poor in salts; these are the most acid and have a limited microflora. The humus of high moors contains less protein and much more cellulose and ether-soluble material than that shown in Table VI–4 (see Waksman, 1938, Chap. 7).

2. THE BACTERIAL POPULATION OF THE SOIL AND ITS CENSUS

A. Soil Bacteria in the Air

It should be made clear that, in any soil, bacteria or fungi of a given type will appear whenever the conditions are suitable for that type, because they are constantly being carried about in the air. This was shown during the "spontaneous generation" controversy (Chap. I) and has subsequently been amplified by many studies of the microbial population of the air. Petri dishes exposed even at 35,000-ft altitude have developed many kinds of organisms. Once carried into the air by wind they settle only very slowly; a cell 1 μ in diameter, in a steady 10-mile-an-hour wind, will be carried 9000 miles before falling 100 yd. When turbulence is taken into account as well, it is clear that organisms may be in the air for very long times; most nonsporeformers doubtless die out by drying, or by exposure to the ultraviolet, long before they return to the soil. In tests with artificially contaminated air, *Serratia marcescens* was found to be 99.9 per cent dead within an hour (Kluyver and Visser, 1950).

Some idea of the spread and survival of bacteria in air is given by ZoBell's exposure of plates at different distances from the sea (1942). He used sea-water agar and fresh-water agar, both with peptone, and exposed them in a sustained onshore breeze. The numbers of colonies obtained are shown in Table VI–5. While the ratio between marine and fresh-water organisms steadily decreases, it should be noted that the marine organisms are still present in good numbers in the air a mile inland.

TABLE VI–5. Average Numbers of Bacteria that Developed on Sea-water and Fresh-water Nutrient Agar Exposed to Air under Comparable Conditions during a Sustained Onshore Breeze

(From ZoBell, 1946)

Distance Inland from Sea Wall (meters)	Sea-water Agar I	Fresh-water Agar II	Ratio $\frac{I}{II}$
0	461	43	10.7
100	548	74	7.4
200	263	109	2.4
400	174	157	1.2
800	128	183	0.7
1600	49	106	0.5

Within the soil, bacteria are also carried short distances by protozoa, worms, insects, and so forth. Evidently, therefore, their ready distribution means that the microbial population of different soils is not limited by difficulty of access, as with higher plants or animals, but is primarily limited and controlled by the conditions of the particular soil sample.

B. Physiological Analysis of Soil Organisms

It is useless to attempt to classify the soil bacteria from the forms developing on plates. Plate methods bring out only the organisms that will grow on them and miss many functionally important groups. For example, a deep or a waterlogged soil, rich in anaerobes, will yield few bacteria able to grow on an aerobic plate, while such organisms as the autotrophic, ammonia-oxidizing bacteria, inhibited in their growth by organic matter, will not develop on any "ordinary" plate. Thus the total numbers of bacteria in soil cannot be determined by simple plating. Much work has been expended in the attempt to find the best medium for total counts by plating. Jensen's dextrose casein agar

(1931) gives perhaps the best all-round results, but even with this the figures generally fall below one-tenth of the number found by direct microscopy (see p. 278).

On this account attempts have been made to determine the numbers in each of the various physiological groups by enrichment methods, i.e., by providing a medium that will allow the development of all the members of a particular physiological group. Thus, a series of dilutions of soil or soil extract will be made with, say, urea, together with salts and peptone, and the highest dilution at which urea hydrolysis occurs will be determined. Calculation from this gives us the total number of urea-hydrolyzing organisms per gram of the original soil. Although extensive analyses along these lines were made by Düggeli (1923), Fehér (1927, 1929, 1930), and others, the numbers found in the different physiological groups account for only a fraction of the total. Among the autotrophs, counts of the bacteria oxidizing ammonia are of special interest. Winogradsky (1933) sowed soil granules upon a plate of silica gel, containing $(NH_4)_2SO_4$ and other salts, and surfaced with $CaCO_3$. The oxidation of NH_3 to HNO_2—the first stage—is accompanied by an increase of acidity; this causes the $CaCO_3$ to dissolve, and a clear zone therefore appears round the soil particle. By counting the number of zones after four to five days, the number of NH_3-oxidizing organisms was determined. Organic manuring, of course, depresses them (Doak, 1952).

On account of their strictly aerobic nature and rather nondescript physiological activities, the Actinomycetes are omitted from the physiological counts. They can, however, be enumerated from plates by their characteristic morphology, and by the hardness and adherence of their colonies to the medium. Since their conidia are small and numerous, plate counts generally yield Actinomycetes in plenty. In garden soils they comprise up to half the total microbes, and Jensen even found them to comprise as high as 65 per cent of the total count in Australian soils. In the wild, the highest numbers, and the largest number of species, were found under grassland (Flaig and Kutzner, 1960). Grassland also yielded the largest numbers of antibiotic-producing strains. They are sensitive to acid and therefore practically absent from the more acid peats; even at pH 5 their numbers are very low (Jensen, 1930). When chalk was added to an acid peat soil of pH 3.85, in which no Actinomycetes at all were detectable, their numbers went up to 85 millions per gram after six weeks. However, the bacterial numbers went up too, and the Actinomycetes still comprised less than a third of the total count (Jensen, 1930). Forest soils, being less acid, usually have moderate numbers of Actinomycetes. At the other extreme, the arid coral soils of the Pacific atolls contain many more Actinomycetes than bacteria, and they represent from 70 up to 99 per cent of the count (Johnstone, 1947).

Many of these soil forms are Nocardias (Erickson, 1949), and they have sometimes been recorded as Corynebacteria (Hopf, 1950). In river muds, where not many ordinary Actinomycetes would be expected, large numbers of the genus Micromonospora are found; the same is true for lake water, in which Micromonospora may constitute up to 20 per cent of the total microbial population (Umbreit and McCoy, 1941).

Spores of fungi are, of course, also present and are often enumerated by plating on malt-peptone agar which has been acidified to pH 4, to suppress the bacteria. From 10,000 to 500,000 fungus spores per gram are often found (Waksman, 1932). Penicillia and Mucorales are the commonest, especially in moist and acid soils, while dry and alkaline soils yield more Aspergilli; alkaline soils also contain Cunninghamella and Rhizopus (Muskat, 1955). Even saline soils yield many fungi. Plates of soil, or mixtures of sand, peat, and soil have also been used, especially for growth studies of soil fungi (e.g., by Likais, 1952; Domsch, 1955). Like the bacteria, the fungi are more numerous around the roots of plants than elsewhere in the soil (see sec. 3, below). Roots of plants resistant to fungus diseases appeared to have the ability to discourage, or select against, those pathogenic fungi (Timonin, 1940–1941; see the review of Stallings, 1954).

Natural waters usually contain fewer bacteria than soil. Recent counts in the Elbe in Germany gave 20,000 to 45,000 per milliliter in the winter and only about 1000 per milliliter in the summer. The decrease in the summer probably reflects a fall in the amount of organic matter due to higher water temperature, especially since the nitrifiers, which are sensitive to organic matter, were more numerous in the summer (Rheinheimer, 1959–1960). Lake water seldom has over 1000 per milliliter, and the open ocean still less. Close inshore the counts are generally higher, but there are much larger numbers in the bottom deposits. In lake bottoms, at the surface of the mud, figures around 100,000 per milliliter of mud were recorded (see ZoBell, 1946a). However, the relatively high oxygen content of sea water leads to vigorous bacterial development in the upper layers of the sea bottom. The numbers fall off rapidly with increasing depth in both cases. Conditions a few centimeters below the surface become very reducing, as shown by the redox potential. Figure VI–3 summarizes the conditions in the sea bottom as shown by three procedures. It will be seen that the surface mud contains over ten millions per gram, which falls to 1000 at 50 cm down. The redox potential is very negative throughout. The ability of the mud to reduce a redox dye, however, which is a measure of

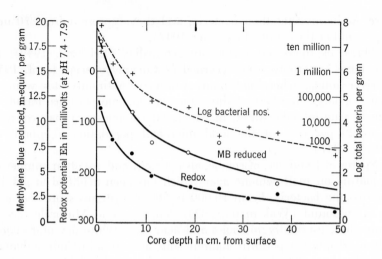

FIGURE VI-3

Bacterial numbers, methylene blue reduction, and redox potential in mud samples from the sea bottom. Note the steep fall in all three from the relatively oxidizing conditions at the mud surface. The water above was 1650 feet deep. (Plotted from data of C. E. ZoBell, *Bull. Am. Assn. Petroleum Geologists*, **30**:477–513, 1946.)

bacterial dehydrogenase activity, decreases along with the bacterial count.

C. Chemical Analysis of Metabolic Products

Since the chemical changes in the soil are mainly due to microorganisms, one can get an idea of their activity by determining the rates of various well-defined soil processes. Of these the oxidation of NH_3 to nitrate, production of NH_3 from protein or peptone, fixation of nitrogen from the air, and production of CO_2 from organic constituents of the soil have been chiefly used. In the past it was hoped that these methods would give a test of fertility that could be agriculturally applied.

1. CARBON DIOXIDE. The significance of the CO_2 in the atmosphere of the soil has already been discussed (p. 264). Determinations of the rate of CO_2 production are usually made using the organic material of the soil, occasionally with the addition of glucose as substrate. The rate of CO_2 production in humus, as a measure of bacterial activity, was apparently first determined by Wollny in 1886; he found the rate to be stimulated by addition of potassium salts. In general, the rate is greatest with neutral or slightly alkaline soils; moisture and aeration are also determining factors.

Occasionally oxygen consumption has been measured instead of CO_2 production, especially in studies of nitrification by soil (see Quastel and Scholefield, 1951). As measure of the total activity of aerobic heterotrophic bacteria, the increase in oxygen consumption that occurs on adding glucose has also been used (Gamble *et al.*, 1952).

The real question is whether CO_2 production or O_2 consumption by soil, or by soil with added organic matter, is any measure either of bacterial numbers or of fertility. Obviously the rate of CO_2 production by a soil must depend not only on the microbes but also on the decomposable matter; the bacterial numbers and types, however, are largely determined by the latter, so that they are not independent variables. In plain soil, therefore, the CO_2 production rate varies roughly with the organic matter, other factors being constant.

Of the types of organic matter, cellulose is probably a major source. Straw added to soil causes an immediate increase in CO_2 production (Schmidt and Starkey, 1951), and Fehér (1927) found the CO_2 evolution to be proportional to the number of cellulose decomposers present. The evolution of CO_2 from soil to which cellulose has been added appears, surprisingly enough, to correlate very well with the agricultural fertility (White *et al.*, 1949). However, this is true only if the soils are not too acid. On soils whose *p*H varied between 7.8 and 4, CO_2 evolution from mannitol was a better criterion (Andrews, 1937), while O_2 consumption with added glucose very roughly paralleled the total plate count (Gamble *et al.*, 1952). All in all, when we consider (1) the wide variety of organisms in the soil, with their different rates of respiration, (2) the presence of algae which consume CO_2, and (3) the presence of weak acids and their salts which can combine with some of the CO_2 produced, it is clear that CO_2 production is a very complex function of microbial activity.

2. AMMONIA. The rate of "ammonification," or ammonia production, is usually determined by adding peptone, casein, or blood to soils; the mixture is incubated, and the NH_3 determined. In a large number of early experiments along these lines, soils of widely differing agricultural productivity have been found to give about the same rate of ammonification. The small differences, however, did parallel differences in nitrifying and nitrogen-fixing power. NH_3 is an intermediate product in soil bacterial activity, being formed from amino acids and then oxidized to nitrite, so that it could accumulate in soil either because of rapid breakdown of protein or of slow further oxidation. Then, too, many organisms important in soil are not actively proteolytic. For this reason the ammonifying power of soil probably has little close connection with total bacterial activity, or with fertility.

3. NITRATE. The oxidation of ammonia to nitrate ("nitrification") is usually determined by incubating soil for several weeks

and determining the nitrate formed (see Chap. X). The soil has to be kept moist but aerobic, i.e., at about half its water-holding capacity. The duration of the experiment should not be too long, as practically any soil will give complete nitrification of added NH_3 if left long enough. The ammonia-oxidizing organisms do not grow at pH more acid than 5.8, and hence nitrifying power will only be high in neutral or alkaline soils.

Many older experiments indicate a parallelism between fertility and nitrifying power. In three soils of different agricultural productivity, the one giving the highest crop had a relative nitrifying power of 93 (arbitrary units), the next, 38, and the least productive, 26 (Ashby, 1904). In another case the most productive soil had a nitrifying power of 54, the next, 29, and the poorest, 4. Waksman and Starkey (1924) treated six plots of identical soil in different ways for 15 years and then determined the crop yield and compared it with nitrifying power; there was very good correlation. The crop yield showed less correlation with the total bacterial plate count, and none at all with the CO_2 production. Both nitrifying power and production of CO_2 from cellulose have correlated well with crop yield in a later study (White et al., 1949). There is no correlation between nitrifying power and total bacteria, however, because readily decomposable organic material, which increases the total bacteria, inhibits the nitrifying organisms. Diesel oil emulsion, for instance, applied to soil at 100 to 500 gal. per acre, increased the total plate count by three or four times, but retarded the rate of oxidation of ammonia for several weeks (Koike and Gainey, 1952).

Along with nitrification, nitrogen fixation has been used as an indicator of soil fertility. The growth of Azotobacter in soil plates to which starch or mannitol has been added is itself a sensitive indicator (Winogradsky, 1924). Only soils of pH 7.2 or greater show appreciable numbers of Azotobacter, or appreciable gain in fixed nitrogen on incubation. If chalk is added to the plate, the nitrogen fixation is a delicate test for other nutrients, especially phosphate (Wieringa, 1939). The fixed nitrogen, of course, can be subsequently oxidized to nitrate.

3. THE RHIZOSPHERE

The immediate vicinity of the roots of plants becomes enriched with organic acids and other substances excreted by roots as well as with sloughed-off cells of the root cap and perhaps root hairs. These materials support the growth of a vigorous microflora, in which the numbers of almost all the physiological types are increased. The rhizosphere organisms can be obtained by lifting the plants from the soil, removing most of the superfluous soil and then shaking the roots, with adhering soil particles, in sterile water. Plate counts made on soil extract media with various additions showed that there were from 5 to 100 times as many bacteria as in control soil, and allowed them to be classified into seven types of increasing nutritional requirements, beginning with those able to develop on a simple glucose-nitrate-salts medium, and proceeding to those growing only in the presence of several added factors (Lochhead and Chase, 1943). This procedure shows that the rhizosphere flora differs from that of the surrounding soil in the following ways: (1) increase in total numbers by about 10 times, (2) increased requirement for amino acids, (3) decreased requirement for yeast extract and for vitamin B_{12} (see Table VI–6). In general, the

Table VI–6. Nutritional Requirements of Bacteria from the Rhizosphere and from the Same Soil Distant from Plants. Average of Two Seasons and Six Crop Plants (Wheat, Oats, Flax, Timothy, Alfalfa, and Red Clover)

(Data of Rouatt and Lochhead, 1955.)

	Control	Rhizosphere
Total count, millions per gram	98	840
Nutrient requirement:*		
Basal medium only	4.2	7.1
Amino acid mixture	15.9	48.7
Yeast extract	48.5	19.8
Yeast extract and vitamin B_{12}	9.3	5.8

* As percentage of the count.

roots of the different crop plants had very similar effects, except that alfalfa specifically encourages organisms having a requirement for B_{12}. This was particularly clearly seen when whole chopped alfalfa plants were mixed in the soil, and probably means that alfalfa roots excrete some B_{12}; higher plants generally do not contain this vitamin but a high B_{12}-synthesizing ability was found to be characteristic of alfalfa root-nodule bacteria (Rouatt and Lochhead, 1955).

Of the amino acids needed for soil bacteria, and particularly for those of the rhizosphere, methionine seems outstandingly important (Wallace and Lochhead, 1950). This may indicate that roots predominantly excrete this amino acid and thus encourage organisms requiring it, or it may only mean that the other amino acids are more readily replaceable by one another. Methionine is apparently irreplaceable, and indeed its existence was first brought to light (by Mueller in 1922) as an unknown compound essential for bacterial growth.

A peculiar feature of soil bacteria is the large proportion that re-

quire one or more vitamins in the medium (in addition to those requiring B_{12}). Some 27 per cent of soil forms isolated had a vitamin requirement (Lochhead and Burton, 1957). As might be expected from
Table VI–6, a somewhat higher percentage of organisms from the
rhizosphere than from ordinary soil were able to synthesize one or more
vitamins; for example, of barley rhizosphere bacteria, 82 per cent
synthesized one or more vitamins (Lochhead, 1957), and it may be
deduced that, except for the amino acids excreted, the proximity of
roots tends to select for increased nutritional independence, perhaps
because they rapidly absorb any B vitamins formed by the bacteria.

Around the roots of plants growing in solution or sand culture,
there is a similar increase in bacterial numbers. Ammonia-liberating,
protein-hydrolyzing, nitrate-reducing, and hemicellulose-hydrolyzing
organisms are all increased from 10 to 100 times above the numbers
in the rest of the medium (Chalvignac, 1958; Balicka, 1958). Chitin-
hydrolyzing organisms are also numerous, amounting in one case to
several hundred thousand per gram of washed roots (Mihaly, 1960),
but since higher plant cell walls do not contain chitin, the meaning of
this is obscure.

The close interrelation between soil microorganisms and the higher
plants growing in the soil deserves fuller exploration. Germination of
fungus spores in the soil may, in some cases, depend on organic compounds excreted by roots, which would be particularly important in
root-rot diseases (see Garrett, 1956). Roots also exude inhibitors of
bacterial growth, and some root extracts are even toxic to bacteria.
Accordingly bacteria can be isolated from the rhizospheres that are not
susceptible to the inhibition (Metz, 1955). Although Azotobacters are
resistant to most of these inhibitions, they are inhibited by *Chelidonium
majus*, due to its alkaloids, to which Azotobacter is much more sensitive
than are other common bacteria (Bukatsch, 1956).

Much has been written, too, about the antibiotics produced by soil
bacteria and their influence on plant pathogens (see Stallings, 1954).
Virtually all our antibiotic-forming organisms have been isolated from
soil (see Chap. XXV), but unfortunately their numbers are probably
too low in most soils to produce effective quantities of antibiotics. These
compounds *can* be produced in soil cultures, the production being promoted by added organic matter; chloramphenicol, formed by *Str.
venezuelae*, and trichothecin, formed by *Trichothecium roseum*, are
good examples (Gottlieb and Siminoff, 1952; Hessayon, 1953, respectively). It is also true that antibiotics *can* exert their typical inhibition
in soil; it is the quantitative data that are lacking.

On the side of growth promotion, the annual sloughing off of dead
nodules with surviving Rhizobia in them probably allows for the

continued reinfection of the roots of leguminous crops by these symbiotic bacteria. But more generally, the excretion or "leakage" of small
amounts of organic nutrients by higher plant tissues doubtless plays a
crucially important part in allowing bacteria, favorable or unfavorable,
to get established on and in the plants. Leaves support on their surfaces
an extensive bacterial flora, which must depend on such sources of
nutrient; in at least one case (the succulent plant, Echeveria), intact
leaves excrete a substance inhibiting the growth of bacteria on them
(Söding, 1959). On the other hand, the spores of plant-disease fungi
must germinate and grow for a while on the leaf surface before they
begin to penetrate the stomata. Thus, the plant-microorganism relationship is rather a subtle and intimate one; it is obviously very widespread,
it involves both promotion and inhibition, and it is reciprocal (see the
discussions by Starkey, 1958, and Thimann, 1959).

4. THE MICROSCOPICAL ANALYSIS OF SOIL
AND ITS RESULTS

It is evident that the plate method is open to serious criticism on the
ground that it leaves out important organisms that cannot develop on
the plates. The method of enrichment cultures, which is the basis of
the physiological chemical analyses, was also called in question, by
Winogradsky in 1925, on the ground that organisms isolated from the
soil become, in culture, more or less laboratory races, adapted to the
aquatic and nutrient-rich conditions of liquid enrichment cultures. In
his early experiments on nitrification (see Chap. X) Winogradsky
found that for a time the artificial medium, a solution of an ammonium
salt, inoculated with soil, underwent no change, but "finally growth,
accompanied by the [nitrification] process, begins again and even becomes intense, despite the maintenance of the same artificial conditions; there has therefore taken place an *adaptation*, the formation of
a new race which prospers in a liquid medium." The same ideas were
expressed in 1915 by Russell. They have been amply substantiated by
later work on selection and adaptation (see Chaps. XVII and XIX). In
enrichment cultures from soil there must necessarily be a rapid selecting out of physiological varieties. Enrichment cultures, then, although
they are invaluable for studying what bacteria *can* do, may not necessarily tell us what they *are doing* under natural conditions.

To get an idea of the actual state of the microorganisms in soil, the
methods of *direct microscopy* have been developed. They are essentially simple. In the first, introduced by Conn as long ago as 1918, a
suspension of soil in dilute gelatin solution as fixative is spread on

slides, dried, stained, and examined. An acid dye, such as rose bengal or erythrosin, in 5 per cent phenol, is used because this does not stain the soil colloids. If 0.5 gm soil be shaken up in 5 ml of solution, and a known volume spread over a measured area on the slide (say 0.02 ml over 1 cm^2), then the counts can give the total number of organisms per gram of soil. Conn's method was perfected and used with great success by Winogradsky (1925–1926). The large soil particles were first allowed to settle, and the suspension and washings centrifuged. Preparations were made by spreading and staining the centrifugate and the supernatant suspension. This procedure is excellent for the Eubacteria, whose colonies are thus seen in the natural state, but the Actinomycetes, fungi, and attached or filamentous bacteria become badly broken up. A better procedure is to grind the soil with water and mix with melted agar on a hemocytometer slide; this has a depression 0.1 mm deep, and hence one obtains a uniform thin film which can be floated off and stained (Jones and Mollison, 1949). In this film filamentous organisms and fungal mycelia are seen in their normal state. Total counts by these methods give values between 10^9 and 21.10^9 per gram of fertile soil (Vandervelde and Verbelen, 1930).

Cholodny, in 1930, introduced another method, simply pushing clean slides vertically into the soil, covering them and leaving them for one to three weeks (cf. also Rossi, 1928). The soil is then carefully broken away, and the slide removed without scraping its surface, fixed in the flame, gently rinsed, and stained as above. A corresponding procedure has been used in culture solutions or in lake and stream waters to study the attached and the filamentous bacteria (Henrici, 1933). These, especially Micromonospora and Sphaerotilus, appear to play a large role in the flora of natural waters. They adhere best to the glass plates when the waters are low in nutrient, probably because the nutrient adsorbs to the test surface (Jannasch, 1955). Up to 10 millions per milliliter have been detected in this way.

A third method is that of *contact preparations;* a clean, moist slide is carefully pressed against the soil, using a freshly exposed vertical surface, removed, and treated as for the growth plate (Rossi, 1928).

These three methods—*spread suspensions,* with or without centrifuging, *growth plates,* and *contact preparations*—provide for the direct examination of the soil. All lead to the same general conclusion, namely, that the distribution of microorganisms in soil is extremely heterogeneous. The bacteria are seen as characteristic small colonies containing from a few dozen to a few hundred individuals; separate individuals are virtually absent (Winogradsky, 1933; Jones and Mollison, 1949), although a few appear on growth plates. Each microcolony is of characteristic form and appears to be a pure culture. It is surrounded by a gelatinous capsule and often embedded in stainable gel fragments which are presumably humic material. Some soil colonies are shown in Figure VI–4. Some of these colonies, on picking out and cultivating, turn out to be Proactinomycetes (Hopf, 1950). These probably include the organisms that live upon the humus of the soil and slowly decompose it. All methods indicate that Proactinomycetes are prominent among the regular or "native" inhabitants of the soil. The organisms seen in spread suspensions are mostly coccoid, many unusually large cocci being present, and some of these may be Azotobacter, which forms cystlike agglomerations. Some others, however, are rather angular in appearance and may be Myxobacteria. These are widely present in soils. Since a soil known not to have been manured for 100 years contained 2000 to 76,000 Myxobacteria per gram (Singh, 1948), they also are certainly among the "native" flora. A few rods are present, particularly an organism which spreads into "veils," or colonies only one cell thick, seen both in suspensions and Cholodny growth plates (Demeter and Mossel, 1933). Growth plates made close to the surface of the soil also show diatoms and filamentous algae, largely blue-greens. Spirilla are apparently absent from this native soil flora; they are essentially water forms. Filamentous forms can be well seen if a small moist chamber, in soil, be constructed on a slide (Cholodny, 1936), or better still when fragments of undisturbed soil are examined directly with a microscope illuminated from above (Kubiena and Renn, 1935). Here the development and fructification of fungi and Actinomycetes, migrating out of the soil, can be watched. Tufts of aerial hyphae of Actinomycetes are seen to bridge the spaces between soil particles. In the water sheath which surrounds the larger fungal hyphae the bacteria are frequently carried, and this doubtless accounts for their close association with the hyphae always seen in soil growth plates. Some organisms evidently also grow on, and destroy, the organic matter of fungus hyphae.

Sporeformers occur in moderate numbers only; Conn estimated 5 to 10 per cent, but Winogradsky found them only rarely. They often accumulate on plant fibers; if the soil is not too well aerated, these are probably clostridia, carrying out a butyric fermentation on the starch and pectin of the plant cells (cf. Chaps. XV and XVII). Curiously enough, sporeformers, aerobic and anaerobic, are greatly inhibited by addition of stable manure to the soil; the same is apparently true for Azotobacter and some Actinomycetes (Demeter and Mossel, 1933). That sporeformers do not grow much in normal soil was proven by adding Bac. mycoides and Bac. subtilis to sterilized soil; they did not grow, but quickly degenerated, while other bacteria, such as Azotobacter and Cytophaga, increased in a normal way (Meyer, 1935).

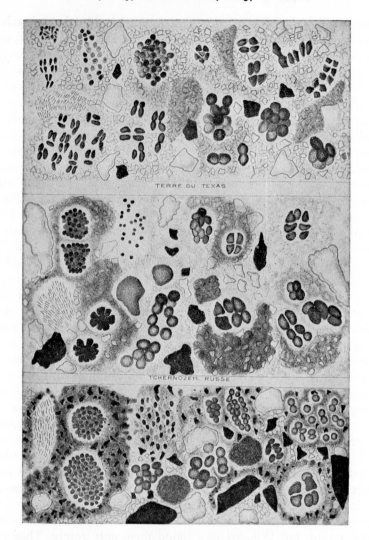

FIGURE VI-4

Colonies of bacteria as seen in soil preparations. Note the preponderance of spherical forms. (From S. Winogradsky, *Ann. Inst. Pasteur*, **39**:299–354, 1925.)

Probably sporeformers grow only where organic residues are being constantly added to the soil (Grundmann, 1934).

Samples of arable soil from France, Russia, Germany, and the United States showed the same types of organisms and the same appearance of the colonies throughout; hence the distribution of these colonies or "glomeruli" is the same all over the world. Demeter and

Mossel compared a sandy and a loamy soil, finding no important differences; Rossi compared different depths and found the bacterial numbers to decrease regularly with depth, but the bulk of the decrease appeared only below those depths that are agriculturally worked.

A clear distinction can be made between (1) the native flora, in resting colonies or growing on slowly decomposed humus, and (2) the transitory populations, developing with enormous rapidity, which are evoked by addition of easily decomposed organic materials. If glucose or mannite be incorporated into the soil, and the water content brought to about 20 per cent of saturation, Winogradsky found (1926) that after 24 hours at 28° to 30° C a large bacillus appeared, but after another 24 hours it had disappeared and the soil was crowded with large cocci—Azotobacter(?)—reaching a maximum of about 200 millions per gram in three to four days. If a little urea be added, it is rapidly decomposed with the growth of two characteristic rods. If a trace of peptone be added instead, there is an "explosive" growth of sporeformers, all microscopic fields being covered with them in 15 hours. The same process was seen by Cholodny (1936), and indeed also by earlier workers, notably by Conn and Joffe, who regarded sporeformers as in "watchful waiting" for the arrival of conditions under which they could grow. When plant material such as straw is added, there is an increase in the rate of CO_2 evolution with simultaneously a synthesis of riboflavin, which is later inactivated (Schmidt and Starkey, 1951). Evidently here, too, there is "explosive" growth of some organisms.

If with the addition of mannite or glucose the water content of the soil is raised to 42 per cent, *Clostridium pasteurianum* appears in enormous numbers and, although a strict anaerobe, approaches to within 2 cm of the soil surface (Winogradsky, 1926).

The addition of stable manure induces a marked development of algae and fungi, especially Oospora and Oidium types (Demeter and Mossel, 1933). This may perhaps be due to the high thiamine content of manure, since thiamine is an essential growth factor for many fungi. The addition of cellulose gave rise to two fungi, *Verticillium chlamydosporium* and a *Humicola* species, as well as to many rod-shaped bacteria (Kubiena and Renn, 1935).

Chronic additions have a different effect, since they produce a kind of enrichment culture. Two examples of this may be mentioned: (1) When 2,4-D is used as a weed killer, its continual addition to the soil, from sprayed plants, develops a culture of organisms active in destroying it. The rate of destruction builds up very quickly (Audus, 1961). (2) By exposing small soil samples to ammonium salts and aerating in a continuous circulator, very active populations of NH_3-oxidizing (=

nitrifying) organisms can be built up (Lees and Quastel, 1946; cf. Chap. X). Such "adapted" soils can be used essentially like enzyme preparations.

The truly native humus-decomposing flora is, of course, not at rest, but is engaged in decomposing the humus. Humic acid in general is a poor nutrient for microorganisms and will not even support Penicillia, although they can derive some nitrogen from it. It is a somewhat better nitrogen source after it has been autoclaved (Flaig and Schmidt, 1957). However, Winogradsky (1925) was able to grow the veil-forming bacterium on plates of silica gel with calcium humate as the sole nutritive addition; it took weeks for colonies to form, but they eventually did so, and were accompanied by clearing of the opaque humus-plate in zones surrounding the colonies. Such cleared zones indicate breakdown of the complex humic acid molecules. These organisms are probably Nocardias (Küster, 1950). In so far as the humus consists of lignin, this can be attacked by the lignin-decomposers, which include Pseudomonads and Flavobacteria (Sørensen, 1962). Some of these could decompose up to 20 per cent of added lignin in 6 to 8 weeks' culture.

5. THE PROTOZOAN THEORY OF MICROBIAL EQUILIBRIUM IN SOIL

Many years ago an entirely different picture of microbial life in the soil, namely, that of a sort of Darwinian struggle for existence, was built up by Russell and his co-workers at Rothamsted. It arose from the observation that if soil is overmanured for a time, it becomes subject to "soil sickness," i.e., poor growth of plants on it. This is commonest when warmth, moisture, and organic manure have been maintained for some time, as in greenhouses. It is paralleled by a large increase in the protozoan population. The trouble could be cured by "partial sterilization," i.e., treating the soil with steam, or with such antiseptics as chloroform, CS_2, or toluene. This treatment has the following remarkable effects:

(1) At first there is a fall, then a permanent rise, in bacterial numbers, the final numbers being higher than before treatment.

(2) Introduction of some untreated soil into the partially sterilized soil causes a fall in bacterial numbers (by plate count).

(3) After the treatment the total bacterial numbers come to vary with the temperature; in untreated soil they do not do this.

Russell and Hutchinson, therefore, concluded that the bacterial numbers in the untreated soil were limited by something. This "something" is reintroduced with a little untreated soil, and furthermore it is destroyed by heat or antiseptics and takes a long time to develop again. "It is difficult to see," concluded Russell (1913), "what agent other than a living organism can fulfill these conditions. Search was therefore made for a larger organism capable of destroying bacteria, and considerable numbers of protozoa were found. Ciliates and amoebae are killed by partial sterilization. Whenever they are killed the detrimental factor is found to be put out of action: the bacterial numbers rise and maintain a high level. Whenever the detrimental factor is not put out of action, the protozoa are not killed. To these rules we have found no exception." As to sensitivity to heat, the thermal death points of protozoa are about as follows: for flagellates, 44° C, amoebae, 48° C, ciliates, 54° C, cysts, about 72° C.

An extensive examination of soils by Sandon (1927), by plating and by growing in hay infusion, showed that many species of protozoa are identical in soils from all over the world, including Arctic soils, frozen for most of the year, tropical soils rich in decomposable material, and the unworked soils of isolated Pacific islets. Flagellates comprise the largest group, both in total numbers (Koffman, 1934, found up to 100,-000 per gram of soil) and also in the number of different species present. The figures for numbers of species, from the analyses of 148 soils, may be summarized as follows:

TABLE VI–7. Distribution of Species of Protozoa in Soils

(From Sandon, 1927)

Source of Soil	No. of Samples	Total N %	pH	AVERAGE NUMBER OF SPECIES OF:				
				Flagellates	Ciliates	Amebae	Thecamebae	Total
Arctic and Antarctic	24	0.78	6.0	4.6	2.4	1.8	3.8	12.6
Temperate oceanic islands	12	1.02	5.6	13.3	5.7	3.8	4.8	27.6
Temperate continental	23	0.16	6.7	7.4	3.1	2.0	2.0	14.5
Tropical and subtropical islands	42	0.39	7.2	6.7	3.9	3.0	1.4	15.6
Tropical and subtropical continental	47	0.11	7.0	6.7	4.3	2.4	0.8	14.2

With the exception of *Colpoda cucullus*, the common species are all small forms; many are, as Koffman (1934) considers, "Lilliput" forms of larger organisms; thus he points out that Chilodon in aquatic conditions measures about 150 μ, but in the soil rarely exceeds 22 μ.

Cutler *et al.* (1922) made daily counts for a year of the four commonest flagellates and two amebae, and found in general an inverse relation between the amebae and the bacteria. The flagellated ameba

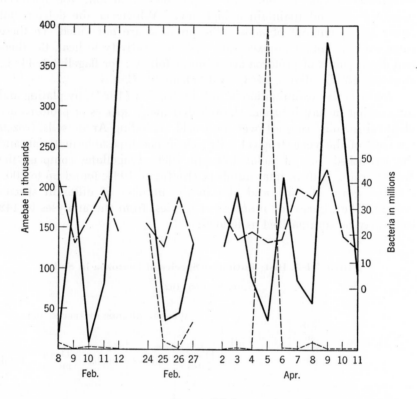

FIGURE VI–5

An example of daily counts of bacteria (*dashed line*) and two ameba species, *Naegleria gruberi* (*solid line*) and *Ameba* α (*dotted line*) in Rothamsted field soil. Counts per gram fresh weight. (From D. W. Cutler, L. M. Crump, and H. Sandon. *Phil. Trans. Roy. Soc. London*, B **211**:317–350. Copyright 1922 by Cambridge Univ. Press.)

Naegleria gruberi and the small Limax ameba, *Ameba* α, were the two organisms involved. Rapid fluctuations in the numbers of bacteria and of these two protozoa were found from day to day (Fig. VI–5). These fluctuations were supposed to be due to the bacteria growing first and then being eaten by the amebae. The resulting growth of amebae would reduce the bacterial numbers till the amebae begin to die off, so that the bacteria increase once again.

To show that these soil amebae really do keep down the bacterial numbers, Cutler (1923) inoculated sterilized field soil with three species of bacteria, with and without the addition of a culture of *Naegleria gruberi*, using a fine spray to ensure good distribution. He

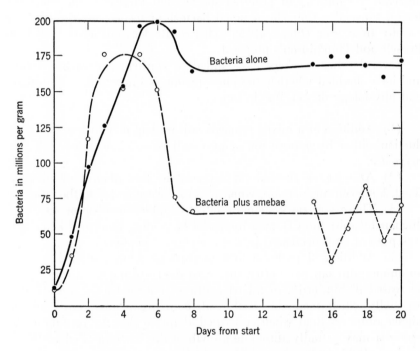

FIGURE VI–6

Counts of soil bacteria (three species, inoculated in sterile soil with and without addition of the ameba, *Naegleria gruberi*). When the bacterial counts settle down to a steady state, the numbers in presence of amebae average one-third that of the bacteria alone. Note also the wide fluctuations in the lower curve (cf., Fig. VI–5). (From D. W. Cutler, *Ann. Appl. Biol.*, **10**:137–141. Copyright 1923 by Cambridge Univ. Press.)

obtained the data of Figure VI–6. It will be seen that, after the fourth day, which is possibly the time required for the amebae to multiply appreciably, the bacterial numbers in the presence of the amebae fall off markedly and settle down to a value about one-third that of the controls. In addition they exhibit the same wide fluctuations of more than 100 per cent that were previously observed in normal soil. On the other hand, the soil containing bacteria alone gives practically constant numbers.

The phenomenon is not limited to laboratory cultures, since recently steam or formalin treatment of soil in the field has been shown to reduce the count of amebae and increase that of bacteria; with formalin the amebic count remains depressed for over a year (Singh and Crump, 1953). Partial steam sterilization of greenhouse soils was also shown to decrease the number of protozoa species, but thereafter the surviving forms, especially Colpoda, a noted bacterium feeder, multiplied more rapidly than ever (Stout, 1955). This result does not agree well with Russell and Hutchinson's proposal.

Several other workers have failed to confirm the earlier results and have doubted whether the phenomenon is important in the microbial physiology of soil. For instance:

(1) Addition of a mixed protozoa culture had no effect on NH_3 production, either by natural soil or by sterilized soil inoculated with *Bac. mycoides*.

(2) Azotobacter showed no decrease in the amount of nitrogen fixed, but even an increase, when protozoa were added to the cultures.

(3) There was no systematic effect of added amebae on CO_2 production by soil; the CO_2 was increased by adding amebae when sugar was present, and decreased in the presence of peptone.

(4) Addition of protozoa to a mixture of toluene-treated soil and an ammonuim salt more often increased the resulting nitrification than decreased it. Similarly, in mixed cultures of Azotobacter and amebae, especially when made in sterile soil, *both* organisms were found in higher numbers than when cultivated alone, so that the feeding of the protozoa may actually stimulate growth of the bacteria (Fedora-Winogradova, 1927, 1928). Now NH_3 and CO_2 production, as also nitrification, have been taken (see sec. 2C above) as indices of bacterial activity. The conclusion would seem to be that the organisms responsible for NH_3 and CO_2 production are not those that are eaten by the protozoa. Yet we know that amebae in culture feed readily on Azotobacter, which are highly active in producing CO_2; that ciliates like Colpoda feed readily on Pseudomonas species, which are active ammonifiers; and that amebae will consume Myxobacteria such as *Myxococcus rubescens*, which are common soil forms (Meyer-Pietschmann, 1956).

(5) There is some doubt whether the soil protozoa behave in quite the same way as aquatic forms. Many are themselves not much larger than an Azotobacter cell and can grow quite well in bacteria-free culture. Neff *et al.* (1958) grew Acanthameba on a peptone-sugar medium,

and it will even grow on a medium of known constituents, containing 18 amino acids, thiamine, and vitamin B_{12} (Adam, 1959). Hartmanella behaves similarly, and when fed C^{14}-glucose, it assimilates 25 per cent and respires 50 per cent of it (Band, 1959). Thus, there is no doubt that the soil amebae *can* grow on a soluble medium, but, of course, this does not prove that they do not consume bacteria as well.

A weakness in the theory, insofar as it attempts to explain the results of partial sterilization, is its failure to take into account the effect of the sterilizing substances themselves as nutrients. Toluene and phenol are readily utilized by many soil bacteria (Gray and Thornton, 1928); indeed, some hydrocarbons produce large increases in soil bacterial population apart from any "antiseptic" effect (Matthews, 1924; Koike and Gainey, 1952). G. H. Wiltshire writes (1957) that from soil that had been perfused with naphthalene and chloronaphthalene a Pseudomonas could be isolated which could grow on these compounds as a sole carbon source. However, formalin does not increase the bacterial count any more than does steam treatment (Singh and Crump, 1953).

In face of all these facts, it is doubtful whether the rapid fluctuations in bacterial numbers observed by the Rothamsted workers are primarily due to the protozoa, although the protozoa may contribute to them. If not, they may be due rather to changes in the microcolonies. It was seen above that the addition to the soil of organic matter brings about the development of the physiologically appropriate organisms from their microcolonies with "explosive" rapidity. Rossi compared this with the excystment of protozoa, but excystment is a direct response to specific excysting substances present in plant infusions (Thimann and Barker, 1934; Strickland and Haagen Smit, 1947) and is not necessarily bound up in any way with the multiplication of the protozoa. The action of CS_2, toluene, and the other partial sterilizing agents could be regarded, partially at least, as a kind of nonspecific excysting stimulus, the resulting individual and separate bacteria having a greater physiological activity than when in colonies. The role of these microcolonies is dramatically described in the following quotation from Rossi (1935):

> The bacteria would emerge from the glomerular forms when the *soil climate* brings about modifications such that—the cyst being as it were opened—the bacteria multiply with their characteristic rapidity, and bring about, in their turn, their specific biochemical functions. . . . Such an interpretation lends itself to a better conception of what may be a state of equilibrium in the bacterial life of the soil, which we must not imagine as a continuous and implacable struggle . . . and it would explain, better than we can do at present, the action of irrigation, of chemical fertilizers,

of green and stable manure, and of tilling. It would explain better the action of heat, cold, rain and snow. The bacterial glomeruli would be like the seeds which agriculture causes to germinate at the opportune moment.

REFERENCES

Adam, K. M. G. 1959. *J. Gen. Microbiol.*, **21**:519–529.

Andrews, W. B. 1937. *J. Am. Soc. Agron.*, **29**:253–268.

Ashby, S. F. 1904. *Trans. Chem. Soc.*, **85**:1158–1170.

Audus, L. J. 1961. Microbiological Breakdown of Herbicides in Soils. In, Handbuch der Pflanzenphysiol. Berlin, Springer Verlag, Vol. XVI.

Balicka, N. 1958. *Ann. Inst. Pasteur*, **95**:480–491.

Band, R. N. 1959. *J. Gen. Microbiol.*, **21**:80–95.

Baver, L. D. 1956. Soil Physics, 3rd. ed. New York, John Wiley.

Bower, C. A. 1949. *Iowa Agric. Expt. Sta. Res. Bull.* 362.

Bukatsch, F. 1956. *Arch. Mikrobiol.*, **24**:281–296.

Chalvignac, M. A. 1958. *Ann. Inst. Pasteur*, **95**:474–479.

Cholodny, N. G. 1930. *Arch. Mikrobiol.*, **1**:620–652.

Cholodny, N. G. 1936. *Arch. Mikrobiol.*, **7**:286–296.

Cutler, D. W. 1923. *Ann. Applied Biol.*, **10**:137–141.

Cutler, D. W.: Crump, L. M.; and Sandon, H. 1922. *Phil. Trans. Roy. Soc.*, **B211**: 317–350.

*Dean, L. A. 1949. Fixation of Soil Phosphorus. *Adv. in Agronomy*, **1**:391–411. New York, Academic Press.

Demeter, K. J., and Mossel, H. 1933. *Zentr. Bakt. II Abt.*, **88**:384–393.

Doak, B. W. 1952. *J. Agric. Sci.*, **42**:162–171.

Domsch, K. H. 1955. *Arch. Mikrobiol.*, **23**:79–87.

Düggeli, M. 1923. Cited from Waksman's Principles of Soil Microbiology (see below).

Erickson, D. 1949. *J. Gen. Microbiol.*, **3**:361–368.

Fedora-Winogradova, T. 1927, 1928. *Zentr. Bakt. II*, **72**:374–379; **74**:14–22.

Fehér, D. 1927, 1929. *Biochem. Z.*, **180**:201–204; **207**:350–360 (1929).

Fehér, D. 1930. *Arch. Mikrobiol.*, **1**:381–417, 464–492.

Flaig, W., and Kutzner, H. J. 1960. *Arch. Mikrobiol.*, **35**:207–228.

Flaig, W., and Schmidt, H. L. 1957. *Arch. Mikrobiol.*, **27**:1–32.

Gamble, S. J. R.; Mayhew, C. J.; and Chappell, W. E. 1952. *Soil Sci.*, **74**:347–350.

Garrett, S. D. 1956. Biology of Root-infecting Fungi. Cambridge Univ. Press.

Glinka, K. D. 1927. (Trans. C. F. Marbut.) The Great Soil Groups of the World and Their Development. Ann. Arbor, Mich., Univ. Michigan Press.

Goring, C. A. I., and Bartholomew, W. V. 1952. *Soil Sci.*, **74**:149–164.

Gottlieb, D., and Siminoff, P. 1952. *Phytopath.*, **42**:91–97.

Gradmann, H. 1928. *Jahrb. wiss. Bot.*, **69**:1–100.

Gray, P. H. H., and Thornton, H. G. 1928. *Zentr. Bakt.*, **73**:74–96.

Grundmann, E. 1934. *Arch. Mikrobiol.*, **5**:57–83.

Henrici, A. T. 1933. *J. Bact.*, **25**:277–286.

Hessayon, D. G. 1953. *Soil Sci.*, **75**:395–404.

Hopf, M. 1950. *Arch. Mikrobiol.*, **14**:661–677.

Jannasch, H. W. 1955. *Arch. Mikrobiol.*, **23**:146–180.

Jenny, H. 1930. Influence of Climate on the N and Organic Matter of the Soil. *Mo. Agr. Expt. Sta. Bull.* **152.**

Jenny, H.; Bingham, F.; and Padilla-Saravia, B. 1948. *Soil Sci.*, **66**:173–186.

Jensen, H. L., 1930. *Soil Sci.*, **30**:59–77.

Jensen, H. L. 1931. *J. Agric. Sci.*, **21**:832–843.

Johnstone, D. B. 1947. *Soil Sci.*, **64**:453–458.

Jones, P. C. T., and Mollison, T. E. 1949. *J. Gen. Microbiol.*, **2**:54–68.

Kluyver, A. J., and Visser, J. 1950. *Ant. v. Leeuwenhoek*, **16**:299–310.

*Koffman, M. 1934. *Arch. Mikrobiol.*, **5**:246–302.

Koike, H., and Gainey, P. L. 1952. *Soil Sci.*, **74**:165–172.

Kubiena, W., and Renn, C. E. 1935. *Zentr. Bakt. II Abt.*, **91**:267–292.

Küster, E. 1950. *Arch. Mikrobiol.*, **15**:1–12.

Lees, H., and Quastel, J. H. 1946. *Biochem. J.*, **40**:803–828.

Likais, R. 1952. *Arch. Mikrobiol.*, **18**:49–100.

Lochhead, A. G. 1957. *Soil Sci.*, **84**:395–403.

Lochhead, A. G., and Burton, M. O. 1957. *Canad. J. Microbiol.*, **3**:35–42.

Lochhead, A. G., and Chase, F. E. 1943. *Soil Sci.*, **55**:185–195.

Matthews, A. 1924. *J. Agric. Sci.*, **14**:1–57.

Metz, H. 1955. *Arch. Mikrobiol.*, **23**:297–326.

Meyer, F. H. 1959–1960. *Arch. Mikrobiol.*, **33**:149–169; **35**:340–360.

Meyer, R. 1935. *Arch. Mikrobiol.*, **6**:461–470.

Meyer-Pietschmann, K. 1956. *Arch. Mikrobiol.*, **24**:297–304.

Mihaly, K. 1960. *Nature*, **188**:251.

Muckenhirn, R. J.; Whiteside, E. P.; Templin, E. H.; Chandler, R. F.; and Alexander, L. T. 1949. *Soil Sci.*, **67**:93–105.

Muskat, J. 1955. *Arch. Mikrobiol.*, **22**:1–20, 21–44.

Neff, R. J.; Neff, R. H.; and Taylor, R. E. 1958. *Physiol. Zool.*, **31**:73–91.

Prát, S. 1962. Literatura o Humusu. Fysiol. rostlin přirodovědecké fakulty Univ. Karlovy, Prague. 555 pp. Titles of 2675 papers, some with abstracts.

Quastel, J. H., and Scholefield, P. G. 1951. See Chap. X.

Quastel, J. H., and Webley, D. M. 1947. *J. Agric. Sci.*, **37**:257–266.

Rahn, O. 1913. *Zentr. Bakt. II Abt.*, **38**:484–494.

Rheinheimer, G. 1959–1960. *Arch. Mikrobiol.*, **34**:358–373; **35**:34–43.

Rossi, G. 1928. Festschr. 70 Geburtstag Stoklasa, Berlin; cf. G. Rossi and G. Gesué, 1930, *Ann. techn. Agr. Roma* **3**:196–248.

Rossi, G. 1935. *Proc. 6th Int. Bot. Congr.*, Amsterdam. **II**:172.

Rouatt, J. W., and Lochhead, A. G. 1955. *Soil Sci.*, **80**:147–154.

* Russell, E. J. 1942. Soil Conditions and Plant Growth, 7th ed. London, Longmans, Green and Co.

Russell, E. J., and Appleyard, A. 1915. *J. Agric. Sci.*, **7**:1–48; **8**:385–417.

Russell, E. J., and colleagues. 1923. The Microorganisms of the Soil. London, Longmans, Green and Co.

Russell, E. J., and Hutchinson, H. B. 1909, 1913. *J. Agric. Sci.*, **3**:111–114; **5**:152–221.

Sandon, H. 1927. Composition and Distribution of the Protozoan Fauna of the Soil. Edinburgh and London, Oliver and Boyd.

Schmidt, E. L., and Starkey, R. L. 1951. *Soil Sci.*, **71**:221–231.

Singh, B. N. 1948. *J. Gen. Microbiol.*, **2**:xvii–xviii.

Singh, B. N., and L. M. Crump. 1953. *J. Gen. Microbiol.*, **8**:421–426.

Söding, H. 1959. *Arch. Mikrobiol.*, **34**:103–131.

Sørensen, H. 1962. *J. Gen. Microbiol.*, **27**:21–34.

*Stallings, J. H. 1954. Soil-produced Antibiotics; Plant Disease and Insect Control. *Bact. Revs.*, **18**:131–146 (107 refs.).

*Starkey, R. L. 1958. Interrelations between Microorganisms and Plant Roots in the Rhizosphere. *Bact. Revs.*, **22**:154–172.

Stolwijk, J. A. J., and Thimann, K. V. 1957. *Plant Physiol.*, **32**:513–520.

Stout, J. D. 1955. *J. Gen. Microbiol.*, **12**:237–240.

Strickland, A. G., and Haagen Smit, A. J. 1947. *J. Cell. Comp. Physiol.*, **30**:381–390.

Thimann, K. V. 1958. *Trans. Bose. Res. Inst. Calcutta* (Bose Centenary Vol.), **25**:69–75.

Thimann, K. V., and Barker, H. A. 1934. *J. Cell. Comp. Physiol.*, **69**:37–57.

Timonin, M. I. 1940, 1941. *Canad. J. Research*, **C18**:444–456; *Soil Sci.*, **52**:395–408.

Thorp, J., and Smith, G. D. 1949. *Soil Sci.*, **67**:117–126.

Umbreit, W. W., and McCoy, E. 1941. Symp. Hydrobiol. Univ. Wis., pp. 106–114.

Vandervelde, A. J., and Verbelen, A. 1930. *Compt. rend.*, **190**:977–979.

*Waksman, S. A. 1932. Principles of Soil Microbiology, 2nd ed. Baltimore, Williams and Wilkins.

*Waksman, S. A. 1938. 2nd ed. Baltimore, Williams and Wilkins.

Waksman, S. A., and Starkey, R. L. 1924. *Soil Sci.*, **17**:151–161.

Waksman, S. A.; Tenny, F. G.; and Stevens, K. R. 1928. *Ecology*, **9**:126–144.

Wallace, R. H., and Lochhead, A. G. 1950. *Canad. J. Research*, **C28**:1–6.

White, J. W.; Holben, F. J.; Jeffries, C. D.; and Richer, A. C. 1949. *Soil Sci.*, **67**:279–285.

*Wieringa, K. T. 1939. Determination of Soil Fertility by Microbiological Methods *Ant. v. Leeuwenhoek*, **6**:56–70.

Wiltshire, G. H. 1957. Private correspondence.

Winogradsky, S. 1924. *Compt. rend. Acad. sci.*, **178**:1236–1238; **179**:861–863.

Winogradsky, S. and H. 1925–1926. *Ann. Inst. Pasteur*, **39**:299–354; **40**:455–521.

Winogradsky, S. and H. 1933. *Ann. Inst. Pasteur*, **50**:350–432.

ZoBell, C. 1942. In, *Aerobiology*, AAAS Publ. No. 17, Washington, D.C., pp. 55–68.

ZoBell, C. E. 1946a. Marine Microbiology. Waltham, Mass., Chronica Botanica Co.

ZoBell, C. E. 1946b. *Bull. Amer. Assoc. Petr. Geologists*, **30**:477–513.

Part Two

The Role of Microorganisms
in the Nitrogen Cycle

CHAPTER VII

Proteolysis

This [the proteins] is the central group in the life structure, and absolutely indispensable in all living plants and animals. It is the very citadel structure of the cell's life. . . . Its strength for the purpose of the vital phenomena lies in its very weakness as a chemical body.

BENJAMIN MOORE: The Origin and Nature of Life, 1912.

The principal nitrogenous compounds of plants and animals are the proteins, and it is therefore as proteins that part of their nitrogen is returned to the soil and to natural waters. The decomposition of proteins is thus the first stage in the setting free of organically bound nitrogen for recirculation.

1. THE NATURE OF PROTEINS

Proteins consist of large numbers of α-amino acids linked together by the elimination of water. Since amino acids in neutral solution are not in the neutral form RCHCOOH but in the doubly charged form

$$\underset{NH_2}{RCHCOOH}$$

$$\underset{+NH_3}{RCHCOO^-},$$ the resulting protein molecules are highly polar; most of them are therefore soluble in water but not in organic solvents. They are usually rendered insoluble ("denatured") by heat. Some, like the fibroin of silk or the elastin of muscle ligaments, are long fibrous "macromolecules" of extremely low solubility; others, like ovalbumin of egg white, are more nearly spherical and highly water soluble. Their molecular weights range from 17,000 up to several millions. Many of them are enzymes, others reserve nutrients (as in eggs and seeds), others are structural (like collagen) or mechanical (like the proteins

of flagella and muscles). The toxins of pathogenic bacteria (tetanus, diphtheria, botulism, etc.) are all proteins.

Proteins are normally composed of 21 different amino acids; however, one of these, hydroxyproline, is thought to be formed *in situ* from protein-bound proline, and cystine is readily formed from cysteine, so that only 19 molecular types are used in protein synthesis. All the amino acids participating in the synthesis have amino groups α to the carboxyl and are of the L-configuration. Some D-amino acids occur in nature, especially in bacteria, e.g., in cell walls and capsules (Chap. III) and in antibiotic substances (Chap. XXV), but they are not found in proteins. The L-form of all the constituent amino acids makes the proteins asymmetric in structure, the typical form being that of a helix (Pauling and Corey, 1951).

The composition of some selected proteins is shown in Table VII–1. The variation is wide. Hydroxylysine is only found in a few; tryptophan and cysteine are completely missing from collagen (and therefore from gelatin which is derived from it); histidine and methionine are absent from some strains of tobacco mosaic virus; glycine is relatively low in most proteins, but in collagen becomes by far the most important constituent; serine reaches a similar status in the fibroin of silk; and so on. In addition to the amino acids many proteins are linked to lipids, metal atoms, or biologically active "prosthetic groups," like hemin, riboflavin, or DPN.

With the exception of links between the S atoms of cystine in the native keratins of skin and wool, and in insulin, all links between amino acids in the protein molecule are of the peptide type, resulting from the loss of the elements of water:

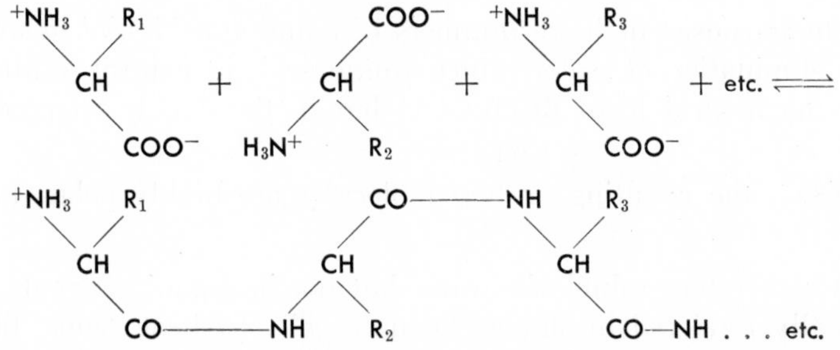

This loss of water comes about initially through the formation of aminoacyl derivatives of adenylic acid; from these "activated amino acids" a series of reactions leads to protein synthesis as shown in Chapter XX. In the reverse process the addition of the elements of water (hydrolysis) at the peptide bond causes protein breakdown.

**TABLE VII-1. Amino Acid Composition of Proteins,
Expressed as Moles Amino Acid per 10^5 Gram Protein**

(From Haurowitz, 1950)

	Oval-bumin	Casein	Insulin	Ribo-nuclease	Botu-linus Toxin	Collagen
Arginine	33	23	20	30	27	51
Histidine	15	21	34	27	6	5
Lysine	42	56	18	71	53	31
Hydroxylysine	0	2	...	.....	...	8
Ammonia	72	101	126	146	152	47
Glutamic acid	109	150	137	88	106	77
Aspartic acid	61	50	50	106	152	47
Glycine	43	6	61	17	18	350
Alanine	75	36	33	.....	44	106
Valine	39	51	84	62	45	29
Leucine* Isoleucine*	121	{80 40}	125	24	{79 90}	42
Proline	28	92	25	31	23	132
Phenylalanine	45	39	48	22	7	25
Serine	77	56	55	114	42	33
Threonine	34	38	27	75	71	20
Tyrosine	22	35	68	44	75	8
Hydroxyproline	0	17	...	.....	...	107
Tryptophan	13	13	...	.....	9	0
Cysteine* Cystine ($\times \frac{1}{2}$)*	}13	3	{5 92	5 13	2 4	0 0
Methionine	35	23	...	30	7	5
Free basic groups	90	102	72	128	86	87
Free acid groups	98	129	61	48	106	77
Nitrogen recovered, %	93.4	98.4	99	98.7	100	99.8

* In some of the proteins the sums of leucine and isoleucine and of cysteine and cystine are recorded, since analyses of the respective amino acids are not available.

In a few proteins, e.g., insulin and the enzyme ribonuclease, the exact sequence of all the amino acids has been determined; in many others, parts of the sequence are known.

Two fundamental stages of proteolysis (= protein hydrolysis) may be distinguished:

(1) The first is a breakdown into relatively large molecules, the polypeptides, each containing two or more amino acids. This is brought about by *proteinases*, i.e., enzymes that can hydrolyze a peptide bond when it is situated within a large molecule. (Most proteinases can also hydrolyze relatively small peptides or even ester linkages as well; see Green and Neurath, 1954.)

(2) The breakdown of polypeptides, or of di- and tripeptides, to the free amino acids is brought about by various types of *peptidases*. These are enzymes that can attack a peptide bond only when one of the adjoining groups of the linked amino acids is free. Some require a free amino group (aminopeptidases), some a carboxyl group (carboxy-peptidases).

The subsequent decomposition of the amino acids takes place in various ways, giving either ammonia, which is the main product, or in some instances other organic nitrogen compounds (Chap. VIII).

2. THE ATTACK UPON PROTEINS

A. Native Protein

Purified proteins, alone or with the usual inorganic salts, seldom provide a good medium for the growth of bacteria, even of organisms that are in general actively proteolytic. Crystalline ovalbumin, serum albumin, and serum globulin, together with inorganic salts, allow prac-tically no growth of organisms of the coliform group or of *M. aureus* or Gonococcus, and very little even of highly proteolytic organisms such as *Bac. subtilis*, *B. prodigiosum*, and *Cl. putrificum* (Sperry and Rettger, 1915). In both cases, however, the addition of peptone (the mixture of polypeptides obtained by treating proteins with pepsin) allowed vigorous growth to take place. With Proteus and others (but not with *E. coli* or *S. typhosa*), this growth was accompanied by active proteolysis. Thus, it seems that the proteinases of many bacteria are elaborated only when vigorous growth takes place, and that some nitrogen source other than pure protein is needed to start the growth. This is particularly true with native, or undenatured, proteins.

Streptomyces griseus, which produces streptomycin (Chap. XXV), excretes a powerful proteinase which does attack egg albumin. The crystalline enzyme also attacks polypeptides and even dipeptides (Nomoto *et al.*, 1959). At the opposite extreme is *Bac. subtilis*, which attacks purified ovalbumin without causing extensive hydrolysis. This organism, or the crystalline enzyme "subtilisin" prepared from it (Guntelberg and Ottesen, 1952; Ottesen, 1957), merely splits off six to seven amino acids to produce a new protein, called plakalbumin (be-cause it crystallizes in plates). Except for minor differences in solu-bility and in immunological properties (Grabar and Kaminski, 1950), the plakalbumin still very strongly resembles the original ovalbumin.

One of the few native proteins readily attacked by bacteria is collagen, the protein of bones, skin, and animal connective tissue. Three aerobes, *Bac. brevis*, *mycoides*, and *mesentericus*, and several anaerobes, including *Cl. histolyticum*, *welchii*, and *lentoputrescens*, hydrolyze native beef tendon or purified collagen (Jennison, 1945). Some 30 strains of *Cl. welchii* hydrolyze hide powder rapidly, and *Cl. histolyticum* is even more active (Evans, 1948). The effective enzyme, *collagenase*, is excreted by these Clostridia and is responsible for their ability to break down living tissue; the enzyme from *Cl. welchii* solubilizes purified collagen in a few hours at 38° C (Delaunay *et al.*, 1949). It is this action that sometimes turns Clostridium-infected wounds into a semiliquid state. The enzyme comprises part of the mixture of toxic substances formed by the most potent type of *Cl. welchii*, type A (Bidwell and van Heyningen, 1948; Bidwell, 1949–1950). Types B and D of this organism, which cannot break down living tissues, do not contain collagenase, but type B instead has an enzyme that hydrolyzes only denatured animal proteins and gelatin (Bidwell, 1950). Several studies of the purified enzyme have been made, especially from *Cl. histolyticum*. Grant and Alburn (1959) have identified at least three separate collagenases from a pure culture filtrate, two with optimum pH about 8, and one near 7. All are activated by Ca^{++} and attack gelatin rapidly, but other proteins only slowly. A nonspecific enzyme attacking several denatured proteins was present as well.

Elastin, the fibrous protein of ligaments, is not attacked by collagenase, and only a few bacteria can hydrolyze it. Besides *Vibrio comma* and a Pseudomonas (Narayanan *et al.*, 1953), one of the few other bacteria attacking it is a Flavobacterium isolated from disease pockets around teeth (Mandl and Cohen, 1960). Its enzyme (elastase), after purification, attacked no other substrate. It had a pH optimum of 7.5 and was inhibited by Zn and Cd but not by other metals. Elastase has also been reported in five Actinomycetes (Sbarra *et al.*, 1960).

Keratin, the protein of hair, wool, horn, and feathers, is also highly resistant to most bacteria, although attacked by certain insects, including of course the clothes moth. Much of its stability is due to S—S linkages between amino acid chains; when these are reduced, the rest of the molecule is more hydrolyzable, and thus keratin hydrolysis depends in the first stage on reduction. For this reason, keratin that has been autoclaved or ground is sometimes attacked by organisms that cannot attack the native keratin, since these treatments may reduce the S—S linkages. The more careful studies have shown that truly native keratin (such as defatted wool or hair) is attacked only by: (1) skin-disease fungi or *dermatophytes*, especially *Microsporum gypseum*, whose ability to attack native keratin has been considered a diagnostic test (Vanbreuseghem, 1952); (2) a few Streptomycetes, among which *Str. fradiae* is very active, solubilizing 90 per cent of the keratin from various sources in about a week at 28° C. The S—S bonds were broken down to —SH compounds, and much of the nitrogen liberated as ammonia (Noval and Nickerson, 1959). Some keratin-digesting activity, promoted by metallic ions, was excreted into the medium. Six other Streptomycetes and two Nocardias had some action on wool. The enzyme of *Str. fradiae* occurs conjugated to an acidic polymer, from which, however, it can be separated and crystallized (Nickerson *et al.*, 1962). The enzyme has maximal activity at its isoelectric point, which lies at *p*H 9.

That members of the Actinomycetacae should be the major keratin decomposers in nature agrees with observations on hair and wool fragments in soil, which by direct microscopy show the presence of many attached Actinomycetes, possibly *Actinoplanes* species (Gaertner, 1955).

B. Bacterial Protein

An interesting substrate is the protein of the bacterial cell itself. Why proteinases do not attack the proteins of the cells that produce them is still a mystery, but it is not more mysterious with bacteria than with any other cells. Perhaps the formation of a proteinase automatically requires the formation of a specific antagonist for it, which remains within the cell when the proteinase diffuses out. However this may be, it is enough to kill bacteria by heat in order to make them sensitive to proteolytic enzymes. Thus, heat-killed pneumococci are digested by trypsin (Dubos, 1937); heat-killed Aerobacter by an enzyme from a soil Actinomycete (Muggleton and Webb, 1952); and heat-killed *M. aureus* and *E. coli* by an enzyme from a *Streptomyces* species (Tai and van Heyningen, 1951; Born, 1952). Living cells are not so attacked. Tai and van Heyningen (1951) have shown that the Streptomyces excretes two enzymes, one active only on casein and the other on the *E. coli* protein, and that the latter is strongly adsorbed by the cells that it can lyse. It appears that simple heat-killing does not suffice to make the cells lysable nor to make them adsorb the enzyme, since heating 10 minutes at 55° C (which kills virtually all), starving them to death for 12 days in distilled water, or killing by antibiotics is ineffective; heating 15 minutes at 75° C or higher is required. Evidently the protein must be extensively denatured. Table VII–2 compares the lysis occurring spontaneously and in the presence of an enzyme, and the enzyme adsorption, following different treatments.

TABLE VII–2. Lysis of *E. coli* in Buffer and with Streptomyces Enzyme

(From data of Tai and van Heyningen, 1951)

Treatment	(% Lysis in 1 hr at 37°C) (in buffer)	(with enzyme)	% Adsorption of Enzyme
Living (contains a few dead cells)	11	14	10
90% dead after 12 days in water	22	34	17
Killed by polymixin (1 gm per liter for three hours)	18	36	34
Autoclaved 20 minutes at 120° C	3	64	70

These lytic enzymes in some ways resemble trypsin; they are activated by Mn and other metals and inhibited by H_2S and —SH compounds and have optima about pH 7 (see below). Trypsin, indeed, has similar effects and also acts only on heat-killed cells. The enzymes do not attack the cell walls, and when their lytic action is complete, the residual walls can be seen more or less intact (Salton, 1953, 1955). An enzyme in *Bac. cereus* spores that lyses the *walls* of the vegetative cells (Strange and Dark, 1957) is probably not a proteinase.

Gram-positive cells are lysed very much more slowly than gram-negative ones, both by trypsin and by the Streptomyces enzymes. *E. coli, Ps. fluorescens, Sp. serpens,* and *Aerob. aerogenes* are sharply distinguished in this respect from *M. aureus, Bac. megaterium,* and *Cl. welchii;* the gram-staining complex apparently protects the cell protein against the enzyme, because *Cl. welchii* cells that have been made gram-negative by autolysis or by extraction with cholate become more sensitive to proteolysis (Muggleton and Webb, 1952). By contrast, the cytoplasm of yeasts, fungi, and even some bacilli is lysed readily by papain (Gorbach and Hoffmann, 1956).

C. Denatured Protein

Since casein and gelatin are not native proteins, they are easily attacked. For instance, the proteinase of yeast attacks casein, gelatin, and denatured ovalbumin, but not native ovalbumin. The hydrolysis of casein by *Penicillium camemberti* is an important part of the ripening and softening of Camembert cheese. It is common bacteriological practice to determine the ability of organisms to hydrolyze gelatin and to take this as a measure of proteolytic activity. The hydrolysis can be detected by observing the clearing of agar containing casein or gelatin (Dion, 1950) but more commonly by inoculating tubes of gelatin medium. A medium containing peptone, salts, and about 10 per cent gelatin is filled deep into test tubes and inoculated by stabbing with a straight needle previously touched with the culture. After incubation at below 25° C, the type of liquefaction (proteolysis) is sometimes classified as shown in Figure VII–1. Evidently these indicate growth and proteolysis, of types: (1) facultatively aerobic or anaerobic, (2) strictly aerobic, and (3) principally anaerobic. If the time, temperature, and composition of the medium are standard, and the stab is carefully made so that the gel closes up again on removing the needle, the results have considerable relative value.

The formation of gelatinase by several bacteria is strongly promoted by calcium (Haines, 1932, 1933); 0.01 M $CaCl_2$, or less, is sufficient (Gorini and Fromageot, 1949). With fungi or Streptomycetes, Mg is often more effective than Ca (Dion, 1950). Sugars, on the other hand,

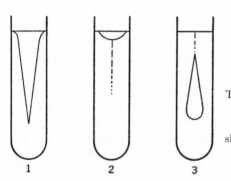

FIGURE VII–1
Types of gelatin liquefaction.
  1. Infundibuliform or funnel-shaped.
  2. Stratiform, salverform, or bow shaped.
  3. Saccate or bag-shaped.

inhibit formation of the enzyme, 1.5 per cent glucose being enough to render *Proteus vulgaris* completely inactive (Kendall, 1923). Similarly, protein hydrolysis by the bacteria of cattle rumen is strongly inhibited by starch, which is itself rapidly metabolized (Warner, 1956). This phenomenon (see Chap. VIII, sec. 6D) seems not to occur in fungi, whose proteinase formation is sometimes increased by sugars. Thus, *Gliocladium roseum* gives increasing yields of proteinase with glucose, up to a maximum at 8 per cent glucose (Dion, 1950); perhaps this is due to the promotion of its growth.

3. THE ATTACK UPON PEPTIDES

The ability to grow on peptone, proteose, and other partially hydrolyzed proteins is common to most organisms. Even bacteria like *E. coli*, which do not attack proteins, will grow well on peptones. Streptococci grow better when given arginine peptides than on arginine itself, because they decompose the amino acid (to ornithine) too rapidly (Gale, 1945). The same is true for peptides of tyrosine (Chap. XII, sec. 3).

The peptidases of bacteria have not been extensively studied. Those of the lactic bacteria have pH optima at 5.5 to 6 or 6.8, while those from four gram-negative rods, three bacilli, and three clostridia have optima between pH 8 and 9 (Berger *et al.*, 1938, 1941). The polypeptidase of yeast and the crystalline proteinase-peptidase of *Str. griseus* (Nomoto *et al.*, 1959) are both optimal between pH 7 and 8. Several bacterial peptidases are activated by Fe or Mn (Maschmann, 1944), thus resembling the Mn- or Co-requiring enzymes of animal tissues (see Smith, 1951), while four gram-negative rods (*E. coli, Proteus, Ps. fluorescens*, and *Ps.* [*Agrob.*] *tumefaciens*) yielded peptidases activated by Mg (Berger *et al.*, 1938), as is the erepsin of animal intestines. The Mycobacteria yield peptidases readily, *Mycob. smegmatis* excreting it into the medium, while *Mycob. tuberculosis* yields them on grinding the cells (Roulet and Zeller, 1948). Glycyl-L-leucine was the most sensitive substrate.

The lactic bacterium *Leuconostoc mesenteroides* has at least two di- and two tripeptidases, activated by metal ions, which can hydrolyze peptides of D-amino acids as fast as those of L-amino acids, in contrast to most animal peptidases which are restricted to the L-isomers (Berger, *et al.*, 1938). It is evident that bacterial peptide hydrolysis requires much more patient study.

4. THE NATURE OF THE ENZYMES

In animal tissues, where proteolytic enzymes have been the most thoroughly studied, four types are recognized:

(1) *Pepsin*, active only at a very acid pH and destroyed by alkalies, attacking some native proteins including hemoglobin, and clotting milk. Pepsin splits peptides if they contain an aromatic amino acid. Pepsin is liberated by acid from its inactive precursor in the stomach, pepsinogen.

(2) *Trypsin*, optimum pH 8, attacking native proteins only weakly, but denatured or modified proteins vigorously (cf. above); it also clots milk. Trypsin can attack amide or ester linkages of peptides with a free basic group such as benzoylarginine amide or benzoylarginine methyl ester (Schwert *et al.*, 1948, and earlier work there cited). In the need for a free basic group and a covered carboxyl, the *aminopeptidases* resemble trypsin. The activity of trypsin is increased by divalent metal ions and inhibited by cysteine. It occurs as the in-

active form, trypsinogen, which is made active by a special enzyme, enterokinase; it also converts itself autocatalytically at pH 8.

(3) *Chymotrypsin*, most active at pH 7 to 8, attacking few native proteins but many peptides, natural and synthetic (see Neurath and Schwert 1950). Chymotrypsin has no requirement for basic or acidic groups, but does require an aromatic ring (or a methionine residue). It occurs in the intestine as an inactive precursor, chymotrypsinogen, which is converted to the active form by trypsin.

(4) *Papain* and some cathepsins, ficin, bromelin, etc., a group of enzymes found in liver, spleen, and in higher plants, optimum pH about 5, requiring to be activated by HCN, H_2S, or —SH groups. Actually papain exists in two forms; a-papain is converted by —SH compounds into β-papain, which with HCN becomes proteolytic. Papain will attack tripeptides. Like trypsin, it can clot milk.

The bacterial proteinases have some similarities to these animal enzymes. In one case the similarity extends to the formation of enzyme from inactive precursor, since a micrococcus has been found to excrete a compound that is autocatalytically converted to a proteinase on standing a few hours (Gorini and Lanzavecchia, 1954). In general, proteinases must of course be excreted from the cell, since proteins cannot pass the permeability barrier to be attacked inside. It is true that the cell's own proteins must also be broken down in normal metabolism, and indeed in nongrowing cells this happens actively, leading to rapid "turnover," as has been shown with *E. coli* by following the fate of selected C^{14}-labeled amino acids (Mandelstam and Halvorson, 1960). During growth this proteolysis is in some way prevented. While these *endoproteinases* are sometimes excreted, especially in old cultures (Berger, *et al.*, 1938), the typical proteolytic bacteria, like *B. prodigiosum* or *Ps. fluorescens*, excrete proteinases vigorously from the start of growth (Virtanen and Tarnanen, 1932; Maschmann, 1937–1938).

The peptidases are more commonly endoenzymes, which can only be extracted by grinding, autolyzing, or repeated freezing and thawing (Berger *et al.*, 1938; Roulet and Zeller, 1948), although they are excreted by *Bac. megaterium*. The two enzyme types thus show a natural separation; for example, *Ps. fluorescens* actively excretes a proteinase during growth, while from the cells a polypeptidase and a dipeptidase could be extracted (Virtanen and Tarnanen, 1932).

Several Clostridia (*Cl. welchii, Cl. chauvoei, Cl. histolyticum*) excrete an enzyme of the papain type, which is activated by cysteine, and hydrolyzes the basic protein clupeine (Maschmann, 1937–1938). The proteinases of other clostridia and of Proteus are also activated by cysteine (Weil *et al.*, 1939). The proteinase that has been crystallized from group A streptococci requires activation by HCN, cysteine, etc., and in this resembles papain (Mycek *et al.*, 1952), but its action on synthetic substrates such as the amides of benzoyl-L-arginine and benzoyl-L-histidine rather resembles that of trypsin. The collagenase of *Cl. histolyticum*, which is the most active of all collagenases and has been extensively purified though not crystallized, is activated both by cysteine and by $FeSO_4$. Several aerobes have proteinases that are inhibited by cysteine but activated by Fe^{++} or by cysteine plus Fe^{++} (Maschmann, 1944).

The enzymes hydrolyzing bacterial proteins, discussed above, resemble trypsin in many ways. So does an enzyme from *Bac. subtilis*, which is sold for industrial use in Japan under the name of "Nagarse." This has been crystallized by Hagihara *et al.* (1958) and found more heat-stable and more resistant to natural inhibitors than is crystalline trypsin, although like trypsin it is inactivated by diisofluorophosphate. However, it has long been known that all hydrolytic enzymes are sensitive to this reagent, because the amino acid serine is an essential part of the active hydrolytic center, and diisofluorophosphate reacts with the OH of serine. This property is therefore not critical. Recently three crystalline enzymes from bacilli, namely, a proteinase from *Bac. cereus*, the Nagarse enzyme, and Ottesen's subtilisin, have been carefully compared (Wieland *et al.*, 1960). All three have *p*H optima 7 to 7.5, coagulate milk (rennin action), and inactivate lactic dehydrogenase at the same rate. They have the same sedimentation constant in the ultracentrifuge, the same amino acid composition, and even the same amino acid at the end of the chain, namely, alanine. Apparently, therefore, they are identical or almost so.

In the pathogenic clostridia it is the variety rather than the similarities that is notable, because there are enzymes of at least four types (Maschmann, 1937–1938); (1) a collagenase that also acts on gelatin, (2) a gelatinase, (3) a less specific proteinase that acts on gelatin, casein, fibrin, and ovalbumin (*Cl. botulinum*), and (4) the papain-like enzyme that attacks clupeine. A number of peptidases are present as well.

The *p*H optima offer limited clues to the nature of the enzymes. The gelatinases from six organisms all have their optima close to *p*H 7 (Maschmann, 1937–1938; Haines, 1933); the proteinase of *Lactob. casei* has optimum close to *p*H 6, as do the gelatinases of several clostridia. The collagenase of *Cl. welchii* has a very narrow *p*H band of action with optimum near 7 (Bidwell, 1950). A number of imperfect fungi form proteinases which have *p*H optima between 7 and 8, are unstable below *p*H 5, and generally are more or less of the trypsin type (Mc-

Connell, 1950). The enzymes from Trichophyton and other dermato-phytes also have optima near 8 (Tate, 1929). On the other hand, yeast proteinase has its optimum at pH 5. The proteinase of *Aspergillus oryzae*, which has been crystallized (Crewther and Lennox, 1950), has potential industrial uses, like the Japanese preparation from *Bac. cereus* of Hagihara *et al.* (1958); industry has shown much interest in these enzymes (see Ledingham, 1953).

REFERENCES

Berger, J.; Johnson, M. J.; and Peterson, W. H. 1938. *J. Biol. Chem.*, **124**:395–408; *J. Bact.*, **36**:521–545.

Bidwell, E. 1949–1950. *Biochem. J.*, **44**:28–32; **46**:589–598.

Bidwell, E., and van Heyningen, W. E. 1948. *Biochem. J.*, **42**:140–149.

Born, G. U. R. 1952. *J. Gen. Microbiol.*, **6**:344–351.

Crewther, W. G., and Lennox, F. G. 1950. *Nature*, **165**:680.

Delaunay, M.; Guillaumie, M.; and Delaunay, A. 1949. *Ann. Inst. Pasteur*, **76**:16–23.

Dion, W. M. 1950. *Canad. J. Res.*, **C28**:577–585, 586–599.

Dubos, R. J. 1937. *J. Exp. Med.*, **65**:873–883; **66**:101–112.

Evans, D. G. 1948. *J. Gen. Microbiol.*, **1**:378–386.

Gaertner, A. 1955. *Arch. Mikrobiol.*, **23**:28–37.

Gale, E. F. 1945. *Biochem. J.*, **39**:46–52.

Gorbach, G., and Hoffmann, M. 1956. *Arch. Mikrobiol.*, **24**:49–59.

Gorini, L., and Fromageot, C. 1949. *Compt. rend.*, **229**:559–563.

Gorini, L., and Lanzavecchia, G. 1954. *Biochem. Biophys. Acta*, **15**:399–410.

Graber, P., and Kaminski, M. 1950. *Bull. Soc. chim. biol.*, **32**:620–629.

Grant, N. H., and Alburn, H. E. 1959. *Arch. Biochem. Biophys.*, **82**:245–255.

Green, N. M., and Neurath, H. 1954. In, The Proteins, ed., H. Neurath and K. Bailey. New York, Academic Press, Vol. 2B.

Guntelberg, A. V., and Ottesen, M. 1952. *Nature*, **170**:802.

Hagihara, B.; Matsubara, H.; Nakai, M.; and Okunuki, K. 1958. *J. Biochem* (Tokyo) **45**:185–194; Matsubara, B., and Nishimura, S. *Ibid.*, 503–510.

Haines, R. B. 1932. *Biochem. J.*, **26**:323–336.

*Haines, R. B. 1933. The Proteolytic Enzymes of Microorganisms. *Biol. Revs.*, **9**:235–261.

Haurowitz, F. 1950. The Proteins. New York, Academic Press.

Jennison, M. W. 1945. *J. Bact.*, **50**:369–370.

Kendall, A. I. 1923. *Physiol. Revs.*, **3**:438–455.

*Ledingham, G. A. 1953. Industrial Fermentations. *Ann. Rev. Microbiol.*, **7**:433–460.

McConnell, W. B., 1950. *Canad. J. Res.*, **C28**:600–611.

Mandelstam, J., and Halvorson, H. 1960. *Biochim. Biophys. Acta*, **40**:43–49.

Mandl, I., and Cohen, B. B. 1960. *Arch. Biochem. Biophys.*, **91**:47–53.

Maschmann, E. 1937–1938. *Biochem Z.*, **294**:1–33; **295**:1–10, 351–368; 391–399, 400–401. 402–405; **297**:284–296.

Maschmann, E. 1944. Bakterien-Proteasen. *Ergebn. d. Enzymforschung*, **9**:166–192.

Muggleton, P. W., and Webb, M. 1952. *Biochim. Biophys. Acta*, **8**:431–441.

Mycek, M. J.; Elliott, S. D.; and Fruton, J. S. 1952. *J. Biol. Chem.*, **197**:637–640.

Narayanan, E. K.; Devi, P.; and Menon, P. S. 1953. *Ind. J. Med. Res.*, **41**:295–299.

Neurath, H., and Schwert, G. W. 1950. *Chem. Revs.*, **46**:69–153.

Nickerson, W. J.; Noval, J. J.; and Robinson, R. S. 1963. *Biochim. Biophys. Acta;* Nickerson, W. J., and Durand, S. C. *Ibid.*

Nomoto, M.; Narahashi, Y.; and Murakami, J. 1959. *Reports Inst. Phys. Chem. Res. (Tokyo),* 35:90–98, 154–166, 261–268; *J. Biochem. (Tokyo),* 46:1645–1651.

Noval, J. J., and Nickerson, W. J. 1959. *J. Bact.,* 77:251–263.

Ottesen, M. 1957. *Compt. rend. trav. lab. Carlsberg, ser. chim.,* 30:211–270.

Pauling, L., and Corey, R. B. 1951. *Proc. Nat. Acad. Sci.,* 37:235–285.

Ramon, G.; Richou, R.; and Ramon, P. 1945. *Compt. rend.,* 220:341–343.

Roulet, F., and Zeller, E. A. 1948. *Helv. chem. Acta,* 31:1915–1926.

Salton, M. R. J. 1953, 1955. *J. Gen. Microbiol.,* 9:512–523; 12:25–30.

Sbarra, A. J.; Gilfillan, R. F.; and Bardawil, W. A. 1960. *Fed. Proc.,* 19:144.

Schwert, G. W.; Neurath, H.; Kaufman, S.; and Snoke, J. R. 1948. *J. Biol. Chem.,* 172:221–239, and literature there cited.

Smith, E. L. 1951. Proteolytic Enzymes. In, The Enzymes, 1(Pt. 2):793–872. New York, Academic Press.

Sperry, J. A., and Rettger, L. F. 1915. *J. Biol. Chem.,* 20:445–459.

Strange, R. E., and Dark, F. E. 1957. *J. Gen. Microbiol.,* 16:236–249.

Tai, T. Y., and van Heyningen, W. E. 1951. *J. Gen. Microbiol.,* 5:110–120.

Tate, P. 1929. The Dermatophytes or Ringworm Fungi. *Biol. Revs.,* 4:41–75.

Vanbreuseghem, R. 1952. *Mycologia* 44:176–182; cf. Page, R. M. 1950. *Ibid.,* 42:591–602.

Virtanen, A. I., and Tarnanen, J. 1932. *Z. physiol. Chem.,* 204:247–258; cf. Virtanen, A. I., and Suolahti, 1937. *Enzymologia,* 2:89–91.

Warner, A. C. I. 1956. *J. Gen. Microbiol.,* 14:749–762.

Weil, L.; Kocholaty, W.; and Smith, L. 1939. *Biochem. J.,* 33:893–897.

Wieland, Th.; Griss, G.; Haider, K.; and Haccius, B. 1960. *Arch. Mikrobiol.,* 35:415–427.

CHAPTER VIII

The Metabolism of Amino Acids

Few products of natural origin are as versatile in their behavior as the amino acids, and few have such a variety of biological duties to perform. . . . They reveal at once uniformity and diversity; in this duality, the array of the amino acids is a partial reflection of the larger biological world which is always the same and always different.

J. P. GREENSTEIN and M. WINITZ:
Chemistry of the Amino Acids (1961)

1. AMMONIFICATION IN THE SOIL

The final products of proteolysis are the amino acids. Bacterial attack on these substances involves reactions of several types, but in the main the nitrogenous product is ammonia. The study of amino acid breakdown is, therefore, in good part the study of ammonia production by bacteria or by their enzymes.

It was a very early observation that nitrogenous material added to soil readily gives rise to ammonia. Marchál, however (1894), showed that sterilized soil gave no ammonia when mixed with nitrogenous matter, so that the process is evidently bacterial. The production of NH_3 from feces is also bacterial (Severin, 1895–1901), about 40 per cent of human feces consisting of bacteria. Of a number of organisms grown upon unpurified ovalbumin, Marchál found that *Bac. mycoides* was the most active ammonifier, converting 40 per cent of the added protein nitrogen to ammonia in 15 days at 30° C. However, *Proteus vulgaris*, an Actinomyces species, and many other bacteria, Aspergillus, Cephalothecium, and other fungi, also produced ammonia; he recognized, therefore, that the faculty of decomposing nitrogenous compounds to ammonia is widely distributed. In the soil, ammonia production is often the result of collusion between different organisms, some being mainly responsible for the initial hydrolysis of polymers such as proteins and aminopolysaccharides, while others rapidly liberate ammonia from the resulting smaller molecules.

Of the main paths of amino acid breakdown, that depending on oxidation is the most important and will be considered first.

2. OXIDATIVE DEAMINATION

A. The Process Itself

Marchál appreciated that ammonification in soil is essentially oxidation, carbon dioxide and water being formed at the same time and in approximately the amounts corresponding to complete oxidation. The first step in this process, in which ammonia is eliminated, is called oxidative deamination. According to the researches of Knoop and of Neubauer on animal tissue, it proceeds in two stages—dehydrogenation to the imino acid, and subsequent hydrolysis to the keto acid:

$$\underset{\displaystyle \underset{NH_2}{\overset{COOH}{\Big|}}}{RCH} \quad \xrightarrow{\tfrac{1}{2}O_2} \quad \underset{\displaystyle \underset{NH}{\overset{COOH}{\Big|}}}{R{-}C} + H_2O \quad \xrightarrow{H_2O} \quad \underset{\displaystyle \underset{O}{\overset{COOH}{\Big|}}}{R{-}C} + NH_3$$

Oxidative deamination is probably the commonest type of amino acid breakdown. Like so many biological oxidations, it may be imitated by quinones (Schaaf, 1929; Kisch, 1931–1932) and other compounds containing two carbonyl groups, as well as by H_2O_2.

Unfortunately, oxidative deamination by microorganisms is nearly always accompanied by secondary reactions, so that the highly reactive keto acids seldom appear. The evidence for its widespread occurrence is therefore in good part indirect, but four types of evidence combine to make it convincing. Most of this was obtained long ago.[1]

(1) Deamination by washed bacteria is often strictly oxidative; Janke and Tayenthal (1937), using *E. coli* and *Bac. mycoides*, found glycine to be attacked only in air, and Stephenson and Gale (1937) found the same for alanine and glutamic acids. In favorable cases, as when *Proteus vulgaris* acts on histidine (Raistrick, 1919), leucine, phenylalanine, or methionine (Bernheim *et al.*, 1935), only one atom

---

[1] The more biochemical aspects of this chapter, especially the work published between 1946 and 1954, are presented in some detail in the *Symposium on Aminoacid Metabolism*, McCollum-Pratt Institute, ed., W. D. McElroy and H. Bentley Glass, Baltimore, Johns Hopkins Press, 1955. Alton Meister's *Biochemistry of the Amino Acids*, New York, Academic Press, 1957, is also a useful biochemical (but not bacteriological) general reference.

of O_2 is absorbed and one mole NH_3 produced as required by the equation shown above.

(2) Where the products are not the corresponding keto acids, they are substances that could have been formed readily from these keto acids. For example, glutamic acid is readily converted to succinic acid by yeast, but α-ketoglutaric acid was converted to succinic acid in a 99 per cent yield (Neuberg and Ringer, 1915, 1918). Similarly, alanine is oxidized to acetic acid by many organisms, but the intermediate keto acid, pyruvic acid, is oxidized to acetic acid even more rapidly. *Proteus vulgaris* also rapidly oxidizes α-keto butyric acid (Stumpf and Green, 1944).

(3) In favorable circumstances the keto acid has actually been isolated. Neubauer and Fromherz (1911), realizing that with natural amino acids the resulting keto acid is readily broken down, chose an amino acid that does not occur naturally, namely, phenylglycine. By exposing this to yeast (in the presence of sugar), they obtained phenylglyoxylic acid, isolated in 20 per cent yield:

$$C_6H_5CHNH_2COOH \rightarrow C_6H_5COCOOH + NH_3$$

Similarly, glycine exposed to washed cells of *E. coli* or *Bac. mycoides* gave rise to glyoxylic acid (Janke and Tayenthal, 1937):

$$CH_2NH_2COOH \rightarrow CHOCOOH + NH_3$$

but some CO_2 was evolved as well, indicating more extensive breakdown. With fungi (*Asp. oryzae*) small yields of phenylpyruvic acid were obtained from phenylalanine, and of isopropylpyruvic acid from leucine (Uyemura, 1937); *Fusarium lini* also converts alanine to pyruvic acid (Wirth and Nord, 1943).

(4) Cell-free preparations, from which some at least of the accompanying enzymes have been removed, give cleaner results. In one such preparation from *Proteus vulgaris*, the keto acids were only very slowly oxidized, if at all, and the theoretical requirements, i.e., equimolecular quantities of oxygen consumed and of NH_3 and keto acid produced, were realized (Table VIII–1). With this same preparation, the formation of keto acids from 11 different amino acids was demonstrated.

In the special case of glutamic acid, the dehydrogenation is carried out with a hydrogen acceptor other than oxygen; in animal tissues, in Treponema, and in *Cl. sporogenes* this is DPN (= NAD) (Olson and Anfinsen, 1952–1953); in *E. coli* and probably most bacteria, it is TPN (= NADP) (Adler *et al.*, 1938), while in yeast both a DPN-linked and a TPN-linked enzyme are present (Holzer and Schneider, 1957). The first step, with the ensuing hydrolysis, is given by equations (1) and (2). The reduced coenzyme reduces flavoprotein, and the re-

TABLE VIII–1. Oxidative Deamination by Cell-free Enzyme from *Proteus Vulgaris*

(From Stumpf and Green, 1944)

All Figures in Micromoles

Substrate	O₂ Consumed	NH₃ Formed	Keto Acid Formed
DL-phenylalanine	34.8	34.8	35.5
L-leucine	38.3	42.3	37.4

duced flavoprotein is reoxidized by oxygen (equations [3] and [4]). The keto acid is then oxidized either by the H_2O_2 (equation [5]) or enzymatically (equation [6], cf. Chap. XII, sec. 2C). In the intact cell the H_2O_2 is decomposed by catalase.

$$RCHNH_3^+COO^- + TPN^+ \rightleftharpoons R\cdot C=NH_2^+COO^- + TPNH + H^+ \tag{1}$$
$$R\cdot C=NH_2^+COO^- + H_2O \rightleftharpoons R\cdot COCOO^- + NH_4^+ \tag{2}$$
$$TPNH + H^+ + FP \rightleftharpoons TPN^+ + FPH_2 \tag{3}$$
$$FPH_2 + O_2 \rightarrow FP + H_2O_2 \tag{4}$$
$$R\cdot COCOO^- + H_2O_2 \rightarrow R\cdot COO^- + CO_2 + H_2O \tag{5}$$
$$R\cdot COCOO^- + \tfrac{1}{2} O_2 \rightarrow R\cdot COO^- + CO_2 \tag{6}$$

Formal proof that it is ammonium ion, NH_4^+, that participates, rather than NH_3, has been given by Fisher and McGregor (1960) from a study of pH sensitivity. Accordingly, all the participants have been shown in their corresponding charged forms.

Neurospora has several mutants that are deficient in nitrogen assimilation. Study of these has brought to light three different glutamic dehydrogenases (Fincham, 1960). One is like that of bacteria, one is activated by a few minutes at 35° C and loses its activity slowly on cooling, and the third differs in having a much higher affinity for all its substrates, especially for ammonia. They are inherited independently. All three use TPN(= NADP) as hydrogen acceptor and are otherwise superficially alike. Thus, what appears to be a single enzyme can occur in various modifications, and one can only suppose that when other organisms receive equally detailed study, many similar cases will come to light.

A second special case is that of L-alanine. This deaminase, or dehydrogenase, has so far only been found in *Bac. subtilis* and other bacilli; the equilibrium is in the direction of alanine synthesis, and apparently for these organisms the reaction is the main path of ammonia assimilation (Hong *et al.*, 1959). In other bacteria (see below) this function is served by glutamic dehydrogenase, which thus has a much greater importance than merely as a deaminase for one amino acid. The L-alanine dehydrogenase of *Bac. cereus* is specific for DPN and has pH optimum 8.8 (for amination) and 9.8 (for deamination), values that allow it to function well in presence of free ammonia (O'Connor and Halvorson, 1960).

In view of the close relation between the functions of these two dehydrogenases in amino acid metabolism, it is truly remarkable that the enzymes themselves are just as closely related. For recent work shows that the glutamic dehydrogenase molecule readily dissociates into four subunits (Frieden, 1959), and one of these acts as alanine dehydrogenase (Tomkins *et al.*, 1961). The dissociation is brought about by certain steroids and metal-chelators, while reassociation is favored by ADP, DPN, and TPN; correspondingly, the first group of reagents inhibits activity on glutamate and promotes activity on alanine, while the second group has the opposite effect.

There is some evidence for a special deaminase for phenylalanine, too, since Proteus characteristically oxidizes it faster than other bacteria. In this case the keto acid, phenylpyruvic acid, is readily identified as the product because of its color reaction with $FeCl_3$ (Henriksen, 1950). The ability to produce this reaction in phenylalanine broth has, therefore, been proposed as a diagnostic test for Proteus; it can be done in 10 minutes (Ben Hamida and le Minor, 1956).

Other amino acids are deaminated directly by a pair of flavoprotein enzymes, the *amino acid oxidases*, whose only specificity is for the L-isomers and the D-isomers, respectively. These enzymes are Nos. 15 and 16 in Table V–5. Some organisms possess only, or mainly, one type, e.g., *Ps. aeruginosa* does not attack D-leucine, D-isoleucine, or D-histidine, and although it oxidizes some other D-forms, they are not deaminated (Webster and Bernheim, 1936). In *E. coli*, D-glutamate is attacked only one-fifth as rapidly as the L-form, while in *Proteus vulgaris*, the enzyme for the L-isomers is the only one present in the cell-free preparation of Table VIII–1. However, in animal tissue the D-forms are generally the more rapidly deaminated, and in several fungi very active D-amino acid oxidases are present (Emerson *et al.*, 1950).

Optimum pH for oxidative deamination, either in vivo or in vitro, is between 6.5 and 8. When the flavoprotein is reoxidized by O_2 (equation [4]), the over-all free energy yield is about 20,000 calories per mole (see Cohen and Brown, 1960), which means that the reaction goes fairly completely. The status of the imino acid as the primary product, although generally accepted for some time, has recently been given direct chemical support, leucine and the L-amino acid oxidase being used (Frieden and Velick, 1957). A peculiar feature is that glucose in the culture medium inhibits formation of these enzymes, although glucose does not affect the deamination process itself (Stephenson and Gale, 1937).

(5) Where oxidative deamination is reversed, i.e., in *reductive amination*, the role of the keto acid is clear. In preparations from yeast or *E. coli*, the reduction of TPN by glutamic acid is at once reversed

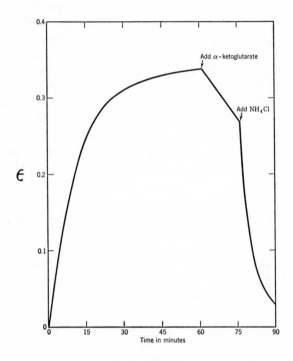

FIGURE VIII–1

The deamination of L-glutamate by an enzyme from *E. coli* in presence of TPN as hydrogen acceptor. The process is followed by the absorption of reduced TPN in the ultraviolet (ordinate). Note reversal on adding the keto acid or ammonium. (From E. Adler, V. Hellström, G. Günther, and H. v. Euler, *Z. physiol. Chem.*, **255**:14–26, 1938.)

by adding α-ketoglutaric acid, especially if NH_4^+ is added too (see Fig. VIII–1):

$$\text{Glutamate}^- + \text{TPN}^+ + H_2O \rightleftharpoons \text{Ketoglutarate}^- + \text{TPNH} + H^+ + NH_3$$

In the figure the extent to which the TPN is reduced was followed by its light absorption at 340 mμ, which provides a convenient assay. The free-energy yield for equations (1) and (2) from left to right is actually negative (−18,000 calories per mole) so that the equilibrium is markedly in favor of synthesis.

Similarly, the amination of pyruvic acid to alanine, first observed in fermenting yeast (Fromageot and Desnuelle, 1933–1934), can be readily carried out with L-alanine dehydrogenase; the enzyme of *Bac. cereus* and its spores aminates pyruvate about 10 times as fast as it deaminates alanine (O'Connor and Halvorson, 1960). Here the equilibrium is even farther toward synthesis. This fact is, as mentioned above, important because these two dehydrogenases appear to provide *the main pathways of ammonia assimilation*, the glutamic system for yeast and most bacteria, the alanine system for a few mutants of these and for the bacilli (Hong *et al.*, 1959). The general importance of glutamic acid as a route of nitrogen assimilation can be shown dramatically by following the appearance of C^{14}-compounds in yeast treated with C^{14}-ethanol (Aubert and Milhaud, 1956). Labeled glutamic acid appears in the cells within five seconds, aspartic acid after one minute, alanine and other amino acids only after 15 minutes. When the yeast has been grown on alcohol, the interconversions are faster, but the order is the same and it is clear that glutamic acid is formed with great speed.

Although the keto acid is optically inactive, its amination generally leads to the L-amino acid. Thus, the keto-analogues of leucine and valine, i.e., α-keto-isocaproic and α-keto-isovaleric acids, are reductively aminated by *Bac. subtilis* to L-leucine and L-valine, with less than 1 per cent of the D-isomer (Shah and King, 1958). (The formation of DL-alanine from pyruvate by this bacillus is an exception due to presence of a *racemase*, which brings D- and L-alanine into equilibrium.) The asymmetric formation of the amino acid must mean that the keto acid is rigidly held on the enzyme at three points while the ammonia reacts with it (see p. 341).

(6) The relationship to keto acids is shown also by growth requirements. A Neurospora mutant requiring leucine for growth would grow immediately on α-keto-isocaproic acid, and another requiring valine would grow on α-keto-isovaleric acid (Bonner *et al.*, 1943). Aerobacter and *E. coli* mutants requiring valine both similarly respond to the keto acid, while another *E. coli* mutant actually accumulates the keto acid and is therefore deficient in the aminating system (Umbarger and Magasanik, 1951; Maas and Vogel, 1953).

B. Transamination

A special kind of reversible deamination leads to the formation, not of free NH_3, but of another amino acid. Alanine, for instance, can be deaminated to pyruvic acid in the presence of α-ketoglutaric acid, which accepts the amino group:

$$
\begin{array}{cccc}
\text{CO·COOH} & \text{CH}_3 & \text{CHNH}_2\text{·COOH} & \text{CH}_3 \\
| & | & | & | \\
\text{CH}_2 & + \quad \text{CHNH}_2 \; \leftrightarrows \; \text{CH}_2 & & + \quad \text{CO} \\
| & | & | & | \\
\text{CH}_2\text{COOH} & \text{COOH} & \text{CH}_2\text{·COOH} & \text{COOH}
\end{array}
$$

This process, *transamination*, is of general importance. At first (Braunstein and Kitzmann, 1937) it was thought to take place with only very few amino acids, but it is now known that virtually all amino acids take part. For example, dried cells of *E. coli* and *Ps. fluorescens* can each use α-ketoglutarate as an amino acceptor for 13 amino acids (Feldman and Gunsalus, 1950); an extract from *Lactob. arabinosus* uses it for 16 (Meister, 1952). In *E. coli* also, α-keto-isovaleric acid acts as an amino acceptor for alanine and α-aminobutyric acid, and in Brucella pyruvate is an amino acceptor for leucine (see the review of Meister, 1955). The role of aspartic acid as an amino group donor has been given special prominence in Virtanen's interpretation of the nitrogen fixation process in nodules (Chap. IX) and has been recorded in large numbers of microorganisms.

Transamination of the γ-amino group of ornithine is an interesting case, because it yields glutamic γ-semi-aldehyde (Fincham, 1953).

$$
\begin{array}{cccc}
 & \text{COOH} & & \text{COOH} \\
 & | & & | \\
\text{CHNH}_2 & \text{CO} & \text{CHO} & \text{HCNH}_2 \\
| & | & | & | \\
(\text{CH}_2)_2 & + \; \text{CH}_2 \; \rightleftarrows \; (\text{CH}_2)_2 & + & \text{CH}_2 \\
| & | & | & | \\
\text{CHNH}_2 & \text{CH}_2 & \text{CHNH}_2 & \text{CH}_2 \\
| & | & | & | \\
\text{COOH} & \text{COOH} & \text{COOH} & \text{COOH} \\
\text{Ornithine} & \begin{array}{c}\alpha\text{-Keto-}\\ \text{glutaric}\end{array} & \begin{array}{c}\text{Glutamic}\\ \gamma\text{-semi-aldehyde}\end{array} & \text{Glutamic acid}
\end{array}
$$

Since this aldehyde is a direct precursor of proline (Vogel and Davis, 1952), this reaction interconnects arginine breakdown with proline synthesis. Several other α-keto acids act as amino acceptors with ornithine. A parallel case is the transamination of glyoxylic acid from glutamic acid to yield glycine; the equilibrium here is in the direction of glycine formation (Metzler *et al.*, 1954).

Even D-amino acids can transaminate; *Bac. subtilis* uses α-ketoglutarate as an amino acceptor for D-alanine, forming D-glutamate (see Meister, 1955). In view of the prevalence of D-glutamate polymers in capsules and elsewhere, this reaction is doubtless of great importance in bacteria. D-Alanine is produced by the racemase mentioned above.

With all these reactions, pyridoxal phosphate is needed as a co-enzyme. Its mode of action is described in section 6D. The apoenzyme (i.e., the protein part) is not a separate one for each amino acid, but like the amino acid oxidases above, is rather unspecific. In *E. coli* there is evidence for only about three separate enzymes, each of which catalyzes a large group of transaminations.

The peculiar readiness with which α-ketoglutarate acts as an amino acceptor, so that glutamic acid will be continually formed in a metabolizing cell, lends special significance to the wide occurrence of glutamic dehydrogenase in bacteria. The two reactions may constitute a major route for the deamination of other amino acids, namely:

$$\text{Amino acid} + \alpha\text{-Ketoglutarate} \rightarrow \text{Keto acid} + \text{Glutamate}$$
$$\text{Glutamate} + H_2O + TPN^+ \rightarrow TPNH + H^+ + \alpha\text{-Ketoglutarate} + NH_3$$

The glutamic acid thus acts as a catalyst. Evidently this pathway is an alternative one to that using the amino acid oxidases. From what was said above, the pathway is a main one in the reverse direction too, glutamate acting as catalyst in the bacterial synthesis of many amino acids.

C. The Secondary Reactions of the Keto Acids[2]

1. REDUCTION. The keto acid may be directly reduced to the hydroxy acid:

$$R\cdot CO\cdot COOH \xrightarrow{2(H)} R\cdot CHOH\cdot COOH$$

For example, tyrosine in presence of glycerol and phosphate was converted by *E. coli* and *Proteus vulgaris* to *p*-hydroxy-phenyl-lactic acid (Sasaki, 1914). In this case R = HOC_6H_4. Similarly, phenylglycine added to a yeast fermentation, in the presence of sugar, was converted to the hydroxy acid (mandelic) as well as partly to the keto acid (phenylglyoxylic [Neubauer and Fromherz, 1911]):

$$C_6H_5CHNH_2COOH \xrightarrow{\frac{1}{2}O_2} C_6H_5COCOOH + NH_3 \xrightarrow{2(H)} C_6H_5CHOHCOOH$$

This change evidently took place *via* the keto acid, because when the keto acid itself was added, it was readily reduced to mandelic acid. Many other examples could be adduced.

There is no evidence at all that organisms produce hydroxy acids from amino acids by direct *hydrolysis*, i.e.:

$$R\cdot CHNH_2\cdot COOH + H_2O \rightarrow R\cdot CHOH\cdot COOH + NH_3$$

[2] Many of the instances in the older literature were reviewed by Janke (1930).

Where hydroxy acids appear, there is every reason to believe they are formed by oxidative deamination and subsequent reduction of the keto acid. Hydrolytic deamination (see sec. 5 below) appears to be restricted to amides.

2. DECARBOXYLATION. In addition to oxidative decarboxylation (sec. 8 of Chap. V) keto acids can be "simply" decarboxylated to produce the aldehyde with one less carbon atom:

$$R \cdot CO \cdot COOH \rightarrow CO_2 + R \cdot CHO$$

Among those rapidly decarboxylated by the enzyme from yeast are the α-keto derivatives of isocaproic and isovaleric acids and of ethyl glutarate (Meister, 1952). All of these could arise by deamination of amino acids.

The resulting aldehyde can react in two ways:

(1) It may be dehydrogenated to an acid, RCOOH, having one carbon atom less than the original amino acid. The over-all reaction is thus not different from oxidative decarboxylation. In the few cases where aldehydes are identifiable intermediately, they are subject either to direct dehydrogenation or to dismutation (Chap. XVI); thus, acetaldehyde dehydrogenase forms acetic acid; its "mutase" forms a mixture of acetic acid and ethanol.

(2) The alternative fate is that the aldehyde may become reduced to the alcohol:

$$RCHO + 2(H) \rightarrow RCH_2OH$$

This reaction was first studied by Ehrlich in attempting to discover the source of the "fusel oils" (amyl alcohol and its isomers) produced in yeast fermentation. Esters of amyl alcohol are responsible for a good deal of the aroma or "bouquet" of fine wines. According to Heinzelmann and Dehnicke (1915), who made an extended study of the conditions, fusel oils are produced by all yeasts; the amount is greater with grain mash than with potato mash, doubtless due to the high-protein content of the grains.

Ehrlich (1907, 1909) showed that isoamyl alcohol arises from leucine:

$$(CH_3)_2CHCH_2CHNH_2COOH \rightarrow (CH_3)_2CHCH_2CH_2OH + NH_3 + CO_2$$
$$\text{Leucine} \qquad\qquad\qquad \text{Isoamyl alcohol}$$

Several fungi that carry out an alcoholic fermentation give the same reaction (Pringsheim, 1908); added leucine is quantitatively converted to isoamyl alcohol. Valine is converted to isobutyl alcohol (Ehrlich, 1906):

$$(CH_3)_2CH \cdot CHNH_2COOH \xrightarrow{\frac{1}{2}O_2 + 2(H)} (CH_3)_2CH \cdot CH_2OH + NH_3 + CO_2$$

and serine to ethylene glycol:

$$CH_2OHCHNH_2COOH \xrightarrow{\frac{1}{2} O_2+2(H)} CH_2OH \cdot CH_2OH + NH_3 + CO_2$$

Phenylalanine and tryptophan (indolealanine) give, analogously, phenyl-ethanol and tryptophol (indole-ethanol) (Ehrlich, 1907, 1912), while phenylglycine gives benzyl alcohol (Neubauer and Fromherz, 1911). A cell-free preparation from yeast converts tyrosine to p-hydroxyphenylethanol (tyrosol), and here the presence of the intermediate p-hydroxy-phenylpyruvic acid was shown (Shanmuganathan and Elsden, 1958). Asparagine or ammonium sulfate prevent fusel oil production, probably by reaminating the intermediates (see Yamada 1932, 1935).

However, fusel oil is not produced only from external amino acids, since it can also be endogenous. Yeast suspended in glucose solution produces fusel oil at a slow but steady rate (Genevois and Lafon, 1957), and some of its constituents, e.g., n-propanol and n-butanol, are not directly related to amino acids. Apparently the fusel oils can be produced from glucose by the same pathways as are used for the amino acids, since a yeast mutant that requires leucine for growth produced a fusel oil containing almost no isoamyl alcohol, and one requiring valine yielded very little isobutyl alcohol (Ingraham and Guymon, 1960). No doubt the synthesis goes as far as the related keto acid, and since the amination of this is genetically blocked in the mutant so that it cannot be converted to an amino acid, it is broken down directly; when a particular pathway is missing, both the amino acid and the fusel oil are affected.

3. OXIDATION. As shown in Chapter V, section 8, α-ketoglutarate is readily oxidized to succinate, and pyruvate to acetate, so that amino acids frequently give rise to an acid with one less carbon atom. Alanine yields acetic acid, and in a parallel reaction indolealanine (tryptophan) yields indoleacetic acid. This reaction, discovered (with mixed cultures) in 1880 by Salkowski, is now important on account of the role of indoleacetic acid as a plant growth hormone. With *Rhizopus suinus* (a Phycomycete) the yield of indoleacetic acid was found approximately proportional to the extent of aeration of the culture (Thimann, 1935):

$$I-CH_2CHNH_2COOH \xrightarrow{\frac{1}{2} O_2} (I-CH_2COCOOH) \xrightarrow{\frac{1}{2} O_2} I-CH_2COOH + CO_2$$

where I represents the indole nucleus. In several bacteria the reaction requires a keto acid, an indication that the first step is a transamination rather than a direct oxidation; pyridoxal phosphate is needed too (Stowe, 1959). With *Acetobacter xylinum* both indoleacetic acid and indole-ethanol are formed, which implicates indole-acetaldehyde as intermediate (Larsen *et al.*, 1962). By either pathway indoleacetic acid can be produced in higher plants by invading microorganisms, and since the substance promotes the growth of the plant in exceedingly low concentrations, this reaction leads to those plant diseases that are characterized by excessive overgrowth, such as galls and nodules (see sec. 1D of Chap. IX). In the case of the galls produced by corn smut (*Ustilago zeae*), it has been shown that a related nonpathogenic species does not carry out the reaction (Wolf, 1952); the indoleacetic acid, which has been isolated chemically, is present in the galls at about 20 times its normal level in the plant (Turian and Hamilton, 1960).

The crown-gall organism, *Agrob. tumefaciens*, produces indolealdehyde, indole-lactic acid, and other products from tryptophan; all of these arise from the breakdown of the indole-pyruvic acid first formed (Kaper and Veldstra, 1958). Some of the fungi that form mycorrhizas (swollen, inhibited, and distorted roots) convert tryptophan to indoleacetic acid very actively (Moser, 1959); mixed cultures with bacteria from the rhizosphere were even more effective. While the reaction may occur in some normal plant tissues, it is not clear whether it is the pathway of formation of indoleacetic acid in the uninfected plant (see the review of Thimann, 1960).

3. DESATURATIVE DEAMINATION

Deamination may lead to the formation of the unsaturated acid:

$$R \cdot CH_2 CHNH_2 \cdot COOH \rightarrow R \cdot CH = CH \cdot COOH + NH_3$$

Thus, histidine is converted by organisms of the coli-typhosum group to good yields of urocanic acid, which had previously only been known from urine of dogs (Raistrick, 1917):

Histidine   Urocanic acid

The enzyme, *histidinase*, can be readily prepared from *Ps. fluorescens* (Tabor and Mehler, 1955); its pH optimum is 9.5. The preparation also contains an enzyme that destroys urocanic acid.

Similarly aspartic acid is converted to fumaric acid by *E. coli*, this reaction being reversible (Quastel and Woolf, 1926):

The deamination of hydroxy-amino acids is slightly more complex. Here H_2O is removed, and the unsaturated acid that results tautomerizes to the imino acid; this is at once hydrolyzed to the keto acid (equation [2], p. 310). L-serine yields pyruvate (Chargaff and Sprinson, 1943).

$$
\begin{array}{cccc}
CH_2OH & CH_2 & CH_3 & CH_3 \\
| & \| & | & | \\
CH\cdot NH_2 \xrightarrow{-H_2O} & C{-}NH_2 \rightarrow C{=}NH \xrightarrow{H_2O} & C{=}O + NH_3 \\
| & | & | & | \\
COOH & COOH & COOH & COOH
\end{array}
$$

Threonine and homoserine similarly yield α-ketobutyrate. Since this compound is the first step on the route to isoleucine, threonine deaminase in *E. coli* controls the formation of this amino acid; the fact that it is inhibited by isoleucine gives a clear-cut case of "feedback control" (p. 347 and Chap. XX, sec. 5B). The enzyme occurs also in *Ps. fluorescens* and has been purified from *B. cadaveris* (Williams and McIntyre, 1955). It appears to need no coenzyme.

The first reaction, carried out by coliform bacteria, is due to the enzyme, *serine deaminase* (Wood and Gunsalus, 1949, 1950). The extracts have been reported to need adenylic acid, zinc ions, and glutathione for activation.

Glutamic acid undergoes a similar reaction, but only after it has been first isomerized to the branched chain form, β-methyl-aspartic acid. This is then deaminated to mesaconic acid:

$$
\begin{array}{ccc}
COOH & COOH & COOH \\
| & | & | \\
CH_2 & CH{-}CH_3 & C{-}CH_3 + NH_3 \\
| \rightleftharpoons & | \rightleftharpoons & \| \\
CH_2 & CHNH_2 & CH \\
| & | & | \\
CHNH_2 & COOH & COOH \\
| & & \\
COOH & &
\end{array}
$$

Barker *et al.* (1958, 1959), studying the soluble enzyme from *Cl. tetanomorphum* which catalyzes this reaction, have found that a derivative of vitamin B_{12} is coenzyme for the isomerization step. Several B_{12} derivatives participate in similar reactions (Chap. XIII).

A parallel reaction is the removal of H_2S from cysteine. The production of H_2S from peptones, presumably therefore from cysteine, is often used as a diagnostic reaction. It is particularly active with *Proteus vulgaris*, which liberates H_2S both from cysteine and its homologue, homocysteine, but not from β-thiolpropionic acid (Tarr, 1934). The amino group is therefore needed. The cell-free enzyme preparation from Proteus, called *cysteine desulfurase,* is partially cyanide-sensitive (i.e., linked to an oxidase) but a similar enzyme preparation from *E. coli* is anaerobic (Gale, 1947). Pyridoxalphosphate acts as coenzyme (Kallio, 1951). The reaction is formulated:

$$\begin{array}{cccccccc}
CH_2SH & & CH_2 & & CH_3 & & CH_3 & \\
| & -H_2S & || & & | & H_2O & | & \\
CHNH_2 & \longrightarrow & C-NH_2 & \rightarrow & C=NH & \longrightarrow & C=O & +NH_3 \\
| & & | & & | & & | & \\
COOH & & COOH & & COOH & & COOH &
\end{array}$$

Probably the initial step in both these reaction types is the formation of a hydrogen ion; it is the resulting electron shift that produces first α-amino acrylic acid and then the imino acid. With serine the steps would be:

$$\begin{array}{cccc}
 & -H^+ & H_2O + & \\
HOCH_2 \cdot CHCOOH \rightarrow & HO-CH_2-C-COOH \rightarrow & CH_2=C-COOH \rightarrow & CH_3-C-COOH \\
| & | & | & || \\
NH_2 & NH_2 & NH_2 & NH
\end{array}$$

In desaturative deamination in general, it is to be noted that a second substituent in the β position is needed. This may be COOH, OH, SH, or even imidazole. Desaturative deamination of simple aliphatic amino acids, at least by bacteria, has not been recorded.

4. REDUCTIVE DEAMINATION

This process leads to the formation of saturated fatty acids:

$$R \cdot CHNH_2COOH \xrightarrow{2(H)} R \cdot CH_2COOH + NH_3$$

It takes place anaerobically, generally by the action of clostridia, or in a few cases through facultative organisms.

Glycine is reduced to acetic acid, and both alanine and serine to propionic acid, by *Cl. putrificum* (Brasch, 1908–1909). Tryptophan is reduced by *E. coli* to β-indole propionic acid, and histidine to β-imidazole propionic acid (Koessler and Hanke, 1919). Aspartic acid is reduced to succinic acid by *Proteus vulgaris* and *Cl. putrificum.* Although hydrogen is evidently needed for these processes, the recorded examples are those in which amino acids alone (with inorganic salts) were the substrate. The hydrogen must come, therefore, from endogenous cell material.

In another type of reaction, the required hydrogen is supplied by the simultaneous dehydrogenation of another amino acid. Stickland

(1934–1935) found that, although neither alanine nor glycine is deaminated alone by *Cl. sporogenes*, when mixed together 2 moles of glycine are reductively deaminated to acetic acid while 1 mole of alanine is "oxidized" to acetic acid, probably via pyruvic acid. The alanine yields 4H:

$$CH_3CHNH_2COOH + H_2O \rightarrow CH_3COCOOH + NH_3 + 2(H)$$
$$CH_3COCOOH + H_2O \rightarrow CH_3COOH + CO_2 + 2(H)$$

The hydrogen is then accepted by glycine:

$$2\ CH_2NH_2COOH + 4(H) \rightarrow 2\ CH_3COOH + 2\ NH_3$$

Cysteine may take the place of alanine as hydrogen donor (Woods, 1936). These "Stickland reactions" suffice to maintain the growth of all of the proteolytic clostridia in a glycine-alanine medium (Nisman, 1954). They are not shown by the anaerobic micrococci, however. These organisms convert serine to pyruvate, and threonine to α-keto-butyrate by the "desaturative" reaction, but they then liberate CO_2 from the ketoacids (Whiteley, 1957).

The nonsporeforming *Diplococcus glycinophilus* can use glycine alone (Cardon and Barker, 1946, 1947); the products are acetic acid, NH_3, and CO_2; one molecule of glycine is completely "oxidized" to $CO_2 + NH_3$, yielding 6(H), which is accepted by three more molecules, as above. Thus, four molecules of glycine yield three of acetic and two of CO_2. If the cultures were shaken, hydrogen gas was evolved; in consequence, less hydrogen was available for reduction and correspondingly less acetic acid was formed and more CO_2 evolved.

This reaction is mediated by tetra-hydro-folic acid which acts as a "one-carbon transfer system" (Chap. XXIV, sec. 4). Cell-free extracts of the Diplococcus require this substance (abbreviated FH_4) as well as DPN, vitamin B_6, and a reducible dye, in order to attack glycine (Sagers and Gunsalus, 1961). Glycine with C^{14} in the CH_3 group transfers some C^{14} to the FH_4, but C^{14} in the carboxyl group appears only as CO_2. The folic acid transfers the "1-carbon" group to another glycine molecule to form serine:

$$NH_2CH_2COOH + FH_4 \rightarrow FH_3 \cdot CH_2OH + CO_2 + NH_3 + 2(H)$$
$$NH_2CH_2COOH + FH_3CH_2OH \rightarrow HOCH_2 \cdot CHNH_2COOH + FH_4$$

The serine is now converted to pyruvate as above (p. 319) and thence to acetate. This seems a complex route, but the Diplococcus does not attack other amino acids. For many other bacteria this reaction provides the normal source of serine (Lascelles and Woods, 1954; Wright, 1955); it is thus of critical importance.

In a modification of the above reactions (Stickland, 1935), proline is reduced to δ-aminovaleric acid at the expense of the dehydrogenation of either alanine or cysteine; only here, of course, the proline is not deaminated:

$$
\begin{array}{ccc}
CH_2\!-\!\!-\!\!-CH_2 & \left(\begin{array}{c}\text{alanine}\\ \text{or}\\ \text{cysteine}\\ \rightarrow 2(H)\end{array}\right) & CH_2\!-\!CH_2 \\
| \qquad\quad | & & | \qquad | \\
CH_2 \quad CH\cdot COOH & \longrightarrow & CH_2 \quad CH_2COOH \\
\diagdown\;\diagup & & \diagdown \\
NH & & NH_2
\end{array}
$$

The addition of dithiols helps to reduce the proline, and the cell-free enzyme from Clostridia contains a dithiol dehydrogenase. DPN, Mg, and pyridoxal phosphate are coenzymes (Stadtman, 1956). Hydroxy-proline and tryptophan can also act as hydrogen acceptors. Ornithine gives the same product by deamination:

$$ NH_2(CH_2)_3CHNH_2COOH \xrightarrow{2(H)} NH_2(CH_2)_3CH_2COOH + NH_3 $$

Cl. sporogenes can also deaminate arginine or ornithine alone, presumably by dehydrogenation of some molecules and hydrogenation of others, or even using O_2 as hydrogen acceptor (see Nisman's review, 1954).

It will be noticed that in the above reactions the δ–NH_2 group is not attacked. Also, the "unnatural" amino acid, β-alanine, which does not occur in proteins but is a constituent of the vitamin, pantothenic acid, and of coenzyme A, is not attacked by *Cl. sporogenes*. In general, only α-amino groups are removed in reactions of the above types.

A slightly more complex reaction is involved with threonine (α-amino β-hydroxy-butyric acid). This is reductively deaminated with reduction also of the hydroxy group by *Cl. propionicum* (Cardon and Barker, 1947):

$$ 3\ CH_3CHOHCHNH_2COOH + H_2O \rightarrow $$
$$ CH_3CH_2CH_2COOH + 2\ CH_3CH_2COOH + 2\ CO_2 + 3\ NH_3 $$

Probably desaturative deamination first produces α-ketobutyric acid as above, and this is then partly dehydrogenated and partly reduced, somewhat as in the Stickland reaction:

$$ 2\ CH_3CH_2CO\cdot COOH + 2\ H_2O \rightarrow 2\ CH_3CH_2COOH + CO_2 + 4(H) $$
$$ CH_3CH_2CO\cdot COOH + 4(H) \rightarrow CH_3CH_2CH_2COOH $$

5. HYDROLYTIC DEAMINATION AND THE SYNTHESIS OF ARGININE

A. Amides

When deamination occurs oxidatively and the resulting keto acid is reduced to a hydroxy acid, the impression is given that a hydrolysis has occurred, the —NH$_2$ being converted to —OH. However, it is only in the case of amides and imides that deamination by hydrolysis can occur:

$$RCONH_2 + H_2O \rightarrow RCOOH + NH_3$$

The same thing happens when amides are heated with alkali. The amide group of *asparagine* is readily hydrolyzed to yield aspartic acid, and that of *glutamine* to glutamic acid.

Asparaginase, the asparagine-hydrolyzing enzyme, is probably widely distributed. Asparagine is an effective nitrogen source in culture media for most bacteria. An L-asparaginase has been prepared from Mycobacteria (Halpern and Grassowicz, 1957) and two separate enzymes, one for D- and one for L-asparagine, from *Brucella abortus* (Altenborn and Housewright, 1954). Glutaminase is present in several bacteria too and has been partially purified from *Cl. welchii* (Hughes and Williamson, 1952) and *E. coli* (Meister *et al.*, 1955).

Glutaminase acting in reverse is probably not the main route of glutamine synthesis, which requires ATP (Chap. XX). However, it may have special importance because glutamine in trace amounts stimulates a number of bacterial activities. It promotes the growth and production of lactic acid by many lactobacilli and streptococci, and it promotes the formation of both toxin and alcohol by *Cl. tetani* (Lerner and Mueller, 1949; Mueller and Miller, 1949). While the mechanism of some of these effects is obscure, the action on growth may be due to a specific *transamidation* (analogous to transamination) from the amide group of glutamine to the 2-position, equivalent to a carbonyl group, of fructose-6-phosphate:

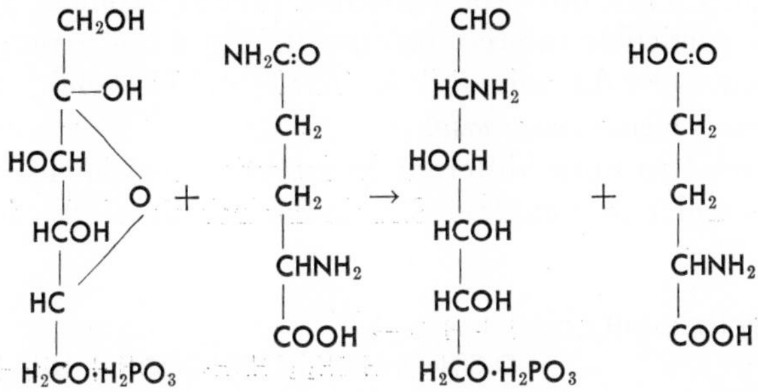

The product, 6-phosphoglucosamine, would obviously be important for cell-wall formation (Chap. III, sec. 1). Discovered in Neurospora by Leloir and Cardini (1953), the transamidase enzyme is present in *E. coli* and has been extensively purified from both (Ghosh *et al.*, 1960). Probably it is universal, and, significantly, its activity is greatest in the early stages of growth when cells are dividing rapidly (Strange and Dark, 1960). Unfortunately, at least in *Bac. cereus* and

E. coli, there is also an enzyme that deaminates the glucosamine under the same conditions; one may guess that unless it is quickly acetylated and polymerized into cell wall, the glucosamine will not accumulate.

B. Guanidine and Arginine Metabolism

Guanidine (not an amino acid) is converted to urea by *Asp. niger* (Ivanov and Avetissova, 1930):

$$NH{=}C{\diagup}^{NH_2}_{\diagdown}{}_{NH_2} + H_2O \rightarrow O{=}C{\diagup}^{NH_2}_{\diagdown}{}_{NH_2} + NH_3$$

Chrzaszcz and Zakomorny (1935) found that this ability is widespread among the fungi, some accumulating urea and others further hydrolyzing the urea to ammonia (see below). A comparable reaction is given by the guanidine derivative, *arginine:*

$$H{-}O{-}\underset{H}{\overset{NH{=}C{\diagup}^{NH_2}}{}} NH{\cdot}(CH_2)_3CHNH_2COOH + H_2O \rightarrow NH_2C{\diagup}^{NH_2}_{\diagdown\!\!\diagdown O} + NH_2(CH_2)_3CHNH_2COOH$$

Ornithine and urea are thus formed. This reaction has been recorded for only a few micrococci and *Bac. subtilis* (Tomota, 1940–1941), but it is of particular interest because it is also the manner in which urea is produced by the animal liver (Krebs and Henseleit), the enzyme involved being termed *arginase.*

There are two quite different hydrolytic breakdowns of arginine, one simple and one complex. Simple hydrolysis of the imide group yields citrulline:

$$NH{:}C(NH_2)NH(CH_2)_3CHNH_2COOH + H_2O \rightarrow$$
$$O{:}C(NH_2)NH(CH_2)_3CHNH_2COOH + NH_3 + Ca\ 6000\ cal$$

This reaction, due to the enzyme arginine desimidase, is brought about by *Sc. fecalis, Ps. aeruginosa,* yeast, and *Cl. perfringens,* a broad enough group of organisms to suggest that the distribution is very wide, though probably irregular (see footnote 1, p. 308).

Streptococci and lactobacilli, however, carry out a more complex breakdown in which CO_2 and 2 moles of NH_3 are liberated without oxygen uptake (Hills, 1940). Like so many bacterial enzymes, the system is largely adaptive, very little being formed when the cells are grown without arginine in the medium (Slade and Slamp, 1952). The nonoxidative nature of the reaction is shown by the presence of the system in *Cl. welchii* (Woods and Trim, 1942). Because the reaction results in a double hydrolysis, the enzyme was first called arginine dihydrolase, but it is not a single enzyme. One might think that the arginine is first hydrolyzed to urea and thence by another enzyme (see below) to $CO_2 + 2$ NH_3, but the streptococci do not hydrolyze urea. A clue to the problem appeared when cell-free preparations of *Sc. lactis* and *Sc. fecalis* were found to convert arginine to citrulline as expected (above), but not to hydrolyze citrulline unless ADP or ATP were added (Knivett, 1954). That the breakdown of citrulline is not a hydrolysis but a phosphorolysis and that the product is not ammonia but a new compound, carbamyl phosphate, were shown by Jones, Spector, and Lipmann (1955):

$$O:C(NH_2)NH(CH_2)_3CHNH_2COOH + {}^=HPO_4 \rightleftharpoons$$
$$NH_2(CH_2)_3CHNH_2COOH + NH_2COO \sim PO_3{}^=$$

The enzyme has been purified from *Sc. lactis* (Ravel *et al.*, 1959). The high-energy bond of carbamyl phosphate is transferred to ADP:

$$NH_2COO \sim H_2PO_3 + ADP \xrightarrow{Mg^{++}} NH_4{}^+ + HCO_3{}^- + ATP$$

However, in *E. coli* it can be simply hydrolyzed (Krebs *et al.*, 1958) to give carbamic acid, which decomposes spontaneously at *p*H 6:

$$H_2O + NH_2COOH_2PO_3 \rightarrow H_3PO_4 + NH_2COOH \rightarrow NH_4{}^+ + HCO_3{}^-$$

It will be noted that citrulline breakdown thus yields ATP without any oxidation, as does the breakdown of phosphotrioses described in Chapters XI and XII. The CONH bond in citrulline must thus be one of high energy. It is suggestive that a Pseudomonas has been isolated from soil which can use citrulline as a sole source of carbon and nitrogen (Slade *et al.*, 1954); perhaps it obtains its ATP from this reaction. Some streptococci can do the same with arginine.

A still more important point is that both the citrulline-ornithine reaction and the carbamyl phosphate-ammonia reaction are reversible, so that in this way citrulline can be synthesized from ornithine, CO_2, and NH_3. These are crucial steps in the *synthesis* of arginine. In a study of the ascomycete *Neurospora crassa*, which ordinarily grows without added arginine, Srb and Horowitz (1944) found seven mutant strains which only grew if arginine were added; one of these required arginine itself, two could use either arginine or citrulline, and four could use arginine, citrulline, or ornithine. They deduced that the sequence was the same as Krebs and Henseleit had earlier worked out in the animal liver, namely:

$$\text{Precursor} \xrightarrow{(1)} \text{Ornithine} \xrightarrow[(2)]{CO_2+NH_3} \text{Citrulline} \xrightarrow[(3)]{NH_3} \text{Arginine}$$

Evidently the first mutant was blocked in reaction (3), the next two at reaction (2), and the last four at reaction (1). The mutants which could not utilize ornithine were not helped by adding urea, proving that the synthesis must go by the route shown.

Using similar mutant strains, from *E. coli* (Davis, 1950), it was shown by growing the cultures side by side on a plate that the mutant requiring arginine excretes into the medium a substance that allows the mutant requiring citrulline to grow; presumably this substance is in fact citrulline. Thus, the organism cannot carry out reaction (3) and therefore accumulates its substrate. Both strains accumulate a substance, presumably ornithine, that allows the ornithine-requiring mutant to grow (see Fig. VIII–2).

Some of the ornithine-requiring mutants of Neurospora and of Penicillium can use glutamic acid instead, and since Neurospora can convert this acid to its semi-aldehyde, and the aldehyde by transamination to ornithine (p. 314), the precursor system in Neurospora is:

$$\text{HOOC·CH}_2\text{CH}_2\text{CHNH}_2\text{COOH} \rightarrow \text{OHC·CH}_2\text{CH}_2\text{CHNH}_2\text{COOH} \rightarrow \text{H}_2\text{N CH}_2\text{CH}_2\text{CHNH}_2\text{COOH}$$

Glutamic acid   Glutamic semi-aldehyde   Ornithine

(see Vogel and Bonner, 1954, 1958). Curiously enough, however, *E. coli* uses another route, since its ornithine-requiring mutants were found to accumulate not glutamic semi-aldehyde, but its acetyl derivative, as well as N-acetylornithine (Vogel, 1953). It was deduced that the *E. coli* route is therefore:

Glutamic → N-acetylglutamic → N-acetylglutamic semi-aldehyde →
N-acetylornithine → Ornithine

Enzymes for the acetylation of glutamic acid, the transamination of the acetylated aldehyde, and the deacetylation of acetylornithine have since been detected (see Vogel and Bonner, 1958). It is important too that N-acetylornithine will not allow growth of those Neurospora mutants that will grow on ornithine, although it will do so for an *E. coli* mutant. Thus, the two pathways are quite separate.

The last step in arginine synthesis has also proved to be complex. Citrulline does not simply add NH_3, since too much energy is required for this (ca. 6000 calories); instead it condenses with aspartic acid to form argininosuccinic acid:

$$\text{HOOC—CH(CH}_2)_3\text{NH—C—NH—CHCH}_2\text{COOH}$$
$$\begin{array}{ccc} | & \| & | \\ \text{NH}_2 & \text{NH} & \text{COOH} \end{array}$$

This compound was first isolated in a study of arginine formation by liver (see Ratner, 1962) and is also formed from malate by dried cells of the green alga Chlorella which had been grown on urea (Walker, 1952). ATP is required in the condensation, and ADP is liberated;

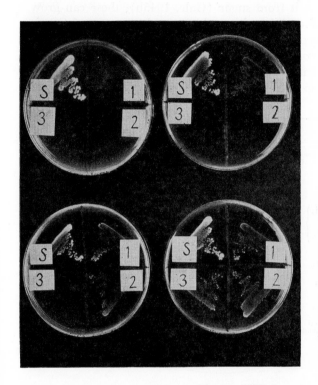
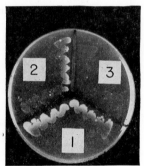

FIGURE VIII–2

Left. Growth of three mutants and of wild-type (S) *E. coli* on minimal medium (*top left*) and the same medium enriched with (*in order*) ornithine, citrulline, or arginine. Mutant 1 grows on all three enriched media; mutant 2 on citrulline and arginine; mutant 3 on arginine only.

Right. The three mutants grown on medium enriched with a trace of casein hydrolysate. The growth of mutant 1 is promoted by diffusate from mutants 2 and 3. The growth of mutant 2 is promoted by the diffusate from mutant 3. In other words, mutant 2 makes ornithine, and mutant 3 makes both citrulline and ornithine. (From B. D. Davis, *Experientia,* **6**:41–50, 1950.)

this satisfies the energy requirement (ATP → ADP + ca. 10,000 calories). Argininosuccinate is broken down readily by bacteria to arginine and fumarate and thus completes the route to arginine.

The series of reactions centering around arginine have many

ramifications in the life of bacteria. Carbamyl phosphate turns out to be an intermediate in the synthesis of pyrimidines (Lieberman and Kornberg, 1954–1955). Glutamic semi-aldehyde is the precursor of proline as well as ornithine (above). The CO_2 given off in arginine breakdown acts as a growth factor for certain streptococci that need CO_2 but cannot produce it from sugar (Gale, 1945b); these can grow on ornithine instead of arginine, but only if another source of CO_2 is supplied. Finally, the synthesis of the enzyme interconverting ornithine and citrulline in *E. coli* is suppressed by arginine, so that added arginine inhibits its own synthesis; this is the phenomenon of "feed-back control" (see Chap. XX, sec. 5).

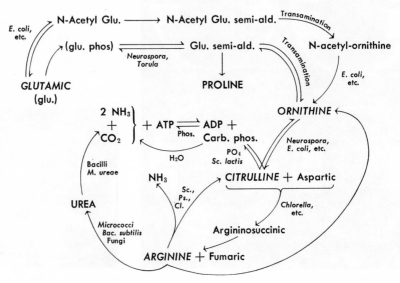

Some of the main microbial reactions of arginine are summarized in the accompanying diagram.

C. Urea Hydrolysis

This important hydrolytic reaction:

$$NH_2CONH_2 + 2 H_2O \rightarrow (NH_4)_2CO_3 \rightarrow 2 NH_3 + CO_2$$

is brought about by a limited number of bacteria. If urea be mixed with peptone and inoculated with soil, the predominating organisms are sporeformers, called by Beijerinck (1901) Urobacillus but now considered as *Bac. pasteurii* and its congeners. These organisms, as well as a nonsporeformer isolated by Söhngen (1909) as *Urobac. jakschii*, can hydrolyze urea in concentrations up to 10 per cent. They grow best on alkaline media (up to pH 11) and can do without urea on media made to pH 9 and containing 1 per cent NH_4Cl (Gibson, 1934). *Bac. pasteurii* has an actual requirement for ammonia in addition to peptone, although other urea-hydrolyzing bacilli do not (Bornside and Kallio, 1956). Beijerinck also isolated a Sarcina (*Sporosarcina ureae*) with similar physiology, which is most unusual because it is motile and forms spores, yet otherwise is a typical-looking Sarcina. It is evidently widely distributed in soils (Gibson, 1934).

If, instead of peptone, calcium malate be used in the enrichment culture with 2 per cent urea, nonsporeformers develop that can hydrolyze urea only at concentrations up to 3 per cent (Söhngen, 1909).

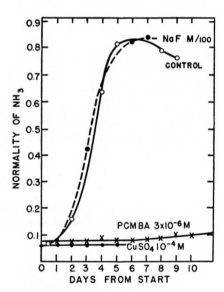

FIGURE VIII-3
Liberation of ammonia from urea by Urobacillus sp. The decrease in the control after reaching the maximum is doubtless due to loss of ammonia from the solution. *PCMBA*, Parachloromercuribenzoic acid. The insensitivity of the reaction to fluoride and its high sensitivity to the sulfhydryl reagents are clear. Urea concentration, 1.6 M (35° C). (Original.)

These include *M. ureae* (often also found in old urine) and a red organism, "*B. erythrogenes*," with a light-sensitive pigment. *M. aureus*, as well as certain yeasts, including Cryptococcus and Rhodotorula, also hydrolyzes dilute urea solutions, and the reaction is reliable enough to help in identifying them (Seeliger, 1956).

None of these organisms can grow in the absence of a carbon source in addition to urea. This is partly because the urea-hydrolyzing bacilli require traces of biotin, thiamine, or nicotinic acid (Bornside and Kallio, 1956) but partly because the energy liberated by urea hydrolysis is small. However, the reaction is so vigorous that very little carbon is needed; 20 mg of asparagine allow hydrolysis of 3600 mg of urea by *Urobac. jakschii*, and *M. ureae* decomposes up to 2000 times its wet weight of urea per hour (Burchard, 1899).

The hydrolysis is due to the enzyme *urease*, which is also present in some leguminous plants, notably the jack bean and soybean, but the urease from *Bac. pasteurii* is much more active than the jack-bean enzyme (Larsen and Kallio, 1954). Its Q_{10}, as would be expected for a hydrolysis, is only about 1.5.

This enzyme is one of many whose activity depends on the presence of sulfhydryl groups (—C—SH). It is strongly inhibited by iodoacetate, arsenite, and copper and mercury salts, as well as organic mercury compounds; these react with the —SH group (cf. Chap. XXIV). In *M. aureus* the sensitivity of urease to —SH inhibitors is limited to organisms grown in the presence of urea in the medium (Yall and Green, 1952). But the growth and urea hydrolysis by Urobacillus can be dramatically inhibited by traces of these reagents. The progress of urea hydrolysis in normal and inhibited cultures is shown in Figure VIII–3.

The importance of urea hydrolysis lies, of course, in the fact that it is a typical animal excretion product, and that large quantities of it are constantly being added to soil and to natural waters.

D. Creatine Breakdown

The bacterial breakdown of creatine (N-methyl-guanidine acetic acid) differs from simple deamination in that it involves splitting off of urea; in this it has much in common with the breakdown of arginine.

Creatine is attacked oxidatively by only a few bacteria. In the case of a Pseudomonas resembling *Ps. aeruginosa*, isolated from urine, the breakdown is rapid, leading to urea and ammonia (Kopper and Beard, 1947). The anhydride of creatine, creatinine, is brought into equilibrium with creatine by an enzyme called creatinomutase:

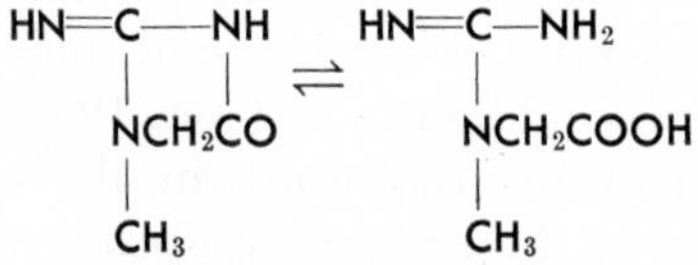
HN=C—NH
NCH₂CO
CH₃
HN=C—NH₂
NCH₂COOH
CH₃

Creatinine Creatine

This equilibrium is brought about by a soil organism obtained from enrichment cultures on a creatinine medium. After growth on this medium the bacterium develops an enzyme system converting creatine to urea and sarcosine (Akamatsu and Miyashita, 1952). The sarcosine is demethylated to glycine, and the glycine liberates ammonia, giving the following sequence:

$$\begin{array}{c} HN=C-NH_2 \\ | \\ N-CH_2COOH \\ | \\ CH_3 \end{array} \xrightarrow{H_2O} \begin{array}{c} H_2N-C-NH_2 \\ \| \\ O \\ + \end{array} \begin{array}{c} \\ \\ NHCH_2COOH \\ | \\ CH_3 \end{array} \xrightarrow{O_2} NH_2CH_2COOH \xrightarrow{1\frac{1}{2}\ O_2} \begin{array}{c} \\ \\ \\ NH_3 + 2CO_2 + H_2O \end{array}$$

The first stage exactly parallels the action of arginase, and an enzyme for it has been prepared from a soil bacterium that did not attack creatinine (Nimmo-Smith, 1949).

6. REACTIONS OTHER THAN DEAMINATION

The breakdown of amino acids is complicated by a number of side reactions that do not yield ammonia and therefore reduce the rate of the nitrogen cycle in nature.

A. Assimilation

In the first place, synthesis of bacterial or fungal protoplasm absorbs amino acids. Those organisms, like *E. coli* or *Asp. niger*, that are able to grow on a single amino acid or on a carbohydrate plus ammonium salts, must have the power of synthesizing all ordinary amino acids from NH_3, like green plants. It usually requires oxygen and, in any event, requires some source of energy (see Chap. XX). If a single amino acid is the sole nutrient, there will in general be an excess either of carbon compounds or of nitrogen; in the latter case ammonia will be excreted into the solution. Alanine seems to give nearly the right balance of C and N, and can be assimilated very efficiently by fungi like Leptomitus (Schade and Thimann, 1940). On the other hand, glutamate and asparagine, when oxidized by *Brucella abortus*, give a partial yield of NH_3 and CO_2 (Gerhardt et al., 1950):

$$\text{Glutamate} + (ca.)\ 2\ O_2 \rightarrow (ca.)\ 3\ CO_2 + 0.7\ NH_3$$

It is evident that part of the amino acid is assimilated while part is being oxidized. Glycine is usually a very poor growth substrate, and few bacteria, protozoa, or fungi will grow on it alone. *Diplococcus glycinophilus* (p. 321) is outstanding in this respect. The polyglutamate capsule (Chap. III) represents another drain on the amino acid supply.

B. Pigment Formation

In the second place, bacteria form a number of pigments in which nitrogen becomes temporarily immobilized. One of these is the group of black compounds called *melanins*, which are formed from tyrosine by the enzyme polyphenol oxidase. In this process, the tyrosine is first oxidized to dihydroxyphenyl alanine or *dopa;*

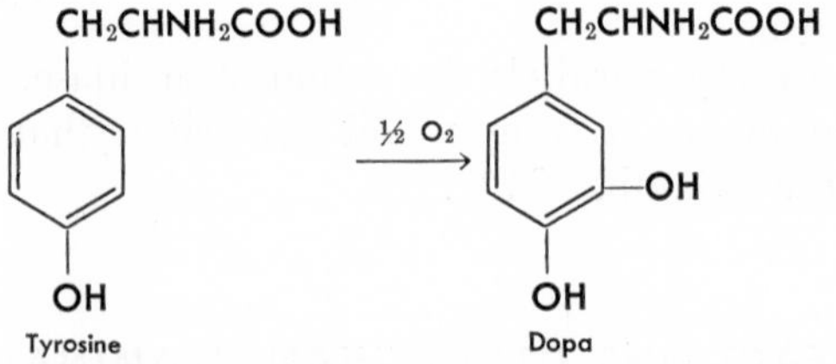

Dopa, being a dihydric phenol, is further oxidized to the orthoquinone, and this undergoes an intramolecular hydrogen transfer to form an indole ring. A second oxidation yields the quinonoid structure called *hallachrome,* a red pigment, and this undergoes hydrogen transfer to form 5,6-dihydroxy-2-indole carboxylic acid. The last-known stage is that this loses CO_2 and condenses to the black melanins. The series of reactions, elucidated by Raper (1928), and confirmed by several workers (Beer *et al.,* 1949, and Clemo *et al.,* 1950, 1952), are as follows:

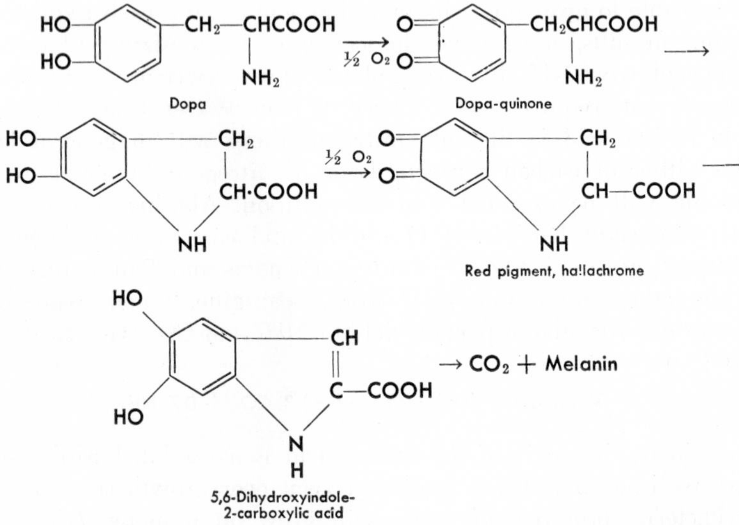

Later C^{14} experiments show, however, that melanin formation is more complex than simple condensation, because about half of the CO_2 that comes off arises from C atoms other than the carboxyl; also some of the C^{14} of the carboxyl survives in the final melanin (Clemo *et al.*, 1952). Doubtless several secondary reactions participate.

Polyphenol oxidase is possessed by many bacteria and Actinomycetes; it is also present in Neurospora (Horowitz and Shen, 1952) and in mushrooms. Its presence can easily be shown by moistening tyrosine agar plates with diluted sewage, when deep black spots appear surrounding the colonies of active organisms. Production of black pigment from tyrosine is sometimes used as a diagnostic character in taxonomy. Beijerinck (1913) found that a soil Actinomycete produced from tyrosine a colorless substance which other bacteria (*Ps.* sp.) oxidized to melanin. The colorless compound is probably dopa.

Of the pigments that are laid down inside the cell itself, the most important are a number of compounds containing three separate or fused rings.

The red pigment of *Serratia marcescens*, formerly called *Bacterium prodigiosum* ("miracle bacterium") because its colonies on moist bread resemble drops of blood (see p. 17), has been the center of an interesting group of studies. Beijerinck in 1912 observed that this organism continually gives rise to yellow and white mutants, and the yellow forms give rise to white ones, so that the ability to form red pigment, *prodigiosin*, is evidently lost by finite steps. His long paper, "Mutation bei Mikroben," was the first contribution to bacterial genetics (see Chap. XXI). Prodigiosin also occurs in members of the genus Streptomyces (Perry, 1961).

The pigment is insoluble in water, but is extracted from the cells by petroleum ether. From the molecular weight of 460, the fact that destructive breakdown yields pyrrole derivatives, and other chemical considerations, Wrede and Rothhaas (1934) assigned it formula III below. Its tri-pyrrole structure suggests some relationship to the all-important tetra-pyrroles which form the hemins and chlorophyll. Thus when *Serratia marcescens* is grown on C^{14}-labeled acetate or glycine, the C^{14} is found in the prodigiosin; and if both acetate and glycine are labeled, the C^{14} of *both* enters the pigment (Hubbard and Rimington, 1950). The special interest of this finding is that the hemin pigments are also formed by the condensation of acetate and glycine (Chap. XXIII). However, the biosynthetic pathway of prodigiosin cannot be the same as that for the hemin pigments, because the C^{14} of proline enters into the prodigiosin molecule even more readily than that of glycine (Marks and Bogorad, 1960).

When prodigiosin is heated with alkali, the breakdown products include $C_{10}H_{17}N$, 2-methyl,3-amyl pyrrole, II. One of the white *Serratia* mutants has now been shown to accumulate this compound while another mutant forms a different pyrrole compound, 2-aldehydo, 3-methoxy,5-pyrryl-pyrrole I. When cultures of this second white mutant are exposed to vapors of the methylamyl-pyrrole, they turn red immediately, i.e., the two pyrrole compounds condense into prodigiosin (Wasserman *et al.*, 1960):

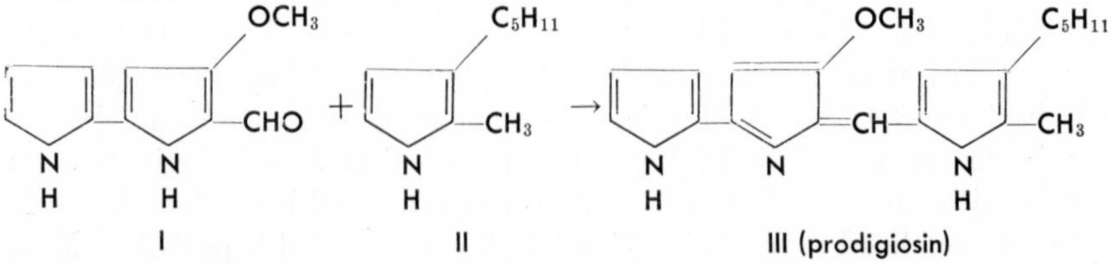

This may give a simple explanation for some of the complex genetical findings with crosses between Serratia strains. It also explains Santer and Vogel's observation (1956) that with two white mutants growing side by side one produces a diffusible precursor from which the other forms red pigment. There may be several related pigments in the Serratia gene-complex, because in some strains (e.g., var. *Kiliensis*) the pigment diffuses out into the medium, while in others it is wholly intracellular. In some the red compound is accompanied by a blue pigment of apparently similar structure, but a molecular weight about 775, i.e., perhaps a double molecule (Green *et al.*, 1956).

Another triple-ring pigment is the beautiful violet compound, violacein, formed by *Chromob.* (= Agrob.) *violaceum*. The elucidation of this structure has proved very difficult; after several attempts by Marchál in France and Beer in England, it was finally shown by Ballantine *et al.* (1958) to be IV:

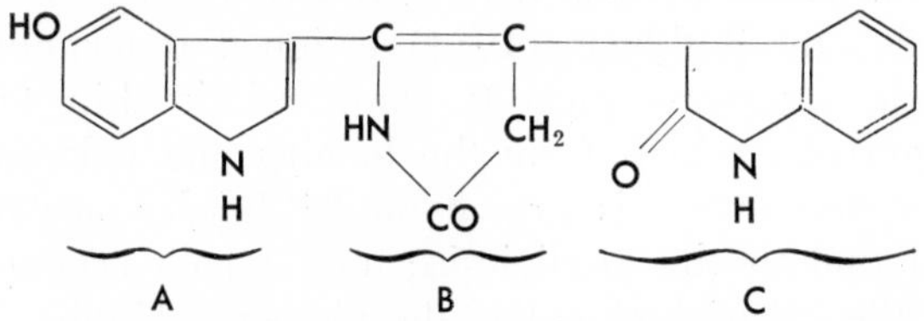

Thus, it contains 5-hydroxyindole (A), pyrrolenone (B), and oxindole (C). A marine strain isolated from codfish yielded the same pigment. Presence of the two indole rings suggests that violacein is an oxidation product of tryptophan. This agrees with the fact that a suspension of *C. violaceum* actively oxidizes tryptophan to the 5-hydroxy derivative and also breaks it down to indoleacetic and 5-hydroxyindoleacetic acids (Mitoma *et al.*, 1956). Indeed, *C. violaceum*, suspended in a solution of L-tryptophan alone, can form the pigment (DeMoss and Evans, 1959). An oxindole compound is known as an oxidation product of indoleacetic acid by the fungus Omphalia (Stowe *et al.*, 1957), so that this too can be formed from tryptophan. Indole is probably an intermediate, and when the cells are lyophilized they convert indole to indigo (p. 345) instead of to violacein (Sebek and Jäger, 1962).

The *phenazine pigments* are a group of compounds formed by Pseudomonads. Pyocyanin, from *Ps. aeruginosa* (originally *Ps. pyo-cy-anea* because it formed "blue pus" in infected wounds), has long been known. Its ready extraction from liquid cultures with chloroform to give a blue underlayer enables easy recognition of this organism. The structure is V and the color probably due to resonance between different forms. *Ps. chlororaphis* similarly produces a deep green pigment believed to be the semiquinone derived from oxychlororaphin, VI, or phenazine-2-carboxamide. Probably one of the N atoms is hydrogenated. *Ps. iodinum* forms the purple compound, iodinin, VII, or 2,7-dihydroxy phenazine. The latest member of the group to be discovered is the pigment of *Ps. aureofaciens* (Kluyver, 1956) which is deposited around the colonies as yellow crystals, especially on a glucose medium. It consists mainly of phenazine-2-carboxylic acid, VIII (see Haynes *et al.*, 1956); hence VI is its amide. Like the others it is readily extracted by chloroform. From what amino acids the phenazine ring is derived is unknown.

Many workers have wondered what function these (and other) pigments serve. The quantity is of course very small—usually only a fraction of 1 per cent of the dry weight. But at this concentration other pigments such as hemins or flavoproteins can be critically important in the life of the cell. However, colorless mutants, e.g., those of Serratia, seem at no disadvantage as regards growth rate or nutrition. Pyocyanin can be reversibly oxidized and reduced and can function as a coupler between some dehydrogenases. Prodigiosin is a fairly effective antibiotic, inhibiting the growth of *M. aureus* at a concentration as low as $1:30,000$ (Efimenko *et al.*, 1956). But whether these functions are served in nature remains obscure.

C. Decarboxylation

This is the most important side reaction. It is widely carried out by members of the coliform group, clostridia, and lactobacilli (Rodwell, 1953), as well as certain fungi, and is comparable to decarboxylation of the keto acids (cf. p. 316):

$$RCHCOOH \rightarrow RCH_2NH_2 + CO_2$$
$$|$$
$$NH_2$$

Amino acid decarboxylations are of great biochemical importance. The resulting amines were isolated by early workers from putrefying meat; they have unpleasant odors, are basic, and are toxic to animals. Brieger (1886) termed these bases *ptomaines* (the word was invented by Selmi in 1878) and considered them responsible for the "ptomaine poisoning" which follows the ingestion of bacterially spoiled meat or fish. However, although such bases are indeed toxic on injection (Berthelot, 1918), yet when fed by mouth, ordinarily spoiled meat has little ill effect (Savage, 1920). For the concentration of the bases to reach anywhere near the toxic level, the meat must be so far gone that it would be completely unpalatable. Further, these bases are present in the normal alimentary canal as a result of bacterial action, so that they cannot be highly toxic.[3]

Examples of the decarboxylation of amino acids (see also Gale, 1946) are:

(1) *Ornithine* produces *putrescine*, isolated by Ellinger (1899, 1900), from a mixed culture and subsequently by Gale (1941) from *Cl. septicum:*

$$NH_2(CH_2)_3CHNH_2COOH \rightarrow NH_2(CH_2)_3CH_2NH_2 + CO_2$$

The same base was obtained from arginine, doubtless by way of ornithine (Ackermann, 1910a).

---

[3] True food poisoning is either due to production of a very active toxin by the anaerobe *Cl. botulinum* or to actual bacterial invasion of the intestine by organisms present in the meat, such as *Salmonella typhimurium*. The noticeable extent of putrefaction in meat has little relation to its toxicity. Thus, many outbreaks of "botulism" have arisen from the eating of quite unsuspected food on which *Cl. botulinum* had grown and produced toxin and died out again, without causing much obvious breakdown. The botulinus toxin is a protein (Abrams *et al.*, 1946) and is not heat-stable, so that 10 minutes' boiling of infected food will render it perfectly safe.

(2) *Arginine* is converted to *agmatine* by intact *E. coli* (Gale 1940), or by the enzyme from it (Umbreit and Gunsalus, 1945):

$$HN:C\cdot NH(CH_2)_3CHNH_2COOH \rightarrow HN:C\cdot NH(CH_2)_3CH_2NH_2 + CO_2$$
$$\quad\quad\quad |\quad\quad\quad\quad\quad\quad\quad\quad\quad\quad\quad\quad\quad |$$
$$\quad\quad NH_2\quad\quad\quad\quad\quad\quad\quad\quad\quad\quad\quad NH_2$$

(3) *Lysine* produces *cadaverine:*

$$NH_2(CH_2)_4CHNH_2COOH \rightarrow NH_2(CH_2)_4CH_2NH_2 + CO_2$$

Cadaverine is so named because of its odor of corpses, in which it doubtless arises by bacterial action.

Both putrescine and cadaverine are produced by *Aspergillus oryzae* from soybean proteins, so that they are by no means products only of bacteria (Yamada and Ishida, 1926).

(4) *Glutamic acid* yields *γ-amino butyric acid:*

$$\begin{array}{lll} CHNH_2COOH & CH_2NH_2 & + CO_2 \\ | & | & \\ CH_2 & \rightarrow \quad CH_2 & \\ | & | & \\ CH_2COOH & CH_2COOH & \end{array}$$

This reaction occurs with *Rhizobium leguminosarum* (Virtanen *et al.*, 1938), *E. coli* (Gale, 1940; King and Fletcher, 1950), and *Cl. welchii* (Gale, 1945). The Aerobacter species differ from Escherichia in being unable to decarboxylate glutamic acid. *Leucine* and *valine* are decarboxylated by *Proteus* (Haughton and King, 1961).

(5) *Aspartic acid* yields *β-alanine:*

$$HOOC\cdot CH_2CHNH_2COOH \rightarrow HOOC\cdot CH_2CH_2NH_2 + CO_2$$

This reaction, exactly comparable to (4) above, is carried out vigorously by cultures of Rhizobium (Virtanen *et al.*, 1938), and also by *Cl. welchii* in the presence of pyruvate (Meister *et al.*, 1951). Very few other bacteria can bring it about.

(6) *Tyrosine* yields *tyramine*, which has interest for its marked pharmacological action on animals:

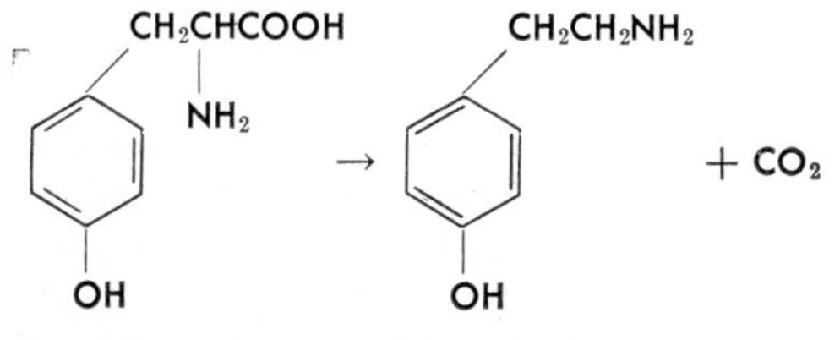

It was first obtained with an intestinal organism (Berthelot and Bertrand, 1912), and with *Proteus vulgaris* and *E. coli* growing on tyrosine solution (Sasaki, 1914). More recently Gale and co-workers

(1940, 1946) found that 500 strains of *Sc. fecalis*, as well as some other streptococci (but not *Sc. lactis*), carry out the reaction. It is less common among coliform bacteria, being found in less than 10 per cent of the strains investigated (Stadler and Neus, 1935; Gale, 1946).

(7) *Tryptophan* (indolealanine) has been reported to yield *tryptamine:*

$$ICH_2CHNH_2COOH \rightarrow ICH_2CH_2NH_2 + CO_2 \quad (I = \text{indole nucleus})$$

No organism capable of doing this has been found since Berthelot and Bertrand's report in 1912, in spite of examination of over 1000 cultures by Gale and co-workers. The corresponding decarboxylation of 5-hydroxytryptophan to 5-hydroxytryptamine, or serotonin, however, goes readily in the presence of a soluble enzyme in the kidney (Udenfriend, 1959) and is important in animal physiology because of the potent neurological action of serotonin. However, this reaction is not yet known in bacteria.

(8) *Histidine* yields *histamine*, which powerfully contracts the animal uterus and also plays a part in surgical shock and in allergic reactions. Unlike tyramine, it lowers the blood pressure. The decarboxylation played an interesting part in the discovery of histamine. Barger and Dale (1910), studying the toxic action of ergot (from rye grains parasitized by the Ascomycete *Claviceps purpureum*), found that neither of the two substances, ergotine and tyramine, known to be present in ergot, was responsible for the uterine contraction that is typical of ergot poisoning. They therefore looked for another, unknown substance in the ergot extract and arrived at the conclusion that it must have arisen during bacterial action on their stored ergot extracts. On allowing their preparation (or later, meat extract and yeast extract) to putrefy, a new base, apparently related to histidine, was isolated from the mixture. At the same time, Ackermann (1910a) had obtained and identified histamine from the partially anaerobic putrefaction of histidine in presence of glucose, peptone, and calcium carbonate. Comparison of their compound with a sample of Ackermann's proved it to be histamine. The organism of Berthelot and Bertrand (above) also produces histamine, as do strains of *S. typhosa* (Mellanby and Twort, 1912) and *E. coli* (Koessler and Hanke, 1919). Berthelot (1918) showed that if proteolytic Clostridia were grown in blood, they set free histidine from the blood protein as expected; if now a decarboxylating organism of the Aerobacter type were introduced, histamine was rapidly formed at 37° C. Thus, infection of wounds by a proteolytic and a decarboxylating organism together could possibly give rise to sufficient histamine to have serious physiological results.

(9) *Diaminopimelic acid* (not found in proteins) yields *lysine*. This is important because it is a normal path of lysine formation; in other words this decarboxylation differs from the others in that its product is a normal amino acid. Diaminopimelic acid occurs in the cell walls of sporeformers and is dehydrogenated to dipicolinic acid during spore formation (Chap. III, sec. 1). In the vegetative cell, however, it is decarboxylated (Powell and Strange, 1957). The decarboxylase is also present in small amount in the spores themselves.

(10) *Threonine* yields *aminoacetone*:

$$CH_3CHOHCHNH_2COOH \xrightarrow{-2 H} CH_3COCH_2NH_2 + CO_2$$

This is an oxidative decarboxylation, and α-amino-isopropanol is not an intermediate (Elliott, 1960); the dehydrogenation thus takes place first.

The enzymes concerned are *decarboxylases*. In *E. coli* they are produced at pH 5, but not at pH 7 (Gale, 1940); presence of the amino acid in the medium generally favors production of its decarboxylating enzyme. Presence of sugar in the medium also favors decarboxylation. The pH optimum for the action of these enzymes is from 4 to 5. The reaction is completely inhibited by cyanide at about 3×10^{-3} M, as well as by silver and mercury ions (Taylor and Gale, 1945), and semicarbazide (Meister *et al.*, 1951).

The decarboxylases are so specific that they can be used to determine certain amino acids precisely. The procedure is to add a washed suspension of the bacteria, or an acetone-dried powder, to the amino acids in a manometer and estimate the CO_2 evolved. Only a few milligrams of amino acid are needed. Since the enzymes act at acid pH, the CO_2 is not absorbed and the determination is complete in about 30 minutes. Only L-amino acids are attacked (i.e., natural forms), but hydroxy-amino acids are attacked along with their nonhydroxy counterparts. The organisms are grown in a protein-hydrolysate medium containing 1 to 2 per cent glucose, since glucose promotes formation of decarboxylases. The following determinations (Gale, 1943–1946; Krebs, 1948; Meister *et al.*, 1951) are quantitative as shown in Table VIII-2.

In the case of tyrosine decarboxylase of *Sc. fecalis*, the purified enzyme was found to require a coenzyme. The latter is pyridoxal-5-phosphate, or vitamin B_6 phosphate (Gunsalus and Bellamy, 1944; Umbreit *et al.*, 1945). The same compound is coenzyme for all other decarboxylations studied, as well as for transaminations (p. 313). The structure below was confirmed by synthesis (Heyl and Harris, 1951) and demonstration that the 3-phosphate is inactive. The highest

TABLE VIII–2. The Quantitative Determination of Amino Acids by Bacterial Decarboxylation

(Data from Gale, 1946, unless otherwise stated)

Amino Acid	Organism	Preparation Used	pH Optimum	Product
Lysine (and hydroxylysine)	B. cadaveris	Powder	6.0	Cadaverine
Arginine	E. coli	Powder	5.2	Agmatine
Histidine	Cl. welchii	Powder	4.5	Histamine
Ornithine	Cl. septicum	Suspension	5.5	Putrescine
Tyrosine	Sc. fecalis	Powder	5.5	Tyramine
Glutamic acid (and hydroxyglutamic)	Cl. welchii	Suspension	5.5	α-Aminobutyric acid
Glutamine (Krebs, 1948)	Cl. welchii	Suspension	4.9	α-Aminobutyric acid (separated from glutamic acid by NH_3 production)
Aspartic acid (Meister et al., 1951)	Cl. welchii	Suspension with added pyruvate	—	β-Alanine

decarboxylase activity is shown by the calcium salt (Viscontini et al., 1951):

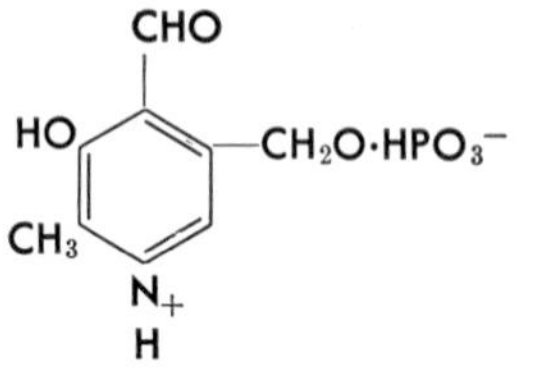

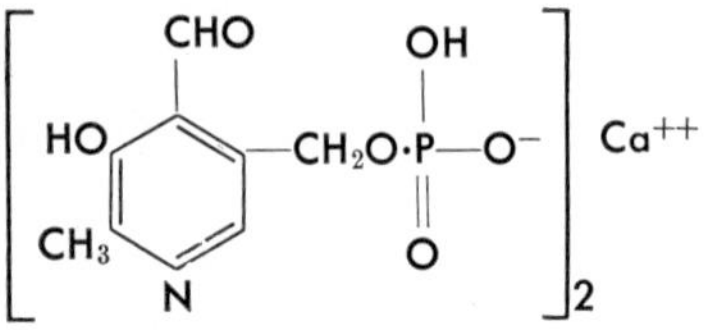

A mixture of pyridoxal with excess of ATP will also act as coenzyme, although with greatly reduced efficiency. Evidently, therefore, phosphorylation is carried out by ATP. The enzyme for this, *phosphokinase*, has been detected in several organisms and purified from yeast (Hurwitz, 1952); it is not specific for pyridoxal but will also use ATP to phosphorylate pyridoxine and pyridoxamine (compounds having $-CH_2O$ and $-CH_2NH_2$ in the 4 position, respectively). It can also phosphorylate other analogues, some of which inhibit decarboxylation by preventing the union of coenzyme with apoenzyme. The apoenzyme, which is, of course, a protein, can be extracted from *Sc. fecalis* which has been grown without vitamin B_6; when pyridoxal phosphate is added to it, it will decarboxylate tyrosine (Umbreit et al., 1945), and it can therefore be used to determine pyridoxal phosphate in tissues (Sloane-Stanley, 1949).

The elucidation of the mode of action of pyridoxal phosphate in decarboxylation was bound up with the study of its action in transamination. The finding that both the aldehyde (pyridoxal) and the amine (pyridoxamine) occur naturally led Snell (1944) to suggest that these two forms might be convertible into one another and thus catalyze transamination to other aldehydes and ketones. This was supported by evidence that transamination in animal tissues, as well as tyrosine decarboxylation in *Sc. fecalis*, was impaired in vitamin B_6 deficiency. Both could be restored by adding pyridoxal phosphate or pyridoxal plus ATP (see Meister, 1955).

The basic reaction (Braunstein and Shemyakin, 1953) is the combination of the amino acid with the aldehyde group of pyridoxal phosphate to form a Schiff base, II; this is then subject to electron withdrawal toward the positively charged N atom, to give a substituted imino acid, III:

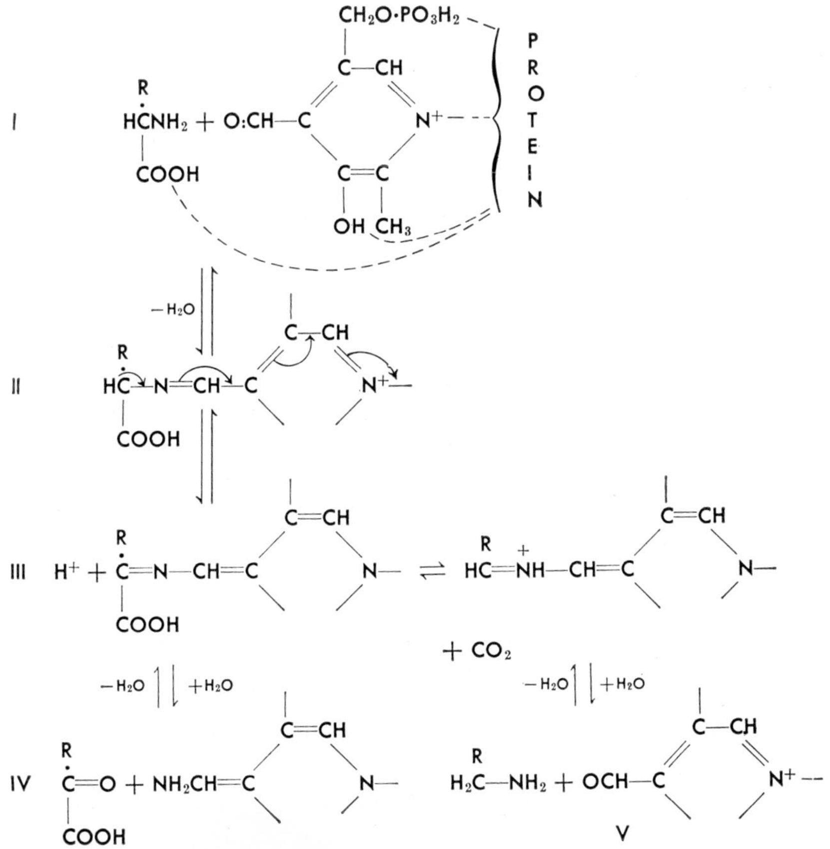

This compound, if the protein is *transaminase*, then hydrolyzes to yield the keto acid, IV, and pyridoxamine (which can then react in the reverse way with another keto acid, thus causing transamination). If the protein is the *decarboxylase*, III can lose CO_2, as shown to the right, and rearrange to liberate the amine and free pyridoxal phosphate, V. The protein, of course, determines not only which of these courses will be followed but also which amino acids can be attacked and held until the reaction occurs. In *Proteus vulgaris* it contains a —SH group which is somehow adjacent to, and protected by, the —CHO of the pyridoxal. When this —CHO has combined with an amino acid (as in II), the —SH can be inactivated by iodoacetate or other —SH reagents (Sutton and King, 1959).

TABLE VIII–3. Activity of Amino Acid Decarboxylases in *E. coli* Grown on Different Media

(Data of Gale, 1946)

(Activity expressed as Q_{CO_2} at 30° C and the optimum pH)

Amino Acid as Substrate in Test	AMINO ACID ADDED TO THE MEDIUM							
	None	All	Lysine	Argi-nine	Orni-thine	Gluta-mate	Histi-dine	Tyro-sine
L(+)Lysine	4	194	210		4			
L(+)Arginine	0	330		27				
L(+)Ornithine	3	145			225			
L(+)Glutamate	45	100				88		
L(−)Histidine	0	18					7	
L(−)Tyrosine	0	63						60

(+) and (−) refer to the actual direction of optical rotation, D and L to the spatial configuration.

Since, during transamination, the optical activities of the amino acids are not changed, they must be attached rigidly to the protein at not less than three points. The formulae above are oversimplified, since Ca^{++} or another divalent metal plays an important part; indeed, some reactions can occur without the protein (i.e., nonenzymatically) if a metal ion is present (see Snell, 1958).

As mentioned above, presence of the amino acid in the growth medium *induces* formation of its decarboxylase (see Chap. XVII, sec. 1; and Chap. XX). The results summarized in Table VIII–3 show that all the decarboxylases, except that for glutamic acid, are inducible.

D. Indole Production

The production of indole and skatole from tryptophan is a change of another type:

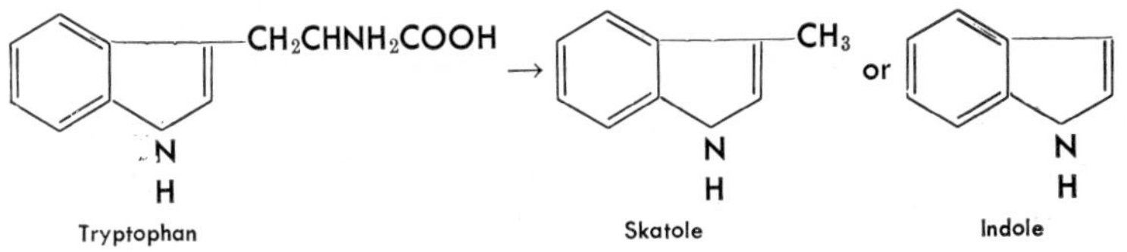

Tryptophan   →   Skatole   or   Indole

Indole was first detected by W. Kühne in 1875 among the products of proteolysis and isolated by Nencki in the same year from protein incubated three days at 40° C; its constant occurrence as a bacterial product led Hopkins and Cole (1903) to search for its precursor and hence to discover tryptophan, a constituent of nearly all proteins. Indole formation is characteristic of *E. coli, Proteus vulgaris*, and many related organisms. It is readily detected because of the numerous sensitive color reactions given by indole and its derivatives, especially with *p*-dimethylaminobenzaldehyde in HCl (see Frieber, 1922); these have made indole formation a routine diagnostic test.

We have seen above that oxidative deamination of tryptophan by many bacteria and fungi may yield indoleacetic acid. One might, therefore, suppose that further breakdown of this acid would yield indole. Bacterial action on indoleacetic acid, however, does not yield indole. (It probably yields skatole [3-methyl indole] by decarboxylation, although this has never been shown with pure cultures). None of the expected intermediates—indoleacetic, indole-pyruvic or indoledicarboxylic acids, indole-ethylamine, indole-aldehyde or skatole— yields indole with *E. coli* under the conditions in which it is formed from tryptophan (Frieber, 1922; Woods, 1935). The only precursor other than tryptophan that Woods could find to produce indole was a mixture of indole-pyruvic acid and ammonia; since oxidative deamination can be reversed (cf. sec. 2 of this chap.) the organism probably synthesized tryptophan from these constituents. In other words, tryptophan itself is required for the production of indole.

The failure of possible intermediates to produce any indole led to the idea that tryptophan is split directly into indole and alanine, but preparation of a cell-free indole-forming enzyme from autolyzed dried *E. coli* has shown that alanine is not produced (Wood *et al.*, 1947; Dawes and Happold, 1949). This enzyme is called *tryptophanase*, and requires pyridoxal phosphate as coenzyme. The combination converts tryptophan into indole, pyruvate, and NH_3, in ratios almost exactly 1:1:1. No oxygen is required. It does not deaminate alanine or serine, which indicates that alanine is not an intermediate product, i.e., the deamination is simultaneous with the reductive separation of the side-chain:

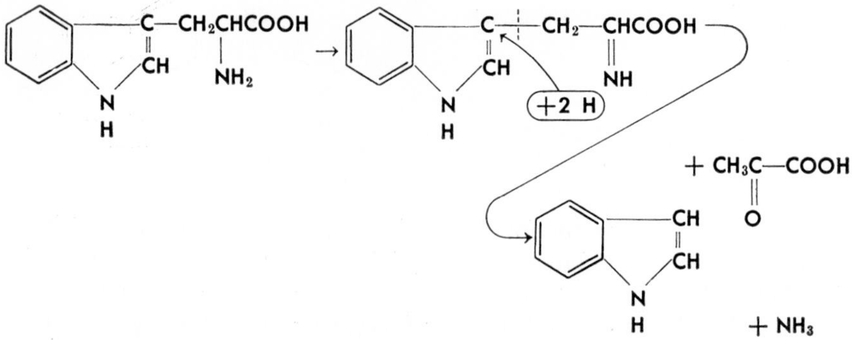

The mechanism for this curiously smooth rupture of a carbon-to-carbon bond has been much discussed (see Happold, 1950; Ek et al., 1952). It is catalyzed by traces of Cu and Co in alkaline medium. The most reasonable mechanism suggested involves preliminary isomerization to pseudotryptophan, formation of an anion by the dehydrogenation, and subsequent migration of the electrons as shown (Ek et al., 1952):

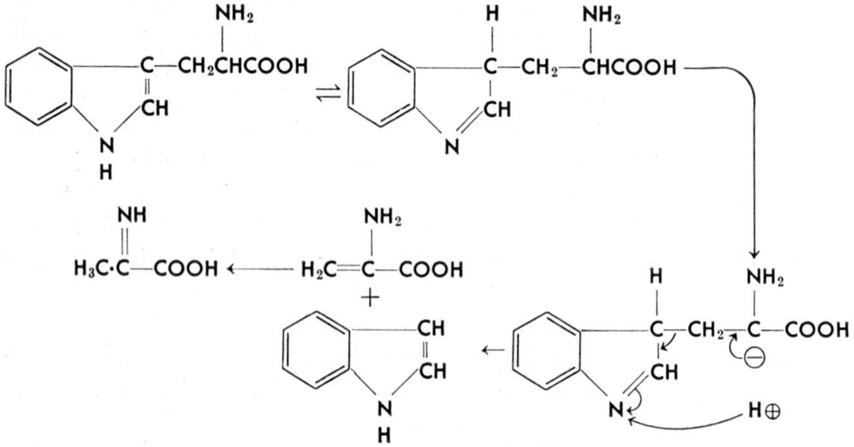

The liberated α-amino acrylic acid in the tautomeric imino-form would be at once converted to pyruvic acid (cf. the reaction suggested for cysteine and serine on p. 319). Intact cells would, of course, oxidize the pyruvate away very rapidly, which accounts for its not appearing in cultures. The cell-free enzyme after purification does not destroy pyruvate.

Tryptophanase is produced in E. coli only in presence of tryptophan, i.e., its formation is induced. When used as an antigen in rabbits, the resulting antisera act as tryptophanase inhibitors; since they appear to be specific for different bacterial species (Dolby and Happold, 1951), a family of closely related enzymes may be involved. Like the amino acid oxidases, histidinase, and other enzymes, tryptophanase formation is prevented by glucose, M/10 glucose in the medium suppressing its production 100 per cent (Freundlich and Lichstein, 1960). The enzyme that catalyses the reverse reaction, synthesizing tryptophan from indole and serine or from indoleglycerol phosphate, reacts to glucose in the opposite way, its formation being promoted (Monod and Cohen-Bazire, 1953). These glucose effects are discussed in Chapter XX, section 5B.

The production of phenol from tyrosine by *"B. coli phenologenes"* (a strain of *E. coli*) has also been reported (Rhein, 1918). As with indole, phenol is not formed from any of the probable intermediates of deamination, either oxidative or reductive:

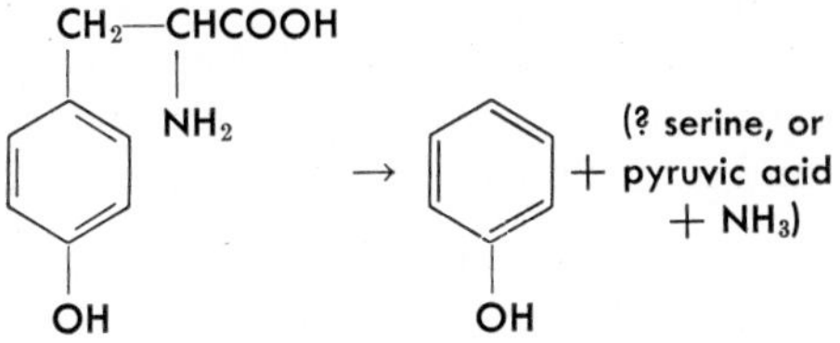

Doubtless the reaction will turn out to be of a type similar to that with tryptophan.

Indole production by *E. coli* in the intestines, if sufficiently vigorous, may occasionally lead to the excretion in the urine of indoxyl, an oxidation product of indole, as a glucoside or sulfate known as indican. In such urine, on standing, the indican is again hydrolyzed to indoxyl, two molecules of which readily oxidize to indigo blue: the urine thus deposits a deep blue precipitate, and the condition is known as indicanuria:

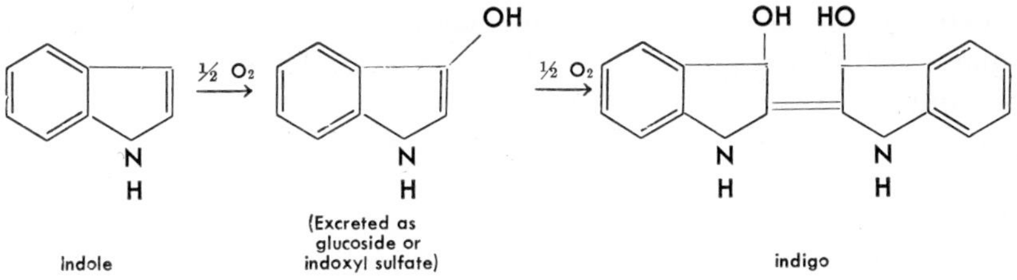

7. A CONSPECTUS OF THE BIOSYNTHESES OF AMINO ACIDS

We have seen in section 2 that alanine deaminase or dehydrogenase normally operates in the direction of synthesis and is thus a major route of ammonia assimilation in the bacilli. Glutamic dehydrogenase fulfills the same function for most other bacteria and many fungi. Alanine and glutamic acid, once formed, readily take part in transamination reactions with α-keto acids. For most other amino acids, therefore, the route of synthesis is merely the route to the corresponding α-keto acid, and the last step is transamination (proline, threonine, serine, and tryptophan are exceptions). For completeness, the known reaction sequences leading to the appropriate α-keto acids in bacteria will be reviewed here; some of them are treated elsewhere.

Pyruvate is formed directly from sugar by aerobic (Chap. V) and anaerobic routes (Chaps. XI and XII). *Oxalacetic* and *α-keto-glutaric acids* similarly lie on the Krebs cycle (Chap. V, sec. 8).

α-keto-isovaleric acid ("ketovaline") is formed from acetolactate (Chap. XIV, sec. 3A). Mutants of *E. coli*, requiring valine, accumulate α-acetolactate; the cell-free extracts will form acetolactate from pyruvate, and normal cells fed C^{14}-acetolactate produce C^{14}-valine in the protein (Umbarger and Brown, 1958). Acetolactate undergoes rearrangement (2) and reduction (3) to α-β-dihydroxy-isovalerate:

$$\overset{1}{\rightarrow} CH_3CO-\overset{\displaystyle OH}{\underset{\displaystyle CH_3}{\overset{|}{C}}}\Big\langle\begin{array}{l} \\ COOH\end{array} \quad \overset{2}{\rightarrow} CH_3\overset{\displaystyle OH}{\underset{\displaystyle CH_3}{\overset{|}{C}}}-\overset{\displaystyle O}{\underset{\displaystyle COOH}{C}}\Big\langle \quad \overset{\displaystyle 3}{\underset{\displaystyle \underset{Mg}{TPNH}}{\rightleftharpoons}}$$

$$CH_3\overset{\displaystyle OH}{\underset{\displaystyle CH_3}{\overset{|}{C}}}-\overset{\displaystyle OH}{\underset{\displaystyle COOH}{\overset{\displaystyle H}{\underset{|}{C}}}}\Big\langle \quad \underset{-H_2O}{\overset{4}{\longrightarrow}} \quad \overset{\displaystyle CH_3}{\underset{\displaystyle CH_3}{}}\Big\rangle CH-C\overset{\displaystyle O}{\underset{\displaystyle COOH}{}} \quad \overset{5}{\rightarrow}$$

The dehydrogenase for reaction 3, using TPN ($=$ NADP), probably also causes, or favors, reaction 2. Step 4 is due to a dehydrase, present in extracts of normal *E. coli* and absent in certain valine-requiring mutants, which accumulate the dihydroxy-acid. The final step (5) is transamination with glutamic acid.

α-keto-β-methylvaleric acid ("keto-isoleucine") is formed by parallel reactions, the lower CH_3 group being replaced by C_2H_5. Instead of forming acetolactate, pyruvate condenses with α-ketobutyrate (formed from threonine [p. 319]) to form α-aceto-α-hydroxy-butyrate:

$$CH_3CH_2CO\cdot COOH + CH_3COCOOH \rightarrow CH_3CH_2\overset{\displaystyle OH}{\underset{\displaystyle COCH_3}{\overset{|}{\underset{|}{C}}}}\cdot COOH$$

The rearrangement, reduction, and dehydration, at least by *E. coli* mutants, are then exactly as for valine. Furthermore the enzymes are actually the same for each step, the condensing enzyme (step 1), the isomerase (step 2), dehydrogenase (step 3), and dehydrase (step 4) operating equally on the two members of each pair of homologs. This is shown not only by biochemical similarities between the enzymes, but also genetically by the fact that many apparently "single-step" mutations cause *E. coli* or *S. typhimurium* to require *both* isoleucine and valine for growth (Umbarger *et al.*, 1960–1961). The fact that the condensing enzyme requires Mg and diphosphothiamine indicates its close relationship to carboxylase, which can cause not only decarboxylation of pyruvic acid to acetaldehyde but also its condensation to acetoin (see Chaps. XII and XIV).

α-*keto-isocaproic acid* ("ketoleucine") is derived from "ketovaline" (see above) by a further condensation with acetyl-CoA (Jungwirth *et al.*, 1961):

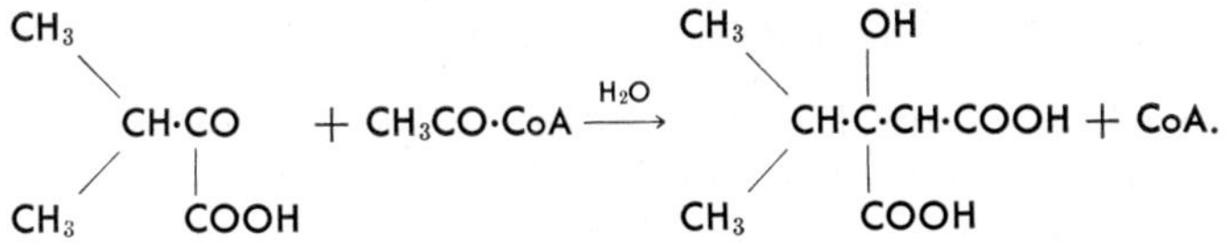

This is isomerized to the α-hydroxy isomer and dehydrogenated to the α-keto acid. The final step is again transamination with glutamic acid.

Thus these three α-keto acids, and therefore the aminoacids valine, isoleucine and leucine, arise on the same pathway:

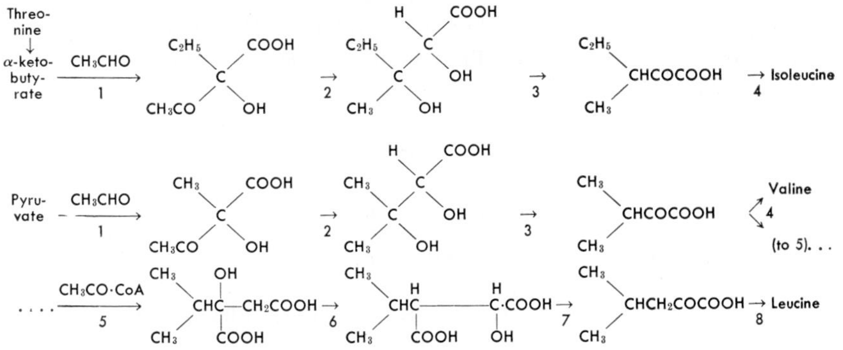

Now, as discussed in Chap. XX, formation of bacterial enzymes is frequently repressed by presence of their products. In this case the presence of excess of *either one*, e.g., valine, would prevent the formation of enzymes synthesizing *all three* amino acids. Perhaps to offset this complication, *E. coli* and *S. typhimurium* show the peculiar effect that enzymes for the early steps, i.e., threonine deaminase and the dehydrase of step 3, are *not* repressed by isoleucine or valine alone, but only when leucine also is added. By contrast, formation of the decarboxylase of step 7, which makes only leucine, *is* repressed by leucine alone (Freundlich *et al.*, 1962).

Phenyl pyruvic and *p-hydroxyphenylpyruvic* acids, precursors of phenylalanine and tyrosine, are formed from sugar via sedoheptulose diphosphate and a 7-carbon deoxy-keto-heptose which undergoes cyclization (Chap. XVI, sec. 9). The product is gradually dehydrogenated to the aromatic state and takes on a pyruvic side chain to form the immediate precursor, prephenic acid. This loses H_2O and CO_2 directly to form phenylpyruvic acid, but just how the *p*-hydroxy group is introduced for tyrosine is still not clear; it may require an oxygenation.

In the formation of *histidine* the expected keto acid is replaced by a keto-phosphate, imidazole-acetol phosphate. After this has been transaminated (by glutamic acid), the phosphate is hydrolyzed off and the resulting alcohol oxidized to an acid (*Im* represents imidazole):

$$ImCH_2CO \cdot CH_2O \cdot H_2PO_3 \text{ (IV)} \rightarrow ImCH_2CHNH_2 \cdot CH_2O \cdot H_2PO_3 \rightarrow$$
$$H_3PO_4 + ImCH_2CHNH_2CH_2OH \rightarrow ImCH_2CHNH_2CHO \rightarrow ImCH_2CHNH_2COOH$$

The remarkable control system exerted over this sequence and the gene-enzyme relationship are discussed in Chapter XX, section 5B.

The imidazole ring is formed in cell-free extracts of Aerobacter and Salmonella by a condensation of ATP with ribosephosphate to N-1-(5 phosphoribosyl)-ATP (I). This is followed by a splitting of the purine ring; carbons 1 and 2 of the ribose, nitrogen 1 and carbon 2 of the purine, plus NH_2 contributed from glutamine, form the imidazole ring. The resulting imidazole glycerol phosphate, II, is dehydrated to the acetol phosphate above, IV. The remainder of the molecule forms a second imidazole compound, III, which can be resynthesized again to adenine (Moyed and Magasanik, 1960):

Lysine, having two amino groups, passes through two keto stages. In Neurospora and other fungi it is formed from α-keto-adipic acid, the α-keto group being transaminated (by glutamic acid) and the ϵ-COOH reduced to the aldehyde and then transaminated. But in bacteria the route is quite different, via aspartic and pyruvic acids which condense to amino-keto-pimelic acid (Chap. III, sec. 1), which is then transaminated to di-amino-pimelic acid. In both cases the diamino acid is decarboxylated to lysine (p. 339).

Of amino acids not formed directly from the keto acid, the *tryptophan* route from anthranilic acid is given in Chapter XX, section 5. It was worked out largely with tryptophan-requiring mutants of Aerobacter and *E. coli*.

Serine is formed by transformylation from glycine (sec. 4 above), the CH_2OH group being carried over by tetrahydrofolic acid (FH_4) (formula on p. 773). The formyl group can come from formic acid (hence from CO_2), from glyoxylic acid or other sources, to produce formyl-tetrahydrofolic acid, which is then reduced (F = folic acid):

$$HCOOH + FH_4 \rightarrow FH_3 \cdot CHO + H_2O$$
$$FH_3 \cdot CHO + DPNH + H^+ \rightarrow \underline{FH_2 \cdot CH_2} + H_2O + DPN^+$$
$$\underline{FH_2 \cdot CH_2} + NH_2CH_2COOH - (B_6) + H_2O \rightarrow HOCH_2 \cdot \overset{\cdot}{C}HCOOH + FH_4 + (B_6)$$
$$\overset{|}{NH_2}$$

In the last step, catalyzed by *serine hydroxymethylase*, the glycine is combined with pyridoxal phosphate (vitamin B_6), accepts the $HOCH_2$-group, and splits off the B_6 again (see Huennekens and Osborn, 1959). The enzyme system isolated from *E. coli* has a vitamin B_{12} derivative as its prosthetic group and requires ATP, DPNH, and FAD as well as the folic acid and B_6 (Hatch *et al.*, 1961). The intermediate $FH_2 \cdot CH_2$ (N^5-N^{10}-methylene-tetrahydrofolic acid) is a general donor of methylene groups; it methylates uracil to thymine and ethanolamine to choline also (Kisliuk and Sakami, 1955). Hence this family of reactions is of central importance.

Threonine is formed from aspartate by the following reactions:

$$\text{Aspartic} \xrightarrow{\text{ATP}} \text{Aspartyl phosphate} \xrightarrow{\text{TPNH}} \text{Aspartic semi-aldehyde} \xrightarrow{\text{TPNH}}$$
$$\text{Homoserine} \xrightarrow{\text{ATP}} \text{O-phosphohomoserine} \longrightarrow \text{Phosphate and threonine.}$$

This route appears the same in Neurospora, yeast, and *E. coli*. Again it offers an example of "feedback control," the first reaction being inhibited by threonine (Chap. XX, sec. 5). The last reaction, due to threonine synthetase (purified from Neurospora), uses pyridoxal phosphate (B_6) as coenzyme; the combination allows electron migration and hence the uptake of OH at the β-position (Flavin and Slaughter, 1960):

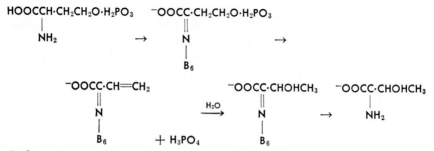

A threonine-requiring mutant did not possess this enzyme.

The biosyntheses of *arginine* and *proline* were discussed in section 5 above. The pyrroline ring is formed from glutamic semi-aldehyde by loss of H_2O and is then reduced to proline. Hydroxylation to *hydroxyproline* occurs (at least in animal tissue) only on proline bound in protein.

Methionine is formed from two amino acids, cysteine and homoserine. Homoserine is not present in proteins, but occurs free in small amounts, especially in seedlings; some mutant fungi require it for growth. In Neurospora, a number of strains which cannot utilize sulfate require sulfur-containing amino acids for growth. Some of these can use only methionine or homocysteine, $HS(CH_2)_2CHNH_2COOH$. One requires methionine itself, and this one excretes into the medium a new compound, cystathionine. This is formed from cysteine and homoserine:

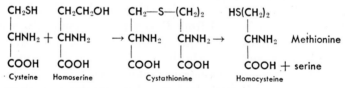

It is readily converted to homocysteine (see Emerson, 1950).

The methylation of homocysteine is carried out by *E. coli* with serine as CH_3 source (Szulmajster and Woods, 1960). The enzyme requires a folic acid derivative as co-factor and forms glycine from serine under the same conditions (cf. above).

8. THE BREAKDOWN OF AMINES

Reasoning that many anaerobic processes lead to formation of compounds relatively resistant to biological decomposition, de Jong (1926) set out to study the organisms responsible for the breakdown of higher alcohols, fatty acids, and amines. While none of the known bacteria tested would grow on the amines as carbon and nitrogen source, organisms could be isolated from natural waters using enrichment cultures of these compounds. These included a group of related Pseudomonads, named *Ps. aminovorans* (four types), two new species of Mycobacterium, and some nonmotile gram-negative forms which could not be placed in any recognized group. Since these last are characterized by ability to grow on simple amines, de Jong named them *Protaminobacter*. All these bacteria are aerobic and catalase-positive, so that the attack is oxidative in all cases. Since the growth was the characteristic studied, the nature of the intermediate products, if any, in the oxidation of these compounds remains unknown.

Table VIII–4 summarizes the growth data. The di- and tri-substituted amines are evidently less attackable than the monoamines. On the higher dialkylamines almost the only organism able to grow is *Protaminob. alboflavum*. The Mycobacteria are clearly limited to monosubstituted amines. The amines formed by decarboxylation of amino acids are somewhat more readily attacked; tyramine is oxidized at least partially by *Ps. pyocyanea* and also by some strains of *E. coli* and its relatives, but only when the organisms were previously grown on a medium containing some tyramine. The same is true for the oxidation of histamine by *Mycob. smegmatis* (Roulet and Zeller, 1945).

Although not much is known about the monoamine oxidases of bacteria, the enzymes attacking diamines have been well studied. Pentamethylene diamine (cadaverine) and histamine are attacked by the two Mycobacteria of Table VIII–4, as well as by *Mycob. smegmatis*. *Mycob. lacticola* oxidizes histamine and putrescine (Franke and Schillinger, 1944), and other Mycobacteria, including those of tuberculosis in man and birds, attack putrescine. *Pseudomonas pyocyanea* oxidizes putrescine, cadaverine, and agmatine (Gale, 1942); *Proteus morganii* oxidizes putrescine and cadaverine and *M. aureus* oxidizes cadaverine. These enzymes seem to be always present irrespective of growth medium, but they can be increased by culturing in presence of the base concerned.

Roulet and Zeller (1945) observed that when two diamines were given simultaneously to *Mycob. smegmatis*, the oxygen uptake was never greater than on one alone, and also that if one of the two diamines was oxidized very slowly and the other rapidly, then the resulting combined oxygen uptake was intermediate between the values found with the diamines separately. For example, the oxygen consumption (corrected for that of blanks without amine) was as follows (in μl):

(Expt. 1): putrescine   920; cadaverine 170; putrescine + cadaverine 625.
(Expt. 2): putrescine 1005; histamine   5; putrescine + histamine   725.

Similar observations were made with *E. coli* (Zeller, 1951). It is, therefore, concluded that all the oxidations are caused by one enzyme,

TABLE VIII–4. Ability of "Protaminophagic" Bacteria to Grow on Various Amines, Added as Hydrochlorides to Agar Containing Mineral Salts

(From den Dooren de Jong)*

(Growth is characterized as: + vigorous; (+) poor; (−) slight; − none.)

STRAIN OR SPECIES	PS. AMINOVORANS				MYCOBACT.		PROTAMINOBACTER				
	α	β	γ	δ	Salmoni-color	Opacum	Alboflavum α	β	γ	δ	Rubrum
Methylamine	+	+	+	+	(−)	(−)	−	(−)	(−)	−	+
Dimethylamine	+	+	(−)	+	(−)	(−)	−	(−)	(−)	−	+
Trimethylamine	+	+	+	+	(−)	(−)	−	−	(−)	−	(+)
Ethylamine	+	+	+	(−)	+	+	+	+	+	+	−
Diethylamine	(+)	+	(+)	−	(−)	(−)	+	+	(−)	−	(+)
Triethylamine	(−)	(−)	−	(−)	(−)	(−)	(−)	(−)	(−)	−	−
Propylamine	(+)	(−)	−	+	+	+	+	+	+	+	−
Isopropylamine	(+)	−	−	−	(−)	(−)	−	−	−	−	(−)
Dipropylamine	(−)	(−)	−	−	(−)	(−)	+	+	−	−	−
Tripropylamine	(−)	(−)	−	−	(−)	(−)	+	(+)	(−)	−	−
Butylamine	(+)	(+)	(−)	(−)	+	+	+	(−)	(+)	−	−
Isobutylamine	(+)	+	(+)	+	+	+	+	+	+	+	−
Dibutylamine	(−)	(−)	−	+	(−)	(−)	+	+	(−)	−	−
Tributylamine	−	(−)	−	−	(−)	(−)	−	(−)	(−)	−	−
Amylamine	+	(+)	−	−	+	+	+	(+)	+	+	(−)
Diamylamine	−	(−)	−	−	(−)	(−)	−	+	−	−	−
Triamylamine	(−)	−	−	−	−	−	−	−	−	−	−
Hexylamine	−	−	−	−	−	−	−	−	−	−	−
Ethanolamine	(+)	(−)	(−)	(+)	+	+	+	+	+	+	(−)
Choline	(+)	−	(+)	+	(−)	(−)	(−)	(−)	−	−	(−)
Glucosamine	+	+	+	(+)	−	+	+	+	+	−	(−)
Pentamethyl-enediamine	+	(−)	−	−	+	+	−	(−)	(−)	−	−
Histamine	−	(−)	−	(−)	(+)	+	−	−	−	−	(−)

* Somewhat condensed from de Jong's Table XXXII (1926).

diamine oxidase. Besides the diamines, this enzyme attacks histamine but not other monoamines. Even with diamines a separation of the two NH_2 groups by 14 or more carbon atoms prevents them from being attacked by the diamine oxidase. The marked differences between the attacking abilities of the organisms in Table VIII–4 indicate that for the monoamines several enzymes must be involved.

Since the optimum *p*H for the oxidations is 7.9 to 9.5, they will not proceed at the *p*H (4.5 to 6) at which the amines were formed (Gale,

1942). As a rule, too, the bacteria that form the amines will not oxidize them. The oxidations are inhibited by some antibiotics, including streptomycin, dihydrostreptomycin, and chloramphenicol (Owen *et al.*, 1951), but the significance of this is uncertain since they are also inhibited by numerous synthetic amines and the pigment pyocyanine.

It is important that the oxidations are inhibited by semicarbazide, dimedon, and hydroxylamine, since all these are reagents combining with aldehydes (Roulet and Zeller, 1945). This indicates that the first product is the aldehyde, and indeed Gale (1942) was able to isolate *p*-hydroxyphenylacetaldehyde when *Ps. pyocyanea* attacked tyramine. A diamine would correspondingly yield an aminoaldehyde. Since the oxidation is accompanied by formation of H_2O_2, which may be secondarily destroyed by catalase, the reduced diamine oxidase ($DO \cdot H_2$) is evidently reoxidized by a flavoprotein which in turn forms H_2O_2 when it reacts with oxygen. With the enzyme which has been purified from animal tissue (Tabor, 1951), the aminoaldehyde can be further oxidized to the acid, either by oxygen, using aldehyde oxidase, or with DPN as hydrogen acceptor. In the early stages of the reaction less than 1 atom of oxygen is used per molecule of NH_3 formed (Fouts, 1953), because the aminoaldehyde can itself act as hydrogen acceptor for the reduced enzyme and thus be converted to an aminoalcohol.

The whole system can be represented thus (diamine oxidase = DO):

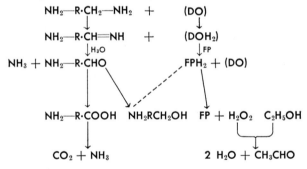

Formation of the imine may also occur in the oxidation of monoamines and would explain why di-substituted amines are so seldom attacked.

9. THE BREAKDOWN OF NUCLEIC ACIDS
AND OF THEIR COMPONENTS

Nucleic acids, as mentioned many times earlier, are of two types: RNA containing ribose with the bases adenine, guanine, cytosine, and uracil, and DNA containing 2-deoxyribose with adenine, guanine, cytosine, and thymine. In the first stages of their breakdown, i.e., depolymerization and hydrolysis to the nucleotides (base-ribose-5-phosphate), a number of enzymes participate; these often differ from one species to another. Active RNA-ases are excreted by *Bac. subtilis*, *megaterium*, and *mesentericus* (MacFadyen, 1934), and by Aspergillus and other fungi (Otani, 1935). A DNA-ase has been prepared from hemolytic streptococci (*Sc. pyogenes* group A, see Chap. XII), which excrete it into the medium (McCarty, 1949). It requires Mg and is inhibited by RNA. A similar enzyme extracted from *E. coli* acts only on denatured or 1-stranded DNA (Lehman, 1960).

In the second stage of breakdown the hydrolysis of phosphate is due to widely distributed phosphatases and pyrophosphatases. The ribose can be hydrolyzed off too, or it may be removed by *phosphorolysis* as ribose-1-phosphate, e.g., *E. coli* converts uracil and cytosine ribosides, with inorganic phosphate, to the free bases and ribosephosphate (Kalckar, 1947). *Lactobacillus pentosus* actively hydrolyzes purine and pyrimidine ribosides, probably by a pair of related enzymes (Wang, 1955), and similar enzymes for uridine and for purine ribosides occur in yeast. The hydrolysis may be associated with deamination, as when *E. coli* and Aerobacter attack adenylic acid to give H_3PO_4, ribose, and NH_3, the adenine being deaminated to hypoxanthine (Stephenson and

Adenylic acid (or adenosine phosphate)   Adenosine   +H_3PO_4

R = Ribose

Inosine   +NH_3 Hypoxanthine   +Ribose

Trim, 1938). A similar reaction is carried out by an enzyme from *Asp. oryzae*, or from the Taka-diastase made from its mycelium, as well as from *Neurospora crassa* (Mitchell and McElroy, 1946); here adenine riboside is substrate, and the deaminated product is hypoxanthine riboside, called inosine. Finally the ribose may be hydrolyzed off. A third type of reaction occurs with guanosine-5-phosphate, in which the intact nucleotide is deaminated by *E. coli* B or *S. aureus* without loss of ribose or phosphate to form xanthosine-5-phosphate (Carter, 1959; Hanka, 1960). With the cell-free enzyme, the equilibrium, in presence of ATP, Mg^{++}, and excess of NH_4^+, is strongly on the side of amination:

Guanosine phosphate   Xanthosine phosphate

In a variant of this, guanosine-5-phosphate is *reductively* deaminated to inosine-5-phosphate by *E. coli* in a reaction that is not reversible (Mager and Magasanik, 1960). These reactions allow Aerobacter to convert adenosine to guanosine:

$$A5P \rightarrow I5P \text{ (above)} \xrightarrow{DPN^+} X5P \xrightarrow[NH_3]{ATP} G5P$$

Deamination of the (phosphate-free) riboside and deoxyriboside of cytosine is carried out by a specific enzyme from *E. coli* (Wang, 1955), producing the uracil derivatives. Direct deamination of the simple purines, as of adenine by the enzyme adenase, is much slower (at least in *E. coli*) than is deamination of the nucleotides. ATP itself is rapidly attacked by *E. coli*, which both dephosphorylates and deaminates it (Lutwak-Mann, 1936).

The pyrimidines, uracil and thymine, are attacked in a different way by a *Mycobacterium species*, being oxidized to barbituric and 5-methylbarbituric acids, respectively. The former is then hydrolyzed to urea and malonic acid (Hayaishi, 1955):

The purines and pyrimidines can also be attacked anaerobically, and here reduction, i.e., hydrogenation, may be the key reaction. From enrichment cultures on orotic acid, (4-carboxy-uracil), an organism called *Zymob. oroticum* was obtained which decomposed orotic acid, I, anaerobically to CO_2 and NH_3 (Lieberman and Kornberg, 1954–1955). Evidently hydrogenation is followed by successive splitting of the two peptide bonds thus:

$$
\begin{array}{ccccccc}
\text{NH—CO} & & \text{NH—CO} & & \text{NH}_2\ \text{COOH} & & \\
|\quad\ | & \xrightarrow{\text{DPNH}} & |\quad\ | & \xrightarrow{\text{H}_2\text{O}} & |\quad\quad | & \xrightarrow{\text{H}_2\text{O}} & \\
\text{CO}\ \ \text{CH} & \rightleftharpoons & \text{CO}\ \ \text{CH}_2 & \rightleftharpoons & \text{CO}\ \ \text{CH}_2 & \rightleftharpoons & \\
|\quad\ \| & & |\quad\ | & & |\quad\quad | & & \\
\text{NH—C·COOH} & & \text{NH—CH·COOH} & & \text{NH—CH·COOH} & & \\
 & & \text{II} & & \text{III} & &
\end{array}
$$

$$
\begin{array}{ccccc}
\text{NH}_3\ \ \text{COOH} & & \text{COOH} & & \text{CO}_2 + \text{CH}_3 \\
+ \quad\quad | & \xrightarrow{\text{RCOCOOH}} & | & & | \\
\text{CO}_2\ \ \text{CH}_2 & \rightleftharpoons & \text{CH}_2 & \rightarrow & \text{CO} \\
+ \quad\quad | & \xleftarrow{\text{RCHNH}_2\text{COOH}} & | & & | \\
\text{NH}_2\text{—CH·COOH} & & \text{CO·COOH} & & \text{COOH} \\
\text{IV} & & \text{V} & & \text{VI}
\end{array}
$$

A Corynebacterium found in the same enrichment culture carried out the same reactions except for using TPNH for the first step. The enzyme that converts ureidosuccinic acid, III, to aspartic acid, CO_2, and NH_3 (IV) was isolated and found to require Mn^{++} or Fe^{++}. The last steps, conversion of aspartic acid to pyruvic acid, CO_2, and NH_3, proceed only in presence of α-ketogluturate and therefore involve transamination first. Uracil is attacked in a similar way by *Cl. uracilicum* (Campbell, 1957), producing CO_2, NH_3, and β-alanine (instead of aspartic acid); the intermediates corresponding to II and III above would be dihydrouracil and β-ureidopropionic acid. In uracil synthesis the place of $CO_2 + NH_3$ is taken by carbamyl phosphate (Chap. XX, sec. 5B). *Clostridium uracilicum* is a butyric acid fermenter (cf. Chap. XV) and requires both amino acids and biotin for growth.

The breakdown of the oxygen-containing purines by anaerobic enrichments is of interest in that the products are only NH_3, CO_2, and acetic acid (Barker *et al.*, 1940, 1942, 1944). The yield of acetic acid increases as the oxygen content of the purines goes down:

$$C_5H_4N_4O_3 + 5\tfrac{1}{2}\ H_2O \rightarrow ca.\ \tfrac{3}{4}\ C_2H_4O_2 + 4\ NH_3 + 3\tfrac{1}{2}\ CO_2$$
Uric acid

$$C_5H_4N_4O_2 + 6\ H_2O \rightarrow ca.\ 1\ C_2H_4O_2 + 4\ NH_3 + 3\ CO_2$$
Xanthine

$$C_5H_4N_4O + 6\tfrac{1}{2}\ H_2O \rightarrow ca.\ 1\tfrac{1}{4}\ C_2H_4O_2 + 4\ NH_3 + 2\tfrac{1}{2}\ CO_2$$
Hypoxanthine

Uric acid   Xanthine   Hypoxanthine

This last case is especially important because the purine molecule does not contain more than one chain of two carbons. The yield of more than 1 mole of acetic acid shows that this acid must be in part synthesized; indeed, $C^{14}O_2$ causes acetic acid to be formed containing C^{14} in both methyl and carboxyl groups (Barker *et al.*, 1940; Karlsson and Barker, 1949). This reaction, which involves folic acid, is discussed further in Chapter XXIV, section 4.

Pure cultures of two new clostridia were isolated from the enrichments, using the purine as the sole nutrient, and strictly anaerobic conditions. These organisms, *Cl. acidi-urici* (terminal spores with swelling, small rods) and *Cl. cylindrosporum* (larger rods, variable spore position without swelling), are specific for purine breakdown and do not attack glucose, peptones, or amino acids. In keeping with the ability of *Cl. acidi-urici* to synthesize acetic acid, it was found also to synthesize riboflavin, folic acid, and biotin and to need no growth factors or amino acids added to the medium (Barker and Peterson, 1944). Such great synthetic power is rare among clostridia.

It should be mentioned in closing that uptake of CO_2 occurs not only in the breakdown, but also in the synthesis, of purines. Growing *E. coli* and Aerobacter incorporate $C^{14}O_2$ into the 6 position of both adenine and guanine, and about 80 per cent of this carbon in fact comes from CO_2 (Koch *et al.*, 1952; Sutton and Werkman, 1953). The adenine and guanine are converted not only to nucleic acids but also to each other. Many other syntheses using CO_2 are discussed in Chapter XIV.

REFERENCES

Abrams, A.; Kegeles, G.; and Hottle, G. A. 1946. *J. Biol. Chem.*, **164**:63–79.
Ackermann, D. 1908. *Z. physiol. Chem.*, **56**: 305–315.
Ackermann, D. 1910a. *Z. physiol. Chem.*, **65**:504–510.
Ackermann, D. 1910b. *Z. physiol. Chem.*, **69**: 273–280.
Adler, E.; Günther, G.; and J. E. Everett, 1938. *Z. physiol. Chem.* **255**:27–35.
Adler, E.; Hellström, V.; Günther, G.; and Euler, H. v. 1938. *Z. physiol. Chem.*, **255**:14–26.

Akamatsu, S., and Miyashita, R. 1952. *Enzymologia*, **15**: 173–176.

Altenborn, R. A., and Housewright, R. D. 1954. *Arch. Biochem. Biophys.*, **49**:130–137.

Aubert, J. P., and Milhaud, G. 1956. *Ann. Inst. Pasteur*, **60**:320–332.

Ballantine, A.; Barrett, C. B.; Beer, R. J. S.; Eardley, S.; Robertson, A.; Shaw, B. L.; and Simpson, T. H. 1958. *J. Chem. Soc.*, pp. 755–760.

Barger, G., and Dale, H. H. 1910. *J. Physiol.*, **40**:xxxviii; *J. Chem. Soc.*, **26**:128.

Barker, H. A. 1937. *Enzymologia*, **2**:175–183.

Barker, H. A., and Beck, J. V. 1942. *J. Bact.*, **43**:291–304.

Barker, H. A., and Peterson, W. H. 1944. *J. Bact.*, **47**: 307–308.

Barker, H. A.; Ruben, S.; and Beck, J. V. 1940. *Proc. Nat. Acad. Sci.*, **26**:477–482.

Barker, H. A.; Weissbach, H.; and Smyth, R. D. 1958. *Proc. Nat. Acad. Sci.*, **44**:1093–1096; Weissbach, H.; Toohey, J.; and Barker, H. A. 1959. *Ibid.*, **45**:521–525.

Beer, R. J.; McGrath, L.; Robertson, A.; and Woodier, A. B. 1949. *J. Chem. Soc.*, pp. 2061–2066.

Beijerinck, M. W. 1901. *Zentr. Bakt. II*, **7**:33–61.

Beijerinck, M. W. 1913. *Proc. Kon. Akad. Wetensch. Amsterdam*, **15**:932–937.

Bellamy, W. D.; Umbreit, W. W.; and Gunsalus, I. C. 1945. *J. Biol. Chem.*, **160**:461–472.

Ben Hamida, F., and Le Minor, L. 1956. *Ann. Inst. Pasteur*, **90**:671–673.

Bernheim, F.; Bernheim, M. L.; and Webster, M. D. 1935. *J. Biol. Chem.*, **110**:165–172.

Berthelot, A. 1918. *Compt. rend.*, **166**:187–189.

Berthelot, A., and Bertrand, D. M. 1912. *C. R. Acad. Sci.*, **154**:1643–1645, 1826–1828.

Bonner, D. M.; Tatum, E. L.; and Beadle, G. W. 1943. *Arch. Biochem.*, **3**:71–91.

Bornside, G. H., and Kallio, R. E. 1956. *J. Bact.*, **71**:627–634, 655–660.

Brasch, W. 1908–1909. *Biochem. Z.*, **18**:380; **22**:403–408.

Braunstein, A. E., and Kritzmann, M. G. 1937. *Biokhimiya*, **2**:242–262, 859–874; cf. also *Nature*, **140**:503–504.

Braunstein, A. E., and Shemyakin, M. M. 1953. *Biokhimiya*, **18**:393–411.

Brieger, L. 1886. Die Ptomaine. Berlin.

Burchard, A. 1899. *Arch. Hyg.*, **36**:264–284.

Campbell, L. L. 1957. *J. Bact.*, **73**:220–224, 225–229.

Cardon, B. P., and Barker, H. A. 1946. *J. Bact.*, **52**:629–634.

Cardon, B. P., and Barker, H. A. 1947. *Arch. Biochem.*, **12**:165–170.

Carter, C. E. 1959. *Biochem. Pharmacol.*, **2**:105–111.

Chargaff, E., and Sprinson, D. B. 1943. *J. Biol. Chem.*, **151**:273–280.

Chrzaszcz, T., and Zakomorny, M. 1935. *Biochem. Z.*, **275**:97–105.

Clemo, G. R., and Duxbury, F. K. 1950. *J. Chem. Soc.*, pp. 1795–1800.

Clemo, G. R.; Duxbury, F. K.; and Swan, G. A. 1952. *J. Chem. Soc.*, pp. 3464–3468.

Clifton, C. E. 1940. *J. Bact.*, **39**:485–497.

Cohen, P. P., and Brown, G. W. 1960. In, Comparative Biochemistry, **2**, Chap.4:161–244 (431 refs.). New York, Academic Press.

Colowick, S. P.; Kalckar, H. M.; and Cori, C. F. 1941. *J. Biol. Chem.*, **137**:343–356.

Davis, B. D. 1950. *Experientia*, **6**:41–50.

Dawes, E. A., and Happold, F. C. 1949. *Biochem. J.*, **44**:349–361.

DeJong, L. E. den Dooren. 1926. Bijdrage tot de kennis van het mineralisatieproces. Rotterdam, Nijgh and van Ditmar.

De Moss, R. D., and Evans, N. R. 1959. *J. Bact.*, **78**:583–588.

Dewan, J. G. 1938. *Biochem. J.*, **32**:1378–1385.

Dolby, D. E., and Happold, F. C. 1951. *Biochem. J.*, **49**:v.

Efimenko, O. M.; Kuznetsova, G. A.; and Yakimov, P. A. 1956. *Biokhimiya*, 21:416.

Ehrlich, F. 1906. *Biochem. Zeit.*, 2:52–70.

Ehrlich, F. 1907. *Ber. deut. chem. Ges.*, 40:1027–1047.

Ehrlich, F. 1909. *Biochem. Zeit.*, 18:391–423.

Ehrlich, F. 1912. *Ber. deut. chem. Ges.*, 45:883–889.

*Ek, A.; Kissman, H.; Patrick, J. B.; and Witkop, B. 1952. Chemical Contributions to the Mechanism of the Biological Oxidation of Tryptophane. *Experientia*, 8:36–40.

Ellinger, A. 1899. *Ber. deut. chem. Ges.*, 31:3183–3186.

Ellinger, A. 1900. *Z. physiol. Chem.*, 29:334–348; *Ber. deut. chem. Ges.*, 32:3542–3546.

Elliott, W. H. 1960. *Biochem. J.*, 74:478–485.

Emerson, S. 1950. *Cold Spring Harbor Symp. Quant. Biol.*, 14:40–48.

Emerson, R. L.; Puziss, M.; and Knight, S. G. 1950. *Arch. Biochem.*, 25:299–308.

Feldman, L. I., and Gunsalus, I. C. 1950. *J. Biol. Chem.*, 187:821–830.

Fincham, J. R. S. 1953. *Biochem. J.*, 53:313–320.

*Fincham, J. R. S. 1960. Genetically Controlled Differences in Enzyme Activity. In, *Adv. in Enzymol.*, 22:1–43.

Fisher, H. F., and McGregor, L. L. 1960. *Biochem. Biophys. Res. Comms.*, 13:629–631.

Flavin, M., and Slaughter, C. 1960. *J. Biol. Chem.*, 235:1103–1108, 1112–1118.

Fouts, J. R. 1953. *Federation Proc.*, 13:210–211.

Franke, W., and Schillinger, A. 1944. *Biochem. Zeit.*, 316:313–334.

Freundlich, M.; Burns, R. O.; and Umbarger, H. E. 1962. *Proc. Nat. Acad. Sci.*, 48:1804–1808.

Freundlich, M., and Lichstein, H. C. 1960. *J. Bact.*, 80:663–638.

Frieber, W. 1922. *Zentr. Bakt. I*, 87:254–276.

Frieden, C. 1959. *J. Biol. Chem.*, 234:809–814, 815–821.

Frieden, C., and Velick, S. F. 1957. *Biochim. Biophys. Acta*, 23:439–440.

Fromageot, C., and Desnuelle, P. 1933–1934. *Bull. Soc. chim.*, 53:541–547; *Biochem. Zeit.*, 273:24–34.

Gale, E. F. 1940. *Biochem. J.*, 34:392–413, 846–852, 853–857.

Gale, E. F. 1941. *Biochem. J.*, 35:66–80.

Gale, E. F. 1942. *Biochem. J.*, 36:64–75.

*Gale, E. F. 1943. Factors Influencing the Enzymic Activities of Bacteria. *Bacteriol. Revs.*, 7:140–173.

Gale, E. F. 1945a. *Biochem. J.*, 39:46–52.

Gale, E. F. 1945b. *Brit. J. Exp. Path.*, 26:225–233.

*Gale, E. F. 1946. The Bacterial Amino Acid Decarboxylases. *Adv. in Enzymol.*, 6:1–32.

*Gale, E. F. 1947. Nitrogen Metabolism. *Ann. Rev. Microbiol.*, 1:141–160.

Gale, E. F., and Rodwell, A. W. 1949. *J. Gen. Microbiol.*, 3:127–142.

Genevois, L., and Lafon, M. 1957. *Chem. and Ind.*, 78:323; *Chim. Anal.*, 40:156–158.

Gerhardt, P.; Levine, H. B.; and Wilson, J. B. 1950. *J. Bact.*, 60:459–467.

Ghosh, S.; Blumenthal, H. J.; Davidson, E.; and Roseman, S. 1960. *J. Biol. Chem.*, 235:1265–1273.

Gibson, T. 1934. *J. Bact.*, 28:295–312, 313–322.

Green, J. A., Rappoport, D. A., and Williams, R. P. 1956. J. Bact., 72: 483–487.

Gunsalus, I. C., and Bellamy, W. D. 1944. *J. Biol. Chem.*, 155:357–358, 685–686.

Halpern, Y. S., and Grassowicz, N. 1957. *Biochem. J.*, 65:716–720.

Hanka, L. J. 1960. *J. Bact.*, 80:30–36.

*Happold, F. C. 1950. Tryptophanase-Tryptophan Reaction. *Adv. in Enzymol.*, 10:51–82.

Hatch, F. T.; Larrabee, A. R.; Cathou, R. E.; and Buchanan, J. M. 1961. *J. Biol. Chem.*, 236:1095–1101.

Haughton, B. G., and King, H. K. 1961. *Biochem. J.*, **80**:268–277.

Hayaishi, O. 1955. In, Methods in Enzymol., ed. S. P. Colowick and N. O. Kaplan. New York, Academic Press, Vol. II, 490–497.

Haynes, W. C.; Stodola, F. H.; Locke, J. M.; Pridham, T. G.; Conway, H. F.; Sohns, V. E.; and Jackson, R. W. 1956. *J. Bact.*, **72**:412–417.

Heinzelmann, G., and Dehnicke, J. 1915. *Z. Spiritus Ind.*, **38**:316–347.

Henriksen, S. D. 1950. *J. Bact.*, **60**:225–231.

Heyl, D., and Harris, S. A. 1951. *J. Amer. Chem. Soc.*, **73**:3434–3437 (and papers immediately preceding and following).

Hills, G. M. 1940. *Biochem. J.*, **34**:1057–1069.

Holzer, H., and Schneider, S. 1957. *Biochem. Zeit.*, **329**:361–369.

Hong, M. M.; Shen, S. C.; and Braunstein, A. E. 1959. *Biochim. Biophys. Acta*, **36**: 288–289.

Hopkins, F. G., and Cole, S. W. 1903. *J. Physiol.*, **29**:451–466.

Horowitz, N. H., and Shen, S. C. 1952. *J. Biol. Chem.*, **197**:513–520.

Hubbard, R., and Rimington, C. 1950. *Biochem. J.*, **46**:220–225.

*Huennekens, F. M., and Osborn, M. J. 1959. Folic Acid Enzymes and One-Carbon Metabolism. *Adv. in Enzymol.*, **21**:369–446.

Hughes, D. E., and Williamson, D. H. 1952. *Biochem. J.*, **51**:45–55.

Hurwitz, J. 1952. *Biochim. Biophys. Acta*, **9**:496–498.

Ingraham, J. L., and Guymon, J. F. 1960. *Arch. Biochem. Biophys.*, **88**:157–166.

Ivanov, N. N., and Avetissova, A. N. 1930. *Biochem. Z.*, **231**:65–78.

Ivanov, N. N., and Smirnova, M. I. 1927. *Biochem. Z.*, **181**:8–16.

Ivanov, N. N., and Toschevikova, A. 1927. *Biochem. Z.*, **181**:1–7.

*Janke, A. 1930. Der Aminosäureabbau durch Mikroben. *Arch. Mikrobiol.*, **1**:304–322.

Janke, A., and Tayenthal, W. 1937. *Biochem. Z.*, **289**:76–86.

Jones, M. E.; Spector, L.; and Lipmann, F. 1955. *J. Am. Chem. Soc.*, **77**:819–200.

Jungwirth, C.; Margolin, P.; and Umbarger, H. E. 1961. *Biochem. Biophys. Res. Comms.*, **5**:435–438.

Kalckar, H. M. 1947. *J. Biol. Chem.*, **167**:461–475.

Kallio, R. E., 1951. *J. Biol. Chem.*, **192**:371–377.

Kaper, J. M., and Veldstra, H. 1958. *Biochim. Biophys. Acta*, **30**:401–420.

Karlsson, J. L., and Barker, H. A. 1949. *J. Biol. Chem.*, **178**:891–902.

King, H. K., and Fletcher, L. I. 1950. *J. Gen. Microbiol.*, **4**:228–241.

Kisch, B. 1931–1932. *Biochem. Z.*, **242**:1–20; **244**:440–450; **249**:63–71.

Kisch, B., and Schuwrith, K. 1932. *Biochem. Z.*, **247**:371–385.

Kisliuk, R. L., and Sakami, W. 1955. *J. Biol. Chem.*, **214**:47–57.

Kluyver, A. J. 1956. *J. Bact.*, **72**:406–411.

Knivett, V. A. 1954. *Biochem. J.*, **56**:602–606, 606–610.

Koch, A. L.; Putnam, F. W.; and Evans, E. A., Jr. 1952. *J. Biol. Chem.*, **197**:105–120.

Koessler, K. K., and Hanke, M. T. 1919. *J. Biol. Chem.*, **39**:539–584; cf. also *ibid.*, **39**:497–519; 521–537.

Kopper, P. H., and Beard, H. H. 1947. *Arch. Biochem.*, **15**:195–199.

Korzenovsky, M., and Werkman, C. H. 1952–1953. *Arch. Biochem. Biophys.*, **41**:233 (1952); **46**:174–185 (1953).

Krebs, H. A. 1948. *Biochem. J.*, **43**:51–57.

Krebs, H. A.; Jensen, P. K.; and Eggleston, L. V. 1958. *Biochem. J.*, **70**:397–402.

Larsen, A. D., and Kallio, R. E. 1954. *J. Bact.*, **68**:67–73.

Larsen, P.; Harbo, A.; Klungsoyr, S.; and Aasheim, T. 1962. *Physiol. Plantarum*, **15**:552–565.

Laseelles, J., and Woods, D. D. 1954. *Biochem. J.*, **58**:486–497.

Lehman, I. R. 1960. *J. Biol. Chem.*, **235**:1470–1487.

Leloir, L. F., and Cardini, C. E. 1953. *Biochim. Biophys. Acta*, **12**:15-22.

Lerner, E. M., and Mueller, J. H. 1949. *J. Biol. Chem.*, **181**:43–45.

Lieberman, I., and Kornberg, A. 1954–1955. *J. Biol. Chem.*, **207**:911–924; **212**:909–920 (1958).

Liebert, F. 1909. *Proc. Kon. Akad. Wetensch., Amsterdam*, **12**:54-64.

Lutwak-Mann, C. 1936. *Biochem. J.*, **30**:1405–1412.

Maas, W. K., and Vogel, H. J. 1953. *J. Bact.*, **65**:388–393.

McCarty, M. 1949. *J. Exptl. Med.*, **90**:543–553.

MacFadyen, D. A. 1934. *J. Biol. Chem.*, **107**:297–308.

Mager, J., and Magasanik, B. 1960. *J. Biol. Chem.*, **235**:1474–1478.

Marchál, E. 1894. *Agric. Sci.* **8**:574; cf. *Zentr. Bakt. II*, **1**:753–758 (1895).

Marks, G. S., and Bogorad, L. 1960. *Proc. Nat. Acad. Sci.*, **46**:25–28.

Meister, A. 1952. *J. Biol. Chem.*, **197**:308–317.

*Meister, A. 1955. Transamination. In, *Adv. in Enzymol.*, **16**:185–246 (261 refs.).

Meister, A.; Levinstow, L.; Greenfield, R. E.; and Abendschein, P. A. 1955. *J. Biol. Chem.*, **215**:441–460.

Meister, A.; Sober, H. A.; and Tice, S. V. 1951. *J. Biol. Chem.*, **189**:577–590, 591–595.

Mellanby, E., and Twort, F. W. 1912. *J. Physiol.*, **45**:53–60.

Metzler, D. E.; Olivard, J.; and Snell, E. E. 1954. *J. Am. Chem. Soc.*, **76**:644–648.

Mitchell, H. K., and McElroy, W. D. 1946. *Arch. Biochem.*, **10**:351–358.

Mitoma, C.; Weissbach, H.; and Udenfriend, S. 1956. *Arch. Biochem. Biophys.*, **63**:122–130.

Monod, J., and Cohen-Bazire, G. 1953. *Compt. rend.*, **236**:530–532.

Moser, M. 1959. *Arch. Mikrobiol.*, **34**:251–269.

De Moss, W. C., and Evans, N. R. 1959. *J. Bact.*, **78**:583–588.

Moyed, H. S., and Magasanik, B. 1960. *J. Biol. Chem.*, **235**:149–153.

Mueller, J. H., and Miller, P. A. 1949. *J. Biol. Chem.*, **181**:39–42.

Neubauer, O., and Fromherz, K. 1911. *Z. physiol. Chem.*, **70**:326–350.

Neuberg, C. 1911. *Biochem. Z.*, **37**:501–506.

Neuberg, C., and Peterson, W. H. 1914. *Biochem. Z.*, **67**:32–45.

Neuberg, C., and Ringer, M. 1915. *Biochem. Z.*, **71**:226–236, 237–244.

Neuberg, C., and Ringer, M. 1918. *Biochem. Z.*, **91**:131–136.

*Nisman, B. 1954. The Stickland Reaction. *Bact. Revs.*, **18**:16–42.

O'Connor, R. J., and Halvorson, H. O. 1960. *Arch. Biochem. Biophys.*, **91**:290–299.

Olson, J. A., and Anfinsen, C. B. 1952. *J. Biol. Chem.*, **197**:69–79.

Otani, H. 1935. *Acta schol. med. Univ. Imp. Kyoto*, **17**:323–329.

Owen, C. A.; Carlson, A. G.; and Zeller, E. A. 1951. *J. Bact.*, **62**:53–62.

Perry, J. J. 1961. *Nature*, **191**:77–78.

Powell, J. F., and Strange, R. E. 1957. *Biochem. J.*, **65**:700–708.

Pringsheim, H. 1908. *Biochem. Z.*, **8**:128–131.

Quastel, J. H., and Woolf, B. 1926. *Biochem. J.*, **20**:545–555.

Raistrick, H. 1917. *Biochem. J.*, **11**:71–77.

Raistrick, H. 1919. *Biochem. J.*, **13**:446–458.

Raper, H. S. 1928. The Aerobic Oxidases. *Physiol. Revs.*, **8**:245–282.

Ratner, S. 1962. Chap. 30 in, The Enzymes, ed. P. Boyer, H. Lardy, and K. Myrbäck. New York, Acad. Press, pp. 495–511.

Ravel, J. M.; Grona, M. L.; Humphreys, J. S.; and Shive, W. 1959. *J. Biol. Chem.*, **234**:1452–1455.

Rhein, M. 1918. *Biochem. Z.*, **87**:123–128.

Rodwell, A. W. 1953. *J. Gen. Microbiol.*, **8**:224–232, 233–237, 238–247.

Roulet, F., and Zeller, E. A. 1945. *Helv. chim. Acta*, **28**:1326–1342.

Sagers, R. D., and Gunsalus, I. C. 1961. *J. Bact.*, **81**:541–549.

Santer, U., and Vogel, H. J. 1956. *Biochim. Biophys. Acta*, **19**:578–579.

Sasaki, T. 1914. *Biochem. Z.*, **59**:429–435.

Savage, W. G. 1920. Food Poisoning and Food Infections. Cambridge Univ. Press; cf. *J. Hyg.*, **20**:61, 1921.

Schaaf, F. 1929. *Biochem. Z.*, **205**:449–450.

Schade, A. L., and Thimann, K. V. 1940. *Am. J. Bot.*, **27**:659–670.

Sebek, O. K., and Jäger, H. 1962. *Nature*, **196**:793–795.

Seeliger, H. R. 1956. *J. Bact.*, **72**:127–131.

Severin, S. A. 1895–1901. *Zentr. Bakt. II orig.*, **1**:97–104, 160–168, 799–817; **3**:628–635 (1897); **7**:369–386 (1901).

Shah, P. C., and King, H. K. 1958. *Biochem. J.*, **68**:19P.

Shanmuganathan, S. S., and Elsden, S. R. 1958. *Biochem. J.*, **69**:210–218.

Slade, H. D.; Doughty, C. C.; and Slamp, W. C. 1954. *Arch. Biochem. Biophys.*, **48**:338–346.

Slade, H. D., and Slamp, W. C. 1952. *J. Bact.*, **64**:455–466.

Sloane-Stanley, G. S. 1949. *Biochem. J.*, **44**:567–573.

Snell, E. E. 1944. *J. Biol. Chem.*, **154**:313–314.

*Snell, E. E. 1958. Chemical Structure in Relation to Biological Activities of Vitamin B_6. *Vitamins and Hormones*, **16**:78–125.

Söhngen, N. L. 1909. *Zentr. Bakt. II orig.*, **23**:91–98.

Srb, A. M., and Horowitz, N. H. 1944. *J. Biol. Chem.*, **154**:129–139.

Stadler, P., and Neus, E. 1935. *Zentr. Bakt. I orig.*, **135**:110–114.

Stadtman, T. C. 1956. *Biochem. J.*, **62**:614–621.

Stephenson, M., and Gale, E. F. 1937. *Biochem. J.*, **31**:1316–1322.

Stephenson, M., and Trim, A. R. 1938. *Biochem. J.*, **32**:1740–1751.

Stickland, L. H. 1934–1935. *Biochem. J.*, **28**:1746–1759; **29**:288–290, 889–898 (1935).

*Stowe, B. B. 1959. *Fortschritte der Chemie org. Naturstoffe*, **17**:248–297.

Stowe, B. B.; Ray, P. M.; and Thimann, K. V. 1957. *Rapp. Comm. 8 Congr. Bot. Internat.*, **11** (Suppl.):135–140.

Stowe, B. B., and Thimann, K. V. 1954. *Arch. Biochem. Biophys.*, **51**:499–516.

Strange, R. E., and Dark, F. A. 1960. *Nature*, **188**:741–742.

Strassman, M.; Locke, L. A.; Thomas, A. J.; and Weinhouse, S. 1955–1956. *Science*, **121**:303; *J. Am. Chem. Soc.*, **78**:1599–1602 (1956).

Stumpf, P. K., and Green, D. E. 1944. *J. Biol. Chem.*, **153**:387–399.

Sumner, J. B. 1926. *J. Biol. Chem.*, **69**:435–441.

Sutton, C. R., and King, H. K. 1959. *Biochem. J.*, **73**:43p.

Sutton, W. B., and Werkman, C. H. 1953. *Arch. Biochem Biophys.*, **47**:1–7.

Szulmajster, J. S., and Woods, D. D. 1960. *Biochem. J.*, **75**:3–12.

Tabor, H. 1951. *J. Biol. Chem.*, **188**:125–136.

Tabor, H., and Mehler, A. H. 1955. In, Methods in Enzymology, **2**:228–233. New York, Academic Press.

Tarr, H. L. A. 1934. *Biochem. J.*, **28**:192–198.

Tatum, E. L., and Bonner, D. 1944. *Proc. Nat. Acad. Sci.*, **30**:30–37; cf. Tatum, E. L.; Bonner, D.; and Beadle, G. W. *Arch. Biochem.*, **3**:477–478.

Taylor, E. S., and Gale, E. F. 1945. *Biochem. J.*, **39**:52–60.

Thimann, K. V. 1935. *J. Biol. Chem.*, **109**:279–291.

*Thimann, K. V. 1960. Plant Growth. In, Fundamental Aspects of Normal and Malignant Growth, ed. W. W. Nowinski. Amsterdam, Elzevier Press, pp. 748–822.

Tomkins, G. M., Yielding, K. L.; and Curran, J. 1961. *Proc. Nat. Acad. Sci.*, **47**:270–278.

Tomota, S. 1940–1941. *J. Biochem. Japan*, **32**:307–315, 401–403, 405–417; **33**:205–214.

Turian, G., and Hamilton, R. H. 1960. *Biochim. Biophys. Acta*, **41**:148–150.

*Udenfriend, S. 1959. Biochemistry of Serotonin and Other Indoleamines. In, *Vitamins and Hormones*, **17**:133–154.

Umbarger, H. E., and Brown, B. 1958. *J. Biol. Chem.*, **233**:1156–1160; Umbarger, H. E. *Fed. Proc.*, **17**:326.

Umbarger, H. E.; Brown, B.; and Eyring, E. J. 1960. *J. Biol. Chem.*, **235**:1425–1432; Leavitt, R., and Umbarger, H. E. *ibid.*, **236**:2486–2491 (1961).

Umbarger, H. E., and Magasanik, B. 1951. *J. Biol. Chem.*, **189**:287–292.

Umbreit, W. W.: Bellamy, W. D.; and Gunsalus, I. C. 1945. *Arch. Biochem.*, **7**:185–199; *J. Biol. Chem.*, **161**:743–744.

Umbreit, W. W., and Gunsalus, I. C. 1945. *J. Biol. Chem.*, **159**:333–341.

Uyemura, T. 1937. *J. Agr. Chem. Soc. Japan*, **13**:1146–1158; (Engl. abstr. 107–108).

Virtanen, A. I., and Laine, T. 1938. *Enzymologia*, **3**:266–270.

Virtanen, A. I.; Rintala, P.; and Laine, T. 1938. *Nature*, **142**:674.

Viscontini, M.; Ebnöther, C.; and Karrer, P. 1951. *Helv. Chem. Acta*, **34**:1834–1841.

Vogel, H. J. 1953. *Proc. Nat. Acad. Sci.*, **39**:578–583.

Vogel, H. J. 1955. In, Aminoacid Metabolism, ed. Glass and McElroy. Baltimore, Johns Hopkins Press, pp. 335–353.

Vogel, H. J., and Bonner, D. M. 1954. *Proc. Nat. Acad. Sci.*, **40**:688–694.

Vogel, H. J., and Bonner, D. M. 1958. The Use of Mutants in the Study of Metabolism. In, *Handb. der Pflanzenphysiol.*, **11**:Chap. 2. Berlin, Springer.

Vogel, H. J., and Davis, B. D. 1952. *J. Am. Chem. Soc.*, **74**:109–112.

Waelsch, H.; Owades, P.; Miller, H. K.; and Borek, E. 1946. *J. Biol. Chem.*, **166**:273–281.

Walker, J. B. 1952. *Proc. Nat. Acad. Sci.*, **38**:561–566.

Wang, T. P. 1955. In, *Methods in Enzymology*, **2**:456–464. New York, Academic Press.

Wasserman, H. H.; McKeon, J. E.; and Santer, U. 1960. *Biochim. Biophys. Res. Comms.*, **3**:146–149.

Webster, M. D., and Bernheim, F. 1936. *J. Biol. Chem.*, **114**:265–271.

Whiteley, H. R. 1957. *J. Bact.*, **74**:324–330.

Wildman, S. G.; Ferri, M.; and Bonner, J. 1947. *Arch. Biochem.*, **13**:131–144.

Williams, V. R., and McIntyre, R. T. 1955. *J. Biol. Chem.*, **217**:467–477.

Wirth, J. C., and Nord, F. F. 1943. *Arch. Biochem.*, **2**:463–468.

Wolf, F. T. 1952. *Proc. Nat. Acad. Sci.*, **38**:106–111.

Wood, W. A., and Gunsalus, I. C. 1949. *J. Biol. Chem.*, **181**:171–182; cf. Gunsalus, I. C. 1950. *Fed. Proc.*, **9**:556–561.

Wood, W. A.; Gunsalus, I. C.; and Umbreit, W. W. 1947. *J. Biol. Chem.*, **170**:313–321

Woods, D. D. 1935. *Biochem. J.*, **29**:640–648, 649–655.

Woods, D. D. 1936. *Biochem. J.*, **30**:1934–1940.

Woods, D. D., and Trim, A. R. 1942. *Biochem. J.*, **36**:501–512.

Wrede, F., and Rothhaas, A. 1934. *Zeit. Physiol. Chem.*, **226**:95–107.

Wright, B. E. 1955. *Biochim. Biophys. Acta*, **16**:165–166; *J. Am. Chem. Soc.*, **77**:3930–3932.

Yamada, M. 1932. *J. Agr. Chem. Soc. Japan*, **8**:428–432, 498–505, 506–508.

Yamada, M. 1935. *Bull. Agr. Chem. Soc., Japan*, **11**:20–28.

Yamada, M., and Ishida, S. 1926. *J. Agr. Chem. Soc. Japan*, **2**:No. 7; from *Chem. Zentr.*, **II**:2568 (1928).

Zeller, E. A. 1951. In, The Enzymes, **2**:Pt. 1, 536–558. New York, Academic Press.

CHAPTER IX

The Fixation of Nitrogen

All the nitrogen in the world found in different nitrogenous compounds ·
has its origin in the atmosphere, and . . . by far the greater part of it has
been formed through the activity of micro-organisms.

A. I. VIRTANEN (1947)

Although the bulk of animals and plants are unable to utilize in any
way the vast stores of nitrogen in the air, there are a number of ways
in which atmospheric nitrogen is "fixed" and converted, directly or
indirectly, to organic matter. The quantities involved are large: an
acre of clover may fix 50 lb of nitrogen per year. In the whole United
States this would amount to a million tons of nitrogen per year.
Nitrogen is also being fixed, in increasing amounts, artificially, although
the methods require rather drastic conditions. Three such processes are
in commercial use: (1) the formation of NO in the electric arc at
3200° C (Birkeland-Eyde process), (2) the production of ammonia by
heating nitrogen and hydrogen at about 500° C under pressures of 200
to 300 atmospheres in the presence of metallic catalysts (Haber
process), and (3) the formation of calcium cyanamide ($CaNCN$) by
passing nitrogen over red-hot calcium carbide in the electric furnace.
The contrast with the smooth quietness of biological fixation, at one
atmosphere and 20° C, is very striking.

1. FIXATION BY LEGUMINOUS PLANTS

A. The Evidence for Fixation[1]

The first clear evidence that legumes actually absorb nitrogen from
the air is due to J. B. Boussingault, the French chemist, who in 1838,

[1] *Root Nodule Bacteria and Leguminous Plants*, by Fred, Baldwin, and McCoy
(1932) gives a detailed treatment of the historical material in this and the following
two sections.

on his farm in Alsace, determined the total nitrogen in plants and in their seeds. In pot experiments, to which no nitrogen fertilizer was added, he obtained striking results, from which the following are selected (Table IX–1). The legumes thus showed an increase while the nonlegumes showed no significant change. Careful field experiments, in which the quantity and composition of all fertilizers were determined, provided confirmation, and he concluded that "nitrogen may enter the living frame of the plants directly."

TABLE IX–1. Boussingault's Data on Nitrogen in Seed and Crop

Plant	N in Seed (mg)	N in Crop after 3 Mos (mg)	Change in N (mg)
Wheat	57	60	3
Oats	59	53	−6
Clover	114	156	42
Peas	47	100	53

However, later on, Boussingault began to be uncertain whether the increase was due to fixation of nitrogen or uptake of ammonia from the air. Liebig, in his celebrated book, *Die Chemie in ihrer Anwendung auf Agricultur und Physiologie* (1840), claimed that Boussingault's nitrogen determinations in his field experiments were unreliable. In later, more rigid experiments, in which the plants were grown in calcined sand or pumice and more precautions taken against contamination, Boussingault (1851–1853) did not obtain any increase in nitrogen with beans or lupines[2]—for a reason which will be obvious below. Similarly, Lawes and Gilbert, in field experiments in England, satisfied themselves at first that legumes increased the nitrogen of crops. In a 10-year period, 10 successive crops of wheat totaled 262 kg of organic nitrogen per hectare, while five crops of wheat interspersed with five crops of beans totaled 827 kg of organic nitrogen. Yet later on, Lawes, Gilbert, and Pugh, growing legume plants very carefully on a calcined clay, found no increase in nitrogen. Thus, in each case the increase in nitrogen disappeared when the experimental precautions were increased. On the other hand, another French chemist, Ville, claimed to obtain nitrogen fixation with all plants, legumes and nonlegumes alike. This introduced confusion and led to much argument. Approaching the problem in another way, later experiments in Germany showed that fertilizing oats led to increased growth only when the fertilizer contained nitrogen, while peas gave a good response to potassium and

[2] Peas were not included in these later experiments.

phosphate alone (Wagner, 1891). Clarity was reintroduced, though only much later, by Atwater in America, who in 1885 fully confirmed the original findings. Some of Atwater's results on peas are given in Table IX–2. A small amount of nitrate was added to the sand cultures, along with other nutrient salts. The third and fourth lines of data indicate that fixation is repressed by giving large amounts of fixed nitrogen (see p. 380).

TABLE IX–2. Experiments of Atwater with Peas
Data in mg

N in Seeds	N Added in Solution	Total N at Start	N in Plants	N Left in Solution	Total N at End	N Fixed
36.7	59.4	96.1	116.4	1.4	117.8	21.7
72.5	59.4	131.9	210.9	2.7	213.6	81.7
34.4	136.9	171.3	178.9	2.0	180.9	9.6
75.2	136.9	212.1	200.6	12.8	213.4	1.3

In reporting his conclusion that leguminous plants could fix free nitrogen of the air, Atwater admitted that this was "contrary to the general belief and the results of the best investigators on the subject." But it was not long before the complete explanation appeared.

B. The Role of Nodules

At about the middle of the century considerable attention was directed to the peculiar outgrowths, or nodules, which commonly occur on the roots of legumes. Lachmann in 1858 and Woronin in 1866 observed that the nodule tissue is filled with small rod-shaped bodies, sometimes motile, resembling bacteria. The fact that these organisms, called by Brunchorst in 1885 "bacteroids," are the *cause* of the nodules was not recognized at that time. A confusing factor was the observation that early in nodule development the organisms are united in a kind of thread, running through the root hair which is first infected, and then from cell to cell (Fig. IX–1). This thread was thought by some to be a fungus hypha. The exact nature of the organism was only settled by isolation in pure culture (Beijerinck, 1888; Prazmowski, 1890). Beijerinck used for growth medium an extract of leaves of the leguminous plant, together with asparagine, sucrose, and 7 per cent gelatin.

In growing cultures the nodule organisms are rods, from about 4

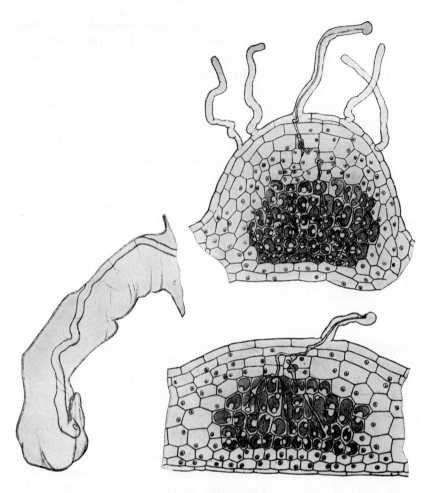

FIGURE IX–1

The infection thread in the development of a nodule.

Left. Root hair of pea showing point of infection, with distortion and curling. 1030 ×.

Top Right. Cross-section through pea nodule with similar infection thread entering the cortex from the epidermis cell out of which the root hair grows. Note outer cortical cells traversed by bacterial thread, and bacteria multiplying in the inner cortex. 350 ×.

Bottom Right. Longitudinal section through a similar young nodule. 350 ×.

(From B. Frank, 1890; courtesy of Paul Parey Verlag, Berlin.)

$\mu \times 1\ \mu$ down almost to cocci; within the nodules, however, especially in older nodules, they show characteristic swollen, branched, and T-shaped forms which differ in different species of legume. These are the "bacteroids" (Fig. IX–2).

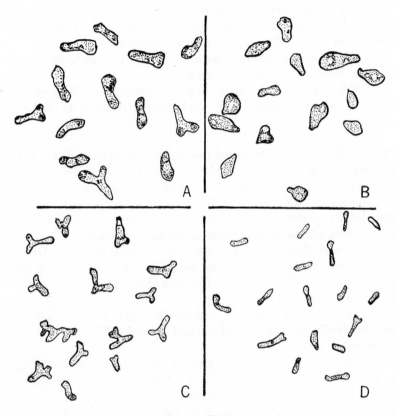

FIGURE IX–2

Rhizobia in the bacteroid form from the nodules of legumes.

A. Alfalfa. *B.* Clover. *C.* Pea. *D.* Soybean. *Ca* 2500 ×. (From camera lucida draw_ings of E. B. Fred, I. L. Baldwin, and E. McCoy: *Root Nodule Bacteria and Leguminous Plants.* Copyright 1932 by Wisconsin Univ. Press.)

Legumes thus differ from most other plants in being able to increase in nitrogen content, and in possessing nodules on their roots. The connection between these two facts was brought to light by Hellriegel and Wilfarth (1886–1888) in a series of researches of unrivaled clarity. Sand cultures were used, and the plants watered with nitrogen-free distilled water. In brief the findings were as follows:

(1) Grass plants grown on sterile, nitrogen-free sand yellowed and made little growth.

(2) Pea plants, on sterile sand, were mostly no better. The yellowing and stunting were typical of nitrogen deficiency. No nodules formed. (A few plants, however, became green and flourished.)

(3) But if the sterile sand were inoculated with an extract of fresh soil, growth of the peas became good, and the plants were green; on pulling them up, nodules were *invariably* observed.

(4) When after inoculation with soil extract the substrate was again sterilized, these effects were not obtained.

(5) When young pea plants that had formed nodules were transplanted to sterile, nitrogen-free sand, they continued to make good growth.

It is evident that greening of the plants, i.e., curing of the nitrogen deficiency in the absence of applied nitrogen, is dependent on formation of nodules, and this in turn is dependent on infection from the soil. Correspondingly, the failure of legumes to gain nitrogen in Boussingault's later experiments was due to a too careful calcining of the soil and therefore killing of the nodule-forming organisms.

Gilbert was chairman of the meeting in Berlin at which Hellriegel reported these results, and it was not long before they were widely confirmed by himself and others. Fixation of nitrogen is thus associated with nodule formation. Yet, curiously enough, the nodule bacteria themselves do not fix nitrogen, and fixation must result in some way from the *symbiosis* between plant and bacteria. This is, in fact, the present status of the problem.

Nodules are present on the roots of many nonleguminous plants too. These include *Alnus* (alder), *Coriaria japonica*, *Elaeagnus* and other members of the *Elaeagnaceae*, many of the *Zygophyllaceae*, *Ceanothus* (New Jersey tea), *Myrica*, *Podocarpus*, *Casuarina*, and some of the Cycads. In some of these the causative organisms resemble the bacteria of legume nodules, in others, e.g., *Ceanothus*, it is a streptomyces (Furman, 1958), and in still others perhaps a fungus related to *Plasmodiophora brassicae*, the cause of "clubroot" in cabbage (see Hawker and Fraymouth, 1951). The organism of *Alnus* is difficult to cultivate in vitro because it has an absolute requirement for a lipid growth factor present in the *Alnus* roots (Quispel, 1960). It is probably an actinomycete, having "hyphae with a diameter of less than 1 μ." In *Tribulus*, one of the *Zygophyllaceae*, the nodules are not bacterial at all (Allen and Allen, 1950a). Nevertheless, some of these nodules definitely fix nitrogen. Isolated *Alnus* nodules treated with isotopic N_2^{15} as described on page 381 show fixation which increases for at least two hours (Virtanen *et al.*, 1954). Similarly N_2^{15} supplied to freshly detached nodules of *Myrica Gale* was converted within two hours to amino acids, mostly glutamine (Leaf *et al.*, 1958, 1959). Earlier work on *Coriaria* (Kataoka, 1930) makes fixation probable there also. The ability of *Ceanothus* to flourish on N-deficient soils is often thought significant, but recent attempts to demonstrate its N-fixing ability have been inconclusive (Hellmers and Kelleher, 1959).

C. The Genus Rhizobium

The nodule bacteria of different legumes are evidently closely related, and it is reasonable to combine them in a single group or genus. The name *Rhizobium*, proposed by Frank (1890), has been generally adopted. Whether they are a genus with many species, or a species with many strains, is hard to decide and is for all practical purposes meaningless. In their ability to act as antigens on injection into animals, giving rise to antibodies that coagulate members of the group, they show clear interrelations (Kleczkowski and Thornton, 1944). On the other hand, there is marked specificity within the group in regard to the host plant. Recognition of this fact goes back to Hellriegel's finding that soil in which beans have grown will not support lupines; soil in which lupines have grown will, similarly, not support beans, but it will support serradella (*Ornithopus*). Cross-inoculation experiments in the field have indicated that there are seven or eight subgroups, each of which is moderately specific. Numerous other legume species fall outside these groups, and their Rhizobia have sometimes been assigned to additional subgroups. When it is remembered that there are some 10,000 species in the *Leguminosae*, of which barely 10 per cent have been examined (Allen and Allen, 1950b), it will be evident that such a grouping must be excessively tentative. Table IX–3, compiled from Fred, Baldwin, and McCoy (1932), gives the shape of the "bacteroids" and some of the cultural characters of the bacteria of the eight main groups. On the whole the first four groups, the "fast-growers," are very similar, while the next three ("slow-growers") are also closely related among themselves.

The growth factor requirements show a few systematic differences (summarized by Allen and Allen, 1950b). All groups but VI and VII require biotin for their growth (Nilsson *et al.*, 1939; West and Wilson, 1940), while only II requires thiamine. The clover organisms also require at least five other vitamins. Some variation in the requirement of different isolates within groups may reflect the uncertainty of the group boundaries. Serological tests, based on agglutination, indicate the existence of only three broad types corresponding to group I.

groups II and III, and groups V, VI, and VII, respectively. The third type is somewhat imperfect. Attempts to find clear-cut cultural differences, or differences in respiratory mechanisms, that could be used to determine host-specificity without the trouble of inoculation experiments, have been largely unsuccessful.

TABLE IX–3. Cultural and Morphological Characters of Eight Groups of Rhizobia

Group	Number of Flagella	Shape of Bacteroids	Growth on Yeast Mannite Agar	Growth in Milk	Growth on Arabinose (in glycero-PO₄ agar)	Growth on Galactose
I. *R. meliloti* (alfalfa, etc.)	1–few	Various, highly vacuolated	Fair, buttery	Clear zone, acid	+	+
II. *R. trifolii* (clover)	4	Mainly swollen, pear-shaped forms	Rapid, gummy	Clear zone, alkaline	−	−
III. *R. leguminosarum* (pea and vetch)	4	Branched forms, usually T or Y	Rapid, gummy	Clear zone, alkaline	+	+
IV. *R. phaseoli* (bean)	4	Mainly rods, smaller than the other groups	Rapid, gummy to slimy	Clear zone, alkaline	−	−
V. *R. lupini* (lupin)	2–3	Rods	Slow	No change, alkaline	++	−
VI. *R. japonicum* (soybean)	1	Long rods, sometimes with swollen ends	Slow, buttery	No change, alkaline	++	−
VII. *R. (cowpea)* (17 genera)	1+		Very slow	No change, alkaline	++	−
VIII. *R. (lotus)* (lotus)	1		Slow			
IX to XXII. (Small groups of 1 to 2 plants apiece)		Various				

The cross-inoculation experiments are not always reliable, and when the bacteria have been cultured on nutrient medium, their specificity seems to be reduced. Using cultures in sterile soil, J. K. Wilson (1939) found much less specificity than generally reported in the field; of 37 strains from nodules of *Amorpha fruticosa* (in one of the small groups IX to XXII), 33 formed nodules when tested back on Amorpha; many formed nodules on plants in group VII; 11 formed nodules on alfalfa (group I) and 14 on clover (group II). One strain produced excellent nodules on plants in three different groups, namely, clover (II), vetch (III), and Desmodium (VII), as well as on Amorpha. An extremely receptive host is *Astragalus nuttallianus*, which bore nodules with Rhizobia from plants in six groups (Wilson, 1944). Similarly, after several transfers on nutrient medium, a strain from peas (group III) formed nodules on clover (II), lupine (V), and several plants in the small groups; a strain from lupines showed similar nonspecificity (Sanchez, 1958). Very often there is incomplete reciprocity too, i.e., plant A forms nodules with bacteria from plant B, but plant B shows no response to the bacteria from plant A (Wilson, 1944).

Within a given species, sensitivity is genetically controlled. Thus, one line of red clover (*Trifolium pratense*) has a recessive gene *i* which, when homozygous, causes strain A of *Rhizobium trifolii* to make "ineffective" nodules, i.e., nodules causing little or no nitrogen fixation, while strain CiF and others form effective nodules. In another line derived from this, a recessive factor *m* modifies the first to make strain A "effective." In a third, unrelated line, a different recessive gene *ie* makes all strains except CiF ineffective (Nutman, 1959). The sites of action of these factors are different (see sec. D). The ineffective nodules are usually small and white, the others being larger, pink, and richer in bacteroidal tissue. Crimson clover nodulated by Rhizobium from white clover formed small white nodules and contained 0.4 to 0.5 mg nitrogen per plant, while when nodulated with its own strains, it had 5.3 to 7.3 mg nitrogen per plant at the same age (Burton and Allen, 1950).

The relationship between the *Rhizobia* and other bacteria is far from clear. The flagellation in some strains, especially groups VI and VII, is purely monotrichous, as in Pseudomonas, while in others there are two or four flagella situated rather at the sides or corners. In alfalfa (group I) different strains show different types of flagellation, from monotrichous to peritrichous. In other groups, especially III and V, flagellation depends on the stage of growth, the smallest coccoid cells being monotrichous, or occasionally with two polar flagella (Bisset and Hale, 1952). An organism called *B. radiobacter*, named from its tendency to form radiating, star-shaped groups, resembles Rhizobium in many ways and can be found on the roots of legumes, but does not form nodules or fix nitrogen. It is the commonest contaminant of Rhizobium isolates, but can be distinguished by its ability to grow in yeast extract-mannitol broth at *p*H 11 and to produce acid from dextrin, inulin, and amygdalin in yeast extract media (Hofer, 1941). The organism of crown-gall disease of plants, *Ps. tumefaciens*, also forms star-shaped groups (see Fig. III–14), and the galls formed by it in some plants superficially resemble nodules. Both these organisms have been included by Bergey in the oddly named genus Agrobacterium which is placed next to Rhizobium in the family *Rhizobiaceae*.[3] All in

[3] The key description of this is as follows: "Heterotrophic rods which may not require organic nitrogen for growth. Usually motile with 1 to 6 or more flagella. Usually form nodules or tubercles on roots of plants, or show violet chromogenesis." The description is, of course, absurd. As to organic nitrogen, Rhizobia require it, Agrobacterium does not, so that the word "may" means only that this criterion does not apply. The alternative between nodule formation and violet chromogenesis does not suggest any particular unity in the group, apart from the fact that *B. radiobacter* does neither.

all, the Rhizobia are probably more nearly related to the Pseudomonads than to any other group.

The "bacteroid" form is thought by some to be connected with nitrogen fixation, and in some types of ineffective nodules the rhizobia are rod-shaped (Virtanen, 1947; Nutman, 1959). In culture, bacteroid forms can be induced by adding alkaloids, metallic chlorides, or malic acid (Fred, Baldwin, and McCoy, 1932). Sometimes bacteroids are seen in young cultures, particularly when growth is slow. The bacteroid shape might point to the Actinomycetes (cf. Fig. IX–2 with Fig. II–14A), and it is suggestive that the symbionts of *Alnus* and other nonlegumes are often placed in this group, but the motility and gram-negativity of Rhizobium are against such a relationship. The barred staining of the bacteroids has been ascribed variously to fat bodies (Lewis, 1941), to cross walls with cytoplasm aggregated on them (Bisset and Hale, 1952), or to their being a kind of sporangium, the darkly staining granules being released as small cocci or "swarmers," which afterward grow again into rods. This "life-cycle" theory might seem supported by the variations in morphology which Rhizobia show, because small coccus-like forms are often seen together with rods of varying length (see especially Bisset and Hale, 1952), and perhaps the large barred rods divide into very small cells. Individual bacteroids, when in single-cell isolations, are quite incapable of growth (Almon, 1933), and since the irregularity of staining is in part due to degeneration of the nuclear material (Bergersen, 1955), it seems likely that they are truly decadent forms. Some viable forms must, of course, remain in vivo, or nodules would not yield cultures.

D. The Physiology of Nodule Formation

The infection process was first described by Marshall Ward in 1887 and by Frank in 1890. The bacteria usually accumulate at the tip of the root hair, which they enter, causing curling or other deformation (Fig. IX–1). The bacteria alone do not produce cellulase or pectinase to attack the root-hair wall (Clarke and Tracey, 1956), but in combination with a clover seedling they do (Ljunggren and Fåhraeus, 1961); it appears that the Rhizobia secrete something that stimulates the root hair to produce a pectinase. (The tip of the root hair contains little or no cellulose.) Within the living root hair some separate motile bacteria can at first be seen (Burgin-Wolff, 1959), but the bacteria soon agglomerate into a thread which penetrates from cell to cell in the root cortex. This infection thread is a peculiar structure; it has a definite membrane of cellulose and also contains pectin; evidently, therefore, it is contributed by the host plant and not by the bacteria that are inside it. In its origin it can be considered as an invagination of the original root-hair wall (Nutman, 1956, 1961), and ultimately it comes to surround each subgroup of rhizobia in the cells (see below). At each cell wall the thread probably passes through the primary pit areas, which have a loose, open structure, doubtless made more so by the pectinase secreted; the rods remain lengthwise in the thread (cf. Fig. IX–3).

Development of the nodule tissue depends on presence of the few tetraploid cells that each root normally contains. When these are entered, the nucleus is stimulated to divide, so that the amount of bacteroidal tissue increases. Since the diploid cells do not respond, the

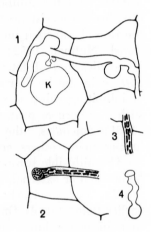

FIGURE IX–3
Details of the infection thread in nodules of *Vicia Faba;* cell contents omitted.

1. General view (*K* = cell nucleus).

2 and *3.* The alignment of the Rhizobia lengthwise in the thread. *2* shows also a cross-section through the thread. Note triangular thickenings where thread passes through cell wall, comparable to those at corners of cells.

4. Cross-section through an old thread at a branch point showing the thick wall of main thread and thin wall of lateral branch. 825 ×.

(From R. Schaede, *Beitr. Biol. Pflanzen*, **27** :165–188, 1941.)

infected core of the finished nodule is largely tetraploid and its cortex diploid (Wipf and Cooper, 1940; Fujita and Mitsuishi, 1953). The infection thread seems to be attracted to the nucleus in each cell, and the same is true in the root hair; if infection occurs on one branch of a forked root hair and the nucleus is in the other branch, the thread will turn outward toward the nucleus rather than inward to the cortex (Fåhraeus, 1957).

Within limits, the number of nodules formed is a function of the number of rhizobia, a minimum of 10^6 to 10^9 per cubic centimeter. of rhizosphere medium being needed for infection (Purchase and Nutman, 1957). But beyond that, several factors control nodulation; just which ones are crucial is still not known. In the first place, only a few per cent of infected root hairs give rise to nodules. This is in part, of course, due to the strain specificity; in Burgin-Wolff's observations on living root hairs (1959), the root hairs of peas could be infected by rhizobia from clover, and even sunflowers and corn had some rhizobia in their root hairs, but of course no nodules resulted. But even with pure strains of the host-specific type, one clover species may form a nodule from each infection, while another forms only one from 100 infections (Nutman, 1961). Obviously many infection threads abort (see the review of Raggio and Raggio, 1962).

In the second place, there is an interrelationship between nodules and the primordia of lateral roots. In clover, young uninoculated plants bear more laterals than inoculated ones, the total number of laterals plus nodules remaining constant for a time. Decapitation of the root tip increases nodule formation, perhaps by increasing the number of lateral root initials. Nodules themselves inhibit the formation of other nodules, and the inhibition is exerted by the uppermost part which contains the meristem; when nodules (or their meristems) are cut off, the rate of infection increases until the original number is about reinstated (Nutman, 1952). All these findings indicate that the formation of nodules and of lateral root initials is subject to a predetermined *pattern* in the host's root system which is mediated by the secretion of inhibiting substances. It is known that lateral roots are subject to such a pattern of control (Torrey, 1952, 1956), and thus, as Nutman (1961) concludes, "the nodule functions essentially as one meristem among many others active in determining the pattern of growth."

The diffusible substances responsible for this interrelationship may be internal or external. Seedlings grown in a medium in which another seedling has previously grown and been removed become nodulated earlier than controls. On the other hand, if many seedlings are together in a limited volume, the number of nodules is decreased (Nutman, 1956). Addition of fine absorbent charcoal increases the number (Turner, 1955), i.e., secretions can be both promotive and inhibitive. Internally, factors come from the cotyledons which control the formation of nodules and of lateral roots (Thornton, 1929; Torrey, 1956, respectively), and since inositol fed through the root base increases nodulation (Raggio *et al.*, 1959), it may itself be one of these factors.

If the number of tetraploid cells is small, this may limit nodulation too. Treatment with colchicine (which doubles the chromosome number) greatly increases the number of nodules on diploid clover and serradella, but has a smaller effect on tetraploid strains (Trolldenier, 1959). This might explain why effective and ineffective strains compete in nodule formation, as they have long been known to do, because clover plants inoculated first with an ineffective strain derive little or no benefit from subsequent inoculation with an effective one, and vice versa (Burton and Allen, 1950).

The various stages of nodulation offer numerous points at which

the process can be interfered with. For example, Nutman's factor *i*
(above), when homozygous, prevents the conversion of the rhizobia
into bacteroids; the bacteria multiply but remain normal, and the
typical degeneration of the nucleus does not occur. The factor *ie*, on the
other hand, prevents multiplication, so that the bacteria remain in a
little clump at the point of discharge from the infection thread. Their
secretion (? indoleacetic acid) stimulates cell division in the normal
way, however, so that a tumor, with little or no bacterial tissue, develops (Bergerson and Nutman, 1957). In another clover, *T. subter-*
raneum, one strain of Rhizobium cannot escape from the infection
thread but multiplies within; the resulting nodules are no more than
tiny bumps.

Thus the control of nodulation seems to be more in the hands of
the host plant than of the parasite. When we consider also that the
plant contributes a wall to the infection thread as well as (probably)
an enzyme to attack its own walls, and that it has to nourish the
Rhizobia throughout and eventually hydrolyze them, it is clear that the
symbiosis is elaborately developed.

Some authors claim that the relationship is not limited to the
nodules. Frank (1890) and others later have claimed that Rhizobia
penetrate to the upper parts of the plant, and although this has been
heartily denied (Allen and Allen, 1950b), it does not seem any more
improbable than the penetration of distant organs by crown-gall
bacteria. Tonzig and Bracci (1951) conclude that "legumes normally
harbor abundant Rhizobia, not only in the nodules and root-system
but in . . . the stem, leaf, different parts of the seed and even, very
probably, parts of the flower." In any event it is only in the nodules that
the plant responds with a growth reaction.

Growth of the nodule, once it is initiated, is associated with, and
perhaps caused by, an excess of indoleacetic acid. It was the finding
that nodules, both of legumes and of *Myrica*, are rich in an auxin that
led to the proposal that they represent lateral roots whose outgrowth
is inhibited in length and increased in diameter by auxin (Thimann,
1936, 1939). These are known effects of auxins on roots. The fact
that the nodule is cortical while the lateral root is initiated on the edge
of the central stele is, however, an important difference (Bond, 1948),
and it is more probable that both represent points of *potential* lateral
outgrowth. Not only are nodules far richer in auxin than ordinary
root tissue, but their auxin is all in the free, or active, form, while in
roots it is only slowly liberated by enzymatic action (Thimann *et al.*,
1942). The curling of root hairs so characteristic of the initial stages
(see above) is also caused by auxin. Rhizobia produce quantities of
indoleacetic acid in culture media also (Chen, 1938; Thimann, 1936,

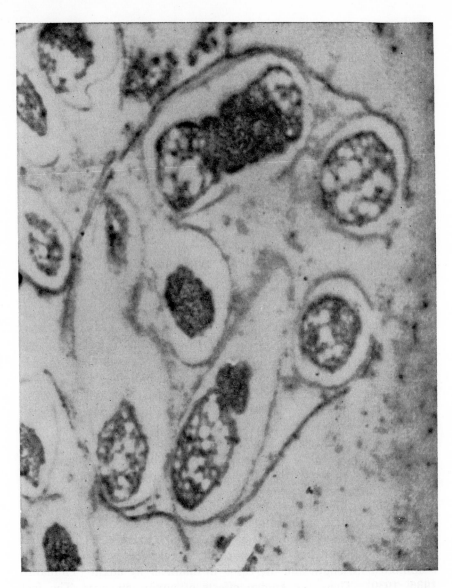

FIGURE IX–4

Rhizobia of a soy bean nodule enclosed within their membrane. RCA-EMU3B. Osmium fixed. Magnification 80,000 ✕. (Photo, F. J. Bergerson, 1957. Cf. Bergerson and Briggs, 1958). Six cells are seen (the space surrounding each is probably due to shrinkage). The hemoglobin is present in the spaces between the cells and the outer membrane. Each nodule cell contains about 10,000 of these membrane-enclosed units

1939). The auxin in Phaseolus nodules increases as they enlarge to reach a maximum at the end of flowering, then decreases as the pods grow and the nodules correspondingly begin to degenerate. Thus, the auxin is probably the major cause of the nodule's growth.

There is also differentiation, since vascular bundles soon develop near the outside of the nodule and establish contact with the bundles in the root. This ensures a good supply of carbohydrates to the nodule and no doubt carries away amino acids to the shoot (Pfennig, 1956). The vascular bundle of the lateral root, in contrast, develops as a branch from that of the main root (Bond, 1948). The core of bacterial tissue normally becomes pink due to hemoglobin (see below), and when the nodules degenerate and their auxin content falls, this turns greenish (cf., α-hemolysis, Chap. XI). The bacteroids then disappear, the nitrogen remaining in the nodule is absorbed into the plant like that in leaves before their fall in the autumn, and finally the nodule is cut off by a cork layer and withers away. In some perennial lupines, however, bacteroidal tissue becomes enclosed within the root and produces a new nodule the next season. What happens in the tropical leguminous trees is not known.

Electron-microscopic study of developing nodules has brought out another suggestive anatomical point (Bergerson and Briggs, 1958). When the bacteria are released from the infection thread, each is surrounded by a fragment of the thread membrane, and as each one divides, the membrane enlarges, so that the resulting group of daughter cells is enclosed in a thin membrane. All the rhizobia in the nodule are thus in little membrane-enclosed units, usually four to six in each one (see Fig. IX–4). This probably means that the microenvironment of the rhizobia is still more anaerobic than that of the host cells.

E. The Mechanism of the Symbiotic Nitrogen Fixation

Since neither the Rhizobia alone nor the legume alone will fix nitrogen, the problem of the fixation mechanism is very difficult. Isolated nodules will fix nitrogen, but only in small amounts and for a few hours (see below). A system intermediate between isolated nodules and intact plants is offered by nodules in culture on isolated root systems, fed with nutrient medium; these have a normal pink color and fix nitrogen in approximately normal amounts (Raggio et al., 1957, 1959). The problem is in part one of nutrition, because fixation in whole plants is greatly reduced by darkening the plants for a few hours, although it continues slowly in the dark (Lindstrom et al., 1952).

The Wisconsin workers at one time assembled much evidence to indicate that nitrogen fixation and the extent to which nodules are formed are dependent on the carbohydrate:nitrogen ratio in the plants (see P. W. Wilson, 1940). Thus, increasing the CO_2 content of the air or adding sugar to the soil, both of which increase the carbohydrate in the plants, increases nitrogen fixation and nodule number. Conversely, manuring with high nitrogen (Table IX–2) inhibits both processes. The conception unfortunately does not shed much light on mechanisms.

Nitrogen fixation is inhibited by hydrogen gas. When combined nitrogen is supplied, hydrogen does not affect the growth of the plants, but when they are growing without added nitrogen and dependent on fixation, hydrogen strongly inhibits growth and fixation. If we assume that N_2 is taken up by a special enzyme, *nitrogenase*, then its K_m, i.e., the N_2 concentration giving 50 per cent saturation, is for soybean nodule slices about 0.025 atmosphere of N_2 (Burris et al., 1955). This value agrees with the K_m found for Azotobacter and Nostoc (see below). Hydrogen, on this basis, would combine at the same enzyme and thus displace N_2; its affinity for the enzyme is about one-fifth that of N_2 (Wilson and Burris, 1953).

Carbon monoxide also inhibits fixation, 0.0001 atmosphere of CO having a detectable effect in red clover. However, unlike the inhibition of cytochrome oxidase, the effect of CO here depends only on the CO pressure and not on the $CO:O_2$ ratio. It might be deduced that nitrogenase is not a cytochrome but a related enzyme of the hemin-protein type.

Combined nitrogen, as we have seen, inhibits fixation too, but in a different way. Since the infected root hairs become curled or deformed (Fig. IX–1), the early stages of infection can be followed by determining the numbers of curled root hairs; this number is decreased by adding *nitrate*. For example, with alfalfa (Medicago) in sterile culture, 13 per cent of the root hairs were deformed; when Rhizobia were added, 64 per cent were deformed; if 0.15 per cent $NaNO_3$ was added as well, the number fell to 16 per cent (Thornton, 1936). If nitrate was supplied to isolated roots through their bases, nodulation was not decreased; only if it reaches the fine roots *externally* is nitrate inhibitory (Raggio, Raggio, and Torrey, 1957). Thus, the effects of nitrate and other oxidizable forms of nitrogen are probably exerted via this first stage rather than on the N_2-fixing process.

In 1933 Virtanen and co-workers in Finland discovered that legumes grown in nitrogen-free sand excrete organic nitrogen compounds into the sand (Virtanen et al., 1933). The excretion is large enough in amount to allow the growth of some grasses (or even spruce-tree seedlings) in the sand. It appears to be a true excretion rather than merely a sloughing off of decayed nodules. Most of the nitrogen appearing in the sand is in the form of aspartic acid, with smaller amounts of its decarboxylation product, β-alanine, and of glutamic acid (Virtanen and Laine, 1939; Virtanen, 1947). This would imply that the fixed nitrogen had become combined with oxalacetic or ketoglutaric acid. It had earlier been shown that clover without nodules grows well with aspartic acid as a sole nitrogen source. The findings were disputed at first, but were later repeated in the United States under growth conditions similar to those prevailing at Virtanen's laboratory in Finland (see Roberts, 1946). There was some evidence that the first fixation product was hydroxylamine, but this was subsequently shown to be improbable both by the Wisconsin group and by Saris and Virtanen (1957). However, the positions of aspartic and glutamic acids as first products have been fully supported. Virtanen's original claim that isolated nodules will fix nitrogen in the presence of oxalacetic acid has not been borne out, because healthy soybean nodules separated rapidly from the parent plant fix nitrogen (supplied as N_2^{15}) only for a few hours, and the period is not prolonged by supplying oxalacetate or any other organic acid (Aprison et al., 1954). Nitrogen fixation by excised Alnus nodules is also not much increased by organic acids (Virtanen et al., 1954). Either the keto acid must be produced endogenously to be effective, or else the system is very fragile. As we shall see below, glutamic acid appears as a primary product of fixation by the free-living Axotobacter and Clostridium. Also, in nodules of the nonleguminous tree Myrica Gale (bog myrtle), after incubation with N_2^{15} most of the isotope was found in the amide N of glutamine and asparagine (Leaf et al., 1959). In Alnus nodules the N_2^{15} goes into glutamic acid and the guanidine N of citrulline (Leaf et al., 1959).

Although there is thus uncertainty about the exact pathway, and perhaps some interspecific differences, this conception does indicate why fixation is so dependent on the plant's nutrition and why isolated nodules fix only transiently (see Prianischnikov, 1951). For if a supply of keto-acid precursors must be maintained, the nodule must be in constant touch with the photosynthetic system. The vascular bundles that supply the nodules are thus very important, both for supply and for product removal. Since nodulated and unnodulated roots of peas have the same amino acid composition (Pfennig, 1956), the fixed nitrogen is probably continuously given off to the rest of the plant. In boron deficiency, vascularization of the nodules is greatly reduced, and correspondingly growth and fixation are seriously decreased.

A remarkable fact about nitrogen fixation in nodules is its dependence on traces of molybdenum and cobalt. Molybdenum has long been known to control fixation by free-living bacteria (see below), but recently this was extended to nodules (Bond and Hewitt, 1961), thus confirming a strong suspicion of some 30 years' standing. A similar requirement for cobalt is shown by several legumes and by Alnus (Ahmed and Evans, 1961; Bond and Hewitt, 1962). When these plants are grown in purified nitrogen-free sand culture and are inoculated, they become yellow and appear N-deficient unless 1 part in 10^8 of cobalt is added; the N content of the plants is then tripled. The same appears to hold for Casuarina.

Some suggestive observations on pigments may bear on the first stage of fixation. It is well known that healthy nodules are usually pink, and the term "beef-steak" has even been used in describing them. As it happens, the term is unexpectedly appropriate because the pigment is actually hemoglobin. It combines with O_2 and with CO to form an oxyhemoglobin and a carboxyhemoglobin, just as does the hemoglobin of blood cells. It readily oxidizes to a brown form in which the iron is trivalent—methemoglobin. In older nodules, or in plants kept in the dark for a few days, it turns greenish. Blood hemoglobin undergoes a similar change when it is metabolized, forming a green bile pigment. Virtanen (1947) points out that the change to green is invariably associated with loss of nitrogen-fixing power in the nodule.

Nodules caused by ineffective Rhizobium strains are almost colorless, as shown by Thornton's (1945) observations with several hundred strains. Their content of total hematin is about one-tenth that of effective nodules (Smith, 1949), and the *brei* from ineffective nodules does not form any porphyrins in vitro, under conditions where the *brei* from effective nodules does (Falk *et al.*, 1959). Rhizobia in culture can form porphyrins, although they never form hemoglobin (Falk *et al.*, 1959). Neither is hemoglobin ever found in higher plants, except in nodules. It is suggestive that the nitrogen-fixing capacity of nodules varies with the effective volume of hemoglobin-containing tissue (Bergersen, 1961).

These facts suggest that the hemoglobin might combine with nitrogen, as the first step in the process. Indeed, observation of the spectrum of soybean-nodule extract in an atmosphere of helium shows the hemoglobin mainly in the ferrous form, and on admission of N_2 it changes to the ferric form (Hamilton *et al.*, 1957). Hydrogen causes the reverse change. This certainly indicates some reaction with nitrogen. However, addition of nodule hemoglobin to Rhizobia in culture does not cause any nitrogen fixation (Tove and Wilson, 1948); added oxaloacetate does not help. The hemoglobin of blood does not combine with nitrogen either, although the two hemoglobins are not necessarily identical. Indeed, Virtanen's preparation (called "leghemoglobin") appears to have a molecular weight (17,000) about one-quarter that of the blood pigment. The hemoglobin of nodules definitely has no function in respiration; effective and ineffective nodules have the same rates of O_2 uptake, and when all the hemoglobin is combined with CO (through exposure to a mixture of CO and air), the O_2 uptake is not reduced (Smith, 1949). It is, however, suggestive that blood hemoglobin combines with hydroxylamine, liberating free N_2 (Colter and Quastel, 1950), but there is as yet no evidence that the reaction is reversible. Thus, the physiological function of the hemoglobin remains obscure, and with it, the whole mechanism of nitrogen fixation in nodules.

2. FIXATION BY FREE-LIVING ORGANISMS

A. Clostridium

In formulating his well-known "Law of the Minimum," according to which the yield of a crop is determined by that element which is present in the soil in minimum (i.e., limiting) amount, Liebig, 100 years ago, recognized that any one of many elements might, under different conditions, be limiting the crop. He considered nitrogen one of these and urged the use of ammonium salts as manures. The need for constantly replacing nitrogen was established experimentally by the classic researches of Lawes and Gilbert in 1843–1855, who found that all plants, with the exception of legumes, need nitrogen added to the soil. In 1847 Liebig changed his views, concluding that meadow land supplied with alkali and phosphate could actually gain in nitrogen. The basis for this view is not clear, since Boussingault's careful experiments showed that plants in general could not gain nitrogen from the atmosphere. However, certain experiments of Berthelot (1885) cast a different light on the matter. Samples of sterilized and unsterilized soil were set aside in the laboratory or outdoors for some months. The unsterilized samples were found to have increased, slightly but definitely, in total nitrogen (see Table IX–4). The increase was almost entirely in the organically combined nitrogen. A few years later, Winogradsky made his well-known study of nitrogen fixation (1895). A culture medium free from nitrogen but containing sugar, phosphate, sulfate, and $CaCO_3$ was inoculated with soil. Vigorous fermentation took place, with the smell of butyric acid. After a time the solution had gained in nitrogen.

In the course of numerous transfers to fresh media, it was soon found that sporeforming rods constituted the major part of the flora. Winogradsky therefore pasteurized the solution to remove nonsporeformers. Furthermore, the sporeformers grew mainly at the bottom of the culture, suggesting that they were anaerobes. He therefore used tall cylinders through which nitrogen was bubbled. In this way he finally isolated a sporeforming anaerobe, which was named *Clostridium pasteurianum*.[4]

TABLE IX–4. Berthelot's Experiments on the Increase in Soil Nitrogen

(Data from Berthelot, 1885)

Treatment	TOTAL N IN MG/KG DRY WEIGHT DETERMINED IN:			Average Gain (mg/kg) per 3 Months
	April	July	October	
Pots indoors	98.9	116.7	120.9	11.0
Pots in the field	26.9	45.8	63.0	18.1
Pots sterilized, open to air through cotton plugs:				
1		116.7	109.2	0
2		150.2	134.8	0
3		35.4	32.2	0

Isolation of an actual nitrogen-fixing organism settled the matter, insofar as gains of nitrogen by soil are concerned. It also caused a stir among agriculturists, who saw the possibility of inoculating soil with this wonderful organism and thus ending forever the need for supplying nitrogenous fertilizer. Within a year or two Caron placed on the market a culture to increase fixed nitrogen, named "alinite." This was useless—for two reasons. First, it was not *Cl. pasteurianum* at all, but an aerobe, *Bac. cereus*, common in soil and, like other bacilli, quite without nitrogen-fixing power. Second, as we know now, the flora of soil is usually determined by the prevailing conditions and not by inoculation. If soil contains attackable carbohydrate and the right salts, the clostridia will develop in any event as soon as conditions become anaerobic enough. Bredemann (1908) found *Cl. pasteurianum* in 137 out of 152 soils examined. Those from which it was absent comprised mainly the peats and peat-sand soils with *p*H more acid than 5. In Winogradsky's work with soil (Chap. VI) it was enough to add glucose and make the soil waterlogged to develop enormous numbers of *Cl. pasteurianum* immediately.

Experiments like those of Berthelot have recently been repeated

[4] Winogradsky's original spelling was *pastorianum*, but the form above is now generally used.

in Nigeria (Moore and Abuelu, 1959); the gain was 28 mg N per kilogram of soil in five months, which agrees well with the data of Table IX–4 (4 to 6 mg/kg/month). Addition of Mo and phosphate to the pots of soil more than tripled the gain, which reached 110 mg per kilogram.

The power of fixing nitrogen is widespread among the Clostridia, with the exception of those that are animal pathogens. As with Rhizobium, the amount of nitrogen fixed depends on the amount of carbohydrate supplied. Winogradsky (1902) found *Cl. pasteurianum* to fix 2 mg N per gram of dextrose fermented, but later workers with shaken cultures have obtained up to 7 mg N per gram of dextrose, with *Cl. saccharobutyricum* and other species. Even so, a gram of sugar gives rise to less fixation with Clostridia than it does with Azotobacter (see below), but since the sugar has to be fermented rather than oxidized, it yields much less energy per gram. In nodules and aerobic organisms the fixation is inhibited by ammonia, but *Cl. pasteurianum* can use both N_2 and NH_3 simultaneously, because when the cells are exposed to N_2^{15}, it is converted to $N^{15}H_3$, which appears in the medium while $N^{14}H_3$ is simultaneously being taken up (Zelitch, 1951). In other respects the action of inhibitors is similar to that in aerobes. Hydrogen inhibits, the inhibition being proportional to the ratio H_2/N_2, i.e., it competes with nitrogen (Hiai *et al.*, 1957); both CO and N_2O inhibit also (Hino, 1955). It is suggestive that CO inhibits ammonia assimilation too, although less powerfully than it does nitrogen fixation. The fixation mechanism is discussed in section 2E2 below.

B. Myxophyceae (Blue-Green Algae)

Nitrogen can also be fixed under aerobic conditions. This was brought out by Beijerinck (1901, 1902) in a study of the flora of tap water containing 0.02 per cent KH_2PO_4. Organisms growing in the presence of only traces of nitrogen he called *oligonitrophilic* (Greek *oligos*, small or few). This medium, inoculated with soil and kept in the light, slowly develops blue-green algae, principally the filamentous forms, Nostoc and Anabaena. Only if ammonium salts were added did grass-green algae (*Chlorophyceae*) appear. Beijerinck, therefore, concluded that the blue-greens could fix nitrogen, and much later this was confirmed by nitrogen determinations (Drewes, 1928; Fogg, 1942); all filamentous types that form heterocysts can fix N (Wilson and Burris, 1953). The amount of nitrogen fixed was originally considered to be very small, Drewes finding only 12 mg N per liter of medium in 50 days; however, it is greatly increased by vigorous shaking to bring the cells in contact with the N_2. *Anabaena cylindrica* in shaken cultures is reported to fix up to 500 mg N per liter (Allen and Arnon, 1955). The large range in the recorded amounts of fixation may be due to contamination by bacteria. Thus *Nostoc calcicola* in pure culture fixed only 10 mg N per liter of medium in 90 days (cf. Drewes' value), but in mixed culture with *Bac. megaterium* 54 mg N were fixed (Bjälfve, 1962).

The fixation by blue-greens is inhibited by H_2 and by CO to about the same extent as that by Azotobacter and by clover nodules. Since blue-green algae are of very wide distribution in lakes and streams, the fixation may be quantitatively important there; they also grow vigorously in flooded rice fields. A number of lichens have Nostoc as the algal partner, and two of these, as well as the liverwort *Blasia pusilla* which contains Nostoc in the tissue, have been shown to fix small amounts of nitrogen (Bond and Scott, 1955). A few marine blue-greens have been found to fix nitrogen also (Watanabe *et al.*, 1951) which again indicates the probable large scale of the process in nature (see also Fogg and Wolfe, 1954).

C. Purple Bacteria

In studying the photosynthetic reactions of Rhodospirillum, a purple bacterium (Chap. XXIII), it was found that from some organic acids hydrogen is given off in the light (Gest *et al.*, 1950). The reaction is inhibited by nitrogen gas, as well as by ammonium. Because of the special relations between hydrogen gas and nitrogen fixation (p. 380), it was thought that the reciprocal relationship might apply here, and that the Rhodospirillum might be able to fix nitrogen. Accordingly, the culture was tested, using N^{15} gas, and found to fix nitrogen vigorously in the light. Nitrogen gas could even be used instead of amino acid as source of nitrogen for growth, provided a trace of biotin were added; after several weeks 56 mg N_2 was fixed per liter of medium (Gest *et al.*, 1956). This is about five times as much fixation as by Nostoc. Under similar conditions, but without biotin, both a Chromatium (of the *Thiorhodaceae*, or sulfur purples) and a Chlorobium have been found to fix up to 100 mg N_2 per liter after two to three weeks (Lindstrom *et al.*, 1950). Nitrogen is also fixed by 19 strains of Rhodopseudomonas, representing all four species, and by Rhodomicrobium (Lindstrom *et al.*, 1951). Hence the ability to fix nitrogen, and in considerable quantities, is characteristic of the *Rhodobacteriinae* as a whole. Fixation by Rhodospirillum is greatly promoted by sulfide, and, as with other organisms, is inhibited by H_2 (Gest *et al.*, 1956).

D. Ordinary Bacteria

In the last few years bacteriologists have come to realize the surprising fact that many "ordinary" bacteria have the ability to fix a little nitrogen. These weak nitrogen-fixers include:

Aerobacter aerogenes
Methanobacterium omelianskii
"*Ps. azotogenesis*," a yellow Pseudomonas from soil, and six other Pseudomonads
Achromobacter, eight strains, and
Nocardia calcarea

With the Methanobacterium, which produces CH_4 from alcohols (see Chap. XVIII), traces of ammonia actually promoted the fixation by promoting growth, but larger amounts inhibited strongly (Pine and Barker, 1954). The Achromobacter (Jensen, 1958) fixed 3 to 17 mg N per liter of medium in four days, at a rate of 1 mg N per gram of carbohydrate used, which is considerable, though much less than with typical nitrogen fixers. It could even fix some nitrogen anaerobically. Some of the Pseudomonads fix as much as 50 mg N per liter of medium (Proctor and Wilson, 1958–1959). They respond to small amounts of ammonium by increased growth, like Methanobacterium, but then the growth slows down and after a lag it restarts, this time with N fixation. This suggests that NH_3 represses formation of the nitrogenase enzyme.

In addition to the bacteria, two red yeasts (Rhodotorula), a Saccharomyces and a black Pullularia, all isolated from soil, fix moderate amounts of nitrogen (Metcalfe and Chayen, 1954; Metcalfe and Brown, 1957; Nemeth, 1959). The Pullularia fixes 4 to 5 mg N per gram of glucose supplied, which is comparable to the Clostridia. Since up to 8000 were found per gram of soil (Metcalfe and Brown, 1957), its contribution may be important. One wonders how many other nitrogen-fixing organisms will be turned up.

E. Azotobacter

1. CHARACTERISTICS. If carbohydrate be added to a medium containing salts but only traces of nitrogen, many bacteria develop aerobically. Of these, one of the most characteristic is Azotobacter, a nitrogen-fixer of the first importance. Beijerinck and van Delden (1902), who isolated it, could obtain fixation only in mixed cultures, but later workers have shown that pure cultures fix nitrogen very actively. The amount is large—up to 20 mg per gram of sugar (Fischer,

1949; Wilson and Burris, 1953), or more than double that of most clostridia. In addition to Beijerinck's original two species, *A. chroöcoccum* and *A. agilis*, several others have since been discovered. They can be distinguished roughly as follows (Kluyver and van Reenen, 1933, and Starkey and De, 1939):

AZOTOBACTER SPECIES	MORPHOLOGY (24-HR CULTURE)	GLUCOSE-AGAR COLONIES AFTER 1 WEEK	MANNITE-AGAR COLONIES AFTER 1 WEEK
Chroöcoccum (soil)	Oval, 2 μ broad, mainly in pairs	Large, slimy, deep brown to black	As on glucose
Agilis (canal water)	Round cells, 3.5 μ broad, singles and in pairs	Very small, pale yellow, trace of greenish diffusible pigment	Tiny, pale yellow, with yellow-green fluorescent pigment diffusing into agar
Vinelandii (soil)	Small oval, 1.5 μ broad, singles and pairs	Large, almost colorless, slimy	Large, colorless to pale yellow with yellow-green diffusible pigment as with *A. agilis*
Beijerinckii (soil)	Long, 2 μ broad, commonly forming definite chains	Large, almost colorless, slimy	Large, colorless to yellow; no diffusible pigment
Indicum	Oval, mainly in pairs	Large, slimy, cream-colored, turning brown very slowly	Large, white to creamy, slight fluorescent pigment

The Azotobacters have been described in detail by Jensen (1958), who considers that *Az. indicum*, because of its long lag period, slow growth, and formation of acetic acid and excessive amounts of gummy polysaccharide, should be placed in a new genus, *Beijerinckia*. On a glucose medium it converts 2 to 3 per cent of the glucose to acetic acid, 30 to 70 per cent to gum, and the rest to CO_2 (Quinnell, 1957).[5] Each cell contains two prominent fat globules. A smaller-celled type with numerous fat globules, and clearly polar flagella, has been placed in a third genus, *Derxia* (Jensen et al., 1960; Roy and Sen, 1962). The other species are fairly closely related, although within the Chroöcoccum type the initial rate of nitrogen fixation indicates two subgroups (Fischer, 1949), since of 68 strains, about half fixed 2 to 4 mg N, and the others, 8 to 12 mg N (in 2 days at 30° C on 50-ml mannite medium). Very few were intermediate. The upper value, 240 mg per liter, is not as high as has been recorded. The more active group was the more motile and more nearly rod-shaped.

Azotobacter cells have been thought to resemble those of blue-green

---

[5] All the Azotobacters form gummy nonreducing polysaccharide to some extent, and its presence makes pure culture isolation troublesome. It is a curious fact that such material is often formed by bacteria growing in the near-absence of combined N (Beijerinck's "oligonitrophiles").

algae (see Fig. IX–5). The relatively broad cells, showing characteristic granules, are easily recognized in enrichment cultures. Their dimensions, unusual in bacteria, correspond to those of small blue-greens such as *Chroöcoccus dispersus* var. *minor*, which is about 2 μ

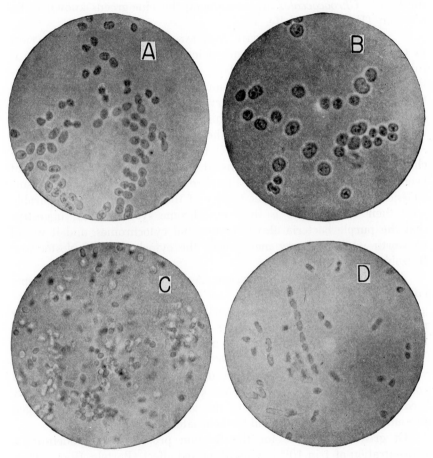

FIGURE IX–5

Four species of Azotobacter.

A. *A. chroococcum*. B. *A. agilis*. C. *A. vinelandii*. D. *A. beijerinckii*. All 900 ×. (From A. J. Kluyver and W. J. van Reenen, *Arch. Mikrobiol.*, 4:280–300, 1933.)

in diameter. The gummy capsule holds the Azotobacter cells together in pairs or small groups (cf. Chap. VI, sec. 3). In addition, single cells form curious cysts, with at least three layers of wall. These might be compared to spores, but the cell inside shows no differences from its normal vegetative form (Tchan *et al.*, 1962) and oxidizes substrates vigorously (Socolofsky and Wyss, 1961). The cyst wall is thus like a capsule which has hardened. The fact that all Azotobacters are motile with peritrichous flagella is an important difference from the blue-greens. Unfortunately also for the parallel, *Chroöcoccus* and the family *Chroöcoccales* are not among the blue-greens known to fix nitrogen (Fogg and Wolfe, 1954).

2. METABOLISM AND THE MECHANISM OF NITROGEN FIXATION IN GENERAL. The Azotobacters are strictly aerobic. Their respiration is fully cyanide-sensitive and is about as rapid per unit of protein as that of any known cell. Theirs is an atypical cytochrome system, and they were used for the direct observation of the bands of the oxidase, cytochrome a_2 (see Table V–2), which replaces cytochrome a_3 in these cells. The bands of a_1 and b_1 take the place of cytochromes a and b. In *Az. vinelandii* (we do not know if the same is true in others) cytochrome c is replaced by the unusual pair c_4 and c_5, which have not been found to interact with the cytochrome systems of other organisms (Tissières, 1956). Thus, a peculiarity of the Azotobacters, comparable with their morphology, is their cytochrome system. It is suggestive that the purple bacteria also have unusual cytochromes, and it would be worth while to know more about the cytochromes of Nostoc and Rhizobium.

As far as substrate is concerned, Azotobacters are not highly specific. Organic acid salts, sugars, and sugar alcohols are favorable for growth, and mannitol is often used in enrichment cultures because not many Clostridia can attack it; Winogradsky's observation of the rapid growth of large cocci when mannitol was added to soil (Chap. VI, sec. 4) doubtless refers to Azotobacter. With a variety of carbon sources, the nitrogen fixation is roughly proportional to the heat of combustion of the compound (Mockeridge, 1915), which probably means that it is proportional to the amount of combined hydrogen present. The rule does not hold for benzoate (Fischer, 1949).

Of great importance for the fixation process is molybdenum, a concentration of 1 in 10^{10} having a marked effect (Bortels, 1930, 1936). However, *Az. vinelandii* and *Az. agile* can fix nitrogen in a highly purified medium about half as fast without Mo as with it (Bové *et al.*, 1957); only *Az. chroöcoccum* fixed no nitrogen without added Mo. In many cases, but not all, molybdenum is replaceable by vanadium but by no other metal.[6] The Mo is antagonized by tungsten (as tung-

---

[6] In this connection it is worth noting that in the Haber nitrogen fixation process, in which nitrogen and hydrogen are combined under high pressure, metallic catalysts are also required. Preparations of uranium and iron are used. The parallel with the need for molybdenum (or vanadium) and iron in Azotobacter is suggestive.

state), giving an apparently competitive inhibition (Takahashi and Nason, 1957), and tungstate inhibits the growth of Azotobacter when N_2 gas is the nitrogen source (Aurich, 1959), although this may be only because it prevents the uptake of Mo (Keeler and Varner, 1957). Vanadium does not reinstate growth in presence of tungstate. Most of the Mo taken up has been found, by using the isotope Mo^{99}, to go into a protein-rich fraction (Keeler et al., 1956; Magee and Burris, 1956). Even in *Aerob. aerogenes* Mo is required for nitrogen fixation, 1 part in 10^8 giving maximum effect; there was no Mo requirement for growth on an ammonium medium (Pengra and Wilson, 1959). Most higher plants require Mo for growth, but legumes fixing nitrogen probably require more than others, and nitrogen fixation in nodules appears dependent on Mo (Bond and Hewitt, 1961). The reduction of nitrate also requires Mo (see Chap. X). All in all, it can be deduced that the nitrogenase enzymes in virtually all organisms contain molybdenum. In Rhizobium, cobalt promotes growth, both of the bacteria and of legumes growing symbiotically with them; it is converted to vitamin B_{12} coenzymes in the cell and in the nodule (Ahmed and Evans, 1960–1961; Kliewer and Evans, 1962). However, a direct action of Co on fixation is doubtful.

As mentioned in connection with nodules, an early candidate for the position of first intermediate in nitrogen fixation was hydroxylamine. This compound was also considered in relation to Azotobacter, but it is quite toxic; N^{15}-labeled hydroxylamine is not used by the bacteria, and oximes are assimilated only poorly (Burris, 1956).

Since the starting material is N_2, an intermediate containing 2 N atoms is obviously attractive, and some interest has centered on hydrazine, N_2H_4. Hydrazine, although it is also toxic, is readily taken up by Azotobacter, and ammonia inhibits the uptake. Chemically, hydrazine is known to react with α-ketoglutarate to form the cyclic compound, I:

Compounds similar to I were found to occur naturally both in *Az. vinelandii* and in soybean nodules (Bach, 1957). Azotobacter exposed to $N_2{}^{15}$ had the isotope at higher concentration in the organic acids (including the fraction in which I occurs) than when they were exposed to $N^{15}H_4{}^+$ salts. Bach points out that I could be reduced directly to glutamine, and doubtless oxalacetate might substitute for α-ketoglutarate to yield an analogue of I which would reduce to asparagine and aspartic acid. Against hydrazine as an intermediate, however, are its toxicity and its failure to take up N^{15} label in active extracts (see below).

Thus, the evidence does not support either NH_2OH or NH_2NH_2 as an intermediate, and ammonium remains the strongest contender for the title. In its favor is the fact that Azotobacter and Clostridium use it very rapidly and convert it to the same products as they do N_2. After three minutes' exposure of Azotobacter to $N^{15}H_4{}^+$, the highest concentration of N^{15} was found in glutamic and aspartic acids, and the same was true after 90 minutes' exposure to $N_2{}^{15}$ gas (see Wilson and Burris, 1953). Unlike most other amino acids, these two compounds are assimilated by Azotobacter when supplied exogenously.

Cell-free preparations convert ammonia into the same products, *Az. vinelandii* extracts incorporating $N^{15}H_4{}^+$ into glutamic acid without delay (Burma and Burris, 1957). Addition of α-ketoglutarate accelerated the $NH_4{}^+$ uptake, as might be expected. It was shown by Winogradsky (1930, 1938) that when Azotobacter grows on sodium lactate or benzoate, its oxidation of the organic anion sets free so much alkali that the cells autolyze and ammonia is evolved. The spectacle of enough NH_3 coming off a *nitrogen-free* culture to turn red litmus paper blue is certainly dramatic. Pertinent to the role of NH_3 also is the long-known fact that ammonium salts (and urea) inhibit fixation, while amino acids have little effect. Against a *primary* role of NH_3, however, are the data with isolated nodules exposed two hours to $N_2{}^{15}$ (Aprison *et al.*, 1954), where most of the N^{15} was found in glutamic and aspartic acids, and the concentration of N^{15} (= "specific activity") was *higher* in these than in the NH_3. Azotobacter in exposures of two to five minutes to $N_2{}^{15}$ shows the same reaction (Allison and Burris, 1957). These data suggest rather that NH_3 is secondarily formed (perhaps very easily) from the primary fixation product.

Most of the recent work has centered on fixation by cell-free systems. Protoplasts from *Az. vinelandii*, made by treating with lysozyme and versene (p. 110), and exposed to $N_2{}^{15}$ for two hours, fix nitrogen at a rate from 1 to 50 per cent of that of whole cells (Jose and Wilson, 1959), but there were many intact cells present. Azotobacter cells broken by ultrasonic vibration give good $N_2{}^{15}$ fixation, too, the enzyme being in the particulate fraction (Nicholas and Wilson, 1962). The best success has been with *Cl. pasteurianum*, similarly broken up by sonic vibration (Wilson and Burris, 1960; Carnahan *et al.*, 1960; Burris, 1962); this preparation in presence of pyruvate or (less effectively) ketoglutarate fixes about half as much N_2 as whole cells, and the enzyme is strictly soluble. Spectroscopic observation of such preparations from Azotobacter and nodules indicated that both flavoprotein and cytochromes could be reduced by hydrogen and reoxidized by N_2 (Hamilton *et al.*, 1957), while Clostridium extracts show only the flavin being so reduced and reoxidized, as might be expected in an anaerobe. Hydrogen gas would normally be activated by the enzyme *hydrogenase* (see Chap. XIV), and indeed both in Azotobacter and Rhodospirillum (but not in Clostridium) the hydrogenase content is higher when they are growing with N_2 gas than when growing on ammonium or glutamate (see Gest *et al.*, 1956). But since the normal supply of hydrogen for reduction would be metabolic, i.e., $H^+ + e$, and would come via the usual oxidation-reduction mechanisms, the role of hydrogenase in fixation may have been made too much of. In any case the Clostridium enzyme has allowed a rigid test of the role of intermediates (Burris, 1962); if, after $N_2{}^{15}$ fixation, unlabeled NH_2OH was added to the enzyme, it could be reisolated as an oxime, and if any $N^{15}H_2OH$ were present, the oxime would be labeled. It was not. Hydrazine similarly received no label whatever. In the same experiments ammonia became intensely labeled. Thus the N_2 is probably reduced directly or indirectly to ammonia on the enzyme. The dominating role of a reduction process fits well with the fact (p. 378) that within nodules the rhizobia must be under anaerobic conditions.

The first step must be for the N_2 to be bound. Fixation in Azotobacter is inhibited specifically and competitively by N_2O and by azide, $N_2 \cdot NH$ (Roberts, 1959). In both these the distance between the N atoms is nearly the same as in nitrogen gas, which could indicate that the enzyme binds both N atoms, and then its action is fundamentally to break the bonds between them. The bond energy of N:N is 225,000 calories, so that very large energy is needed to separate them. Because in cytochrome oxidase the atoms of O_2 are separated through a change in valency of the metal (iron) in the enzyme, so one visualizes the same thing here, only with more extreme change of valency because of the higher energy requirement. Molybdenum, having valencies from 2 to 6, is thus most appropriate. Furthermore, the function of the nitrogenase is not only to bind the N_2, but also to bring it into contact with protons; then, presumably by the change of metallic valency, to donate enough electrons to allow the hydrogen to combine, as shown below, E being the enzyme (cf. Bach, 1957). Finally the two amino groups would be removed by keto acids, while the electron-transfer chain reduces the metal back to its original valency state. But understanding of the details is for the future.

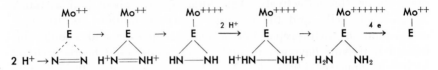

REFERENCES

Ahmed, S., and Evans, H. J. 1960, 1961. *Soil Science,* **90**:205–211; *Proc. Nat. Acad. Sci.,* **47**:24–36.

Allen, E. K., and Allen, O. N. 1950a. *Proc. Soil Sci. Soc. Am.,* **14**:179–183.

*Allen, E. K., and Allen, O. N. 1950b. Biochemical and Symbiotic Properties of the Rhizobia. *Bacteriol. Revs.,* **14**:273–330.

Allen, M. B., and Arnon, D. I. 1955. *Plant Physiol.,* **30**:366–372.

Allison, R. M., and Burris, R. H. 1957. *J. Biol. Chem.,* **224**:351–364.

Almon, L. 1933. *Zentr. Bakt. II,* **87**:289–297.

Aprison, M. H.; Magee, W. E.; and Burris, R. H. 1954. *J. Biol. Chem.,* **208**:29–39.

Arnon, D. I. 1958. In, Trace Elements; New York, Academic Press, pp. 1–32.

Atwater, W. O. 1885–1886. See Fred, Baldwin, and McCoy (1932) and Wilson (1940).

Aurich, H. 1959. *Arch. Mikrobiol.,* **33**:46–49.

Bach, M. K. 1957. *Biochim. Biophys. Acta,* **26**:104–113.

Beijerinck, M. W. 1888. *Bot. Ztg.,* **46**:725–735, 741–750, 757–771, 781–790, 791–802.

Beijerinck, M. W. 1901–1902. *Zentr. Bakt. II,* **7**:561–582; Beijerinck, M. W., and van Delden, A., *ibid.,* **9**:3–43 (1902).

Bergersen, F. J. 1955. *J. Gen. Microbiol.,* **13**:411–419.

Bergersen, F. J. 1961. *Biochim. Biophys. Acta,* **50**:576–578.

Bergersen, F. J., and Briggs, M. J. 1958. *J. Gen. Microbiol.,* **19**:482–490.

Bergersen, F. J., and Nutman, P. S. 1957. *Heredity,* **11**:175–184.

Berthelot, M. 1885. *Compt. rend. Acad. sci.,* **101**:775–781; cf., also *Compt. rend. Acad. sci.,* **115**:569 and 738 (1892).

Bisset, K. A., and Hale, C. M. F. 1952. *J. Gen. Microbiol.,* **5**:592–595.

Bjälfve, G. 1962. *Physiol. Plantarum,* **15**:122–129.

Bond, G., and Hewitt, E. J. 1961, 1962. *Nature,* **190**:103–104; **195**:94–95.

Bond, G., and Scott, G. D. 1955. *Ann. Bot.,* **19**:67–77.

Bond, L. 1948. *Bot. Gaz.,* **109**:411–434, 435–447.

Bortels, H. 1930. *Arch. Mikrobiol.,* **1**:333–342.

Bortels, H. 1936. *Zentr. Bakt. II,* **95**:193–218.

Bortels, H. 1940. *Arch. Mikrobiol.,* **11**:155–186.

Boussingault, J. B. See Fred, Baldwin, and McCoy (1932).

Bové, J.; Bové, C.; and Arnon, D. I. 1957. *Plant Physiol.,* **32** (suppl.): xxiii.

*Bredemann, G. 1908. *Zentr. Bakt. II,* **23**:385–568.

Burgin-Wolff, A. 1959. *Ber. schweiz. bot. Ges.,* **69**:75–111.

Burma, D. P., and Burris, R. H. 1957. *J. Biol. Chem.,* **225**:723–733.

Burris, R. H. 1956. In, Symp. on Inorganic Nitrogen Metabolism, eds. W. McElroy and B. Glass; Baltimore, Johns Hopkins Press, pp. 316–343.

Burris, R. H. 1962. *Science*, **136**:324–325.

Burris, R. H.; Magee, W. E.; and Bach, M. K. 1955. *Ann. Acad. Sci. Fennicae AII*, **60**:190–199.

Burton, J. C., and Allen, O. N. 1950. *Proc. Soil Sci. Soc. Am.*, **14**:191–195.

Carnahan, J. E.; Mortenson, L. E.; Mower, H. F.; and Castle, J. E. 1960. *Biochim. Biophys. Acta*, **38**:188–189.

Chen, H. K. 1938. *Nature*, **142**:753–754.

Clarke, P. H., and Tracey, M. V. 1956. *J. Gen. Microbiol.*, **14**:188–196.

Colter, J. S., and Quastel, J. H. 1950. *Arch. Biochem.*, **27**:368–389.

Drewes, K. 1928. *Zentr. Bakt. II*, **76**:88–100.

Dugdale, R.; Menzel, D.; and Ryther, J. W. 1961. *Deep Sea Research* **7**:297–299.

Fåhraeus, G. 1957. *J. Gen. Microbiol.*, **16**:374–381.

Falk, J. E.; Appleby, C. A.; and Porra, R. J. 1959. In, Utilization of Nitrogen and Its Compounds by Plants. *Symp. Soc. Exp. Biol.*, **XIII**:73–86.

Fischer, W. K. 1949. *Arch. Mikrobiol.*, **14**:353–406.

Fogg, G. E. 1942. *J. Exp. Biol.*, **19**:78–87.

Fogg, G. E., and Wolfe, M. 1954. In, Autotrophic Microorganisms, *Symp. Soc. Exp. Biol.*, **IV**:99–125.

Frank, B. 1890. Ueber die Pilzsymbiose der Leguminosen. Berlin, Paul Parey. 118 pp.

*Fred, E. B.; Baldwin, I. L.; and McCoy, E. 1932. Root Nodule Bacteria and Leguminous Plants. Madison, Wis., Univ. Wisconsin Press.

Fujita, T., and Mitsuishi, S. 1953. Cited from Nutman, 1956.

Furman, T. E. 1958. *Dissertation Abstracts*, **19**:1182.

Gest, H.; Judis, J.; and Peck, H. D. 1956. Symp. on Inorganic Nitrogen Metabolism. Eds. W. McElroy and B. Glass; Baltimore, Johns Hopkins Press, pp. 298–315.

Hamilton, P. B.; Shug, A. L.; and Wilson, P. W. 1957. *Proc. Nat. Acad. Sci.*, **43**:297–304.

Hawker, L., and Fraymouth, J. 1951. *J. Gen. Microbiol.*, **5**:369–386.

Hellmers, H., and Kelleher, J. M. 1959. *Forest Sci.*, **5**:275–278.

Hellriegel, H., and Wilfarth, H. 1886–1888. The original paper, Untersuchungen über die Stickstoff-nährung der Gramineen und Leguminosen, *Zeit. Ver. Rubenzucker-Ind. deut. Reichs*, pp. 863–877, is very rare and almost nowhere available; see *Zentr. Bakt.*, **1**:133–136 (1887) for a long abstract (this abstract omits Wilfarth's name).

Hiai, S.; Mori, T.; Hino, S.; and Mori, T. 1957. *J. Biochem* (Tokyo), **44**:839–847.

Hino, S. 1955. *J. Biochem.* (Tokyo), **42**:775–784.

Hofer, A. W. 1941. *J. Bact.*, **41**:193–224.

Horner, C. K.; Burk, D.; Allison, F. E.; and Sherman, M. S. 1942. *J. Agr. Res.*, **65**:173–193.

Jensen, V. 1958. *Arch. Mikrobiol.*, **29**:348–356.

Jensen, H. L.; Petersen, E. J.; De, P. K.; and Bhattacharya, R. 1960. *Arch. Mikrobiol.*, **36**:182–193.

Jose, A. G., and Wilson, P. W. 1959. *Proc. Nat. Acad. Sci.*, **45**:692–697.

Kataoka, T. 1930. *Jap. J. Bot.*, **5**:209–218.

Keeler, R. F.; Bulen, W. A.; and Varner, J. E. 1956. *J. Bact.*, **72**:394–396.

Keeler, R. F., and Varner, J. E. 1957. *Arch. Biochem. Biophys.*, **70**:585–590.

Kleczkowski, A., and Thornton, H. G. 1944. *J. Bact.*, **48**:661–672.

Kliewer, M., and Evans, H. J. 1962. *Arch. Biochem. Biophys.*, **97**:427–429.

Kluyver, A. J., and van Reenen, W. J. 1933. *Arch. Mikrobiol.*, **4**:280–300.

Leaf, G.; Gardner, I. C.; and Bond, G. 1958, 1959. *J. Exp. Bot.*, **9**:320–331 (1958); *Biochem. J.*, **72**:662–667 (1959).

*Lewis, I. M. 1941. The Cytology of Bacteria, *Bacteriol. Revs.*, **5**:181–230.

Lindstrom, E. S.; Lewis, S. M.; and Pinsky, M. J. 1951. *J. Bact.*, **61**:481–487.

Lindstrom, E. S.; Newton, J. W.; and Wilson, P. W. 1952. *Proc. Nat. Acad. Sci.*, **38**: 891–896.

Lindstrom, E. S.; Tove, S. R.; and Wilson, P. W. 1950. *Science*, **112**:197–198.

Ljunggren, H., and Fåhraeus, G. 1961. *J. Gen. Microbiol.*, **26**:521–528.

Magee, W. E., and Burris, R. H. 1956. *J. Bact.*, **71**:635–643.

Metcalfe, G., and Brown, M. E. 1957. *Nature*, **180**:282.

Metcalfe, G., and Chayen, S. 1954. *Nature*, **174**:841–842.

Mockeridge, F. A. 1915. *Biochem. J.*, **9**:272–283.

Moore, A. W., and Abuelu, J. N. 1959. *Nature*, **184**:75.

Nemeth, G. 1959. *Nature*, **183**:1460–1461.

Nicholas, D. J. D., and Wilson, P. W. 1962. *Science*, **136**:328.

Nilsson, R.; Bjalfve, G.; and Burström, H. 1939. *Ann. Agric. Coll. Sweden*, **7**:51, 301.

Nutman, P. S. 1952. *Ann. Bot. N. S.*, **16**:79–101.

Nutman, P. S. 1956. The Influence of the Legume in Root Nodule Symbiosis. *Biol. Revs.*, **31**:109–151.

Nutman, P. S. 1959. In, Utilization of Nitrogen and Its Compounds by Plants. *Symp. Soc. Exp. Biol.*, **XIII**:42–58.

Nutman, P. S. 1961. In, Handbuch der Pflanzenphysiol.; Berlin, Springer, Chap. XV.

Pengra, R. M., and Wilson, P. W. 1959. *Proc. Soc. Exptl. Biol. Med.*, **100**:436–439.

Pfennig, N. 1956. *Arch. Mikrobiol.*, **24**:8–30.

Pine, M. J., and Barker, H. H. 1954. *J. Bact.*, **68**:589–591.

Prazmowski, A. 1890, 1891. *Landw. Versuchssta.*, **37**:161–238; **38**:5–62.

Prianischnikov, D. N. 1951. Nitrogen in the Life of Plants; Madison, Wis., Kramer Business Service, Inc., 109 pp. (Trans. S. A. Wilde.)

Proctor, M. H., and Wilson, P. W. 1958–1959. *Nature*, **182**:891 (1958); *Arch. Mikrobiol.*, **32**:254–260 (1959).

Purchase, H. F., and Nutman, P. S. 1957. *Ann. Bot. N.S.*, **21**:439–454.

Quinnell, C. M. 1957. *J. Bact.*, **73**:688–689.

Quispel, A. 1960. *Acta Bot. Néerl.*, **9**:380–396.

*Raggio, M., and Raggio, N. 1962. Root Nodules. *Ann. Rev. Plant Physiol.*, **13**:109–128.

Raggio, M.; Raggio, N.; and Burris, R. H. 1959. *Science*, **129**:211–212; *Biochim. Biophys. Acta*, **32**:274–275.

Raggio, M.; Raggio, N.; and Torrey, J. 1957. *Am. J. Bot.*, **44**:325–334.

Roberts, E. R. 1959. In, Utilization of Nitrogen and Its Compounds by Plants. *Symp. Soc. Exp. Biol.*, **XIII**:24–41.

Roberts, R. H. 1946. *J. Amer. Soc. Agron.*, **38**:947–953.

Roy, A. B., and Sen, S. 1962. *Nature*, **194**:604–605.

Sanchez, E. C. de H. 1958. *An. Edafol. Fisiol. Veg.*, **17**:669–678, 755–764.

Saris, N., and Virtanen, A. I. 1957. *Acta Chem. Scand.*, **11**:1438–1440, 1440–1442; *Chem. Abstr.*, **52**:11174 (1958).

Schaede, R. 1941. *Beiträge Biol. Pflanzen*, **27**:165–188.

Smith, J. D. 1949. *Biochem. J.*, **44**:585–591, 591–598.

Socolofsky, M. D., and Wyss, O. 1961. *J. Bact.*, **81**:946–954.

Starkey, R. L., and De, P. K. 1939. *Soil Sci.*, **47**:329–342.

Takahashi, H., and Nason, A. 1957. *Biochim. Biophys. Acta*, **23**:433–435.

Tchan, Y. T.; Birch-Anderson, A.; and Jensen, H. L. 1962. *Arch. Mikrobiol.*, **43**: 50–66.

Thimann, K. V. 1936, 1939. *Proc. Nat. Acad. Sci.*, **22**:511–514; *Trans. 3rd Comm. Int. Soc. Soil Sci.*, **A**:24–28 (1939).

Thimann, K. V.; Skoog, F.; and Byer, A. 1942. *Am. J. Bot.*, **29**:598–606.

Thornton, H. G. 1929. *Proc. Roy. Soc.*, **B104**:481–492.

Thornton, H. G. 1936. *Proc. Roy. Soc.*, **B119**:474–492.

Thornton, H. G. 1945. *Nature,* **156**:654.

Tissières, A. 1956. *Biochem. J.,* **64**:582–589.

Tonzig, S., and Bracci, L. 1951. *Nuovo Giornale Bot. Ital. N.S.,* **58**:237–257, 258–270.

Torrey, J. G. 1952. *Plant Physiol.,* **27**:591–602.

Torrey, J. G. 1956. *Physiol. Plant.,* **9**:370–388.

Tove, S., and Wilson, P. W. 1948. *Proc. Soc. Exp. Biol. Med.,* **69**:184–186.

Trolldenier, G. 1959. *Arch. Mikrobiol.,* **32**:328–345.

Turner, E. R. 1955. *Ann. Bot., N. S.,* **19**:149–160.

*Virtanen, A. I. 1947. The Biology and Chemistry of Nitrogen Fixation by Legume Bacteria. *Biol. Revs.,* **22**:239–269.

Virtanen, A. I.; v. Hausen, S.; and Karström, H. 1933. *Biochem. Z.,* **258**:106–117.

Virtanen, A. I., and Laine, T. 1939. *Biochem. J.,* **33**:412–427.

Virtanen, A. I.; Moisio, T.; Allison, R. M.; and Burris, R. H. 1954. *Acta Chem. Scand.,* **8**:1730–1731.

Wagner, P. 1891. Dungungsversuchen in Lichtdruckbilden mit erlaütern den Vorträge, 2nd ed. Darmstadt.

Watanabe, A.; Nishigaki, S.; and Konishi, C. 1951. *Nature,* **168**:748.

West, P. M., and Wilson, P. W. 1940. *Enzymologia,* **8**:152–162.

Wilson, J. K. 1939. *Cornell Univ. Agr. Expt. Sta. Mem.,* No. **221**:48 pp.; *Trans. 3rd Comm. Int. Soc. Soil Sci.,* **A**:49–63.

Wilson, J. K. 1944. *Soil Sci.,* **58**:61–69.

*Wilson, P. W. 1940. The Biochemistry of Symbiotic Nitrogen Fixation; Madison, Wis., Univ. Wisconsin Press. 302 pp.

Wilson, P. W., and Burris, R. H. 1953. Biological Nitrogen Fixation, a Re-appraisal. *Ann. Rev. Microbiol.,* **7**:415–432.

Wilson, P. W., and Burris, R. H. 1960. *Science,* **131**:1321.

Winogradsky, S. 1895. *Arch. sci. biol. St. Petersburg,* **3**:297–352.

Winogradsky, S. 1902. *Zentr. Bakt. II,* **9**:43–54, 107–112.

Winogradsky, S. 1930. *Compt. rend. Acad. sci.,* **190**:661–665.

Winogradsky, S. 1938. *Zentr. Bakt. II,* **97**:399–413.

Wipf, L., and Cooper, D. C. 1940. *Amer. J. Bot.,* **27**:821–824.

Zelitch, I. 1951. *Proc. Nat. Acad. Sci.,* **37**:559–565.

CHAPTER X

Nitrification, Denitrification, and the Nitrogen Cycle

The immediate principles of living bodies would be, to a degree, indestructible if, of all the organisms created by God, the smallest and apparently most useless were to be suppressed. And because the return to the atmosphere and to the mineral kingdom of everything which had ceased to live would be suddenly suspended, life would become impossible.

Louis Pasteur

For up and down and round, says he,
Goes all appointed things,
And losses on the roundabouts
Means profits on the swings.

Patrick R. Chalmers

1. NITRIFICATION

A. The Nitrification Process and Its Causative Organisms

The preceding chapters have shown that the end product of protein breakdown, so far as the nitrogen is concerned, is ammonia. Yet ammonia does not accumulate in the soil, since most of the soil nitrogen is in the form of nitrate. Since solutions of ammonium salts do not change to nitrate when simply exposed to the air, it was early realized that ammonia must be converted to nitrate only under very special conditions.

Solution to the problem came through the finding that the process is biological, not chemical. Schloesing and Müntz (1877–1879) in France passed sewage water very slowly through a column of sandy soil and chalk, and found that after 20 days ammonia no longer issued at the other end, but its place was taken by nitrate. The process ran for four months. The reaction was very slow at 50° C and had its optimum temperature at 30° to 35° C. It was stopped completely by drawing through the tube either chloroform or boiling water. However, when, after boiling, a little fresh soil was added to the column, the power of oxidizing ammonia soon returned. They deduced, therefore, that the conversion of ammonia to nitrate, or (as it is usually called) *nitrification*, is due to living creatures.

In parallel studies with solution cultures, Warington (1878–1891) confirmed the French workers' findings and established the following facts:

(1) A minute seeding (0.1 gm of soil in a large flask of sterile ammonium sulfate solution) suffices to start nitrification.

(2) Seedings of soil taken from more than 18 in. in depth were inactive, i.e., the organisms must be only in the upper layers of the soil.

(3) The ammonium sulfate solution without seeding keeps indefinitely.

(4) Small amounts of phosphate are needed; this recalls the slogan based on the analysis of animal tissues, "*Ohne Phosphor kein Leben.*"

(5) The solution becomes acid during the process, because the NH_4^+ cation is being converted to the $^-NO_3$ anion and hydrogen ions. Addition of $CaCO_3$, therefore, promotes nitrification by providing a reserve of base. (Its second function, that of providing essential Ca ions, was not discovered until 50 years later.)

(6) Ordinary bacteria isolated from air do not nitrify, so that a special organism must be concerned. Schloesing and Müntz also had had no success using highly oxidative fungi.

(7) Organic materials such as urine and milk could only be nitrified when in high dilution, and then always more slowly than ammonium salts. Addition of glucose also slowed the reaction.

(8) Sometimes the reaction went only as far as nitrite. Increased aeration did not affect this. Successive seedings from the nitrite-producing solutions gave only nitrite, but when fresh soil was added, nitrate quickly appeared.

(9) The complementary phenomenon of seedings which only converted nitrite to nitrate and did not oxidize ammonia was also occasionally found.

It followed from this work that two kinds of special, aerobic organisms must be responsible, respectively, for the two stages of oxidation, $NH_3 \rightarrow HNO_2$ and $HNO_2 \rightarrow HNO_3$. However, all attempts to isolate these organisms from the enrichment cultures failed. The method which had just been introduced by Koch, of plating out in nutrient gelatin medium, although brilliantly successful with other organisms, gave no satisfactory results here. Several other workers were equally unsuccessful. Although numbers of very short rods could be observed in the nitrifying solutions, no colonies could be obtained on nutrient gelatin.

The problem was finally solved through the introduction of a quite new viewpoint by the young Russian, Winogradsky (1890, 1891).

The difficulties of the problem, and the originality and resourcefulness brought to bear upon it, have made his researches a classic of micro-biology. Pointing out that the oxidation of ammonia yields energy, Winogradsky realized that this energy could be applied to the forma-tion of organic matter by *reduction of CO_2*. The process would resemble photosynthesis, but, instead of light, the energy required would be supplied by a chemical oxidation. This idea was supported by the inhibiting effect of organic matter (noted by Warington) and by Winogradsky's finding that nitrification proceeded most vigorously in the absence of any added source of carbon except carbonate.

The conception of the nitrifying bacteria as *chemosynthetic*, i.e., synthesizing their organic matter through energy supplied by a chemical reaction, at once enabled their isolation. Using a gelatin medium, free from organic nutrients and containing only $(NH_4)_2SO_4$ and other inorganic salts, Winogradsky made inoculations from the small floccules attached to the $CaCO_3$ particles in liquid enrichments. From these, colonies developed which were not the nitrifying organ-isms. By then picking from where no visible colonies grew and inoculating into fresh inorganic medium, he obtained pure cultures of the nitrifiers. He afterward found that they would form colonies, although only minute ones, if the medium were solidified with silica gel (see Fig. X–1). Two types were isolated, *Nitrosomonas*, oxidizing ammonia to nitrite, and *Nitrobacter*, oxidizing nitrite to nitrate. Exam-ination of soils from all over the world led to the recognition of two species of Nitrosomonas, *N. europeaensis*, from Russian, Swiss, and French soils, and *N. javenensis*, from East Indies soil. The various strains of Nitrobacter were all indistinguishable. As the photographs (Fig. X–1) show, Nitrosomonas is a very short rod with a long polar flagellum.

In a later return to the subject, Winogradsky and his sister (1933) distinguished four Nitrosomonas species, a *Nitrosococcus* and a spiril-lum, *Nitrosospira*. From pine-forest soils, on which nitrification is very slow (largely due to the acidity), some organisms forming cystlike zoogloeae, *Nitrosocystis*, *Nitrosogloea*, and *Nitrocystis*, were isolated and *N. javenensis* placed in the first of these genera. These organisms are probably Myxobacteria and not nitrifiers at all, because Imsenecki (1946) found that nitrifying cultures were readily overgrown by a member of the genus Sorangium (p. 72) forming hard, angular fruiting bodies. Bisset and Grace (1954), therefore, assign both these "genera" to Sorangium and consider them nonnitrifiers. Others believe them to be "hard-colony" variants of Nitrosomonas. When it is con-sidered, too, that Actinoplanes forms sporangia from which polarly motile "spores" emerge (p. 66), one wonders how many possible

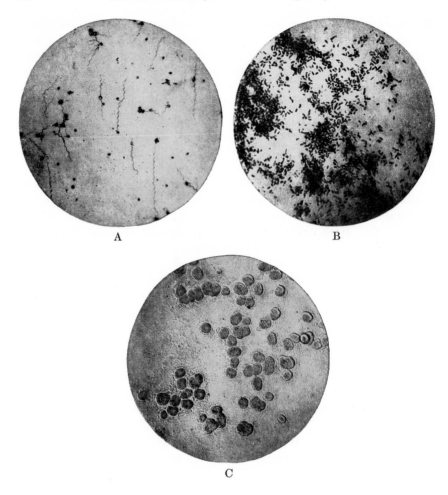

FIGURE X–1

Nitrifying bacteria.

A. *Nitrosomonas javenensis.* Loeffler's flagella stain. 1100 ×.

B. Nitrobacter (Quito). Edge of membrane from bottom of nitrate liquid culture. 1100 ×.

C. Nitrosomonas (Zurich). Surface colonies on silica gel. 55 ×. (All from S. Winogradsky, 1892.)

organisms may be involved. The figures and description suggest that Nitrosospira may also be a Myxobacterium. All in all, Nitrosomonas and Nitrobacter are the only well-defined and active nitrifiers.

The isolation and pure culture of nitrifying bacteria, although often repeated (Gibbs, 1919; Nelson, 1931; Kingma Boltjes, 1935;

Bömeke, 1939, 1951; Lees, 1952; Meiklejohn, 1954; Bisset and Grace, 1954), are tedious by ordinary methods. Even after continued transfers in inorganic media from the enrichment cultures, Nelson found that nitrifiers were still in a minority of 1 to 1000. What the other 999 organisms were living on, in a purely inorganic medium, is not clear, but it seems certain that the slow growth of the nitrifiers is due to inadequate aeration (Lees, 1951). Since their oxygen requirement for growth is so much greater than that of ordinary bacteria (up to 100 atoms of oxygen per atom of carbon assimilated), their growth is greatly favored by growing them on glass beads percolated at intervals with the liquid medium (cf. sec. D below). This ensures a very thin layer of medium and free access to air. While the simple process of plating and picking colonies from flask cultures would scarcely ever give pure cultures, the percolation method, after only five transfers, gave cultures apparently free from heterotrophic organisms.

The difficulties of culture are increased by the fact that the colonies are minute and are firmly attached to the silica gel. They can, however, be enlarged in size by adding traces of peptone (Fred and Davenport, 1921), "*Nährstoff Heyden*," a peptone product (Kingma Boltjes, 1935), or even soil extract (Hes, 1937). The rate of nitrification, however, is not enhanced by soil extract or peptone, and the latter, even at 0.2 per cent, is quite toxic (Meiklejohn, 1952).

Two older methods are worth mention. In one, silica gel plates, soaked in a salt solution containing ammonium sulfate, are coated with a cream of $CaCO_3$ which is allowed to dry (Winogradsky, 1933). Minute grains of soil are then placed at intervals on the plate. After 6 to 15 days, clear zones appear around some grains, owing to the nitrous acid, which dissolves the $CaCO_3$. By picking from these zones, making serial dilutions in water, and again plating, pure cultures can be obtained. In addition, by counting the percentage of grains that develop clear zones, the numbers of nitrifiers in different soils can be compared. In the other method (Engel and Skallau, 1937) a very large number of transfers (say 100 or more) are made from one vigorously nitrifying liquid culture; on individual examination, one or more of these may be found to be pure cultures by their ability to nitrify but inability to produce any growth in broth. Probably neither of these can compete with Lees' percolation procedure.

B. The Influence of *p*H and of Substrate

Meyerhof (1916, 1917) found by measuring oxidation rates that the optimum *p*H of Nitrosomonas is 8.5 to 8.8, and that of Nitrobacter about the same (Fig. X–2). The steep decrease in rate on the acid side has not been wholly confirmed, because Hofman and Lees (1953) found a much more gradual fall, reaching 50 per cent of the maximum rate at pH 6.5. For Nitrobacter they also found the curve somewhat more to the acid side, the optimum pH being 7.7. The fall in rate on the alkaline side may be due to the inability of the cells to use the

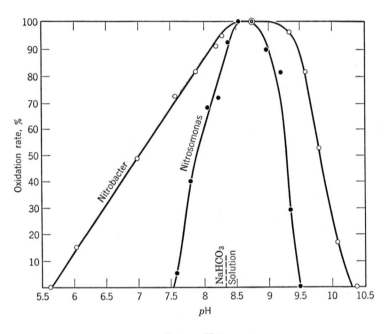

FIGURE X–2

Dependence of oxidation of ammonia and nitrate upon pH. The substrates are NH_4^+ and $^-NO_2$, respectively. The oxidation rates are calculated as percentages of the maximum, which is reached at 8.5 to 8.7 in each case. (Plotted from data of O. Meyerhof, *Pflüger's Arch. ges. Physiol.*, 1916a and b.)

$^=CO_3$ ion as source of CO_2, while they could use $^-HCO_3$. The narrow pH optimum, with a steeper fall on the alkaline than on the acid side, favors this view. The suggestion that the fall on the alkaline side is due to penetration of Nitrosomonas cells by free NH_3 (Meyerhof, 1917) can hardly be valid, because Nitrobacter shows a similar sensitivity to alkali. Indeed, in the case of Nitrobacter, ions must enter the cell freely, since (1) at the optimum pH both nitrite and bicarbonate are very largely dissociated, and (2) unionized NO_2 and NO groups in the form of metallic complexes or organic nitroso-compounds (Meyer-hof, 1917) could not be used.

The original medium of Winogradsky (1890, 1891) used $MgCO_3$ instead of $CaCO_3$. When this was made up with purified chemicals, it gave very poor growth and nitrification. In an elegant study of the influence of impurities, Kingma Boltjes (1935) established that the missing factor was $CaCl_2$ Apparently the Ca ion is essential for

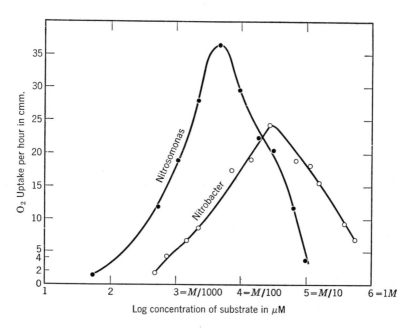

FIGURE X–3

Dependence of oxidation of ammonia and nitrate upon substrate concentration. The substrates are NH_4^+ and $^-NO_2$, respectively. (Plotted from data of O. Meyerhof, *Pflüger's Arch. ges. Physiol.*, 1916a and b.)

Nitrosomonas. Solid $CaCO_3$ thus fulfills two functions, that of pH control and of Ca supply. Solid $CaCO_3$ is not necessary for Nitrobacter, however (Meyerhof, 1916).

Part of the difficulty in culturing nitrifying bacteria doubtless resides in their sensitivity to excess substrate, when in cultures. Nitrobacter is inhibited by nitrite and Nitrosomonas by ammonia. The inhibition may be slowly overcome, but is powerful at first. In Figure X–3 the oft-quoted data of Meyerhof have been recalculated as absolute concentrations and plotted on a logarithmic scale; the sharp substrate optimum for both bacteria is remarkable and is quite unlike the behavior of most other organisms with their substrates. What happens is that the efficiency of Nitrosomonas decreases as nitrite accumulates. Correspondingly, growth of Nitrobacter slows down as nitrate accumulates, but if the nitrate is continually dialyzed away, as much as 6 gm nitrate per liter can be formed without loss of activity (Gould and Lees, 1959). Nitrobacter is also inhibited by free NH_3 (Meyerhof, 1916), and, therefore, it will often not develop until Nitrosomonas has lowered the NH_3 level. When most of the NH_3 has disappeared, nitrate suddenly begins to be formed. Lees and Simpson (1957) have to some extent circumvented these inhibitions by using an aerated suspension of metal phosphates as medium. The cells remain attached to the particles, which can be easily washed; the suspensions are convenient material for experiments.

Both forms are inhibited by divalent metal ions, the inhibition of Nitrobacter increasing sharply with pH (Meyerhof, 1916, 1917), and also by lowered oxygen pressure (Meyerhof, 1916; Amer and Bartholomew, 1951), which suggests that at least one stage of the oxidation involves an oxidase with much less affinity for O_2 than cytochrome oxidase.

C. The Influence of Organic Matter

Since the nitrifiers are autotrophic, it is easy to see why their growth is not supported by organic matter. But what is remarkable is that many organic compounds actually inhibit nitrification. Not only gelatin, but many amines, alkaloids, and even amino acids inhibit. Guanidine and aniline derivatives were particularly potent, both in solution cultures (Meyerhof, 1917) and in soil enrichments (Lees and Quastel, 1946). Metal-combining agents such as cyanide, thiourea (Quastel and Scholefield, 1951), and especially allylthiourea (Hofman and Lees, 1953) inhibit, as also do the urethanes. Hydroxylamine, a possible intermediate, also inhibits somewhat (Meyerhof), although it is itself slowly oxidized. Early workers found sugars inhibitory too, but this has not been confirmed, and the inhibition caused by glucose is in fact due to a decomposition product formed on autoclaving (Jensen, 1950). Thus, it appears that the strongest inhibitions are due either to interfering with the metal-enzyme oxidase system (cyanide, etc.) or to chemical relationship with the substrate ammonia (the organic bases).

Antibiotics seem not to affect nitrification directly. Concentrations of streptomycin that strongly inhibit growth have no direct effect on ammonia oxidation (Lees, 1952). The actual growth promotion by Nährstoff-Heyden is in marked contrast to the general inhibition by nitrogenous compounds.

Nitrobacter is less sensitive to organic compounds, and its colonies can be obtained on nitrite agar; they are very small, tough, and difficult to transfer. Besides excess nitrite, it is inhibited by cyanide and azide (Lees, 1954), by chlorate (Meiklejohn, 1952), and among organic compounds, by methionine, nitrourea, thiourea, and antibiotics (Quastel and Scholefield, 1951).

D. Nitrification in Soil

Nitrification usually proceeds fast enough that little free ammonia remains in soil, although some grass-clover pastures have been found to have about equal amounts of ammonia and nitrate (Richardson, 1938). Correspondingly, the nitrate is reduced back to NH_3 and amino acids fast enough in the plants that they rarely contain more than traces of nitrate, which is fortunate because nitrate and nitrite are toxic to animals. After a long dry summer has rendered the soil very aerobic, rains may cause so much nitrification that the crops become rich in nitrate; this seems to occur often in New Zealand (Bathurst and Mitchell, 1958; Butler, 1959) where rye-grass (*Lolium* spp.) and oats reach high nitrate levels. The fluctuations in nitrification rate and in soil nitrate are evidently very wide.

Neither in pure nor in enrichment cultures can any of the nitrifiers yet known grow at pH more acid than 6. In the extensive Rothamsted trials with grassland, soils more acid than 6 tended to accumulate NH_3 (Richardson, 1938). This raises the question of how nitrification can proceed in acid soils. It does take place, though slowly, in soil at pH 4.5 to 5.[1] No doubt the nitrifying bacteria act mainly when attached to mineral particles, i.e., at points where the pH is locally less acid. This is easily visualized from the discussion in Chapter VI, which shows how heterogeneous the conditions of growth in soil usually are.

An alternative explanation was advanced by Indian workers who claim that, in tropical soils at least, ammonia may be oxidized photochemically (Dhar and Rao, 1933). Zinc oxide and TiO_2, which are present in many soils, were claimed to act as catalysts. However, in view of the stability of ammonium salts in the presence of sterile soil, it is unlikely that this factor could be of general importance.

The attachment of nitrifying bacteria to particles explains also the nitrification in soil in spite of the presence of organic matter. For on a soil particle, local areas can be freed of organic matter by oxidizing

[1] The claim of Meek and Lipman (1922) to have obtained organisms from peat soil that can nitrify down to pH 4.1 has never been confirmed.

organisms and thus made suitable for the growth of nitrifiers. The same holds for the sand filters of sewage outfall works, which must be well supplied with organic matter, but from which Nitrosomonas can be readily obtained. In this connection it is worth noting that marine nitrifying bacteria (i.e., salt-tolerant races) can be obtained from the sea bottom, but very seldom from sea water itself (Issatschenko, 1926; Carey, 1938).

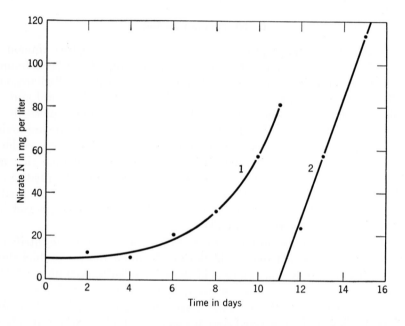

FIGURE X–4

Course of nitrate formation in a soil sample perfused with M/100 NH₄Cl. *Curve 1.* First perfusion. *Curve 2.* Second perfusion (with fresh solution). (From J. H. Quastel and P. G. Scholefield, *Bact. Revs.*, **15**:1–53, 1951. By courtesy of the Williams and Wilkins Co., Baltimore, Md.)

For several years Quastel and co-workers studied nitrification in soil under laboratory conditions by continually perfusing solutions through a small column of soil on a filter. The technique is reminiscent of that of Schloesing and Müntz, but aeration is much more efficient, and the apparatus is cyclic and completely enclosed. The soil perfused with ammonium salt becomes an enrichment culture, and the rate of nitrification increases steadily during the perfusion (Fig. X–4). If the process is stopped and then restarted with fresh solution, the rate begins at once at the maximal value previously reached and does not increase further (Lees and Quastel, 1946). This means that the surfaces of the soil particles are now saturated with the organisms.

With these enriched soils many of the findings on liquid cultures have been readily reproduced. The most important findings (Quastel and Scholefield, 1951) are:

(1) Calcium carbonate improves nitrification on most soils. Sodium salts of organic acids have a similar effect owing to their rapid conversion to bicarbonate.

(2) Although amino acids in general do not appreciably inhibit, methionine and methionine sulfoxide do.

(3) Many inhibitors exert quite different action on the two processes. Urethanes, guanidines, thiourea, and p-aminosalicylic acid inhibit ammonia oxidation; nitrourea, thiourea, and chlorates inhibit nitrite oxidation, but urethanes do not. Since chlorate does not affect Nitrosomonas, soils in presence of N/1000 chlorate accumulate nitrite, and this permits study of ammonia oxidation alone.

(4) Enrichment of Nitrosomonas and Nitrobacter on perfusion with nitrite takes place only after a lag, which is doubtless due to the inhibitory effect of nitrite on the organisms (see Fig. X–4). That they develop at all indicates either selection of a nitrite-resistant strain or development of a protective mechanism.

(5) Amines and amino acids in general are only nitrified after conversion to ammonium. An exception, however, is pyruvic oxime, $CH_3C \cdot COOH$, which appears to be converted directly to nitrite by the

$$\overset{\parallel}{N}OH$$

soil enrichments. This conversion is not due to Nitrosomonas, however, but to three groups of heterotrophic bacteria (Jensen, 1951). A proactinomycete, *Nocardia corallina*, is the most active of these.

E. The Nitrogen:Carbon Ratio and the Biochemistry of Nitrification

By comparison with other bacteria, the nitrifiers are not highly active. A Nitrosomonas cell takes nearly an hour to produce twice its weight of nitrite (Engel, 1929). Yet Urobacillus hydrolyzes 1000 times its weight of urea in an hour. On the other hand, since Nitrosomonas can live only by an oxidative process, the oxygen consumption is relatively high. As a result the yield of cells per unit of time, or per unit of oxygen consumed, is low.

Autotrophic growth with ammonia oxidation can be considered as a pair of linked reactions, the second of which has two alternatives:

(1) Nitrite formation: $2\ NH_4^+ + 4\ H_2O \rightarrow 2\ {}^-NO_2 + 4\ H^+ + 12(H)$
(2a) Oxidation by oxygen: $12(H) + 3\ O_2 \rightarrow 6\ H_2O$
(2b) "Oxidation" by CO_2: $12(H) + 3\ CO_2 \rightarrow 3(CH_2O) + 3\ H_2O$

Winogradsky measured the ratio N:C (i.e., NH_4^+ oxidized:CO_2 reduced) and found it to be about 35. By similar methods, Nelson (1931) obtained 15; Hes (1937), values close to 33; and Bömeke (1951), 35 to 53.[2] Old cultures give higher figures, i.e., they are less efficient in assimilating carbon (Hes, Bömeke). Apparently there is a steady increase in the figure with increase of nitrite in the solution. Hofman and Lees (1952) have found that the results of different workers, with different amounts of nitrite formed, all agree with the approximate equation:

$$\log C = 0.73 \log N - 0.35$$

where C = organic carbon formed and N = nitrite formed, both in milligrams per liter.

On thermodynamic grounds, but assuming rather different (and improbable) reactions, Baas-Becking and Parks (1927) calculated that with a ratio N:C of about 30, Nitrosomonas is only about 5.9 per cent efficient. That is, of the energy liberated by ammonia oxidation only 5.9 per cent is used for CO_2 reduction. For Nitrobacter they found about 9 per cent. However, it follows from the equation that very young Nitrosomonas cultures would be much more efficient. Actually, when the nitrite is below 20 mg per liter, efficiencies up to almost 50 per cent have been found (Hofman and Lees, 1952). This would still correspond to about 10 of reaction (2a) to 1 of (2b). The free energies are such that the organism should need to oxidize only 2 or 3 molecules of ammonia to reduce one of CO_2, i.e., 3 of reaction (2a) would support one of (2b).

The wide variation and the influence of age and nitrite suggest that the method of linkage between reactions (1) and (2b) is a highly sensitive one. It has been suggested that the low thermodynamic efficiency is due to loss of organic matter by respiration, but the respiratory rate of the nitrifiers is extremely slow (Bömeke, 1939); Nitrobacter oxidizes formate one-fifth as fast as nitrite and also (more slowly) acetate (Silver, 1960). It is more likely that whatever high-energy linkage is produced as a result of the oxidation of ammonia is very easily destroyed or sidetracked before it has caused reduction of CO_2. Perhaps some of the strong inhibitions by organic compounds are due to their reacting with this linkage.

[2] Values obtained in the author's laboratory with Nelson's culture vary between 20 and almost 100.

Another sign of sensitivity is that resting cultures of Nitrobacter soon lose their ability to oxidize nitrite; on supplying nitrite, O_2, and CO_2 (all three essential), the power returns, but only after 40 hours or so (Seeler and Engel, 1959). The inhibition of respiration by pure O_2, observed by Meyerhof, suggests peroxide accumulation and therefore participation of a flavoprotein enzyme.

Reaction (1) above probably comprises three parts. As to the first, thiourea and allylthiourea inhibit the oxidation of ammonia but not that of hydroxylamine (Hofman and Lees, 1953). Added hydroxylamine is rapidly oxidized and without any time lag (Engel and Alexander, 1958). Hydrazine, on the other hand, prevents the formation of nitrite, and instead some hydroxylamine accumulates. All these facts indicate that the first step is:

$$NH_4^+ + \tfrac{1}{2} O_2 \rightarrow NH_2OH + H^+$$

Since this step requires the actual incorporation of oxygen, it may well be the one using a special noncytochrome type of oxidase. Noting that thiourea and its derivatives chelate most strongly with copper, Lees (1954) suggested that the oxidase may contain copper.

The succeeding stages would correspondingly be written (Lees, 1954):

$$NH_2OH + H_2O \xrightarrow{-2\,H} [NH(OH)_2]? \xrightarrow{-2\,H} HONO$$

The nature of the highly unstable intermediate is unknown, but a possible structure is that corresponding to trimethylamine oxide, namely $\pi_\circ N \rightarrow O$. Recently a cell-free preparation from Nitrosomonas was
$\quad|$
$\quad OH$
found to carry out these last two stages (Nicholas and Jones, 1960). It oxidizes NH_2OH to HNO_2, using cytochrome c as electron acceptor. Ammonia promotes the reaction but is not itself oxidized, while (in accord with the experiments above) hydrazine strongly inhibits.

Comparable success with an enzyme from Nitrobacter has also been achieved, when a preparation of fine particles from sonically broken Nitrobacter was found to oxidize nitrite. The particles contain a cytochrome, and if ADP[32] is added, the P[32] is incorporated into ATP (Aleem and Nason, 1959–1960). The phosphorylation could not be easily "uncoupled" (see Chap. XI). Oxygen was also taken up with succinate or DPNH, but only one-tenth as fast as with nitrite.

These discoveries give hope that the mysteries of both the nitrifying bacteria may be yielding to biochemical attack.

2. NITRATE REDUCTION OR DENITRIFICATION

A. The Flora of Nitrate Enrichment Cultures

When mixed fermentations go on in the presence of nitrates, it is common for nitrite and even N_2O or N_2 to be produced. This was observed as long ago as 1868 by Schloesing and was first studied using a mixture of KNO_3 with ammonium citrate and asparagine (Gayon and Dupetit, 1882). Two organisms were isolated, one (probably *Ps. pyocyanea*) producing N_2 and N_2O, the other (*Ps. stutzeri*) forming mainly N_2.

In essence, the reduction of nitrate is the use of the oxygen of nitrate as a hydrogen acceptor. Consequently, a source of combined hydrogen and a limitation on the supply of free oxygen are needed. Recognition of these two conditions by Beijerinck and Minkman (1909) led to their making enrichment cultures from soil under anaerobic conditions but in the presence of KNO_3, using various organic compounds as hydrogen donors. They found, however, that inclusion of a small bubble of oxygen at the start ("stimulus oxygen") improved the growth. Much nitrous oxide was evolved. A crude culture (mostly sporeformers) decomposed in three days the whole of 2 gm KNO_3 added, producing 159 ml N_2O, 75 ml N_2, and 11.5 ml CO_2. Since the theoretical yield of N_2 or N_2O is 222 ml, the agreement is within 5 per cent.

Both the composition of the gas and the bacterial flora obtained depend on the nitrate concentration and the carbon source. In broth containing 5 to 12 per cent KNO_3 (0.5 to 1.2 M), with alcohol or organic acids as hydrogen donor, the gas contains much N_2O, and sporeformers (such as Beijerinck's *Bac. nitroxus*) predominate. When protein is used as hydrogen donor, e.g., in a study of denitrifiers growing in cans of salted ham (which contains KNO_3), thermophilic sporeformers resembling *Bac. subtilis* were obtained (Verhoeven, 1950). All of these are now regarded as strains of one species, *Denitrobacillus licheniformis* (Verhoeven, 1952).

In media containing only 1 to 2 per cent KNO_3, mostly Pseudomonads develop. With alcohol or propionate as hydrogen donor, *Ps. aeruginosa* often appears, giving a gas containing about two-thirds N_2O; with other organic acid salts, *Ps. stutzeri*, the gas from which is largely nitrogen, and *Ps. vulpinus* are obtained (van Iterson, 1903). Tartrate gives rise to *Ps. stutzeri* with great regularity, and pure cultures can be obtained in two transfers (van Niel and Allen, 1952). With sugar as hydrogen donor, Korsakowa (1927–1929) obtained a strain of *Ps. fluorescens*, giving almost wholly nitrogen. Even hydrogen gas can be used as donor in the special case of *M. denitrificans* (Kluyver, 1953). From sea water an organism giving almost pure N_2 has been isolated (Lloyd and Cranston, 1930); as with Beijerinck's cultures, a trace of oxygen was necessary to start growth, but nitrate reduction did not take place in aerobic conditions. Among other denitrifiers the Rhizobia should be mentioned (Wilson, 1947), while very many facultative anaerobes, especially the coliform bacteria, can reduce nitrate to the stage of nitrite.

B. The Physiology of Nitrate Reduction

1. COMPETITION WITH O_2. Since, as stated above, the reduction of nitrate (as also of nitrite) is essentially the use of bound oxygen as hydrogen acceptor, it might be expected that free oxygen would inhibit nitrate reduction. Experiments of this sort with *E. coli*, using the reduction only to nitrite, gave the data shown in Table X–1. Similarly,

TABLE X–1. Effect of O_2 on Nitrate Reduction by *E. coli*

(From Stickland, 1931)

Oxygen in Gas (per cent)	Inhibition of Nitrate Reduction (per cent)
0	0
0.4	21
1.1	61
3.8	93
21	94
99	96

nitrate reduction by Aerobacter almost stops when an anaerobically grown culture is aerated (Lewis and Hinshelwood, 1948). With *Ps. denitrificans* 2.5 per cent oxygen in the gas gave 45 per cent inhibition, while air (*ca.* 21 per cent) gave 73 per cent inhibition (Sacks and Barker, 1949); comparison with the table shows that in this more powerful denitrifier the process is not so readily suppressed by oxygen. However the oxygen content of the medium is undoubtedly much lower than that of the gas. Nitrate reduction by the sporeforming *Denitrobac. licheniformis* is inhibited only by very vigorous aeration (Verhoeven, 1952).

The standard test of the SAB for nitrate reduction in more or less aerobic broth cultures is therefore almost meaningless, since the extent of nitrite formation will depend on whether the growth is strong enough to consume the dissolved oxygen. The phenomena of selection and of induction (see below) also complicate the test.

2. THE NATURE OF THE ENZYME SYSTEM. In order for the oxygen of nitrate to combine with the hydrogen of organic compounds, it has to be activated by a special enzyme, called nitrate reductase or *nitratase*. Evidence for this comes from inhibition experiments. Cyanide strongly inhibits reduction of both nitrate (Stickland, 1931) and nitrite (Elema *et al.*, 1934; Yamagata, 1939), and so does carbon monoxide. In *E. coli*, nitrite reduction is inhibited also by iodoacetate (dehydrogenase type of poisoning), so that it behaves just as normal oxidation with O_2 would (Aubel, 1938). Evidently, therefore, the process requires, as well as a dehydrogenase, a metallo-enzyme of the oxidase type. This enzyme is a complex of the nitrate-reducing system and the cytochromes. Nitrate-reducing bacteria are rich in cytochromes; *Ps. stutzeri* growing on potato forms so much cytochrome that the normally colorless colonies become pink (van Niel and Allen, 1952); so do those of *Ps. aeruginosa* grown anaerobically with nitrate (Verhoeven and Takeda, 1956). *Ps. denitrificans* and *M. denitrificans* both contain two cytochromes, a *c* apparently identical with mammalian cytochrome *c*, and a *b*, with peaks at 559, 528, and 426 $m\mu$ (Kamen and Vernon, 1955; Vernon, 1956).

The formation both of cytochromes and of nitratase is readily inducible by the medium. Nitratase appears in *E. coli* when the cells are incubated in mannitol and nitrate; no growth need occur, but amino acids and Mg are necessary for formation of the enzyme (Pollock, 1946; Pollock and Wainwright, 1948), indicating that protein synthesis is involved. When mutants requiring a specific amino acid were used, that amino acid was also needed for the formation of nitratase (Wainwright and Nevil, 1956). *Ps. aeruginosa* grown on nitrate is rich in nitrate-reducing enzyme, while on nitrite it forms much of the nitrite-reducing system that yields N_2.

This last observation shows that there are two enzyme systems, *nitratase* and *nitritase*. The first is readily isolated by suspending *E. coli* in fluoride-phosphate mixture, when the enzyme goes into solution (Yamagata, 1939), or by breaking up the cells (Nicholas and Nason, 1955). After it was shown that nitratase from green leaves and from Neurospora contains molybdenum and flavoprotein, similar properties were shown for the *E. coli* enzyme, and cells grown on a medium free of Mo were found deficient in nitratase (Nicholas and Nason, 1955). The cell-free enzyme uses DPNH to reduce nitrate. When isotopic Mo or Fe was present in the medium, the metal became concentrated in the purified enzyme (Fewson and Nicholas, 1961). Furthermore, when repeated precipitation had lowered the activity, it was restored by adding flavin-adenine-dinucleotide, FAD. The enzyme contained cytochrome c, which was seen to be reduced by the DPNH and reoxidized by nitrate or molybdate. It can also be reoxidized with N_2O itself (Verhoeven and Takeda, 1956). The electron-transport system can therefore be represented (Fewson and Nicholas, 1961):

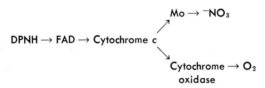

Correspondingly, if the oxidase is inhibited by CO, aeration no longer prevents nitrate reduction; i.e., nitrate (via the Mo) and oxygen (via the oxidase) *compete* for the reoxidation of the reduced cytochrome c.

Nitritase appears to contain no Mo, but contains a flavin (Taniguchi *et al.*, 1952), and that from *Ps. stutzeri* contains both Cu and Fe (Chung and Najjar, 1956). While the cells of *Ps. aeruginosa* convert nitrate to N_2, the cell-free enzyme after purification forms only NO (Walker and Nicholas, 1960); that from *Ps. stutzeri* forms N_2 and NO (Chung and Najjar, 1956). Using reduced FAD as hydrogen donor the reaction is:

$$FADH_2 + 2\ ^-NO_2 \rightarrow 2\ NO + FAD + 2\ OH^-$$

The preparation of Chung and Najjar also reduced NO, using DPNH or TPNH and a flavoprotein. Although the enzymes evidently contain a cytochrome c, it did not appear to be reduced in the process.

3. SUBSTRATES. If nitratase operates as an alternative to cytochrome oxidase, any substrate oxidizable through the cytochrome system would be expected also to be oxidizable with nitrate reduction. As shown in section A., alcohols, organic acids, and sugars can be so used, depending on the organism and the nitrate concentration. In addition, many strains of *E. coli* use H_2 for the reduction to nitrite (McNall and Atkinson, 1956), and the case of *M. denitrificans*, using H_2 for the full reduction to N_2, was noted above. Glucose as substrate is completely dehydrogenated by *Ps. aeruginosa* to CO_2 and H_2O, the nitrate being converted to N_2 with about 10 per cent of N_2O (Verhoeven and Goos, 1954). In one rare case, even sulfur reacts (Chap. XXII, sec. 5). Two groups of compounds are exceptions to this rule: aromatic acids and aliphatic hydrocarbons. The reason for the first is clear; oxidation of the benzene ring requires the introduction of OH groups, and there-

fore *oxygen atoms* are required and are incorporated (Chap. XVI, sec. 7). To provide oxygen is not the same as to accept hydrogen. As to the second case, *Ps. stutzeri* will oxidize several hydrocarbons in air, but not anaerobically with nitrate (Hansen and Kallio, 1957); however, their corresponding alcohols *can* be oxidized with nitrate. Hansen and Kallio, therefore, believe that the first step in hydrocarbon oxidation is the introduction of OH groups. Evidently, then, nitrate can act as *hydrogen acceptor* but not as *oxygen donor*.

4. THE INTERMEDIATE STAGES. Three stages could be recognized:

$$HNO_3 + 2(H) \rightarrow HNO_2 + H_2O \tag{1}$$
$$HNO_2 + 2(H) \rightarrow \tfrac{1}{2}(H_2N_2O_2) + H_2O \tag{2}$$
$$(H_2N_2O_2) + 2(H) \rightarrow N_2 + 2\ H_2O \tag{3}$$
over-all: $$2\ HNO_3 + 10(H) \rightarrow N_2 + 6\ H_2O \tag{4}$$

The postulated intermediate product in equations (2) and (3) is unstable and could alternatively break down thus:

$$(H_2N_2O_2) \rightarrow H_2O + N_2O$$

This is, no doubt, the source of the nitrous oxide so often produced, especially by the sporeformers. In general, high temperatures lead to N_2O production; at lower temperatures the $(H_2N_2O_2)$ presumably survives long enough to be further reduced. For example, Denitrobacillus produced 49 per cent N_2O (with 10 per cent CO_2 + 41 per cent N_2) at 30° C, rising to 63 per cent N_2O at 51° C (Verhoeven, 1950). Low pressures also favor N_2O formation, by allowing the gas to escape as fast as it is formed; high pressures correspondingly prevent N_2O formation, and nitrogen appears instead (Verhoeven, 1952).

The denitrification process has been followed in anaerobic cultures by oxidation-reduction measurements (Elema, 1932). Since anions are being removed, the pH becomes alkaline, so that the potentials must be compared with those of a hydrogen electrode in the same solution (Fig. X–5). As soon as nitrite appears, the potential rises to about 475 mv above the hydrogen electrode. This apparently is due to the $^-NO_3$-$^-NO_2$ system. When all nitrate is reduced, the value drops about 25 mv and remains there until all nitrite is used up; then it falls precipitously. If at the end more nitrate is added, the potential rises again to the nitrite level, to fall again when all nitrite is consumed (cf. Elema *et al.*, 1934). It may be concluded that there are two characteristic potentials (i.e., reducing tendencies); one for the nitrate-nitrite system and a lower one for the nitrite-$H_2N_2O_2$ system. In these experiments the necessary reversible oxido-reduction system to react at the electrode was furnished by some excretion product of the bacteria (*M. denitrificans* or *Ps. vulpinus*), so that addition of a reversible dye was not necessary.

These experiments show that the postulated intermediate between nitrite and oxygen really exists, but they give no evidence as to what it is. It cannot be N_2O, because *Ps. denitrificans,* which reduces nitrate rapidly to nitrogen without forming any appreciable N_2O, is unable to reduce N_2O itself until after a time lag (Sacks and Barker, 1952). This indicates that it has to form a special induced enzyme for N_2O

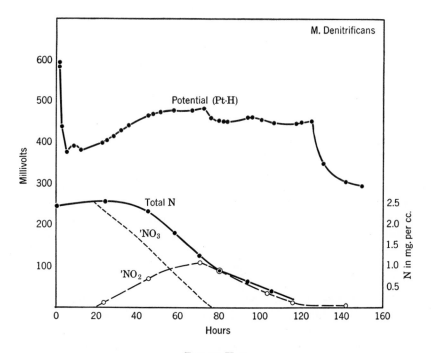

FIGURE X–5

Oxidation-reduction potential (corrected for changes in pH) of *Micrococcus denitrificans* in 2% KNO_3 with 1.5% ethanol as hydrogen donator. In the nitrogen analyses (lower curves and scale at right) the curve for nitrate is the difference between total nitrogen and nitrite. (Data of B. Elema, 1932.)

reduction; the formation of this enzyme, like that of many other induced enzymes, is inhibited by azide or dinitrophenol. Yet these reagents do not inhibit the conversion of nitrite to N_2. Besides, in *Ps. stutzeri* the different reductions show different sensitivity to cyanide. For example, $M/100$ KCN at pH 7.3 completely inhibits the reduction of N_2O, but only causes 60 per cent inhibition of the reduction of nitrite (van Niel and Allen, 1952). In other words, nitrite can be converted to nitrogen under conditions where N_2O cannot.

Alternative intermediates are nitroxyl, NOH, hyponitrous acid, HON:NOH, nitramide, NH_2NO_2, and nitric oxide, NO. Evidence for one or two of these has been brought up from time to time and then discarded. Hyponitrite is attacked by a few denitrifiers, but *Ps. stutzeri*, one of the most active, produces no more gas from it than is yielded by spontaneous decomposition (van Niel and Allen, 1952).[3] The fact that NO is formed by two of the cell-free systems (above), and can be reduced also by them, makes it a strong candidate for the position of intermediate, although like N_2O it could lie just off the main pathway. However, in the case of *Thiobacillus denitrificans*, NO is produced best in presence of M/1000 KCN, and in the case of *Ps. aeruginosa*, by cells more than 40 hours old (Verhoeven, 1956). Furthermore, NO is reduced very slowly and not only by denitrifiers but also by *Ps. fluorescens* and even yeast. For these reasons NO is probably not an intermediate either, and it seems that the true intermediate remains bound to the enzyme. The case is oddly parallel to that of the reduction of nitrogen itself.

The production of alkali in the process is important. Emphasis has been laid on denitrification in the sea as a cause of calcium carbonate precipitation, because, if sea water (containing Ca $[HCO_3]_2$) is made alkaline, $CaCO_3$ will be deposited. In warm tropical waters, as at the Bahama banks, $CaCO_3$ is being precipitated in great quantities. Various investigators, particularly Molisch and Drew, attempted to implicate specific organisms in this process (see ZoBell, 1946). However, any organism producing alkali would have the same effect. Precipitation of calcium carbonate from peptone media, as by Molisch's "*B. calciprecipitans*," is due merely to the ammonia resulting from deamination. Sulfate reduction also removes a strong anion and thus makes the solution alkaline; it too has been considered responsible for $CaCO_3$ precipitation (Bavendamm, 1932). There is evidently no reason to believe that any particular "chalk-precipitating" organisms are involved in the process.

C. The Decomposition of Nitrous Oxide

So far as is known, N_2O does not occur in the atmosphere, although it is found in traces in soil; it must therefore be readily decomposed. *Ps. stutzeri* and *Ps. aeruginosa* rapidly reduce N_2O to N_2 (Beijerinck and Minkman, 1909); the former converted a gas containing 85 per cent N_2O to one containing 90 per cent N_2 in six days at 37° C. Denitrobacillus can convert 40 per cent of N_2O to N_2 in eight days at 30° C

---

[3] The decomposition of hyponitrite by heat is a complex reaction, part being oxidized to nitrite and part reduced to N_2. Some N_2O is formed as well, its amount depending on the water content of the hyponitrite (Oza and Oza, 1953, and literature there cited).

(Verhoeven, 1952). The adaptation of *Ps. denitrificans* to N_2O was mentioned above. Oxidation of the reduced cytochrome c by N_2O is striking; the band at 556 mμ disappears (Sato and Egami, 1949). In adapted cells of *Ps. stutzeri*, and in Chung and Najjar's enzyme prepared from it, or in Verhoeven and Takeda's enzyme from *Ps. aeruginosa*, nitrate, nitrite, or N_2O causes it to disappear at once. The band will of course disappear in oxygen too.

D. The Reduction of Nitrate to Ammonia

This is the most extreme reduction possible; however, it is not uncommon, having been recorded for Azotobacter, Radiobacter, *Cl. welchii*, Desulfovibrio, Denitrobacillus, *Bac. subtilis* (the Marburg strain), and some strains of *E. coli* (Beijerinck and van Delden, 1903; Stoklasa, 1908; Woods, 1938; Baumann and Denk, 1951; Verhoeven, 1952, respectively). *Cl. welchii* and *E. coli* strain Bn can use H_2 gas as reducer, thus:

$$HNO_3 + 4\ H_2 \rightarrow NH_3 + 3\ H_2O$$

The *E. coli* strain can also reduce nitrite, hyponitrite, and hydroxylamine to ammonia, using H_2. For this reason it can grow aerobically on any of these as sole nitrogen source, or anaerobically on lactate and nitrate (McNall and Atkinson, 1956, 1957). With Desulfovibrio, lactate was the hydrogen donor, and the rapid nitrate reduction did not interfere with the reduction of sulfate, which went on simultaneously (Baumann and Denk, 1951).

Nitrite is of course the first intermediate, and much evidence indicates that hydroxylamine is the last. With *Cl. welchii* it yields NH_3 more rapidly than nitrite or nitrate (Woods, 1938), and Desulfovibrio reduces it readily (Pichinoty and Senez, 1956). *Bac. pumilus* reduces NH_2OH about as well as nitrite, using reduced FAD or methylene blue as H donor (Taniguchi *et al.*, 1956). *E. coli* will reduce it, with glucose, in well-aerated cultures, and the strain *E. coli* B, which grows on nitrate or nitrite in an atmosphere of hydrogen, also can use NH_2OH or N_2O (McNall and Atkinson, 1957). Small amounts of NH_2OH have been detected in denitrifying cultures (Verhoeven, 1952).

Strangely enough, aeration *promotes* the reduction to ammonia. Denitrobacillus, in shallow-layer cultures with glucose as H donor, gives a 40 to 90 per cent yield of ammonia (Verhoeven, 1952). *Bac. subtilis* does the same, and when fed $KN^{15}O_3$, the reduction is so rapid that within 45 minutes highly labeled $N^{15}H_3$ is found in the medium (Hall and MacVicar, 1955).

Evidently, therefore, reduction to ammonia is a different process from the other denitrification reactions. It can be brought about by such organisms as *Bac. subtilis*, which do not produce N_2 or N_2O, and as mentioned it may even be promoted by aeration. Kluyver (1953), who devoted several of his last years to the study of *Micrococcus denitrificans*, made the attractive suggestion that while N_2 requires the union of two molecules of nitrite (or the next intermediate), NH_3 does not; thus, the action of O_2 would be just to inhibit *dimerization* rather than denitrification as a whole:

$$2\ \ ^-NO_3 \rightarrow 2\ \ ^-NO_2 \longrightarrow 2\ NH_2OH \rightarrow 2\ NH_3\ or\ 2\ RNH_2$$
$$\text{inhib. by } O_2$$
$$\longrightarrow H_2N_2O_2 \rightarrow N_2O\ or\ N_2$$

It must be remembered, too, that many organisms can readily grow on nitrate as sole nitrogen source. This means that nitrate must be reduced to amino acids, and hence probably to NH_3, in the small amounts needed for growth, by a wide variety of organisms. It seems that a sharp distinction must be made between *bulk* nitrate reduction, with accumulation of N_2O, NH_3 or other reduced products, and *assimilatory* nitrate reduction, in which the only product is cells. The first case, in which nitrate acts as terminal electron acceptor for all substrates, could be called nitrate respiration.

E. Agricultural Importance of Denitrification

It was the loss of nitrogen from soil that led Gayon and Dupetit (1882) to discover denitrification. Counts of denitrifying organisms show them to represent about 1 in 10,000 of the total soil bacteria; Düggeli, for example (Chap. VI), found 830 out of 8.4 million total count in garden soil, and 1720 out of 3.6 million in vineyard soil. Nitrifiers are probably present in similar numbers. Russell (1950) states that crops typically absorb only about one-half the nitrogen supplied them, while the rest is lost, partly by leaching and partly by denitrification.

Nitrate reduction is probably most active in the lower layers of ordinary soil or in waterlogged soils such as rice fields. In these, during the period when they are flooded, nitrate often disappears entirely and ammonia may accumulate. When the soil dries out again, nitrate reappears, in amount about equal to the ammonia, and the cycle continues. Waterlogged soils frequently contain appreciable amounts of nitrite, which may be toxic to the crop. Liming of such soils, to bring the *p*H up, may cause loss of nitrogen, probably through promoting activity of denitrifiers. Similarly, liming of (waterlogged) peat soils has been claimed to cause serious nitrogen loss by denitrification. Rice-field soils have been stated to lose nitrogen spontaneously.

Appreciable denitrification can occur aerobically also. Soil aerated in cylinders with added nitrite or nitrate shows a small utilization of the added nitrogen for growth of microorganisms, but loses N when much organic matter is present (Table X–2). This means, in the first place, that a readily available hydrogen donor is needed for appreciable reduction to occur; the humus is too slowly decomposed (see Chap. VI) to allow of much nitrate reduction. Second, it means that moderate aeration does not prevent denitrification any more in soil than in culture vessels. Important losses of nitrogen are claimed to take place

TABLE X–2. Loss of Nitrogen during the Aeration of Soils

(From Corbet and Wooldridge, 1940)

N ADDED TO 5-GM SOIL		Increase in Organic N	Loss of N
Form	Amount (mg N)		
Normal Garden Soil; Organic N 5.6 mg			
Nitrite	2.7	0	0
Nitrite	10.8	0.5	0.4
Nitrate	2.8	0.2	0
Nitrate	11.0	0.1	0.3
Special Soil; Organic N 9.9 mg			
Ammonium	3.2	2.8	(+0.2)
Nitrite	3.4	0.7	2.7
Nitrate	3.3	0.7	2.3

from tropical soils even under aerobic conditions (see Corbet and Wooldridge, 1940, and Verhoeven, 1952, and literature there cited). These losses are no doubt partly due to leaching into the subsoil, but in part they are due to reduction to N_2, caused by the addition of fresh, decomposable organic matter. They have also been ascribed to photochemical decomposition of NH_4NO_2 (Dhar and Mukherji, 1935). The loss of nitrogen from standing manure heaps is mainly due, however, to volatilization of ammonia, set free by urea organisms and by deamination; it is largely aerobic in nature, because in air the temperature of manure goes very high (up to 72° C), and this drives off "torrents of ammonia" (Gayon, 1884).

In experiments on sewage decomposing under aerobic conditions (activated sludge process), a large loss, apparently as N_2, occurred when extra nitrite or nitrate was added (Corbet and Wooldridge, 1940). Activated sludge plants in which nitrification is occurring may, therefore, be subject to some (probably small) loss of nitrogen. It may well be that in addition to the losses of nitrogen in fires, burning of agricultural refuse, cremation, and the like, a very considerable drain on the nitrogen cycle is that due to nitrate reduction.

3. THE NITROGEN CYCLE

The principal reactions of nitrogen compounds brought about by microorganisms can be summarized in Figure X–6.

The breakdown of amines is represented as leading mainly to bacterial protein (see Chap. VIII, sec. 7). The humus reactions are very slow and are, therefore, shown in dotted lines only. Many organ-

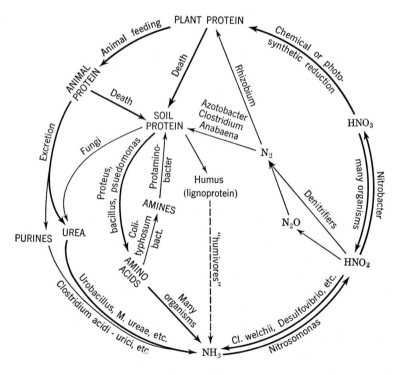

FIGURE X–6
The nitrogen cycle.

isms participating in a minor way have been omitted, and doubtless many more of importance will be brought to light in future.

It will be noted that the animal kingdom is not an essential part of the cycle and may be regarded as parasitic on it.

Although the details of many reactions are doubtless not yet known, the picture shows no serious gaps, and its elucidation represents a major achievement of microbiology.

REFERENCES

Aleem, M. I. H., and Nason, A. 1959, 1960. *Biochem. Biophys. Res. Comms.*, **6**:323–325; *Proc. Nat. Acad. Sci.*, **46**:763–768 (1960).

Amer, F. M., and Bartholomew, W. V. 1951. *Soil Sci.*, **71**:215–219.

Aubel, E. 1938. *Compt. rend. Acad. sci.*, **207**:348–349.

Baas-Becking, L. G. M., and Parks, G. S. 1927. Energy Relations in the Metabolism of Autotrophic Bacteria. *Physiol. Revs.*, **7**:85–106.

Bathurst, N. O., and Mitchell, K. J. 1958. *N. Z. J. Agric. Res.*, **1**:540–552; *Chem. Abstr.*, **53**:5537.

Baumann, A., and Denk, V. 1951. *Arch. Mikrobiol.*, **15**:283–307.

*Bavendamm, W. 1932. *Arch. Mikrobiol.*, **3**:205–276.

Beijerinck, M. W., and van Delden, A. 1903. *Arch. Nèerl. Sci.*, Ser. 2, **8**:319–373.

Beijerinck, M. W., and Minkman, D. C. J. 1909. *Zentr. Bakt. II*, **25**:30–63.

Bisset, K. A., and Grace, J. B. 1954. In, Autotrophic Microorganisms (IVth Symp. Soc. Gen. Microbiol.), Cambridge Univ. Press (eds. Fry and Peel), pp. 28–53.

Bömeke, H. 1939. *Arch. Mikrobiol.*, **10**:385–445.

Bömeke, H. 1951. *Arch. Mikrobiol.*, **15**:414–427.

Butler, G. W. 1959. *Proc. N. Z. Soc. Animal Production*, **19**:99–110.

*Carey, C. L. 1938. *J. Mar. Res.*, **1**:291–304; cf. also Chap. XI in C. E. Zobell's Marine Microbiology (1946).

Chung, C. W., and Najjar, V. A. 1956. *J. Biol. Chem.*, **218**:617–625, 627–632.

Corbet, A. S., and Wooldridge, W. R. 1940. *Biochem. J.*, **34**:1015–1025, 1026–1035, 1036–1040.

Dhar, N. R., and Mukherji, S. K. 1935. *J. Ind. Chem. Soc.*, **12**:756–763.

Dhar, N. R., and Rao, G. G. 1933. *J. Ind. Chem. Soc. P.C. Ray Commem. Vol.* (Suppl. to Vol. **10**), pp. 81–91; cf. Dhar, N. R., and Mukherji, S. K. *Ann. Agron.*, **11**:87–91.

Elema, B. 1932. De bepaling van oxydatie-reductie potentiaal in bacteriencultures en here beteekenis voor de stofwisseling. Dissertation, Delft.

Elema, B.; Kluyver, A. J.; and Dalfsen, J. W. 1934. *Biochem. Z.*, **270**:317–340.

Engel, H. 1929. *Planta*, **8**:423–426.

Engel, H., and Skallau, W. 1937. *Zentr. Bakt. II*, **97**:305–311.

Engel, M. S., and Alexander, M. 1958. *J. Bact.*, **76**:217–222.

Fewson, C. A., and Nicholas, D. J. D. 1961. *Biochim. Biophys. Acta*, **49**:335–349; Walker, G. C., and Nicholas, D. J. D., *ibid.*:350–360, 361–368.

Fred, E. B., and Davenport, A. 1921. *Soil Sci.*, **11**:389–407.

Gayon, U. 1884. *Compt. rend. Acad. sci.*, **98**:528–531.

Gayon, U., and Dupetit, G. 1882. *Compt. rend. Acad. sci.*, **95**:644–646.

Gibbs, W. M. 1919. *Soil Sci.*, **8**:427–471.

Gould, G. W., and Lees, H. 1958. *Biochem. J.*, **69**:38P.

Hall, L. M., and MacVicar, R. 1955. *J. Biol. Chem.*, **213**:305–310.

Hansen, R. W., and Kallio, R. E. 1957. *Science*, **125**:1198–1199.

Hes, J. W. 1937. Zur Stoffwechselphysiologie von Nitrosomonas. Dissertation, Groningen.

Hofman, T., and Lees, H. 1952. *Biochem. J.*, **52**:140–142.

Hofman, T., and Lees, H. 1953. *Biochem. J.*, **54**:579–583.

Imsenecki, A. A. 1946. *Nature*, **157**:877.

Issatschenko, B. 1926. *Compt. rend. Acad. sci.*, **182**:185–186.

Jensen, H. L. 1950. *Nature*, **165**:974.

Jensen, H. L. 1951. *J. Gen. Microbiol.*, **5**:360–368.

Kamen, M. D., and Vernon, L. P. 1955. *Biochim. Biophys. Acta*, **17**:10–22.

Kingma Boltjes, T. Y. 1935. Untersuchungen über die nitrifizierenden Bakterien. Dissertation, Delft; also *Arch. Mikrobiol.*, **6**:79–138.

Kluyver, A. J. 1953. *Proc. Int. Microbiol. Cong. Rome*, pp. 71–91, (Symp. Microbial Metabolism).

Korsakowa, M. P. 1927–1929. Cited by Elema, 1932.

Lees, H. 1951. *Nature*, **167**:355–356.

Lees, H. 1952. *Biochem. J.*, **52**:134–139.

Lees, H. 1954. In, Autotrophic Microorganisms, IVth Symp. Soc. Gen. Microbiol.; Cambridge Univ. Press, pp. 84–98.

Lees, H., and Quastel, J. H. 1946. *Biochem. J.*, **40**:803–814, 815–823, 824–828.

Lees, H., and Simpson, J. R. 1957. *Biochem. J.*, **65**:295–305.

Lewis, P. R., and Hinshelwood, C. N. 1948. *J. Chem. Soc.*, pp. 824–847.

Lloyd, B., and Cranston, J. A. 1930. *Biochem. J.*, **24**:525–528, 529–547.

McNall, E. G., and Atkinson, D. E. 1956, 1957. *J. Bact.*, **72**:226–229; **74**:60–66 (1957).

Meek, C. S., and Lipman, C. B. 1922. *J. Gen. Physiol.*, **5**:195–204.

Meiklejohn, J. 1952. *Proc. Soc. Appl. Bact.*, **15**:77–81.

Meiklejohn, J. 1954. In, Autotrophic Microorganisms (IVth Symp. Soc. Gen. Microbiol.), Cambridge Univ. Press (eds. Fry and Peel), pp. 68–83.

Meyerhof, O. 1916. *Pflüger's Arch. ges. Physiol.*, **164**:353–427; **165**:229–284.

Meyerhof, O. 1917. *Pflüger's Arch. ges. Physiol.*, **166**:245–280.

Nelson, D. H. 1931. *Zentr. Bakt. II*, **83**:280–311.

Nicholas, D. J. D., and Jones, O. T. G. 1960. *Biochem. J.*, **74**:19P.; *Nature*, **185**:512–514 (1960).

Nicholas, D. J. D., and Nason, A. 1955. *J. Bact.*, **69**:580–583.

van Niel, C. B., and Allen, M. B. 1952. *J. Bact.*, **64**:413–422.

Oza, T. M., and Oza, V. T. 1953. *J. Chem. Soc.*, pp. 909–913.

Pichinoty, F., and Senez, J. C. 1956. *Compt. rend. soc. biol.*, **150**:744–745.

Pollock, M. R. 1946. *Brit. J. Exp. Path.*, **27**:419–432.

Pollock, M. R., and Wainright, S. D. 1948. *Brit. J. Exp. Path.*, **29**:223–240.

*Quastel, J. H., and Scholefield, P. G. 1951. *Bacteriol. Revs.*, **15**:1–53.

*Richardson, H. L. 1938. *J. Agric. Sci.*, **28**:73–121.

Russell, Sir E. J. 1950. Soil Conditions and Plant Growth, 8th ed.; London, Longmans, Green and Co.

Sacks, L. E., and Barker, H. A. 1949. *J. Bact.*, **58**:11–22.

Sacks, L. E., and Barker, H. A. 1952. *J. Bact.*, **64**:247–252.

Sato, R., and Egami, F. 1949. *Bull. Chem. Soc. Japan*, **22**:137–143.

Schloesing, Th., and Müntz, A. 1877–1879. Sur la nitrification par les ferments organisées. *Compt. rend. Acad. sci.*, **84**:301–303 (1877); **85**:1018–1020 (1877); **86**:892–895 (1878); **89**:891–894 (1879).

Seeler, G., and Engel, H. 1959. *Arch. Mikrobiol.*, **33**:387–394.

Silver, W. S. 1960. *Nature*, **185**:555–556.

Stickland, L. H. 1931. *Biochem. J.*, **25**:1543–1554.

Stoklasa, J. 1908. *Zentr. Bakt. II*, **21**:484–509, 620–632.

Taniguchi, S.; Mitsui, T.; Toyoda, T.; Yamada, T.; and Egami, F. 1952. *J. Biochem. Tokyo*, **40**:175–186.

Taniguchi, S.; Sato, R.; and Egami, F. 1956. In, Inorganic Nitrogen Metabolism (ed. McElroy and Glass), pp. 87–108; Baltimore, Johns Hopkins Univ. Press.

Verhoeven, W. 1950. *Ant. v. Leeuwenhoek*, **16**:269–281.

Verhoeven, W. 1952. Aerobic Spore-forming Nitrate-reducing Bacteria. Dissertation, Delft.

*Verhoeven, W. 1956. In, Inorganic Nitrogen Metabolism (eds. McElroy and Glass), pp. 61–86, Baltimore, Johns Hopkins Univ. Press.

Verhoeven, W., and Goos, J. J. C. 1954. *Ant. van Leeuwanhock*, **20**:93–101.

Verhoeven, W., and Takeda, Y. 1956. In, Inorganic Nitrogen Metabolism (ed. McElroy and Glass), pp. 159–162; Baltimore, Johns Hopkins Press.

Vernon, L. P. 1956. *J. Biol. Chem.*, **222**:1035–1044.

Wainwright, S. D., and Nevill, A. N. 1956. *J. Gen. Microbiol.*, **14**:47–56; *J. Bact.*, **71**:254–255.

Walker, G. C., and Nicholas, D. J. D. 1960. *Biochem. J.*, **77**:4P–5P.

Warington, R. 1878–1891. On Nitrification, I–IV. *J. Chem. Soc.*, **33**:44–51 (1878); **35**:429–456 (1879); **45**:637–672 (1884); **59**:484–529 (1891).

Wilson, J. K. 1947. *Proc. Soil Sci. Soc. Amer.*, **12**:215–216.

Winogradsky, S. 1890, 1891. *Ann. Inst. Pasteur*, **4**:213–231, 257–275, 760–771; **5**:92–100, 577–616.

Winogradsky, S. 1892. *Arch. sci. biol. St. Petersburg* **1**:87–137 (4 plates).

Winogradsky, S., and Winogradsky, H. 1933. *Ann. Inst. Pasteur*, **50**:350–432.

Woods, D. D. 1938. *Biochem. J.*, **32**:2000–2012.

Yamagata, S. 1939. *Acta Phytochim.*, **11**:145–157.

*ZoBell, C. E. 1946. Marine Microbiology. Waltham, Mass., Chronica Botanica Co.

Part Three

The Metabolism of

Carbohydrates

CHAPTER XI

The Alcoholic Fermentation

And wine which maketh glad the heart of man . . .
and bread which strengtheneth man's heart.

Psalm 104

1. INTRODUCTORY: THE SIX TYPES OF
FERMENTATIONS

The action of microorganisms on carbohydrates falls naturally under
four heads:

The fermentation of simple sugars
The hydrolysis of di- and trisaccharides to simple sugars
The breakdown of complex polysaccharides and
The synthesis of polysaccharides

Since these processes typically do not require oxygen, they can all be
regarded as fermentations.

Of the fermentations of simple sugars there are six main types
caused by bacteria and fungi. These can be classified as follows:

(1) Alcoholic fermentation, in which sugar is converted to ethanol
$+ CO_2$ (this chapter).

(2) Lactic fermentation, in which sugar is converted either to
lactic acid alone, or to a mixture of lactic acid with alcohol or acetic
acid (Chap. XII).

(3) Propionic fermentation, in which sugar (or lactic acid) is
converted to propionic and acetic acids $+ CO_2$ (Chap. XIII).

(4) Formic fermentation, a more complex type in which formic

acid is the characteristic product, along with many other compounds in varying amounts (Chap. XIV).

(5) Butyl-butyric fermentations, a still more complex group characterized by production of three four-carbon compounds, namely, butanol, butyric acid, and acetoacetic acid, usually together with alcohol and acetic acid (Chap. XV).

(6) The so-called "oxidative fermentations," which are not fermentations at all but oxidation of the sugars and their breakdown products to various acids, and especially to acetic acid (Chap. XVI).

Of the six types the alcoholic fermentation is the most famous and also the most widely investigated. It is carried out par excellence by the yeasts; also by some other fungi, when growing under anaerobic or semianaerobic conditions. A few bacteria give a modified alcoholic fermentation (sec. 10). It will be simplest, therefore, to consider first the fermentation as it is carried out by yeast.

The yeasts are a large group of fungi belonging to the Ascomycetes (see Bessey, 1950). They are normally single-celled, but some grow out into a limited mycelium. They include: (1) the organisms forming ascospores and belonging to the family *Endomycetaceae;* (2) another group not forming ascospores (probably through having lost this ability), comprising the family *Torulopsidaceae;* and (3) several other genera which seem similar but may not actually be very closely related. The first group includes Saccharomyces, often referred to as "yeast"; the second group includes many which do not ferment at all but only oxidize. Yeast cells may be diploid or haploid, but only diploid cells form asci, and even that is erratic and uncertain. Many media have been devised to promote ascus formation; high K, low N, addition of vegetable juices and acetate, all tend to promote the process (see McClary *et al.*, 1959). Light also promotes it in some yeasts, but inhibits in others (Oppenoorth, 1956). The controlling mechanisms remain unknown.

2. SOCIAL AND INDUSTRIAL IMPORTANCE OF YEAST FERMENTATIONS

A. Wine

Wine is the fermentation product of the fresh juice of sweet fruits, usually grapes, though pears, figs, and others are occasionally used. The juices are somewhat acid, commonly having a pH around 5, which is near the optimum for alcoholic fermentation. The infection is spontaneous, and Pasteur was the first to show that yeasts are present on the surface of grapes—especially as they approach maturity—and form vigorous colonies at points of injury where the sweet juice exudes. The yeasts are carried from one grape to another by insects, especially wasps. Wortmann showed that carefully expressed sterile juice did not ferment until a wasp alighted on the solution. Among the yeasts on the surface of grapes and figs are: (1) Saccharomyces, the principal alcohol-fermenting genus; (2) several of those types which fuse to produce ascospores, particularly Zygosaccharomyces species; and (3) nonsporeforming yeasts belonging to the genera Torulopsis and Candida (see Mrak and Phaff, 1948). The yeasts in the fermenting vats of wines are often Saccharomyces *"ellipsoideus,"* a variety of *Sacch. cereviseae.* They convert the dextrose and fructose in the fruit juice into alcohol, up to a maximum of 14 per cent, at which concentration both fermentation and growth of the yeasts stops. Wines higher in alcohol than 14 per cent are made by distilling the fermented liquor and adding the distillate (grape brandy) to ordinary wine. The flavor of wines is in large part due to the amyl alcohols and their esters, along with acetic and lactic acids and ethyl acetate. The acids are partly present in the fruit and partly formed in traces as by-products in the fermentation; the amyl and other organic radicals besides ethyl are produced in part by deamination of leucine and the other amino acids, in part synthesized directly (see p. 316).

B. Beer

Beer differs from wine in being made from seeds. Cereal seeds, including wheat, barley, rye, and corn, are allowed to begin germination, and then mashed and boiled with water. The resulting extract—wort—contains a moderate concentration of dextrose which has been set free from the starch in the grain by amylase. Since the amylase begins to act soon after soaking, and the resulting sugar is rapidly used up in growth and respiration of the seedling, careful control of the time and temperature of soaking is needed in order to control the sugar content of the wort. Molasses or other forms of sugar may be added as well. Hops (the flowers of *Humulus lupulus* or, in America, *Humulus americana*) are also added, usually when the boiling is nearly over, both for their bitter flavor and because the extract has mild antiseptic properties, due to the resins humulon and lupulon. The antiseptics discourage the growth of Lactobacilli and Sarcinae, which occasionally damage the beer. The wort is cooled and at once inoculated, usually with *Saccharomyces cereviseae;* the fermentation produces not more than about 6 per cent alcohol. The yeast is added in large quantities ("pitched") usually from a previous fermentation. Bottom yeasts, which grow as a sediment, and top yeasts, which grow mainly near the surface, carry out essentially the same fermentation, the former having a lower optimum temperature. Both are races of *Sacch. cereviseae.* The stability of the froth ("head retention"), color, and flavor are largely controlled by the nitrogen compounds in the wort. In dark ales and stout, a slow fermentation carried out by *Brettanomyces* species follows the main one, giving additional flavor and darker color. Molasses and roasted grain may be added for darkening.

C. Industrial Alcohol

This product is usually made from molasses (as a cheap source of sugar), in which the sucrose is rapidly hydrolyzed by invertase in the yeast. In recent years acid-hydrolyzed sawdust has been used on an experimental scale, and sulfite waste liquor from paper factories is also sometimes fermented (Kolachov and Nicholson, 1951). As far as possible, pure cultures of *Sacch. cereviseae* are used. In wine and beer fermentations, "wild yeasts," of the family *Torulopsidaceae,* cause trouble by producing bitter tastes, but in industrial alcohol production their effect is to reduce the yield of alcohol, because these are mainly aerobic forms which oxidize away the carbohydrate. To obtain as nearly pure culture Saccharomyces as possible, small pure cultures are used to inoculate successively larger vessels (as done originally by Hansen), the last being the so-called "propagation plant" in the distillery. It may be as large as 7000 liters, so that 5 per cent of the fermentation tank itself (30,000 gal) is supplied by this inoculum. In using molasses, urea is often added, since the nitrogen content of the molasses is too low to allow really vigorous yeast growth. An acid *p*H (about 4.7) is maintained to suppress bacteria.

D. Bread

Essentially this is also an alcoholic fermentation product. The source of sugar is the small amount in flour, plus a little which is usually incorporated in the dough. The fermentation is of short duration (4 to 12 hours) and is intended to produce gas to "leaven" or *lift* the dough. The French word for yeast (*levure*) and the old English "leaven" refer to this use of yeast. The alcohol is, of course, driven off in the baking. Baker's yeast is a "top yeast" form of *Sacch. cereviseae.*

In ancient days bread and beer were made together from wheat flour. The models of the life and times of 2000 B.C., excavated at Thebes in Egypt, show (*inter alia*) a brewery and bakery in one building. "In the first room two women grind corn into flour and a man makes it into cakes of dough, which another treads into mash in a barrel. Nearby, the rising mash stands in four tall crocks while the yeast ferments, when . . . another man pours it into a row of stoppered jugs which stand along the wall" (Winlock, 1921). In the next room is the bakery, doubtless being supplied with yeast from this mash. This is probably the oldest known representation of a microbial process.

E. Yeast

Yeast itself is produced in quantity when the medium is aerated. The yield of alcohol decreases (see sec. 11), and the yeast grows much more than under anaerobic conditions. A cereal mash, as for beer, is used, glucose being added to increase the yield. In recent years ammonium salts have been used as a main source of nitrogen; the yeast converts this in 50 per cent yield to protein. Hence this "grain-ammonia process" is more efficient than agricultural methods, like pasturing cattle, for the formation of concentrated protein, while the resulting yeast cake is at least as good a food as beef. When sugar, ammonium, and phosphate are added steadily as the yeast grows, yields as high as 90 per cent, calculated on the nitrogen, are obtained.

The effectiveness of grain as basal medium is due to the need of yeast for vitamins as growth substances. These compounds, formerly known collectively as "Bios," and later separated into Bios I, II, III, and so on, are present in cereal seeds. They comprise:

(1) *myo*-Inositol, $C_6H_{14}O_6$, or hexahydroxycyclo-hexane

(2) Biotin, a compound containing nitrogen and sulfur

(3) Nicotinic acid, or its amide (p. 224)

(4) Thiamine,
or vitamin B_1

(5) Riboflavin

(6) Pantothenic acid, which comprises part of the molecule of coenzyme A, and is a peptide of pantoic acid and β-alanine:

$$CH_2OH \cdot C \cdot CHOHCO \cdot NHCH_2CH_2COOH,$$
$$\underset{(CH_3)_2}{|}$$

Some yeasts do not require the whole molecule but can synthesize it if supplied with β-alanine, or even with peptides of β-alanine (Betz, 1960–62).

(7) Folic acid, which contains the pteridine nucleus, linked with p-aminobenzoic acid and up to 7 molecules of glutamic acid (see Chap. XXIV, sec. 4).

The functions of these substances are more or less understood. Nicotinic acid and riboflavin are converted to coenzymes and flavoproteins (Chap. V). Biotin catalyzes carboxylation reactions (Chap. XIII); thiamine, converted to its pyrophosphate, is the coenzyme for carboxylase (p. 441); pantothenic acid is converted to coenzyme A (see p. 244); and folic acid is required for certain one-carbon syntheses (Chap. XXIV, sec. 4 and Chap. VIII, sec. 7).

All yeasts do not require all the vitamins, and a few can grow on synthetic medium; one of these, *Torulopsis utilis*, was proposed as a food during World War I, being raised on hydrolyzed sawdust and ammonium salts. It can also be raised on sulfite waste liquor from paper mills after this has first been fermented by Saccharomyces. The Saccharomyces attacks only the hexoses, and Torulopsis then grows on the pentoses; urea and phosphate are added to the liquor as nutrients. In this way a ton of waste will yield 20 gal of alcohol and 40 to 100 lb of yeasts, which are used as high-protein cattle feed (Kurth, 1946).

3. EARLY WORK ON THE ALCOHOLIC FERMENTATION[1]

The nature of fermentation was always part of the "spontaneous generation" controversy (Chap. I). It was Schwann, in 1837, who showed that the alcoholic fermentation of grape juice is entirely dependent on germs reaching it from the atmosphere. From the morphology of yeast, and its susceptibility to different poisons (Hg'' and arsenate, but not to strychnine, which poisons mammals), Schwann deduced that yeast belongs to the plants rather than the animals. Cagniard-Latour and Kützing in the same year also made quite clear that yeast is a plant.

However, Liebig and other chemists had always held that fermentation is due to the presence of unstable molecules, which in their breaking down carry along other molecules, thus causing them to break down also (Chap. I, sec. 3). The need for a trace of yeast was thus viewed as merely the need for what we should now call a catalyst, i.e., (in Liebig's view), some unstable matter in the process of breakdown. In 1828 Wöhler synthesized urea, a typical biological product, and thus he and Liebig were satisfied that in the end all biological processes would prove to be chemical in nature. In alcoholic fermentation, they were supported in their contention by the simple molecular relationships expressed in the Gay-Lussac equation:

$$C_6H_{12}O_6 \rightarrow 2\ C_2H_5OH + 2\ CO_2$$

This equation satisfies the law of simple proportions and thus gives a deceptively "chemical" appearance to the fermentation. Actually, as Pasteur showed, it does not truly describe the fermentation, because small quantities (fractions of a mole) of glycerol and succinic acid also appear.

The biological concept of fermentation as something resulting from the life of microorganisms, therefore, seemed absurd to Liebig. He and Wöhler published an anonymous paper, mocking at the idea that living yeast could be responsible for fermentation, and at the use of the microscope in what they regarded as purely chemical studies. This appeared in Liebig's journal, the *Annalen*, in 1839. A free translation of part of it is as follows:

> I am in process of developing a new theory of wine fermentation . . . This discovery shows how simple are the means used by Nature to cause the most wonderful phenomena. I owe this to the application of the microscope . . . .
> Beer yeast broken up in water is resolved by this instrument into in-

[1] For detailed treatment and an excellent historical outline see Harden (1932).

numerable small spheres . . . . When placed in sugar water it can be seen
that these are the eggs of animals; they swell, burst, and there develop
small animals which multiply with incredible rapidity in a most unprecedented way. The form of these animals differs from that of the 600 spp.
already described; it is the shape of a Beindorf's distilling flask (without
the condenser). The tube of the stillhead is a kind of sucking snout covered
internally with fine 1/2,000-line cracks; although teeth and eyes are not to
be seen, one can distinguish a stomach, intestine, the anus (a rose-pink
spot), and the organs of urine secretion. From the moment of emergence
from the egg, the animals suck in sugar, which can clearly be seen in the
stomach. It is immediately digested and the digestion is followed by excretion. In a word these infusoria feed on sugar; they excrete from the intestine alcohol and from the urine organs carbon dioxide. The urine bladder
in the full condition is shaped like a champagne bottle . . . .

This paper may have had considerable influence in delaying the
further study of fermentation and of spontaneous generation. At any
rate it was 20 years before Pasteur elaborated and repeated Schwann's
experiments. He confirmed that there is no spontaneous generation,
and that fermentation is due to the living yeast (Pasteur, 1860):

I am of the opinion that alcoholic fermentation never occurs without
simultaneous organization, development, multiplication of cells, or the
continued life of cells already formed. The results expressed in this memoir
seem to me to be completely opposed to the opinions of Liebig and Berzelius.
If I am asked *in what* consists the chemical act whereby the sugar is decomposed and what is its real cause, I reply that I am completely ignorant
of it.

He thus took the "vitalist" position that fermentation is inseparable
from life. He considered (cf. Chap. V, sec. 2) that the organism,
deprived of oxygen from the air, draws its oxygen from organic
compounds: *"La fermentation est la vie sans l'air."*[2]

Shortly before Pasteur, Moritz Traube, in 1858, put forward the
theory that *all fermentations produced by living organisms are in
reality caused by ferments in the organism.* Ferments were considered
definite substances *closely related to proteins.* This incredibly accurate
prophetic view was supported when Berthelot, in 1860, isolated invertase from yeast, but there was no experimental support forthcoming
for actual *fermentation* by cell-free products. Pasteur himself and
many other workers, including Claude Bernard, the physiologist, tried
grinding, freezing, and plasmolyzing yeast, and even extracting it
with glycerol, without success. It was in 1897 that Buchner, grinding
yeast with sand to make an extract for therapeutic purposes, found
that the extract decomposed rapidly and attempted to preserve it by

[2] In spite of Pasteur's clear distinction, followed by almost all workers since, a
famous bacteriology text, in its 1946 edition, called fermentation "the oxidation of
carbohydrate to acids."

adding sugar. The mixture gradually frothed, CO_2 was evolved, and cell-free fermentation was discovered. The papers of Buchner (1897) and Buchner and Rapp (1897–1899) created a sensation. Liebig had been half right after all.

Later, numerous fermenting preparations were made from yeast. *Zymin* is made by treating yeast with alcohol and ether, or with acetone, and drying. Lebedev made "maceration juice" by drying the yeast and then macerating it in water at 35° C. All such preparations ferment, although only from 2 to 10 per cent as fast as living yeast; they also give a slow "autofermentation" due to the breakdown of stored glycogen which is hydrolyzed to sugar by the killed preparation. They ferment glucose, fructose, and mannose, also sucrose and maltose; raffinose is attacked very slowly. Preparations from yeasts other than *Sacch. cereviseae* may attack galactose. Pentoses are not fermented by these preparations, but phosphorylated pentoses are, and Lebedev juice ferments ribose phosphate as fast as glucose (Dickens, 1938).

4. THE ROLE OF PHOSPHATE

So long as the living cell is required, research on biological processes is slow. In fermentation, as soon as cell-free preparations could be used, a major discovery was made which opened up a whole new vista in biological chemistry. Buchner in 1903 observed that CO_2 production was stimulated by adding phosphate and attributed this to the increased acidity of the medium. It was in a more careful study of the influence of phosphate that the major discovery referred to was made, by Harden and Young (1906). They found that the addition of phosphate to fermenting yeast juice caused the rate to rise by as much as 20 times for a while; it then returned to normal. On adding a second quantity of phosphate the rise was again obtained (see Fig. XI–1). Each addition caused production of one additional mole of CO_2 per mole of phosphate added, and alcohol was also produced in proportion to the CO_2. A smaller effect was obtained with zymin, but none with intact yeast, probably because the cells contained enough phosphate already. The full explanation of this effect of phosphate took about 40 years to elucidate.

When at the end of the experiment the liquid was examined, the phosphate was no longer free as $=HPO_4$ ions, but as organically bound phosphate *esters*.[3] They isolated a hexosediphosphate, afterward found to be fructose (fructofuranose)-1-6-diphosphate. By careful hydrolysis

[3] Independent of Harden and Young's experiment with the juice, Ivanov (1905–1907) showed that intact yeast and zymin also convert phosphate to organic esters.

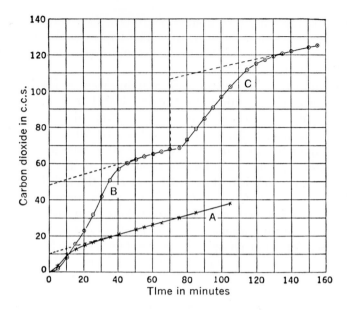

FIGURE XI–1

The experiment of Harden and Young, 1906, with yeast juice.

Curve A. Glucose only.

Curve B. Glucose + 0.3 M phosphate; at 70 minutes 0.3 M phosphate is again added to curve B, giving *curve C.* The extra CO_2 due to the phosphate is shown graphically as 38 and 39 cc, respectively.

(From A. Harden, *Alcoholic Fermentations.* Copyright 1932 Longmans Green and Co. Ltd., London.)

of this, Neuberg (1918) subsequently prepared a fructose (fructo-furanose)-monophosphate, while Robison (1922) isolated from fermentation liquor a third ester, glucose (glucopyranose)-6-phosphate. Subsequently another compound, glucose-1-phosphate, intermediate in the breakdown and resynthesis of starch and glycogen, was identified by Cori and Cori. The four esters are shown below:

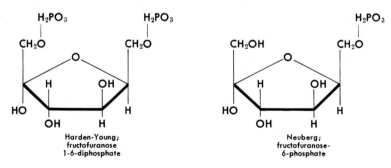

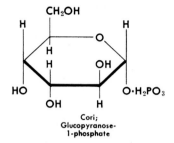

Hexose phosphates are normally present in yeast, as the following analysis of fresh pressed brewer's yeast (Boyland, 1930) shows:

Orthophosphate	1.37 mg P per gram yeast
Pyrophosphate	0.68
Hexosediphosphate	0.38 ⎫
Hexosemonophosphate	0.72 ⎬ total 1.10
Nucleic acid	0.07
	———
Total P	3.25

Altogether, no less than 16 phosphate compounds participate in fermentation, five as hexose esters, eight as intermediate substrates, and three as coenzymes. The old slogan, *"Ohne Phosphor kein Leben,"* thus receives its full explanation.

5. COENZYMES

When yeast juice is thoroughly dialyzed,[4] then neither the dialyzate (small molecules) nor the residue (large molecules) can carry out fermentation, but on mixing them together they ferment as before. This discovery was made independently by Buchner and Antoni and by Harden and Young, both in 1905. The residue, called *apoenzyme*, is inactivated by heat and thus proteinaceous, while the dialyzate, called *coenzyme* or *cozymase*, is thermostable. The cozymase cannot be replaced by phosphate ions, but is organic in nature.

In this connection a discovery of great importance for comparative biochemistry was made by Meyerhof (1918). He found that when animal muscle is ground up and thoroughly washed, it becomes unable to carry out its typical fermentation, namely, the formation of lactic acid from carbohydrate. If, however, the washings are added to the residue, the mixture is again able to form lactic acid. If, instead of the washings, yeast cozymase be added, the effect is the same as that of

[4] To dialyze, a solution is placed in parchment or cellophane bags, surrounded by water; molecules small enough to pass through the pores in the bag diffuse out into the water, proteins and other large molecules remain behind.

the muscle washings. In a corresponding way, the hot-water washings of muscle, added to yeast apozymase, will enable it to carry out its alcoholic fermentation. In other words, yeast and muscle have the same, or at least interchangeable, coenzymes. Evidently lactic acid fermentation in muscle is very closely related to alcoholic fermentation in yeast (see Chap. XII).

Extensive study of the cozymase, particularly by von Euler, Myrbäck, Lohmann, and their co-workers, led to the recognition that three substances are involved, all containing phosphate. Two of them also contain the base adenine and the pentose D-ribose. The three are:

(1) *Adenosine triphosphate* (ATP), the phosphate-carrying coenzyme, first isolated from muscle (Lohmann, 1935):

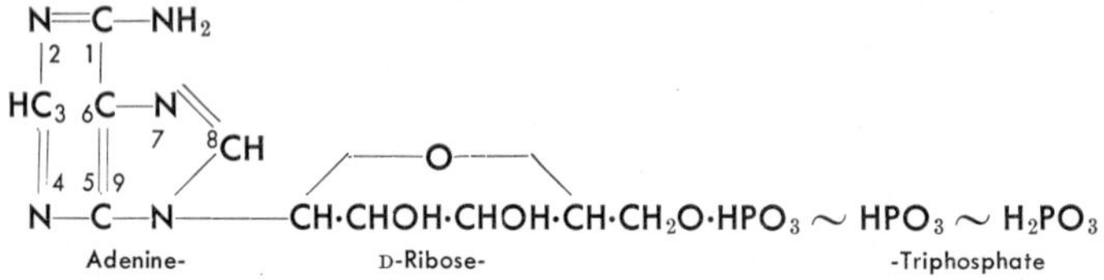

(The bonds marked ∼ are of high energy; cf. Chap. V, sec. 3.)

Its structure has been confirmed by synthesis (Michelson and Todd, 1949). The parent substance, adenosine, was previously shown by synthesis to be 9-β-D-ribosido-adenine (Davoll, Lythgoe, and Todd, 1948). ATP, together with magnesium ions, is the means whereby hexose is converted to one of the hexose phosphates; in donating the required phosphate group the ATP becomes adenosine *di*phosphate (ADP). The enzyme *hexokinase* catalyzes this reaction. The ADP accepts another phosphate group (being reconverted to ATP) from phosphorylated 3-carbon compounds as shown below.

(2) *Diphosphopyridinenucleotide* (DPN), *nicotinamide-adenine-dinucleotide* (NAD), or coenzyme I, the hydrogen-carrying coenzyme, isolated by Euler and Schlenk (1937), and containing two bases, adenine and nicotinic acid amide (nicotinamide or niacin):

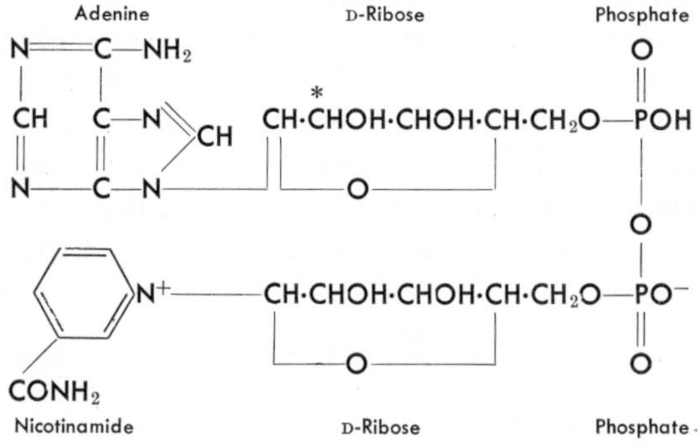

This substance is closely related to coenzyme II (p. 224); it differs only in containing but two phosphoric groups while in the other, called triphospho-pyridine nucleotide, TPN, or NADP, the C atom marked with an asterisk is also phosphorylated. However, their actions are quite specific, each working most efficiently with its own group of dehydrogenases.

(3) *Thiamine pyrophosphate*, diphosphothiamine, or *cocarboxylase*, the CO_2-releasing coenzyme (Lohmann and Schuster, 1937):

| 2 Methyl-6-amino pyrimidine- | 1,2 Dimethyl-3-ethyl thiazole | -Pyrophosphate |

————Thiamine————

Yeast cocarboxylase, if carefully purified at pH 6, contains the diphosphothiamine and also magnesium attached to the protein, in a ratio of 1 Mg atom and 1 diphosphothiamine molecule for 75,000 gm of protein (Kubowitz and Lüttgens, 1941). At pH 8 the coenzyme dissociates off, leaving the apo-carboxylase, but the whole enzyme, *carboxylase*, can be resynthesized in presence of a metal ion and pyrophosphate, and its activity fully restored (Boffi *et al.*, 1959). Yeast incubated with thiamine and phosphate synthesizes first the cocarboxylase and then thiamine triphosphate, which is inactive (Kiessling, 1956–1959). Cell-free extracts of *Mycob. lacticola* do the same thing (Rossi-Fanelli *et al.*, 1960); however, they can also split off the phosphate groups again, so that the net synthesis soon stops.

In addition to the organic coenzymes, the ions Mg^{++}, Mn^{++} and NH_4^+ are also essential for the fermentation.

6. THE REDUCING POWER OF YEAST

The next important step in the understanding of the fermentation is the appreciation that yeast, particularly in the presence of sugar, constitutes a strongly reducing system. Fermenting yeast can reduce powdered sulfur, methylene blue, or thiosulfate. This last reaction:

$$Na_2S_2O_3 + 2(H) \rightarrow Na_2SO_3 + H_2S$$

even goes (very slowly) in the absence of sugar, doubtless in connection with autofermentation (Kossowicz and Loew, 1913). Yeast which is fermenting sugar can also reduce aromatic nitro compounds to amines, ketones to secondary alcohols, and—of particular importance— aldehydes to primary alcohols. Most notable is the great readiness with which acetaldehyde is reduced to ethyl alcohol (Kostytschev and Hubbenet, 1912–1913), a reduction carried out equally well by living yeast, pressed dried yeast-cake, or zymin. The significance of this is seen in connection with the fundamental theory that acetaldehyde is an intermediate product in the fermentation.

7. ACETALDEHYDE AS AN INTERMEDIATE PRODUCT

It was Neuberg and co-workers who in 1911–1912 discovered that yeast decomposes keto acids to CO_2 and aldehydes. Thus α-ketobutyric acid yields propionaldehyde and CO_2:

$$CH_3CH_2CO\cdot COOH \rightarrow CH_3CH_2CHO + CO_2$$

Oxalacetic and α-ketoglutaric acids are also decomposed, as well as a number of the keto acids formed by oxidative deamination of amino acids (Meister, 1952). Especially vigorous is the decomposition of pyruvic acid:

$$CH_3COCOOH \rightarrow CH_3CHO + CO_2$$

The rate of production of CO_2 from pyruvic acid is faster than the production of CO_2 from glucose itself. The enzyme concerned, *carboxylase*, is widely distributed in yeasts, fungi, and higher plants. It has a pH optimum between pH 4 and 5, and requires the diffusible coenzyme, *cocarboxylase*, or diphosphothiamine, described above.

The presence of carboxylase, and the ease with which acetaldehyde is reduced by yeast, led both Neuberg and Kostytschev to conclude that fermentation proceeds via the formation and decarboxylation of pyruvic acid and subsequent reduction:

$$\text{Hexose} \rightarrow CH_3COCOOH \rightarrow CH_3CHO \xrightarrow{2(H)} CH_3CH_2OH + CO_2$$

Thus, the CO_2 of fermentation comes from the carboxyl group of pyruvic acid. This was the first instance of the general rule that *all* CO_2 produced biologically comes from carboxyl groups.

Several proofs of the scheme above have been given. If $CaCO_3$ be added during fermentation of glucose, calcium pyruvate is precipitated

(Fernbach and Schoen, 1914). The best evidence, however, is given by Neuberg's fixation process, or *Abfangverfahren*. This consists in adding sodium bisulfite to a fermenting mixture of yeast and sugar. The acetaldehyde-bisulfite compound is precipitated, and a new substance, *glycerol*, accumulates. Simultaneously the yield of alcohol and CO_2 decreases.

The production of glycerol from sugar attracted great interest, because no sooner had it been worked out than Germany found herself in World War I, with a drastic shortage of glycerol, due to the lack of imported fats. By 1917 it is estimated that the process was making over 1000 tons of glycerol per month, giving a 15 to 20 per cent yield on the basis of sugar fermented. Some writers have claimed that without this process the Germans would not have been able to wage war after the end of 1917.[5] In place of sulfite, two other substances that combine with acetaldehyde, namely, dimedon and semicarbazone, have been used in later experiments with similar results. With *Sacch. rouxii* oxygen has the same effect (Spencer and Shu, 1957). This yeast forms arabitol as well as glycerol. The fermentation has also been carried out with yeasts "adapted" to the presence of magnesium sulfite (Underkofler *et al.*, 1951).

Not only does the formation of acetaldehyde-bisulfite prove the theory outlined above, but the appearance of the glycerol proves something else. One mole of glycerol appears for every mole of acetaldehyde-bisulfite formed. Had the acetaldehyde not been removed, it would have been hydrogenated to alcohol. Hence the glycerol *must contain the hydrogen which would have been accepted by acetaldehyde.* The only compound that could be hydrogenated to glycerol, $C_3H_8O_3$, would be a *triose*, $C_3H_6O_3$. This triose actually consists of a mixture of the phosphorylated derivatives of glyceraldehyde and dihydroxyacetone:

$$
\begin{array}{ccc}
\text{CHO} & & \text{CH}_2\text{OH} \\
| & \xrightleftharpoons[\text{Isomerase}]{} & | \\
\text{CHOH} & & \text{CO} \\
| & & | \\
\text{CH}_2\text{O·H}_2\text{PO}_3 & & \text{CH}_2\text{O·H}_2\text{PO}_3 \\
\text{3-Phosphoglyceraldehyde} & & \text{Phosphodihydroxyacetone}
\end{array}
$$

These two substances are in equilibrium with each other through the enzyme isomerase. (Under physiological conditions the equilibrium ratio is about 95 per cent phosphodihydroxyacetone.)

Neuberg considered the normal fermentation the *first form*, and

[5] In spite of his great scientific services to his country through development of the glycerol fermentation, Carl Neuberg was unceremoniously driven out of Germany by the Nazis early in 1935.

the bisulfite-glycerol fermentation the *second form*. He also discovered
a *third form* of fermentation, occurring in the presence of weak alkali.
Here acetic acid is produced, and the yield of alcohol falls to half the
normal. This process is *dismutation;* two molecules of acetaldehyde
react together to form one of alcohol and one of acetic acid:

$$CH_3CHO + CH_3CHO \rightarrow CH_3CH_2OH + CH_3COOH$$

The reaction is catalyzed by two enzymes, aldehyde dehydrogenase
and alcohol dehydrogenase, linked by DPN (Racker, 1949). Since

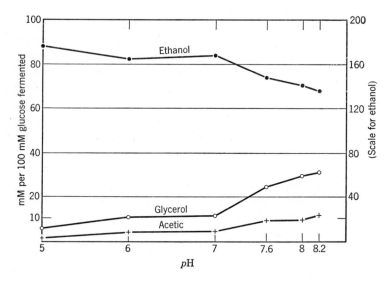

FIGURE XI–2

Industrial glycerol fermentation. Increase in the yield of glycerol by maintaining
the alcoholic fermentation at alkaline *p*H. Note corresponding decrease in ethanol
and increase in acetate. (From A. C. Neish and A. C. Blackwood, *Canad. J. Technol.*,
29:123–129, 1951. By courtesy of Canadian National Research Council.)

acetaldehyde is thus removed and cannot act as hydrogen acceptor,
glycerol accumulates here too. For each mole of acetic acid, two (to
three) moles of glycerol appear.

This reaction has been considered for industrial glycerol manufacture, but the fermentation slows down markedly in alkali. By adding
acid or alkali continuously, the *p*H can be held constant, giving results
shown in Figure XI–2 (Neish and Blackwood, 1951). Increasing the
glucose concentration to 25 per cent also increases the formation of
glycerol, giving yields above 30 per cent of the glucose fermented.

From all the above experiments it is clear that the acetaldehyde theory is fully established, and it has not been seriously questioned.

8. THE EARLY STAGES OF HEXOSE BREAKDOWN

Understanding of the first stages, which were for a long time puzzling, only became possible by the recognition that both hexoses and trioses react in the form of their *phosphate esters*. The recognition of the phosphotrioses[6] is due to Meyerhof and Kiessling (1933–1935) and to Barrenscheen (1933), who showed that phosphoglyceraldehyde is fermented at least as fast as glucose. Synthesis of (racemic) phosphoglyceraldehyde is due to Fischer and Baer (1932), and its isolation (in the D-form) to Meyerhof and co-workers.

STEP 1. The two phosphotriose molecules, phosphoglyceraldehyde and phosphodihydroxyacetone, are formed from one diphosphofructose molecule by the enzyme *aldolase*. This aldolase reaction is reversible (Warburg and Christian, 1943) which is very important for synthesis, since it means that hexose can be formed directly from triose (see Fig. XI–3).

STEP 2. The phosphoglyceraldehyde first takes up a molecule of inorganic phosphate and at the same time is dehydrogenated to 1,3-diphosphoglyceric acid, or phosphoglyceryl phosphate (isolated by Negelein and Brömel, 1939):

$$
\begin{array}{l}
H_2CO\!-\!H_2PO_3 \\
\mid \\
HCOH \qquad + DPN^+ + H_3PO_4 \rightarrow \\
\mid \\
O\!=\!CH
\end{array}
\qquad
\begin{array}{l}
H_2CO\!-\!H_2PO_3 \\
\mid \\
HCOH \qquad + DPNH + H^+ \\
\mid \\
O\!=\!CO \sim H_2PO_3
\end{array}
$$

The hydrogen is accepted by DPN (cozymase, NAD), the hydrogen-transferring enzyme being *phosphoglyceraldehyde dehydrogenase*. This complex reaction was demonstrated very elegantly by Warburg and Christian (1939), who called it the "oxidizing reaction of fermenta-

---

[6] The names of the phosphorylated compounds are confusing and completely inconsistent. There were good historical reasons for this, but there seems very little reason to retain this nomenclature today. The phosphate compound of glucose is called glucose-*phosphate*, that of glycerol is glycero*phosphoric acid*, and that of glyceric acid is *phospho*glyceric acid. In the present treatment, order has been introduced, perhaps rashly, by adopting the prefix *phospho-* for all but the hexose compounds (these being more hallowed by time than the others). Thus glycerophosphoric acid becomes *phosphoglycerol*, glyceraldehyde-phosphate becomes *phosphoglyceraldehyde*, and dihydroxyacetone phosphate becomes *phosphodihydroxyacetone*, while *phosphoglyceric* and *phospho(enol)pyruvic* acids remain unchanged.

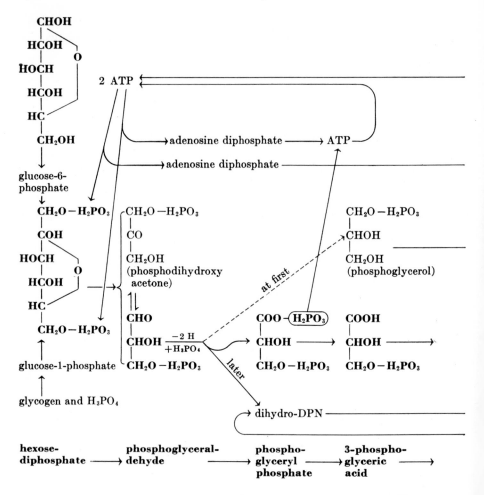

FIGURE
The alcoholic

tion." If phosphoglyceraldehyde is mixed with DPN and crystalline phosphoglyceraldehyde dehydrogenase (which they isolated), the DPN is not reduced unless inorganic phosphate is added. The rate of formation of reduced DPN varies with the phosphate concentration; arsenate will shift the equilibrium drastically (see below).

These phenomena are explained by the nature of the aldehyde dehydrogenase enzyme, which contains both two reactive —SH groups and two molecules of the coenzyme DPN (Racker and Krimsky, 1952; Velick et al., 1953). The aldehyde combines with the SH, then trans-

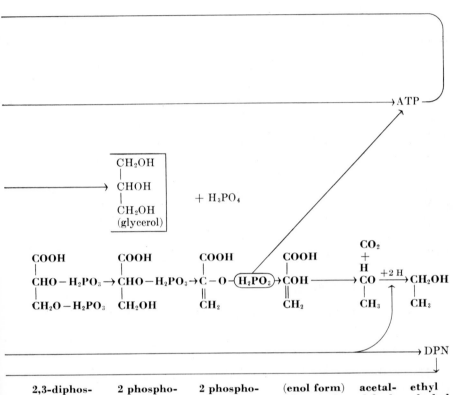

2,3-diphos-   2 phospho-   2 phospho-   (enol form)   acetal-   ethyl
phoglyceric → glyceric → enolpyruvic → of) pyruvic → dehyde →alcohol
acid   acid   acid   acid

XI-3
fermentation.

fers its hydrogen to the DPN, which makes the carbon-sulfur linkage very reactive, so that it is attacked by a phosphate ion, setting free the acyl phosphate:

where R = $\begin{array}{c} \text{H}_2\text{CO}-\text{H}_2\text{PO}_3 \\ | \\ \text{HCOH} \\ | \end{array}$ and E is the enzyme. When the SH group is

attacked and bound by Hg-compounds (Chap. XXIV, sec. 1), the enzyme can no longer bind DPN, so that the two groups are, probably, very close together (Velick, 1953), and it is this which doubtless makes the hydrogen transfer possible.

The phosphate linkage to a double-bonded carbon atom in 1,3-diphosphoglyceric acid is "energy-rich" (cf. Table V–1, p. 202); it would not have been formed in appreciable concentration by phosphorylation of 3-phosphoglyceric acid, since its formation requires about 10,000 calories. This energy is furnished by the dehydrogenation of the phosphoaldehyde (Meyerhof and Oesper, 1947).

Because of the high bond energy, diphosphoglyceric acid can phosphorylate a phosphate acceptor, which is adenosine diphosphate, converting this to the triphosphate, ATP. The enzyme responsible is called *phosphoglyceric phosphokinase*. The resulting dephosphorylated compound is 3-D-phosphoglyceric acid:

$$\begin{array}{ccc} \text{H}_2\text{C}\cdot\text{O}\cdot\text{H}_2\text{PO}_3 & & \text{H}_2\text{C}\cdot\text{O}\cdot\text{H}_2\text{PO}_3 \\ | & & | \\ \text{HCOH} & + \text{ADP} \rightleftarrows & \text{HCOH} \quad + \text{ATP} \\ | & & | \\ \text{O}{=}\text{C}\cdot\text{O} \sim \text{H}_2\text{PO}_3 & & \text{O}{=}\text{C}\cdot\text{OH} \end{array}$$

Hence the over-all change is that the inorganic phosphate which was taken up in the first step is converted to ATP, while the phosphoglyceraldehyde is dehydrogenated to the acid. This compound was first identified in an alcoholic fermentation proceeding in presence of fluoride (Nilsson, 1930). The over-all reaction:

3-Phosphoglyceraldehyde + DPN$^+$ $\rightleftarrows$ 3-Phosphoglyceric acid + DPNH + H$^+$

yields 7500 to 10,000 calories (Meyerhof and Oesper, 1947) in going from left to right.

STEP 3. The 3-phosphoglyceric acid now undergoes a curious set of changes (Sutherland, Posternak, and Cori, 1949). A small amount of it is rephosphorylated, probably by ATP, to form the 2,3-diphospho-derivative. (Both phosphate groups in this are ordinary esters linked by low-energy bonds.) The diphospho- compound then gives up the phosphate group in the 3 position to phosphorylate the 2 position of another molecule:

$$\underset{\text{2,3-Diphospho-}}{\overset{\displaystyle CH_2O \cdot H_2PO_3}{\underset{\displaystyle COOH}{\overset{\displaystyle |}{\underset{\displaystyle |}{CHO \cdot H_2PO_3}}}}} + \underset{\text{3-Phospho-}}{\overset{\displaystyle CH_2O \cdot H_2PO_3}{\underset{\displaystyle COOH}{\overset{\displaystyle |}{\underset{\displaystyle |}{CHOH}}}}} \rightleftharpoons \underset{\text{2-Phospho-}}{\overset{\displaystyle CH_2OH}{\underset{\displaystyle COOH}{\overset{\displaystyle |}{\underset{\displaystyle |}{CHO \cdot H_2PO_3}}}}} + \underset{\text{2,3-Diphospho-}}{\overset{\displaystyle CH_2O \cdot H_2PO_3}{\underset{\displaystyle COOH}{\overset{\displaystyle |}{\underset{\displaystyle |}{CHO \cdot H_2PO_3}}}}}$$

Thus, a new molecule of 2-3-diphosphoglyceric acid is formed, which can now react with a second molecule of the 3-phospho acid. The net result is conversion of one molecule of 3-phospho acid to a molecule of the 2-phospho acid. The 2,3-diphospho acid is acting as a coenzyme. The enzyme catalyzing this reaction (*phosphoglyceromutase*) is thus a phosphate-transferring enzyme or "trans-phosphatase."

STEP 4. The resulting 2-phosphoglyceric acid loses a molecule of water under the influence of another enzyme, *enolase*, to produce phosphoenol-pyruvic acid, i.e., pyruvic acid in the enol form, phosphorylated at the OH group:

$$\underset{\text{2-Phosphoglyceric}}{\overset{\displaystyle CH_2OH}{\underset{\displaystyle COOH}{\overset{\displaystyle |}{\underset{\displaystyle |}{HC-O \cdot H_2PO_3}}}}} \underset{\text{enolase}}{\rightleftharpoons} \underset{\text{Phosphoenolpyruvic}}{\overset{\displaystyle CH_2}{\underset{\displaystyle COOH}{\overset{\displaystyle \|}{\underset{\displaystyle |}{C-O \sim H_2PO_3}}}}} + H_2O$$

This reaction is comparable to the conversion of malate to fumarate by fumarase (see Chap. V). It is of special interest because of its sensitivity to poisoning by fluoride. Enolase requires magnesium ions for its activity, and in presence of fluoride a magnesium fluorophosphate is formed which combines with the protein enzyme and inactivates it (Warburg and Christian, 1942). As a result, 3-phospho- and 2-phosphoglyceric acids accumulate and could be isolated by Nilsson and by Meyerhof, respectively.

STEP 5. The next step is the dephosphorylation of the phosphoenolpyruvic acid. Like the 1-phosphate bond in 1,3-diphosphoglyceric acid, the phosphate bond here is linked to a doubly bonded carbon atom and is therefore energy-rich. As before, it phosphorylates ADP, which as a result is converted to the triphosphate.

Thus, in these steps two molecules of ADP have been converted to ATP. Since both energy-rich phosphate bonds retain their energy in ATP, they can react with other substrates and phosphorylate them. In this system they react with glucose, in presence of the enzyme *hexokinase*, to produce first the 6-phosphate, then fructose-1,6-diphosphate (Harden-Young ester). Thus, the cycle is started again (*step 1*).

A little of the phosphoenol-pyruvate suffers a different fate; it combines with CO_2 (see Chap. XIII). The phosphate is split off at the same time, and oxaloacetate results. This is then reduced to malic and succinic acids or can be transaminated to aspartic acid (p. 313). These reactions, which account for a group of minor products, are inhibited by oxygen (Stoppani *et al.*, 1958), and hence the amounts of these acids vary with the conditions.

STEPS 6 AND 7. In the formation of phosphoglyceric acid, a molecule of DPN has been reduced. The reduced DPN has two alternative fates. At first it is dehydrogenated by phosphodihydroxyacetone to produce 3-phosphoglycerol:

$$
\begin{array}{cc}
CH_2O \cdot H_2PO_3 & CH_2O \cdot H_2PO_3 \\
| & | \\
CO \quad + DPNH + H^+ \rightarrow & CHOH \quad + DPN^+ \\
| & | \\
CH_2OH & CH_2OH
\end{array}
$$

which is hydrolyzed to glycerol by a phosphatase. It is in this way that small amounts of glycerol are formed in the normal fermentation (Pasteur).

Later, however, acetaldehyde appears, and this is much more reducible than phosphodihydroxyacetone. Therefore, from now on, whenever phosphoglyceraldehyde is dehydrogenated, the 2(H) resulting is taken up eventually by acetaldehyde. The role of DPN in carrying 2(H) from triose to acetaldehyde is parallel to that of ATP in carrying phosphate from triose to hexose. The cycle is thus complete. In Figure XI–3 the changes in sugar and triose are shown alongside the changes in the two coenzymes.

9. SOME ADDITIONAL POINTS

It remains to explain Harden and Young's initial finding that the fermentation by yeast juice, with added phosphate, comes to a stop, with accumulation of hexosediphosphate (Fig. XI–1). This is due to the peculiar mechanism of the reaction from phosphoglyceraldehyde to phosphoglyceric acid (*step 2*, above). Here the intermediate, 1,3-diphosphoglyceric acid, is produced by uptake of inorganic phosphate. Since the 1-phospho group has high energy, however, it phosphorylates ADP. Inorganic phosphate is thus continuously removed from the system and transferred to ATP which at once phosphorylates hexose with it. Hence hexosediphosphate accumulates, and the system comes to a standstill for want of ionic phosphate.

If arsenate is added, phosphorylation is interfered with because, instead of phosphoglyceryl phosphate, phosphoglyceryl arsenate is formed, and this hydrolyzes spontaneously to phosphoglyceric acid (Warburg and Christian, 1939). Hence inorganic phosphate is not taken up:

$$H_3AsO_4 + \begin{array}{c} CH_2O \cdot H_2PO_3 \\ | \\ CHOH \\ | \\ CHO \end{array} \rightleftharpoons \begin{array}{c} CH_2O \cdot H_2PO_3 \\ | \\ CHOH \\ | \\ CO \cdot O \cdot H_2AsO_3 \end{array} \rightarrow \begin{array}{c} CH_2O \cdot H_2PO_3 \\ | \\ CHOH \\ | \\ COOH \end{array}$$

The same result could be secured (Harden and MacFarlane, 1930) by adding a phosphatase preparation. In the living cell ATP is continuously being hydrolyzed by a pyrophosphatase (ATP-ase), but this enzyme is too unstable to survive the grinding of yeast into juice. Indeed, it is destroyed by autolysis, slow drying, or acetone treatment; i.e., by the very treatments used for most biochemical studies (Meyerhof, 1949). If yeast is quickly dried, and then broken by vibrating supersonically, its ATP-ase is largely retained. After washing, it needs the addition of DPN, ATP, phosphate, Mg^{++}, and either K^+ or NH_4^+, and will then ferment glucose at a steady rate (Meyerhof and Kaplan, 1951). Hexosephosphates definitely do not accumulate; phosphate is neither absorbed nor liberated to an appreciable extent. This behavior confirms the above explanation of the Harden and Young phenomenon.

It should be noted that this reaction is the only one using inorganic phosphate and is, therefore, of great importance; it is the route whereby free phosphate is able to enter the cycle.

The validity of the whole fermentation scheme was confirmed by fermenting glucose containing C^{14} in the 1 position (Koshland and Westheimer, 1950). About 95 per cent of the C^{14} was found in the CH_3 group of the alcohol, as predicted. The CO_2 contained about 3 per cent of the activity, probably owing to a small exchange of phosphate between the 1 and 3 positions of dihydroxyacetone.

Lastly, one of the initial steps shown in Figure XI–3 has not yet been mentioned. Yeast produces a small amount of alcohol and CO_2 when simply suspended in water. This "autofermentation" is at the expense of glycogen stored in the cell. The splitting of glycogen is a phosphorolysis, brought about by ATP, and yields glucose-1-phosphate. This compound enters the fermentation by being converted to glucose-6-phosphate, which involves a system exactly comparable to that converting 3-phosphoglyceric to 2-phosphoglyceric acid. The enzyme is called *phosphoglucomutase*, and its coenzyme is glucose-1,6-diphosphate (Leloir *et al.*, 1948–1949). Small amounts of this diphosphate are formed from glucose-1-phosphate, using ATP, by the enzyme glucose-1-phosphate-kinase. The diphosphate can then convert the 1-phosphate to the 6-phosphate:

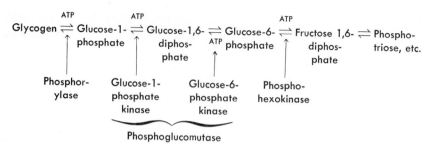

Phosphoglucomutase requires Mg and, like enolase, is readily poisoned by fluoride. Its reverse action leads to glycogen synthesis, but another enzyme, using uridine-diphosphoglucose (p. 467), is more important for this synthesis and probably controls it (Madsen, 1963).

10. ALCOHOLIC FERMENTATIONS BY BACTERIA

As mentioned in section 1, some bacteria produce alcohol from sugar. In several cases this involves routes differing from that followed by yeast. The best example is *Ps. lindneri* (formerly *Zymononas mobilis*) which, unlike other Pseudomonads, is an obligate sugar fermenter. Its fermentation produces the Mexican alcoholic drink, "pulque," made from the juice of Agave plants. *Ps. lindneri* ferments glucose or fructose (not mannose) to 45 per cent CO_2, 45 per cent ethanol, and up to 7 per cent of lactic acid (Kluyver and Hoppenbrouwers, 1931). When glucose labeled with C^{14} in the 1 position is fermented by this organism, practically all the activity is found in the CO_2 (Gibbs and de Moss, 1951). Now in the normal breakdown of hexosediphosphate (see sec. 8 above), it is carbon atoms 3 and 4 that produce the aldehyde groups and therefore the final CO_2; carbon atom 1 appears as CH_3 (Koshland and Westheimer, 1950). Thus, the alcohol represents carbon atoms 1 and 2, 5 and 6. With *Ps. lindneri*, glucose with C^{14} in the 3 and 4 positions yields half its C^{14} as CO_2 and half as ethanol, i.e., CO_2 comes from positions 1 and 4 and hence ethanol from 2 and 3, 5 and 6 (Gibbs and de Moss, 1954). "Thus," says Kluyver (1956), "the Mexican who enjoys his alcohol as produced by *Ps. lindneri* imbibes different carbon atoms of the sugar than does the American who takes it in the form of Bourbon whisky."

The key to understanding this fermentation was furnished by an aerobic organism, *Ps. saccharophila*, which produces pyruvic acid and a triose (Entner and Doudoroff, 1952; McGee and Doudoroff, 1954). In this case the first step is conversion of the glucose-6-phosphate, not to a diphosphate, but to 6-phospho-gluconic acid, I. This loses H_2O to form a new intermediate compound, 2-keto, 3-deoxy, 6-phosphogluconic acid, II, which Doudoroff and co-workers isolated. The compound splits to pyruvate and phosphoglyceraldehyde, III, and in *Ps. lindneri* this can be converted to a second molecule of pyruvate. Final formation of alcohol liberates carbon atoms 1 and 4 as CO_2:

CHO	COOH	COOH	COOH	CO_2	1
HCOH	HCOH	CO	CO $\xrightarrow{2(H)}$	CH_2OH	2
HOCH	→ HOCH	→ CH_2	→ CH_3	CH_3	3
HCOH	HCOH	HCOH	HCO	COOH	4
HCOH	HCOH	HCOH	HCOH $\xrightarrow[-2(H)]{}$	CO $\xrightarrow{2(H)}$	5
CH_2O—(P)	CH_2O—(P) +2(H)	CH_2O—(P)	CH_2O—(P)	CH_3	CH_2OH 6
G-6-P	6-Phospho-gluconic, I	II	III		

This explains the distribution of carbon atoms found for *Ps. lindneri* by Gibbs and de Moss; evidently, therefore, this organism uses the same pathway but carries the process all the way to alcohol and CO_2.

A peculiarity of this fermentation is that one of the two molecules of pyruvic acid arises directly from the hexonic acid and not via phosphoglyceraldehyde. As a result *no ATP* is produced in its formation. The second molecule arises via triosephosphate, and therefore ATP is produced as with yeast. Thus, the whole process yields only one ATP instead of two.

The alcohol produced by heterofermentative lactic bacteria such as Leuconostoc (see Chap. XII) arises in a somewhat different way; these bacteria produce lactic acid and alcohol. Here again glucose-1-C^{14} gives all its C^{14} in the form of CO_2, while glucose-3, 4-C^{14} gives half its C^{14} in the lactic acid and half in the ethanol (de Moss *et al.*, 1951). Phosphogluconic acid is the first intermediate, as above, but apparently this is decarboxylated to a phosphopentose, which is split, carbon atoms 1 and 2 becoming ethanol, while numbers 3, 4, and 5 yield lactate (Gunsalus and Gibbs, 1952):

COOH	CO_2 +		
HCOH	CH_2OH	CH_2OH	
HOCH	HOCH	CH_3 +	
HCOH →	HCOH →	CHO	COOH
HCOH	HCOH	HCOH	→ → → HCOH
CH_2O—(P)	CH_2O—(P)	CH_2O—(P)	CH_3

The last conversion, from triose to lactic acid, is described in Chapter XII. In presence of oxygen, the products are 1 mole each of lactic and acetic acids and CO_2 (Johnson and McCleskey, 1958).

Table XI–1 brings out several features of the fermentations by Leuconostoc. The results with glucose are as just stated. With fructose some of the hydrogen that would have formed ethanol is used to produce mannitol—a reduction characteristic for this genus. Correspondingly the dehydrogenated product acetate appears. As the hydrogen content decreases, through gluconate to ketogluconate, the ethanol continues to decrease and the acetate to take its place. The exact reactions leading to alcohol are obscure. Another peculiarity is that the intermediate can hardly be an ordinary phospho-pentose, since neither Leuconostoc nor *Ps. lindneri* can attack any of the pentose phosphates (de Moss, 1953).

TABLE XI–1. Fermentations by *Leuconostoc mesenteroides* (glucose in pH 7 buffer for 6 hours at 28° C, others with peptone and $CaCO_3$, for one week at 30° C)

(Data of de Moss [1953] and Blackwood and Blakley [1956], respectively.)
(Moles per 100 moles glucose fermented.)

	D-Glucose	D-Fructose	D-Gluconate	2-Keto-D-gluconate
CO_2	103	67	96	98
Ethanol	96	47 }63	41 }94	tr
Acetate	—	16	53	101
Lactate	89	64	98	99
Mannitol	—	33	—	—

The alcohol formed in the complex fermentations of the coliform bacteria (Chap. XIV) arises by yet another route, namely, from reduction of acetyl-coenzyme A. The giant sarcina, *Zymosarcina ventriculi*, making alcohol, acetic acid, CO_2, and H_2, may operate similarly (Chap. XV). Alcohol is also formed, along with traces of butanol and butyric acid, by a strain of *Cl. tetani* (Lerner and Pickett, 1945), but the pathway has not been studied.

The bacterial alcohol fermentations are thus based generally on hexose monophosphate instead of the diphosphate, and yield half as much ATP as does the yeast fermentation.

11. INHIBITION OF FERMENTATION BY OXYGEN: THE PASTEUR EFFECT

As stated on p. 203, Pasteur discovered that in air the growth of yeast was accelerated, while the consumption of sugar was reduced.

In air the yeast (in his own words) "ceases to be a ferment." With intermediate amounts of oxygen the rate of sugar consumption was decreased proportionately.

Evidently two phenomena are to be distinguished. The effect of oxidation on growth is easy to understand, since, as seen in Chapter V, the oxidation of a molecule of glucose can produce 30 to 40 energy-rich phosphate bonds, while its fermentation can produce only 4. These bonds are the main mechanism whereby the energy of respiration becomes built into the chemical energy of synthesis. We should expect, therefore, that for each glucose molecule broken down, 8 to 10 times as much yeast would be produced in air as anaerobically. Pasteur actually found this, for in his experiments (1861) 1 gm of yeast was produced by 4 to 10 gm of sugar aerobically, or by 60 to 80 gm anaerobically, a ratio of 8 to 15 times.

The second phenomenon is more obscure; clearly oxidation in some way slows down the attack on sugar. The phenomenon is shown not only by yeasts and their relatives but also to varying extents by Lactobacilli and Propionibacteria; it is found also in animal tissue, especially retina, and in higher plants. At least five explanations have been advanced but none of them has been proved.

One of the most widely accepted is that oxidation leads to such efficient phosphorylation that all the adenylic acid and ADP in the aerobic cell are converted to ATP, and thus not enough ADP remains to accept the phosphate from diphosphoglyceric and phosphoenol-pyruvic acids. Sugar utilization is thus decreased because of a shortage of ADP.[7] In support of this idea, Meyerhof and Fiala (1951) found that, with the quickly dried yeast described in section 9, nitrophenol decreases the production of CO_2 anaerobically and increases it aerobically, i.e., it prevents the Pasteur effect. Since nitrophenols are known to "uncouple" phosphorylation from oxidation, i.e., to prevent phosphate from being converted to ATP, it can be concluded that the Pasteur effect is prevented by decreasing the ATP formation.

An attractive and simpler view depends on the ready oxidizability of phosphoglyceraldehyde dehydrogenase. Admittedly the critical work has been done on this enzyme in pea-seed extract rather than in yeast, but the pea-seed extract shows a typical Pasteur effect (Hatch and Turner, 1959, 1960).

Phosphoglyceraldehyde dehydrogenase depends for its activity on

[7] As originally advanced by Johnson (1941) the theory proposed that not only ADP but also inorganic phosphate are limiting factors under aerobic conditions. As far as the phosphate is concerned, therefore, it would be identical with the theory in section 9. However, in view of the fact that added phosphate does not prevent the Pasteur effect, it seems that the limitations by ADP and adenylic acid are the main ones.

an —SH group with which the aldehyde combines (p. 446). In air this group oxidizes to the —S—S— form, which is inactive. Hatch and Turner found that within an hour in air the total content of protein —SH in the extract fell by a third, and phosphoglyceraldehyde dehydrogenase activity by 70 per cent. The oxidation is catalyzed by a metal. Addition of DPNH or of a mixture of hexose phosphate with DPN reactivated the enzyme; in the second case the hexose phosphate was being metabolized to reduce the DPN. The DPNH reduces the —S—S—, a special *protein —S—S reductase* catalyzing the reaction. It is clear that if phosphoglyceraldehyde is not dehydrogenated to phosphoglyceric acid, it will accumulate in the form of hexose phosphate (since the aldolase reaction is readily reversible), and thus oxygen, by oxidizing the —SH, prevents the breakdown of sugar.

In view of the lessened yield of ATP under anaerobic conditions, (one or two per hexose instead of 32 in air) the increased rate of sugar consumption represents a most appropriate control mechanism.

REFERENCES

Barrenscheen, H. K., and Klebermass-Messiner, L. 1933. *Biochem. Z.*, **265**:157–159; Barrenscheen, H. K., and Beneschovsky, H. 1933. *Biochem. Z.*, **265**:159–168.
*Bessey, E. A. 1950. Morphology and Taxonomy of Fungi. Philadelphia, Blakiston, pp. 334–360.
Betz, A. 1960–1962. *Arch. Mikrobiol.*, **35**:1–33; **44**:253–258 (1962).
Blackwood, A. C., and Blakley, E. R. 1956. *Canad. J. Microbiol.*, **2**:741–746.
Boffi, V.; Cavallero, G.; and Lucarelli, A. 1959. *Arch. Sci. biol.* (Bologna), **43**:428–437.
Boyland, E. 1930. *Biochem. J.*, **24**:350–354.
Buchner, E. 1897. *Ber.*, **30**:117–124, 1110–1113.
Buchner, E., and Rapp, R. 1897–1899. *Ber.*, **30**:2668–2678; **31**:209–217, 1084–1094, 1531–1533; **32**:127–137, 2086–2094.
Cori, C. F. 1942. Phosphorylation of Carbohydrates. In, A Symposium on Respiratory Enzymes. Madison, Wis., Univ. Wisconsin Press, pp. 175–189.
Davoll, J.; Lythgoe, B.; and Todd, A. R. 1948. *J. Chem. Soc.*, pp. 967–969.
Dickens, F. 1938. *Biochem. J.*, **32**:1645–1653.
Entner, N., and Doudoroff, M. 1952. *J. Biol. Chem.*, **196**:853–862.
Euler, H. von, and Schlenk, F. 1937. *Z. physiol. Chem.*, **246**:64–82; also *Naturwiss.* **24**:794–795 (1936).
Fernbach, A., and Schoen, M. 1914. *Compt. rend. Acad. sci.*, **158**:1719–1722.
Fischer, H. O. L., and Baer, H. 1932. *Ber. d. chem. Ges.*, **65**:337–345; also *Naturwiss.* **25**:588 (1937).
Gibbs, M., and de Moss, R. D. 1951. *Federation Proc.*, **10**:189; *Arch. Biochem. Biophys.*, **34**:478–479.
Gibbs, M., and de Moss, R. D. 1954. *J. Biol. Chem.*, **207**:689–694.
Gunsalus, I. C., and Gibbs, M. 1952. *J. Biol. Chem.*, **194**:871–875.
*Harden, A. 1932. Alcoholic Fermentation, 4th ed. London, Longmans, Green and Company. 243 pp.

Harden, A., and MacFarlane, M. G. 1930. *Biochem. J.*, **24**:343–349; cf. also Harden, A., and Young, W. J., 1911. *Proc. Roy. Soc.*, **B83**:451–475.

Harden, A., and Young, W. J. 1906. *Proc. Roy. Soc.*, **B77**:405–420.

Hatch, M. D., and Turner, J. F. 1959, 1960. *Biochem. J.*, **72**:524–532; **75**:66–72; **76**:556–562 (1960).

Ivanov, L. 1905–1907. *Sc. Trav. Soc. Naturalistes de St. Petersbourg*, **34**:(1905); *Z. physiol. Chem.*, **50**:281–288 (1907).

Johnson, M. J. 1941. *Science*, **94**:200.

Johnson, M. K., and McCleskey, C. S 1958. *J. Bact.*, **75**:98–101.

Kiessling, K. H. 1956–1959. *Arkiv. Kemi*, **10**:279–282; *Biochim. Biophys. Acta*, **20**: 293–298; *Acta chem. Scand.*, **12**:663–667 (1958); **13**:1358–1362 (1959).

Kluyver, A. J. 1956. In, The Microbe's Contribution to Biology. A. J. Kluyver and C. B. van Niel. Cambridge, Mass., Harvard University Press, p. 39.

Kluyver, A. J., and Hoppenbrouwers, W. J. 1931. *Arch. Mikrobiol.*, **2**:245–260.

Kolachov, P., and Nicholson, L. W. 1951. *Econ. Botany*, **5**:60–81.

Koshland, D. E., and Westheimer, F. H. 1950. *J. Amer. Chem. Soc.*, **72**:3383–3388.

Kossowicz, A., and Loew, W. 1913. *Z. Gärungsphysiol.*, **2**:87; cf. also Neuberg, C., and Welde, E. 1914. *Biochem. Z.*, **67**:111–118.

Kostytschev, S., and Hübbenet, E. 1912–1913. *Z. physiol. Chem.*, **79**: 359–374; **85**: 408–411; cf. Kostytschev, S. 1912. *Ibid.*, **79**: 130–145.

Kubowitz, F., and Lüttgens, W. 1941. *Biochem. Z.*, **307**:170–180.

Kurth, E. F. 1946. *Ind. Eng. Chem.*, **38**:204–207, 617–619.

Leloir, L. F.; Trucco, R. E.; Cardini, C. E.; Paladini, A.; and Caputto, R. 1948–1949. *Arch. Biochem.*, **19**:339–340; **22**:87–100; **23**:55–56.

Lerner, E., and Pickett, M. J. 1945. *Arch. Biochem.*, **8**:183–196.

*Lipmann, F. 1941. Metabolic Generation and Utilization of Phosphate Bond Energy. *Adv. in Enzymol.*, **1**:99–162.

Lohmann, K. 1935. *Biochem. Z.*, **282**:120–123.

Lohmann, K., and Schuster, P. 1937. *Biochem. Z.*, **294**:188–214.

Madsen, N. B. 1963. *Canad. J. Biochem. Physiol.*, **41**:561–571.

McClary, D. O.; Nulty, W. L.; and Miller, G. R. 1959. *J. Bact.*, **78**:362–368.

McGee, W., and Doudoroff, M. 1954. *J. Biol. Chem.*, **210**: 617–626.

Meister, A. 1952. *J. Biol. Chem.*, **197**:309–317.

Meyerhof, O. 1918. *Z. physiol. Chem.*, **101**:165–175; **102**:1–32.

Meyerhof, O. 1949. *J. Biol. Chem.*, **180**:575–586.

Meyerhof, O., and Fiala, S. 1951. *Biochim. Biophys. Acta*, **6**:1–12.

Meyerhof, O., and Kaplan, A. 1951. *Arch. Biochem. Biophys.*, **33**:282–297.

Meyerhof, O., and Kiessling, W. 1933–1935. *Biochem. Z.*, **264**:40–71 (1933); **267**:313–348 (1934); **276**:239–253; **280**:99–109 (1935).

Meyerhof, O., and Kiessling, W. 1935. *Biochem. Z.*, **279**:40–48.

Meyerhof, O., and Oesper, P. 1947. *J. Biol. Chem.*, **170**:1–22.

Michelson, A. M., and Todd, A. R. 1949. *J. Chem. Soc.*, pp. 2487–2490.

de Moss, R. D. 1953. *J. Cell. Comp. Physiol.*, **41** (Suppl.): 207–224.

de Moss, R. D.; Bard, R. C.; and Gunsalus, I. C. 1951. *J. Bact.*, **62**:499–511.

*Mrak, E. M., and Phaff, H. J. 1948. Yeasts. *Ann. Rev. Microbiol.*, **2**:1–46.

Negelein, E., and Brömel, H. 1939. *Biochem. Z.*, **301**:135–136; **303**:132–144.

Neish, A. C., and Blackwood, A. C. 1951. *Canad. J. Techn.*, **29**:123–129.

Neuberg, C. 1918. *Biochem. Z.*, **88**:432–436.

Neuberg, C., and Karczag, L. 1911. *Biochem. Z.*, **44**:2477–2479; Neuberg, C., and Kerb, J. 1912. *Ibid.*, **47**:405–412, 413–420.

Nilsson, R. 1930. Studien über den enzymatischen Kohlehydratabbau. *Arkiv. Kemi Min. Geol.*, **A10**, No. 7: 135 pp.

Oppenoorth, W. F. F. 1956. *Nature*, **178**:992–993.

Pasteur, L. 1860. Memoire sur la fermentation alcoolique. *Ann. chim. phys.*, **58**:323–426.

Pasteur, L. 1861. *Compt. rend.*, **52**:1260–1264.

Pasteur, L. 1873. Etudes sur le vin, ses maladies, etc., 2nd ed. Paris, F. Savy.

Racker, E. 1949. *J. Biol. Chem.*, **177**:883–892.

Racker, E., and Krimsky, I. 1952. *J. Biol. Chem.*, **198**:731–743.

Robison, R. 1922. *Biochem. J.*, **16**:809–824; Robison, R., and King, E. J. 1931. *Ibid.*, **25**:323–328.

Rossi-Fanelli, A.; Ipater, P. L.; Fasella, P.; and Marchetti, A. 1960. *Rendiconti Acad. Naz. Lincei*, **29**:22–27.

Schwann, Th. 1837. *Poggendorf's Ann.*, **41** (Series 2, vol. 11): 184–193.

Spencer, J. F. T., and Shu, P. 1957. *Canad. J. Microbiol.*, **3**:559–567.

Stoppani, A. O. M.; Conches, L.; de Favelukes, S. L. S.; and Sacerdote, F. L. 1968. *Biochem. J.*, **70**:438–455.

Sutherland, E. W.; Posternak, T. Z.; and Cori, C. F. 1949. *J. Biol. Chem.*, **179**:501–52.

Underkofler, L. A.; Fulmer, E. I.; Henry, R. J.; and Lees, T. M. 1951. *Iowa State Coll. J. Sci.*, **26**:111–133, 135–147.

Velick, S. F. 1953. *J. Biol. Chem.*, **203**:563–573.

Velick, S. F.; Hayes, J. E., Jr.; and Harting, J. 1953. *J. Biol. Chem.*, **203**:527–1544.

Warburg, O., and Christian, W. 1939. *Biochem. Z.*, **303**:40–68.

Warburg, O., and Christian, W. 1942. *Biochem. Z.*, **310**:384–421.

Warburg, O., and Christian, W. 1943. *Biochem. Z.*, **314**:149–176.

Winlock, H. E. 1921. *Bull. Natl. Mus. of Art* (USA), **16**:12–32.

Wöhler, F., and Liebig, J. v. 1839. *Liebig's Ann.*, **29**:100–104.

CHAPTER XII

The Lactic Fermentation

Remember, I beseech thee, that thou hast fashioned me as clay; and wilt thou bring me into the dust again? Hast thou not poured me out as milk, and curdled me like cheese? . . .

JOB 10:10

In contrast to the alcoholic fermentation, which is mainly carried out by fungi, the conversion of sugar to lactic acid is typically a bacterial process. The same fermentation occurs in animal muscle, and indeed much of the work on the mechanism of fermentation has been carried out on preparations of muscle. Lactic acid may also be a product of mixed fermentations by both bacteria and fungi, in which it is produced along with acetic acid, CO_2, and other products.

1. THE LACTIC BACTERIA

A. The Group as a Whole

The thorough studies of Orla-Jensen (1919) made clear that the true lactic acid bacteria are gram-positive, nonmotile, and nonspore-forming, and include both spheres and rods. Except for some strains of *L. plantarum* they do not usually contain catalase, and consequently many of them produce H_2O_2 when growing in air (Chap. V, sec. 6).

Three groups produce lactic acid from sugar in 80 to 98 per cent yield (in acid media), with only traces of by-products. These *homofermentative* forms include:

Thermobacterium: long rods, optimum temperature about 40° C or higher, making either inactive or laevolactic acid in concentrations up to 3 per cent (0.33 M).

Streptobacterium: chain-forming rods, optimum temperature about 30° C, making inactive or dextrolactic acid up to about 1.5 per cent.

Streptococcus:[1] chain-forming spheres with various optimum temperatures, making dextrolactic acid in concentrations below 1 per cent. Some are hemolytic (see below). *Sc. pyogenes* is not strictly a "lactic" organism at all, in the special sense that it will not grow in milk. A few strains of cocci, called Tetracoccus or *Pediococcus* (Pederson *et al.*, 1954) form tetrads instead of chains; they are often called Sarcinae but are evidently related to the lactic Streptococci. Three typical streptococci are shown in Figure XII–1, *A-C*, and a long-chain streptobacterium in XII–1, *D*.

Three other groups are *heterofermentative*, i.e., produce a mixed fermentation in which only about half the sugar is converted to lactic acid, the remainder appearing as CO_2, H_2, alcohol, formic or acetic acid. These are:

Betabacterium: growing on vegetables or cheese, but not milk, making inactive lactic acid (this genus name is no longer used).

Betacoccus (or *Leuconostoc*): growing on ensilage and other plant material, in which they attack pectins and the resulting pentoses; when the ensilage is fed to cattle, the organisms appear in the milk. These bacteria are noted for growth in sucrose solution with formation of much slimy polysaccharide. The "frog's egg bacterium" (*Leuconostoc mesenteroides*) often makes trouble in sugar refineries for this reason.

Bacterium bifidum: a strict anaerobe showing branched and forked forms, found in the intestinal flora of milk-fed infants. This and a related similar organism are probably anaerobic Corynebacteria, being of very variable morphology (Hayward *et al.*, 1955). They produce lactic and acetic acids, without CO_2. Several other anaerobic branched forms occur in feces or tissue fluids (Prévot, 1938).

The major properties of the lactic organisms are summarized in Table XII–1, which is condensed from Orla-Jensen, Henneberg, Bergey, and others.

In addition to the true lactic acid bacteria, milk, cream, and cheese often contain members of the coli-aerogenes group of gram-negative rods, which produce lactic acid among other substances (see Chap. XIV); also colored micrococci, and some very small gram-positive rods, perhaps related to the propionic bacteria, which occur sometimes in feces and were named by Orla-Jensen Microbacteria. These last are facultative anaerobes but contain catalase (Doetsch and Pelczar, 1948). Of the three known species, one is motile and thermophilic (optimum 50° C); it is homofermentative (Bolcato, 1957). Furthermore, recent

[1] Streptococcus is abbreviated *Sc.* throughout.

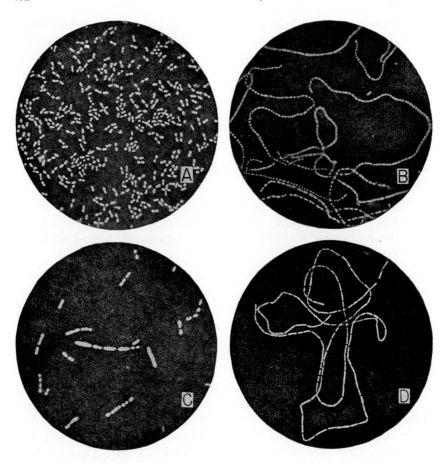

FIGURE XII–1

A–C. Lactic streptococci.
    A. Streptococcus lactis.
    B. Streptococcus cremoris.
    C. Streptococcus thermophilus.
    D. A lactic Streptobacterium, *L. casei.*
    Bacteria mounted in nigrosine. 1150 ×.
    (Photos S. Orla-Jensen. From *Dairy Bacteriology.* Copyright 1931 by the Blakiston Co., Philadelphia and New York.)

work on removing bacteria from milk by centrifuging has led to the recognition that much of the flora consists of saprophytic Mycobacteria, some of which are thermoduric.

The terminology of Orla-Jensen has been altered by Bergey *et al.*, who have combined all the rod-shaped lactic bacteria into one genus,

TABLE XII–1. Summary of the Lactic Bacteria

Group	Species	Lactic Acid Formed	Fermentation Type	Optimum Temp. °C	Morphology	Habitat	Pentose Fermentation	Casein Liquefaction	Other Features
Lactobacillus: (Thermobact.)	8	l- or L-, up to 3%	Homo-	37–60 usually ca. 40	Long rods with granules; the rough strains longer and thinner than the smooth	Milk, cheese, yogurt, etc.; *L. delbrückii* from plant mashes	–	+ most	All ferment lactose
(Streptobact.)	3	l- or D-, up to 1.5%	Homo-	28–32	Long rods, forming long chains	Milk and cheese; *L. plantarum* from mashes and pickles	±	+	All ferment lactose
(Betabact.)	4 or 5*	l	Hetero-	28–40	Rods, usually short	Plants and yeast; *L. pastorianus* from spoiled beer	+	–	Fructose reduced to mannitol
Streptococcus:† Pyogenes group. (Lancefield's groups A, B, and C)	5?	D-	Homo-	35–40 *No growth at 45*	Spheres (to short rods) forming long chains in broth	Human and animal parasites	–	+	β-hemolytic
Viridans group.	5 or 6‡	D-	Homo-	35–40 *Will grow at 45*	Spheres in pairs or short or long chains	Saliva, respiratory tract, and feces; *Sc. thermophilus* in milk	(+) a few strains	?	Usually α-hemolytic
Lactis group.	2 or 3§	D-, up to 0.7%	Homo-	25–30 *No growth at 45*	Short (*Sc. lactis*) or long (*Sc. cremoris*) chains	Milk and cheese	Usually –	(+) some	
Enterococcus group. (Lancefield's group D)	3 or 4	D-	Homo-	35–40 *Will grow at 45*	Pairs and short chains	Milk; feces	+ a few	*Sc. liquifaciens* only +	α or β hemolytic; can grow at pH 9.6
Pediococcus	1 to 3	l, up to 0.9%	Homo-	22–32	Spheres in tetrads	Beer, fermenting vegetables	weakly +	–	"Sarcinae of beer"
Leuconostoc (= Betacoccus)	3	L- or DL-	Hetero-‖	ca. 25	Short or long chains	Plant mashes, sugar, milk#	+	–	Fructose reduced to mannitol
Bovis	1			37	Short or long chains	Rumen of cattle			Starch hydrolyzed

* *Leptotrichia buccalis*, a long-chain-forming rod common in the mouth, producing not over 0.1 per cent lactic acid heterofermentatively, may belong here.
† The proteolytic, anaerobic streptococci do not produce appreciable lactic acid and are therefore omitted here.
‡ *Pneumococcus*, considered a separate genus (*Diplococcus*) by Bergey, should probably be included here; it may form short chains, and some other "viridans" streptococci appear in pairs.
§ *Sc. diacetilactis*, if a true species, would belong here.
‖ *Ln. citrovorum* is mainly homofermentative, the CO_2 and other products found in milk coming from the citric acid present; it has recently been renamed *Pediococcus cereviseae*. The strain P60 of *Ln. mesenteroides*, much used in work on growth factors, has been assigned to *Sc. equinus*. True strains of *Ln. mesenteroides*, like *Ln. dextranicus*, form dextran gum on sucrose media (Garvie, 1959–1961).
Leuconostoc comes into milk and cheese from the beets or ensilage used as fodder.

463

Lactobacillus. The word is unfortunate, but the grouping is logical and is now generally used. The cell walls of the rods are very similar both in amino acid and in sugar content (Ikawa and Snell, 1960). Only *L. casei* is separated from the others in containing little or no ribitol phosphate but has a glycerol-phosphate instead (cf. Chap. III, sec. 1). Their very weak ability to synthesize amino acids and vitamins, discussed in section 3 below, is another common and characteristic property of the group. Furthermore, because the rod-shaped and the coccoid forms have so much in common, Orla-Jensen combined them together with the propionic acid bacteria into one family—the *Lactobacteriaceae* —which is still recognized.

B. The Streptococci

Within the streptococci, classification is often made on the basis of "hemolysis," i.e., discoloration surrounding the colony on blood-agar plates. Those producing a green zone, without lysis of the erythrocytes (α-hemolysis), are called the "viridans" group, and include *Sc. thermophilus, Sc. lactis, Sc. bovis, Pneumococcus,* and an organism called *Sc. salivarius,* found in the mouth and on restaurant glassware. *Sc. bovis,* which lives in the rumen of cattle, is exceptional in being a true anaerobe (Hungate *et al.,* 1952).

The streptococci producing a colorless zone in which the erythrocytes are lysed are the truly hemolytic or "β-hemolytic" forms. These were subdivided by Lancefield (1925) on serological grounds as follows:

Group A: *Sc. pyogenes,* including all the important *human* pathogens.

Group B: *Sc. agalactiae* (= *Sc. mastiditis*), the cause of mastitis in the udder of the cow and thus a common form in milk.

Group C: the so-called "animal pyogenes," causing many infections of animals, and *Sc. equi,* the cause of strangles in horses.

Group D: *Sc. durans,* a thermoduric organism found in pasteurized milk, *Sc. zymogenes, Sc. liquefaciens,* which liquefies gelatin, and *Sc. fecalis,* from animal intestines. The last includes a motile strain. This group D has been termed the *Enterococci* (Sherman, 1938). Skadhåuge (1950) considers it as having only three true species, *Sc. durans, Sc. fecalis,* and *Sc. pseudofecalis.*

Groups A and C produce a characteristic viscous polysaccharide different from those of Pneumococci (below), and probably identical with hyaluronic acid (Lancefield, 1954). This substance is the intercellular material of animal tissues; it is a polymer of N-acetyl-glucosamine and glucuronic acid.

The Pneumococci are near to the viridans group but are distinguished by greater fragility of their cell walls. For example, they are dissolved by bile or 10 per cent bile salt (sodium taurocholate). When treated with penicillin, horse serum, and a Mg salt in presence of 10 to 20 per cent sucrose, they readily give rise to "L-forms" (p. 84); these grow into colonies with large bodies (possibly fused wall-less cells) and long chains of fine granules, quite unlike the L-forms of streptococci (Madoff and Dienes, 1958). For the same reason pneumococci autolyze rapidly, so that old cultures often lose their gram-positivity. A few strains are strict anaerobes though otherwise typical; these can mutate to aerobic forms (Smith, 1936). The polysaccharide capsular materials of pneumococci were discussed in Chapter III.

Both Streptococci and Lactobacilli occur in moderate numbers in the human mouth and may be the cause of dental caries, through the acid they produce. Four homofermentative and three heterofermentative species of rods, and four Streptococcus species are found (see Bisset and Davis, 1960). Other common mouth organisms include Leptotrichia—long, slightly tapered rods or filaments—and two spirochaetes of the genus Treponema.

2. THE LACTIC FERMENTATION

A. Products

The fermentation proper can be very nearly expressed by the simple equation:

$$C_6H_{12}O_6 \rightarrow 2\ C_3H_6O_3$$

In animal tissues this reaction is termed *glycolysis* (literally, "sugar-splitting," although the splitting of the hexose into trioses is only one of 11 reactions which together constitute the lactic fermentation).

The homofermentative forms, especially the Thermobacteria, give nearly quantitative yields of lactic acid from hexose sugars in acid or unbuffered media. Alkaline media favor the formation of other products; for instance, *Sc. liquefaciens*, which at pH 5 gives 87 per cent lactic acid, yields only 61 per cent lactate at pH 9 (Gunsalus and Niven, 1942). Along with lactic acid are produced small amounts of formate, acetate, and alcohol, approximately in the ratio 2:1:1 (Friedemann, 1939). Table XII–2 shows how all the homofermentative cocci studied give a similar pattern of products, while the two heterofermentative forms differ, producing more ethanol.

Many species ferment pentoses, and in some, including also some strains of *E. coli* which have been grown on xylose, the reaction is nearly:

$$6\ C_5H_{10}O_5 \rightarrow 8\ C_3H_6O_3 + 3\ C_2H_4O_2$$

i.e., they produce more than one mole of lactic acid per mole of pentose (Orla-Jensen, 1919). These organisms must, therefore, carry out the complex recombination described in Chapter XIV. These pentose fermentations have played a valuable part in elucidating the hetero-fermentation (p. 469).

TABLE XII–2. Products of Lactic Fermentations by Cocci, Initial pH 7.6

(Data from Friedemann, 1939)

Organism	Fermentation type	YIELD IN mM PER 100 "mM" OF C_3			
		Lactate	Formate	Acetate	Ethanol
Sc. fecalis	Homo-	74	14	6	7
Sc. viridans (mean of 2 strains)	Homo-	81	6.5	2	2
Sc. lactis	Homo-	89	4	1	1
D. pneumoniae	Homo-	70–78	6–20	3–8	2–7
Ln. mesenteroides	Hetero-	81	0	4	10
Ln. dextranicus	Hetero-	44	1	6	44

The optical rotation of the lactic acid is characteristic of the organism. A bacterium that forms D-lactic acid in milk will form D-lactic acid in any other medium "whether the source of energy be alcohols, aldoses, ketoses, pentoses, hexoses, or polysaccharides" (Orla-Jensen). The same is true for organisms producing the L- or I-forms. Thus the optical activity does not derive directly from that of the sugar. However, the optically active hydroxy fatty acids formed by *L. casei* (Camien *et al.*, 1959) are probably formed directly from amino acids, like the fusel oils (p. 316).

Some lactic bacteria show an induction period between inoculation and the onset of rapid fermentation (Fromageot and Roux, 1931, 1933). It is independent of sugar concentration, pH, and O_2, but is shortened by adding phosphate; the shorter the induction period, the faster the sugar is subsequently fermented. This period is perhaps due to the formation of induced enzymes. The initial fermentation rates vary with the organism, fructose being the most rapidly attacked by some, lactose by others.

B. Mechanism of the Homofermentative Process

The coenzymes of yeast, DPN (NAD) and ATP, function equally well for the lactic fermentation of muscle, and indeed researches on yeast and on muscle have been carried out in parallel. The major difference between the alcoholic and lactic fermentations, and therefore between yeast and most of the lactic bacteria, is the absence of functional *carboxylase* in the latter. Apart from this the fermentations go through the same intermediate stages. When pyruvic acid is formed, therefore, it becomes the hydrogen acceptor for reduced DPN (in place of acetaldehyde in yeast) and is thus reduced directly, without decarboxylation, to lactic acid:

Phosphohexose → Phosphotriose → Phosphoglyceric acid → Phosphopyruvic acid
$+2$ H → DPN

Lactic ← ——————— Pyruvic acid
acid

The protein part or apoenzyme of the hydrogen-accepting enzyme system is here lactic dehydrogenase, instead of alcohol dehydrogenase. To reduce pyruvic acid, the oxidation potential has to go lower than for acetaldehyde. The E_0 value for acetaldehyde $\rightleftharpoons$ alcohol is -0.068 volt, while that of pyruvic $\rightleftharpoons$ lactic is -0.154.

Yeast contains lactic dehydrogenase too, but normally forms only traces of lactic acid, because it decarboxylates the pyruvic acid first. Lactic dehydrogenase is readily purified from yeast; it is a pink complex containing cytochrome b_2 and riboflavin phosphate linked to a colorless protein (see, e.g., Appleby *et al.*, 1960).

The high yields of lactic acid from lactose mean, of course, that the galactose moiety of lactose is fermented just as well as the glucose. Lactose is readily hydrolyzed to glucose and galactose by β-galactosidase, and the subsequent changes were elucidated by Leloir and coworkers (see Leloir, 1951) using strains of yeast that ferment galactose. These organisms interconvert glucose and galactose, using a special coenzyme, uridine-diphosphoglucose or UDPG:

shows the group that becomes inverted

When this is incubated with the enzyme, 25 per cent of the glucose in the molecule is converted to galactose, by inversion at the 4 position, a "Walden inversion" (discovered with chlorosuccinic acid by P. Walden in 1893). The enzyme is hence named galactowaldenase. The reaction occurs in two steps (see Leloir and Trucco, 1955); first galactose-1-phosphate displaces glucose-1-phosphate in the UDPG, and then the inversion takes place:

$$\text{Gal-1-P} + \text{UDPG} \rightleftharpoons \text{G-1-P} + \text{UDP·Gal}$$
$$\text{UDP·Gal} \rightleftharpoons \text{UDPG}$$

The UDPG is readily hydrolyzed to release glucose-1-phosphate, and this is then converted to the fermentable 6-phosphate by phosphoglucomutase (Chap. XI, sec. 9). In reverse these processes cause the synthesis of lactose in mammary glands, UDP·Gal plus glucose forming lactose rapidly (Watkins and Hassid, 1961). A whole family of similar systems is now known, interconverting several sugars, especially hexoses with the methylpentoses (Kornfeld and Glaser, 1960).

The action of poisons has helped to elucidate the intermediate steps in this fermentation, though not primarily with the lactic bacteria. *Cyanide*, of course, has no effect, either on the fermentation or on sugar oxidation by lactic bacteria. *Iodoacetate* prevents lactic acid formation, and the discovery by Lundsgaard (1930) that muscle poisoned with iodoacetate could still contract disposed of the view that lactic acid formation is an essential result of muscular contraction. The principal action of iodoacetate is exerted on the dehydrogenase of phosphoglyceraldehyde, whose —SH group combines directly with the aldehyde (p. 446). *Fluoride* poisons the conversion of phosphoglyceric acid to phosphopyruvic acid (enolase reaction) by combining with Mg as a fluorophosphate-protein complex (Warburg and Christian, 1942). It also poisons phosphatases and phosphoglucomutase.

Most of the intermediate compounds and the enzymes have been discussed extensively in Chapter XI. Figure XII–2 summarizes the information of both chapters, and includes the role of galactose-phosphates. The numerous subsidiary reactions are omitted from the diagram.

C. Formation of Lactic Acid from Pentoses and the Heterofermentative Mechanism

The above mechanism, which is known as that of Embden, Meyerhof, and Parnas, owes its characteristic high yields of lactic acid to the action of aldolase, which cleaves the hexose diphosphate into two equal parts, both of which form pyruvate and hence lactate. Also, two ATP

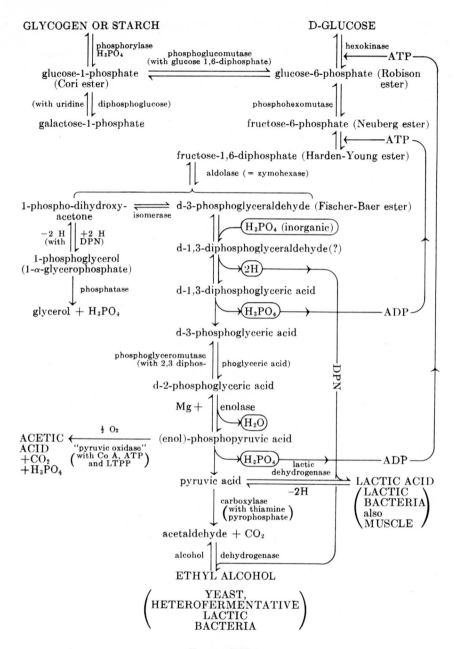

FIGURE XII–2

Fermentation of sugar to lactic acid or alcohol.

are formed. With pentoses, which cannot be equally cleaved, there are two possible results: (1) the 2-carbon fragment appears as ethanol or acetic acid (or both), giving a mixture of products exactly like that produced by heterofermentative organisms from hexoses; or (2) the 2-carbon fragment recombines with a pentose molecule, and after a complex series of changes, the products are trioses:

$$
\begin{aligned}
2\ C_5 &\rightarrow 2\ C_3 + 2\ C_2 \\
C_5\ +\ \ C_2 &\rightarrow\ \ \ C_7\ \rightarrow C_3 + C_4 \\
C_4\ +\ \ C_2 &\rightarrow\ \ \ C_6\ \rightarrow 2\ C_3
\end{aligned}
$$
$$\text{Total: } 3\ C_5 \rightarrow 5\ C_3$$

In this second pathway (see Chap. XIV for details) the ultimate fermentation products are thus the same as those from hexoses, and hence the yield of pyruvate is high; however, this is not found with lactic bacteria. In the first pathway, which they use, the products differ, and the unraveling of the process has helped to explain the reactions of the heterofermentative bacteria in general.

Just as glucose has to be converted to the 2-keto form (fructose) in order to be cleaved, so pentoses are first converted to their 2-keto forms; these are apparently all isomerized to 2-keto-xylose or *xylulose*, which is cleaved (cf. also the cleavage of 2-keto-3-deoxy-gluconic acid in Chap. XI). The first reactions, in which the three aldopentoses— arabinose, ribose, and xylose—are isomerized and phosphorylated, all forming 5-phospho-xylulose, are due to a series of *kinases* (phosphorylating enzymes, using ATP as phosphate donor) and *isomerases* or *epimerases*, all of which have been prepared either from *L. plantarum* or *L. pentosus* (Stumpf and Horecker, 1956; Hurwitz and Horecker, 1956; Heath *et al.*, 1956, 1958). The steps, of which the last are formulated below, are:

D-ribose $\rightleftharpoons$ 5-Phospho-D-ribose $\rightleftharpoons$ 5-Phospho-D-ribulose

D-xylose $\rightleftharpoons$ D-Xylulose $\xrightleftharpoons{\qquad}$ 5-Phospho-D-xylulose

L-arabinose $\rightleftharpoons$ L-Ribulose $\rightleftharpoons$ 5-Phospho-L-ribulose

These epimerases are evidently comparable to the galactowaldenase above.

The 5 phospho-D-xylulose now undergoes a peculiar reaction, due to the enzyme phosphoketolase, again prepared both from *L. plantarum* and *L. pentosus*; in this a molecule of inorganic phosphate is taken up and the C_5 chain is cleaved to acetyl phosphate and phosphoglyceraldehyde (Heath *et al.*, 1956, 1958). Thiamine pyrophosphate and Mg are coenzymes:

CH₂OH
|
CO
|
HCOH   ⟵3-Epimerase⟶
|
HCOH
|
CH₂O·H₂PO₃
5-P-D-Ribulose

CH₂OH
|
CO
|
HOCH
|
HCOH
|
CH₂O·H₂PO₃

CH₃
|
CO·O·H₂PO₃   ⇌
|
CHO
|
HCOH
|
CH₂O·H₂PO₃

          ADP
CH₃ ⟶ CH₃
| | + ATP
COOH COOH

          ADP
COOH ⟶ COOH
| Pᵢ |
HCOH   CO   + ATP
| |
CH₂O·H₂PO₃   CH₃ ⟍2H
                    COOH
                    |
                    HCOH
                    |
                    CH₃

CH₂OH
|
CO   ⟵4-Epimerase⟶
|
HOCH
|
HOCH
|
CH₂O·H₂PO₃
5-P-L-Ribulose

5-P-D-xylulose

Acetyl phosphate
+
Phosphoglyceraldehyde

The acetyl phosphate yields acetate, and the phosphoglyceraldehyde yields pyruvate and thence lactate. *L. pentosus* and *L. plantarum* thus produce equimolar amounts of acetic and lactic acids. Since both acetyl phosphate and phosphoglyceraldehyde produce 1 mole of ATP in the last steps, the pentose fermentation yields as much chemically available energy for growth as does that of the hexoses.

Now the fermentation of glucose by *Ln. mesenteroides* and other heterofermentative forms yields equimolar amounts of lactate, ethanol, and CO_2 (Chap. XI, sec. 10), while *Lactobac. brevis* gives lactic and acetic acids and CO_2. Since the CO_2 comes from C_1 of glucose, the remainder is evidently a pentose and hence is further broken down by the route just described. The only difference is that the acetyl phosphate, instead of yielding acetate + ATP, is reduced by the Leuconostoc to ethanol. Hence, this fermentation yields only one ATP. In accord with this interpretation, 13 homofermentative lactic bacteria (all that were tested) were found to contain the enzyme aldolase (which causes cleavage of hexose to two C_3 units), while none of the heterofermentative species contained it (Buyze *et al.*, 1957). All four heterofermentative Leuconostoc strains contained the enzymes to dehydrogenate and decarboxylate glucose-6-phosphate to pentose-5-phosphate, as did some homofermenters too.

Aerobically, gluconate is converted to lactate, acetate, and CO_2 with uptake of one-half O_2 (Johnson and McCleskey, 1958); 2-ketogluconate, which can be considered as having taken up O_2, gives the same products anaerobically, xylulose and ribulose being intermediates

(Blackwood and Blakley, 1956; also Blakley and Blackwood, 1960).

The formation of acetoin and of diacetyl (Chap. XIV, sec. 3A) from citrate or pyruvate is important in dairying, since diacetyl is responsible for much of the flavor of butter. The reactions are due to *Ln. citrovorum, Sc. cremoris,* and *Sc. diacetilactis,* using the small amount of citrate in milk (see Sandine *et al.,* 1962). *Ln. citrovorum,* which forms acetoin from pyruvate, forms it only from C atoms 5 and 6 of glucose, C atom 4 being lost as CO_2 (Busse and Kandler, 1961).

The deoxypentoses are fermented in yet another way; when *L. plantarum* is grown on deoxyribose, it develops a specific enzyme which cleaves the C_5 into C_3 and C_2 without introducing phosphate; i.e., in the same way as aldolase:

$$
\begin{array}{lllll}
\text{CHO} & \text{CHO} & & & \\
| & \quad\rightarrow\quad | & & & \\
\text{CH}_2 & \text{CH}_3 & & & \\
| & \overline{} & & & \\
\text{HCOH} & \text{HCO} & 2(\text{H}) + \text{COOH} & \text{COOH} \\
| & | & | & | \\
\text{HCOH} & \rightarrow \ \text{HCOH} & \rightarrow & \text{CO} & \rightarrow \text{HCOH} \\
| & | & | & | \\
\text{CH}_2\text{O}\cdot\text{H}_2\text{PO}_3 & \text{CH}_2\text{O}\cdot\text{H}_2\text{PO}_3 & \text{CH}_3 & \text{CH}_3
\end{array}
$$

The reaction is readily reversible and has been used to synthesize pure 5-phospho-D-ribose (Pricer and Horecker, 1960).

D. Pyruvic Acid Oxidation and Other Associated Reactions

The acetate and CO_2 that appear along with lactate can also be formed aerobically from pyruvate by oxidative decarboxylation:

$$CH_3COCOOH + \tfrac{1}{2}\ O_2 \rightarrow CH_3COOH + CO_2 \tag{1}$$

L. delbrückii (= *Thermob. helveticum*), although homofermentative anaerobically, readily oxidizes pyruvate in air. *Sc. fecalis, M. aureus,* Gonococcus, and the fungus *Neurospora crassa* carry out the same reaction. Like the "plain" decarboxylation by pyruvate, it requires cocarboxylase (diphosphothiamine); thus the lactic organisms, not possessing the apoenzyme of carboxylase, may still possess the coenzyme. Fungi like Neurospora, which ferment pyruvate to alcohol, presumably have both. A Neurospora mutant which could not oxidize pyruvate could still make alcohol and hence is probably lacking only the pyruvic oxidation factor (Strauss, 1952).

The oxidation of pyruvate is a complex process and can go in more than one way. Lipmann (1940), using an enzyme prepared from *L.*

delbrückii, found that phosphate was essential and identified an inter- mediate compound as acetylphosphate, $CH_3CO \cdot OH_2PO_3$. However, at least with *Sc. fecalis*, this is not the first but the fourth step in the series of reactions. Cell-free enzymes prepared from *Sc. fecalis* oxidize pyruvate only in the presence of a special "oxidation factor" (Gunsalus *et al.*, 1952), which in *E. coli* is a complex of cocarboxylase and the amide of dithio-octanoic acid, called lipoic acid (Reed and de Busk, 1952–1953; Reed, 1953). In its absence the extracts oxidize glucose only to pyru- vate, which may accumulate as such or be condensed to acetoin (Chap. XIV).

The first step in pyruvate oxidation is the same as in its anaerobic decarboxylation; the pyruvate combines with thiamine pyrophosphate (TPP), most probably on the 2-carbon of the thiazole ring, as shown below (Breslow, 1958; Breslow and McNelis, 1959). The first evidence for this was that the H at that position readily exchanges with deu- terium when thiazole stands in D_2O solution, which means that the intermediate dipolar ion has a reasonable stability:

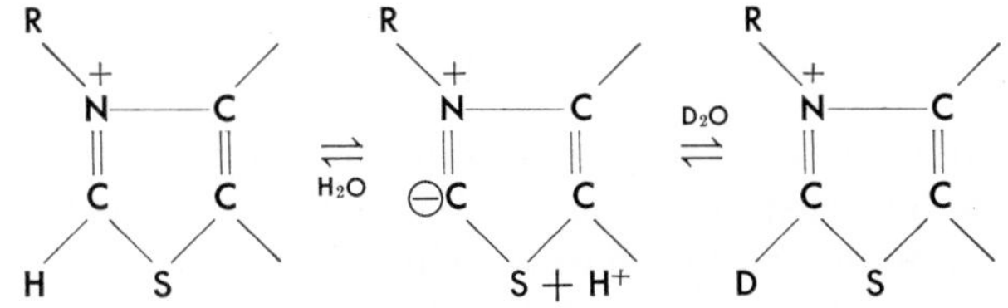

Pyruvate can thus combine with this intermediate, and when it does so it tends to withdraw electrons from the carboxyl group and release the CO_2 (since the resulting product III is stabilized by resonance):

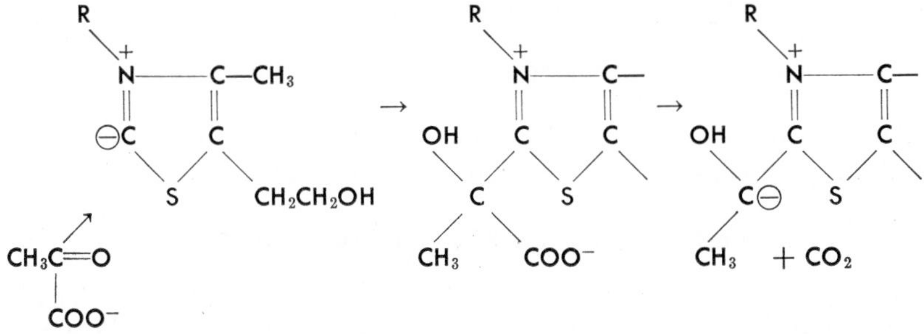

Compound III was subsequently identified as an intermediate when C^{14}-pyruvate was incubated either with yeast pyruvic decarboxylase or pyruvic oxidase (Holzer and Beaucamp, 1959; Holzer *et al.*, 1960– 1961). Thiamine alone, in solution, catalyzes detectably the decarboxy- lation of pyruvate and other reactions for which cocarboxylase is coenzyme, including the condensation to acetoin (Chap. XIV, sec. 3) (Mizuhara *et al.*, 1951).

Compound III, which thus contains "active acetaldehyde," $CH_3C\text{-}OH$, can lose this (1) by condensing two molecules to acetoin, (2) directly as free acetaldehyde in presence of the apo-carboxylase enzyme, as would happen in yeasts, or (3) by transference to another acceptor, as in the present case. The acetaldehyde is in fact transferred to the sulfur of the associated lipoic acid, reducing the —S—S bond and forming 6-acetyl-lipoic acid (Gunsalus *et al.*, 1956):

$$[CH_3C^-\text{—OH}] + \underset{(TPP)}{} \begin{array}{c} CH_2 \\ \diagup \quad \diagdown \\ CH_2 \qquad CH\cdot(CH_2)_4COOH \\ \diagdown \quad \diagup \\ S\text{—}S \end{array} \rightleftharpoons \begin{array}{c} CH_2 \\ \diagup \quad \diagdown \\ CH_2 \qquad CH\cdot(CH_2)_4COOH \\ \diagdown \quad \diagup \\ S^- \quad S\cdot COCH_3 \end{array} + H^+ + TPP \qquad (3)$$

Next the acetyl-lipoic acid (whether complexed with thiamine pyrophosphate or not) transfers its acetyl group to coenzyme A (cf. p. 244):

$$(CoA)\cdot SH + CH_3COS(lipoic)S^- \rightarrow (CoA)\cdot SCOCH_3 + HS(lipoic)S^- \qquad (4)$$

The reduced lipoic acid that is liberated is dehydrogenated by DPN and thus reconverted to its original —S—S form, and the DPNH passes on the hydrogen to a flavoprotein, whose reoxidation by air (in the case of *L. delbrückii*) produces H_2O_2. Note that this is the *only* oxidation step in the whole process; it is here that the $\frac{1}{2}$ O_2 of equation (1) participates.

In the fourth step, acetyl-coenzyme A (in presence of the enzyme transacetylase) comes to equilibrium with acetyl phosphate:

$$CH_3CO\cdot SCoA + HO\cdot H_2PO_3 \rightleftharpoons CH_3CO\cdot O\cdot H_2PO_3 + CoA\cdot SH \qquad (5)$$

Finally, since acetyl phosphate has a high-energy phosphate bond, it can phosphorylate ADP. In so doing it is converted to acetic acid:

$$CH_3COO\cdot H_2PO_3 + ADP^= \rightleftharpoons CH_3COO^- + ATP^= \qquad (6)$$

The same reaction was noted above when xylulose-phosphate is cleaved by phosphoketolase to produce triose and acetyl phosphate. Alternatively, acetyl phosphate is directly hydrolyzed, though slowly, to acetic acid and free phosphate.

To a small extent pyruvate can be split into acetyl-CoA and formate, as by the formic bacteria (Chap. XIV). The hydrogen that would have reduced the pyruvate to lactate probably reduces the acetyl-CoA to ethanol, thus accounting for the products shown in Table

XII–2. Also, some organisms convert pyruvate to acetate anaerobically by using a second molecule of pyruvate as hydrogen acceptor:

$$CH_3COCOOH + DPNH + H^+ \rightleftharpoons CH_3CHOHCOOH + DPN^+ \tag{7}$$
$$CH_3COCOOH + DPN^+ + HO \cdot H_2PO_3 \rightleftharpoons CH_3CO \cdot O \cdot H_2PO_3 + CO_2 + DPNH + H^+ \tag{8}$$
$$CH_3CO \cdot O \cdot H_2PO_3 + H_2O \rightleftharpoons CH_3COOH + H_3PO_4 \tag{9}$$

or in sum: 2 Pyruvate → Acetate + CO_2 + Lactate

L. brevis carries out this reaction anaerobically, while in air the lactate is removed by oxidation to acetate and CO_2 (Walker, 1959). Soluble preparations from E. coli and Sc. fecalis carry out reactions (7) and (8), accumulating acetyl phosphate (Korkes et al., 1952). Further, if the condensing enzyme is present and oxalacetate is added, these preparations form citrate (Stern et al., 1952):

2 Pyruvate + Oxalacetate → Citrate + CO_2 + Lactate

Evidence for the participation of lipoic acid is given by the powerful inhibition exerted by arsenite, which combines with its two adjacent S atoms.

An alternative to lactic acid formation is the reaction in L. delbrückii and Proteus vulgaris, where pyruvic acid, linked with cocarboxylase, reduces FAD (Moyed and O'Kane, 1952; Hager et al., 1954). In Proteus this is reoxidized via the cytochrome system. Arsenite does not inhibit this process, and indeed lipoic acid was shown to be absent from the purified enzyme. The products are acetyl phosphate and CO_2.

Third, Mycob. phlei and Mycob. avium oxidize lactate to acetate and CO_2 without going through pyruvate (Sutton, 1954–1957). The enzyme, which contains riboflavin-5-phosphate, is in fact inhibited by pyruvate, and the intermediate appears to be a free radical (Commoner et al., 1958). Since neither of these bacteria is a lactic organism, the relationship to the lactic system is probably remote.

E. Other Mechanisms of Lactic Acid Formation

There are several of these. Glycerol can be oxidized to lactic acid by Sc. fecalis:

$$\begin{array}{ccc} CH_2OH & & COOH \\ | & & | \\ CHOH + O_2 \rightarrow & CHOH + H_2O_2 \\ | & & | \\ CH_2OH & & CH_3 \end{array}$$

If catalase is added, the reaction goes more vigorously and only $\frac{1}{2}$ O_2 is used per mole of glycerol oxidized. This reaction apparently goes by way of phosphoglycerol, triosephosphate, and phosphoglyceric acid (Gunsalus and Umbreit, 1945).

The formation of lactic acid by fungi of the genera Rhizopus and Mucor, especially *M. rouxii*, is accompanied by other acids and ethyl alcohol (Takahashi and Asai, 1933). These fungi do not attack lactose. Anaerobically the mycelium of *Rhizopus MX* produces almost equal quantities of lactic acid, alcohol, and CO_2, essentially as with *Ln. mesenteroides*. Aerobically, alcohol production is largely suppressed (Waksman and Foster, 1939); instead, carbon is assimilated into the mycelium and some fumaric acid is formed (Margulies and Vishniac, 1961). The yield of lactic acid is unchanged in air, and the earlier belief that it was increased is explained by formation of the fumaric acid. With C^{14} in the 2 position of glucose, the isotope is mainly found in the carbinol of lactic acid and of ethanol; when the C^{14} is in the 1 position, it appears as the methyl group and also (in air) in the fumaric acid. In addition, some $C^{14}O_2$ is fixed into the fumaric acid carboxyls. Margulies and Vishniac conclude that the fermentation is essentially by the Embden-Meyerhof route (as with Leuconostoc), and indeed all the enzymes needed for this pathway are present in the Rhizopus. The formation of fumarate is probably due to the combination of CO_2 with phospho-enolpyruvate to form oxalacetate (p. 493), followed by its reduction to fumarate.

Rhizopus MX can also form some lactic acid from formate, by a complex condensation with a 2-carbon unit (Jefferson *et al.*, 1952). C^{14} formate yields the C^{14} mainly in the methyl group of lactate.

Yeasts also form very small amounts of lactic acid in the course of fermenting sugars to ethanol. While some of this may be derived from alanine or other amino acids, just as are the fusel oils (Chap. VIII), some lactic acid is formed from sugar (about 1 per cent yield; Hohl and Joslyn, 1941). One of the Zygosaccharomyces, *Z. acidifaciens*, which produces acetic acid, alcohol, and glycerol anaerobically as in Neuberg's third form of fermentation, makes appreciable amounts of lactic acid (Nickerson and Carroll, 1945), although the maximum yield is only one-fifth to one-tenth of that produced by *Sc. lactis* growing on milk.

Several lactic bacteria decarboxylate malate to lactate and CO_2. These organisms are important in wine making, since they can destroy completely the malic acid in grape juice. The strains isolated include a Leuconostoc and a Lactobacillus similar to *L. plantarum* (Radler, 1958). Apparently fruit juices contain all the necessary amino acids and vitamins for their growth.

The water mold *Blastocladia pringsheimii* produces from glucose 85 per cent of lactate and 11 per cent of succinate (Cantino, 1949). Aeration does not alter this ratio, and the mechanism of the reaction is not clear. If CO_2 is bubbled through the medium, more succinate is formed at the expense of lactate, doubtless by CO_2 fixation (cf. Chap. XIII).

F. Geotrichum candidum

After milk has soured and been kept for some days, its surface often becomes covered with a fungus, *Geotrichum candidum* (formerly *Oöspora lactis*). This organism is probably an imperfect member of the

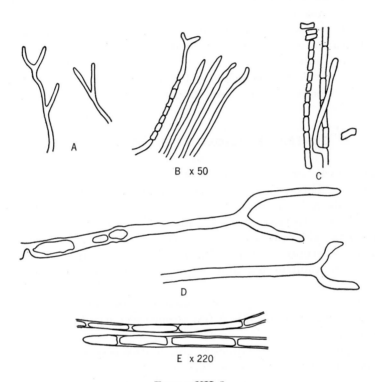

FIGURE XII–3

Geotrichum candidum (= *Oöspora lactis*).

 A and *B*. Hyphal tips.

 C. Older hyphae broken up into oidia. 100 ×.

 D. Older hyphae showing vacuolation.

 E. Hyphal tip and sub-apical region showing relatively thick transverse walls. 220 ×.

 (Note that other Geotrichum spp. do not show the dichotomy at the hyphal tips.) (Original.)

Ascomycetes, related to Candida, although its position is not fully clear. Its dichotomously branching mycelium breaks up, especially on lateral branches, into rectangular or oval fragments called oidia, each of which can give rise to a new mycelium (see Fig. XII–3).

Geotrichum is oxidative in its metabolism and destroys the lactic acid of sour milk. However, there are strains which grow on lactose rather than lactic acid (Geffers, 1937). Cultures on wort agar produce some acid and later destroy it again. It is also proteolytic and deaminates amino acids. For these reasons the pH of soured milk may return to neutrality or even go alkaline when infected by it. Geotrichum forms quantities of fat, some strains containing as much as 50 per cent of the dry weight in the form of neutral fat (Geffers, 1937). Some commercial interest attaches to the fact that it can be grown on acid-hydrolyzed straw or oat-hulls and will form 22.5 per cent fat on such media (see Dunn, 1952).

Unlike the lactic bacteria, Geotrichum possesses catalase and can synthesize riboflavin and other vitamins (Kuchar, 1950).

3. GENERAL PHYSIOLOGY OF LACTIC BACTERIA

True lactic organisms do not produce large colonies on ordinary solid media. This is due to three peculiarities, whose understanding has required about 30 years:

(1) They are microaerophilic for the reason that they possess no cytochrome oxidase or catalase and can respire only by spontaneous oxidation of reduced flavoprotein. This process produces H_2O_2, which thus can accumulate and inhibit growth (Chap. V). Some heterofermentative rods, like *L. cereale*, are exceptions, while some streptococci have a flavoprotein peroxidase, which uses up the H_2O_2 to oxidize DPNH (Dolin, 1953–1955). A few streptococci, e.g., *Sc. bovis*, are true anaerobes.

(2) Their ability to synthesize amino acids is small. Some peptones are inadequate for growth, because of low content of one or another amino acid. Casein peptone is generally reliable, but Orla-Jensen (1919) found yeast extract better for the Streptobacteria and Thermobacteria. In recent years pure amino acids have been used as a medium —19 are required, together with sugar, phosphate, Fe^{++}, Mg^{++}, Mn^{++}, acetate, and the bases, adenine, guanine, and uracil. Vitamins are needed in addition (see below). The relative concentrations are often critical, because even low levels of cystine can be inhibiting, while high concentrations of alanine or leucine inhibit growth, by preventing the utilization of glycine or isoleucine, respectively (Kihara and Snell, 1960). In the latter case, growth can be reinstated by large amounts of glycine or isoleucine, or, even better, by their peptides. Sometimes the use of peptides is preferable, e.g., peptides of tyrosine for *Sc. fecalis*, of histidine for *Pediococcus cereviseae* (Florsheim *et al.*, 1962), of both for *L. delbrückii*, and of glycylserine for Leuconostoc,

since the growth is then less subject to inhibition by related amino acids (O'Barr and Pierce, 1960).

Nevertheless, the nutrient requirements are very useful, since any one constituent of the medium can be omitted and an unknown preparation added in varying amounts; the extent of growth will then be a measure of the amount of the missing amino acid in the unknown. *L.*

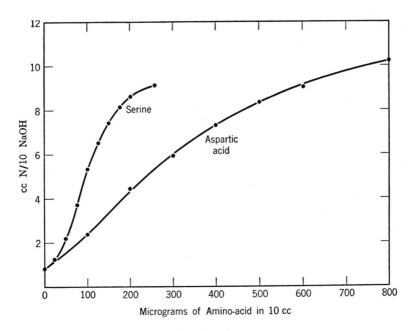

FIGURE XII–4

Assay of two amino acids with *L. delbrückii* LD5. Synthetic medium, similar to that of Table XII–3. The lactic acid is titrated with NaOH after 72 hours' incubation at 37° C. (Redrawn from J. L. Stokes and M. Gunness, *J. Biol. Chem.*, **157**:651–659, 1945.)

arabinosus strain 17-5, *L. casei*, *Leuconostoc mesenteroides* (strain P-60) (= *Sc. equinus*), *L. delbrückii*, and *Sc. fecalis* have been mainly used. In these assays growth is determined either by the turbidity of the medium or simply by the concentration of lactic acid formed under stated conditions, such as 72 hours at 35° C. Two examples are shown in Figure XII–4. There is an extensive literature on this, mainly dealing, however, with the amino acid composition of proteins (cf., e.g., Neumann, 1949, and the review of Snell, 1945).

By contrast, the "pseudo-lactic" bacteria, the coliforms, grow well with single amino acids, or even ammonium, as source of nitrogen, and sugar or lactic acid as carbon source.

The amino acid requirement makes the growth of lactic bacteria very susceptible to inhibition by amino acid analogues (Chap. XXIV, sec. 5). For example, cyclohexyl-alanine competes with phenylalanine, and cyclopentyl-alanine with leucine (Pal *et al.*, 1956). *Ln. dextranicus* and *L. arabinosus* are powerfully inhibited by 3-aminomethyl-cyclo-hexylglycine, IV, which competes with lysine, V (Davis *et al.*, 1960):

$$NH_2CH_2\text{—}CH\cdot CH_2\cdot CH\text{—}CHNH_2COOH \qquad\qquad IV$$
$$\overset{|}{}\qquad\overset{|}{}$$
$$CH_2\cdot CH_2\cdot CH_2$$

$$NH_2CH_2\text{—}CH_2\cdot CH_2\cdot CH_2\text{—}CHNH_2COOH \qquad\qquad V$$

(3) The lactic bacteria also need vitamins of the B group. The need for riboflavin will be obvious because of their flavoprotein system, and the requirement is relatively large. Several lactic bacteria have, therefore, been used for the determination of riboflavin in unknown materials (Snell and Strong, 1939; Williams *et al.*, 1941). Nicotinic acid, thiamine, folic acid, *p*-aminobenzoic acid, pyridoxine (vitamin B_6), and vitamin B_{12} are also required by many strains and can therefore be assayed by omitting any one of them from the medium, and measuring the growth, or the lactic acid, when known amounts have been added.

The use of the lactic organisms for bioassay of vitamins has become widespread in recent years, but it needs caution. For instance:

(a) The growth-promoting activities of pyridoxal and pyridoxamine, two forms of vitamin B_6, are very different.

(b) These B_6 vitamins are often more active in the phosphorylated form, and indeed *L. lactis* cannot use them except when phosphorylated (Hendlin *et al.*, 1950).

(c) If *Sc. fecalis* is given B_6, it decarboxylates tyrosine in the medium and has to be supplied with tyrosine in the form of a peptide (Kihara *et al.*, 1952). Peptides, both of tyrosine and histidine, also stimulate *L. delbrückii*.

(d) Several different forms of pteroylglutamic acid (folic acid) exist, with widely different activities for different organisms, one (Leucovorin) being as much as 10^5 times as active as folic acid on *Ln. citrovorum* (Wieland *et al.*, 1952).

(e) *L. arabinosus* and *L. casei* can synthesize folic acid if *p*-aminobenzoic acid (Sarett, 1947) or certain amino acids (Harry, 1951) are given.

(f) The response to vitamin B_{12} (by *L. leichmannii*) depends on the oxygen tension, so that repeatable results are only obtained if a reducing agent is present in the medium.

(g) Thymidine will substitute for B_{12} and also for folic acid (after a lag period) in the case of *L. leichmannii* (Franklin *et al.*, 1949).

(h) *Ln. citrovorum* 8081 does not require either folic acid or thymidine if it is supplied with a purine-like factor present in liver (Sauberlich and Baumann, 1948, 1949).

(i) *Sc. fecalis* and some Lactobacilli do not require any aspartic acid if biotin is present (Stokes *et al.*, 1947).

(j) *L. casei* in the absence of vitamin B_6 requires D-alanine, as well as L-alanine which must be supplied as a peptide (Kihara *et al.*, 1952).

(k) Biotin in yeast is present as biotinyl-lysine (Wright *et al.*, 1952).

Points *a*, *b*, and *d* make the vitamin assays difficult to interpret; points *c*, *i*, and *j* have the result that the vitamin and amino acid assays can interlock. No doubt some of the differences between different peptones as substrates for lactic bacteria, recorded in the older literature, were due to different contents of vitamins rather than of amino acids. Besides amino acids and vitamins, several purines and pyrimidines, and one or more fatty acids may be required. Lactobacillic acid, a cyclopropane derivative of stearic acid (Hofmann *et al.*, 1958), was iso-

$$
\begin{array}{c}
CH_2 \\
\diagup \; \diagdown \\
CH_3(CH_2)_5C\!\!-\!\!-\!\!-\!\!-\!\!C(CH_2)_9COOH \\
\;\;H \qquad\;\; H
\end{array}
$$

lated from *L. arabinosus* and *L. casei* and also from *Agrob. tumefaciens*, in which it comprises 13 per cent of the cell lipids. This and three related acids promote the growth of *L. arabinosus*, *L. casei*, and *L. delbrückii* on biotin-deficient media; they may be essential metabolites (Hofmann and Panos, 1954). For further details the reviews of Knight (1945), van Lanen and Turner (1949), and Jukes and Stokstad (1951) should be consulted. The method has been very successful.

An example of the media used in assays of this type is given below (Table XII–3).[2] The great spread in concentrations required, between nutrients and salts at one end and vitamins at the other, is notable. The extremes, dextrose and biotin, show a ratio of 50 million times in concentration. It is clear that with the appropriate omission such a medium can be used to assay almost any amino acid or vitamin, and the Lactobacilli have become laboratory reagents.

---

[2] Details of the procedure, both for vitamins and amino acids, have been assembled by the National Dairy Research Laboratories (1949).

TABLE XII–3. Synthetic Medium for Lactic Acid Bacteria

(From *National Dairy Res. Labs. Manual*, 1949)

Constituent	Final Concentration (parts per million)
Nutrients	
Dextrose	10,000
Sodium acetate	6,000
Salts (added as 2 solutions of mixed salts)	
NH_4Cl	2,500
$(NH_4)_2SO_4$	2,500
KH_2PO_4	500
K_2HPO_4	500
NaCl, $FeSO_4$, and $MnSO_4$, each:	5
Amino acids	
Arginine, cystine, glycine, histidine, hydroxyproline, proline, tryptophan, and tyrosine, each:	200
Alanine, aspartic and glutamic acids, isoleucine, leucine, lysine, methionine, norleucine, phenylalanine, serine, threonine, and valine, each:	100
Glutamine	25
Purines	
Adenine, guanine, and uracil, each:	10
Vitamins	
Pyridoxamine-HCl	0.4
Riboflavin, thiamine, niacin, and pantothenic acid, each:	0.2
Para-aminobenzoic acid	0.04
Folic acid	0.02
Biotin	0.0002

REFERENCES

Appleby, C. A.; Morton, R. K.; and Simmonds, D. H. 1960. *Biochem. J.*, **75**:72–76 and lit. there cited.

*Bisset, K. A., and Davis, G. H. G. 1960. The Microbial Flora of the Mouth. London, Heywood and Co., 100 pp. (has good bibliography of dental literature).

Blackwood, A. C., and Blakley, E. R. 1956. *Canad. J. Microbiol.*, **2**:741–746.

Blakley, E. R., and Blackwood, A. C. 1960. *Canad. J. Microbiol.*, **6**:107–114.

Bolcato, V. 1957. *Antonie v. Leeuwenhoek*, **23**:351–355.

Breslow, R. 1958. *J. Am. Chem. Soc.*, **80**:3719–3726.

Breslow, R., and McNelis, E. 1959. *J. Am. Chem. Soc.*, **81**:3080–3082.

Busse, M., and Kandler, O. 1961. *Nature*, **189**:774–775.

Buyze, G.; van den Hamer, C. J. A.; and de Haan, P. G. 1957. *Antonie v. Leeuwenhock*, **23**:345–350.

Camien, M. N.; Fowler, A. V.; and Dunn, M. S. 1959. *Arch. Biochem. Biophys.*, **83:** 408–418.

Cantino, E. C. 1949. *Am. J. Bot.*, **36:**95–112.

Commoner, B.; Lippincott, B. B.; and Passoneau, J. V. 1958. *Proc. Nat. Acad. Sci.*, **44:**1099–1110.

Davis, A. L.; Skinner, C. G.; and Shive, W. 1960. *Arch. Biochem. Biophys.*, **187:**88–92.

Doetsch, R. N., and Pelczar, M. 1948. *J. Bact.*, **56:**37–49.

Dolin, M. I. 1953–1955. *Arch. Biochem. Biophys.*, **46:**483–490; **55:**415–435.

*Dunn, C. G. 1952. Food Yeast. *Wallerstein Lab. Communications*, **15:**61–79.

Florsheim, H. A.; Makineni, S.; and Shankinan, S. 1962. *Arch. Biochem. Biophys.*, **97:**243–249.

Franklin, A. L.; Stokstad, E. L. R.; Hoffmann, C. E.; Belt, M.; and Jukes, T. H. 1949. *J. Am. Chem. Soc.*, **71:**3549–3550.

Friedemann, T. E. 1939. *J. Biol. Chem.*, **130:**757–761.

Fromageot, C., and Roux, J. 1931, 1933. *Biochem. Z.*, **243:**175–190; **265:**13–20 (1933).

Garvie, E. I. 1959–1961. *Nature*, **183:**1411–1412; *J. Dairy Res.*, **27:**283–292 (1961).

Geffers, H. 1937. *Arch. Mikrobiol.*, **8:**66–98.

Gunsalus, I. C.; Barton, L. S.; and Gruber, W. 1956. *J. Am. Chem. Soc.*, **78:**1763–1766.

Gunsalus, I. C., and Niven, C. F., Jr. 1942. *J. Biol. Chem.*, **145:**131–136.

Gunsalus, I. C.; Struglia, L.; and O'Kane, D. J. 1952. *J. Biol. Chem.*, **194:**859–869; cf. O'Kane, D. J., and Gunsalus, I. C., *J. Bact.*, **56:**499–506 (1948).

Gunsalus, I. C., and Umbreit, W. W. 1945. *J. Bact.*, **49:**347–357.

Hager, L. P.; Geller, D. M.; and Lipmann, F. 1954. *Fed. Proc.*, **13:**734–738.

Harry, E. G. 1951. *Biochem. J.*, **49:**5–10.

Hayward, A. C.; Hale, C. M.; and Bisset, K. A. 1955. *J. Gen. Microbiol.*, **13:**292–294.

Heath, E. C.; Hurwitz, J.; and Horecker, B. L. 1956. *J. Am. Chem. Soc.*, **78:**5449.

Heath, E. C.; Hurwitz, J.; Horecker, B. L.; and Ginsburg, A. 1958. *J. Biol. Chem.*, **231:** 1009–1029; Heath, E. C.; Horecker, B. L.; Smyrniotis, P. Z.; and Takegi, Y. *Ibid.*, **231:**1031–1037.

Hendlin, D.; Caswell, M. C.; Peters, V. J.; and Wood, T. R. 1950. *J. Biol. Chem.*, **186:** 647–652.

Hofmann, K.; Marco, G. J.; and Jeffrey, G. A. 1958. *J. Amer. Chem. Soc.*, **80:**5717–5719.

Hofmann, K., and Panos, C. 1954. *J. Biol. Chem.*, **210:**687–693.

Hohl, L. A., and Joslyn, M. A. 1941. *Plant Physiol.*, **16:**343–360.

Holzer, H., and Beaucamp, K. 1959. *Angew. Chem.*, **71:**776.

Holzer, H.; Goedde, H. W.; Göggel, K. H.; and Ulrich, B. 1960–1961. *Biochem. Biophys. Res. Comms.*, **3:**599–602; **5:**445–451 (1961).

Hungate, R. L.; Dougherty, R. W.; Boyaut, M. P.; and Cello, R. M. 1952. *Cornell Vet.*, **42:**423–449.

Hurwitz, J., and Horecker, B. C. 1956. *J. Biol. Chem.*, **223:**993–1008.

Ikawa, M., and Snell, E. E. 1960. *J. Biol. Chem.*, **235:**1376–1382.

Jefferson, W. E.; Foster, J. W.; Phares, E. F.; and Carson, S. F. 1952. *J. Am. Chem. Soc.*, **74:**1477–1478.

Johnson, M. K., and McCleskey, C. S. 1958. *J. Bact.*, **75:**98–101.

*Jukes, T. H., and Stokstad, E. L. R. 1951. The Role of Vitamin B_{12} in Metabolic Processes. *Vitamins and Hormones*, **9:**1–26.

Kihara, H.; McCullough, W. G.; and Snell, E. E. 1952. *J. Biol. Chem.*, **197:**783–789; Kihara, H., and Snell, E. E. *J. Biol. Chem.*, **197:**791–800; Kihara, H.; Klatt, O. A.; and Snell, E. E. *J. Biol. Chem.*, **197:**801–807.

Kihara, H., and Snell, E. E. 1960. *J. Biol. Chem.*, **235:**1409–1414, 1415–1418.

*Knight, B. C. J. G. 1945. Growth Factors in Microbiology. *Vitamins and Hormones,* 3:108–217.

Korkes, S.; del Campillo, A.; Gunsalus, I. C.; and Ochoa, S. 1952. *J. Biol. Chem.,* **193:** 721–735; also *Fed. Proc.,* **10:**210 (1951).

Kornfeld, S., and Glaser, L. 1960. *Biochim. Biophys. Acta,* **42:**548–551.

Kuchar, K. W. 1950. *Sydowia (Ann. Mycol. Ser.* II), **4:**409–449.

Lancefield, R. 1925. *J. Exp. Med.,* **42:**337–395, 397–412.

Lancefield, R. C. 1954. In, Streptococcal Infections, ed. M. McCarty. New York, Columbia Univ. Press, Chap. 1.

*van Lanen, J. M., and Tanner, F. W., Jr. 1948. Vitamins in Microorganisms. *Vitamins and Hormones,* **6:**164–224.

Leloir, L. F. 1951. Metabolism of Hexosephosphates. In, Phosphorus Metabolism, ed. W. D. McElroy and B. Glass. Vol. I, pp. 67–93. Baltimore, Johns Hopkins Press.

Leloir, L. F., and Trucco, R. E. 1955. In, Methods in Enzymology, ed. Colowick and Kaplan, Vol. 1, pp. 290–293. New York, Academic Press.

Lipmann, F. 1940. *J. Biol. Chem.,* **134:**463–464.

Lundsgaard, E. 1930. *Biochem. Z.,* **217:**162–177.

Madoff, S., and Dienes, L. 1958. *J. Bact.,* **76:**245–250.

Margulies, M., and Vishniac, W. 1961. *J. Bact ,* **81:**1–9.

Mizuhara, S.; Tamura, R.; and Arata, H. 1951. *Proc. Japan Acad.,* **27:**302–308.

Moyed, H. S., and O'Kane, D. J. 1952. *Arch. Biochem. Biophys.,* **39:**457–458.

*National Dairy Research Laboratories, Inc. 1949. Manual of Microbiological Methods of Assaying Vitamins and Amino Acids. Oakdale, L. I., New York. 75 pp.

Neumann, R. E. 1949. *Arch. Biochem.,* **24:**289–298.

Nickerson, W. J., and Carroll, W. R. 1945. *Arch. Biochem.,* **7:**257–271.

O'Barr, T. P., and Pierce, D. A. 1960. *J. Bact.,* **79:**519–523.

O'Kane, D. J. 1950. *J. Bact.,* **60:**449–458.

*Orla-Jensen, S. 1919. The Lactic Acid Bacteria. Publ. Danish Acad. Sci., Pt. 8, Ser. V, No. 2.

Orla-Jensen, S. 1931. Dairy Bacteriology. Philadelphia, Blakiston Company. (Trans. P. S. Arup.)

Pal, P. R.; Skinner, C. G.; Dennis, R. L.; and Shive, W. 1956. *J. Am. Chem. Soc.,* **78:** 5116–5118.

Pederson, C. S.; Albury, M. N.; and Breed, H. S. 1954. *Wallerstein Lab. Comm.,* **17:** 7–17.

Prévot, A. R. 1938. *Ann. Inst. Pasteur,* **60:**285–307.

Pricer, W. E., Jr., and Horecker, B. L. 1960. *J. Biol. Chem.,* **235:**1292–1298.

Radler, F. 1958. *Arch. Mikrobiol.,* **30:**64–72; **32:**1–15.

*Reed, L. J. 1953. Metabolic Functions of Thiamine and Lipoic Acid. *Physiol. Revs.,* **33:**544–560.

Reed, L. J., and de Busk, B. G. 1952–1953. *J. Am. Chem. Soc.,* **74:**3457, 3964–3965, 4727–4728; *J. Biol. Chem.,* **199:**873–880 (1953).

Sandine, W. E.; Elliker, P. R.; and Hays, H. 1962. *Canad. J. Microbiol.,* **8:**161–174.

Sarett, H. P. 1947. *J. Biol. Chem.,* **171:**265–272.

Sauberlich, H. E., and Baumann, C. A. 1948. *J. Biol. Chem.,* **176:**165–173.

Sauberlich, H. E., and Baumann, C. A. 1949. *Arch. Biochem.,* **24:**263–269.

Sherman, J. M. 1938. *J. Bact.,* **35:**81–93.

Skadhåuge, K. 1950. Studies on Enterococci. Copenhagen, E. Munksgaard. 197 pp.

Smith, F. 1936. *Brit. J. Exp. Path.,* **17:**329–334.

*Snell, E. E. 1945. The Microbiological Assay of Amino Acids. *Advances in Protein Chem.,* **2:**85–118.

*Snell, E. E., and Strong, F. H. 1939. *Ind. Eng. Chem.,* Anal. ed., **11:**346–348.

Stern, J. R.; Shapiro, B.; Stadtman, E. R.; and Ochoa, S. 1952. *J. Biol. Chem.*, **193:** 703–720.

Stokes, J. L., and Gunness, M. 1945. *J. Biol. Chem.*, **157:**651–659.

Stokes, J. L.; Larsen, A.; and Gunness, M. 1947. *J. Bact.*, **54:**219–230; *J. Biol. Chem.*, **163:**613–614.

Strauss, B. S. 1952. *Arch. Biochem. Biophys.*, **36:**33–47.

Stumpf, P. K., and Horecker, B. L. 1956. *J. Biol. Chem.*, **218:**753–768; cf. Lampen, J. O. 1953. *Ibid.*, **204:**999–1010.

Sutton, W. B. 1954–1957. *J. Biol. Chem.*, **210:**309–320; **216:**749–759 (1955); **226:** 395–405 (1957).

Takahashi, T., and Asai, T. 1933. *Zentr. Bakt. II Abt.*, **89:**81–84.

Waksman, S. A., and Foster, J. W. 1939. *J. Agr. Res.*, **57:**873–899.

Walker, J. R. L. 1959. *Biochem. J.*, **72:**188–192.

Warburg, O., and Christian, W. 1942. *Biochem. Z.*, **310:**384–421.

Watkins, W. M., and Hassid, W. Z. 1961. *Biochem. Biophys. Res. Comms.*, **5:**260–264.

Wieland, O. P.; Hutchings, B. L.; and Williams, J. H. 1952. *Arch. Biochem. Biophys.*, **40:**205–217.

Williams, R. J., *et al.* 1941. Studies on the Vitamin Content of Tissues. Univ. of Texas Pub. No. 4137.

Wright, L. D.; Cresson, E. L., Skeggs, H. R.; Wood, T. R.; Peck, R. L.; Wolf, D. E.; and Folkers, K. 1952. *J. Am. Chem. Soc.*, **74:**1996–1999.

CHAPTER XIII

The Propionic Fermentation

. . . that awful volcanic cheese that has horrible holes in it, as if it had come in boiling and unnatural milk from mysterious and unearthly cattle.

G. K. CHESTERTON: *Alarms and Discursions*

1. THE PROPIONIC BACTERIA

The Propionic bacteria are closely related to the lactic bacteria. They are gram-positive, nonsporeforming, nonmotile rods. Aerobic cultures show rods somewhat on the large side (as bacteria go) but "mostly bent, locally swollen, and sometimes branched" (van Niel, 1928; see Fig. XIII–1). These general properties suggest relationship to the Corynebacteria.

However, their physiology does not resemble that of most Coryne-bacteria, which are typically aerobic. Only in two cases are there indications of a relationship. The pathogen *C. diphtheriae* does convert sugars to acids under partially anaerobic conditions (de Wolff, 1927), and although this is not a typical propionic fermentation, still some of its strains form considerable amounts of propionic acid, along with acetic, lactic, and succinic acids (Tasman and Brandwijk, 1938). Another Corynebacterium, *C. acnes*, is actually microaerophilic and does carry out a propionic fermentation; on this account some would class it as a Propionibacterium (Douglas and Gunter, 1946). Both these organisms are morphologically of the diphtheroid type.

The true Propionibacteria grow under anaerobic or at least micro-aerophilic conditions, like the homofermentative Lactobacilli. Unlike these, however, they contain a cytochrome system (Chaix and From-ageot, 1942), and generally catalase also (Virtanen, 1931; Hitchner,

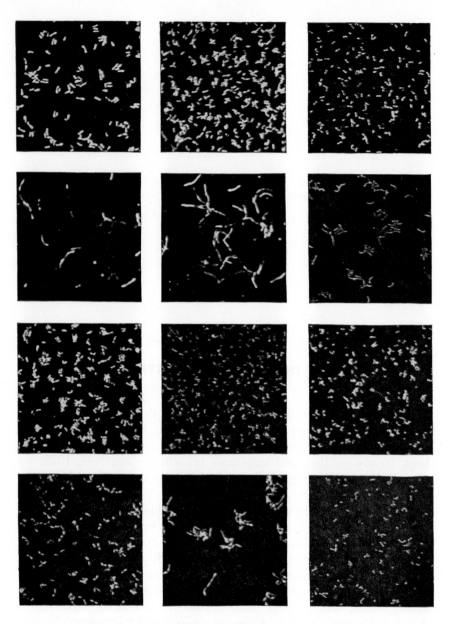

FIGURE XIII–1

Nigrosine preparations of Propionibacteria.

    Left. Pr. jensenii. Center. Pr. pentosaceum. Right. Pr. shermanii.

    Top row from anaerobic (yeast extract-dextrose) plates; second row from aerobic plates; third row from neutral liquid (yeast extract-lactate); fourth row from acid liquid.

    Note in the top row from left to right: short rods, irregular rods, and streptococci, respectively. 650 ×.

    (From C. B. van Niel, *The Propionic Acid Bacteria*, 1928.)

1934). However, they never produce large colonies on the surface of solid media. They can oxidize glycerol and various organic acids, probably via the tricarboxylic acid cycle (Delwiche and Carson, 1953).

Eleven species of Propionibacteria have been described (see van Niel, 1928, and Bergey, 1957). On yeast extract–glucose media two (*Pr. freudenreichii* and *Pr. shermanii*) grow as small streptococci, seven (including *Pr. jensenii*) as rods, and two (*Pr. arabinosum* and *Pr. pentosaceum*) as highly irregular long rods or spheres (see Fig. XIII–1, which shows one of each group). Further distinction is by their carbohydrate fermentations and their pigments.

Pure cultures were first obtained using enrichments inoculated from Swiss cheese, by von Freudenreich and Orla-Jensen (1906). This is a hard cheese with large holes in it, produced by gas bubbles. The propionic acid is partly responsible for its characteristic taste and smell, and it contains 10,000 to 300,000 propionic bacteria per gram. The holes in the cheese are due to CO_2, as will be shown below.

2. OTHER ORGANISMS FORMING PROPIONIC ACID

Besides the Propionibacteria, several other bacteria produce propionic acid. An important group exists in the rumen of cattle and other animals; some of these are anaerobic gram-negative cocci (e.g., *Veillonella gazogenes* = *Micrococcus lactilyticus*, and *M. aerogenes*), while others are gram-positive and resemble the *C. acnes* mentioned above; these readily form propionic from lactic acid (Gutierrez, 1953). The micrococci can produce propionic acid from pyruvic, α-ketoglutaric, and lactic acids (Whiteley and Ordal, 1957), as well as from sugar. However, lactic acid is not an important intermediate in the rumen itself (being mainly converted to acetate there), nor do the rumen bacteria attack it very rapidly (Jayasuriya and Hungate, 1959).

Propionic acid can also be formed from alanine, lactic and pyruvic acids, and other compounds by *Cl. propionicum*, although by a different route from that in the Propionibacteria (see sec. 3C). Finally, *Rhodo-sp. rubrum*, acting on pyruvate in the dark, produces propionic and acetic acids (Kohlmiller and Gest, 1951).

3. THE FERMENTATION

A. Formation and Dehydrogenation of Pyruvic Acid

Propionic acid is formed by the Propionibacteria from glucose, lactose, or, with some species (e.g., *Pr. arabinosum*), from pentoses. It can also be formed from lactic acid, malic acid, and glycerol.

The early stages in hexose fermentation by propionic bacteria are almost certainly the same as with yeast; the dried bacteria do form hexosephosphate (Virtanen and Karström, 1931). They can transfer phosphate groups from ATP to glucose, glycerol, arabinose, and erythritol; the phosphoglycerol, in presence of fumarate as hydrogen acceptor, is dehydrogenated to phosphoglyceric acid (Barker and Lipmann, 1949). Toluene-treated cells can also form phosphoglycerate from hexosediphosphate, or from hexose, using pyruvate as hydrogen acceptor (Werkman et al., 1937). These reactions have to be carried out in presence of fluoride, in order to inhibit hydrolysis of the esters by phosphatases. It can be concluded that the fermentation uses essentially the same intermediates, and involves the same phosphorylations, as the alcoholic fermentation in yeast and the glycolytic process in animal tissues.

Metabolism of pentoses probably involves the interconversions described in Chapter XII for lactic bacteria. In the case of arabinose, which is fermented by *Pr. arabinosum* and *Pr. pentosaceum*, a highly specific enzyme isomerizing 5-phospho-D-arabinose to 5-phospho-D-ribulose has been demonstrated (Volk, 1960). No doubt this is subsequently converted to the fermentable 5-phospho-D-xylulose.

In cheese the main substrate is lactic acid, and it was this fermentation that was first studied. The general equation (Fitz, 1878) is approximately:

$$3 \ CH_3CHOHCOOH \rightarrow 2 \ CH_3CH_2COOH + CH_3COOH + CO_2 + H_2O^1 \qquad (1)$$

Von Freudenreich and Orla-Jensen (1906) found with pure cultures, however, that the ratio *propionate:acetate* was not quite 2, but 1.6 to 1.8; van Niel (1928) generally obtained similar results, but found the ratio *acetate:CO₂* to be always 1.

The constancy of the latter ratio suggested that the acetic acid and CO_2 must arise from the same precursor, which would have to be pyruvate. The reaction must, therefore, be similar to the oxidative decarboxylation of pyruvate (pp. 472 ff.) but without oxygen:

$$CH_3COCOOH + H_2O \rightarrow CH_3COOH + CO_2 + 2(H) \qquad (2)$$

---

[1] Instead of 3 moles of lactic acid, 1½ moles of glucose could be substituted: the equation then describes very well the results in the literature. Thus, van Niel's results (mean of strains 20 and 23 in his Table VII, 1928) give:

$$1\tfrac{1}{2} \ C_6H_{12}O_6 \rightarrow 2.04 \ C_2H_5COOH + 0.82 \ CH_3COOH + 0.80 \ CO_2$$

Similarly with "*Coryneb.*" *acnes* we have (Douglas and Gunter, 1946):

$$1\tfrac{1}{2} \ C_6H_{12}O_6 \rightarrow 1.85 \ C_2H_5COOH + 1.10 \ CH_3COOH + 0.95 \ CO_2$$

Since the conditions are anaerobic, another compound must act as hydrogen acceptor. But the formation of pyruvate from lactate is itself a dehydrogenation:

$$CH_3CHOHCOOH \rightarrow CH_3COCOOH + 2(H) \tag{3}$$

Thus, for every mole of acetic acid formed there are 4(H) to be accepted.

The intermediate role of pyruvate is confirmed by (1) its isolation in the form of its bisulfite derivative (Wood and Werkman, 1936); (2) the fermentation of added pyruvate, which gives, for every mole, 1 acetic + 1 CO_2 (van Niel, 1928).

When pyruvate is dehydrogenated by *M. aureus*, *Gonococcus* and *Sc. fecalis* under anaerobic conditions, a second molecule acts as hydrogen acceptor and is reduced to lactate (Krebs, 1937):

$$2\ CH_3COCOOH \rightarrow CH_3COOH + CO_2 + CH_3CHOHCOOH$$

This "dismutation" is suggestively similar to one of the two main routes whereby bacteria form propionic acid. It is in the hydrogen acceptors that the two kinds of propionic fermentation differ.

B. The Formation of Propionic Acid by *Cl. propionicum*

It will be convenient to consider this special case first. *Cl. propionicum* ferments pyruvate and lactate with the same over-all products as the Propionibacteria and in addition ferments alanine, serine, and acrylic acid as follows (Cardon and Barker, 1947):

$$3\ CH_3CHNH_2COOH + 2\ H_2O \rightarrow 2\ CH_3CH_2COOH + CH_3COOH + CO_2 + 3\ NH_3$$
$$3\ HOCH_2CHNH_2COOH + H_2O \rightarrow\ CH_3CH_2COOH + 2\ CH_3COOH + 2\ CO_2 + 3\ NH_3$$
$$3\ CH_2{=}CHCOOH + 2\ H_2O \rightarrow 2\ CH_3CH_2COOH + CH_3COOH + CO_2$$

Each reaction can evidently be considered as an oxidation of one or two molecules of the substrate and reduction of the remainder to propionic acid. The intermediate, and direct precursor of propionic acid, would be acrylic acid. The correctness of this interpretation is shown by what happens with threonine (Cardon and Barker, 1947). This amino acid yields a mixture of butyric and propionic acids:

$$3\ CH_3CHOHCHNH_2COOH + H_2O \rightarrow$$
$$CH_3CH_2CH_2COOH + 2\ CH_3CH_2COOH + 2\ CO_2 + 3\ NH_3$$

Thus, two molecules are deaminated, decarboxylated, and oxidized to propionic acid, as in Chapter VIII, section 4; this provides 4(H) with which the third molecule is hydrogenated to butyric acid.

Proof that in these organisms propionic acid arises by direct reduction of a 3-carbon precursor is given by labeling experiments (Leaver *et al.*, 1955). Lactate with C^{14} in the C-3 (methyl) position gave rise to propionate labeled *only* in the C-3 position:

$$C^{14}H_3CHOHCOOH \xrightarrow{-H_2O} C^{14}H_2{=}CH{\cdot}COOH \xrightarrow{+2H} C^{14}H_3{\cdot}CH_2COOH$$

By contrast, with Propionibacteria *both* the C-3 and the C-2 positions of the propionate contained isotope. The same was true using pyruvate or lactate labeled in the 2-position. Evidently, therefore, the C-3 and C-2 carbons of propionate *become equivalent* at some stage in the process, and this can only mean that succinate is an intermediate. Indeed, the addition of a second carboxyl group to pyruvate (as first step on the route to succinate) is one of the two "key reactions" of the propionic fermentation, as will appear below:

$$CH_3CO{\cdot}COOH + [CO_2] \rightarrow HOOC{\cdot}CH_2CO{\cdot}COOH \tag{4}$$

C. Steps in the Propionic Fermentation Proper

It was originally thought that the 4 (H) produced in the conversion of lactate to pyruvate and of pyruvate to acetate (equations [2] and [3]) were directly transferred by Propionibacteria to lactate, reducing it to propionate, as with *Cl. propionicum:*

$$2\ CH_3CHOHCOOH + 4(H) \rightarrow 2\ CH_3CH_2COOH + 2\ H_2O \tag{5}$$

The equation of Fitz would then be merely the sum of reactions (2), (3), and (5). But the process is much more complex.

An early indication of this was Barker and Lipmann's finding (1944) that dried bacteria treated with fluoride can make propionate from pyruvate but not from lactate. The only other simple intermediate between pyruvate and propionate is acrylate; yet acrylate yielded no propionate. Since several Propionibacteria could form propionate by decarboxylating succinate (Delwiche, 1948; Johns, 1951), a roundabout route from pyruvate via the 4-carbon acids was possible. Succinyl-coenzyme A appeared to be an intermediate (Whiteley, 1953; Wood *et al.*, 1956).

Succinate was found to be decarboxylated, too, by bacteria growing in the rumen of cattle, both the anaerobic cocci alone (Johns, 1951; Whiteley, 1953) and preparations of total rumen bacteria (Sijpestijn and Elsden, 1952). Since some other rumen organisms *accumulate* succinate, it is apparent that they fail to decarboxylate it, and thus all these organisms probably operate by pathways similar to those of the Propionibacteria. The total rumen organisms actually form propionate from succinate more rapidly than do the Propionibacteria. Since rumen metabolism is dealt with in Chapter XVII, attention here will be focused on propionic acid formation itself.

At first there were conflicts and inconsistencies in regard to succinate decarboxylation; some Propionibacteria seemed not to attack succinate, and labeling experiments with $C^{14}O_2$ and other compounds did not agree well with the proposed route. Fortunately these have now been resolved through experiments on the process going in the opposite direction, namely, the *oxidation* of propionate by the mitochondria of animal tissues (Flavin *et al.*, 1955; Lardy and Adler, 1956). These results show that in the oxidation of propionate to succinate:

(1) CO_2 is taken up,

(2) Both ATP and coenzyme A are needed,

(3) Some tissues produce not only succinate but also its isomer, methyl malonate, $HOOC \cdot \overset{\cdot}{CH} \cdot COOH$.

$$CH_3$$

Ochoa and his co-workers speedily explained this last fact by showing that methylmalonic and succinic acids, in the form of their CoA derivatives, are equilibrated by an isomerase enzyme in liver tissue. The whole reaction is therefore:

$$\text{Propionic} \xrightarrow[\text{CoA}]{\text{ATP}} \text{Propionyl-CoA} \xrightarrow{CO_2} \text{Methylmalonyl-CoA} \xrightarrow{\text{isomerase}^2}$$

$$\text{Succinyl-CoA} \rightarrow \text{Succinic}$$

The enzyme that carboxylates propionyl-CoA contains biotin (see Kosow and Lane, 1961). The application of these facts to the understanding of the propionic fermentation is direct.

In the first place the organisms have long been known to form succinic acid, and in fact it was with them that the carboxylation of pyruvic to oxalacetic acid was discovered (Wood and Werkman, 1936, 1938). The succinic acid produced here, and in the alcoholic fermentation, had been ascribed to the deamination of aspartic acid, but Wood and Werkman showed that the CO_2 evolved is actually taken up again in the propionic fermentation and an equal amount of succinic acid formed. It was deduced that oxalacetic acid was the intermediate:

$$\begin{array}{ccccc} CH_3 & & CH_2COOH & & CH_2COOH \\ | & + CO_2 \rightarrow & | & \xrightarrow{4(H)} & | & + H_2O \\ CO \cdot COOH & & CO \cdot COOH & & CH_2COOH \end{array}$$

---

[2] This enzyme and a related one from *Cl. tetanomorphum*, which isomerizes glutamic acid to β-methyl-aspartic acid, contain members of the vitamin B_{12} group as coenzymes. The methylmalonyl-CoA isomerase uses dimethylbenzimidazolyl-cobamide (= B_{12} coenzyme) (Stadtman *et al.*, 1960); it functions also in the flagellate Ochromonas, which cannot oxidize propionate when deficient in B_{12} (Arnstein and White, 1962). Both isomerases have been purified and studied in detail (Barker *et al.*, 1960–1961; Stjernholm and Wood, 1961). Because of these enzymes the Propionibacteria are unusually rich in B_{12}.

When glycerol was the substrate, there were actually a *net* uptake of CO_2 by *Pr. pentosaceum* and an equivalent production of succinate (Wood and Werkman, 1940). Whereas on lactate 32 μl of CO_2 were evolved, on glycerol 355 μl CO_2 were *absorbed*. The CO_2 uptake was inhibited by fluoride, and at the same time formation of succinate was prevented. The reaction was confirmed with $C^{14}O_2$, because then the isotope was found in the carboxyl groups of *both* succinic and propionic acids (Wood *et al.*, 1940; Carson *et al.*, 1941).

In the second place, participation of coenzyme A in the fermentation was indicated in several ways; the cell-free enzyme from *M. lactilyticus* requires ATP and CoA to convert succinate to propionate (Whiteley, 1953), and, in the reverse process, extracts of *Pr. pentosaceum* carboxylate propionate to succinate rapidly in presence of CoA but only slowly in its absence (Phares *et al.*, 1956). A purified extract from *Pr. shermanii* will transfer carboxyl from succinate to propionate only if CoA is added (Swick and Wood, 1960).

In the third place, the *Pr. shermanii* extract will rapidly decarboxylate methylmalonyl-CoA to propionate, while succinyl-CoA is only one-tenth as effective (Swick and Wood, 1960). The reaction goes in presence of pyruvate, which accepts the carboxyl and becomes oxalacetate:

$$
\begin{array}{c}
\text{CH}_3 \\
|　 \\
\text{CH·COOH} \\
|　 \\
\text{CO·CoA}
\end{array}
\ +\
\begin{array}{c}
\text{CH}_3 \\
|　 \\
\text{CO·COOH}
\end{array}
\ \rightleftharpoons\
\begin{array}{c}
\text{CH}_3 \\
|　 \\
\text{CH}_2 \\
|　 \\
\text{CO·CoA}
\end{array}
\ +\
\begin{array}{c}
\text{CH}_2\text{·COOH} \\
|　 \\
\text{CO·COOH}
\end{array}
$$

No acid other than pyruvate will accept the carboxyl.

Fourth, the enzyme system transfers coenzyme A from propionyl-CoA to succinate, forming succinyl-CoA and thus completing the cycle.

A complication is that while the intact bacteria certainly fix CO_2 in the process, the purified extracts do not. When the methylmalonyl-CoA carboxylates pyruvate, the carboxyl does not come off as CO_2 but remains attached to the enzyme. This enzyme is thus a *transcarboxylase*; it contains biotin as coenzyme and is strongly inhibited by the biotin-combining compound avidin (Swick and Wood, 1960; Lynen, 1961). The carboxyl transfer explains some of the discrepancies alluded to above, especially in regard to the uptake and transfer of $C^{14}O_2$. (The other discrepancies are probably due to failure of some preparations to form succinyl-CoA.) Both the transcarboxylase and also the isomerase that interconverts methylmalonyl-CoA and succinyl-CoA have recently been purified from *Pr. shermanii* (Wood and Stjernholm, 1961; Stjernholm and Wood, 1961).

The complete conversion of pyruvate to propionate is thus given by the following cycle:

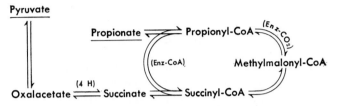

It is a wry twist that the very reaction in which CO_2 fixation was discovered should turn out not to involve CO_2 fixation as an essential part. However, when sugar is fermented by intact cells, some at least of the CO_2 is released and reabsorbed, since CO_2 comes off, and isotopic CO_2 enters the carboxyl groups. Besides, the yield of propionate from succinate with *M. lactilyticus,* and of propionate from pyruvate with Rhodospirillum, is strongly influenced by the CO_2 pressure (Johns, 1951; Kohlmiller and Gest, 1953). The fact that some of the rumen bacteria produce succinate and others propionate (p. 598) also indicates that the two acids are alternative final products, and therefore that transcarboxylation can be replaced by net CO_2 uptake in some cases. When CO_2 is taken up, the most probable pathway is, of course, the carboxylation of phospho-enol pyruvate to oxalacetate, as this is responsible for the CO_2 uptake of yeast and takes place best under anaerobic conditions (Stoppani *et al.,* 1958):

$$\begin{array}{c} CH_2 \\ \parallel \\ C\!-\!O\!\sim\! HPO_3^- \\ \mid \\ COOH \end{array} + CO_2 + H_2O \rightarrow \begin{array}{c} COOH \\ \mid \\ CH_2 \\ \mid \\ C\!=\!O \\ \mid \\ COOH \end{array} + H_2PO_4^-$$

Direct carboxylation of pyruvate to oxalacetate does not readily occur because the equilibrium lies in the direction of decarboxylation; energy can be supplied to drive it either by converting the high-energy phosphate bond to inorganic phosphate, as here, or else by simultaneously hydrogenating the product to malate, as by the "malic enzyme" of green plants, which converts pyruvate directly to malate.

A suggestive parallel to the formation of propionate is furnished by the bacterial decarboxylation of malonate to acetate and CO_2 (Hayaishi, 1953). A purified enzyme from the aerobic *Ps. fluorescens* brings this about, but only in presence of ATP and CoA, so that malonyl-CoA is evidently an essential intermediate. It can be appreciated, too (since COOH is an electron-withdrawing group), that the two carboxyls linked to the same C atom in malonate and methyl-malonate would be much more reactive than those of succinate.

4. INTEGRATION

Finally, the hydrogen balance of the whole fermentation should be noted. Conversion of triose to pyruvate yields 2H. When the pyruvate has been carboxylated to oxalacetate, 4H are required to reduce it to succinate. Formation of *two* moles of pyruvate can thus produce only *one* of succinate (hence, one of propionate). What happens to the second pyruvate? The answer is that a third mole of triose yields pyruvate + 2H, and this pyruvate is converted to acetate, CO_2 + 2H. The resulting 4H + CO_2 gives rise to a second succinate. Both the CO_2 and the CoA cycle continuously during the fermentation, so that it is represented *in toto* (final products underlined):

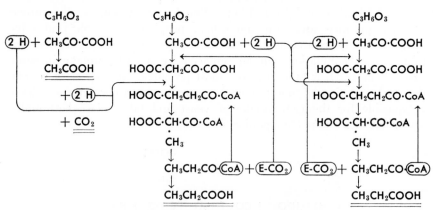

or $3 \ C_3H_6O_3 \rightarrow 2 \ CH_3CH_2COOH + CH_3COOH + CO_2$

REFERENCES

Arnstein, H. R. V., and White, A. M. 1962. *Biochem. J.*, **83**:264–270.
Barker, H. A., and Lipmann, F. 1944. *Arch. Biochem.*, **4**:361–370.
Barker, H. A., and Lipmann, F. 1949. *J. Biol. Chem.*, **179**:247–257.
Barker, H. A.; Smyth, R. D.; Weissbach, H.; Toohey, J. I.; Ladd, J. N.; and Volcani, B. E. 1960. *J. Biol. Chem.*, **235**:480–496; Volcani, B. E.; Toohey, J. I.; and Barker, H. A. *Arch. Biochem. Biophys.*, **92**:381–391, 1961.
Bergey's Manual of Determinative Bacteriology. 1957. Baltimore, Williams and Wilkins.
Cardon, B. P., and Barker, H. A. 1946–1947. *J. Bact.*, **52**:629–634 (1946); *Arch. Biochem.*, **12**:167–180 (1947).
Carson, S. F.; Foster, J. W.; Ruben, S.; and Barker, H. A. 1941. *Proc. Nat. Acad. Sci.*, **27**:229–235.

Chaix, P., and Fromageot, C. 1942. *Trav. mem. Soc. Chim. Biol.*, **24**:1125–1127, 1128–1131; *Chem. Abstr.*, **39**:2138.

Delwiche, E. A. 1948. *J. Bact.*, **56**:811–820.

Delwiche, E. A., and Carson, S. F. 1953. *J. Bact.*, **65**:318–324.

Douglas, H. C., and Gunter, S. E. 1946. *J. Bact.*, **52**:15–23.

Fitz, A. 1878–1880. *Ber. deut. chem. Ges.*, **11**:1890–1899 (1878); **12**:474–481 (1879); **13**:1309–1312 (1880).

Flavin, M.; Ortiz, P. M.; and Ochoa, S. 1955–1957. *Nature*, **176**:823–826 (1955); Flavin, M., and Ochoa, S., *J. Biol. Chem.*, **229**:965–979 (1957); Flavin, M.; Castro-Mendoza, H.; and Ochoa, S. *Ibid.*, **229**:981–996; Beck, W. S.; Flavin, M.; and Ochoa, S. *Ibid.*, **229**:997–1010.

von Freudenreich, E., and Orla-Jensen, S. 1906. *Zentr. Bakt.*, II **17**:529–546; see also Orla-Jensen, S. *Ibid.*, II **13**:161–170 (1904).

Hayaishi, O. 1953. *J. Amer. Chem. Soc.*, **75**:4367.

Hitchner, E. R. 1934. *J. Bact.*, **28**:473–479.

Gutierrez, J. 1953. *J. Bact.*, **66**:123–128.

Jayasuriya, G. C. N., and Hungate, R. E. 1959. *Arch. Biochem. Biophys.*, **82**:274–287.

Johns, A. T. 1951. *J. Gen. Microbiol.*, **5**:326–336, 337–345.

Kohlmiller, E. F., and Gest, H. 1951. *J. Bact.*, **61**:269–282.

Kosow, D. P., and Lane, M. D. 1961. *Biochem. Biophys. Res. Comms.*, **4**:92–95.

Krebs, H. A. 1937. *Biochem. J.*, **31**:667–671.

Lardy, H. A., and Adler, J. 1956. *J. Biol. Chem.*, **219**:933–942.

Leaver, F. W.; Wood, H. G.; and Stjernholm, R. 1955. *J. Bact.*, **70**:521–530.

Lynen, F. 1961. In, Mechanism of Action of Water-soluble Vitamins, Ciba Foundn. Study Group II. London, J. A. Churchill.

van Niel, C. B. 1928. The Propionic Acid Bacteria. Haarlem, J. W. Boissevain and Co., 187 pp.

Phares, E. F.; Delwiche, E. A.; and Carson, E. F. 1956. *J. Bact.*, **71**:604–610.

Sijpestijn, A. K., and Elsden, S. R. 1952. *Biochem. J.*, **52**:41–45.

Stadtman, E. R.; Overath, P.; Eggerer, H.; and Lynen, F. 1960. *Biochem. Biophys. Res. Communs.*, **2**:1–5.

Stjernholm, R., and Wood, H. G. 1961. *Proc. Nat. Acad. Sci* (U.S.,) **47**:303–313.

Stoppani, A. M.; Conches, L.; de Favelukes, S. L. S.; and Sacerdote, F. L. 1958. *Biochem. J.*, **70**:438–455.

Swick, R. W., and Wood, H. G. 1960. *Proc. Nat. Acad. Sci.*, **46**:28–41.

Tasman, A., and Brandwijk, A. C. 1938. *J. Inf. Dis.*, **63**:10–20.

Virtanen, A. I. 1931. *Acta Chem. Fennica (Suomen Kemistilekti)*, **B6**:14.

Virtanen, A. I., and Karström, H. 1931. *Acta Chem. Fennica (Suomen Kemistilekti)*, **B7**, 17; **4**, Nos. 8–9. Suppl. 17–18; (see *Chem. Zentr.*, **103**:402, 1932).

Volk, W. A. 1960. *J. Biol. Chem.*, **235**:1550–1553.

Werkman, C. H.; Stone, R. W.; and Wood, H. G. 1937. *Enzymologia*, **4**:24–30; *Biochem. J.*, **31**:349–359.

Whiteley, H. R. 1953. *Proc. Nat. Acad. Sci.*, **39**:772–779, 779–785.

Whiteley, H. R., and Ordal, E. J. 1957. *J. Bact.*, **74**:331–336.

de Wolff, H. 1927. Biochemische Eigenschappen van der Diphtherie- en van de Pseudodiphtherie-bacteria. Dissertation, Utrecht.

Wood, H. G., and Stjernholm, R. 1961. *Proc. Nat. Acad. Sci.* (U.S.), **47**:289–303.

Wood, H. G.; Stjernholm, R.; and Leaver, F. W. 1956. *J. Bact.*, **72**:142–152.

Wood, H. G., and Werkman, C. H. 1936. *Biochem. J.*, **30**:48–53.

Wood, H. G., and Werkman, C. H. 1938. *Biochem. J.*, **32**:1262–1271.

Wood, H. G., and Werkman, C. H. 1940. *Biochem. J.*, **34**:7–14, 129–138.

Wood, H. G.; Werkman, C. H.; Hemingway, A.; and Nier, A. O. 1940. *J. Biol. Chem.*, **139**:365–376, 377–381.

CHAPTER XIV

The Formic Fermentation

The production of formic acid is the common result of a group of related fermentations with many variants. These variants have so confused the issue that the simple term *formic fermentation* has not been used. However, this term characterizes the process very well, since its "key-reaction," comparable to those given in the preceding chapters, is:

$$H_2O + CH_3COCOOH \rightarrow (CH_3COOH) + HCOOH$$

The acetic acid is bracketed because it is not an essential product, while the formic acid is.

1. THE ENTEROBACTERIACEAE AND THEIR SIGNIFICANCE

The formic-fermenting bacteria, often termed the coli-typhosum or colon-typhoid-dysentery group, have probably received more study than any others. One of them, *Escherichia coli* or *Bacterium coli*,[1] is the most widely used of all bacteria both in biochemical and genetical researches. The name *Enterobacteriaceae* was put forward by Rahn (1937) because so many of them are inhabitants of the animal intestine. Earlier they were sometimes called the enteric bacilli, but the

---

[1] Escherich described this organism as *Bacterium coli commune* in 1885. The name Bacterium is no longer recognized by Bergey's Manual (1957) as referring to a particular genus.

name *Bacillus* has long been restricted to sporeformers by all but the most inveterate medical writers.

These bacteria are gram-negative rods, with their flagella always peritrichous, if present at all. They all produce acid from glucose, and most of them from other carbohydrates as well. Unlike the lactic bacteria, however, they are facultatively aerobic and contain catalase. Most of them, in the "wild" type, do not require the addition of vitamins to the medium, but there are many mutants which do. Many strains of *E. coli* will grow well on ammonium lactate with KH_2PO_4 and salts; *Aerobacter* will grow even with citrate as the sole carbon source. Their morphology is simple, except for *Proteus*, which is claimed to form pleomorphic rods in young cultures; however, these are doubtless really chains of short rods of which cross walls are not easily seen (cf. Chap. III). Some species of Proteus spread rapidly over agar in a characteristic swarming movement. Fimbriae (p. 126) are very common in the group. These thin, stiff filaments are found on virtually all strains of Proteus and Serratia, and on 60 to 80 per cent of Salmonella and Klebsiella as well as on other genera (Duguid and Gillies, 1957–1958).

Some members of the group, particularly Proteus and Aerobacter, are normally present in soil, but *E. coli* is a regular inhabitant of the large intestines, and therefore of the feces of mammals. It grows simply on the nutrients of the feces and is therefore not a parasite, but rather a *commensal* (literally, feeding at the same table) with the host. Researches on vitamin K, however, have cast a new light on so-called commensalism. Mammals and birds need vitamin K for the normal clotting of blood; hemorrhages occur in its absence. Nevertheless, all but the newborn are independent of the vitamin in the diet, because it is synthesized by bacteria in the intestines. Pure cultures of *E. coli* on a synthetic medium synthesize and excrete into the medium relatively large amounts of vitamin K-active substances (Dam *et al.*, 1941). We should therefore regard *E. coli* as a symbiont rather than a commensal. The formation of vitamin B_{12} from cobalt by rumen bacteria (p. 162) and probably by *E. coli* (Barker *et al.* 1960) is a comparable case.

The synthesis of vitamins is not limited to vitamins K and B_{12} nor, indeed, to the activity of *E. coli*. Other members of the *Enterobacteriaceae* do the same, and so do some of the aerobic sporeformers. The amounts of B vitamins produced by some pure cultures on a strictly synthetic medium are shown in Table XIV–1 (see also Huhtanen and Gall, 1953).

These are large. A yield of 115 micrograms of thiamine per gram of *E. coli* is interesting in regard to human nutrition. The human colon has a volume of about 4.5 liters, and some 40 per cent of human feces represents bacteria, mainly *E. coli*. The colon could thus contain 1800 gm of bacteria which would correspond to 200 mg of thiamine. When it is considered that the daily human requirement is only about 2 mg, it is evident that the process of defecation, however desirable for other reasons, is unfortunate from the viewpoint of vitamin nutrition.

TABLE XIV–1

(From Burkholder and McVeigh, 1942)

ORGANISM	YIELD IN MICROGRAMS PER GRAM FRESH BACTERIA (AFTER 48 HR AT 36° C)			
	Biotin	Riboflavin	Thiamine	Nicotinic Acid
Escherichia coli	2.3	106	115	62
Proteus vulgaris	3.2	57	95	? 0
Aerob. aerogenes	1.1	41	43	89
"*Alcaligenes fecalis*"	0.5	78	132	77
*Bac. mesentericus vulgatus**	0.8	82	72	709

* Probably a strain of *Bac. subtilis.*

The presence of *E. coli* in such enormous numbers in feces means that when it is found in water, milk, or food, these are probably contaminated with traces of feces or of sewage. The identification of *E. coli* is, therefore, an important part of the routine bacteriological examination of foods and water. For this purpose distinction must be made between (1) intestinal types, including *E. coli* and pathogens, and (2) soil forms like Aerobacter. A number of laboratory tests have been worked out for this and are widely used by public health bacteriologists (see American Public Health Association, *Standard Methods*, 1960, Parr, 1939). These tests depend on differences in the fermentations as described below.

The group as a whole may be subgrouped physiologically (Table XIV–2) by their ability to produce hydrogen from dextrose and lactose, along with proteolysis as measured by gelatin liquefaction. The table shows that the ability to attack lactose is typical of Escherichia and Aerobacter. A lactose-negative Escherichia ("*E. coli mutabile*") continuously throws mutants, about 1 in 100,000, which can attack lactose (see Chap. XVII). *Aerobacter cloacae* is the species that liquefies gelatin. Serratia, or *B. prodigiosum*, is really to be considered as a group of red-pigmented *Aerobacter cloacae*, or in some isolates which

TABLE XIV–2. The Formic–Fermenting Bacteria

(The sign (+) means that some strains are positive.)

Common or Old Names	Bergey Genus	FROM DEXTROSE		FROM LACTOSE		Voges-Proskauer Reaction	Prote-olysis	Other
		Acid	H₂	Acid	H₂			
B. coli, B. freundii	Escherichia	+	+	+	+	–	–	–
Aerobacter:	Aerobacter							
B. lactis aerogenes	(+ Klebsiella?)	+	+	+	+	+	(+)	Form gum on sugar media
B. cloacae								
B. acidi lactici								
B. carotovorum	Erwinia	+	+	±	±	(+)	(+)	Hydrolyze pectin
B. proteus	Proteus	+	+	–	–	–	+	(See Chap. VII)
B. prodigiosum	Serratia	+	+	(+)	(+)	+	+	Scarlet pigment
B. paratyphosum,	Salmonella	+	+	–	–	–	–	Pathogenic
B. aertrycke								
B. typhosum	Salmonella	+	–	–	–	–	–	Form up to 3 % formic acid
(Eberthella)								
B. dysenteriae	Shigella	+	– (+)	(+)	··	–	–	Pathogenic

do not attack lactose, as red-pigmented Proteus. All its isolates tested form acetoin, which is responsible for the "Voges-Proskauer reaction" shown in Table XIV–2. The pigment (p. 334) is a pyrrole derivative and is apparently attached to the cell membrane (Purkayastha and Williams, 1960; Yoshida, 1962). Several organisms differing from Escherichia and Aerobacter only in that their fermentation of lactose is delayed have been grouped in a separate genus, Paracolobactrum (Bergey, 1957). But to give *generic* rank to what may prove to be only a single gene difference is quite unjustified.

A number of related organisms cause lesions, wilts, or soft rot in plant tissues. These bacteria, of which *B. carotovorum* is the best known, are common on market vegetables, on which they cause soft brown spots or areas, and some of them cause rot diseases on growing plants. In Bergey's manual they are treated as a separate tribe with the single genus *Erwinia*. However, they clearly cause a formic fermentation, in most cases attacking lactose; in some acetoin is produced (p. 513), which is characteristic of Aerobacter, while some are proteolytic. Frequently they will grow on citrate as sole carbon source, a behavior typical of Aerobacter (Taylor, 1951). Thus they are closely related to Aerobacter. Their only distinguishing character is that of rapidly macerating plant tissue, especially carrot and turnip, which is not shown by other members of the *Enterobacteriaceae* (Elrod, 1942); nevertheless, this character alone scarcely justifies classifying them in a separate tribe. The same considerations hold for an animal pathogen,

"Friedländer's bacterium," causing some pneumonias in man. This differs from Aerobacter only in being heavily capsulated, but rough forms (R-forms) without capsule certainly exist, while Aerobacter often forms capsules too. Its listing in Bergey's manual as a separate genus, Klebsiella, therefore has little basis. Some taxonomists, indeed (cf. Wood, 1950), would not only include this organism in Aerobacter, but would also, and with good reason, eliminate Serratia as a separate genus.

The Salmonella group is a rather homogeneous one. All are intestinal pathogens, causing enteric fevers and "food poisoning" of varying degrees of severity. Over 150 strains or isolates exist, distinguished mainly on serological grounds. The transduction phenomenon (sec. 5 of Chap. XXI) indicates a close interrelationship, and some workers would reduce them all to three species. *S. typhimurium (B. aertrycke)* is the commonest cause of food poisoning. The Salmonella fermentations are marked by failure to attack lactose, and, in the case of *S. typhosa*, failure to decompose formate. They are not proteolytic. As a rule they can reduce trimethylamine oxide to trimethylamine, a reaction responsible for the characteristic smell of decaying fish:

$$(CH_3)_3N:O + 2(H) \rightarrow (CH_3)_3N + H_2O$$

However, this reaction is not very specific since it is given by many Proteus, Escherichia, Serratia, and Aerobacter as well (Wood and Baird, 1943).

The dysentery bacteria (genus Shigella) are less homogeneous. Their pathogenicity varies from slight to extreme, their serology is complex, and the fermentations vary, a few producing hydrogen and some attacking lactose slowly. Some reduce trimethylamine oxide; none is proteolytic. The genus as such may not have much more validity than Klebsiella.

The intestinal diseases caused by these last two groups are characterized by inflammation of the intestinal wall. Because the area of tissue involved is quite large and relatively uniform, the onset of the diseases is typically very rapid. The flow of fluid to the area, which is characteristic of the "inflammatory process," leads to dilution of the feces with fluid (as well as blood) and often thence to dehydration of the body as a whole. Cholera, caused by a vibrio, has many similarities to typhoid and dysentery. The endotoxins of these bacteria add a complicating factor to the disease. Of course normal strains of *E. coli* do not attack the intestines in which they live, although strains biochemically indistinguishable from them may sometimes cause inflammations in the bladder and elsewhere.

2. THE "COLI" TYPE OF FERMENTATION

A. Products

The products of the fermentation were first determined by Harden (1901), whose analyses indicated that the fermentation can be formulated:

$$2 \; C_6H_{12}O_6 + H_2O \rightarrow$$
$$2 \; CH_3CHOHCOOH + C_2H_5OH + CH_3COOH + 2 \; CO_2 + 2 \; H_2 \quad (1)$$

Succinic acid was later added to the list of products. Later analyses give results agreeing in principle with Harden's, although not in detail. Two independent sets of analyses are summarized in Table XIV–3.

TABLE XIV–3. Products of *E. coli* Fermentations

(Experiments 1 and 2 in presence of $CaCO_3$ [Scheffer, 1928]; Experiment 3 held at pH 6.0 by adding ammonia [Blackwood *et al.*, 1956].)

PRODUCT	MOLES PER 100 MOLES OF GLUCOSE FERMENTED				
	Experiment 1	Experiment 2	Ratio	Experiment 3	Ratio
CO_2	45	43	1	88	2
H_2	44	41	1	75	2
HCOOH	2	2	—	2	—
CH_3COOH	45	43	1	37	1
C_2H_5OH	45	40	1	50	1
Lactic acid	84	85	2	80	2
Succinic acid	27	31	½	11	¼

Different members of the *Enterobacteriaceae* give significantly different products, as was seen above in Table XIV–2. Attention to these variations has been partly responsible for elucidation of the reaction mechanism. For example, *S. typhosa* gives little or no hydrogen gas, and in this case formic acid is found instead (Harden, 1901). With *Aerobacter aerogenes* the modifications are more extensive and will be discussed in section 3.

Many substrates besides sugars are fermentable. Glycerol gives more alcohol and less lactic acid (see sec. 5 below). Ethylene glycol gives mainly lactic and acetic acids, while malic and tartaric acids yield acetic, succinic, and CO_2 in about equal amounts (Grey, 1924). Succinic acid itself is converted to formic and acetic acids and hydrogen. Glyceric acid yields 50 per cent of acetic acid, formic acid, and a trace of alcohol; the L-form is used much faster than the D- (Virtanen and Peltola, 1930). Access of oxygen during the fermentation decreases the yield of formic acid and increases the lactic and succinic acids (Grey and Young, 1921). Acid pH has similar effects (see below).

Three types of substrate involve special consideration.

(1) Fermentation of *pentoses* is described in detail in section 3C.

(2) Fermentation of the *sugar alcohols* depends on the development of specific dehydrogenases, which are induced. When *E. coli* strain B is grown on sorbitol, it can dehydrogenate 6 phospho-D-sorbitol but not when grown on mannitol or dulcitol (Wolff and Kaplan, 1956). When grown on mannitol (or to a less extent on sorbitol) it can dehydrogenate 1-phospho-D-mannitol, and this dehydrogenase can be readily prepared from the cells. Thus, there are two different inducible dehydrogenases, and probably a third for dulcitol. Special kinases for phosphorylating the alcohols probably exist too, like the glycerokinase of Aerobacter (Rush *et al.*, 1957) which enables those strains that possess it to form phosphoglycerol; those that do not contain it dehydrogenate the glycerol to dihydroxyacetone like Acetobacter (Chap. XVI).

(3) The fermentation of *uronic acids*, as worked out by Ashwell and co-workers (1960), proceeds via the 2 keto-3-deoxy-gluconic acid route described in Chapter XI, section 10. Glucuronic and galacturonic acids are first isomerized to the keto forms, fructuronic and tagaturonic acids (by an isomerase whose formation is induced by growth on either acid). The keto groups are reduced by DPNH with specific dehydrogenases, and the resulting mannonic and altronic acids then lose H_2O to give 2 keto-3-deoxygluconic acid. This is phosphorylated and cleaved to pyruvate and phosphoglyceraldehyde as described on page 453. *E. coli*, *A. aerogenes*, and *Serratia marcescens* behave similarly.

B. Mechanism of Formation

1. HYDROGEN AND FORMIC ACID. The first characteristic in which this complex fermentation differs from those in the three preceding chapters is the production of hydrogen. The key to this is given by the typhoid bacteria, which produce formic acid instead. Having regard to the biological similarities of these bacteria to *E. coli* and the general similarities of the two fermentations in other respects, Harden (1901) and also Pakes and Jollyman, independently, correctly deduced that the hydrogen arises from formic acid. It was noted in Table XIV–3 that *E. coli* also produces small amounts of formic acid, and indeed Blackwood *et al.* (1956) found that if the pH is maintained at 7.8 by

adding ammonia, *E. coli* forms much formic acid and very little H_2. Whether this is an effect of pH or of excess ammonia is not clear.

All the analyses show that the hydrogen formed is about equivalent to the CO_2, so that the reaction evidently is:

$$HCOOH \rightarrow CO_2 + H_2 \tag{2}$$

The first clue to the origin of formic acid was Neuberg's finding (1914) that it arose from the fermentation (by mixed cultures) of pyruvic acid:

$$CH_3COCOOH + H_2O \rightarrow CH_3COOH + HCOOH \tag{3}$$

Oxalacetic acid similarly yields acetic, formic, and CO_2 (although the mechanism of this reaction is far from clear):

$$HOOC \cdot CH_2CO \cdot COOH + H_2O \rightarrow CH_3COOH + HCOOH + CO_2 \tag{4}$$

Reaction (3) resembles those discussed in Chapter V, section 8, except that the pyruvic acid is not oxidized. Instead, pyruvic acid reacts directly with coenzyme A to acetylate it at the S atom and liberate formic acid:

$$CH_3COCOOH + HS \cdot (CoA-enzyme) \rightleftharpoons CH_3CO \cdot S(CoA-enzyme) + HCOOH \tag{5}$$

The enzyme is transacetylase.

The acetyl-coenzyme A rapidly takes up phosphate from the solution to produce acetyl phosphate:

$$CH_3CO \cdot S(CoA-enzyme) + HO \cdot H_2PO_3 \rightleftharpoons CH_3CO \cdot O \cdot H_2PO_3 + HS(CoA) + enzyme \tag{6}$$

Both these reactions are reversible (Stadtman *et al.*, 1951), but the excess of pyruvate drives them from left to right and the over-all reaction is thus:

$$CH_3COCOOH + H_3PO_4 \rightleftharpoons CH_3COO \cdot H_2PO_3 + HCOOH \tag{7}$$

Its reversibility was shown in cell-free extracts of *E. coli* by fermenting pyruvate in the presence of acetate or formate containing C^{13} in the carboxyl group (Lipmann, 1946). After a short period $HC^{13}OOH$ gave rise to $CH_3COC^{13}OOH$, the rate depending on the concentration of phosphate present. Cocarboxylase (thiamine pyrophosphate), cysteine, Mn^{++}, and Mg^{++} are needed to catalyze the reaction.

Unlike formate, isotopic acetate is not converted to pyruvate unless ATP is present. The reason for this is that acetate does not directly react with the enzyme. The function of ATP is to form the adenylate of the enzyme, which then exchanges with coenzyme A to form an enzyme-coenzyme complex. It is this that reacts with acetate (Jones, Lipmann, Hilz, and Lynen, 1953). The resulting acetyl-enzyme transfers the acetyl group to coenzyme A to form acetyl-Co A, which is then converted to acetyl phosphate as shown above (cf. Fig. V–13). The reactions are thus:

1. $CH_3COCOOH + HS\ CoA \rightleftharpoons CH_3CO \cdot S\ CoA + HCOOH$ (cf. 5)

2. a. $Ad\ (P)(P)(P) + Enz.OH \rightleftharpoons Enz.(P)\ Ad + (P)(P)OH$
   b. $Enz.\ (P)\ Ad + HS\ CoA \rightleftharpoons Enz.S\ CoA + Ad(P)H$
   c. $\underline{CH_3COOH + Enz.S\ CoA \rightleftharpoons CH_3CO \cdot S\ CoA + Enz.OH}$

3. $\underline{CH_3CO \cdot S\ CoA + (P)OH \rightleftharpoons CH_3CO \cdot O(P) + HS\ CoA}$ (cf. 6)

1 + 3. $CH_3COCOOH + (P)OH \rightleftharpoons CH_3CO \cdot O(P) + HCOOH$ (cf. 7)

2 + 3. $CH_3COOH + (P)OH + Ad\ (P)(P)(P) \rightleftharpoons$
$$CH_3CO \cdot O(P) + Ad(P)H + (P)(P)OH \quad (8)$$

Sum, (reversing [8]):

$$CH_3COCOOH + (P)(P)OH + Ad(P)H \rightleftharpoons CH_3COOH + HCOOH + Ad(P)(P)(P)$$

where Ad = adenosine and (P) = phosphate, so that $Ad\ (P)(P)(P)$ = ATP, and $(P)(P)OH$ = pyrophosphate. The reverse of equation (8) yields free acetic acid.

In sum, therefore, this fermentation rests on the conversion of pyruvic acid to acetic and formic acids, with the intervention of co-enzyme A, ATP, and phosphate, and the decomposition of formic acid to CO_2 and H_2.

2. ALCOHOL. Although the splitting of pyruvate explains the production of formic acid, it does not by any means explain the whole fermentation, because (see analyses above) alcohol is formed roughly equivalent to the acetic and formic acids. This alcohol cannot be formed as in yeast by decarboxylation of pyruvate and reduction of the acetaldehyde, since if so an equal quantity of CO_2 would be formed. We have seen that CO_2 equivalent to the H_2 comes from formic acid, and as a rule the ratio $CO_2:H_2$ for *E. coli* is close to 1. (With Aerobacter it is nearer 3, but there are special reasons for this which will be seen below.[2]) Besides, pyruvic decarboxylase is not present, because

[2] The value of 1 for the $CO_2:H_2$ ratio has, however, not always been obtained. For example, the data of Grey and Young (1921), obtained under anaerobic conditions, lead to the following quantities, per 100 moles of glucose fermented:

CO_2	119
H_2	34.2
HCOOH	37
CH_3COOH	133
C_2H_5OH	46
Lactic acid	8.2
Succinic acid	0.5

Compared to those quoted above, they show much more CO_2 and acetic acid and much less lactic and succinic acids. Variations in yields of the acids may be ascribed to the pH, but the high ratio of CO_2 to H_2 conflicts not only with Scheffer's data but also with common experience of many workers.

cell-free extracts do not act on pyruvate (Dawes and Foster, 1956). On the other hand acetaldehyde is formed in the fermentation, as shown both by adding bisulfite (Neuberg and Nord, 1919) and by sampling and testing during the first hour (Dawes and Foster, 1956). There is also a reversible DPN-linked alcohol dehydrogenase present (Still, 1940), which could convert acetaldehyde to alcohol.

These conflicting considerations were harmonized by the following observations (Dawes and Foster, 1956):

(1) Fluoride, cyanide, and iodoacetate, all of which inhibited pyruvate formation, also stopped the production of ethanol; arsenite, which caused an accumulation of pyruvate by preventing its metabolism, also stopped the production of ethanol. Thus, ethanol is probably formed from pyruvate.

(2) A mutant that requires pantothenate for growth, and is therefore presumably deficient in coenzyme A, metabolizes pyruvate and produces ethanol, in proportion to the amount of pantothenate added. Thus ethanol formation requires coenzyme A.

(3) The cell-free acetaldehyde dehydrogenase of E. coli, using DPN, acts only in presence of coenzyme A. With DPNH it reduces acetyl-coenzyme A; i.e., it establishes the equilibrium:

$$CH_3CHO + DPN^+ + HS \cdot CoA \rightleftharpoons CH_3CO \cdot SCoA + DPNH + H^+$$

It follows that the ethanol formed by E. coli comes from acetyl-CoA via acetaldehyde and subsequent reduction:[3]

$$CH_3COCOOH \longrightarrow CH_3CO\text{—}S \cdot CoA + HCOOH \tag{9a}$$

$$CH_3CO\text{—}S \cdot CoA \xrightarrow{2(H)} CoA \cdot SH + CH_3CHO \xrightarrow{2(H)} CH_3CH_2OH \tag{9b}$$

The yield of alcohol in the natural fermentation is more constant than that of the acids. The wide variation in yields of the latter may well be due to differences in pH, which often has not been controlled. With increasing alkalinity the yield of acetic and formic acids goes up and that of lactic acid goes down, as Table XIV-4 shows. In this table the H_2 gas has been considered as coming from formic acid and has therefore been added to the formic acid found as such. It is clear that the production of lactic acid or of formic plus acetic acid represent, roughly speaking, alternative fates for pyruvic acid, while the production of alcohol remains constant. In general, the effect of pH resembles that noted with the heterofermentative lactic organisms; alkalinity lowers the yield of lactate and increases the yield of acetate.

[3] It is interesting that this route was proposed in the first edition of this book (1955) as the only feasible explanation of all the data.

TABLE XIV–4. Change of Products with pH; Yields in % of Glucose Used

(Calculated from Data of Tikka, 1935)

Initial pH	Lactic Acid	Acetic Acid	Formic Acid + H_2 Gas	Ethanol
6.4	43.5	5.2	18.1	20.2
7.1	21.0	19.2	18.3	21.5
7.4	4.1	29.4	22.8	22.1
7.6	2.7	34.1	30.2	21.1

3. Lactic Acid. Cell-free enzyme preparations from Escherichia and Aerobacter can split hexosediphosphate into the two triose derivatives, phosphoglyceraldehyde and phosphodihydroxyacetone, and can also establish equilibrium between these two products (Utter and Werkman, 1941–1942). The dehydrogenation of phosphoglyceraldehyde to phosphoglyceric acid (Still, 1940) and the conversion of phosphoglyceric to phosphopyruvic acid, as well as the transfer of phosphate from this product to adenylic acid (Utter and Werkman) have been similarly established. The bacteria thus produce pyruvic acid in the "standard" manner. When it is considered that they can also dehydrogenate lactic acid (Tables V–3 and V–4), and that such dehydrogenations are reversible, it is evident that the lactic acid produced in this fermentation arises in exactly the same way as in the lactic fermentation. The difference between the *Enterobacteriaceae* and the homofermentative Lactobacilli lies in the fact that the former have an additional method of dealing with pyruvic acid (namely, its conversion to formic and acetic acids).

4. Succinic Acid and the Fixation of CO_2 as a Factor in Growth. The fact that succinic acid (containing 4 carbon atoms) can be produced by *E. coli* from glycerol (containing 3 carbon atoms) just about as freely as from glucose (Grey, 1924) indicates that it arises by the addition of CO_2 to pyruvate and subsequent reduction of the oxaloacetate formed (pp. 245–46 and 493–95). This was proved by using cell-free extracts of *E. coli*, with isotopic CO_2 (Kalnitsky and Werkman, 1943–1944). These preparations are free of cocarboxylase and hence do not destroy pyruvate; they thus convert added CO_2 to succinate. ATP and biotin are essential for the reaction, as well as either Mn or Mg. The succinate produced in the formic fermentation, therefore, comprises part of the total yield of CO_2.

Werkman and his co-workers have elucidated several other reactions by which CO_2 is "fixed" into organic acids. These may not account for an appreciable consumption of CO_2 in the fermentation, but they indicate how widely CO_2 enters into combination:

(1) The first step in the oxidative decarboxylation of pyruvate to acetate and CO_2 (Chap. XII) is reversible, so that acetyl-CoA can absorb CO_2, to form pyruvate and thus eventually citrate:

$$\text{CH}_3\text{CO·C}^{13}\text{OO}^- + \text{HS·CoA} + \text{DPN}^+ \overset{\text{TPP}}{\rightleftharpoons} \text{CH}_3\text{CO—S·CoA} + \text{C}^{13}\text{O}_2 + \text{DPNH}$$

This was first shown by incubating washed cells or a cell-free preparation of *M. pyogenes* var. *aureus* with pyruvate and $C^{13}O_2$, when the pyruvate came to contain C^{13} in its carboxyl (Wikén *et al.*, 1947; Watt and Werkman, 1950). A similar fixation occurs with a cell-free preparation from *Cl. butylicum* which evolves H_2 (Wilson *et al.*, 1948):

$$\text{CH}_3\text{CO·C}^{13}\text{OO}^- + \text{HS·CoA} \overset{\text{TPP}}{\rightleftharpoons} \text{CH}_3\text{CO—S·CoA} + \text{C}^{13}\text{O}_2 + \text{H}_2$$

In both cases ATP promoted the reaction as would be expected; coenzyme A was not added but would have been present in the preparation along with cocarboxylase.

(2) The oxidative decarboxylation of α-ketoglutarate to succinate and CO_2 (Chap. V, sec. 8) is also to some extent reversible (Ajl and Werkman, 1948–1950). A cell-free enzyme from *E. coli* will decarboxylate α-ketoglutarate, and the resulting succinate will accumulate if malonate is added to inhibit its oxidation (cf. p. 216). If now $C^{13}O_2$ is introduced and the reaction stopped, the α-ketoglutarate contains C^{13} in the carboxyl adjacent to the C=O group. The fixation is promoted by ATP and involves succinyl phosphate as intermediate.

(3) CO_2 is fixed in the formation of purines and pyrimidines. With *A. aerogenes*, isotope analysis shows that the 4, 5, and 7 positions of its adenine and guanine come from glycine, the 2 and 8 positions from formate, and the 6 position from CO_2 (Sutton and Werkman, 1953). The N at position 1, 3, and 9 comes from glutamine.

(4) The formation of carbamyl phosphate, and therefore the synthesis of citrulline, arginine, and pyrimidines involves CO_2 fixation (Chap. VIII, sec. 5B).

(5) Serine is formed from glycine, either with CO_2 or with formate (Lascelles *et al.*, 1951). Folic acid and pyridoxal are needed as coenzymes (see pp. 321, 349).

All of these reactions using CO_2 account for the fact that many bacteria require CO_2 for growth. If cultures are very vigorously aerated with CO_2-free air, growth may be reduced; yeast extract will then substitute for CO_2 (Lwoff and Monod, 1947). Anaerobic growth is often dependent on CO_2 also, especially among the coliforms. In the absence of CO_2, growth of Escherichia and Aerobacter is reinstated by many organic acids, but for *Serratia marcescens*, the replacement of CO_2 requires asparagine, arginine, uracil, adenine, and guanine; each alone gives rise to a little growth and together they replace 93 per cent of the fixed CO_2 (McLean and Purdie, 1952). Evidently, therefore, CO_2 is fixed in dicarboxylic acids, purines, and also in arginine. Thus CO_2 fixation provides an important part of nutrition.

5. ASSIMILATE. The bacteria grow during the fermentation. In oxidations, approximately a third of the carbohydrate decomposed appears as *E. coli* cell substance (Cook and Stephenson, 1928). In fermentation the assimilation is much less, although it is not negligible. A complete accounting of all carbon in the form of fermentation products is therefore not to be expected. The assimilate has approximately the composition of carbohydrate (see Chap. XX). In the scheme below we have shown ½ mole of pyruvic acid from a total of 4 moles, i.e., 12.5 per cent, diverted to cell substance.

C. Over-all Scheme

The above arguments give rise to a general scheme for the formic fermentation of glucose roughly as shown on page 512.

The scheme accounts fairly well for the quantitative distribution of products commonly found. Intermediate steps, such as the formation and degradation of acetyl-CoA, have been omitted. The relative amounts of the various products will necessarily depend on the relative activities of the enzymes taking part and thus will vary somewhat with the particular organism and the growth conditions.

3. THE AEROBACTER MODIFICATION

Among the bacteria that can ferment lactose to formate, there are those like *E. coli* that produce CO_2 and H_2 in a ratio about 1, and others, including Aerobacter and Serratia, in which the ratio is 3 or much higher, approaching 100 with some strains of Serratia and also with *Bac. subtilis* (see sec. D. below).

The presence of two such clearly defined groups has long been recognized (Harden, 1905; Harden and Walpole, 1906) and is of great importance because organisms of the second type are soil forms, while *E. coli* is intestinal in origin. Establishment of the presence of a formic-fermenting organism in a sample of food or water is thus only of significance for public health (i.e., showing fecal contamination) if it is clear that the organism is not a native soil form.

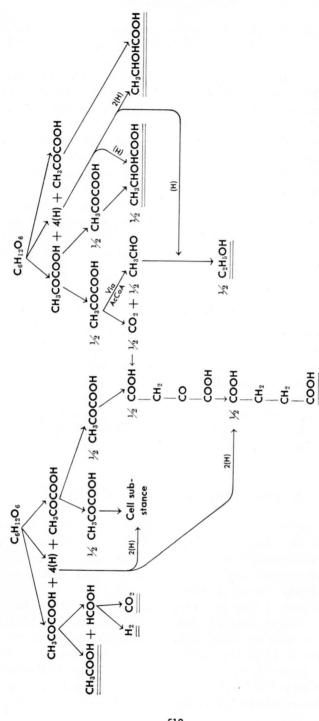

Final products underlined

$$2\ C_6H_{12}O_6 \rightarrow 1\frac{1}{2}\ CH_3CHOHCOOH + CH_3COOH + \frac{1}{2}\ HOOCCH_2CH_2COOH + \frac{1}{2}\ C_2H_5OH + H_2 + CO_2 + \text{Cell substance}$$

512

A. The Formation of Acetoin

The principal difference lies in the formation by Aerobacter of a new substance, acetoin, or acetylmethylcarbinol, $CH_3CO \cdot CHOHCH_3$ (Harden, 1906; Harden and Walpole, 1906). The mode of formation of this substance was touched on in Chapter XII, section D. Pyruvate combines with thiamine pyrophosphate at the 2 position of the thiazole ring, but on losing its CO_2 the acetyl residue, instead of being passed to lipoic acid as described there, is passed to another molecule of pyruvate to form D-α-aceto-lactate; this is decarboxylated (Juni, 1952):

$$[CH_3CO \cdot H] + CH_3CO \cdot COOH \rightarrow CH_3C \overset{\displaystyle COCH_3}{\underset{\displaystyle OH}{\big|}} COOH \rightarrow CH_3CHOHCOCH_3 + CO_2 \quad (10)$$

Thus, each molecule of acetoin formed releases 2 CO_2. The enzyme appears to be the same as pyruvic decarboxylase and to have *two* sites, for holding on to two acetyl residues (Juni, 1961). Its pH optimum is about 6, which agrees with the optimum pH of acetoin formation.

The acetolactate may have an alternative fate, because there is a second enzyme system, of optimum pH 7.8, producing it, and this one is inhibited by valine (Halpern and Umbarger, 1959). This system is thought to be the one by which valine is *formed*, by way of a molecular rearrangement and transamination (p. 346).

Acetoin can be oxidized to diacetyl, and it can also be reduced to 2,3-butanediol, and it is this compound which is mainly found in the fermented liquor:

$$\underset{\text{Diacetyl}}{CH_3COCOCH_3} \underset{\frac{1}{2} O_2}{\overset{2 H}{\rightleftharpoons}} \underset{\text{Acetoin}}{CH_3COCHOHCH_3} \underset{\frac{1}{2} O_2}{\overset{2 H}{\rightleftharpoons}} \underset{\text{2,3-Butylene glycol}}{CH_3CHOHCHOH \cdot CH_3} \quad (11)$$

It will be remembered that every mole of pyruvate formed involves the simultaneous reduction of DPN, and the 2(H) is doubtless at once transferred to acetoin, just as it would be to acetaldehyde in fermentation by yeast.

The above reductions are slowly reversible in air. If an Aerobacter fermentation liquor is made strongly alkaline and exposed to air, it slowly turns bright pink (Voges-Proskauer reaction). Addition of α-naphthol and creatine hastens the reaction and makes it more sensitive, since it depends on condensation of the diacetyl (formed by reversal of reaction [11]) with traces of creatine or guanidine derivatives in the peptone.

The Voges-Proskauer reaction is one of the four standard tests used for differentiating the Aerobacter and coli fermentations. The four tests, abbreviated IMViC, are:

Indole (formed by *E. coli* from tryptophan)
Methyl red (turned red by *E. coli*, due to the acetic acid formed)
Voges-Proskauer reaction
Citrate (utilized as sole carbon source by Aerobacter)

Because of the acetic acid produced, the *E. coli* fermentation typically reaches pH 4 in about 24 hours, while that with Aerobacter goes only to pH 5.3, so that methyl red remains orange-yellow in it.

Like the other fermentation types, that by Aerobacter is strongly pH sensitive. The formation of acetoin and 2,3-butylene glycol takes place only on the acid side of pH 6.3 (Watt and Werkman, 1951). At more alkaline pH the products are mainly lactate, acetate, and ethanol, so that the fermentation more nearly resembles that by *E. coli.*

Diacetyl has another importance. It possesses a characteristic odor, like that of good butter. It is indeed probably responsible for the aroma of butter (van Niel *et al.*, 1929) and is sometimes added in minute amounts to margarine to give it a buttery flavor. Its production in soured cream is largely due to *Sc. cremoris* and *Sc. diacetilactis,* which form it from citric acid (p. 472).

B. General Scheme

Because so much pyruvic acid is converted to acetoin (at acid pH) there is less of it to be converted into acetic acid (cf. the methyl red test). Furthermore, since each mole of acetoin corresponds to the formation of 2 moles of CO_2 (equation [10]), the total CO_2 derives partly from formic acid and partly from this extra source. Hence the ratio $CO_2:H_2$ is much above 1. Typical analyses of the products from 100 moles of glucose fermented by *"Aerobacter indologenes"* (a variant of *A. cloacae*) (Reynolds and Werkman, 1937), and of three other organisms are as follows:

	Aerobacter		Escherichia		Serratia		Bac. subtilis
CO_2	172		44		106		102
H_2	36 ⎱54		43 ⎱45		1 ⎱41		0
HCOOH	18 ⎰ HCOOH		2 ⎰ HCOOH		40 ⎰ HCOOH		6
CH_3COOH	0.5		44		0		1
C_2H_5OH	70		42		42		14
Lactic acid	3		84		33		35
Succinic acid	ca 0		29		3		2
2,3-Butanediol	66.5		—		51		53

Allowing 2 CO_2 for each mole of 2,3-butanediol (i.e., 133 CO_2), 39 moles of CO_2 remain; this just corresponds to the 36 moles of H_2. Hence the remaining CO_2, like the H_2, came from formic acid. In general, in these fermentations, the CO_2 plus the succinic acid (which represents additional CO_2 that has been fixed) should be equal to the H_2 plus twice the butanediol. In the data for Serratia (from Neish, 1950), very little H_2 is evolved, and the yield of CO_2 is thus just twice that of the butanediol. Unlike Aerobacter, Serratia's optimum pH for butanediol formation is about 7, and presence of $CaCO_3$ allows good yields (Bahadur and Dube, 1958). The data for *Bac subtilis* agree well.

Only the Escherichia forms acetic acid, although the other organisms shown may form a little in the earlier stages. The Aerobacter data were obtained after 209 hours; at 31 hours there were 7 moles of acetic acid formed, but even then there were 21 moles of formic acid. It is evident, therefore, that ethanol is appearing instead of acetic acid, in other words, that the acetyl group is being reduced before it can be hydrolyzed to acetic acid (cf. p. 508).

The balance sheet of this fermentation, in terms of pyruvic acid, would be as follows:

PRODUCT	MOLES PYRUVIC ACID REQUIRED	"MOLES" 2(H) REQUIRED
3 moles lactic acid	3	3
66.5 " 2,3-butylene glycol	133	67
70 " ethanol	70	70
54 " formic acid	. . .	54
	206	194
Total expected for 100 moles glucose	200	200

The appearance of small amounts of acetate early in the fermentation and its subsequent disappearance indicate that equation (3) is being reversed; acetate is being condensed with formate to pyruvate. It is important to observe that in this condensation and its sequel the carboxyl of acetic acid is reduced. In other words, *carboxyl* carbon of acetate is converted to *carbinol* carbon of butylene glycol:

$$CH_3\overset{*}{C}OOH \rightarrow CH_3\overset{*}{C}OOH_2PO_3 \rightarrow CH_3\overset{*}{C}OCOOH \rightarrow$$

$$CH_3\overset{*}{C}HOHCOCH_3 \rightarrow CH_3\overset{*}{C}HOHCHOHCH_3$$

Thus, $CH_3C^{13}OOH$ added to fermenting Aerobacter gave rise to $CH_3C^{13}HOHC^{13}OCH_3$, and $C^{13}H_3C^{13}OOH$ gave rise to butylene glycol with C^{13} equally distributed between the methyl and the carbinol carbons (Reynolds *et al.*, 1937). Not more than an eighth of the total butylene glycol seemed to be formed from acetic acid, the bulk of it presumably coming direct from pyruvate by reaction (10).

The general course of the fermentation is thus clear, and the differences from that of Escherichia are all seen to be results of the formation of acetoin. It is of interest that the methyl red test, the $CO_2:H_2$ ratio, and the Voges-Proskauer reaction were all used by public health bacteriologists to distinguish the two types of organism long before the underlying mechanism was understood.

It should be added that *E. coli* also can produce small amounts of acetoin, especially in vigorously aerated cultures containing 2 per cent $NaHCO_3$ (Reynolds and Werkman, 1937). If the reaction products are distilled and the test carried out on the distillate, the sensitivity is higher, and even at the ordinary *p*H a positive reaction is given (Kluyver and Molt, 1939); with some strains the yield approaches 1 per cent (Blackwood *et al.*, 1956). However, *E. coli* does not normally show the test on the fermentation liquor directly.

C. Fermentation of Pentoses

As noted above, when pentoses are the substrate, the products are often the same as with hexoses. In this respect the gram-negative rods differ from the lactic bacteria, in which pentoses give quite a different type of fermentation from hexoses (p. 469). In the lactic organisms, as also in *Ps. lindneri*, the pentose is split into a 3-C and a 2-C fragment, the one yielding lactic acid and the other alcohol or acetic acid. Since the Enterobacteriaceae convert pentoses to the *same* products as hexoses, the 2-carbon fragment must be somehow resynthesized to triose. This is in fact what occurs. The resynthesis is brought about by the enzymes, transketolase and transaldolase, and the coenzyme, thiaminepyrophosphate. Aerobacter provides the best bacterial example of this remarkable series of reactions, which were worked out mostly on peas, spinach, and liver extracts (see Axelrod and Beevers, 1956).

The first steps are the phosphorylation of the pentose (shown below as ribose, I) and its conversion to the ketopentose, ribulose (II), followed by its being brought to equilibrium with 5-phospho-xylulose, III, all as with the heterofermentative lactic bacteria (p. 470). The xylulose is then cleaved to phosphoglyceraldehyde and a glycollic aldehyde radical which remains attached to the coenzyme; the transketolase reaction now transfers this 2-carbon unit to a second 5-phosphoribose molecule to form the phospho-derivative of the 7-carbon sugar sedoheptulose IV:

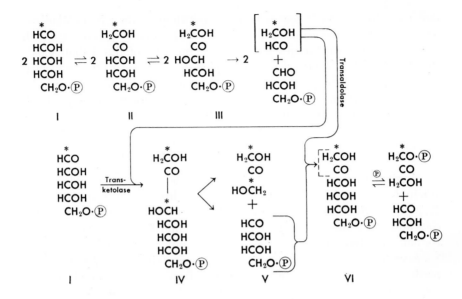

This is again cleaved to a triose and a tetrose, 4-phospho-erythrose, V. A second glycollic aldehyde group condenses with this (catalyzed by transaldolase) to form fructose-phosphate, VI, which is phosphorylated and cleaved as usual to two phosphotrioses. In all, three pentoses are converted to five trioses.

In the above scheme, if the 1-carbon of the ribose ($\overset{*}{C}$) is an isotope, three of the resulting trioses will be unlabeled, one will be labeled in the 1 position, and one labeled in *both* 1 and 3 positions. As a result (cf. diagram on pp. 446–47) one of the 5 molecules of pyruvate will have isotope in the methyl group, and one will have isotope in *both* methyl and carboxyl groups. Exactly this pattern was found when *A. aerogenes* fermented D- and L-arabinose labeled in the 1 position (Neish and Simpson, 1954); the C^{14} activity in the CH_3 groups of the lactic and acetic acids, butane-diol, and ethanol was 40 per cent of that in the original C-1 of the sugar, while in the COOH of the lactic acid, in the formic acid, and in the CO_2 the activity was just one-half as great (i.e., 17 to 23 per cent). Similar though less complete evidence indicates that *A. cloacae* and *E. coli* use the same route (Simpson and Wood, 1956; Nutting and Carson, 1952).

The methylpentose rhamnose may be metabolized in the same way, since the first step is conversion to the keto-form rhamnulose, which is then phosphorylated (Englesberg and Baron, 1958).

When a hexose molecule is fermented, the net gain in ATP is 2 molecules, or ⅓ ATP per carbon atom. When pentose is metabolized by this route, 3 molecules (requiring 3 ATP) give 5 trioses of which two need phosphorylation (= 2 ATP), and each of the 5 then yields 2 ATP; in all, 5 ATP result from 3 pentoses or ⅓ ATP per carbon atom. It would be expected, therefore, that growth on pentose would be just as rapid as on hexose, and in general this expectation is justified. *A. aerogenes* grows well on six different aldopentoses.

D. Acetoin Formation by Other Bacteria

Aerobacillus polymyxa, as mentioned above, converts added acetaldehyde to acetoin and butylene glycol (Stahly and Werkman, 1942). This organism forms alcohol and acetone, as well as acetoin, from glucose and other sugars, from sugar alcohols, and from pectins (p. 548). Its close relative *Aerobac. macerans* does not form acetoin.

Lactobacillus plantarum, one of the streptobacteria (Chap. XII), produces acetoin and CO_2 from pyruvate (Rowatt, 1951). The luminous pseudomonads, *Photobacterium* (Chap. XXII, sec. 7), carry out a fairly typical formic fermentation and produce varying amounts of acetoin (Doudoroff, 1942). Among other organisms forming traces of acetoin are certain yeasts, especially *Pichia indica*, in which the acetoin may reach 2.5 per cent of the sugar fermented (Bahadur and Ranganayaki, 1958); here the production is promoted by adding zinc.

More remarkable are the high yields of acetoin and butanediol produced by *Bac. subtilis*. Although this sporeformer is strongly aerobic, it can ferment glucose to the following products, in order of decreasing concentration; CO_2, butane-diol (and acetoin), lactic acid, glycerol, ethanol, and a little formic, succinic and acetic acids (Neish, 1953). Except for the reduction of about one-sixth of the triose to glycerol, the fermentation resembles that of Serratia above. When carried out in air, the yield of butanediol can be as high as 87 moles per 100 moles glucose fermented (Blackwood and Simpson, 1950). Indeed it was observed as long ago as 1906 by Harden that *Bac. subtilis* and *Bac. mesentericus* (a closely related form) gave strong Voges-Proskauer reactions.

Formation of acetoin by the heterofermentative lactic bacteria, *Leuconostoc citrovorum*, was mentioned above. Here carbon atoms 1, 2, and 3 yield alcohol and CO_2, while 4, 5, and 6 yield pyruvate and thence lactate. This pyruvate together with pyruvate derived from citric acid in the milk is converted to acetolactate and thence acetoin (reaction [10] above). Added citrate or pyruvate yields acetoin more readily than glucose does (Busse and Kandler, 1961).

Several Pseudomonads, especially *Ps. fermentans* and *Ps. trifolii*

($= B.\ herbicola$), produce acetoin from sugars; the former attacks lactose and thus, except for its polar flagellation, is closely related to Aerobacter. The latter shows its relationship to Aerobacter in another way, i.e., by the ability to form much gum on sugar media.

4. ENZYMES CONCERNED WITH HYDROGEN GAS

Although hydrogen comes almost always from formate, formate can be decomposed in several ways:

(1) Washed bacteria incubated with formate and methylene blue reduce the dye (Quastel and Whetham, 1925):

$$HCOOH + MB \rightarrow MBH_2 + CO_2 \qquad (12)$$

The enzyme, which is present in Escherichia, Aerobacter, and others of the group, is called *formic dehydrogenase*. Instead of methylene blue, it can reduce nitrate (in the presence of the enzyme nitratase) and it can also react with cytochrome c. This last property is explained by the fact that formic dehydrogenase, like succinic and lactic dehydrogenases, is closely bound to a cytochrome of the b type. Recently such a complex has been extracted from $E.\ coli$; it contains both cytochrome b_1 and a flavin, as well as 30 per cent RNA (Wrigley and Linnane, 1961). In the spectophotometer formate could be seen to reduce *both* the cytochrome *and* the flavin. Succinic dehydrogenase and nitratase activity were absent. In another preparation (Itagaki *et al.*, 1961) reduction of the cytochrome requires participation of a lipid fraction, replaceable by vitamin K_3; without this, the formate will reduce methylene blue but not the cytochrome (cf. the role of coenzyme Q, p. 208).

(2) Washed $E.\ coli$ can also reduce methylene blue with hydrogen gas (Stephenson and Stickland, 1932), which means that hydrogen is being brought into chemical combination, as by palladium black or Raney nickel:

$$H_2 \rightleftharpoons 2\ H^+ + 2\ e^-$$

This enzyme, which is called *hydrogenase*, is apparently a hemin derivative; it is inactivated reversibly by oxygen and by NO (Fisher *et al.*, 1954); it is also inhibited by CO though not by cyanide (Joklik, 1950). Its activity depends on a —SH group and is inhibited by mercury compounds. In $Ps.\ saccharophila$ it is present in two forms, one of which reduces DPN and the other, methylene blue. In the cell-free preparation these could be separated on the centrifuge (Bone, 1960). The enzyme occurs widely, especially in Azotobacter, in purple bacteria, and in those "Knallgasbakterien" that can grow by oxidizing hydrogen (Chap. XXI). In the purple *Rh-ps. palustris* it is in particles, probably chromatophores; like the much stronger *E. coli* enzyme, it is inhibited by CO but not by HCN (Izawa, 1962).

(3) The evolution of H_2 by *E. coli* does not quite follow either of these patterns. It proceeds optimally at pH 6 and is inhibited by cyanide, 10^{-5} M KCN giving 50 per cent inhibition (Stephenson and Stickland, 1932). For these reasons Woods (1936) at first ascribed it to a separate enzyme, *hydrogenlyase*, catalyzing the reversible reaction:

$$HCOOH \rightleftharpoons H_2 + CO_2$$

Evidently this enzyme, combined with formic dehydrogenase, would allow H_2 gas to reduce methylene blue, in other words, would duplicate the action of hydrogenase.

Hydrogenlyase is developed in *E. coli* as a function of its growth medium. Grown on plain broth, the organisms produce no hydrogen when suspended in glucose. They do, however, contain hydrogenase and formic dehydrogenase, i.e., they can reduce methylene blue with H_2 or with formate. If the bacteria are grown briefly on broth containing 1 per cent formate they then contain the hydrogenlyase. Nongas-producing strains of *S. paratyphosa* can also develop the enzyme after growth in formate medium (Pot and Tasman, 1932–1933). Such *induced* formation of an enzyme by its substrate is discussed in Chapter XX, section 5. The other two enzymes are not induced under these conditions. If the formate contains deuterium instead of hydrogen (i.e., $DCOO^-$), the rate of gas evolution is halved, but the rate of methylene blue reduction is not changed (Abei and Frei, 1957).

The special nature of the "lyase" was brought out unexpectedly by experiments with iron-deficient cells (Waring and Werkman, 1944). *E. coli* grown on broth very low in Fe contain little or no catalase or peroxidase and show no visible cytochrome bands; they also have no activity of formic dehydrogenase, hydrogenase, or hydrogenlyase. On *partially* Fe-deficient media the cells have formic dehydrogenase and hydrogenase, but in fermenting glucose they produce no H_2, producing instead large amounts of formic acid; hence they have no hydrogenlyase. Since there is still enough Fe present for growth, it seems that the "lyase" is "more easily suppressed by Fe deficiency than any other system studied." Since also the "lyase" is powerfully inhibited by KCN, Waring and Werkman (1944) postulate that liberation of H_2 from formate requires (1) formic dehydrogenase, (2) hydrogenase, and (3) an intermediate electron mediator, containing Fe, probably similar to cytochrome. This makes unnecessary a separate "lyase" enzyme but accounts for the special nature of the system. The reaction could be written:

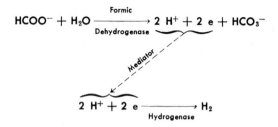

$$\text{HCOO}^- + \text{H}_2\text{O} \xrightarrow[\text{Dehydrogenase}]{\text{Formic}} 2\ \text{H}^+ + 2\ \text{e} + \text{HCO}_3^-$$

Mediator

$$2\ \text{H}^+ + 2\ \text{e} \xrightarrow[\text{Hydrogenase}]{} \text{H}_2$$

5. GLYCEROL AND THE E. FREUNDII MODIFICATION

Glycerol is readily fermented by the *Enterobacteriaceae*. With *E. coli* the products are mainly alcohol, lactic acid, formic acid, and extra CO_2 (Harden, 1901); with Aerobacter they are mainly alcohol and acetic and formic acids (Braak, 1928). However, when carried out under anaerobic conditions, the fermentation comes to a stop long before all the glycerol is used; addition of more peptone or yeast extract will start it again, but only for a time. Braak (1928) deduced that the dehydrogenation of glycerol

$$CH_2OHCHOHCH_2OH \rightarrow CH_2OHCHOHCHO + 2(H)$$

was the limiting reaction and that the peptone was needed to act as hydrogen acceptor. Acetaldehyde acts similarly as an acceptor (increasing the yield of ethanol), or the fermentation could be carried out in air, oxygen being then the acceptor. (The subsequent stages from glyceraldehyde, or more probably phosphoglyceraldehyde, are doubtless essentially as in the fermentation of sugar.)

It was, however, observed by Freund in the 1880's that some fermentations of glycerol gave rise to trimethylene glycol, $CH_2OH \cdot CH_2 \cdot CH_2OH$, and Voisenet (1918) isolated organisms carrying out this process, although he was mainly interested in the fact that they produced acrolein, $CH_2 = CH \cdot CHO$, which accounted for a bitter taste in infected wine. Braak, in his enrichment cultures, obtained two organisms that fermented glycerol rapidly with no added hydrogen acceptor. Evidently, therefore, the glycerol itself was being used as hydrogen acceptor, and trimethylene glycol was identified in the residues:

$$CH_2OHCHOHCH_2OH + 2(H) \rightarrow CH_2OHCH_2CH_2OH$$

The total products, for comparison with those listed in sections 2 and 3, were as follows:

	MOLES OF PRODUCTS PER 100 MOLES GLYCEROL FERMENTED, IN MINERAL MEDIUM	
	Strain 19 (mean of 2 expts.)	Strain 20
CO_2	21	36
H_2	21	37
HCOOH	3.3	13
CH_3COOH	13	5.0
C_2H_5OH	15	50
Lactic acid	5.8	12
Succinic acid	3.8	2.2
Trimethylene-glycol	35.5	24

It will be seen that the second strain produces more formic acid and alcohol, but less trimethylene glycol, than the first. Both were termed *B. freundii* (now *E. freundii*). Other organisms reducing glycerol to trimethylene glycol are found among the lactobacilli (Sobolev and Smiley, 1960) and *Aerobacter aerogenes* (Mickelson and Werkman, 1940). The *Lactobacillus* species can obtain the 2(H) for reducing the glycerol either from glucose, or from the formation of β-hydroxypropionate. Small amounts of acrolein are produced as well, nonenzymically, so that in all probability the intermediate for all three products is β-hydroxypropionaldehyde:

$$HOCH_2CHOHCH_2OH$$
$$\downarrow -H_2O \quad _{-H_2O}$$
$$HOCH_2CH_2CHO \longrightarrow CH_2{:}CH{\cdot}CHO$$
$$_{+2(H)}\diagup \quad \diagdown _{-2(H)}$$
$$HOCH_2CH_2CH_2OH \qquad HOCH_2CH_2COOH$$

E. freundii, on the other hand, derives the 2(H) direct from glycerol to form trimethylene glycol, and in strain 19 of the table we see that each mole of trimethylene glycol equals the sum of lactic, succinic, and acetic acids and alcohol. Strain 20, however, ferments additional glycerol to alcohol and formic acid, doubtless via:

$$Glycerol \rightarrow Triose + 2(H) \rightarrow Pyruvate + 4(H)$$
$$\diagup \quad \diagdown$$
$$Formate \qquad Acetyl\text{-}CoA \longrightarrow Ethanol$$

Braak (1928) found that some strains of *E. coli* and Aerobacter could be adapted to carry out this reaction.

Dihydroxyacetone is fermented in a comparable way. *E. coli* attacks it only very slowly but does so rapidly after being grown in its presence (Virtanen *et al.*, 1930), most probably due to induced formation of the kinase which phosphorylates it. The fermentation then yields mainly one mole of glycerol and one mole each of acetic and formic acids. Evidently 1 mole is reduced, while the other is phosphorylated, converted to phosphoglyceric acid and thence to acetic and formic acids:

REFERENCES

Abei, H., and Frei, E. 1957. *Helv. Chem. Acta*, **40**:1695–1705.

Ajl, S. J., and Werkman, C. H. 1948–1950. *Proc. Nat. Acad. Sci.*, **34**:491–498; *Iowa State Coll. J. Sci.*, **24**:279–286 (1950).

Ajl, S. J., and Werkman, C. H. 1949. *J. Bact.*, **57**:579–593.

American Public Health Association. 1960. Standard Methods for the Examination of Water and Wastewater, etc. 11th ed. New York, A.P.H.A. Inc.

Ashwell, G.; Wahba, A. J.; and Hickman, J. 1960. *J. Biol. Chem.*, **235**:1559–1565; Hickman, J., and Ashwell, G. *Ibid.*, 1566–1570; Smiley, J. D., and Ashwell, G. *Ibid.*, 1591–1595; Cynkin, M. A., and Ashwell, G. *Ibid.*, 1576–1579.

*Axelrod, B., and Beevers, H. 1956. Mechanisms of Carbohydrate Metabolism in Plants. *Ann. Rev. Plant Physiol.*, **7**:267–298.

Bahadur, K., and Dube, J. N. 1958. *Arch. Mikrobiol.*, **32**:16–19.

Bahadur, K., and Ranganayaki, S. 1958. *Arch. Mikrobiol.*, **32**:309–311.

Barker, H. A.; Smyth, R. D.; Weissbach, H.; Toohey, J. I.; Ladd, J. N.; and Volcani, B. E. 1960. *J. Biol. Chem.*, **235**:480–488; Volcani, B. E.; Toohey, J. I.; and Barker, H. A. *Arch. Biochem. Biophys.*, **92**:381–391, 1961.

Blackwood, A. C.; Neish, A. C.; Brown, W. E.; and Ledingham, G. A. 1947. *Canadian J. Res.*, **B25**:56–64.

Blackwood, A. C.; Neish, A. C.; and Ledingham, G. A. 1956. *J. Bact.*, **72**:497–499.

Blackwood, A. C., and Simpson, F. J. 1950. *Canadian J. Res.*, **C28**:613–622.

Bone, D. H. 1960. *Biochem. Biophys. Res. Comms.*, **3**:211–214.

Braak, H. R. 1928. Onderzoeking over vergisting von Glycerine. Dissertation, Delft.

Burkholder, P. R., and McVeigh, I. 1942. *Proc. Nat. Acad. Sci.*, **28**:285–290.

Busse, M., and Kandler, O. 1961. *Nature*, **189**:774–775.

Cook, R. P., and Stephenson, M. 1928. *Biochem. J.*, **22**:1363–1386.

Dam, H.; Glavind, J.; Orla-Jensen, S.; and Orla-Jensen, A. D. 1941. *Naturwiss.*, **29**:287–288.

Dawes, E. A., and Foster, S. M. 1956. *Biochim. Biophys. Acta*, **22**:253–265.
Doudoroff, M. 1942. *J. Bact.*, **44**:461–467.
Duguid, J. P., and Gillies, R. R. 1957–1958. *J. Path. and Bact.*, **74**:397–403; **75**:519–520 (1958).
Elrod, R. P. 1942. *J. Bact.*, **44**:433–440.
Englesberg, E., and Baron, L. S. 1959. *J. Bact.*, **78**:675–686.
Fisher, H. F.; Krasna, A. I.; and Rittenberg, D. 1954. *J. Biol. Chem.*, **209**:569–578; *Proc. Nat. Acad. Sci.*, **40**:225–227.
Fred, E. B., and Peterson, W. H. 1920. *J. Infec. Dis.*, **27**:539–59.
Grey, E. C., 1924. *Proc. Roy. Soc.*, **B96**:156–169.
Grey, E. C., and Young, E. G. 1921. *Proc. Roy. Soc.*, **B92**:135–150.
Halpern, Y. S., and Umberger, H. E. 1959. *J. Biol. Chem.*, **234**:3067–3072.
Harden, A. 1901. *J. Chem. Soc.*, **79**:610–628.
Harden, A. 1905. *J. Hyg.*, **5**:488–493.
Harden, A. 1906. *Proc. Roy Soc.*, **B77**:424–425.
Harden, A., and Walpole, G. S. 1906. *Proc. Roy. Soc.*, **B77**:399–405.
Huhtanen, C. N., and Gall, L. S. 1953. *J. Bact.*, **65**:554–559.
Itagaki, E.; Fujita, T.; and Sato, R. 1961. *Biochem. Biophys. Res. Comms.*, **5**:30–34.
Izawa, S. 1962. *Plant and Cell Physiol.*, **3**:23–42.
Joklik, W. K. 1950. *Austr. J. Exp. Biol. Med.*, **28**:321–329, 331–338.
Jones, M. E.; Lipmann, F.; Hilz, H.; and Lynen, F. 1953. *J. Amer. Chem. Soc.*, **75**:3285–3286.
Juni, E. 1952. *J. Biol. Chem.*, **195**:715–726.
Juni, E. 1961. *J. Biol. Chem.*, **236**:2302–2308.
Kalnitsky, G., and Werkman, C. H. 1943–1944. *Arch. Biochem.*, **2**:113–124; **4**:25–40.
Katagiri, H.; Takeda, I.; and Imai, K. 1959. *J. Vitaminol.*, **5**:287–297.
Kluyver, A. J. 1931. The Chemical Activities of Microorganisms. London, University Press.
Kluyver, A. J., and Molt, E. L. 1939. *Proc. Kon. Akad. Wetensch. Amsterdam*, **42**:118–124.
Kosow, D. P., and Lane, M. D. 1961. *Biochem. Biophys. Res. Comms.*, **4**:92–95.
Lascelles, J.: Cross, M. J.; and Woods, D. D. 1951. *Biochem. J.*, **49**:lxvi.
*Lipmann, F. 1946. Acetyl Phosphate. *Adv. in Enzymol.* **6**:231–267.
Lwoff, A., and Monod, J. 1947. *Ann. Inst. Pasteur* **73**:323–347.
McLean, D. J., and Purdie, E. F. 1952. *J. Biol. Chem.*, **197**:539–545.
*Martius, C., and Lynen, F. 1950. Probleme des Citronensäure-Zyklus. *Adv. in Enzymol.*, **10**:167–222.
Mickelson, M. N., and Werkman, C. H. 1940. *Enzymologia*, **8**:252–256.
Neish, A. C. 1950. Report 46-8-3, Nat. Res. Council of Canada, 56 pp.
Neish, A. C. 1953. *Canad. J. Bot.*, **31**:265–276.
Neish, A. C., and Simpson, F. J. 1954. *Canad. J. Biochem and Physiol.*, **32**:147–153.
Neuberg, C. 1914. *Biochem. Z.*, **67**:90–101.
Neuberg, C., and Nord, F. F. 1919. *Biochem. Z.*, **96**:133–157.
van Niel, C. B.; Kluyver, A. J.; and Derx, H. G. 1929. *Biochem. Z.*, **210**:234–251.
Nutting, L. A., and Carson, S. F. 1952. *J. Bact.*, **63**:575–580, 581–589.
*Parr, L. W. 1939. Coliform Bacteria. *Bact. Revs.*, **3**:1–48.
Pot, A. W., and Tasman, A. 1932–1933. *Zentr. Bakt. I orig.*, **126**:348–351; **130**:357–366.
Purkayastha, M., and Williams, R. P. 1960. *Nature*, **187**:349–350.
Quastel, J. H., and Whetham, M. D. 1925. *Biochem. J.*, **19**:520–531.
Rahn, O. 1937. *Zentr. Bakt. II*, **96**:273–286.
Rauss, K. F. 1936. *J. Path. Bact.*, **42**:183.

Reynolds, H.; Jacobssen, B. J.; and Werkman, C. H. 1937. *J. Bact.*, **34**:15–20.

Reynolds, H., and Werkman, C. H. 1937. *J. Bact.*, **33**:603–614; *Arch. Mikrobiol.*, **8**: 149–152.

Rowatt, E. 1951. *Biochem. J.*, **49**:453–462.

Rush, D.; Karibian, D.; Karnovsky, M. L.; and Magasanik, B. 1957. *J. Biol. Chem.*, **226**:891–899.

Scheffer, M. A. 1928. De suikervergisting door Bakterien der Coli-group. Dissertation, Delft.

Silverman, M., and Werkman, C. H. 1941. *J. Biol. Chem.*, **138**:35–48.

Simpson, F. J., and Wood, W. A. 1956. *J. Am. Chem. Soc.*, **78**:7452–7453.

Sobolev, M., and Smiley, K. L. 1960. *J. Bact.*, **79**:261–266.

Stadtman, E. R.; Novelli, G. D.; and Lipmann, F. 1951. *J. Biol. Chem.*, **191**:365–376.

Stahly, G. L., and Werkman, C. H. 1942. *Biochem. J.*, **36**:575–581.

Stephenson, M., and Stickland, L. H. 1932. *Biochem. J.*, **26**:712–724.

Stephenson, M., and Stickland, L. H. 1933. *Biochem. J.*, **27**:1517–1528, 1528–1532.

Still, J. L. 1940. *Biochem. J.*, **34**:1177–1182; 1374–1382.

Sutton, W. B., and Werkman, C. H. 1953. *Arch. Biochem. Biophys.*, **47**:1–7.

Tanko, B., and Munk, L. 1940. *Z. physiol. Chem.*, **262**:144–157; Tanko, B.; Munk, L.; and Aronzi, I. 1940. *Z. physiol. Chem.*, **264**:91–107.

Taylor, C. B. 1951. *Proc. Soc. Appl. Bact.*, **14**:95–100.

Tikka, J. 1935. *Biochem. Z.*, **279**:264–288.

Utter, M. F., and Werkman, C. H. 1941–1942. *J. Bact.*, **42**:665–676; *Biochem. J.*, **36**:485–493 (1942).

Utter, M. F.; Werkman, C. H.; and Lipmann, F. 1944. *J. Biol. Chem.*, **154**:723; **158**: 521–531.

*Virtanen, A. I.; Karström, H.; and Turpeinen, O. 1930. *Z. physiol. Chem.*, **187**:7–44.

Virtanen, A. I., and Peltola, E. 1930. *Z. physiol. Chem.*, **187**:45–52.

Voisenet, E. 1918. *Ann. Inst. Pasteur*, **32**:476–510.

Waring, W. S., and Werkman, C. H. 1944. *Arch. Biochem.*, **4**:75–87.

Watt, D., and Werkman, C. H. 1950. *Arch. Biochem.*, **28**:30–35.

Watt, D., and Werkman, C. H. 1951. *Arch. Biochem.*, **31**:383–390.

*Werkman, C. H., and Wood, H. G. 1942. Heterotrophic Assimilation of CO_2. *Adv. in Enzymol.*, **2**:135–182. New York, Interscience Press.

Wikén, T.; Watt, D.; White, A. G. C.; and Werkman, C. H. 1947. *Arch. Biochem.*, **14**:478–480.

Wilson, J.; Krampitz, L. O.; and Werkman, C. H. 1948. *Biochem. J.*, **42**:598–600.

Wolff, J. B., and Kaplan, N. O. 1956. *J. Bact.*, **71**:557–564; *J. Biol. Chem.*, **218**: 849–869.

Wood, A. J., and Baird, E. A. 1943. *J. Fisheries Res. Bd.*, *Canada*, **6**:194–201.

Wood, E. J. Ferguson, 1950. *Proc. Linnean Soc. N.S.W.*, **75**:158–166.

Woods, D. D. 1936. *Biochem. J.*, **29**:640–655.

Wrigley, C. W., and Linnane, A. W. 1961. *Biochem. Biophys. Res. Comms.*, **4**:66–70.

Yoshida, S. 1962. *Canad. J. Biochem. Physiol.*, **40**:1019–1024.

CHAPTER XV

Fermentations of the Butyric Type

Time is the best appreciator of scientific work, and I know that an industrial discovery rarely bears all its fruits in the hands of its first inventor.

Louis Pasteur (1876)

1. THE BUTYRIC AND BUTYLIC BACTERIA

The fermentations considered in the four preceding chapters have all been the work of facultative anaerobes. The butyl-butyric-acetone fermentations, on the other hand, are brought about by Clostridia, which are strict anaerobes, and in this chapter it will be convenient to consider also some other processes due to clostridia.

The fermentations are characterized by production, from sugars or related compounds, of butyric acid together with one or more of the following: butyl alcohol; the C_3-compounds acetone and isopropyl alcohol; acetic acid; formic acid; ethyl alcohol; usually also hydrogen; and some CO_2. Butyric acid is produced not only by clostridia but also by some anaerobic Neisserias, by *Zymosarcina maxima*, and (though not from sugar) by the nonsporeforming anaerobic rods called *Butyribacterium*. Butyric acid is formed also from threonine by a special fermentation due to *Clostridium propionicum* (p. 322).

Butanol is not produced by other microorganisms, but isobutanol is produced by yeast as a constituent of fusel oil (p. 316). Acetone can be produced by certain facultative anaerobes (sec. 5 below), and the other products are of course common to many fermentations.

The butyric fermentation was discovered in 1861 by Pasteur, who named the causative organism the *vibrion butyrique*, saw that it was killed by air, and coined the term *anaerobic* for it (cf. Chap. I). Fitz in the 1880's and both Gruber and Grimbert later studied the fermentations but did not distinguish between the butyric acid- and the butanol-producing forms. Pure cultures of a butyric acid-producing form were obtained from soil in 1895 by Winogradsky, the main purpose of whose work was the study of nitrogen fixation (Chap. IX, sec. 2).

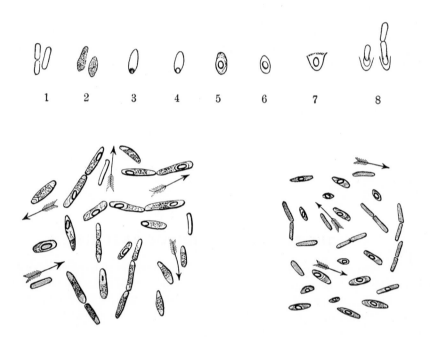

FIGURE XV–1

Classical drawings of butyl-butyric-acetone organisms.

Top. Cl. pastorianum (from S. Winogradsky, *Zentr. Bakt.* II **9**:43–54, 1902). *1.* Young rod "1.5–2 × 1.2 μ". *2.* Spindle-forms with granular contents. *3–6.* Stages of spore formation, the iodine staining having disappeared in 6. *7.* Ripe spore 1.3 × 1.6 μ with the mother-cell characteristically opened. *8.* Spore germination. All about 1000 ×.

Bottom. Left, "*Granulobacter*" (= *Cl.*) *butylicum; right,* "*Granulobacter*" (= *Aerobac.*) *polymyxa.* Both 700 ×. The arrows indicate direction of motion. (From M. W. Beijerinck, *Arch. Néerl,* **29**:1–68, 1896.)

Winogradsky's organism, named *Cl. pastorianum*[1] (Fig. XV–1), produced butyric acid and is readily obtained by fermenting potato slices with a little $CaCO_3$. He noted, however, the formation of small amounts of butyl and ethyl alcohols. Bacteria producing appreciable amounts of

---

[1] In accordance with the abbreviations listed at the front of the book, *Clostridium* is shortened to *Cl.* throughout.

butanol were first obtained in pure culture by Beijerinck (1894), who clearly recognized the difference between them and the butyric organisms; his name *Granulobacter butylicum* was based on presence of a starchlike substance in the cell, staining blue with iodine, which he called *granulose*. From their ability to attack starch vigorously, forming a clear zone on starch agar plates, the organisms have also been called *Amylobacter*. Another of Beijerinck's isolates attacked pectin as well as starch and was called *Granulobacter pectinovorum*. The name *Granulobacter* was later dropped in favor of *Clostridium*, an old term referring to the swollen rods containing spores (see Figs. II–3, XV–1).

An organism with the useful ability of making both butanol and acetone was isolated by Fernbach in 1911 and another by Weizmann in 1915. Because the latter, *Cl. acetobutylicum*, also known as "BY" bacterium, was the more actively fermenting strain and would attack corn, it has become the basis of the butanol-acetone industry.[2] The setting up of this industry in the United States resulted from the establishment of a plant in Canada during World War I, when acetone was in great demand as a solvent for cordite. At present the butanol and butyl esters formed from this fermentation are just as much in demand as the acetone, but synthetic chemicals provide serious competition.

Aerobic bacilli making acetone together with ethanol and acetic acid were isolated by Schardinger (1905) under the name of *Bac. macerans*. A related form, which produces 2,3-butane-diol, was first studied by Prazmowski in 1880 and by Beijerinck (1894) and named *Clostridium* (or *Granulobacter*) *polymyxa* because morphologically like the butanol bacteria (Fig. XV–1), and making *much gum* (= *poly-myxa*). Neither of these produces more than a trace of butanol. Because these organisms produce a fermentation similar to that of Aerobacter they were made into a separate genus—Aerobacillus—by Donker (1926).

A group of nonsporeforming gram-positive rods which form acetic and butyric acids and CO_2, but no hydrogen, was characterized by Barker and Haas (1944) as a new genus, *Butyribacterium*. These organisms are probably more nearly related to the heterofermentative lactobacilli than to the clostridia.

The clostridia as a group are morphologically quite alike. They are mostly gram-positive rods; in the early stages of a fermentation when traces of oxygen are still present, they are medium-sized and actively

[2] Both Fernbach and Weizmann patented their organisms, as both were working in industry (Strange and Graham, Ltd., England), though Weizmann had left the firm when he isolated his organism. Dr. Weizmann afterward became interested in Zionism, of which he was World President for many years, and the patent profits on *Cl. acetobutylicum* were largely used to promote the Zionist cause. As President of Israel from 1949 to 1952, Dr. Weizmann was one of the few microbiologists to become successful in politics.

motile; in later stages, when conditions become really anaerobic, they become larger and either boat-shaped or drumstick-shaped, with good-sized spores $(1 \times 2\ \mu)$ inside. They differ from one another in size, spore position (central or terminal), heat resistance of the spores (Table 5 of Chap. IV), and in their ability to fix nitrogen.

On physiological grounds it is convenient to regard the butyric organisms as falling into five groups, though the border lines are not too sharply drawn.

(1) Butyric bacteria (*Cl. saccharobutyricum, pasteurianum*, and others) make butyric and acetic acids from glucose; most of these also produce traces of butanol or ethanol, depending on the growth conditions.

(2) Butylic bacteria (*Cl. butylicum, acetobutylicum*, and others) convert sugars to butanol in good yield, along with either acetone or isopropanol.

(3) Caproic acid bacteria (*Cl. kluyveri*) do not attack sugars, but convert certain acids and ethanol to caproic acid, $C_7H_{15}COOH$, and other fatty acids, with butyric acid as a probable intermediate. Other organisms, in groups 1, 2, and 5, also form some caproic acid.

(4) Aerobacilli (*Bac. macerans, polymyxa, acetoethylicum*) make acetone, 2,3-butylene glycol, and ethanol, but not butanol, and only traces of butyric acid (Fig. XV–3, p. 547).

(5) Certain nonsporeformers make butyric acid with acetic acid (*Butyribacterium*) or with acetic and lactic acids and ethanol (*Zymosarcina maxima*); another Zymosarcina, however (*Zs. ventriculi*), makes only acetic acid, ethanol, H_2, and CO_2 with no butyric acid (Milhaud *et al.*, 1956).

Some of the clostridia are not primarily butyric fermenters. These "Peptoclostridia" (including *Cl. sporogenes, tetani, histolyticum*, and *botulinum*) attack amino acids in a characteristic way, in which one amino acid is oxidized and another reduced, with deamination (p. 321). Generally they are strongly proteolytic, attacking intact animal tissues, especially muscle (see Chap. VII). Two of them are remarkable for deaminating γ-aminobutyric and δ-aminovaleric acids, hydrogenating one molecule to butyric or valeric acid, respectively, and dehydrogenating a second molecule to NH_3 and acetic acid (Hardman and Stadtman, 1960):

$$NH_2(CH_2)_3COOH + 2\ H_2O \rightarrow NH_3 + 2\ CH_3COOH + 2(H)$$
$$NH_2(CH_2)_3COOH + 2(H) \rightarrow NH_3 + CH_3(CH_2)_2COOH$$

Cl. acidi-urici and *Cl. cylindrosporum* are notable for fermenting purines (p. 357). Some members of this group can ferment sugars to butyric acid, etc., but others do this weakly, if at all. Their main importance is as animal pathogens, because they cause tetanus, gangrene of wounds (especially *Cl. welchii*), and botulism.

Most of the industrial interest has centered on the butylic group (group 2). These are rather homogeneous. Under comparable conditions the fermentation products of the four principal members are quantitatively similar, as shown in Table XV–1. *Cl. felsineum* is distinguished by its orange pigment and its vigorous attack on pectins, which makes it important in the retting of flax (p. 589). *Cl. beijerinckii* may have industrial application in the fermentation of waste sulfite liquors from paper mills; a little corn meal, yeast extract, and salts added to the liquor make it an excellent medium, and the pentosans in it can be fermented to useful products (Gfeller, 1954). *Cl.*

TABLE XV–1. Neutral Products of the Butanol Fermentations from Glucose

(Data of van der Lek, 1930)

(Medium: Yeast-Water, 2% Glucose; Duration 4 to 5 Days at 30° C or 37° C.)

Organism	PER CENT OF THE FERMENTED GLUCOSE				
	Butanol	Acetone	Isopropanol	Ethanol	H$_2$
Cl. acetobutylicum	23.0	7.2	...	2.4	1.5
Cl. beijerinckii	26.7	5.7	...	2.4	1.3
Cl. butylicum	27.6	...	9.2	2.5	1.0
Cl. felsineum	21.0	6.2	...	6.8	1.5

TABLE XV–2. Products of Butyric Acid Fermentations from Glucose

Product	*Cl. saccharobutyricum* (Data of Donker, 1926)		*Zs. maxima* (Data of Smit, 1930)	
	% of Glucose Fermented	Moles per 100 Moles Glucose Fermented	% of Glucose Fermented	Moles per 100 Moles Glucose Fermented
Butyric acid	36.9	75	37.1	76
Acetic acid	14.2	43	10.0	30
Formic acid	Trace	...	1.1	4
Lactic acid	....	...	10.7	21
CO$_2$	47.8	196	36.3	149
H$_2$	2.6	233	2.6	233

acetobutylicum is a similar organism though more actively proteolytic. *Cl. butylicum* makes isopropanol instead of acetone, as shown.

Among the butyric group, *Cl. pasteurianum* is distinguished by fermenting mannitol, sorbitol, and inulin, and *Cl. amylobacter* by fermenting pectin. *Cl. saccharobutyricum* does not attack these, but all three can ferment starch, dextrin, and glycogen (Brown, 1937). *Cl. lactoacetophilum* ferments lactate or glycerol only in presence of acetate (Bhat and Barker, 1947–1948). In Table XV–2 the products of a typical fermentation by a Clostridium of group 1 are compared with those formed by *Zymosarcina maxima*, of group 5. Except for the lactic acid in the latter and correspondingly less acetic acid and CO_2, they are remarkably similar. Some others of group 1, e.g., *Cl. uracilicum* (Campbell, 1957), produce less CO_2 and more acids.

2. THE ACETONE-BUTANOL FERMENTATION AND ITS COURSE

A. The Influence of pH

The formation of the "neutral solvents," acetone and butanol, takes place only in acid media. When the fermentations are allowed to go normally, using sugars or corn mash, the *p*H goes down to 4.5; if chalk is added to hold the *p*H to 7 or 8, the yield of butyric acid goes up roughly four times and that of butanol falls to about a tenth; similarly the acetic acid is doubled and the ethanol halved. The acetone almost disappears (van der Lek, 1930; Bernhauer *et al.*, 1936[3]). The data of van der Lek, using *Cl. butylicum*, are shown in columns 1 and 2 below. Column 3, for comparison, repeats the data from Table XV–2 for *Cl. saccharobutyricum:*

MOLES PER 100 MOLES HEXOSE

	1 Butylic, Un- neutralized	2 Butylic + $CaCO_3$	3 Butyric
Butyric acid	18	71	75
Acetic acid	12	41	43
CO_2	206	196	196
H_2	170	224	233
Butanol	58	4	—

This shows that butylic organisms behave exactly like those of the

[3] Bernhauer's organism bore the old name *Cl. butyricum* (ATCC No. 824), but it is a butanol-acetone bacterium.

butyric group if the acids formed are neutralized. We may conclude that *the butyric fermentation is the fundamental type* and that the butylic process comprises additional enzymes which come into action only when sufficient free acids accumulate. The decreases in the yields of reduced compounds (butanol and ethanol) are accompanied by an increase in hydrogen gas.

B. The Influence of Other Factors

In fermentations on synthetic media, the addition of extracts of corn or other natural products increases the yield of butanol. The alcohol-soluble proteins from several other grains have the same effect. Even on corn mash the addition of potato extract or aqueous soybean extract (Hoshino, 1953) causes a further increase. Much of this effect was traced to aspartic acid, asparagine, or glutamic acid (Tatum *et al.*, 1934–1935). With *Cl. butylicum* on corn mash, asparagine raised the yield of butanol to 17 per cent; however, Table XV–1 shows that yeast extract can be more effective, raising it to 27 per cent. Since the optimum concentration of asparagine is 0.01 M (Brown *et al.*, 1938), it can hardly be itself a precursor of butanol.

Metallic ions, especially iron, strongly influence the fermentation. With *Cl. perfringens*, whose products are mainly butyric and acetic acids with ethanol and H_2, the absence of iron in the medium changed the products over to lactic acid and only small amounts of other compounds (Pappenheimer and Shaskan, 1944). Carbon monoxide, which combines with iron enzymes (Chap. V, sec. 4), also changes the fermentation to a lactic type, both with butyric organisms (Kubowitz, 1934) and typically butylic ones (Simon, 1947). Since low iron favors riboflavin synthesis (sec. 6), some relation between this and the lactic fermentation may be guessed at. *Added* iron, on the other hand, depresses the yields, especially of butanol (Imai, 1956). It seems that molasses heated with Fe salts forms a fermentation-inhibiting factor, and that this may act by promoting the growth of bacteriophages (Hoshino, 1953), but the full explanation is uncertain.

If corn is extracted with dilute acid or alkali, its fermentation is slowed down and cannot be accelerated by adding asparagine or proteins. In this case the effect has been traced to potassium ions (Davies, 1942), KCl restoring the acetone yield of *Cl. acetobutylicum* almost to normal.

Finally, autoclaving glucose with the yeast extract medium gives much less butanol and acetone than autoclaving it separately (van der Lek, 1930).

These and many other causes of variation have been encountered in large-scale applications and in study of the fermentation. Their complete elucidation will require considerable research.

C. The "Break"

In butylic fermentations the acidity (due to acetic and butyric acids) increases at first and then, after some hours, breaks sharply. At the same time much CO_2 is evolved (Fig. XV–2). This "break" in-

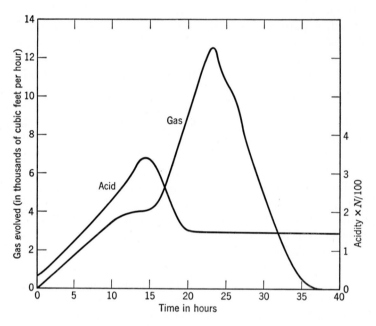

FIGURE XV–2

Normal course of a butanol fermentation. Note the "break" at 15 hours. (Plotted from data of J. Reilly, W. J. Hickinbottom, F. R. Henley, and A. C. Thaysen, *Biochem. J.*, **14**:228–251, 1920.)

dicates the beginning of acetone and butanol formation (Reilly *et al.*, 1920). If it does not occur, butyric and acetic acids are the main products. Failure to break under industrial conditions is not always understood; autoclaving glucose with yeast extract can have this result (cf. above), and so can addition of base (cf. above, p. 533). Both these can also influence the growth of the bacteria, and some workers regard the break as merely marking the cessation of the growth phase (Dyr and Protiva, 1956).

3. MECHANISM OF THE FERMENTATIONS

A. The Source of Acetone

It was an early observation, made during the industrial acetone fermentations of World War I, that the yield of acetone can be increased by adding acetic acid (Reilly et al., 1920). In more recent experiments with nongrowing cell suspensions of Cl. acetobutylicum BY, which convert about 22 per cent of the fermented glucose into butanol, the yield of acetone was raised from 4 to 16 per cent by adding acetate. Since 1 mole of acetate yields about ½ mole of acetone and 1 mole of CO_2, the process evidently goes via acetoacetate:

$$2 \ CH_3COOH \rightarrow CH_3COCH_2COOH \rightarrow CH_3COCH_3 + CO_2 \tag{1}$$

In confirmation: (1) added acetoacetate is rapidly and quantitatively converted to acetone and CO_2 (Johnson et al., 1933); (2) isotopically labeled acetate yields labeled acetone (Wood et al., 1945). Acetyl-coenzyme A is an intermediate (see eq. 3 below).

Acetic acid alone is not converted to acetone, but simultaneous fermentation of glucose or other substrate has to go on (Janke and Siedler, 1937; Davies, 1942). This is because the condensation of acetic to acetoacetic acid, which goes via acetyl-coenzyme A, requires energy $(-\Delta F = -16,000 \ \text{cal})$.

The acetone-forming enzyme, acetoacetic decarboxylase, has been prepared from Cl. acetobutylicum (Davies, 1943). Its pH optimum is 4.5 to 5, as might be expected. It does not decarboxylate any other known keto acid. The reaction is probably due to combination of the ketone group with an amino group of the enzyme to form a Schiff base (Hamilton and Westheimer, 1959; cf. the action of vitamin B_6 coenzymes in Chap. VIII, sec. 6).

B. The Source of Isopropanol

Isopropanol is almost certainly formed by reduction of acetone. As with acetone formation by Cl. acetobutylicum, so with isopropanol formation by Cl. butylicum, addition of acetic acid increases the yield. One mole of acetic acid gives about ½ mole isopropanol (see p. 540). Added acetone also increases the yield of isopropanol, and with Cl. toanum, acetone appears first and then decreases while isopropanol is formed (Baba, 1953–1954). C^{14}-labeled acetone produces labeled isopropanol, leaving little doubt that the reduction goes easily.

C. Butyric Acid Formation

The appearance of butyric acid was first ascribed to the splitting of hexose into a C_4 + a C_2 fragment, but this is negatived by the old observation that some organisms can convert C_3 compounds to butyrate.[4] Calcium pyruvate is fermented by *Cl. butylicum* to acetate and butyrate (Brown *et al.*, 1938), and glycerol similarly by *Cl. acetobutylicum* (Simon, 1947).

Following Neuberg's *Abfangverfahren* with yeast (cf. Chap. XI), the formation of acetaldehyde was demonstrated in the butyric fermentation (Neuberg and Arinstein, 1921). This led to a second theory, namely, that both butyric and acetoacetic acids were formed via acetaldehyde, which would be condensed to acetaldol. This could undergo an internal oxido-reduction to butyric acid, could be dehydrogenated to acetoacetic acid, or reduced to butanol. Unfortunately for this theory, neither acetaldehyde nor acetaldol yielded much butyric acid or butanol in the fermentation (Janke and Siedler, 1937). Furthermore, the observations have not been confirmed, and even the identity of Neuberg's culture is uncertain.[5]

It is now clear that butyric acid is indeed formed from a C_2 compound, but that this is acetyl-coenzyme A, formed from acetate or from pyruvate. The evidence for the intermediate role of acetate is three-fold:

First, the addition of labeled acetic acid, $C^{13}H_3COOH$, to active fermentations gives rise to labeled butyric acid (Wood *et al.*, 1945).

Second, the caproic bacterium, *Cl. kluyveri*, forms butyric acid from acetic acid and alcohol (see sec. 4 below):

$$CH_3COOH + C_2H_5OH \rightarrow C_3H_7COOH + H_2O$$

If $CH_3C^{13}OOH$ is used, the resulting butyric acid has the isotope in both the carboxyl and β-carbon atoms (Barker *et al.*, 1945; Barker, 1947). This means that two molecules of the labeled acetic acid must be reductively condensed (the hydrogen being provided by the ethanol):

$$2\ CH_3C^{13}OOH + 4(H) \rightarrow CH_3C^{13}H_2CH_2C^{13}OOH + 2\ H_2O$$

Third, the same reaction can occur in cell-free extracts. If dried *Cl. kluyveri* is extracted with dilute sodium sulfide solution, the re-

[4] Beijerinck (1894) described an organism converting calcium lactate to calcium butyrate, H_2, and CO_2, and referred its origin to Pasteur.

[5] They used "*Bac. butylicus* Fitz" (which according to Beijerinck is *Cl. saccharobutyricum*) and also *Cl. amylobacter;* both are butyric organisms producing only small amounts of butanol.

sulting extract converts a mixture of ethanol and acetate to butyrate (as well as caproate, see p. 541). Labeled acetate gave rise to labeled butyrate (Stadtman and Barker, 1949a). In an atmosphere of hydrogen, butyrate was formed from a mixture of acetate and acetyl phosphate:

$$CH_3COOPO_3^= + CH_3COO^- + 2\ H_2 \rightarrow CH_3CH_2CH_2COO^- + HPO_4^= + H_2O \quad (2)$$

Butyrate is formed less readily from pyruvate, doubtless because of the need for extra hydrogen, which pyruvate does not supply. *Cl. butyricum* and *Cl. acetobutylicum* convert pyruvate only to acetate, CO_2, and H_2 (Kubowitz, 1934); but a cell-free extract of *Cl. butylicum* converts pyruvate plus phosphate into acetyl phosphate, CO_2, and H_2 (Koepsell *et al.*, 1944). This observation is critical because acetyl phosphate can come into equilibrium (via phosphotransacetylase) with acetyl-coenzyme A (p. 245).

The participation of CoA was first indicated by work with pigeon liver extracts, which showed that this coenzyme is essential when acetate plus ATP brings about the acetylation of aromatic compounds, and especially by the isolation of acetyl-CoA from yeast and the evidence that it acts as an acetylating agent therein (Lynen *et al.*, 1951–1952; Lynen, 1954). The existence of the phosphotransacetylase, which catalyzes the equilibrium between acetyl phosphate and acetyl-CoA, was then discovered in *Cl. kluyveri* extracts (Stadtman, 1952; see Barker, 1957). Thus pyruvate is converted to acetyl phosphate (and vice versa) via acetyl-coenzyme A.

But it is the next step that is most characteristic; two molecules of acetyl-CoA condense to form acetoacetyl-CoA (Lynen, 1954); this C_4 compound is the key to all the C_4-forming reactions of the Clostridia:

$$2\ CH_3CO \cdot SCoA \rightleftharpoons CH_3COCH_2CO \cdot SCoA + HSCoA \quad (3)$$

In liver this condensation requires CO_2 and goes via malonyl-CoA, but this probably does not occur in Clostridia (see sec. 5).

Acetoacetyl-CoA is now reduced. The reaction takes place in three steps, namely, (1) to β-hydroxybutyryl-CoA, (2) to crotonyl-CoA, (3) to butyryl-CoA (Stadtman, 1956; Barker, 1957):

$$\text{Glucose} \rightarrow 4\ H + 2\ \text{Pyruvate} \xrightarrow{\text{ATP} + \text{CoA}} 2\ CH_3CO \cdot SCoA \rightleftharpoons CH_3COCH_2CO \cdot SCoA \xrightarrow{2\ H}_{\text{step 1}}$$

$$CH_3CHOHCH_2CO \cdot SCoA \xrightleftharpoons[\text{step 2}]{-H_2O} CH_3CH{=}CHCO \cdot SCoA \xrightarrow{2\ H}_{\text{step 3}}$$

$$CH_3CH_2CH_2CO \cdot SCoA \xrightarrow{H_2O\ \text{or}\ \text{acetate}} CH_3CH_2CH_2COOH \quad (4)$$

Free butyric acid may be formed either by hydrolysis or by the transfer of coenzyme A to acetate by the CoA-transphorase enzyme of Stadtman (1952), to form acetyl-CoA again; the latter would ensure the rapid recirculation of the coenzyme. Three of the key enzymes required for these reactions have been shown in *Cl. acetobutylicum* and *Cl. sticklandii* (Stern *et al.*, 1956), as well as in *Cl. kluyveri*, although here the source of acetyl-CoA may be acetaldehyde (cf. the reaction with *E. coli*, p. 508). The two reductions make use of TPNH. The enzyme crotonase, which catalyzes step (2), has been crystallized from liver and shown to act on CoA esters of all the unsaturated acids with 4 to 9 carbon atoms (Stern *et al.*, 1956).

The formation of butyrate by condensation of two C_2 units explains the curious fermentations of lactate, which go only in presence of a second substance; with *Cl. lacto-acetophilum* this is acetate, but with *Butyribacterium rettgeri* it is, surprisingly enough, CO_2. In the former case about 1 mole of acetate is used per mole of butyrate formed (Bhat and Barker, 1947–1948), and it is deduced that the lactate is converted to acetate, which is then condensed (via acetyl-CoA) and reduced to butyrate:

$$2\ CH_3CHOHCOOH + 2\ H_2O \rightarrow 2\ CH_3COOH + 2\ CO_2 + 8(H)$$
$$2\ CH_3COOH + 4(H) \rightarrow CH_3CH_2CH_2COOH + 2\ H_2O \qquad (5)$$

Although some hydrogen is lost as gas, nevertheless, more remains than can be accepted by the 1 mole of acetate formed; hence *more* acetate must be added. The Butyribacterium evolves no hydrogen at all, the excess being somehow combined with CO_2 to form a second mole of acetate (Barker *et al.*, 1945):

$$CH_3CHOHCOOH + CO_2 + 4(H) \rightarrow 2\ CH_3COOH + H_2O$$

The acetate then yields butyrate as in equation (5). If $C^{14}O_2$ was supplied, the acetate and butyrate were found to be labeled in all C atoms.

Three subsidiary points remain to be mentioned: (1) the β-hydroxybutyryl-coenzyme A, intermediate in butyrate formation, may suffer another fate: it can be converted to poly-β-hydroxy-butyric acid. This is a common bacterial polymer, found in bacilli, pseudomonads, Rhizobia, and in purple bacteria (Forsyth *et al.*, 1958). *Bac. megaterium* possesses an enzyme which causes the polymerization very rapidly (Merrick and Doudoroff, 1961); some Clostridia may do the same.

(2) The butyric fermentation is inhibited by CO, and the inhibition is reversed by light (Kubowitz, 1934). Absence of iron has the same effect; in both cases only lactate is produced. Evidently, therefore, a hemin-containing enzyme is involved, and it perhaps functions at the initial split of pyruvate to acetyl-CoA or acetyl phosphate:

$$CH_3COCOOH \xrightarrow{^-HPO_4} CO_2 + H_2 + CH_3CO\cdot OPO_3^- \underset{}{\overset{HSCoA}{\rightleftharpoons}} CH_3CO\cdot SCoA + {}^-HPO_4$$

The enzyme is not the same as formic hydrogenlyase (p. 520), since extracts of *Cl. butylicum* which evolve H_2 from pyruvate do not decompose formate (Koepsell et al., 1944). It may be a related heminenzyme that operates with pyruvate instead.

(3) Although the intermediate steps between glucose and pyruvate are presumably the same as in the alcoholic and lactic fermentations, it is an odd fact that neither hexose-1,6-diphosphate nor phosphoglycerate produced any butyric acid when incubated with fresh or acetone-dried *Cl. acetobutylicum* (Simon, 1947). Even glucose-6-phosphate gave only very small yields of butyrate. Probably the phosphate esters are poorly taken up.

D. The Source of Butanol

The experiments on the influence of pH (p. 532) show that when butanol is not formed, butyric acid appears in its place. This and other facts have led to the view that butanol arises indirectly, by reduction of butyrate. Addition of butyric acid to *Cl. acetobutylicum* fermentations, however, has given conflicting results. Simon and Weizmann (1937) got an increase in the "oil," which may or may not have been butanol; Bernhauer and Kürschner (1935) in one experiment got a 90 per cent yield of butanol from butyric acid added to corn mash; Lerner (1941) found that about half the added butyrate was converted to acetate, the remainder being recovered unchanged. However, with *Cl. butylicum* reduction was clearly shown (Osburn et al., 1938). Table XV–3 shows that added butyric acid gave rise to about ½ mole butanol; the rest was converted to acetic acid, CO_2, and a little isopropanol. Acetic acid did not yield butanol, but only isopropanol, i.e., the acetoacetic acid formed via equation (3) must have been decarboxylated. With *Cl. beijerinckii*, Gfeller (1954) similarly found that addition of butyric acid nearly doubled the yield of butanol and increased the acetone plus isopropanol by 35 per cent.

At the "break," when butanol and acetone begin to be formed, both acetate and butyrate in the mash decrease (Peterson and Fred, 1932). The decrease of acetate is of course expected, since it is the source of acetone, or of isopropanol, but the decrease of butyrate points to its reduction to butanol. Fermenting with H_2 under pressure (20 atmos) decreases the yield of butyric acid and raises that of butanol (Eliasberg, 1930).

Finally, the reduction has been confirmed by isotope studies. Doubly labeled butyric acid, $CH_3C^{13}H_2CH_2C^{13}OOH$, was added to fermentations of corn meal, and 84 per cent of the C^{13} was recovered in the butanol (Wood, Brown, and Werkman, 1945). With *Cl. aceto-butylicum*, 2 per cent was recovered as acetone, and with *Cl. butylicum* 3 per cent as isopropanol. These results seem conclusive. Also, $C^{13}H_3COOH$ was converted to butanol, more indeed (55 per cent) than to acetone (15 per cent) or CO_2 (18 per cent). This indicates that when the acetic acid has been converted to acetoacetyl-CoA as above, its subsequent reduction by these organisms is faster than its decarboxylation. With an extract from *Cl. kluyveri*, butyryl phosphate is

TABLE XV–3. Increase in Yields of Products (as M per 100 M Glucose Fermented) When Butyric or Acetic Acids Are Added to Glucose Fermentation by Cl. Butylicum

(Data of Osburn *et al.*, 1938)

(For simplicity, only the increases resulting from the addition, and not the absolute amounts, are here shown.)

Added	Butanol	Isopropanol	Butyric Acid	Acetic Acid	CO_2	H_2
Butyric acid:						
38.5	19	8	−7	15	8	−27
41.5	19	5	7	23	12	−5
64.3	35	12	−5	23	26	
Acetic acid:						
43.2	−5	30	−3	−4	18	−34
65.3	3	32	−6	0	1	

readily reduced to butanol (Stadtman and Barker, 1950). Now the formation of butyrate already involves a reduction (acetoacetyl-CoA + 4[H]), so that when part of the acetoacetate is converted to acetone, the hydrogen acceptor necessary for the conversion of pyruvate to acetate is lost: it is for this reason that the extreme reduction of another acetoacetate molecule to butanol is essential (see Barker, 1957). The formation of butanol could therefore be considered a *necessary consequence* of the formation of acetone:

$$C_6H_{12}O_6 \rightarrow 2\ CH_3COCOOH + 4(H) \rightarrow 2\ H_2$$

$$2\ CH_3COOH + 2\ CO_2 + 4(H) \text{-----}$$

(loss of H acceptor)

$$\begin{bmatrix} CH_3COCH_2COOH \\ \downarrow \\ CH_3COCH_3 + CO_2 \end{bmatrix} \xrightarrow{4\ H} CH_3CH_2CH_2COOH \xrightarrow{4\ H} CH_3CH_2CH_2CH_2OH$$

4. THE CAPROIC FERMENTATION

Barker, in 1935, discovered a related fermentation while studying the formation of methane. In this process a large anaerobe, named *Cl. kluyveri*, grew on a mixture of ethyl alcohol and acetate to form a mixture of butyric and caproic acids (Barker and Taha, 1942). The medium at first contained alcohol only, and the organism was always associated with a methane-producing form, but it developed that the role of the latter was only to produce acetic acid from the alcohol (Barker, 1947). If sufficient acetate is added, *Cl. kluyveri* grows well in pure culture (requiring biotin and *p*-aminobenzoate as growth factors) and converts ethanol and acetate quantitatively to butyrate, caproate, and H_2. Sugars are not used, and no CO_2 is formed.

The formation of butyrate has been described above: the alcohol is dehydrogenated, forming acetyl-CoA which condenses to acetoacetyl-CoA and is then reduced. The formation of caproate follows a similar pattern, a third molecule of acetyl-CoA condensing with the butyryl-CoA and the product being again reduced:

$$C_3H_7CO{\cdot}CoA + CH_3CO{\cdot}CoA \rightleftharpoons C_3H_7COCH_2CO{\cdot}CoA \overset{2\,H}{\rightleftharpoons} C_3H_7CHOHCH_2CO{\cdot}CoA \overset{-H_2O}{\rightleftharpoons}$$

$$C_3H_7CH{:}CHCO{\cdot}CoA \overset{2\,H}{\rightleftharpoons} C_3H_7CH_2CH_2CO{\cdot}CoA \quad (6)$$

By analogy with animal cells, the condensing unit may actually be malonyl-CoA.

The need for alcohol is as source of hydrogen for the reduction, although some of the hydrogen is lost as gas. Caproate is also formed in small yield by *Butyrib. rettgeri* from acetate and lactate, the lactate here evidently substituting for the ethanol.

The validity of reaction (6) is supported: (1) by a fermentation with butyrate-1-C^{14} (butyric acid labeled in the carboxyl), the caproic acid then containing almost all the isotope in the β-position; and (2) by experiments with cell-free extracts (Stadtman and Barker, 1949a) which convert mixtures of ethanol and acetate to butyrate and caproate.

If propionate was substituted for acetate in the medium (with live cells), then acetate and valerate were the main products, and some heptanoate also occurred (Bornstein and Barker, 1948):

$$C_2H_5OH + C_2H_5COOH \rightarrow C_4H_9COOH + H_2O$$
$$C_2H_5OH + C_4H_9COOH \rightarrow C_6H_{13}COOH + H_2O$$

Propionate is thus not converted to caproate, i.e., two C_3 acids do not produce a C_6 acid.

A curious variant on the process is supplied by two organisms called *Cl. caproicum* and *valerianicum* which (despite their names) form mainly *iso*caproic acid, $(CH_3)_2CH \cdot CH_2CH_2COOH$ (Prévot *et al.*, 1958). This, it is suggested, is derived from leucine by reductive deamination, but more likely it is formed on the way to *synthesizing* leucine, by reduction of the ketoacid precursor $(CH_3)_2CH \cdot CH_2CO \cdot COOH$.

Although the reactions are synthetic, they are exergonic, the condensation of alcohol and acetate to butyrate yielding $(-\Delta F_{25°})$ 11,700 cal (Bornstein and Barker, 1948). They thus suffice to supply the organism with all the energy it needs for synthesis of protoplasm.

Finally, the fermentation also involves a parallel to the butanol process, because in the presence of H_2 caproylphosphate is reduced by dried cells of *Cl. kluyveri* to small amounts of capryl alcohol (Stadtman and Barker, 1950). However, capryl alcohol is not formed in vivo, nor indeed is any alcohol higher than propanol.

5. THE SYNTHESIS OF LIPIDS IN BACTERIA

The two preceding sections show how short-chain fatty acids are synthesized. This is an appropriate point, therefore, to consider what is known of the synthesis of more complex lipids in bacteria. Most of this work, which is very recent, stems from Barker's studies of *Cl. kluyveri*.

A. Straight-chain Fatty Acids

The condensation of acetyl-CoA to chains of 4 or 6 carbon atoms (equations [3] and [6]) might appear to be the basis for the formation of chains of any length. However, in animal tissues long-chain fatty acids are not formed in quite this way. Instead, the acetyl-CoA is first carboxylated to form malonyl-CoA, and it is this that condenses with acetyl-CoA (Brady, 1958; Wakil and Ganguly, 1959; Lynen *et al.*, 1959):

$$\begin{array}{ccccc}
 & & CH_3 & & CH_3 \\
 & & | & & | \\
 & COOH & + CO \cdot SCoA & CO & + CO_2 + CoASH \\
 & | & & | \\
CH_3 & \xrightarrow{CO_2} CH_2 & \longrightarrow & CH_2 \\
| & | & & | \\
CO \cdot SCoA & CO \cdot SCoA & & CO \cdot SCoA
\end{array}$$

Biotin functions as the CO_2 carrier and may form N-carboxy-biotin as intermediate. The replacement of the new COOH by a second acetyl group is believed to occur after malonyl-CoA has been bound to the enzyme by an SH group on it (Lynen *et al.*, 1959; Brady, 1961). The resulting acetoacetyl-CoA is reduced (reactions [4] above) and can then accept a second malonyl-CoA to form a C-6 chain, and so on.

Although the enzyme system that fixes CO_2 into malonyl-CoA, and exchanges it in presence of a higher fatty acid, is present in *Cl. kluyveri* (Vagelos and Alberts, 1960), still this system is not necessary for the formation of butyrate; acetyl-CoA alone will form butyrate, and malonyl-CoA does not even enter the molecule (Goldman *et al.*, 1961). The malonyl-CoA system therefore functions only for the long-chain acids; specifically, it works with caproyl-CoA and higher members of the group, thus (Vagelos and Alberts, 1960):

$$\overset{*}{HOOC} \cdot CH_2CO \cdot SCoA + C_5H_{11}CO \cdot SCoA \rightleftharpoons \overset{*}{CO_2} + C_5H_{11}CO \cdot CH_2CO \cdot SCoA + CoASH$$

Thus it is used to make *Cl. kluyveri's* own cell lipids rather than the excreted mass products.

Among the bacterial acids are found a number of monounsaturated compounds. These are probably formed by oxidation of saturated acids, but in the Clostridia, where such oxidation could not occur, they are formed by loss of water from the hydroxy acids. Octanoic and decanoic acids give rise to C_{18}-acids with the double bond at C_7 and C_9 from the CH_3 end, respectively (Scheuerbrandt and Block, 1962). The corresponding C_{10} and C_{12} acids with OH groups at C_7 and C_9 from the CH_3 end (3-hydroxy-decanoic and dodecanoic acids) occur in Serratia (Bishop and Still, 1962); probably these are membrane constituents. Unlike higher organisms, no trace of polyunsaturated acids seems to be found in bacteria (Goldfine and Bloch, 1961).

B. Branched-chain Acids

Steroids, carotenoids, and such branched C_5H_8 units as those in co-enzyme Q (Chap. V, sec. 4C) are synthesized from a basic branched unit which is probably 5-phospho-mevalonic acid (Chaykin *et al.*, 1958):

The synthesis of this begins, in yeast, with the condensation of acetyl-CoA and acetoacetyl-CoA to produce β-hydroxy β-methyl glutaryl-CoA (HMGCoA) (Rudney and Ferguson, 1959):

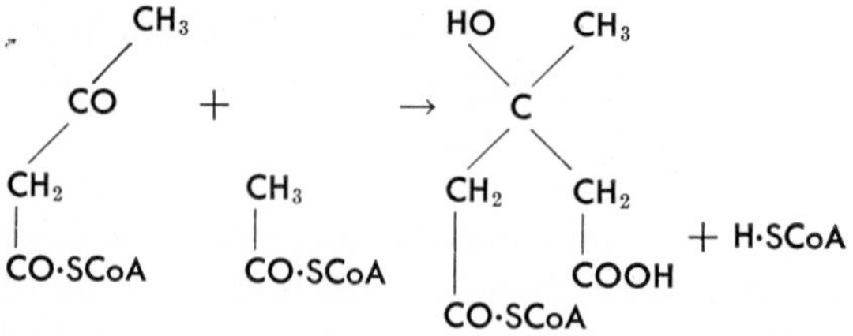

The reaction is specific, apparently irreversible, and is inhibited by excess of either substrate or product (Rudney, 1961). Mycobacteria make the same product by carboxylating and hydrating β-methylcrotonyl-CoA (Lynen et al., 1959):

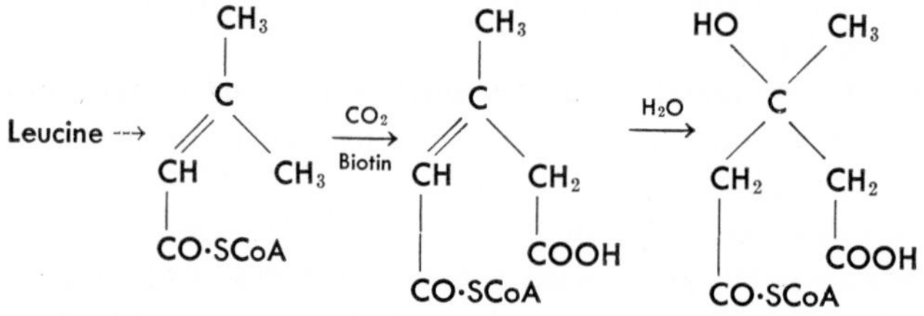

The HMGCoA is reduced by TPNH to mevalonic acid, and CoA liberated, by an irreversible reaction which takes place while the substrates are bound to the enzyme (Popják and Cornforth, 1960):

$$RCO \cdot SCoA + 2\ TPNH + 2\ H^+ \rightarrow RCH_2OH + CoA \cdot SH + 2\ TPN^+$$

The condensation of mevalonic acid via its phosphate and the related isopentenyl pyrophosphate involves loss of both phosphate and carboxyl, producing a highly reactive C_5H_8 unit, which yields the long branched-chain isoprenoid structures with the basis:

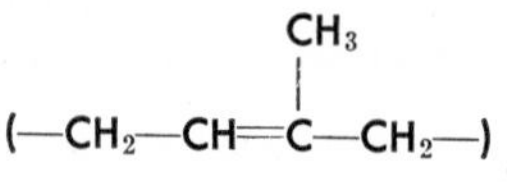

$$\text{CH}_3$$
$$|$$
$$(-CH_2-CH=C-CH_2-)$$

The Mycobacteria, as described in Chapter II, are notable for high-lipid content, and their lipids contain some branched acids of a quite different type. Typical of one group is phthienoic acid, a mixture of α and β unsaturated acids of form:

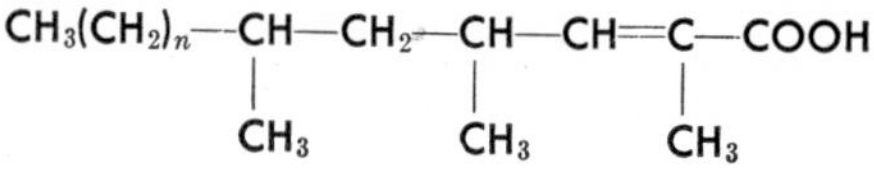

$$CH_3(CH_2)_n-CH-CH_2-CH-CH=C-COOH$$
$$\qquad\qquad\quad |\qquad\quad\ |\qquad\quad\ |$$
$$\qquad\qquad\ CH_3\qquad CH_3\qquad CH_3$$

where n is 17 in the principal member, but can vary from 11 to 21 (see Asselineau and Lederer, 1960, for review). Phthienoic acid is present in both human and bovine strains of *Mycob. tuberculosis,* and is among the preparations that produce marked tubercles in mice; suggestively, it is absent (along with some other saturated acids) from the avirulent strains (Cason *et al.,* 1956). Mycocerosic acid:

$$CH_3(CH_2)_nCHCH_2CHCH_2CHCH_2CH\ COOH$$
$$\quad\quad\quad\quad\ |\quad\ \ |\quad\ \ |\quad\ \ |$$
$$\quad\quad\quad\quad CH_3\ \ CH_3\ \ CH_3\ \ CH_3$$

is very similar. Lederer and co-workers (Lederer, 1961) have found labeled propionic acid to be incorporated entire into this acid, and it seems likely that the Mycobacteria condense *propionyl-CoA* in the same way as the Clostridia use acetyl-CoA:

$$CH_2CO{\cdot}CoA\quad CH_2CO{\cdot}CoA\quad\quad CH_2COCHCOOH\ \ \underset{-H_2O}{\overset{+4\ H}{\longrightarrow}}\ CH_2CH_2CHCOOH$$
$$|\qquad\quad +\ |\qquad\quad \rightarrow\ |\qquad\quad |\qquad\qquad\qquad |\qquad\quad\ |\qquad etc.$$
$$CH_3\qquad\qquad CH_3\qquad\qquad CH_3\quad\ CH_3\qquad\qquad\ CH_3\quad\ CH_3$$

After three or four propionic units have been thus condensed, malonyl-CoA units are added to give the remaining straight chain. Details of this reaction remain obscure.

The second branched type is the *mycolic acids,* β-hydroxyacids with two or more long straight chains, e.g., corynomycolic acid, the simplest, isolated from *C. diphtheriae:*

$$CH_3(CH_2)_{14}CHOHCHCOOH$$
$$\quad\quad\quad\quad\quad\quad |$$
$$\quad\quad\quad\quad\quad (C_{14}H_{29})$$

Since this bacterium contains much palmitic acid, $CH_3(CH_2)_{14}COOH$, two of these units might condense in the α position, just as propionic acid above:

$$CH_3(CH_2)_{14}COOH\ +\ CH_2COOH\ \rightarrow\ CH_3(CH_2)_{14}CHOH{\cdot}CHCOOH$$
$$\quad\quad\quad\quad\quad\quad\quad\quad\quad |\quad\quad\quad\quad\quad\quad\quad\quad\quad\quad\quad |$$
$$\quad\quad\quad\quad\quad\quad\quad\quad (CH_2)_{13}\quad\quad\quad\quad\quad\quad\quad\quad (CH_2)_{13}$$
$$\quad\quad\quad\quad\quad\quad\quad\quad\quad |\quad\quad\quad\quad\quad\quad\quad\quad\quad\quad\quad |$$
$$\quad\quad\quad\quad\quad\quad\quad\quad\ CH_3\quad\quad\quad\quad\quad\quad\quad\quad\ CH_3$$

This was proven by growing the cells on palmitic acid-1-C^{14}, when the corynomycolic acid contained C^{14} only in the COOH and CHOH groups (Gastambide-Odier and Lederer, 1960). The reaction is important, for these acids occur widely in the group:

Corynebacteria	contain the C_{32} acid
Nocardias	contain the C_{50} acid
Mycob. avium and *phlei*	contain the C_{54} acid
Mycob. tuberculosis	contain the C_{88} acid

The higher members probably have four branches, two of C_{18} and two of C_{24} or C_{26} (Lederer, 1961). A mutant Mycobacterium actually needs $C_{26}H_{54}O_2$ for growth, so perhaps uses it to form a mycolic acid (Karlsson, 1956).

A third branched type bears a single CH_3 group, like 10-methyl-stearic acid, present in several Mycobacteria, or a cyclopropane group as in lactobacillic acid (Chap. XI, sec. 3). These are probably formed by addition of a single formyl group to an unsaturated acid. C^{14}-formate is incorporated into lactobacillic acid by *L. arabinosus*, and the un-saturated acid, 11-Δ-octadecenoic, is converted to lactobacillic acid with high efficiency (Hofmann and Liu, 1960):

$$CH_3(CH_2)_5CH{=}CH{\cdot}(CH_2)_9COOH + HCHO \rightarrow CH_3(CH_2)_5\underset{H}{C}\overset{CH_2}{\diagup\diagdown}\underset{H}{C}(CH_2)_9COOH$$

The formyl transfer may be made by folic acid (Chap. XXIV).

Why should bacteria synthesize such a variety of specific lipids? Some are perhaps formed incidentally as by-products of another synthesis, just as, in a way, lactic or butyric acid is produced in the course of acquiring energy for growth. But most are doubtless essential for the cell's life. Many of the cell's lipids are present in the membrane, which contains both true fats and phospholipids or phosphatidic acids (Asselineau and Lederer, 1960). Although the composition and structure of membranes are not yet understood, the fact that they control all the relations between the cell and its environment makes their properties critically important and specific. It is significant that the excreted precursor of cellulose in Acetobacter is a glucose-*lipid* complex. In gram-negative cells, lipids enter not only into the membrane but into the cell walls as well, e.g., Salmonella walls are 22 per cent lipid, and lipoprotein makes up some 80 per cent of the total wall weight. In a Myxococcus 50 per cent of the (trypsin-treated) wall was lipid (Mason and Powelson, 1958). It is safe to predict that the study of the role of lipids in walls and membranes will extend greatly in the future.

6. THE MACERANS AND POLYMYXA FERMENTATIONS

These processes have been comparatively little studied. In Schard-inger's original study of *Aerobac. macerans* (1905), he found that 7 per cent of the potato starch used in the medium was converted to acetone and 21 per cent to ethanol. Acetic and formic acids, but no

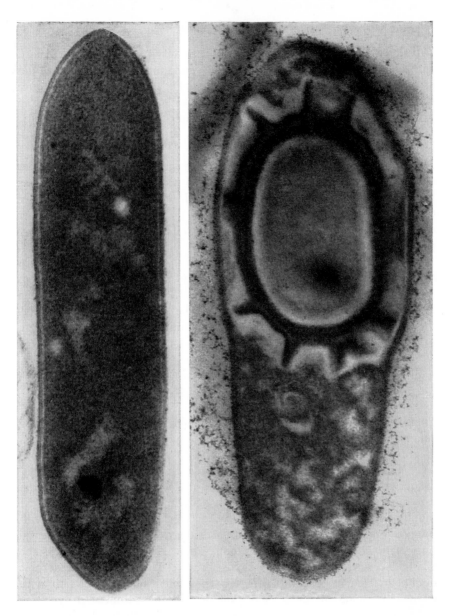

FIGURE XV-3

Electron micrographs of *Bacillus* (= *Aerobac.*) *polymyxa*. *Left,* vegetative cell; *right,* mature cell with spore. The radiating ridges on the spore wall explain why some strains were called *Bac. asterosporus* ("star-spore"). (From Pauline Holbert, 1960. Left, unpublished; right, *J. Biophys. Biochem. Cyt.,* **7:**373–376.)

butyric, were formed. *Aerobac. polymyxa* was regarded by Beijerinck (1894) as giving, from malt, mainly CO_2 and gum, with small quantities of hydrogen and traces of butanol, but later it was found to produce 2,3-butylene glycol in quantity, a 25 per cent yield from glucose (Donker, 1926) and a 27 per cent yield from cornstarch being recorded (Kooi, 1946). Another 20 per cent is converted to ethanol, and 4 to 10 per cent to acetone. Thus, in general the fermentation is like that of Aerobacter (cf. p. 511), except for the acetone formation. Under the name of *Bacillus acetoethylicum*, the *macerans* fermentation has been patented (Northrop, 1919). The yield of acetone is about 13 per cent when corn is used as substrate, and that of ethanol up to 30 per cent, or on glycerol up to over 40 per cent. The fermentation is greatly promoted by addition of iron as $Fe(OH)_3$ suspension (Roberts, 1947).

The special polysaccharides ("Schardinger dextrins") formed in the *macerans* fermentation are discussed on page 587.

A recent portrait of *Bac. polymyxa* or *"asterosporus,"* one of the Aerobacilli, is shown in Figure XV–3. Like *Aerobac. macerans*, it ferments practically all carbohydrates, including starch, inulin, pectin, and hemicellulose.

7. ANAEROBES AND OXYGEN

Although the Aerobacilli are morphologically like the clostridia (cf. Fig. XV–1) and often accompany them in butanol enrichments of grain mash, they are aerobic and die off when the fermentation is well advanced. Correspondingly, of course, the clostridia die off if conditions become aerobic, yet at least some of the enzymes of the clostridia can function under aerobic conditions. Stadtman and Barker (1949b) found that an enzyme from *Cl. kluyveri* can oxidize alcohol to acetaldehyde and acetyl phosphate, and can oxidize butyrate to acetyl phosphate and acetate. Nisman and Vinet (1950) found that some Clostridia can oxidize amino acids by O_2. Thus, strictly anaerobic organisms use, in fermentation, enzymes that can also function with oxygen. It should be noted, too, that the crotonase-thiolase-β-hydroxybutyryl-CoA dehydrogenase group of enzymes functions also in animal tissues that are well supplied with oxygen. Dried cells of *Cl. kluyveri* can oxidize butyrate, and H_2O_2 accumulates (Lieberman and Barker, 1954), doubtless because of the participation of flavoprotein as H acceptor. Apparently the H_2O_2 inhibits the fission of acetoacetyl-CoA to acetate (reaction [3] above), but this in itself does not seem of fatal importance for growth.

If we recall that part at least of the fermentation, namely, the formation of acetone, can be carried out by an aerobe (*Aerobac. macerans*), the exact reason for the strictly anaerobic nature of the clostridia becomes difficult to give. The absence of the cytochrome system in these cells may well make oxygen inert for them, but would not explain why oxygen kills them.

Beijerinck (1894) was convinced that the strict anaerobiosis of the butylic clostridia was a function of the high-sugar media usually used. On a poor medium, containing 1 per cent peptone and ½ per cent starch, at 10° to 12° C, he could obtain appreciable growth and butanol formation only under aerobic conditions. His conclusion, that the bacteria when growing in the natural media of soil and water need occasional contact with oxygen in order to maintain growth, suggests some sort of aerobic vitamin synthesis. This might repay investigation by modern methods.

8. THE PRODUCTION OF RIBOFLAVIN

The butylic fermentation liquor is bright yellow; it is rich in riboflavin, synthesized by the bacteria. This has turned out to be a most valuable by-product. Addition of unpolished rice increases the yield of riboflavin, while excess iron decreases it, since steel fermenting tanks give poor yields. The addition of α,α-dipyridyl, which forms a stable complex with iron, has been patented as a means of improving the yield (see van Lanen and Tanner, 1948); the optimum iron concentration is 1 to 3 ppm. Amino acid mixtures, especially arginine plus asparagine, as well as biotin, also increase the yield of riboflavin (Imai, 1956), which at its maximum may reach 0.3 mg per gram dry matter, or 300 ppm. The *polymyxa* fermentation also produces riboflavin, but in lesser amounts (Adams and Leslie, 1946).

Some of the yeastlike Ascomycetes. including *Eremothecium ashbyi* (Guilliermond, 1936), *Ashbya gossypii*, and several Candida species also form much riboflavin from sugars and compete with the clostridia in industrial importance. Iron and zinc are both critical, the optimum Fe level for Candida being about 0.01 ppm; about 5 mg of iron per liter inhibits riboflavin formation drastically (Goodwin and McEvoy, 1959). For Candida, Zn is essential, and Fe acts only on growth (Knüsel, 1957). With Eremothecium growing on a synthetic medium, thiamine was the main factor promoting riboflavin formation, although it did not promote growth (Osman and Kamel, 1960). *Aspergillus niger* can form riboflavin also, and again the process is separate from the growth, because the addition of sugars like sucrose and arabinose, or the use of nitrate as sole N source, or limitation of the Mg supply, or Hg salts, all retard growth but increase the riboflavin yield (Sarasin, 1953).

Numerous additions of C^{14}-labeled substrates, followed by breakdown of the riboflavin and location of the isotope, have led to the recognition that ring A is formed from acetyl groups or acetoin, while ring C is derived from purines, especially adenine; the ribityl group comes from glucose (McNutt, 1954; Goodwin and Jones, 1956; Brown *et al.*, 1958). Specific C atoms are contributed as shown. In general,

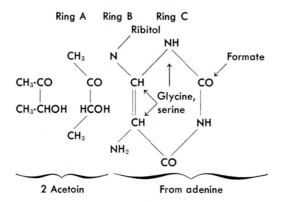

however, adding these substrates in quantity to Ashbya or Eremothecium cultures increases the riboflavin very little. Adenine and serine do increase the yield somewhat. From both Aerobacter and Eremothecium an enzyme system that catalyzes the final steps in riboflavin synthesis from precursors, including acetoin, has been extracted (Katagiri *et al.*, 1959).

REFERENCES

Adams, G. A., and Leslie, J. D. 1946. *Canad. J. Res.*, **24F**:12–28.
Asselineau, J., and Lederer, E. 1960. In, Lipide Metabolism, ed. K. Bloch, New York, Wiley, pp. 336–406.
Baba, T. 1953–1954. *Bull. Fac. Eng. Hiroshima Univ.*, 2:241–250; 3:147–152.
Barker, H. A. 1947. *Antonie v. Leeuwenhoek*, **12**:167–176.
Barker, H. A. 1957. Bacterial Fermentations, Chap. 2, New York, John Wiley.
Barker, H. A., and Haas, V. 1944. *J. Bact.*, **47**:301–305.
Barker, H. A.; Kamen, M. D.; and Bornstein, B. T. 1945. *Proc. Nat. Acad. Sci.*, **31**:373–381.
Barker, H. A.; Kamen, M. D.; and Haas, V. 1945. *Proc. Nat. Acad. Sci.*, 31:355–360.
Barker, H. A., and Taha, S. M. 1942. *J. Bact.*, **43**:347–363.
Beijerinck, M. W. 1896. *Arch. Néerl.*, **29**:1–68.
Bernhauer, K.; Iglauer, A.; Groag, W.; and Kottig, R. 1936. *Biochem. Z.*, **287**:61–64.

Bernhauer, K., and Kurschner, K. 1935. *Biochem. Z.*, **280**:379–387.

Bhat, J. V., and Barker, H. A. 1947–1948. *J. Bact.*, **54**:387–391; **55**:223–230.

Bishop, D. G., and Still, J. L. 1962. *Biochem. Biophys. Res. Comms.*, **7**:337–341.

Bornstein, B. T., and Barker, H. A. 1948. *J. Biol. Chem.*, **172**:659–669.

Brady, R. O. 1958. *Proc. Nat. Acad. Sci.*, **44**:993–998.

Brady, R. O. 1961. Proc. 5th Int. Biochem. Cong. (Moscow). London, Pergamon.

Brown, E. G.; Goodwin, T. W.; and Jones, O. T. G. 1958. *Biochem. J.*, **68**:40–49.

Brown, R. W. 1937. *Iowa State Coll. J. Sci.*, **11**:39–41.

Brown, R. W.; Osburn, O. L.; and Werkman, C. H. 1938. *Proc. Soc. Exp. Biol. Med.*, **36**:203–205; Brown, R. W., Stahly, G. L., and Werkman, C. H. *Iowa State Coll. J. Sci.*, **12**:245–251.

Campbell, L. L. 1957. *J. Bact.*, **73**:270–274, 275–279.

Cason, J.; Allen, C. F.; Acetis, W. de; and Fonken, G. J. 1956. *J. Biol. Chem.*, **220**: 893–904.

Chaykin, S.; Law, J.; Phillips, A. H.; Tchen, T. T.; and Bloch, K. 1958. *Proc. Nat. Acad. Sci.*, **44**:998–1004.

Davies, R. 1942. *Biochem. J.*, **36**:582–599.

Davies, R. 1943. *Biochem. J.*, **37**:230–238.

Donker, H. J. L. 1926. Bijdrage tot de kennis der boterzuur-, butyl-alcohol en ace-tongistingen. Dissertation, Delft; *Tijdsschr. vergel. Geneeskunde*, **11**:78–98 (1924).

Dyr, J., and Protiva, J. 1956. *Ceskoslav. mikrobiol.*, **1**:151–157; from *Chem. Abstr.*, **50**:15738.

Eliasberg, P. 1930. *Biochem. Z.*, **220**:259–277.

Forsyth, W. G.; Hayward, A. C.; and Roberts, J. B. 1958. *Nature*, **182**:800–801.

Gastambide-Odier, M., and Lederer, E. 1960. *Biochem. Zeit.*, **333**:285–295.

Gfeller, P. 1954. Mikrobiologische Verwertung der Sulfitablaugen auf dem Gärwege. Thesis, ETH Zurich.

Goldfine, H. and Bloch, K. 1961. *J. Biol. Chem.*, **236**:2596–2601; Bloch, K. 1962. *Fed. Proc.*, **21**:1058–1063.

Goldman, P.; Alberts, A. W.; and Vagelos, P. R. 1961. *Biochem. Biophys. Res. Comms.* **5**:280–284.

Goodwin, T. W., and Jones, O. T. G. 1956. *Biochem. J.*, **64**:9–13.

Goodwin, T. W., and McEvoy, D. 1959. *Biochem. J.*, **71**:742–748.

*Guilliermond, A. 1936. *Rev. Mycol.*, **1**:115–156.

Hamilton, G. A., and Westheimer, F. H. 1959. *J. Am. Chem. Soc.*, **81**:6332–6333.

Hardman, J. K., and Stadtman, T. C. 1960. *J. Bact.*, **79**:544–548.

Hoffman, K., and Liu, T. Y. 1960. *Biochim. Biophys. Acta*, **37**:364–365.

Hoshino, K. 1953. *J. Agric. Chem. Soc.*, Japan, **27**:222–228, 285–295.

Imai, K. 1956. *Mem. Coll. Agric. Kyoto Univ.*, **73**:31 pp.

Janke, A., and Siedler, V. 1937. *Biochem. Z.*, **292**:101–115.

Johnson, M. J.; Peterson, W. H.; and Fred, E. B. 1933. *J. Biol. Chem.*, **101**:145–157.

Karlsson, J. L. 1956. *J. Bact.*, **72**:813–815.

Katagiri, H.; Takeda, I.; and Imai, K. 1959. *J. Vitaminol.*, **5**:287–297.

Knüsel, F. 1957. *Arch. Mikrobiol.*, **27**:219–259.

Koepsell, H. J.; Johnson, M. J.; and Meek, J. S. 1944. *J. Biol. Chem.*, **154**:535–547.

Kooi, E. R. 1946. *Iowa State Coll. J. Sci.*, **21**:36–37.

Kubowitz, F. 1934. *Biochem. Z.*, **274**:285–298.

*van Lanen, J. M., and Tanner, F. W., Jr. 1948. Vitamins in Microorganisms. *Vitamins and Hormones*, **6**:164–224 (esp. pp. 157–180).

Lederer, E. 1961. Proc. 5th Int. Biochem. Cong. (Moscow). London, Pergamon.

Lek, J. B. van der. 1930. Onderzoekingen over de Butylalkoholgisting. Dissertation, Delft.

Lerner, E. M. 1941. A Consideration of the Butyl Alcohol Fermentation. Thesis. Harvard Univ.

Lieberman, I., and Barker, H. A. 1954. *J. Bact.*, **68**:61–62.

Lynen, F. 1954. *Harvey Lect.*, **48**:210–244.

*Lynen, F.; Knappe, J.; Lorch, E.; Jutting, G.; and Ringelmann, E. 1959. *Angew. Chem.*, **71**:481–486.

Lynen, F.; Reichert, E.; and Rueff, L. 1951–1952. *Ann. Chem.*, **574**:1–32; Lynen, F.; Wessely, L.; Wieland, O., and Rueff, L. *Angew. Chem.*, **64**:687 (1952).

McNutt, W. S. 1954. *J. Biol. Chem.*, **210**:511–519.

Martin, D. B., and Vagelos, P. R. 1961. *Biochem. Biophys. Res. Comms.*, **5**:16–21.

Mason, D. J., and Powelson, D. 1958. *Biochim. Biophys. Acta*, **29**:1–7.

Merrick, J. M., and Doudoroff, M. 1961. *Nature*, **189**:890–892.

Milhaud, G.; Aubert, J-P.; and van Niel, C. B. 1956. *Ann. Inst. Pasteur*, **91**:363–368.

Neuberg, C., and Arinstein, B. 1921. *Biochem. Z.*, **117**:269–314.

Nisman, B., and Vinet, G. 1950. *Ann. Inst. Pasteur*, **78**:115–133.

Northrop, J. H. 1919. U.S. Patent No. 1,293,172, Feb. 14, 1919. *Chem. Abstr.*, **13**:1075.

Osburn, O. L.; Brown, R. W.; and Werkman, C. H. 1938. *Iowa State Coll. J. Sci.*, **12**: 275–284.

Osman, H. G., and Kamel, M. Y. H. 1960. *Egyptian J. Chem.*, **2**:385–395.

Pappenheimer, A. M., Jr., and Shaskan, E. 1944. *J. Biol. Chem.*, **155**:265–275.

Peterson, W. H., and Fred, E. B. 1932. *Ind. Eng. Chem.*, **24**:237–242.

*Popják, G., and Cornforth, J. W. 1960. Biosynthesis of Cholesterol. *Adv. in Enzymol.* (ed. F. F. Nord), **22**:281–335.

Prévot, A. R.; Blass, J.; Aladame, N.; and Azoulay, E. 1958. *Ann. Inst. Pasteur*, **95**: 369–373.

Reilly, J.; Hickinbottom, W. J.; Henley, F. R.; and Thaysen, A. C. 1920. *Biochem. J.*, **14**:228–251.

Roberts, J. L. 1947. *Soil Sci.*, **63**:135–140.

Rudney, H. 1961. *Proc. 5th Int. Biochem. Congr.* (Moscow). London, Pergamon.

Rudney, H., and Ferguson, J. T. 1959. *J. Biol. Chem.*, **234**:1072–1075, 1076–1080.

Sarasin, A. 1953. *Ber. Schweiz. bot. Ges.*, **63**:287–316.

Scheuerbrandt, G., and Bloch, K. 1962. *J. Biol. Chem.*, **237**:2064–2068.

Simon, E. 1947. *Arch. Biochem.*, **13**:237–243; **14**:39–51.

Simon, E., and Weizmann, C. 1937. *Enzymologia*, **4**:169–188.

Smit, J. 1930. Die Gärungssarcinen. Pflanzenforschung, ed. R. Kolkwitz. Jena, G. Fischer.

Stadtman, E. R. 1952. *J. Biol. Chem.*, **203**:501–512.

Stadtman, E. R. 1956. *Fed. Proc.*, **12**:692.

*Stadtman, E. R., and Barker, H. A. 1949a. *J. Biol. Chem.*, **180**:1085–1093, 1117–1124, 1169–1186 (pts. I, III, and IV).

*Stadtman, E. R., and Barker, H. A. 1949b. *J. Biol. Chem.*, **180**:1095–1115 (pt. II).

Stadtman, E. R., and Barker, H. A. 1950. *J. Biol. Chem.*, **184**:769–793.

Stern, J. R.; del Campillo, A.; and Raw, I. 1956. *J. Biol. Chem.*, **218**:971–984.

Tatum, E. L.; Peterson, W. H.; and Fred, E. B. 1934–1935. *J. Bact.*, **27**:207–217 (1934); **29**:563–572 (1935).

Vagelos, P. R., and Alberts, A. W. 1960. *J. Biol. Chem.*, **235**:2786–2791.

Wakil, S. J., and Ganguly, J. 1959. *J. Amer. Chem. Soc.*, **81**:2597–2599; Wakil, S. J. 1961. *J. Lipid Res.*, **2**:1–12.

Wood, H. G.; Brown, R. W.; and Werkman, C. H. 1945. *Arch. Biochem.*, **6**:243–260.

CHAPTER XVI

The "Oxidative Fermentations" and Aromatic Metabolism

It is possible to prepare vinegar by bacterial oxidation of dilute alcohol, (which) . . . is sprayed over beech shavings packed in earthenware towers and impregnated with the bacillus [*sic*]. There is a wonderful plant in existence, consisting of 960 units all of which are controlled electrically from a common centre, so that definite quantities are sprayed at definite intervals. It gives an eerie feeling to stand in this factory, where the human element is absent except as a watchman, whilst all around in silence and without fuss the enzymic agents are busily at work; nowhere else have I been brought so close to an understanding and admiration of the silent processes which are happening under similar directed control in plants and animals.

E. F. Armstrong (1933)

Pasteur's definition of fermentation as life without air obviously cannot apply to any oxidative process. However, the oxidations with which we are here concerned involve many of the same substrates as the fermentations and have so much in common chemically with them that the contradiction in terms ("oxidative fermentation") is partially justified. In any event, the term *fermentation* is sometimes used now, especially in industry, to indicate any biochemical process carried out by microorganisms (cf. Chap. V, sec. 2).

Of the microbial oxidations that are related to fermentation, three types are important:

(1) The conversion of ethanol to acetic acid,

(2) The oxidation of hexoses and sugar alcohols to related acids and ketones, and

(3) The conversion of sugars to citric, fumaric, and oxalic acids. These last are more characteristic of fungi than of bacteria and so will not be discussed here.

1. THE ACETIC BACTERIA

The flora of wine or beer exposed to the air and turning sour (acetifying) were studied by Pasteur in the 1860's in response to requests from the wine makers of France. In his "Etudes sur le Vinaigre" (1868) Pasteur describes two forms of "*Mycoderma aceti*," one forming a delicate dry veil on the surface of the liquid, the other producing "a sort of moist skin, swollen, gelatinous and slippery" and finally filling the whole liquid. Although Pasteur considered they were not bacteria, the name *Mycoderma* is unfortunate since it really applies to a group of nonsporeforming yeasts which are also found on the surface of souring wines. These are aerobic, nonfermentative, budding cells, described by Persoon as early as 1822, and now classified in the *Torulopsoideae* (see Lodder, 1934). They oxidize sugars, alcohol, and organic acids. Other organisms sometimes found in souring wines are true yeasts of the genus Zygosaccharomyces, and also, if the acetic acid content is not above 1 M, a group of nematodes, *Turbatrix aceti*. Little is known about the metabolism of these interesting animals. They can survive pH values from 1.6 to 11 (Peters, 1928); it is not clear whether they make or destroy acetic acid. The most active acetifying organisms were recognized as bacteria by Hansen (1879, 1893) and by Brown (1888), both of whom described additional species.

A definitive study of the group was made by Beijerinck in 1899. Dropping the term "Mycoderma," he coined the name "Acetobacter" for them and recognized them as a group with many morphological and physiological similarities. The most important common property, of course, is the ability to oxidize alcohol to acetic acid. Some make acid from dextrose, but none attack starch, glycogen, or insulin. Many additional species were isolated from malt, beer, wine, and vinegar by Henneberg (1909), and others have been added by Kluyver and his students. Pasteur's two forms are now *A. aceti* and *A. xylinum*, respectively.

The Acetobacters are longish gram-negative rods, one or two with a tendency to curve. The surface films on liquid media, which were particularly studied by the early workers (e.g., Hansen, 1895), contain very long chains and filaments up to 400 μ in length. The strictly aerobic nature of the group and their gram-negativity suggest relationship to the Pseudomonadaceae, but this is only justified for those members that (when motile) have polar flagella. These are designated *Acetomonas* and may be a single rather variable species (Shimwell and Carr, 1959). They do not have the ability to oxidize acetic acid, while the other members, which when motile have peritrichous flagella, can do so (Leifson, 1954). It is this larger group that is designated *Acetobacter* proper.

Even Acetomonas has important differences from Pseudomonas (Shimwell *et al.*, 1960):

(1) They can form acid on ethanol-agar; some of the Pseudomonads can oxidize ethanol to acetic acid (Stanier, 1947), but only in presence of a growth-supporting medium;

(2) They can oxidize glycerol to dihydroxyacetone;

(3) They can grow at an initial pH of 4.5, as indeed can the Acetobacters too;

(4) They cannot oxidize calcium lactate to calcium carbonate as the Pseudomonads can.

The inability of Pseudomonads to grow at pH below 5 or to make surface films distinguishes them from the acetic group as a whole. In addition, of course, they attack proteins and peptides vigorously, and most of them form green, blue, or fluorescent pigments; neither Acetomonas nor the Acetobacters have these properties.

2. THE VINEGAR INDUSTRY

This ancient industry has played an important part in microbiology. Vinegars are made from wines, beers, and ciders by oxidation. In the French process, as carried out at Orleans and elsewhere, wine is stored in broad shallow vats; the acetifying bacteria grow on the surface as a delicate papery skin. Thin pieces of wood may be floated on the wine to help support this membrane, since acetification is most active when the membrane is at the surface; vinegar makers know that it must not be submerged or the process will be slow and the vinegar cloudy. From time to time the vinegar is run off at the bottom of the vat and new wine added, without disturbing the film. The exact species of Acetobacter responsible for the Orleans process is not quite certain. *A. orleanense*[1] was isolated by Henneberg (1909) from such a vat, but the property of forming a coherent film and leaving the liquid clear—as in the vinegar vats—is not present in this culture. Other species, such as *A. ascendens*, may cause turbidity, which is hard to get rid of. The Orleans process is said to furnish vinegars of the finest quality. They may contain up to 9.3 per cent ($= 1.55$ M) acetic acid.

In the "quick" vinegar process, as first developed in Germany, aqueous alcohol or beer is trickled continuously through vats or barrels packed with beech shavings and is converted to vinegar on the way through. A gentle stream of air may be blown through the vat to promote oxidation and to keep the contents cool, since the heat liberated (ca. 113 kcal per mole of acetic acid) is considerable. Here the organisms grow as an almost invisible film on the shavings, and until Pasteur's work it was supposed that the shavings themselves caused the oxidation.

[1] Now considered (Frateur, 1950) as a variety of *A. mesoxydans* (var. *lentum*).

Shavings from actively functioning vessels were used as starter (inoculum) for new vessels. *A. aceti*, isolated by Pasteur and Beijerinck from such vats, is probably the organism of the quick vinegar process. Sometimes its place is taken by the less active mucilaginous or leathery *A. xylinum*, which continues to grow in the vinegar and may give a bad smell to the product.

3. THE OXIDATION OF ALCOHOL

The oxidation of alcohol is the most characteristic activity of Acetobacter and Acetomonas. It is formulated as

$$CH_3CH_2OH + O_2 \rightarrow CH_3COOH + H_2O$$

and mediated (at least in *A. rancens* var. *pasteurianum*) by cytochrome oxidase (Kubowitz and Haas, 1932). As might be expected, it is inhibited by CO in the dark (Tanaka, 1933). There are two steps:

$$C_2H_5OH \xrightarrow{\text{alcohol dehydrogenase}} CH_3CHO + 2(H)$$

$$CH_3CHO \cdot H_2O \xrightarrow{\text{acetaldehyde dehydrogenase}} CH_3COOH + 2(H)$$

In very acid media or with concentrated suspensions, acetaldehyde may accumulate (Janke and Kropacsy, 1935). This may be because the aldehyde dehydrogenase functions best in alkaline solution; the enzyme from beef liver has a sharp optimum at pH 8.3 (Racker, 1949). However, the over-all optimum for alcohol oxidation is nearer pH 6.

The first step (alcohol to aldehyde) can also be brought about by H_2O_2 through the medium either of catalase (Keilin and Hartree, 1945) or of peroxidase (Wieland and Pistor, 1936). One or other of these oxidases is present in all Acetobacters (see sec. 6).

In alkaline media acetic acid can be produced anaerobically from acetaldehyde by dismutation (Neuberg and Windisch, 1925):

$$2\ CH_3CHO \rightarrow CH_3COOH + CH_3CH_2OH$$

In this process the hydrogen is carried from one molecule to the other by DPN, which links together the two enzymes, alcohol dehydrogenase and aldehyde dehydrogenase (Racker, 1949). Because the optimum for dismutation is at pH 8.4 or above (Janke and Kropacsy, 1935), it cannot play a significant part in the formation of acetic acid under natural conditions, where the pH is usually acid.

4. OTHER OXIDATIONS

Many other oxidations are carried out.

(1) *Acetic acid* itself can be oxidized to $CO_2 + H_2O$. In the production of vinegar this is known as overoxidation and can cause serious loss. Some species oxidize acetate rapidly, others not at all. The mechanism of the oxidation, though not specifically established for Acetobacter, is doubtless that described in section 8 of Chapter V, namely, conversion of the acetate to acetyl-CoA, condensation with oxalacetate to citrate, and continued cyclic oxidation thereafter. Uncertainties about the functioning of this cycle in microorganisms (Krebs *et al.*, 1952) have been largely settled with the discovery of its modification in which isocitrate splits to yield succinate and glyoxylate (see Kornberg, 1959).

(2) *Propyl alcohol* is oxidized to propionic acid by nearly all Acetobacters:

$$CH_3CH_2CH_2OH \xrightarrow{O_2} CH_3CH_2COOH + H_2O$$

The reaction was first described by Brown (1886). The enzyme is doubtless the same as for ethanol; at least, the alcohol dehydrogenase of yeast can oxidize alcohols up to amyl. Similarly, ethylene glycol is converted to glycolic acid by some species:

$$
\begin{array}{ccc}
CH_2OH & & CH_2OH \\
| & \xrightarrow{O_2} & | \\
CH_2OH & & COOH + H_2O
\end{array}
$$

(3) *Secondary alcohols* are oxidized to ketones by many, but not all, species; *e.g.*:

$$
\begin{array}{ccccccc}
CH_2OH & & CH_2OH & & CH_2OH & & CH_2OH \\
| & & | & & | & & | \\
HCOH & \xrightarrow{\frac{1}{2}\,O_2} & CO & & HCOH & \xrightarrow{\frac{1}{2}\,O_2} & CO \\
| & & | & & | & & | \\
CH_2OH & & CH_2OH & & HCOH & & HCOH \\
\text{Glycerol} & & \text{Dihydroxyacetone} & & | & & | \\
& & & & CH_2OH & & CH_2OH \\
& & & & \textit{i-}\text{Erythritol} & & \text{L-(+)-Erythrulose}
\end{array}
$$

One special case of this reaction, namely, that of the sugar alcohols, will be discussed in section 5. Another special case is lactic acid, which is similarly oxidized:

$$CH_3CHOHCOOH \xrightarrow{\frac{1}{2}\,O_2} CH_3COCOOH + H_2O$$

With *A. aceti*, the pyruvic acid may be further oxidized to $CO_2 + H_2O$ (Tanaka, 1935); with Acetomonas, the oxidation goes only as far as acetate (Visser't Hooft, 1925). A third sequence leads from pyruvic acid to acetylmethyl carbinol (Chap. XIV); *A. rancens* can give a 25 per cent yield of the carbinol from calcium lactate (Frateur, 1950).

(4) *Aldose sugars*, like aldehydes, can be oxidized to acids. Glucose is converted to gluconic acid (Brown, 1886), galactose to galactonic, and arabinose to arabonic acid (Hermann and Neuschul, 1931; Bernhauer and Görlich, 1935). Some Acetobacters are unable to carry out these reactions, which thus become important for distinguishing species (cf. sec. 6). A number of Pseudomonads, especially *Ps. putida* and *Ps. fluorescens*, oxidize glucose, arabinose, xylose, and ribose in the same way (Lockwood and Nelson, 1946). In the case of glucose, if the further oxidation of gluconic acid is prevented, the oxidation can be almost quantitative (Entner and Stanier, 1951).

The first product of oxidation is the lactone. *Ps. saccharophila* converts arabinose rapidly to arabono-γ-lactone, DPN being hydrogen acceptor (Palleroni and Doudoroff, 1957). Similarly *Acetomonas oxydans* converts glucose to glucono-δ-lactone (King and Cheldelin, 1957–1958), and in this case two enzymes are present: one is in the particles that contain the cytochromes and has optimum pH 5.5, the other is soluble and has optimum pH 8.6. The cells also contain an enzyme to hydrolyze the lactone to gluconic acid. Evidently they are equipped to carry out the oxidation under a variety of conditions.

Often the resulting acid, which contains secondary carbinol groups, undergoes a second stage of oxidation as in (3) above, yielding a ketonic acid. Glucose yields 5-ketogluconic acid:

Glucose	Gluconolactone	Gluconic acid	5-Ketogluconic acid	2-Ketogluconic acid

The 5-keto acid is formed by many Acetobacters and often in good yield (Bernhauer and Görlich, 1935); in media with $CaCO_3$ added, the calcium salt often crystallizes out characteristically.

The 2-keto acid is also formed by many Acetobacters, though sometimes only in traces (Frateur, Simonart, and Coulon, 1954). It is formed more actively by many Pseudomonas species, yields as high as 80 per cent having been recorded (Lockwood *et al.*, 1941). The acid is of especial interest because on decarboxylation it yields arabinose, which may thus be derived under natural conditions from glucose. In fact, the almost constant association of glucose and arabinose in cell-wall materials of higher plants suggests that this path of breakdown may be of wider occurrence than in Acetobacter alone. The conversion of 6-phospho-gluconic acid to ribulose and ribose (Chap. V, sec. 8) is a comparable reaction. The 2-keto acid is further oxidized, by pigment-forming strains of Acetomonas, to the 2,5-diketo acid; this is the precursor of a characteristic brown pigment (Beijerinck, 1911a; Katznelson *et al.*, 1953), which gave the name *A. melanogenum* to these strains; it occurs also in two strains of *A. aceti* (Carr and Shimwell, 1960). Glucose and gluconic acid yield the same product. Slow further oxidation, at least with *Ps. fluorescens*, leads eventually to α-ketoglutaric acid (Lockwood and Stodola, 1946), though some cultures can oxidize glucose without being able to oxidize the 2-keto acid (Entner and Stanier, 1951). Since α-ketoglutaric acid is also the end product of the oxidation of aromatic and hydroaromatic compounds (see sec. 7), it seems likely that (either directly or after amination to glutamic acid) it is assimilated readily by the cells.

The clarity of the sugar oxidations was greatly enhanced by the discovery of "Acetobacter suboxydans," now *Acetomonas oxydans*, an organism that does not "overoxidize" the products (Kluyver and de Leeuw, 1924; Visser t'Hooft, 1925). Not only does this bacterium not oxidize acetic acid at all, but it does not oxidize 5-keto-gluconic acid, so that in four-day-old cultures its conversion of glucose to 5-keto-gluconic acid is virtually 100 per cent (Kluyver and Boezaardt, 1938). That the lactone is intermediate was noted above. Gluconic acid is similarly converted.

A 2-keto acid is also formed from arabonic acid by *Ps. saccharophila* (Palleroni and Doudoroff, 1957). This is not an oxidation but a dehydration like that of phosphogluconic acid caused by this and other pseudomonads (p. 453). The resulting 2-keto-3-deoxy-arabonic acid splits to yield pyruvic and glycolic acids, and the whole reaction may well be more general, both as to the substrates attacked and the organisms carrying it out.

Some Acetobacters contain many of the enzymes active in glucose fermentation. Thus, *A. suboxydans* and *A. rancens* var. *pasteurianum* could convert hexosediphosphate to triose, acetaldehyde, and acetate (Simon, 1930). These organisms, therefore, have all the enzymic outfit needed for conversion of glucose to vinegar. Anaerobically, in heavy suspensions, they can ferment glucose to alcohol and CO_2, an unusual fermentation for bacteria (cf. Chap. XI, sec. 10).

5. OXIDATIONS OF SUGAR ALCOHOLS: THE "SORBOSE BACTERIUM"

The berries of the rowan tree or European mountain ash, *Sorbus aucuparia*, yield the sugar alcohol sorbitol, $C_6H_{14}O_6$. Because certain samples of the berry juice yielded also the rare keto sugar *sorbose*, which is not present in the fresh juice, Bertrand (1904) subjected the juice to an extensive study, which turned out to be most illuminating. The fresh juice contained no sorbose, but did contain glucose (4.4 per cent). On setting aside, it underwent spontaneous fermentation by a yeast, which consumed most of the glucose, but formed no sorbose. This was followed by growth of a fine pellicle of "Mycoderma" which oxidized the alcohol formed by the yeast, and also by a Penicillium; neither of these, however, produced sorbose. Finally he observed that a Drosophila[2] visited the solution and laid eggs; almost immediately afterward a pellicle of a different type appeared—gelatinous and consistent, becoming greenish as it dried. Now the solution was highly reducing (to Fehling's solution) and contained quantities of sorbose.

Examination of the new pellicle showed it to be an almost pure culture of a rod-shaped bacterium, subsequently identified with *A. xylinum*. Bertrand found that the bacterium gave an 80 per cent yield of sorbose from sorbitol and that it also formed reducing sugars from other alcohols in yeast extract medium, including mannitol, erythritol,

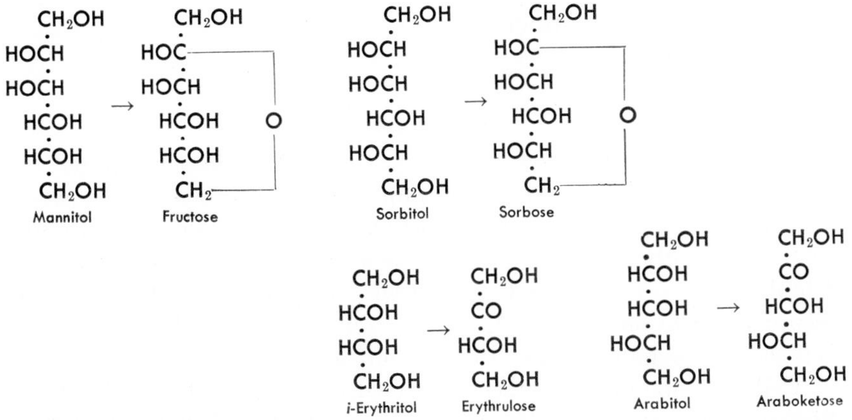

[2] Known as the vinegar fly, Drosophila feeds on decaying fruit, exuding tree sap, and other fermenting sugary materials, and on yeast itself; probably it stands in the same relation to Acetobacter as wasps do to Saccharomyces.

and arabitol. When grown on glucose, the reducing power of the solution disappears at first, due to formation of gluconic acid, but later it partly reappears, with the formation of 5-ketogluconic acid.

Later it was shown that the 7-carbon alcohol, α-glucoheptitol, is converted to a hitherto unknown sugar, D(-)-glucoheptulose (Bertrand and Nitzberg, 1928):

$$
\begin{array}{ccc}
\text{CH}_2\text{OH} & \text{CH}_2\text{OH} & \text{CH}_2\text{OH} \\
\text{HCOH} & \text{CO} & \text{HOC}\!\!-\!\!\rule{0pt}{0pt} \\
\text{HCOH} & \text{HCOH} & \text{HCOH} \\
\text{HOCH} \;\rightarrow\; \text{HOCH} & \text{or} \quad \text{HOCH} \quad \text{O} \\
\text{HCOH} & \text{HCOH} & \text{HCOH} \\
\text{HCOH} & \text{HCOH} & \text{HC}\!\!-\!\!\rule{0pt}{0pt} \\
\text{CH}_2\text{OH} & \text{CH}_2\text{OH} & \text{CH}_2\text{OH}
\end{array}
$$

Related compounds differing only in steric arrangement, such as xylitol and dulcitol, were not attacked. From all these observations, therefore, Bertrand deduced that the OH group can be oxidized only if it is next to the terminal position and also *adjacent* to another OH group; a pair of OH groups in positions 2 and 3 (or 4 and 5) must be in the *cis* position to be susceptible of oxidation.

$$
\begin{array}{cc}
\text{CH}_2\text{OH} & \text{CH}_2\text{OH} \\
| & | \\
\text{HOCH} & \text{HCOH} \\
| & | \\
\text{HCOH} & \text{HOCH} \\
| & | \\
\text{HCOH} & \text{HCOH} \\
| & | \\
\text{HOCH} & \text{CH}_2\text{OH} \\
| & \\
\text{CH}_2\text{OH} & \\
\text{Dulcitol} & \text{Xylitol} \\
\text{(not attacked)} &
\end{array}
$$

It will be noted that the formation of 5-ketogluconic acid (p. 559) is in accordance with the rule; 2-ketogluconic acid is, however, an exception. There are other exceptions too (see Hann, Tilden, and Hudson, 1938), especially outside the acetic bacteria; a Pseudomonas can form dehydrogenases for dulcitol and iditol (both with the terminal OH groups *trans* to one another), and *E. coli* forms a similar enzyme for dulcitol-1-phosphate (Shaw, 1956; Wolff and Kaplan, 1956).

Cell-free enzymes have been obtained for many of these oxidations. *Acetomonas oxydans* yields two different mannitol dehydrogenases, one active at pH 5 and linked to cytochrome in particles, the other with optimum at pH 8, soluble and reducing DPN (Arcus and Edson,

1956; cf. the two glucose dehydrogenases above). *E. coli* apparently carries out the same oxidations *via* the phosphates, because when it is grown on the alcohols, enzymes reducing DPN with mannitol-1-phosphate, sorbitol-6-phosphate, and dulcitol-1-phosphate are developed (Wolff and Kaplan, 1956). The first-named, which forms fructose-6-phosphate, was purified; it is probably the basis for the utilization of mannitol by Streptococci and Pneumococci also (p. 463).

The conversion of sorbitol to sorbose in high yield has become of importance in the industrial manufacture of ascorbic acid (vitamin C), which is prepared by oxidizing sorbose. Since naturally occurring sorbose is rare, its production from sorbitol is essential. Besides *A. xylinum,* Acetomonas strains also give good yields of sorbose (Bernhauer and Görlich, 1935; Boeseken and Leefers, 1935). The D-forms, but not the L-forms, of many sugar alcohols are oxidized by Acetomonas according to Bertrand's rule (Hann *et al.,* 1938), and it is evident that the rule is an expression of a reaction mechanism characteristic for the acetic bacteria but not for other groups.

6. PHYSIOLOGICAL GROUPING OF ACETOBACTER TYPES

As with other bacteria, the same Acetobacter has often been isolated under different names, while different cultures have sometimes been given the same name. For example, *A. aceti* Hansen is not the same as *A. aceti* Beijerinck and two organisms named *A. ascendens* have quite different properties. Many of the characters described are not permanent; for example, "*A. pasteurianum*" contained a starchlike compound staining blue with iodine (cf. p. 529), but this seems to be lost on continued culture, and the resulting organism is then indistinguishable from *A. rancens* (Frateur, 1950).

Apart from minor morphological differences and flagellation, it is the biochemical characters that are most characteristic. These may vary slightly with age, for *Acetomonas oxydans* in very young cultures oxidizes glucose to CO_2, but in older cultures converts it only to 5-ketogluconic acid (Butlin, 1938; Kluyver and Boezaardt, 1938). In general, however, the biochemical properties are fairly stable. The yields of various acids, ketones, sorbose, and so on, obtained after three to four months' incubation, show a continuous series of increasing oxidizing power from *A. gluconicum* (probably a variety of *Acetomonas*) to *A. ascendens* (Hermann and Neuschul, 1931).

A much more extensive series has been worked out by Frateur (1950), using Kluyver's extensive collection of Acetobacters. This

TABLE XVI-1. General Physiology of the Species of *Acetobacter* and *Acetomonas*

(According to Frateur, 1950, modified)

Group	Organism	Catalase	Oxidation of Acetate and Lactate	Ketone* Formation	Gluconic Acid Formation	Ability to grow on NH_4' as Sole N Source in an Alcohol Medium†	Other
Peroxydans	*A. paradoxum*	−	++	−	−	−	
	A. peroxydans	−	+	−	−	+	
Oxydans	*A. ascendens*	+	++	−	−	−	Turbidity in beer
	A. rancens (6 varieties)‡	++	++	(+)	++	+	
	A. lovaniense	++	} ++	(+)	++	+	
Mesoxydans	*A. mesoxydans*§ (4 varieties)	+	+	+	+	−	
	A. xylinum (3 varieties)	++	} may be slow ++	++	++		Thick cellulosic veil Some form brown pigment
	A. aceti	++	++	++	++	+	
Suboxydans (*Acetomonas*)	*Acetomonas oxydans* (4 varieties)	+	−	+	} abundant +		Polarly flagellate
	Acetomonas melanogenum‖ (3 varieties)	+	−	+#	+		Brown-black pigment on 10% glucose-yeast agar

* Ketone formation established qualitatively by (1) conversion of 2 per cent glycerol to dihydroxyacetone, (2) conversion of 2 per cent mannitol to levulose, (3) conversion of 10 per cent glucose (with 3 per cent $CaCO_3$) to 5-ketogluconate and 2-ketogluconate. The sign (+) means that some strains produce small amounts of 2-ketogluconate (Frateur et al., 1954).

† I.e., alcohol the sole carbon source.

‡ Including the one formerly called *A. pasteurianum*.

§ Two of the varieties grow rapidly on beer, and two (including one formerly called *A. orleanense*) very slowly.

‖ Probably not a distinct species.

Forms 2,5-diketogluconic acid (Katznelson et al., 1953).

makes possible a classification based primarily on the oxidizing power. Frateur's system is summarized in Table XVI–1. The most oxidizing species do not form ketones or gluconic acid, because the oxidations go to CO_2 and water; the least oxidizing species, which give good yields of ketones and gluconic acid, cannot attack acetate or lactate. Some strains of the Oxydans group form a little 2-ketogluconic acid (Frateur et al., 1954). The absence of catalase in the Peroxydans group does not mean a flavoprotein type of respiration as in the Lactobacilli, because the respiration is inhibited by cyanide and azide, and there is no detectable accumulation of H_2O_2. Probably the oxidizing enzyme is cytochrome peroxidase (Lenhoff and Kaplan, 1956).

The ability to grow on a mineral medium, with nitrogen derived only from NH_4^+ and carbon derived only from alcohol, is a valuable criterion, especially for A. aceti, but has of course no relation to the oxidations; it relates only to the synthetic abilities of the organisms. Many Acetobacters require preformed amino acids and vitamins in the medium, while some, like A. melanogenum, can form all needed amino acids from ammonium, but require several vitamins (Foda and Vaughn, 1953).

7. THE FORMATION OF CELLULOSE

One of the striking properties of these bacteria is the ability to produce cellulose. The material has been pictured in Figure III–2, and here we need only mention its bacteriological and biochemical aspects.

Cellulose formation is limited to A. xylinum and the related A. acetigenum (which Frateur considers a variety of xylinum). The cellulose fibrils, which do not differ in any major respect from the fibrils formed in plant cell walls, are not in the bacterial wall but outside it. They form a tangled mass at the surface of the medium. In some media they become impregnated with nitrogenous material and, consequently, when tannic acid is added, they form a heavy insoluble mass; in World War I it was even proposed to make "bacterial leather" in this way.

In order to deposit the insoluble cellulose fibrils outside the cell, a soluble precursor that can polymerize has to be excreted. When the cells take up C^{14}-glucose, the isotope is transferred to the cellulose— the C_6 position almost 100 per cent, the C_1 and C_2 less completely, due to being partly oxidized away (Schramm et al., 1957). This shows that polymerization of glucose units is the source of cellulose. But the precursor is not an oligosaccharide nor a sugar phosphate, although these are excreted to some extent (Walker and Wright, 1957; Ziegler and Weigl, 1959). Instead, extracts of *Acetobacter xylinum*, on mixing with an ultrafiltrate from the cells, deposit microfibrils insoluble in alkali and apparently true cellulose (Colvin, 1959; Khan and Colvin, 1961). The active extracts are *soluble in alcohol* and contain a complex of glucose and an aliphatic alcohol, approximately $C_{28}H_{58}O_3$; the ultra-filtrate contains an enzyme. *A. acetigenum* behaves similarly (Brown and Gascoigne, 1960). Thus the cells take up glucose, combine it with lipid to form precursor, probably at the cell membrane, and excrete it together with an enzyme that removes the hexose residues and orients them into fibrils. This ready excretion may be connected with the presence of small modified areas on the cell surface (Webb and Colvin, 1962, 1963). The lipid is then reabsorbed.

The whole remarkable phenomenon may be a model for the excretion of polysaccharide and polyuronide capsules, as well as the sheaths of Chlamydobacteria (Chap. XXII) and Myxophyceae.

8. OXIDATIONS OF AROMATIC AND HYDROAROMATIC COMPOUNDS

Under this head, oxidations brought about by Acetobacter, Pseudomonas, Vibrio, and certain other organisms will be treated together.

It was first shown by Beijerinck (1900) that an Actinomycete (obtained from tree roots) produces a brown pigment on gelatin media and at the same time hardens the gelatin and makes it insoluble in hot water. This phenomenon was traced to the formation of benzo-quinone by the organism as an oxidation product of an amino acid. Evidently the Actinomycete is oxidizing the side-chain of aromatic amino acids (just as "*B. coli phenologenes*," p. 345) and at the same introducing extra OH groups into the benzene ring to form either catechol or quinol, which is then oxidized to the ortho- or para-quinone:

Similar steps occur in the formation of melanin from tyrosine (p. 332), although this Actinomycete does not attack tyrosine. It also cannot attack the final quinone, which accumulates.

A more powerful oxidation is exerted by *Pseudomonas fluorescens*, which oxidizes several aromatic acids to straight-chain aliphatic compounds. This action is inducible; cells grown on yeast extract and suspended in the aromatic acid take up oxygen at only the basal rate for a time, but then suddenly increase their respiration (Fig. XVI–1*A*).

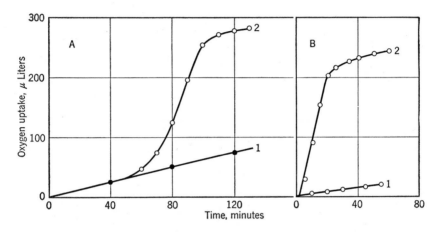

FIGURE XVI–1

Oxygen consumption of *Ps. fluorescens* alone and in the presence of 2 micromoles of benzoate.

Curve 1. Endogenous. Curve 2. Benzoate.

A. Organisms grown on yeast-extract agar. B. Organisms grown on mineral-benzoate agar.

(From R. Y. Stanier, *J. Bact.*, **54**:339–348, 1947. By courtesy of the Williams & Wilkins Co., Baltimore, Md.)

If grown on the acid as sole carbon source, they are "preinduced" and oxidize it without any delay (Fig. XVI–1*B*). The induction can be prevented by antibiotics, or hastened by supplying ammonium and succinate (Bernheim and de Turk, 1953). Evidently it does not differ from induced enzyme formation in general (Chap. XX, sec. 5). The phenomenon was used by Stanier (1947) to study the pathway of oxidation. For example, if mandelic acid is oxidized by way of benzoic acid, then cells preinduced to oxidize mandelate must also be preinduced to benzoate, but not vice versa.

CHOHCOOH   CHO   COOH

$\frac{1}{2}$ O₂ $\frac{1}{2}$ O₂   → ?

+ CO₂

Mandelic acid   Benzaldehyde   Benzoic acid

Figure XVI–2 shows two examples of the "sequential induction." At the left, cells grown on parahydroxybenzoate are seen to oxidize para-hydroxybenzoate without delay, while the other acids are attacked only after an induction period. (Note that complete oxidation of the substrates requires 310 to 400 microliters of O_2.) At the right, cells grown on mandelate attack both mandelate and benzoate without delay. Evidently benzoic acid lies on the oxidation path of mandelic, but parahydroxybenzoic acid does not. Phenylacetic acid was similarly shown to be oxidized without going via either of the others. A vibrio,

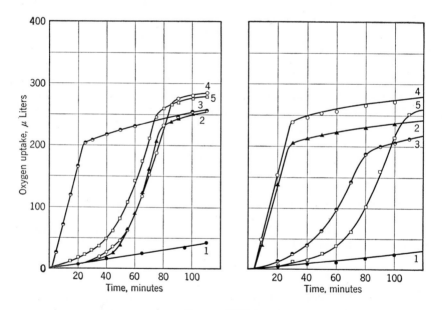

FIGURE XVI-2

Oxygen consumption of *Ps. fluorescens*, showing "sequential induction" by aromatic substrates.

Curve 1, endogenous; *Curve 2*, benzoate; *Curve 3*, parahydroxybenzoate; *Curve 4*, mandelate; *Curve 5*, phenylacetate.

Left. Organisms grown on parahydroxybenzoate. *Right*. Organisms grown on mandelate.

(From R. Y. Stanier, *J. Bact.*, **54**:339–348, 1947. By courtesy of the Williams & Wilkins Co., Baltimore, Md.)

"OI," and another soil rod produce a similar set of induced or adaptive enzymes (Parr *et al.*, 1949; see Elsden and Peel, 1958).

Further study of the same sort has shown that benzoic acid, phenol, and also anthranilic acid are all oxidized to catechol. If benzoic acid isotope-labeled in the carboxyl is used, unlabeled catechol results, but benzoic acid labeled at C-1 gives rise to catechol labeled at C-1 and C-2 (Sleeper, 1951). The carboxyl group is thus evidently replaced by OH, and then a second OH inserted (Parr *et al.*, 1949):

However, this is not the only route, since in another organism salicylic acid is an intermediate (Bhat *et al.*, 1959).

Catechol in turn is oxidized by two different routes. The first, by a pair of enzymes extracted from *Ps. fluorescens* (Hayaishi and Hashimoto, 1950; Evans and Smith, 1951) or *Vibrio OI* (Parr *et al.*, 1949), splits the ring *between* the two OH groups to form *cis-cis*-muconic acid and thence β-keto-adipic acid (which finally yields succinate and acetyl-CoA). The second, by an enzyme obtained from two Pseudomonads, splits the ring bond *adjacent* to one of the OH groups, to form α-hydroxy-muconic semi-aldehyde and thence pyruvate (see Dagley *et al.*, 1960):

The latter organisms do not attack *cis-cis*-muconic acid.

Protocatechuic acid, which is 4-carboxy-catechol, yields the carboxylated analogues in each case; some Pseudomonads produce β-carboxy-*cis-cis*-muconic acid (MacDonald *et al.*, 1954; Gross *et al.*, 1956), while others form the γ-carboxy derivative of α-hydroxy-muconic semialdehyde (Dagley *et al.*, 1960). The former compound yields β-keto-adipic acid (via muconic acid lactone and two other routes), while the latter splits to oxalacetic and lactic acids. The conversion of protocatechuic to oxalic acid by *Asp. niger* (Bernhauer and Waelsch, 1932) suggests the latter route. Meta- and para-hydroxy-benzoic acids follow the first route, yielding β-keto-adipic acid; each first adds a hydroxyl to form protocatechuic acid, which is further oxidized as above.

Phenylacetic acid lies on a separate pathway, because cells that can oxidize it require a further induction period to oxidize benzoate (Dagley *et al.*, 1952). Again there are two routes, both taken by strains of *Ps. fluorescens*; one goes via the 3,4- and the other by the 2,5-dihydroxy acid (Kunita, 1955). The latter is homogentisic acid (see below).

Since mandelic acid is oxidized to benzoic acid (Fig. XVI–2), probably via benzoylformic acid and benzaldehyde, and since anthranilic acid can be formed by the oxidation of tryptophan, a large number of oxidation pathways for aromatic compounds are known, as on page 571. The muconic semialdehyde routes are omitted, for clarity.

Tyrosine and phenylalanine lie on a different pathway (Stanier, 1950) since tyrosine is oxidized first to DOPA (see p. 332) and thence to 2,5-dihydroxy-phenylacetic, or homogentisic acid. This is split to maleyl-acetoacetic and finally yields fumarate and acetoacetate. *Ps. fluorescens* and Vibrio OI when adapted to oxidize tyrosine also oxidize homogentisate, and young cultures accumulate the latter (Dagley *et al.*, 1952; Chapman and Dagley, 1960). Gentisic acid, with one CH_2 group less, behaves similarly, yielding maleyl-pyruvate and hence fumarate and pyruvate (Lack, 1959; Dagley *et al.*, 1960). These reactions of gentisic acid are important because it is itself an oxidation product of salicylic and metahydroxybenzoic acids by *Ps. fluorescens* (see diagram).

In general these oxidations follow recognizable patterns; introduction of OH groups, splitting the benzene ring in two ways as noted above, and stepwise oxidation and decarboxylation of the aliphatic products. Many of the oxidases have been prepared cell-free, and in some cases work with bacteria has been paralleled by feeding experiments with animals.

A few Pseudomonads and many Mycobacteria can oxidize the aromatic hydrocarbons themselves, in spite of their insolubility in water, as well as the phenols, which are normally very toxic (Tausson,

1927; Gray and Thornton, 1928). Application of the sequential induction technique to the attack of naphthalene by five of these has shown that when grown on succinate, they oxidized naphthalene only after a lag, but when grown on naphthalene, they all oxidized it immediately (Treccani *et al.*, 1954). They also oxidized the 1:2 diol, **I**, salicylic acid, **II**, and catechol, **III**. Only two of them oxidized α- and β-naphthol (**IV** *and* **V**), and since also these two compounds did not support growth, it is concluded that they are not on the direct oxidation route. Indeed, the addition of the naphthols actually decreases the oxidation of naphthalene. Presence of **I, II,** and **III** could all be detected in the medium after growth on naphthalene. The route is therefore as shown, and the last product, catechol, **III,** brings us back to the benzene series above.

Growth on aliphatic hydrocarbons, by contrast, is mainly limited to the Mycobacteria and Nocardias (Chap. II, secs. 3 and 4). In these cases the study of phenyl-substituted hydrocarbons has made clear that the mode of attack is by repeated β-oxidation (Webley *et al.*, 1956). However, *Ps. aeruginosa* can dehydrogenate n-heptane to hepta-1-ene, using DPN as H acceptor (Chouteau *et al.*, 1962). The complex hydrocarbon structure of rubber can also be oxidatively attacked, mainly by fungi and Streptomycetes (Rook, 1955).

Many hydroaromatic compounds are also oxidized. These compounds are derivatives of cyclohexane and include myo-inositol, $C_6H_6(OH)_6$, an essential growth factor for many bacteria and fungi. Some of them act as intermediates in the formation of aromatic compounds (see sec. 9), to which they are readily oxidized. Thus, quinic acid, $C_6H_7(OH)_4COOH$, is oxidized to protocatechuic acid or catechol by *Ps. fluorescens, Ps. calcoacetica,* and *Ps. aromatica* (Beijerinck, 1911b), *A. gluconicum,* and several fungi (Bernhauer and Waelsch, 1932; Bernhauer and Gorlich, 1935); quercitol is oxidized to pyrogallol. Inositols are also oxidized to mono- and di-ketones, apparently following rules suggestive of Bertrand's rule (see Rao, 1957, for summary).

The halophilic organism, *Ps. beijerinckii*, isolated from salted beans (12 per cent NaCl), turns the beans bright purple (Hof, 1935). The pigment was produced only on a medium containing aqueous bean extract, the essential component of which turned out to be myo-inositol (Kluyver *et al.*, 1939). Although not fully proved, the purple pigment is probably the Ca salt of tetrahydroxy-quinone:

$$\text{HOH} \quad \text{HOH} \quad \xrightarrow{2 \ O_2} \quad \text{tetrahydroxy-quinone} \quad + \ 4 \ H_2O$$

This compound is further oxidized in air to a colorless substance; correspondingly the beans, or their extract, fade on boiling. A mono- or di-ketoinositol would probably be an intermediate in the oxidation.

9. BACTERIAL SYNTHESIS OF AROMATIC COMPOUNDS

A parallel development of recent years has been the understanding of how bacteria synthesize aromatic compounds. This has benefited from the work on hydroaromatics (above), but mainly developed from the finding that a number of mutants of *E. coli* require tyrosine, phenylalanine, tryptophan, *p*-aminobenzoate or *p*-hydroxybenzoate (Davis, 1950). Some require more than one such compound for normal growth. These strains evidently fail to form the benzene ring, and in several cases they accumulate significant intermediate compounds in the medium; the identification of these and study of their metabolism by other mutants (largely due to B. D. Davis and his co-workers) have made it possible to construct the route of biosynthesis of the benzene ring in bacteria.

A crucial step was the recognition of 5-dehydroquinic acid, **VII,** which is accumulated by several aromatic acid-requiring mutants growing on sugar (Davis and Weiss, 1953) and is therefore considered to lie on the direct pathway. Shikimic acid, **IX** (then known only from plants), was recognized in a similar way. A specific enzyme common in bacteria, yeasts, and higher plants converts **VII** by loss of water to 5-dehydroshikimic acid, **VIII.** This substance and its reduced product, shikimic acid, **IX,** can satisfy the requirement of some mutants for two or more aromatic compounds and are therefore doubtless also on the direct pathway (Davis, 1952). Since these compounds contain 7 carbon atoms they obviously are not formed directly from hexose, but they arise from the 7-carbon sugar, sedoheptulose. Sedoheptulose-7-phosphate and the 1,7-diphosphate were slowly converted to shikimic acid by a cell-free system prepared from the *E. coli* mutant, 83-2, which accumulates this acid. However, a mixture of the 4-carbon and 3-carbon compounds, erythrose-4-phosphate and phospho-enol-pyruvate, was much more effective, giving 88 per cent conversion to dehydroshikimic acid in one hour. Closer study of this system with purified enzymes showed that the initial condensation product was a new 7-carbon acid, 2-keto,3-deoxy-D-araboheptonic acid 7-phosphate, **VI**, and that this then cyclizes to 5-dehydroquinic acid, **VII** (Srinivasan *et al.*, 1959):

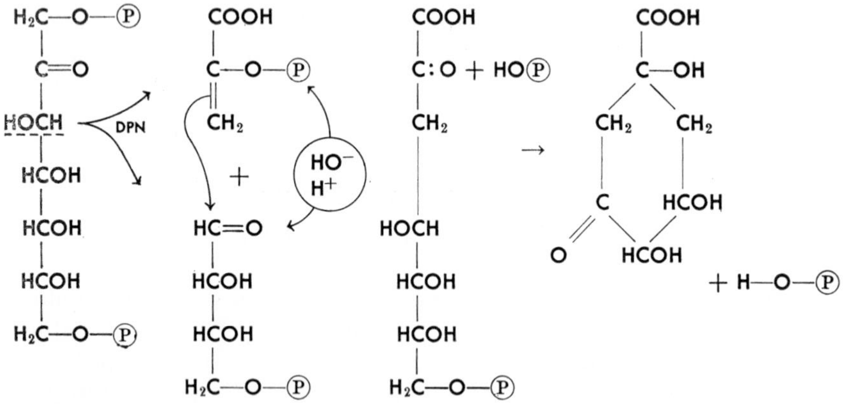

Sedoheptulose 1,7-diphosphate — Phosphopyruvate + erythrose-4-phosphate — VI — VII 5-Dehydroquinic acid

This, then, is the elusive reaction in which the 6-carbon ring is first formed. The condensation is shown as due to a hydrolysis, the phosphate radical of pyruvic acid attracting a hydroxyl, which drives the electrons toward the carbon, liberating the phosphate and setting up a bond to the carbon-1 of the erythrose, which has combined with the proton. The formation of phosphoenolpyruvic acid from the first 3 C-atoms of the heptulose proceeds as described in Chapter XI, section 8. Direct connection of the whole scheme with pentose metabolism is provided by the formation of the acid **VI** by *E. coli* from ribose 5-phosphate (Weissbach and Hurwitz, 1959).

The steps beyond **VII**, also elucidated by the use of *E. coli* mutants, are:

The step from **VII** to **VIII** is due to a single enzyme, purified from *E. coli* 83-2 or W, and also present in an Aerobacter that can grow on quinic acid (Mitsuhashi and Davis, 1954). The reactions from shikimic acid via prephenic to phenylpyruvic, involving addition of pyruvic acid and loss of CO_2 and water, are no doubt multiple; they take place nonenzymatically by heating with acid (Gilvarg, 1955). The conversion of **IX** to **X** entails phosphorylation at the 5 position; it is this which activates the shikimic acid to condense with pyruvic. The 5-phospho-derivative also reacts in several other ways.

Quinic acid is interconverted with its 5-dehydro-form by a dehydrogenase present in Aerobacter. This acid does not lie on the main pathway, although it occurs fairly widely in plants.

In this section we have come a long way from the simple oxidation of alcohol to acetic acid and have moved away from the acetic bacteria to the coliforms, but the path of research in this area, though perhaps a winding one, has been continuous and logical.

REFERENCES

Arcus, R. C., and Edson, N. L. 1956. *Biochem. J.*, **64**:585–594.
Beijerinck, M. W. 1899. *Arch. Néerl. Sci. Exactes Nat.*, **2**:180–189.
Beijerinck, M. W. 1900. *Arch. Néerl. Sci. Exactes Nat.*, **2**:327–340.
Beijerinck, M. W. 1911a. *Zentr. Bakt.*, II **29**:169–176.
Beijerinck, M. W. 1911b. *Proc. Kon. Akad. Wetensch. Amsterdam*, **13**:1066–1077.
Bernhauer, K., and Görlich, B. 1935. *Biochem. Z.*, **280**:367–374, 394–395.

*Bernhauer, K., and Waelsch, H. 1932. *Biochem. Z.*, **249**:223–226 (and literature there cited).

Bernheim, F., and de Turk, W. E. 1953. *J. Bact.*, **65**:65–68.

Bertrand, G. 1904. *Ann. Chim. et Phys. 8éme Ser.*, **3**:181–288.

Bertrand, G., and Nitzberg, G. 1928. *Bull. soc. chim. 4éme Ser.*, **43**:663–667, 1019–1923.

Bhat, M. G.; Ramakrishman, T.; and Bhat, J. V. 1959. *Canad. J. Microbiol.*, **5**: 109–118.

Boeseken, J., and Leefers, J. L. 1935. *Rec. trav. chim. Pays-Bas*, **54**:861–865.

Brown, A. J. 1886. *Trans. Chem. Soc. (London)*, **49**:172–187.

Brown, A. M., and Gascoigne, J. A. 1960. *Nature*, **187**:1010–1012.

Butlin, K. R. 1938. *Biochem. J.*, **32**:508–512.

Carr, J. G., and Shimwell, J. L. 1960. *Nature*, **186**:331–332.

Chapman, P. J., and Dagley, S. 1960. *Biochem. J.*, **75**:6 P.

Chouteau, J.; Azoulay, E.; and Senez, J. C. 1962. *Nature*, **194**:577–8.

Colvin, J. R. 1957–1959. *Arch. Biochem. Biophys.*, **70**:294–295; *Nature*, **183**:1135–1136 (1959).

Colvin, J. R.; Martin, S. M.; and Dearing, G. G. 1961. *Canad. J. Biochem. Physiol.*, **39**:493–497.

*Dagley, S.; Evans, W. C.; and Ribbons, D. W. 1960. *Nature*, **188**:560–566.

Dagley, S.; Fewster, M. E.; and Happold, F. C. 1952. *J. Bact.*, **62**:327–336.

Davis, B. D. 1950–1952. *Experientia*, **6**:41–50; *J. Bact.*, **64**:729–748, 749–763 (1952).

Davis, B. D., and Weiss, U. 1953. *Arch. exp. Path. Pharmakol.*, **220**:1–15.

*Elsden, S. R., and Peel, J. L. 1958. Metabolism of Carbohydrates. *Ann. Rev. Microbiol.*, **12**:144–202.

Entner, N., and Stanier, R. Y. 1951. *J. Bact.*, **62**:181–186.

Evans, W. C., and Smith, B. S. W. 1951. *Biochem. J.*, **49**:x; *Nature*, **168**:772.

Foda, I. O., and Vaughn, R. H. 1953. *J. Bact.*, **65**:79–82.

Frateur, J. 1950. *La Cellule*, **3**:287–392.

Frateur, J.; Simonart, P.; and Coulon, T. 1954. *Ant. van Leeuwenhoek*, **20**:111–128.

Gilvarg, C. 1955. In, Aminoacid Metabolism. Baltimore, Johns Hopkins Press, pp 812–816.

Gray, P. H. H., and Thornton, H. G. 1928. *Zentr. Bakt.*, **II 73**:74.

Gross, S. R.; Gafford, R. D.; and Tatum, E. L. 1956. *J. Biol. Chem.*, **219**:781–796.

Hann, R. M.; Tilden, E. B.; and Hudson, C. S. 1938. *J. Am. Chem. Soc.*, **60**:1201–1203.

Hansen, E. C. 1879. *Comptes rendus lab. Carlsberg*, **1**:49 pp.; 1895, *ibid.*, **3**:182–216; see Lafar's full abstr. in *Zentr. Bakt.*, **II 1**:31–37.

Hayaishi, O., and Hashimoto, K. 1950. *Med. J. Osaka Univ.*, **2**:33; *J. Biochem.* (Japan), **37**:371–374.

Henneberg, C. 1909. Gärungsbakteriol. Praktikum. Berlin.

Hermann, S., and Neuschul, P. 1931. *Biochem. Z.*, **233**:129–216.

Hof, T. 1935. *Rec. trav. bot. Néerl.*, **32**:92–173.

Janke, A., and Kropacsy, S. 1935. *Biochem. Z.*, **277**:268–272; **278**:30–36, 37–59.

Katznelson, H.; Tanenbaum, S. W.; and Tatum, E. L. 1953. *J. Biol. Chem.*, **204**:43–59.

Keilin, D., and Hartree, E. F. 1945. *Biochem. J.*, **39**:293–301.

Khan, A. W., and Colvin, J. R. 1961. *Science*, **133**:2014–2015.

King, T. E., and Cheldelin, V. H. 1957–1958. *J. Biol. Chem.*, **224**:579–590; *Biochem. J.*, **68**:31P. (1958).

Kluyver, A. J., and Boezaardt, A. G. J. 1938. *Rec. trav. chim. Pays-Bas*, **57**:609–615.

Kluyver, A. J.; Hof, T.; and Boezaardt, A. G. J. 1939. *Enzymologia*, **7**:257–272.

*Kluyver, A. J., and de Leeuw, F. J. G. 1924. *Tijdschr. vergelijk. Geneeskunde*, **10**:Afl. 2–3.

*Kornberg, H. L. 1959. *Ann. Rev. Microbiol.*, **13**:49–78.

Krebs, H. A.; Gurin, S.; and Eggleston, L. V. 1952. *Biochem. J.*, **51**:614–628.

Kubowitz, F., and Haas, A. R. 1932. *Biochem. Z.*, **255**:247–277.

Kunita, N. 1955. *Med. J. Osaka Univ.*, **6**:697–702, 703–708.

Lack, L. 1959. *Biochim. Biophys. Acta*, **34**:117–123.

Leifson, E. 1954. *Ant. v. Leeuwenhoek*, **20**:102–110; cf. Shimwell, J. L. *Ibid.*, **24**:187–192 (1958).

Lenhoff, H. M., and Kaplan, N. O. 1956. *J. Biol. Chem.*, **220**:967–982.

Lockwood, L. B., and Nelson, G. E. N. 1946. *J. Bact.*, **52**:581–586.

Lockwood, L. B., and Stodola, F. H. 1946. *J. Biol. Chem.*, **164**:81–83.

Lockwood, L. B.; Tabenkin, B.; and Ward, G. E. 1941. *J. Bact.*, **42**:51–61.

*Lodder, J. 1934. Die anaskosporogenen Hefen. *Verhandel. Kon. Akad. Wetensch. Amsterdam*, **32**:256 pp.

MacDonald, D. L.; Stanier, R. Y.; and Ingraham, J. L. 1954. *J. Biol. Chem.*, **210**: 809–820.

Mitsuhashi, S., and Davis, B. D., 1954. *Biochim. Biophys. Acta*, **15**:54–61.

Neuberg, C., and Windisch, F. 1925. *Biochem. Z.*, **166**:454–481.

Palleroni, N. J., and Doudoroff, M. 1957. *J. Bact.*, **74**:180–185.

Parr, W. H.; Evans, R. A.; and Evans, W. C. 1949. *Biochem. J.*, **45**:xxix–xxx; cf. Smith, B. S. W.; Jones, J. D.; and Evans, W. C. 1952. *Ibid.*, **50**:xxviii.

Pasteur, L. 1868. Etudes sur le Vinaigre. Paris.

Peters, B. G. 1928. *J. Helminthol.*, **6**:1–38.

Racker, E. 1949. *J. Biol. Chem*, **177**:883–892.

*Rao, M. R. R. 1957. Acetic acid bacteria. *Ann. Rev. Microbiol.*, **11**:317–338.

Rook, J. J. 1955. *Applied Microbiol.*, **3**:302–309.

Schramm, M.; Grommet, Z.; and Hestrin, S. 1957. *Nature*, **179**:28–29; see also Hestrin, S., and Schramm, M. 1954. *Biochem. J.*, **58**:345–352.

Shaw, D. R. D. 1956. *Biochem. J.*, **64**:394–405.

Shimwell, J. L., and Carr, J. G. 1959. *Ant. v. Leeuwenhoek*, **25**:353–368.

Shimwell, J. L.; Carr, J. G.; and Rhodes, M. E. 1960. *J. Gen. Microbiol.*, **23**:283–286.

Simon, E. 1930. *Biochem. Z.*, **224**:253–291.

Sleeper, B. P. 1951. *J. Bact.*, **62**:657–662.

Srinivasan, P. R.; Katagiri, M.; and Sprinson, D. B. 1959. *J. Biol. Chem.*, **234**:713–715; Srinivasan, P. R., and Sprinson, D. B. *Ibid.*, pp. 716–727.

Stanier, R. Y. 1947. *J. Bact.*, **54**:191–194, 339–348.

Stanier, R. Y. 1950. Problems of Bacterial Oxidative Metabolism. *Bact. Revs.* **14**: 179–191.

Tanaka, Kyoshi. 1933. *Acta Phytochim. (Japan)*, **7**:265–297.

Tanaka, Kyoshi. 1935. *Acta Phytochim. (Japan)*, **8**:285–313.

Tausson, W. O. 1927. *Planta*, **4**:214–256.

Treccani, V.; Walker, N.; and Wiltshire, G. H. 1954. *J. Gen. Microbiol.*, **11**:341–348.

Visser 't Hooft, F. 1925. Biochemische onderzoekingen over het geslacht Acetobacter. Dissertation, Delft.

Walker, T. K., and Wright, H. B. 1957. *Arch. Biochem. Biophys.*, **69**:361–371.

Webb, T. E., and Colvin, J. R. 1962. *Canad. J. Microbiol.*, **8**:841–846; **9**: (1963).

Webley, D. M.; Duff, R. B.; and Farmer, V. C. 1956. *Nature*, **178**:1467–1468.

Weissbach, A., and Hurwitz, J. 1959. *J. Biol. Chem.*, **234**:705–709.

Wieland, H., and Pistor, H. J. 1936. *Ann.*, **522**:116–137.

Wolff, J. B., and Kaplan, N. O. 1956. *J. Bact.*, **71**:557–564; *J. Biol. Chem.*, **218**: 849–869.

Ziegler, H., and Weigl, J. 1959. *Naturwiss.*, **46**:20.

CHAPTER XVII

The Breakdown of Disaccharides

and Polysaccharides

Let's talk of graves, of worms, and epitaphs;
Make dust our paper, and with rainy eyes
Write sorrow on the bosom of the earth.

SHAKESPEARE: *King Richard II*

1. BREAKDOWN OF DISACCHARIDES

A. The Disaccharidases

The disaccharides are in general attacked by bacteria only after hydrolysis to monosaccharides. The main exception to this rule occurs in the oxidation of sugars to -onic acids. Since this bacterial oxidation (p. 559) involves only one end of the sugar molecule, it is perhaps not surprising that it can take place when a carbon atom farther down the molecule is attached to a second saccharide. For example, maltose, which is 4-α-glucosidoglucose, is oxidized to maltobionic acid, and lactose to lactobionic acid, by certain Pseudomonads (*Ps. quercito-pyrogallica* and related species; Kluyver *et al.*, 1950). Apparently the bionic acids are slowly hydrolyzed after formation, and the resulting hexose and hexonic acid then further oxidized.

The fermentations, however, involve breakdown of the monosaccharide structure and require that the hexose (or pentose) be free. Hence, if a disaccharide is not hydrolyzed, it cannot usually be fermented. For this reason the ability to hydrolyze disaccharides is generally measured by their fermentation. Because this ability is highly characteristic for different organisms, it has been widely applied in the taxonomy of bacteria and fungi as well as in the bioassay of disaccharides. As seen in Chapter XIV, the coliform bacteria are

579

divided on the basis of lactose fermentation, Escherichia and Aerobacter attacking lactose, Proteus and Salmonella not. All four attack maltose. The increasing knowledge of bacterial genetics and of the control of enzyme formation (Chaps. XX and XXI) makes these separations less satisfactory.

At one time the hydrolyzing enzymes or disaccharidases of different organisms were used for the quantitative analysis of sugar mixtures. By determining the reducing power of the solution before and after fermentation by a series of species of Torulopsis, Monilia, and Saccharomyces, the amounts of glucose, fructose (or mannose), galactose, sucrose, and maltose could be determined (Kluyver and Hoogerheide, 1933; Harding and Nicholson, 1933; van Voorst, 1938–1939). These methods have now been superseded by chromatography; by suitable choice of solvents, the sugars can be cleanly separated as spots on paper, revealed by spraying with ammoniacal $AgNO_3$ or aniline, or eluted and the reducing power determined (see, e.g., Linskens, 1959).

The β-galactosidase of E. coli has been more extensively purified than any other such enzyme (probably to 98 per cent purity) and found very stable and specific (Cohn, 1957). It has a molecular weight of about 700,000, and 1 mole hydrolyzes some 4000 moles of the test substrate (o-nitrophenyl-β-galactoside) per second, a relatively high activity. Moreover, it not only hydrolyzes β-galactosides but also transfers galactose residues to other acceptors, forming trisaccharides, etc. The specificity varies somewhat with the monovalent ion used to activate the enzyme, activity on lactose being highest with K^+ and on nitrophenylgalactoside highest with Na^+. Apparently the enzymes of several E. coli strains, of Aerobacter, and Shigella are all the same, while those of yeast and Lactobacillus differ both immunologically and in their affinity to inhibitors.

Other disaccharidases are less well studied. The α-galactosidase of E. coli resembles its β-counterpart in that its formation is induced by substrates, like melibiose and raffinose (see below), but it cannot yet be obtained cell-free (Sheinin and Crocker, 1961), although it can be prepared from yeast. It is not highly specific in its substrates. Enzymes hydrolyzing maltose and other α-glucosides (hence α-glucosidases) are readily obtained from brewer's yeast or Aspergillus oryzae by autolyzing. They have their optimum pH at 4.5, while the bacterial enzymes act optimally at 6.5 to 7; differences in specificity also make it probable that these enzymes are not the same. Invertase again has been mainly studied from yeast (see Hestrin et al., 1955); it hydrolyzes sucrose, the β-fructoside linkage in raffinose, and some fructose polymers (inulins and levans) but does not attack β-galactosides or α-glucosides.

Like β-galactosidase, it can transfer fructose residues to other sugars and alcohols (see Chap. XX).

B. Induced Formation of the Enzymes

The disaccharidase content of an organism commonly varies in amount according to the medium used for culture. As long ago as 1899, Duclaux found that a strain of *Aspergillus niger* produced invertase when it was grown on a sucrose medium. Similarly, Aspergillus grown on a milk medium could hydrolyze casein, and yeast grown on a galactose medium could ferment galactose (Dienert, 1901). These phenomena were investigated systematically by Karström (1931, 1938), who found that certain enzymes were always present, irrespective of the medium, while others were formed only when the medium contained their substrate. The behavior of *Ln. mesenteroides* is shown in Table XVII–1. Glucose is fermented in all cases, but fermentation of the other sugars is in large part dependent on their presence in the growth medium. Note that growth in lactose permits the fermentation of galactose, but not vice versa; i.e., lactose leads to formation of the galactose-fermenting system *galactozymase* which has three constituents, an enzyme, uridine-diphosphoglucose as coenzyme, and DPN as hydrogen transferring agent (p. 467; cf. Kalekar and Maxwell, 1958). However, galactose does not lead to formation of the lactose-hydrolyzing enzyme β-galactosidase. *E. coli* gave similar results (Table XVII–1) and so have several yeasts (Kluyver and Custers, 1940).

Karström termed the enzymes that are always present "constitutive," and those that are formed only in the presence of the substrate "adaptive." The distinction is sometimes quantitative rather than qualitative, since cells grown in the absence of sucrose do hydrolyze sucrose slowly. Also, hydrolysis even of lactose may begin after a long induction time (see Table XVII–1, lower half); this time may be that needed to synthesize the enzyme. The term "adaptive" has since been replaced by "induced."

Induction, as we have seen in earlier chapters, is widespread and appears in the metabolism of almost every group of substances; indeed, there is reason to believe that in the bacteria all enzymes are interrelated with the induction process even when their formation is constitutive (see Chap. XX). Sometimes their formation can be induced not only by the substrate but also by a related compound. Genetic analysis has shown in several cases that the formation of an enzyme is controlled by a pair of genes at the same locus, i.e., "alleles," and that *inducible* is dominant over *constitutive*.

TABLE XVII–1. "Adaptive" Formation of Carbohydrases by *Leuconostoc mesenteroides* and *E. coli*

(From Karström, 1931)

(Figures in parentheses in lower table indicate the induction time in minutes before fermentation began. The whole experiment lasted 225 minutes.)

GROWTH MEDIUM CONTAINS:	LEUCONOSTOC ORGANISMS CAN THEN FERMENT:					
	Glucose (or Fructose)	Sucrose	Maltose	Lactose	Galactose	Arabinose
Glucose	+	(+)	0	0	0	0
Sucrose	+	+	0	0	0	0
Maltose	+	+	+	0	0	0
Lactose	+	+	0	+	+	0
Galactose	+	+	0	0	+	0
Arabinose	+	+	0	0	0	+
No sugars	+	+	+	0	0	0
	E. COLI					
Glucose	+*	(105)	0	(165)		0
Sucrose	+	+	0	0		
Maltose	+	+	+	0		
Lactose †	0†	0†	+†	+†		

* Also fructose and mannose.
† Another strain of *E. coli.*

In the present connection the inducible enzymes include not only the disaccharidases but also those attacking monosaccharides, such as the phosphorylase or kinase involved in the initial phosphorylation, or systems like that required for the galactose-glucose conversion in galactose-grown yeast (see p. 467). For example, *E. coli*, when grown on xylose, ferments xylose but not arabinose, and when grown on arabinose, it ferments arabinose but not xylose. Grown on glucose it ferments neither (Karström, 1931).

Sucrose occupies a special position since it need not be hydrolyzed, but can be phosphorylized. The enzyme *sucrose phosphorylase*, obtained from *Ps. saccharophila*, establishes equilibrium between glucose-1-phosphate and fructose, and sucrose and phosphate (Fig. XVII–1). Hence *Ps. saccharophila*, in which this enzyme is inducible, can synthesize sucrose from the mixture (Hassid *et al.*, 1944). It can also grow on sucrose or on trehalose and exhibits the curious behavior of oxidizing these faster than their constituent hexoses (Doudoroff, 1940). Similarly in *Ps. putrificans* the induced cells not merely oxidize but also *grow* faster on sucrose than on hexose (Doudoroff *et al.*, 1949). The reason in both cases is that the phosphorylative split occurs more readily than does direct phosphorylation of hexose. *Neisseria meningitidis* contains a maltose phosphorylase which acts similarly, forming glucose and glucose-1-phosphate (Fitting and Doudoroff, 1952).

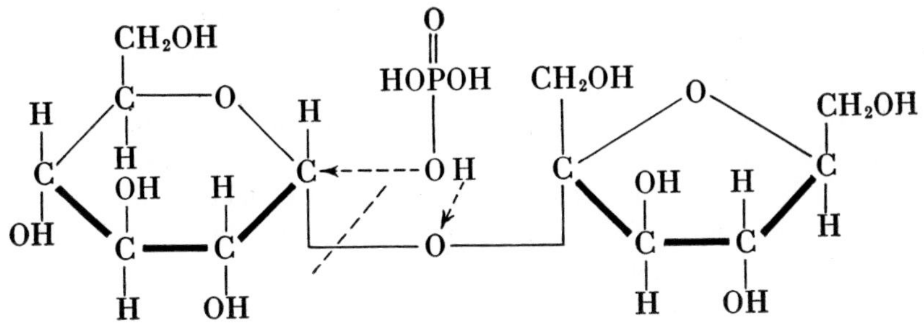

FIGURE XVII–1
Phosphorolysis of sucrose.

Two phenomena are involved in adaptation; they may be considered as "Darwinian" and "Lamarckian." The former is that of *selection*. If, out of the whole population in a culture, one or two cells mutate and begin to produce the enzyme for attacking the disaccharide, then when the disaccharide is added to the medium, these cells are greatly favored and multiply faster than the others. Suppose, for instance, that the favored cells are in a minority of one in a million, but that they divide every 20 minutes, while the others divide only once in an hour. Then we have:

	FAVORED	OTHERS
At start	1	10^6
After 1 hour	8	2×10^6
After 2 hours	64	4×10^6
After 10 hours	*ca.* 10^9	*ca.* 10^9
After 20 hours	10^{18}	10^{12}

In other words, the favored cells, after one day's culture, outnumber the others by a million to one.

The selection process undoubtedly underlies many of the earlier cases of adaptation. It is seldom as rapid as the above figures indicate and may require several transfers before the organisms are "trained" to utilize the new substrate. It requires, of course, that the organisms produce, in small numbers, mutant cells containing the new enzyme. This interpretation has been worked out in the classic case of "*B. coli mutabile*," a lactose-negative strain of *E. coli*, in which Neisser (1906) and Massini observed that old colonies on lactose-peptone agar produced daughter colonies, or "papillae," which could ferment lactose. The change was detected because the medium (Endo's agar) contained fuchsin sulfite; this turns deep pink in the presence of aldehydes and thus indicates whether the sugar is being fermented. In this case the white colonies, growing only on the peptone, developed pink papillae. The explanation is that the strain produces in every generation about two cells in 10^7 that can ferment lactose[1] (Lewis, 1934; Ryan, 1952). Presence of lactose in the medium naturally allows these to overgrow the others, and in a short time the whole culture is lactose-positive. Even in the absence of lactose, the bacteria can grow sufficiently on traces of impurities so that lactose-fermenting mutants can be produced (Ryan, 1952). The rate of mutation is not affected by the presence of lactose, nor indeed of any of a variety of related glucosides, but depends strictly on chance.

Mutation can of course occur in the opposite direction, producing lactose-negative strains; in *E. coli* K12 many different lactose-negative strains have been identified.

Adaptation to ferment lactose can also occur without cell multiplication. In these cases a new enzyme is being formed in the cells as a response to the substrate. This "Lamarckian" phenomenon is *induction* proper. It has been studied on enzymes of many types in addition to the disaccharidases, and is described in Chapter XX.

2. ACTION OF BACTERIA ON STARCH

Starch is attacked by so many organisms, both bacteria and fungi, that there can hardly be said to be a special microflora of starchy products. There are characteristic differences between products, however, as exemplified by Beijerinck's observation that certain samples of barley flour regularly underwent butanol fermentation, while others gave only butyric organisms, and still others only *Bac. polymyxa* (cf. Chap. XV). All these bacteria hydrolyze starch actively; so also do many other sporeformers, both aerobic and anaerobic, and many fungi, but very few yeasts. The ready attack on starch is probably due

[1] The mutation rate in other cases is nearer to 1 in 10^8 (cf. Chap. XIX, sec. 5).

to its similarity to glycogen, which is a true storage and reserve product in many bacteria (cf. Strange *et al.*, 1961; Madsen, 1963).

Understanding of the nature of starch is essential to an understanding of its attack by microorganisms. Its structure depends on the following facts (Myrbäck, 1948):

(1) Starch contains two constituents; *amylose*, a straight chain polymer containing about 200 to 300 glucose units, and *amylopectin*, a branched structure of molecular weight greater than that of amylose and containing phosphate groups. Similar to amylopectin is the glycogen of animal tissue and many plant starches which turn red with iodine, as, for instance, that in Oscillatoria (Hough *et al.*, 1952).

(2) When starch is hydrolyzed by enzymes, maltose and glucose are the only reducing sugars produced. Since glucose is produced from maltose by hydrolysis, it is deduced that both amylose and amylopectin consist of large numbers of maltose units linked together.

(3) When starch is fully methylated, so that all free hydroxy groups have reacted, and is then hydrolyzed, 2, 3, 6-trimethyl glucose is nearly the entire product. It follows that almost all the molecules are linked through the 1-4 positions. Amylopectin, however, yields a little 2,3-dimethylglucose, which shows that a few of its hexose units are linked at *both* the 4 and the 6 positions. These introduce "branch points" into the chain. Also, in both constituents the few terminal units yield a little tetramethyl glucose. Hence amylose must be a polymer of 1:4-linked α-glucose units, and amylopectin the same with occasional 1–6 links in addition.

Starch-hydrolyzing enzymes or amylases are of two kinds. The commonest, called α-amylase, causes rapid disappearance of the iodine color with only very small liberation of reducing groups. Starch gels are rapidly liquefied, and at the completion of the hydrolysis low molecular-weight "dextrins" remain. With Taka-amylase (from *Aspergillus oryzae*), these dextrins contain from 3 to 7 hexose units. If pure amylose is the substrate, however, it is completely hydrolyzed.

The other enzyme, β-amylase, rapidly sets free reducing sugar but does not destroy the iodine color. Hydrolysis stops when 60 per cent of the possible maltose is formed, and the remaining material, called "limit β-dextrin," has a very high molecular weight, about half that of the original starch. Again, pure amylose is hydrolyzed completely.

It is clear that β-amylase breaks off maltose molecules from the "outside" of the amylopectin molecule, leaving a good part of it intact, while α-amylase attacks interior linkages, breaking up the molecule into fragments of fairly large size. Its action is stopped by the branch-points, where a glucose residue is linked at both the 4 and 6 positions. The average length of the branches is about 25 glucose residues and the type of branching is probably bushlike and multiple, rather than short branches on a long straight chain (see Fig. XVII–2).

The amylases of bacteria and fungi are of the α type. The enzyme from *Bac. subtilis* resembles that of malt, both in reaction kinetics (rapid fall of viscosity, slow liberation of reducing sugar) and in the nature of residual dextrins (Hopkins *et al.*, 1942; Bernfeld and Fuld, 1948). The amylase of *Cl. acetobutylicum*, which breaks down starch

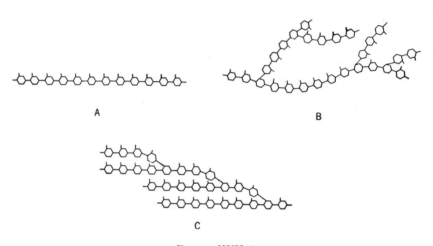

A

B

C

FIGURE XVII–2

Structure of starch.

    A. Amylose, Haworth's structure.

    B. Amylopectin, Meyer's structure. This probably holds for glycogen also.

    C. Amylopectin, Haworth's structure.

completely to a 100 per cent yield of maltose (Hockenhull and Herbert, 1945), is probably a mixture. The amylase from *Bac. subtilis*, which has been crystallized (Meyer *et al.*, 1947), requires free SH groups for its activity and is therefore inhibited by heavy metals; it also requires Ca ions (Di Carlo and Redfern, 1947–1948). Many streptococci contain a starch, which hydrolyzes completely to maltose with pure α- or β-amylase, and is therefore a straight-chain amylose (Crowley and Jevons, 1955; Baum and Crowley, 1960); these organisms form amylases too. The formation of bacterial α-amylase is readily induced by suspending cells of *Ps. saccharophila* in a starch medium (Markovitz and Klein, 1955) and, being an extracellular enzyme, this makes a favorable system for studying enzyme induction (see Chap. XX). There is in the same bacteria an *intracellular* β-amylase.

The action of *Bac. macerans* on starch yields very peculiar dextrins, known as Schardinger dextrins. These consist of rings of 6, 7, or 8 glucose units (i.e., molecular weight about 1000), linked 1–4; they are nonreducing, are resistant to β-amylase, and give characteristic crystals with iodine (French, 1957). They are not synthesized from maltose, but are formed direct from amylose, and appear when the average chain length has fallen to about 100 glucose units. Their formation has been considered as evidence that the amylose chain is a spiral in which one complete turn occupies 6–8 hexose units, but it is more likely that the *macerans*-enzyme twists the starch molecule into spirals (Myrbäck and Neumüller, 1950); in either case it appears that as the dextrins are hydrolyzed off from the parent molecule, their ends at once recombine. The purified enzyme, *dextrinogenase*, is free from true amylase (Schwimmer, 1953); it forms 43,000 moles of dextrin per mole of enzyme per minute.

With the increasing interest in amylase for industrial use (de-starching of textiles, preparation of potato and grain for fermentations), some attention has been given to bacilli as a source. The most active amylase-formers are strains of *Bac. subtilis*, *mesentericus*, *macerans*, and *polymyxa*. The enzyme, which is freely excreted into the liquid medium, generally along with proteases, is produced best in shallow cultures or with vigorous aeration; in other words, enzyme formation is linked to oxidative metabolism. Since amylase formation is inducible, it is produced in largest amounts on a starchy substrate such as potato or cereal mash.

3. HYDROLYSIS OF PECTINS

The bulk of the organic material of plants is made up of the polysaccharides, polyuronides, and aromatic material of the plant cell wall. Because of the importance of these substances in the world's cycle of carbon, their breakdown will be considered here systematically.

The pectins form the "intercellular substance" of higher plants, linking the cellulose walls of one cell to those of the adjacent one. They also occur in water-soluble form. They are essentially methylated polymers of D-galacturonic acid; the demethylated product is called pectic acid. Thus they are not polysaccharides, but polyuronides. Most of the preparations contain small amounts of galactan and araban (i.e., polymers of galactose and arabinose, respectively) in some kind of ester linkage (see Pigman, 1957).

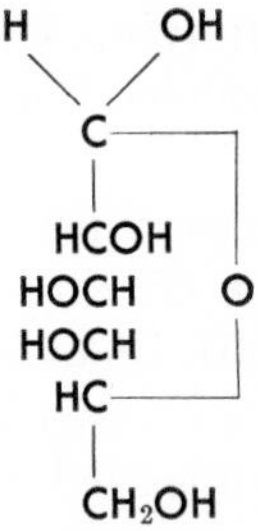

D-Galactose

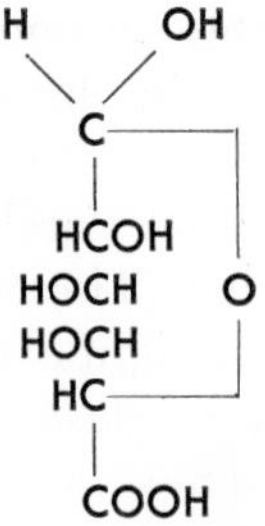

D-Galacturonic acid

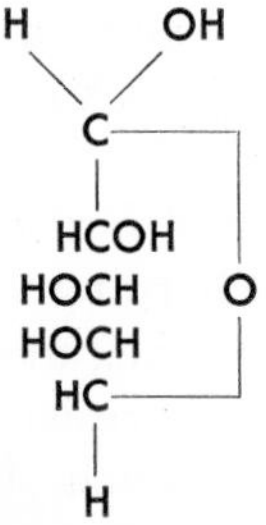

L-Arabinose

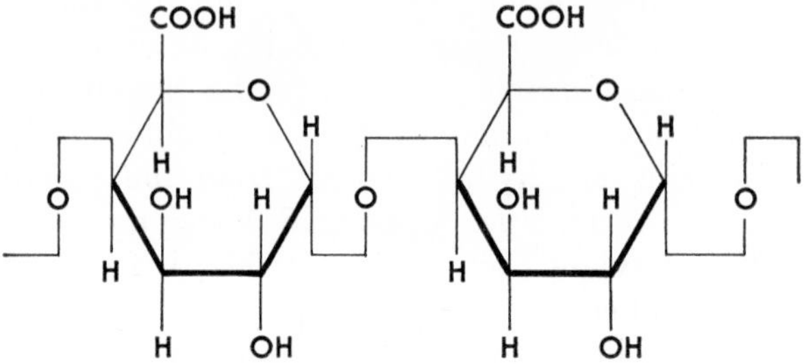

Pectic acid

Pectins are attacked by numerous organisms, especially *Entero-bacteriaceae* and the sporeformers. One of the main groups of pectin-decomposers is the soft-rot organisms. These bacteria grow in the middle lamellae of many tubers, leaves, and stems, causing the tissue to break up into a soft mass. In the early stages, intact loose plant cells can be seen, but later these are killed. One such organism was first isolated by Jones (1901, 1905) from carrots, under the name of *Bacillus carotovorus*, later changed to *Erwinia carotovorum*. It is highly nonspecific and is a common pest in commercial vegetables such as cabbage, beets, and celery. The rapid spread of cellular breakdown convinced Jones that an exoenzyme was produced, and though cell-free filtrates were at first inactive, the presence of exo-cellular enzyme was shown by separating the bacteria from the plant tissue by a layer of agar.

These bacteria are gram-negative rods, carrying out a typically formic fermentation of sugars or pectins. Except for the ability to attack pectin, and therefore to macerate plant tissue, the Erwinias could be assigned to the genera Proteus and Aerobacter (Elrod, 1942). Besides them, some 5 per cent of a large group of soil Pseudomonads could liquefy pectate gel and macerate cucumber tissue (Paton, 1958). Pectin is also decomposed by the Aerobacilli and numerous clostridia, the latter being the main organisms causing the "retting" of flax, hemp, and jute.

Retting is the removal of carbohydrates other than cellulose from the stems of the fiber plants. The method, which until the last 50 years was essentially the same as that used in ancient Egypt and by the European lake dwellers, consists simply of immersing the flax (or hemp) stalks in small ponds for several days. Coconut fiber is obtained in a similar way (Heyn, 1951). The changes occur in three stages:

(1) In the first 6 to 12 hours (at 20° C) the tissue swells and becomes waterlogged; some of the soluble matter diffuses out.

(2) For about four days aerobes, including lactic bacteria and yeasts, develop, fermenting the solutes and using up the dissolved oxygen.

(3) Thereafter clostridia develop, hydrolyzing the starch and pectin and carrying out a butyric fermentation on the products. As a result the parenchyma breaks up, and the vascular bundles with their strong bast fibers (linen) can be separated. The end point comes when the total acids reach a constant value. From this point on, cellulose-attacking clostridia may cause damage to the fibers.

Attempts have been made, especially in Italy, to use known enrichment cultures as "starters" in the retting pit. *Cl. felsineum* has given the best results. Aerobes, including *Bac. comesii*, also ret very efficiently, but under aerobic conditions (obtained by blowing air through the pit or tank) cellulose-destroying organisms may develop rapidly and begin degrading the fibers.

The breakdown of pectins requires at least three enzymes. The first stage, conversion of insoluble protopectin to pectin, is what causes separation of the plant cells or *maceration*. The enzyme causing this, protopectinase, has been found in many Aspergilli, and in *Cl. felsineum* (Heyn, 1951). The second stage is the demethylation of pectin to pectic acid; this enzyme, called pectin methyl esterase, is widely present in bacteria and higher plants. The final stage, hydrolysis of the 1–4 linkages to break up the macromolecule, is due to a third enzyme, pectinase, obtainable from cultures of *Asp. oryzae, Rhizopus tritici*, and *Erwinia carotovorum*. Its *p*H optimum is near 3. From its products, yields as high as 85 per cent of crystalline D-galacturonic acid have been obtained (Pigman, 1957).

4. HYDROLYSIS OF OTHER NATURAL POLYSACCHARIDES

Plant cell walls contain various insoluble and fibrous constituents: cellulose is the best known of these, but in addition many other polysaccharides, called *hemicelluloses*, are soluble in dilute alkali and hydrolyzed by dilute acids. The commonest are the xylans, which constitute about half the weight of grass and straw, and are often present in wood. One xylan (that from esparto grass) comprises chains of about 19 xylose units with an arabinose residue at the ends, while in the xylan of wood hemicellulose there are 7 to 19 xylose units combined with a molecule of methylglucuronic acid (see Chap. 12 of Pigman, 1957). All these are classed as *pentosans*. Xylan is more readily attacked by bacteria than cellulose. It can be fermented by "*Aerobac.*" *macerans* and *polymyxa*, yielding their typical fermentation products (pp. 518, 547). It is also attacked oxidatively by three species of Cytophaga, the cellulose-attacking Myxobacteria which will be discussed in the next section (Fuller and Norman, 1942). Probably many of the organisms active in retting can attack it.

A number of fungi and several bacilli excrete soluble enzymes that hydrolyze the water-soluble *pentosan* obtained from wheat flour (Simpson, 1954–1959). The presence of the pentosan itself, or wheat bran, xylan, etc., in the medium generally promoted formation of the enzyme, especially by *Bac. subtilis* and *pumilus*. Some sugars, especially xylose, and with *Asp. niger* arabinose, were also effective, so that stimulation of enzyme formation is by no means limited to substrates (see Chap. XX).

Agar is a compound of rather peculiar structure (see Chap. IV, sec. 4), a polygalactoside containing galactose-6-sulfate. It is attacked slowly by only a few bacteria and fungi. Straw manure and especially marine algae often yield cultures whose colonies sink slowly into the agar, making a little well or depression. There is rarely any over-all liquefaction like that of gelatin. Biochemically the attack can be shown by pouring iodine on the agar; the normal red-violet color does not develop where the agar has been attacked. Colorless zones surrounding the colonies thus indicate formation of a diffusible enzyme, termed *gelase*.

The agar-liquefying organisms described are all aerobic and oxidize many sugars with little acid formation. Of seven species isolated from seaweeds, six attacked cellulose, but none attacked chitin (Stanier, 1941). The most active agar-liquefiers reported from soil are commonly vibrios, and this group includes one sulfate-reducer (Stüven, 1960). The remainder are gram-negative rods (Gorseline, 1933; Buck and Cleverdon, 1960), an Actinomycete (Stanier, 1942), and several Cytophagas (see below). Some of the Myxomycetes can liquefy agar too; this is particularly true for *Fuligo septica* and three species of Badhamia (Cohen, 1940).

The special carbohydrates forming the capsular polysaccharides of Pneumococcus are, of course, not immune to attack by other bacteria, and early in the study of the actions of bacteria on one another, Sickles and Shaw (1934, 1950) isolated a Bacillus (*Bac. palustris*) which attacks some of them. Enzymes attacking type III and type VIII polysaccharides are formed only in presence of these specific substrates or their breakdown products, the latter requiring also that no other carbon sources be present (Torriani and Pappenheimer, 1962). Both enzymes apparently attack the 1–4 β glucuronic-glucose linkage (p. 123), a tetrasaccharide being the end product.

Chitin is the main constituent of crab shells and of the exoskeletons of insects; it is also the major fibrillar material in fungal cell walls. The 2-N-acetyl-glucosamine of which it is a long-chain polymer occurs also in less polymerized form in the walls of bacteria (Chap. III). Because it occurs so widely, it is necessarily attacked by many organisms, including Aspergilli (Grassmann and Rubenbauer, 1931), some of the Basidiomycetes (Tracey, 1955), Streptomycetes, and several Eubacteria. These include Aerobacter, Serratia and Klebsiella, some Pseudomonads, Vibrios and two Clostridia (Clarke and Tracey, 1956), and the marine luminous *Photobacteria* (Spencer, 1961). Among the most active of all chitin-decomposers are Streptomycetes, which have been isolated from soil by enrichment cultures in media containing finely powdered chitin as sole organic constituent (Reynolds, 1954; Jeuniaux, 1951, 1958). These organisms, grown in a shaken aerobic medium, excrete a soluble stable chitinase, with optimum pH 7, the amount of which is either dependent on, or increased by, chitin in the medium. Apparently it comprises three enzymes which act together in synergism (Jeuniaux, 1957). It does not remove the acetyl-group, but breaks down the chitin to N-acetyl-glucosamine or the corresponding biose, N,N-diacetyl-chitobiose (Reynolds, 1954). Formation of the biose parallels strikingly the production of maltose from starch (above).

Lignin is not a polysaccharide, but its breakdown may be mentioned here, since it is a major insoluble polymer of plant cell walls. It is an amorphous material of phenolic composition, probably consisting of C_6—C_3—O units linked in a multiple (nonlinear) pattern. The breakdown of lignin is not a hydrolysis but rather an oxidation and is most actively brought about in nature by white-rot fungi, especially Polyporus and Stereum species (Gottlieb and Pelczar, 1951). Although chemically processed lignins and their breakdown products have been found attackable by bacteria, native lignin is very resistant. Virtanen (1946) found finely powdered wood to be attacked by some thermophiles in soil, and later Fischer (1953) obtained by enrichment cultures a group of gram-negative rods, probably Pseudomonads, forming red and brown pigments on potato, which attack lignin rather selectively; none could hydrolyze cellulose, and they oxidized phenol only weakly. Oxygen was essential, and addition of protein or peptone promoted the action. A number of Fusaria and other imperfect fungi were also active. There is some relation between the lignin bacteria and the humus-decomposing organisms discussed in Chapter VI.

5. THE BREAKDOWN OF CELLULOSE

Since it is the major insoluble and fibrous constituent of plant material, the rate of cellulose breakdown probably exerts a major influence on the carbon cycle in nature. Because cellulose also forms many of the commercial textile fibers, such as cotton, linen, jute, and hemp, its breakdown has been extensively studied, although in recent years emphasis has shifted from the bacteria to the fungi.

Cellulose consists of long chains of glucopyranose united by β-1:4 linkages, i.e., as cellobiose. The molecular weight of these fiber-

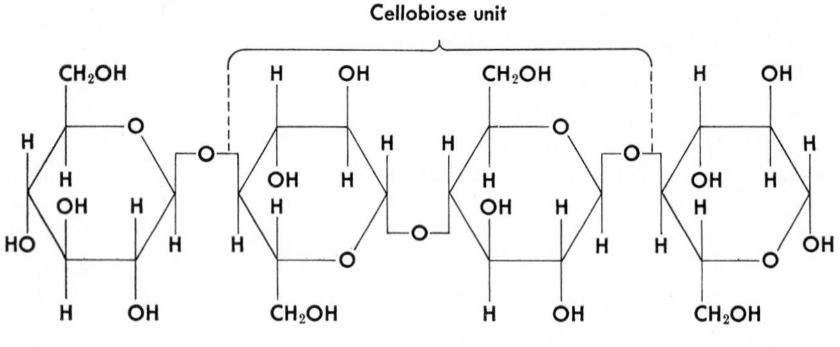

Cellobiose unit

molecules is from 200,000 to 1,000,000 (see Pigman, 1957). It follows that there can be only a minute percentage of terminal reducing groups. This fact and its insolubility make cellulose resistant to many organisms. Soluble cellulases, producing hydrolysis to cellobiose, are formed in snails and a few fungi, but not in many bacteria. The main active organisms are:

Cytophagas and related aerobic Myxobacteria.
Certain aerobic sporeformers and nonsporeformers.
Clostridia.
The anaerobic nonsporeformers of the rumen of herbivores.
Several Actinomycetes.
Some of the Chytridiales, a primitive group of the Phycomycetes, that produce a soluble cellulase.

Many imperfect fungi, including (1) *Chaetomium globosum*, often used as a test organism in evaluating preservatives for textiles; (2) *Memnoniella echinata* and *Stachybotrys*, common on cotton fabrics; (3) *Myrothecium verrucaria*, one of the most active of the fungi, and common in soils, especially forest soils.

Detailed discussion of all these would be out of place, but four bacterial groups will be considered.[2]

A. The Cytophagas

Although these organisms were found by van Iterson as early as 1904, in enrichment cultures with paper as the sole carbon source, their nature was not made clear till the detailed study of Hutchinson and Clayton (1919) at Rothamsted. These workers, from the knowledge that cellulose decomposition is fastest in a light, sandy soil, set out to look for aerobic cellulose-destroying organisms therein. Using as enrichment medium filter paper and salt solutions (with NH_4^+ as source of N), they obtained threadlike, slightly curved rods together with large micrococci, both being adherent to the paper fibers. The two forms could not be separated by heat, disinfection, or even spraying through an atomizer. When an almost pure culture of the thread forms was picked and diluted, the cocci eventually appeared even in the highest dilution. The organism therefore exists in two forms, rod and sphere (Fig. XVII–3).

By placing filter paper on agar or silica gel containing the salts, and inoculating at intervals with tiny soil crumbs, Winogradsky (1929) obtained several such organisms distinguished by forming different pigments. However, in the form he studied in detail, only rods and no cocci were formed. The explanation for this, given by Krzemieniewska (1933), is that there are two types, those that (like Hutchinson and Clayton's organism) round up to form spheres (Sporocytophaga), and those that do not (Cytophaga proper). They all belong to the Myxobacteria, which are characterized by forming fruiting bodies through creeping together and piling up (see Chap. II). The Cytophagas, however, are regarded as imperfect members in which fruiting-body formation is either reduced to the rounding up of single cells (Sporocytophaga) or is entirely absent (Cytophaga).

The Cytophagas were long believed to be limited to cellulose as a growth medium, but this was due to the toxicity of autoclaved sugar solutions. They will grow on glucose and cellobiose (when sterilized by Seitz-filter); *C. rubra*, a red form, also attacks xylose and mannose (Stanier, 1942a). The two marine forms attack agar

[2] The fungi and their action are discussed in Siu's book (1951).

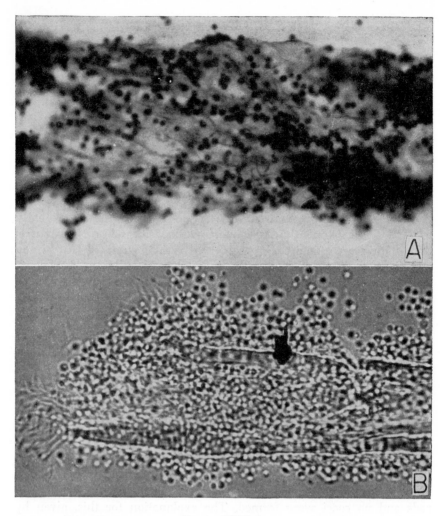

FIGURE XVII–3

Sporocytophaga myxococcoides.

A. Attacked filter-paper fiber showing microcysts and vegetative cells, Wino-gradsky's stain. 830 ×.

B. A similar fiber photographed in the living state.

Note vegetative cells at left-hand end. 850 ×.

(From R. Y. Stanier, *Bact. Revs.*, **6:**143–196, 1942a. By courtesy of the Williams and Wilkins Co., Baltimore, Md.)

and many sugars, but their action on cellulose is slow; they require peptone or yeast extract as nitrogen source, while the soil forms can use NH_4^+, nitrate, aspartic acid, or asparagine. Most Cytophagas are obligate aerobes. In cultures with paper or cotton dipping into a nutrient salt solution, the strongest attack is right at the liquid surface, where a strip of filter paper may be completely cut through in 7 to 10 days at 25° C. Only two species so far are facultative: *Cyt. fermantans*, which ferments glucose to acetate, propionate, and succinate,

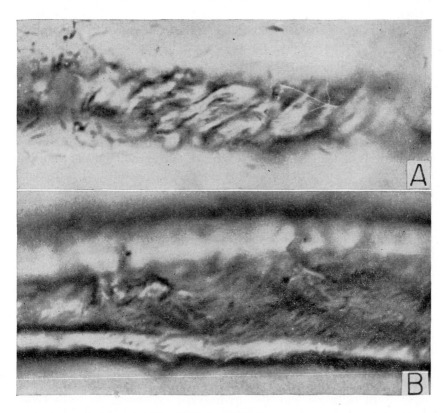

FIGURE XVII-4

The attack of cellulose by Cytophaga. Cotton wool fibers previously swollen in 15 per cent NaOH and then inoculated with *C. hutchinsonii*.

A. The organisms lie in the spiral furrows which probably follow the orientation of the microfibrils. 950 ×.

B. Fiber from which the organisms have been detached, showing furrows formed. 950 ×.

(From R. Y. Stanier, *Bact. Revs.*, **6**:143–196, 1942a. By courtesy of the Williams and Wilkins Co., Baltimore, Md.)

and *Cyt. succinicans*, which ferments glucose to pyruvate and, with the uptake of CO_2, to succinate (Bachmann, 1955; Anderson and Ordal, 1961).

Along with the Cytophagas, more complex Myxobacteria occur on cotton in the field (Heyn, 1957). Isolations on cellulose-salts agar showed that *Angiococcus cellulosum* and *Polyangium cellulosum* grow on raw cotton fibers. Both of these form large fruiting cysts, those of Angiococcus being yellowish pink and borne on stalks, those of Polyangium red to brown, stalkless, and up to 150 μ in diameter. The former, which is common, was first isolated from soil (Mishustin, 1938).

The mode of attack on cellulose is not understood. No reducing sugars are produced, and no cell-free cellulase has been obtained, although a preparation hydrolyzing the polysaccharide, lichenin, has been reported (see Greathouse, 1950). The organisms are closely adherent to the cellulose, the rods being aligned with the orientation of the microfibrils (Fig. XVII–4A). If cotton preswollen in NaOH is used, and the cells washed off after growth, indentations can be seen where the cells have lain (Fig. XVII–4B). Apparently, therefore, hydrolysis takes place at the surface of the cell, and the resulting sugars are consumed as fast as they are liberated. Polyangium penetrates the fiber so deeply that its fruiting bodies may be formed within the lumen (Heyn, 1957). The idea that cellulose destruction is simply a function of growth is supported by the observation that for every milligram of nitrogen taken up, about 30 mg of cellulose are destroyed (Hutchinson and Clayton, 1919).

B. The Aerobic Eubacteria

The aerobes include the sporeforming Cellulobacillus, which yields a good instance of a bacterial cellulase. These organisms, of which two species, *C. myxogenes* and *C. mucosus*, were isolated, formed both glucose and cellobiose when grown in paper pulp in the presence of toluene (Simola, 1931). The cell-free culture fluid produced reducing sugar from cellulose and also hydrolyzed cellobiose. As with Cytophaga, a good deal of the cellulose was assimilated by the bacteria; there were also formed colored reducing acids related to humic acid, and, with uptake of nitrogen, a protein. As with Cytophaga, about 30 mg of cellulose were destroyed for every milligram of inorganic nitrogen taken up, which suggests that the basic process is similar in these otherwise unrelated types.

There is also a group of nonsporeformers known as Cellulomonas; the name is unfortunate since some of them are peritrichously flagellated. These are probably the forms that were isolated from cellulose decomposing in sewage (Maki, 1954); they appeared to be the major cellulolytic organisms present. In pure culture they convert cellulose to alcohol, CO_2, and formic, acetic, and lactic acids. Their role in nature is not yet clear.

C. The Anaerobic Sporeformers

Anaerobic cellulose breakdown has been studied ever since Omelianski (1902) obtained two sporeformers in cellulose-enrichment cultures from ditch mud. They had terminal spherical spores (*plectridia*). Omelianski considered that the cellulose was fermented directly, without hydrolysis to sugars, but this was disproved when toluene or iodoform was added to the cultures, since the fermentation was then arrested, and both glucose and cellobiose could be identified in the medium (Pringsheim, 1912). Pure cultures hydrolyze cellulose to glucose and cellobiose much faster than the sugars are subsequently fermented. Methane is often formed in enrichment cultures, doubtless due to a secondary fermentation.

Pure cultures of these bacteria proved difficult to obtain. The insolubility of the cellulose makes dilution methods ineffective, and the requirement of the organisms for rich organic media often makes their growth on agar poor. It was not until 1944 that definitely pure cultures were obtained by Hungate. Thermophilic forms were later obtained by using partially degraded cellulose in colloidal or soluble form, incorporated in a rich agar medium and incubating at 55 to 60° C (McBee, 1950; Enebo, 1951, 1954). The cells produce a soluble cellulase, which yields mainly cellobiose and glucose; there is no soluble cellobiase, but most of the glucose is probably formed direct from cellulose (unlike the action of amylase). The *Cl. thermocellulaseum* of Enebo formed about the same products as Hungate's mesophilic form, (column 2 in Table XVII–2).

Many years ago Khouvine studied the cellulolytic bacteria in the alimentary tract of man (1923) and various farm animals (1926). By anaerobic enrichment cultures at 40° C she isolated *"Bac. cellulosae dissolvens"* in what may have been pure culture. This organism, shown in Figure XVII–5, has somewhat unusual morphology: it is a long gram-negative rod with terminal oval "spores." It converts cellulose mainly to acetic acid and ethanol. As Table XVII–2 shows, the products are similar to those of some clostridia from soil (Hungate, 1950). They are also similar to the products of some thermophilic forms (*Cl. thermocellum*), which give 150 millimoles of acetic acid and 35 of ethanol from 100 "millimoles" of cellulose. Other clostridia gave a fermentation characterized by much succinic acid (column 2 of Table XVII–2). Two Clostridia, *Cl. lochheadii* and *Cl. longisporum*, isolated from the rumen of cattle being fed timothy hay, are extremely rapid cellulose digesters (Hungate, 1957). Like the above they form very long, apparently curved rods, but differ in producing large spindle-shaped clostridia in which the spores are formed. Again acetic acid and ethanol are prominent breakdown products of cellulose, along with CO_2, H_2, HCOOH, and in one case butyric acid. However, in general the sporeformers are not the main organisms responsible for cellulose utilization in the alimentary tract of animals (see below).

The thermophiles offer a striking contrast in rates. Omelianski's

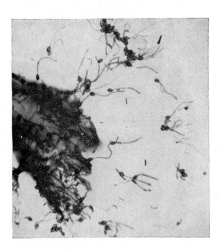

FIGURE XVII–5

Bac. cellulosae dissolvens on paper fiber. Stained with Hucker's methyl violet. From a seven-day enrichment culture. 700 ×. (From A. K. Sijpestijn, 1948.)

bacteria took three to four months at room temperature to ferment a few grams of cellulose; *Cl. thermocellum* began to produce gas from cellulose in 24 hours at 50° C, and a thermophile growing at 65° C (Woodman and Stewart, 1928) completed the whole fermentation in seven days. Most of these cultures were not pure.

D. Bacteria of the Rumen of Herbivorous Animals

One of the most important uses of cellulose biologically is as feed for animals. Many of the herbivorous animals belong to the order *Ruminantia*, which means that the food after eating is transferred to a digestive pouch, the rumen, where it remains stirred and salivated for many hours before return to the mouth for chewing or passage on to the abomasum or "fourth stomach." In nonruminants like the horse and pig, the cecum and colon are enlarged and doubtless play a similar part. Ruminants have very voluminous stomachs; the four organs together in cattle have a volume close to 250 liters, while that of the intestine is only 100 liters. Of the grasses and other plant foods, a third or more is cellulose, and a good deal of this is decomposed. In the classic experiments of Thomas and Pringsheim (1918) a ram was fed for 11 days on potatoes and filter paper; determinations of paper fiber in the feces showed that 57 per cent had disappeared. Later experiments on steers showed a 90 per cent disappearance. Much of the carbon is converted to gas; a cow forms about 700 liters of CO_2 and methane daily. Since there are no cellulose-hydrolyzing enzymes known in mammals, the decomposition is due to micro-organisms acting in the rumen. Accordingly, numerous isolations have been attempted of bacteria living in the rumen of cattle and sheep.

The first such studies always yielded enrichment cultures of Omelianski's organisms, rods with terminal spherical spores, producing acetic and butyric acids with CO_2 and hydrogen or methane. Khouvine's isolations from human feces and the cecum of herbivores were mentioned above. Many others obtained similar organisms. In addition an anaerobic actinomycete, *Micromonospora propionici*, has been isolated from the gut of termites (Hungate, 1946), where it decomposes cellulose. However, direct microscopic study of the flora of the rumen or cecum of herbivores did not support the importance of sporeformers in the breakdown of cellulose. Instead, the plant fragments mostly carried cocci of various sizes, often in chains like streptococci, together with vibrios (Baker and Martin, 1937–1939). These organisms gave a blue color with iodine like that of the "granulose" of clostridia (pp. 126, 529). The normal flora of the rumen and cecum was thus considered to consist in large part of coccoid bacteria (Baker, 1942), and approximate counts by the dilution method indicated that spore-formers were only present in very small numbers (Hungate, 1946). The predominance of sporeformers in enrichment cultures is probably due to the change of conditions from those prevailing in vivo, and to the less exacting nutritional needs of the clostridia, although the two clostridia of Hungate (1957) probably do qualify as of real importance in cellulose breakdown in the rumen.

By adding rumen fluid to the medium, cultures of a chain-forming coccus and a short ovoid gram-negative rod were obtained (Hungate, 1950; Sijpestijn, 1948, 1951). The great effectiveness of these in fermenting cellulose is shown by comparing rates; the sporeformers, even under their optimum conditions, took 13 days at 38° C for 80 per cent decomposition of added paper, while the cattle rumen cocci, in presence of rumen fluid, did the same in four days (Sijpestijn, 1948).

Since four days is supposed to correspond to the actual time of digestion in cattle, the nonsporeformers evidently fit the physiological requirements.

Sijpestijn's organisms comprised a gram-negative rod, *Ruminobacter parvum*, and a yellow gram-positive streptococcus, *Ruminococcus flavefaciens* (Fig. XVII–6). Hungate later (1959) obtained the gram-negative *Ruminococcus albus*, while *R. flavefaciens* was found in the cecum of rabbits (Hall, 1952). Often yeast extract could be substituted for rumen fluid. Two gram-negative rods of variable morphology isolated in a similar way were *Bacteroides succinogenes*

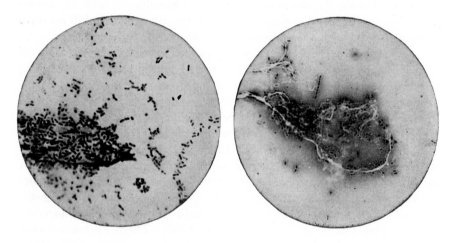

FIGURE XVII–6

Ruminococcus flavefaciens on fiber remnants.

   Left. Methyl violet stain. *Right.* Gram-stain and nigrosine counterstain. 780 ×.
   (From A. K. Sijpestijn, 1948.)

(Hungate, 1950), which attacks cellulose, and *Bacteroides amylophilus* (Hamlin and Hungate, 1956), which attacks only starch and maltose. Another form less active on cellulose appears to convert acetic to butyric acid and may be related to Butyribacterium (cf. p. 529). The difficulty of culturing Ruminococcus without rumen fluid is due to its nutritional requirements, which are like those of the lactobacilli; *R. flavefaciens* needs a complete amino acid mixture, folic acid, purines, cellulose or cellobiose, CO_2, and strict anaerobiosis (Ayers, 1958). Glucose is not used.

The products of cellulose fermentation of some of these organisms are compared in Table XVII–2. All of them form much acetic acid as a principal product. With three of the five rumen forms listed, ethanol is less prominent than with the sporeformers. It is perhaps just as well that the role of the sporeformers in the rumen is a minor one, since otherwise it might be difficult for cows to remain sober (up to 60 mole per cent yield of alcohol!). Three of the rumen bacteria apparently form either propionic or succinic acid as a second main product. The Actinomycete mentioned above forms propionic acid. Since Hungate's *B. succinogenes* (column 5) actually takes up CO_2, these two acids are in reality physiologically equivalent, by way of the decarboxylation of succinic acid (Chap. XIII, sec. 3c). Succinate, indeed, is vigorously decarboxylated by washed rumen bacteria (Sijpestijn and Elsden, 1952) and also by pure cultures of the rumen micrococcus called *Veillonella gazogenes* (Johns, 1951). This organism, although probably the main source of propionic acid in the rumen, does not attack cellulose, or indeed any of the sugars. Presumably its main substrates are lactate and succinate formed by other bacteria.

As to the other products, it is evident that they vary with the organism. Some of the bacteria (especially those in column 7) produce reducing sugar in moderate amounts, but this has been largely corrected for. Small amounts of aromatic fatty acids are found, these being produced by deamination of tyrosine and phenylalanine (Scott *et al.*, 1963). The products are altered, too, by differences in the CO_2 tension, which influences the decarboxylation of both succinic and pyruvic acids. Low CO_2 tensions would thus favor the formation of alcohol, high tensions that of succinate.

It will be noted that methane is not a product in these pure culture fermentations. On the other hand, methane does appear in fermentations carried out by the total bacteria centrifuged out of rumen fluid (Marston, 1948). As far as is known, the methane fermentation is undergone only by organic acids or alcohol, and not by cellulose. The methane that is produced in the rumen, therefore, is due to a secondary fermentation of the products (see p. 612 ff), and two Methanobacteria have been isolated from rumen that do this: *Mb. formicicum*, which utilizes formate (Opperman *et al.*, 1957), and *Mb. ruminantium*, which is present in larger numbers, up to 200 million per milliter, and makes methane most actively from hydrogen and CO_2 (Smith and Hungate, 1958). These are very strict anaerobes, especially the latter, which requires dithionite, or growing *E. coli*, to make the redox potential sufficiently negative for growth.

The conclusion that the rumen contains many organisms, closely related physiologically, and mostly of short rod, oval, or coccus morphology, which actively ferment cellulose to organic acids, agrees well with studies of cattle nutrition, which have shown the presence of large amounts of acetic and propionic acids in the rumen after cellulose ingestion. Both these acids can be converted in the animal

TABLE XVII-2. Products of Cellulose Fermentation by Sporeformers (1–3) and Rumen Bacteria (4–7)

All data corrected for cellulose unfermented and recalculated to the same basis, i.e., millimoles of product per 100 "millimoles" of cellulose decomposed.* Dashes indicate that the compound was not determined.

| | SPOREFORMERS | | | RUMEN BACTERIA | | | | |
| | 1 | 2 | 3 | 4 | 5 | 6 | 7 | |
	From Soil (two forms) (Hungate, 1950)	From Soil via Enrichments (Hungate, 1950)	From Intestines (Khouvine, 1923)	Short Rod (Sijpestijn, 1948)	Short Rod (Hungate, 1950)	Coccus (yellow) (Sijpestijn, 1948, 1951)	Coccus (Hungate, 1950) (yellow)	(colorless)
Acetic	49–57	112	73	43	82†	65	40	110†
Propionic	0	0	—	78	9	0	0	0
Butyric	0	0	6	trace	5	0	0	0
Formic	—	—	—	—	trace	64	0	25
Lactic	1	23	—	—	0	(27)‡	63	10
Succinic	0	49	—	—	146	51	trace	—
Ethanol	40–60	16	30	—	—	0	31	52
CO₂	++	132	66	++	−45 (i.e., used)	} little	27	48
H₂	++	174	69	—	0		20	21

* 1 "mM" cellulose ($C_6H_{10}O_5$) = 162 mg.

† Mean of two experiments.

‡ The 27 mM of lactic acid were found in a combined fermentation with *Cl. sporogenes* and may not all have been formed by the Ruminococcus.

body into glucose, glycogen, and (in the case of acetic acid) to fat. Further, the bodies of the bacteria, rich in granulose, should also be assimilable after hydrolysis. These comprise from 7 to 18 per cent of the total combustible energy of the cellulose. It has been calculated from fermentations with combined rumen bacteria that at least 70 per cent of the energy requirement of cattle comes from the fermentation acids of the rumen (Carroll and Hungate, 1954) and cellulose provides a good part of these. It is clear, therefore, that ruminal and intestinal cellulose breakdown is an important and effective part of the natural carbon cycle.

REFERENCES

Anderson, R. L., and Ordal, E. J. 1961. *J. Bact.*, **81**:120–128, 129–146.
Ayers, W. A. 1958. *J. Bact.*, **76**:504–509.
Bachmann, B. J. 1955. *J. Gen. Microbiol.*, **13**:541–551.
Baker, F. 1942. *Nature*, **149**:220, 582; **150**:479.
Baker, F., and Martin, R. 1937–1939. *Zentr. Bakt. II orig.*, **96**:18–35; **97**:201-221; **99**:400–424.
Baum, H., and Crowley, N. 1960. *Nature*, **187**:413.
Bernfeld, P., and Fuld, M. 1948. *Helv. chim. Acta*, **31**:1423–1427.
Bryant, M. P. 1952. *J. Bact.*, **64**:325–335.
Buck, J. D., and Cleverdon, R. C. 1960. *Canad. J. Microbiol.*, **6**:594–595.
Carroll, E. J., and Hungate, R. E. 1954. *Applied Microbiol.*, **2**:205–214.
Clarke, P. H., and Tracey, M. V. 1956. *J. Gen. Microbiol.*, **14**:188–196.
Cohen, A. L. 1940. The Nutrition of the Myxomycetes. Thesis. Cambridge, Mass., Harvard Univ. Chap. 4.
*Cohn, M. 1957. *Bact. Revs.*, **21**:140–168.
Crowley, N., and Jevons, M. P. 1955. *J. Gen. Microbiol.*, **13**:226–234.
DiCarlo, F. J., and Redfern, S. 1947–1948. *Arch. Biochem.*, **15**:333–342, 343–350; **17**:1–2.
Dienert, F. 1901. Sur la fermentation du galactose et sur l'accoutumance des levures à ce sucre. *Ann. Inst. Pasteur*, **14**:139–189.
Doudoroff, M. 1940. *Enzymologia*, **9**:59–72.
Doudoroff, M.; Wiame, J. M.; and Wolochow, H. 1949. *J. Bact.*, **57**:403–427.
Elrod, R. P. 1942. *J. Bact.*, **44**:433–440.
Enebo, L. 1951. *Physiol. Plantarum*, **4**:652–666.
Enebo, L. 1954. Studies in Cellulose Decomposition by an Anaerobic Thermophilic Bacterium and Two Associated Non-cellulolytic Species. Thesis, Stockholm.
Fischer, G. 1953. *Arch. f. Mikrobiol.*, **18**:397–424.
Fitting, C., and Doudoroff, M. 1952. *J. Biol. Chem.*, **199**:153–159.
*Foster, J. W. 1951. Metabolism of Fungi. *Ann. Rev. Microbiol.*, **5**:101–120.
French, C. D. 1957. *Baker's Digest*, **31**:24–36; *Proc. Int. Symp. Enzyme Chem.; Tokyo and Kyoto*, **2**:530–532; Adv. in Carbohydrate Chem. New York, Academic Press, **12**:189–200.
Fukumoto, J. 1949. See *Chem. Abstr.*, **43**:1450.
Fuller, W. H., and Norman, A. G. 1942. *J. Bact.*, **44**:256.
*Gorseline, H. E. 1933. *J. Bact.*, **26**:435–457.

*Gottlieb, S., and Pelczar, M. J., Jr. 1951. Microbiological Aspects of Lignin Degradation. *Bact. Revs.*, 15:55–76 (97 refs.).

Grassmann, W., and Rubenbauer, H. 1931. *Münch. med. Wochenschw.*, 78:1817–1819.

Greathouse, G. A. 1950. Microbiological Degradation of Cellulose. *Textile Res. J.*, 20:227–238.

Hall, E. R. 1952. *J. Gen. Microbiol.*, 7:350–357.

Hamlin, L. J., and Hungate, R. E. 1956. *J. Bact.*, 73:548–554.

Harding, V. J., and Nicholson, T. F. 1933. *Biochem. J.*, 27:1082–1094.

Hassid, W. Z.; Doudoroff, M.; and Barker, H. A. 1944. *J. Am. Chem. Soc.*, 66:1416–1418.

Hestrin, S.; Feingold, D. S.; and Schramm, M. 1955. In, Methods in Enzymol., 1:231–258; New York, Academic Press.

Heyn, A. N. J. 1951. Studies on the Microbiological Retting Process for the Preparation of a Hard Fiber, and Influence of This Process on the Fiber Properties. *Verhandel. Kon. Akad. Wetensch. Amsterdam*, II: pt. 48, No. 1, 59 pp.

Heyn, A. N. J. 1957. *Textile Res. J.*, 27:591–603.

Hockenhull, D. J. D., and Herbert, D. 1945. *Biochem. J.*, 39:102–106.

Hopkins, R. H., and Kulka, D. 1942. *J. Inst. Brewing*, 48:170–174; Hopkins, R. H.; Dolby, D. E.; and Stopher, E. G. *J. Inst. Brewing*, 48:174–178; cf. also *Wallerstein Lab. Comm.*, 5:115–124, 125–130.

Hough, L.; Jones, J. K. N.; and Wadman, W. H. 1952. *J. Chem. Soc.*, pp. 3393–3399.

Hungate, R. E. 1946. *J. Bact.*, 51:51–56.

*Hungate, R. E. 1950. The Anaerobic Mesophilic Cellulolytic Bacteria. *Bact. Revs.*, 14:1–49.

Hungate, R. E. 1957. *Canad. J. Microbiol.*, 3:289–311.

Hutchinson, H. B., and Clayton, J. 1919. *J. Agr. Sci.*, 9:143–173.

Jeuniaux, Ch. 1951, 1958. *Arch. internat. de Physiol. Biochemie*, 59:242–246; 66:408–427 (1958) and literature there cited.

Jeuniaux, Ch. 1957. *Biochem. J.*, 66:29 P.

Johns, A. T. 1951. *J. Gen. Microbiol.*, 5:317–336.

Jones, L. R. 1901. *Zentr. Bakt. II*, 7:12–21, 61–68.

Jones, L. R. 1905. *N. Y. Agr. Expt. Sta. Tech. Bull.*, No. 11, pp. 291–368. Geneva, N. Y.

*Kalckar, H. M., and Maxwell, E. S. 1958. Biosynthesis and Metabolic Function of UDPG. *Physiol. Revs.*, 38:77–90.

Karström, H. 1931. Ueber die Enzymbildung in Bakterien. Dissertation, Helsinki.

*Karström, H. 1938. Enzymatische Adaptation bei Mikroorganismen. *Ergebn. der Enzym-Forschung*, 7:350–376.

Kertesz, Z. I. 1937. *J. Biol. Chem.*, 121:589–598.

Khouvine, Y. 1923. *Ann. Inst. Pasteur*, 37:711–752.

Khouvine, Y. 1926. *Compt. rend. soc. biol.*, 94:1072–1074.

Kluyver, A. J. 1914. Biochemische suikerbepalingen. Dissertation, Leiden.

Kluyver, A. J., and Custers, M. T. J. 1940. *Ant. v. Leeuwenhoek*, 6:121–162.

Kluyver, A. J., and Hoogerheide, J. C. 1933. *Proc. Kon. Akad. Wetenschap. Amsterdam*, 36:605–608.

Kluyver, A. J.; deLey, J.; and Rijven, A. 1950. *Ant. v. Leeuwenhoek*, 16:1–14.

Krzemieniewska, H. 1933. *Arch. Mikrobiol.*, 4:394–408.

Lederberg, E. 1952. *Genetics*, 37:469–483.

Lewis, I. M. 1934. *J. Bact.*, 28:619–638.

Linskens, H. F. 1959. Papierchromatographie in der Botanik, 2nd ed. Berlin, Springer, 408 pp.

McBee, R. H. 1950. The Anaerobic Thermophilic Cellulolytic Bacteria. *Bact. Revs.*, 14:51–63.

Madsen, N. B. 1963. *Canad. J. Biochem. Physiol.*, **41**:561–571.

Maki, L. R. 1954. *Ant. v. Leeuwenhoek*, **20**:185–200.

Markovitz, A. and Klein, H. P. 1955. *J. Bact.*, **70**:641–648, 649–655.

Marston, H. R. 1948. *Biochem. J.*, **42**:564–574.

Meyer, K. H.; Fuld, M.; and Bernfeld, P. 1947. *Experientia*, **3**:411–412.

Mishustin, E. N. 1938. *Mikrobiologia (USSR)*, **7**:427–444.

*Myrbäck, K. 1948. Products of the Enzymic Degradation of Starch and Glycogen. *Adv. in Carbohydrate Chemistry*, **3**:252–310. New York, Academic Press.

Myrbäck, K., and Neumüller, G. 1950. Amylases and the Hydrolysis of Starch and Glycogen. In, The Enzymes, Vol. 1, Chap. 19, New York, Academic Press.

Neisser, M. 1906. *Zentr. Bakt. I (Ref.)*, **36**:98; cf. also Massini, R. *Arch. Hyg.*, **61**: 250–292 (1907).

Omelianski, W. 1902. *Zentr. Bakt. II (orig.)*, **8**:193–201, 225–231, 257–263, 289–294, 321–326, 353–361, 385–391.

Opperman, R. A.; Nelson, W. O.; and Brown, R. E. 1957. *J. Dairy Sci.*, **40**:779–788.

Paton, A. M. 1958. *Nature*, **181**:61–62.

Pigman, W. W. 1957. The Carbohydrates; Chemistry, Biochemistry, Physiology. New York, Academic Press.

Pringsheim, H. 1912. *Z. physiol. Chem.*, **78**:266–291.

Reynolds, D. M. 1954. *J. Gen. Microbiol.*, **11**:150–159.

Ryan, F. J. 1952. *J. Gen. Microbiol.*, **7**:69–88.

Schwimmer, S. 1953. *Arch. Biochem. Biophys.*, **43**:108–117.

Scott, T. W.; Ward, P. F. V.; and Dawson, R. M. C. 1963. *Biochem. J.*, **86**:3–4P.

Sheinin, R., and Crocker, B. F. 1961. *Canad. J. Biochem. Physiol.*, **39**:55–61.

Sickles, G. M., and Shaw, M. 1934. *J. Bact.*, **27**:475–481; **28**:415–421; *J. Immunol.*, **64**:21–26, 27–33 (1950).

*Sijpestijn, A. K. 1948. Cellulose Decomposing Bacteria from the Rumen of Cattle. Dissertation, Leiden. 184 pp.

Sijpestijn, A. K. 1951. *J. Gen. Microbiol.*, **5**:869–879.

Sijpestijn, A. K., and Elsden, S. 1952. *Biochem. J.*, **52**:41–45.

Simola, P. E. 1931. *Ann. Acad. Sci. Fennicae, Ser. A.*, **34**: No. 1, 91 pp. and No. 6, 115 pp.; *Chem. Abstr.*, **25**:4574; and **26**:1316.

Simpson, F. J. 1954–1959. *Canad. J. Microbiol.*, **1**:131–139; **2**:28–38 (1956); **5**:99–107 (1959).

* Siu, R. G. H. 1951. Microbial Decomposition of Cellulose. New York, Reinhold.

Smith, P. H., and Hungate, R. E. 1958. *J. Bact.*, **75**:713–718.

Spencer, R. 1961. *Nature*, **190**:938.

Stanier, R. Y. 1941–1942. *J. Bact.*, **42**:527–556; **44**:555–570 (1942).

*Stanier, R. Y. 1942a. The Cytophaga Group: a Contribution to the Biology of Myxo-bacteria. *Bact. Revs.*, **6**:143–196.

Strange, R. E.; Dark, F. A.; and Ness, A. G. 1961. *J. Gen. Microbiol.*, **25**:61–76.

Stüven, K. 1960. *Arch. Mikrobiol.*, **35**:92–104.

Thomas, K., and Pringsheim, H. 1918. *Arch. Anat. u. physiol.*, pp. 25–52.

Torriani, A., and Pappenheimer, A. M., Jr. 1962. *J. Biol. Chem.*, **237**:3–13.

Tracey, M. V. 1955. *Biochem. J.*, **61**:579–588.

Virtanen, A. I. 1946. *Nature*, **158**:795–796.

van Voorst, F. T. 1938–1939. *Chem. Weekblad*, **35**:338–341, 677–678 (1938); **36**:253–256 (1939).

Weidenhagen, R. 1928. *Z. ver. deut. Zuckerind.*, pp. 125–134, 406–418, 539–542; *Naturwiss.*, **16**:654–655.

Winogradsky, S. 1929. *Ann. Inst. Pasteur.*, **43**:549–633.

Woodman, H. E., and Stewart, J. 1928. *J. Agr. Sci.*, **18**:713–723.

CHAPTER XVIII

Fermentations Making Use of Inorganic

Hydrogen Acceptors

When we analyze . . . fermentation processes, we may conclude that they are chains of reactions in which one organic molecule or part of such a molecule is oxidized whilst a second . . . undergoes a reduction. It is obvious that the extreme form which can be conceived for such a process will be that part of the carbon atoms . . . attain their highest reduction stage, i.e., methane, another part of these carbon atoms their highest stage of oxidation, i.e., carbon dioxide.

A. J. KLUYVER (1931)

Holland, country of odoriferous canals and great microbiologists, contributed most to our early knowledge of (these organisms).

K. R. BUTLIN (1949)

The fermentations of simple carbohydrates were grouped in Chapters XI through XV according to the ultimate reduced products—alcohol, lactic acid, and so forth. They could almost as well have been grouped by their final hydrogen acceptors—acetaldehyde, pyruvic acid, oxalacetic acid, etc. The general similarity between these hydrogen acceptors accounts for the basic similarities between the fermentations. On the other hand, the fermentations described below utilize inorganic hydrogen acceptors, and correspondingly they have a much more individual quality.

1. SULFATE REDUCTION

Any reasonably sensitive nose can detect that H_2S is often produced in nature; besides the special case of sulfur springs, H_2S can be noted above sewage, certain kinds of swamps and mud, and salt-water pools. Some of this may come from proteins, as in the case of rotten eggs; H_2S is readily liberated from cysteine (cf. pp. 319–320). However, the H_2S that is usually detected where vegetation is decaying comes from another source. Beijerinck, doubtless stimulated by the odor of the Delft canals in summer, made a classic investigation of this (1895).[1] Enrichment cultures made from ditch mud in a medium con-

[1] The first article in the first volume of the new Zweite Abteilung of the *Zentralblatt für Bakteriologie*.

taining lactate as organic nutrient, with inorganic salts and 2 per cent
CaSO₄, yielded H₂S on incubation.[2] The organism responsible, a short
spirillum or vibrio, was a strict anaerobe and was only obtained by
making mixed cultures together with a facultative anaerobe (Aerobacter) which consumed the last traces of oxygen in the medium.
Later, pure cultures were obtained by including enough H₂S to react
with the residual oxygen (van Delden, 1904). The bacteria, subsequently named Desulfovibrio, were producing H₂S by *reduction of
sulfate:*

$$H_2SO_4 + 8(H) \rightarrow 4\ H_2O + H_2S \tag{1}$$

The organisms are curved rods and gram-negative—typical vibrios,
with a single polar flagellum (or occasionally two) (Fig. XVIII–1).
In addition a straight rod, *Clostridium nigrificans* (Fig. XVIII–2) has
the same physiology (Campbell *et al.*, 1957; Stüven, 1960). The action
of this organism has been thought to explain the occasional appearance
of spores in sulfate-reducing cultures, especially at temperatures above
50° C, and by an odd chance the spores are vibrio-shaped (Stüven,
1960). However, another true vibrio, *D. orientis*, has been reported
to reduce sulfate and to form spores (Adams and Postgate, 1959);
the spores are said to occur rarely but "on three occasions we have
observed *ca.* 90% sporulation."

The sulfate-reduction process explains the frequent association of
H₂S in nature with salt waters. Most such waters contain sulfate, and
decaying vegetation in them provides organic matter and establishes
anaerobic conditions. The H₂S often combines with iron salts to precipitate black FeS; hence, H₂S is associated with "black mud." The
Black Sea is named for this, and the association is common everywhere
in marine inlets; the shores of the Great Salt Lake provide another
example. The peculiar conditions prevailing in oil fields, where quantities of organic matter are found at great depths, favor the growth of
the anaerobic sulfate-reducers. A connection between H₂S formation
and petroleum deposits was pointed out by Murray Stewart in 1923
and by Bastin (1926; see also ZoBell, 1946). Since many oil fields are
near the sea, which contains sulfate, the relationship is readily under-

---

[2] The media used by different workers are very similar (see Starkey, 1948). Van
Delden's, the simplest, is, in grams per liter: Na lactate, 5; asparagine, 1.9; K₂HPO₄,
0.5; MgSO₄·7H₂O, 1.0; FeSO₄, a trace. By using ammonium nitrogen the growth of
sporeformers is discouraged. Elion's "first-rate culture medium" (1924) was: Na
lactate, 3; NH₄Cl, 1.0; K₂HPO₄, 0.5; MgSO₄·7H₂O, 2.0; CaSO₄, 1.0; ferrous amm.
sulfate, 0.5, or metallic iron. A similar medium with one small iron nail added per tube
has been used for counting sulfate-reducers in natural waters (Abd-el-Malik and Rizk,
1958). Oxidation of the iron helps to establish anaerobic conditions and allows the
growth of sulfate-reducers in tubes open to the air.

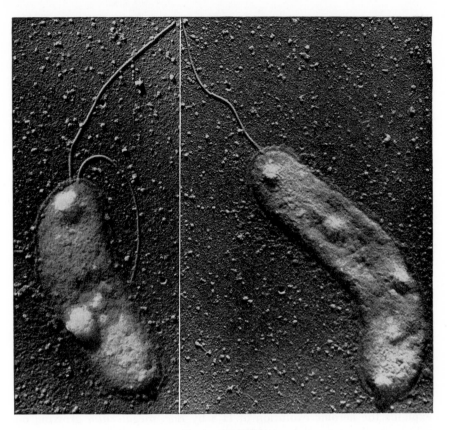

FIGURE XVIII–1

Desulfovibrio desulfuricans. Cells of a strain from a marine mud, cultured in Starkey's medium. 35,000 ×. (Photo, Dr. Klaus Stüven, *Arch. Mikrobiol.*, **35**:152–180, 1960.)

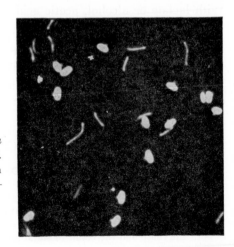

FIGURE XVIII–2

Rods and spores of *Clostridium nigrificans;* four-day culture at 55° C. Preparation in nigrosine. 850 ×. (From R. L. Starkey, *Arch. Mikrobiol.*, **9**:268–304, 1938.)

stood,[3] although it has not yet been shown that paraffin hydrocarbons can serve as hydrogen donors for the reduction.

There are other sites besides oil fields where sulfate-reducers have played a major part in geology. In some German salt mines the carnallite ($KCl \cdot MgCl_2 \cdot 6H_2O$) is blackened with flecks of FeS; elsewhere it contains red ferric oxide and residues of the highly aerobic iron bacteria (Chap. XXII), so that H_2S must have permeated the salt after deposition, suggesting the activity of a very halophilic Desulfovibrio (Müller and Schwartz, 1953). Elemental sulfur is often found in rock deposits, where it has been ascribed to H_2S produced bacterially from sulfate; since the H_2S could not have been subsequently oxidized in the anaerobic deposits, it probably reacted chemically with sulfate or SO_2 to deposit sulfur (Jones et al., 1956).

Many microbes, and all algae and green plants, must be able to reduce sulfate in small quantities because they grow and form protein when sulfate is their sole source of sulfur. In the ascomycete *Ophiostoma multiannulatum* this ability is genetically controlled, and mutants can be readily obtained that cannot reduce sulfate, although these can still use cysteine, cystine, or sulfide for growth (Fries, 1946). At least three genes control sulfate-reduction, and some of the mutants can be adapted back to growth with sulfate. Such reduction of sulfate *for growth* is to be clearly distinguished from its reduction *in bulk* with evolution of H_2S. Perhaps the former process, followed by autolysis, explains the aerobic evolution of H_2S by *Bac. megaterium* growing on sulfate media (Bromfield, 1953).

As organic compounds (i.e., hydrogen donors) for Desulfovibrio, a variety of substances will serve, including lactate, ethyl, propyl or butyl alcohol, glycols, some amino acids, and glucose (Baars, 1930). With lactate or alcohol, acetic acid is the main product, and the data fit well with the following equations (Baars):

$$2\ CH_3CHOHCOOH + H_2SO_4 \rightarrow 2\ CH_3COOH + 2\ CO_2 + H_2S + 2\ H_2O \quad (2)$$
$$2\ CH_3CH_2OH \quad\quad + H_2SO_4 \rightarrow 2\ CH_3COOH \quad\quad\quad\quad + H_2S + 2\ H_2O \quad (3)$$

In terms of equation (1), each molecule of these substances acts as a source of 4(H), e.g.:

$$CH_3CH_2OH + H_2O \rightarrow CH_3COOH + 4(H)$$

Butyrate goes almost completely to CO_2, with a little acetate, i.e.,

$$C_3H_7COOH + 6\ H_2O \rightarrow 4\ CO_2 + 20(H)$$

[3] It has also been suggested that the H_2S is responsible for the *formation* of petroleum, by acting as a chemical reducing agent to reduce acids or sugars to hydrocarbons (ZoBell, 1945). It requires some ingenuity, however, to visualize the organic matter as both the cause and the result of sulfate-reduction.

This reaction, along with other fatty acid oxidations, was ascribed to *D. rubentschickii*, but the existence of this organism is now doubtful (Postgate, 1959).

Some of the sulfate-reducers can utilize hydrogen gas as hydrogen donor, in addition to organic compounds, i.e., they have the enzyme hydrogenase (Stephenson and Stickland, 1931):

$$4\ H_2 + H_2SO_4 \rightarrow H_2S + 4\ H_2O$$

This removes the need for an organic compound as source of hydrogen, and made it possible to obtain pure cultures that develop in a strictly mineral medium with hydrogen and 5 per cent CO_2 (Butlin *et al.*, 1949). Sulfite was used to reduce the number of contaminants in the enrichment, since it is inhibitory to most bacteria, but can be reduced by Desulfovibrio. Evidently growth in such media is *autotrophic*, like that of bacteria oxidizing hydrogen by means of O_2 (Chap. XXII).

The use of $C^{14}O_2$ has confirmed that CO_2 is actually fixed, and some 10 to 20 gm-ions of $=SO_4$ are reduced per mole CO_2 fixed (Sorokin, 1954). That Desulfovibrio can grow autotrophically may be of importance in the corrosion of iron pipe, because iron will combine with the ‾OH ions of water provided an acceptor, or "depolarizer," can be found for the hydrogen. Correspondingly, iron wire can be used in the cultures instead of hydrogen, but the exact role of sulfate-reducers in corrosion is far from clear (see Starkey, 1958).

Desulfovibrio is remarkable for the variety of conditions in which it can grow. Van Delden (1904) isolated two organisms, *D. desulfuricans* being a fresh-water form and *D. estuarii* (obtained from a river mouth) growing only in 3 per cent NaCl. Baars' adaptation (1930) of *D. desulfuricans* to, and from, marine conditions (p. 163) appears to show that the marine "species" *D. estuarii* is only a salt-adapted form of *D. desulfuricans*. On the other hand a thermophilic form, first called *D. thermodesulfuricans* (Elion, 1924), has since been identified with *Cl. nigrificans* (Campbell *et al.*, 1957), so that the claim of Baars that *D. desulfuricans* can be trained to grow at 55° C is not supported, although there are moderately heat-resistant strains of the vibrio (Postgate, 1959). Sulfate-reduction occurs over a wide range of temperatures from 30° to 55° C, but this is probably due to the occurrence of many mutants, since no one pure strain grew over so wide a range (Butlin *et al.*, 1949).

Sulfate-reduction is mediated by an unusual cytochrome designated c_3 (see p. 211), which can be reduced by pyruvate, formate, and H_2 (with hydrogenase) and reoxidized by sulfate, sulfite, or thiosulfate (Postgate, 1956; Ishimoto and Koyama, 1957; Senez and Pichinoty, 1958). Because cytochrome c_3 has a very low redox potential, it can also be oxidized by hydroxylamine, nitrite, and even O_2, but the significance of this is doubtful, in so strict an anaerobe as Desulfovibrio. *D. orientis* has a different cytochrome, with band at 557 mμ. These phenomena strikingly parallel nitrate reduction (Chap. X), where also the nitrate acts as hydrogen acceptor by way of a cytochrome. *M. denitrificans* reducing nitrate with hydrogen gas also compares with the autotrophic growth of Desulfovibrio.

The first product of sulfate-reduction is probably adenosine-5-phosphosulfite, since cell-free preparations reduce $^=SO_4$ to $^=SO_3$ by H_2 only in presence of ATP (Peck, 1959), 1 mole of ATP being used, and one pyrophosphate split off, for each H_2. TPNH can also function as reducing agent. Further reduction can occur all the way to sulfide (Ishimoto, 1959). The reaction between ATP and sulfate, yielding adenosine-5-phosphosulfite, has been studied in yeast (Robbins and Lipmann, 1956; Wilson and Bandurski, 1958; Hilz and Kittler, 1958, 1960); it is specific for ATP but not for sulfate, and occurs also with selenate, sulfite, chromate, molybdate, and tungstate. Since all these except sulfite inhibit sulfate-reduction, they probably do so by competing for ATP. Thus the combination with adenosine evidently makes the sulfate group more easily reducible. The sulfate reductase appears to contain lipoic acid.

Among other, less drastic, reductions, that of tetrathionate to thiosulfate is interesting (Knox and Pollock, 1944–1950):

$$^=S_4O_6 + 2\ e \rightarrow 2\ ^=S_2O_3$$

This reaction, due to the enzyme tetrathionase, is brought about by Salmonella, in which it is readily induced. It is the reverse of the conventional iodine titration of thiosulfate; with its aid, the tetrathionate is made available for growth.

Since H_2S is continually being produced, it must also be removed. This is done by oxidation, supporting the growth of both chemosynthetic and photosynthetic autotrophs (Chaps. XXII and XXIII). Many minor sulfur compounds are also involved, especially in soil (see Starkey, 1950). The resulting "sulfur cycle" is comparable, though not in complexity, with the nitrogen cycle (see e.g., Gregory and Robbins, 1960, and p. 422).

2. METHANE FORMATION

Methane is readily formed when plant material decays in waterlogged anaerobic soil. A flickering blue light, seen over swamps, was formerly said to have lured travelers deeper and deeper into the bog and so to their doom. This *ignis fatuus* or false fire is due to the ignition of the methane, probably by traces of phosphorus hydrides. Methane is produced in such large quantities in the anaerobic decomposition of sewage that the gases from the Imhoff tank are sometimes piped off for heating or lighting purposes. Its formation indirectly from cellulose in the rumen of cattle was discussed in the preceding chapter.

It was Söhngen (1906, 1910) who first made enrichment cultures that fermented the lower fatty acids to methane. No other hydrocarbon resulted. A large sarcina was the most prominent organism. Later, a thermophilic bacterium was found to produce methane from fatty acids or glucose, while crude cultures from feces would attack cabbage and cellulose in the same way (Coolhaas, 1928). Other fermentable substrates are methanol, ethanol, butanol, formate, butyrate, formaldehyde, and acetone. The methane is accompanied by CO_2, and for the fatty acids the general process can be represented (Buswell and Neave, 1930):

$$C_nH_{2n}O_2 + \frac{n-2}{2} H_2O \rightarrow \frac{n+2}{4} CO_2 + \frac{3n-2}{4} CH_4$$

The fermentation goes best when n is an even number (Söhngen, 1910). In this reaction the fatty acids are not decarboxylated, because no matter what the length of the carbon chain, only methane is produced; higher hydrocarbons have never been obtained in appreciable quantities (Thayer, 1931). The absence of higher hydrocarbons means that compounds of two or more carbon atoms are not being reduced; the corollary is that methane arises because a compound of one carbon atom, namely CO_2, is being reduced. This brilliant suggestion made by van Niel in 1933 to Barker[4] has been amply confirmed (Barker, 1936–1943). It was, indeed, earlier observed that certain rods will form CH_4 from hydrogen and CO_2 (Söhngen, 1906; Fischer et al., 1932; Stephenson and Stickland, 1933):

$$CO_2 + 4\ H_2 \rightarrow CH_4 + 2\ H_2O \tag{4}$$

In Barker's studies, pure cultures were obtained for the first time by using Na_2S to remove the last traces of oxygen (cf. p. 608). Minute colonies, made evident by gas production in deep agar tubes, yielded pure cultures of four types:

(1) A large sarcina, evidently Söhngen's organism, called *Methanosarcina (Ms.) methanica*, and gram-variable, unlike other *Sarcinae*; this organism had also been studied by Smit (1930; Fig. XVIII–3);

(2) A coccus, also gram-variable, called *Methanococcus (Mc.) Mazei* (Fig. XVIII–4);

(3) A gram-negative rod forming long threads, called *Methanobacterium (Mb.) Sohngenii* (Fig. XVIII–5);

---

[4] Made also to the present writer at about the same time.

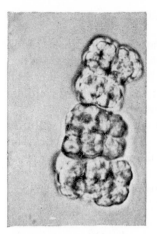

FIGURE XVIII–3

Methanosarcina methanica, from fermenting sewage.
Unstained. 700 ×. Original photo, Jan Smit. (Cf.
Die Gärungssarcinen, 1930.)

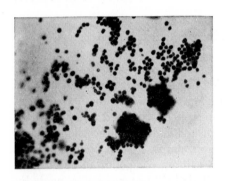

FIGURE XVIII–4

Methanococcus Mazei. Cells in crushed
colony in agar. Stained with erythrosin.
650 ×. (From H. A. Barker, *Arch.
Mikrobiol.,* 7:420–438.)

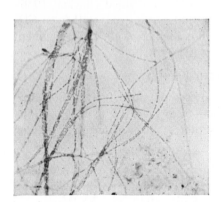

FIGURE XVIII–5

Methanobacterium Söhngenii. Stained
with erythrosin. 650 ×. (From H. A.
Barker, *Arch. Mikrobiol.,* 7:420–438.)

614

(4) Another rod, forming "sporelike bodies" of low heat resistance and called *Methanobacterium* (*Mb.*) *Omelianskii*. This too is mostly gram-negative.

The first three ferment acetic and butyric acids, the last ferments alcohols. Two other rods and another Sarcina were obtained later (Kluyver and Schnellen, 1947; Mylroie and Hungate, 1954), and the methane-forming bacterium of cattle rumen (Chap. XVII, sec. 5D) has since been added (Carroll and Hungate, 1955); this last is a gram-positive nonmotile rod, *Mb. ruminantium*, which can use H_2 or, more weakly, HCOOH as reducing agent.

With these organisms the following facts have been established:

(1) Ethyl alcohol and CO_2 are converted quantitatively to acetic acid and methane:

$$2 \ CH_3CH_2OH + CO_2 \rightarrow 2 \ CH_3COOH + CH_4 \tag{5}$$

Note the similarity to equation (3) of the *Desulfovibrio* above.

(2) Butanol is similarly converted to butyric acid and methane:

$$2 \ C_3H_7CH_2OH + CO_2 \rightarrow 2 \ C_3H_7COOH + CH_4 \tag{6}$$

(3) In cooperation with *Cl. kluyveri* (cf. Chap. XV, sec. 4), ethanol can be converted, via acetic acid, to butyric and caproic acids. This is, of course, a side reaction.

(4) $C^{14}O_2$ is reduced to $C^{14}H_4$ by *Mb. Omelianskii*, fermenting alcohol (Barker *et al.*, 1940; Stadtman and Barker, 1949), and by *Mb. ruminantium*, using CO_2 and H_2 (Smith and Hungate, 1958). In the former case the cells had some radioactivity, indicating that 1.5 per cent of the CO_2 was assimilated; the inactive carbon of ethanol was also assimilated (Barker and Beck, 1941).

(5) Even with methanol, using *Ms. methanica*, $C^{14}O_2$ gave radioactive methane. This is of special interest because the equation for the over-all process,

$$4 \ CH_3OH \rightarrow CO_2 + 3 \ CH_4 + 2 \ H_2O \tag{7}$$

could be interpreted as a reduction of methanol rather than of CO_2. Evidently the real reaction has two phases:

$$(a) \ CH_3OH + H_2O \rightarrow CO_2 + 6(H)$$
$$(b) \ CO_2 + 8(H) \qquad \rightarrow CH_4 + 2 \ H_2O$$

Equation (7) represents four of (a) and three of (b).

(6) Hydrogen gas can be used by *Mb. Omelianskii*, *Mb. ruminantium*, *Mb. formicicum*, and another sarcina, *Ms. Barkeri* (Kluyver and Schnellen, 1947; Smith and Hungate, 1958).

(7) A striking variant is the use of CO. A mixture of CO and H_2 passed over a natural sludge gave rise to CH_4 and CO_2 (Fischer *et al.*, 1931–1932). By varying the gas concentration it could be shown (with enrichment cultures) that the reaction occurs in two steps:

$$\left.\begin{array}{l} CO + H_2O \;\rightarrow CO_2 + H_2 \\ CO_2 + 4\ H_2 \rightarrow CH_4 + 2\ H_2O \end{array}\right\} CO + 3\ H_2 \rightarrow CH_4 + H_2O$$

With pure cultures of *Ms. Barkeri* the same thing was shown by analyzing the mixture before the reaction was over (Kluyver and Schnellen, 1947). *Mb. formicicum*, which ferments formate, similarly attacks CO and hydrogen (Mylroie and Hungate, 1954).

Methane can even be produced by *Ms. Barkeri* from pure CO alone. Here the first of the two reactions is the only source of hydrogen, and the over-all equation would be:

$$4\ CO + 2\ H_2O \rightarrow 3\ CO_2 + CH_4$$

(8) Only in the fermentations of acetate and benzoate is methane formed from other sources than CO_2. With acetate (using enrichment cultures of Methanococcus) the methane comes mostly from the methyl group and the CO_2 from the carboxyl group, although toward the end a little CO_2 is converted to methane (Stadtman and Barker, 1949). This anomaly may mean that both CO_2 and acetate are converted into methane only via an intermediate compound that is common to both. The direct decarboxylation of acetate seems open to doubt. With benzoate (using enrichment cultures from sewage sludge) high yields of CH_4 and CO_2 were obtained, but very little of the CO_2 added was reduced to methane (Clark and Fina, 1952). Apparently most of the methane came directly from benzoic acid.

With the exception of these last two special cases the data all show that the fundamental reaction in the methane fermentation is:

$$CO_2 + 4\ H_2A \rightarrow CH_4 + 4\ A + 2\ H_2O \tag{8}$$

In the case of hydrogen, A of course is missing. This representation of CO_2 reduction shows great similarity to the reactions of photosynthesis to be discussed in Chapter XXIII. But whereas in photosynthesis the CO_2-reducing enzymes are rather well understood, the methane-forming enzymes remain totally unknown.

3. ACETIC ACID FORMATION FROM CO_2

A series of bacterial processes differing only moderately from the methane fermentation will be described quite briefly.

In studying the conversion of CO and CO_2 to methane (see above), Fischer *et al.* (1932) found that in certain cultures acetic acid is formed rather than methane, and the reaction approximates (cf. equation [4] above):

$$2\ CO_2 + 4\ H_2 \rightarrow CH_3COOH + 2\ H_2O \tag{9}$$

Later a *Clostridium*, *Cl. aceticum*, was obtained in pure culture that carried out reaction (9) alone (Wieringa, 1936). Evidently this represents an alternative form of the generalized reaction (8), with acetic acid replacing methane. It appears now that this is a widespread bacterial reaction type, and four instances have been elucidated by Barker and his students.

(1) The butyric fermentation due to *Butyribacterium rettgeri* (see p. 529) differs from that caused by the butyric clostridia in that lactate is readily fermented. The yield of acetic and butyric acids is relatively high and that of CO_2 is low. Accordingly Barker *et al.* (1945) considered that some of the CO_2 might be converted to fatty acids. The fermentation was allowed to proceed in presence of $C^{14}O_2$; as a result about 25 per cent of the C^{14} was recovered as acetic acid and about 50 per cent as butyric:

$$CH_3CHOHCOOH + H_2O \rightarrow CH_3COOH + CO_2 + 4(H)$$

Then:

$$2\ CO_2 \qquad + 8(H) \rightarrow CH_3COOH + 2\ H_2O \tag{10}$$
$$2\ CH_3COOH + 4(H) \rightarrow C_3H_7COOH + 2\ H_2O \tag{11}$$

Reactions (10) and (11) compete for the active hydrogen. The butyric acid, of course, gets its isotope from the acetic acid formed by CO_2 reduction. Reaction (10) is the analogue of reaction (9).

(2) The anaerobic fermentation of uric acid by *Cl. acidi-urici* produces acetic acid, CO_2, and ammonia (p. 356):

$$2\ C_5H_4N_4O_3 + 11\ H_2O \rightarrow 1\tfrac{1}{2}\ CH_3COOH + 7\ CO_2 + 8\ NH_3$$

Other purines give similar reactions. When the fermentation was carried out in the presence of $C^{14}O_2$, both the acetic acid and the non-volatile material contained the isotope (Barker *et al.*, 1940). Evidently, therefore, CO_2 is being reduced to acetic acid, as in equation (10), as well as other compounds. *Cl. cylindrosporum* gives a similar fermentation which produces glycine in addition, and here $C^{14}O_2$ yields isotope in the CH_3 of acetic acid and the COOH of glycine (Barker and Eldsen, 1947).

(3) Perhaps the most remarkable example is the fermentation of sugars carried out by *Cl. thermoaceticum* (Barker, 1944; Barker and

Kamen, 1945). Glucose or xylose is converted almost completely to acetic acid, anaerobically, by this organism:

$$C_6H_{12}O_6 \rightarrow 3\ C_2H_4O_2$$

Added $C^{14}O_2$ is readily recovered in the acetic acid. Hence the sugar must first be converted to acetic acid and CO_2:

$$C_6H_{12}O_6 + 2\ H_2O \rightarrow 2\ CH_3COOH + 2\ CO_2 + 8(H)$$

and the resulting CO_2 then reduced as in equation (10). Pyruvic acid is probably an intermediate, since it is also fermented to acetic acid and CO_2.

4. AEROBIC AND ANAEROBIC CO$_2$ REDUCTION

All the cases surveyed above involve strict anaerobes and consist of the transfer of either hydrogen gas or the hydrogen from organic compounds to the acceptors, sulfate or carbon dioxide. When the acceptor is CO_2, the organism has at least the potentiality of growing autotrophically. As shown in Chapter XXVI, the most primitive organisms on earth were probably anaerobes. When oxygen became available, it would have been preferred, as a hydrogen acceptor, to any other compound, organic or inorganic, because the combination with oxygen is more strongly exergonic than any alternative. Correspondingly, the aerobic organisms are now the dominant forms. Although CO_2 still has to be reduced, we find the aerobes linking the reduction to an oxidation that provides the energy for it. Thus, *Hydrogenomonas*, which reduces CO_2 with the oxidation of hydrogen, will not combine CO_2 with hydrogen anaerobically (Kluyver and Manten, 1942). Yet CO_2 and H_2 are combined by the anaerobes described above. It follows that the linkage to an oxidation process in the aerobic forms (if one dare assume the direction of evolution) has become obligate over the years. These matters are discussed further in Chapter XXII.

REFERENCES

Abd-el-Malik, Y., and Rizk, S. G. 1958. *Nature*, **182**:538.
Adams, M. E., and Postgate, J. R. 1959. *J. Gen. Microbiol.*, **20**:252–257.
*Baars, J. K. 1930. Over Sulfaatreductie door Bacterien. Dissertation, Delft.
Barker, H. A. 1936–1943. Studies upon the Methane Fermentation. I and II, *Arch. Mikrobiol.*, **7**:404–419, 420–438; III, *ibid.*, **8**:415–421 (1937); IV, *Ant. v. Leeuwenhoek*, pp. 201–220 (1940); V, *J. Biol. Chem.*, **137**:153–167 (1940); VI, *Proc. Nat. Acad. Sci.*, **29**:184–190 (1943).

Barker, H. A. 1944. *Proc. Nat. Acad. Sci.*, **30**:88–90; Barker, H. A., and Kamen, M. D. 1945. *Proc. Nat. Acad. Sci.*, **31**:219–225.

Barker, H. A., and Beck, J. V. 1941. *J. Biol. Chem.*, **141**:3–27.

Barker, H. A., and Elsden, S. R. 1947. *J. Biol. Chem.*, **167**:619–620.

Barker, H. A.; Kamen, M. D.; and Haas, V. 1945. *Proc. Nat. Acad. Sci.*, **31**:355–360.

Barker, H. A.; Ruben, S.; and Beck, J. V. 1940. *Proc. Nat. Acad. Sci.*, **26**:477–482.

Barker, H. A.; Ruben, S.; and Kamen, M. D. 1940. *Proc. Nat. Acad. Sci.*, **26**:426–430.

Bastin, E. S. 1926. *Bull. Amer. Asscc. Petr. Geol.*, **10**:1270–1299.

Beijerinck, M. W. 1895. *Zentr. Bakt. II*, **1**:1–9, 49–59, 104–114.

Bromfield, S. M. 1953. *J. Gen. Microbiol.*, **8**:378–390.

Buswell, A. M., and Neave, S. L. 1930. *Bull. Illinois State Water Survey*, No. 30.

Butlin, K. R.; Adams, M. E.; and Thomas, M. 1949. *J. Gen. Microbiol.*, **3**:46–59.

Campbell, L. L., Jr.; Frank, H. A.; and Hall, E. R. 1957. *J. Bact.*, **73**:516–521.

Carroll, E. J., and Hungate, R. E. 1955. *Arch. Biochem. Biophys.*, **56**:525–536.

Clark, F. M., and Fina, L. R. 1952. *Arch. Biochem. Biophys.*, **36**:26–32.

Coolhaas, C. 1928. *Zentr. Bakt. II*, **75**:161–170.

van Delden, A. 1904. *Zentr. Bakt. II*, **11**:81–94, 113–119.

Elion, L. 1924. *Zentr. Bakt. II*, **63**:58–67.

Fischer, F.; Lieske, R.; and Winzer, K. 1931–1932. *Biochem. Z.*, **236**:247–257; **245**:2–12 (1932).

Fries, N. 1946. *Svensk Bot. Tidskrift*, **40**:127–140.

*Gregory, J. D., and Robbins, P. W. 1960. *Ann. Rev. Biochem.*, **29**:347–364.

Hilz, H., and Kittler, M. 1958–1960. *Biochim. Biophys. Acta*, **30**:650–651; *Biochem. Zeit.*, **332**:151–166; *Biochem. Biophys. Res. Comms.*, **3**:140–142 (1960).

Ishimoto, M. 1959. *J. Biochem., Tokyo*, **46**:105–108.

Ishimoto, M., and Koyama, J. 1957. *J. Biochem. Tokyo*, **44**:233–242, 413–423, 707–715. and earlier papers there cited.

Jones, G. E.; Starkey, R. L.; Feely, H. W.; and Kulp, J. L. 1956. *Science*, **123**:1124–1125.

Kluyver, A. J. 1931. The Chemical Activities of Microorganisms. Univ. of London Press.

Kluyver, A. J., and Manten, A. 1942. *Ant. v. Leeuwenhoek*, **8**:71–85.

Kluyver, A. J., and Schnellen, C. G. T. P. 1947. *Arch. Biochem.*, **14**:57–70.

Knox, R., and Pollock, M. R. 1944–1950. *Biochem. J.*, **33**:299–304; Pollock, M. R. *Brit. J. Exp. Path.*, **26**:410–416 (1945); Knox, R. *Ibid.*, pp. 146–150 (1945); *J. Gen. Microbiol.*, **4**:388–392 (1950).

Müller, A., and Schwartz, W. 1953. *Zeit. deut. geol. Ges.*, **105**:789–802.

Mylroie, R. L., and Hungate, R. E. 1954. *Canad. J. Microbiol.*, **1**:55–64.

Peck, H. D. 1959. *Proc. Nat. Acad. Sci.*, **45**:701–708.

*Postgate, J. R. 1956. *J. Gen. Microbiol.*, **14**:545–572.

*Postgate, J. R. 1959. Sulphate Reduction by Bacteria. *Ann. Rev. Microbiol.*, **13**:505–520 (with 146 refs.).

Robbins, P. W., and Lipmann, F. 1956. *J. Am. Chem. Soc.*, **78**:2652, 6409–6410.

Senez, J. C., and Pichinoty, F. 1958. *Biochim. Biophys. Acta*, **27**:569–580; **28**:355–369.

*Smit, J. 1930. Die Gärungssarcinen. Pflanzenforschung, ed. R. Kolkwitz. Jena, G. Fischer Verlag. 59 pp.

Smith, P. H., and Hungate, R. E. 1958. *J. Bact.*, **75**:713–718.

Söhngen, N. L. 1906. *Zentr. Bakt. II*, **15**:513–517; Het ontstaan en verdwijnen van Waterstof en Methaan onder den invloed van het organische Leven. Dissertation, Delft.

Söhngen, N. L. 1910. *Rec. trav. chim. Pays Bas*, **29**:238–274.

Sorokin, Y. I. 1954. *Compt. rend. U.R.S.S.*, **95**:61; *Proc.* (Trudy) *Inst. Mikrobiol.*, *Akad. Nauk SSR*, **3**:21–34.

Stadtman, T. C., and Barker, H. A. 1949. *Arch. Biochem.*, **21**:256-264; cf. Boswell, A. M., and Sollo, F. W. *J. Am. Chem. Soc.*, **70**:1770 (1948).

*Starkey, R. L. 1938. *Arch. Mikrobiol.*, **9**:268–304.

Starkey, R. L. 1948. *J. Am. Waterworks Assoc.*, **40**:1291–1298.

*Starkey, R. L. 1950. Relations of Microorganisms to Transformations of Sulfur in Soils. *Soil Sci.*, **70**:55–65.

Starkey, R. L. 1958. *Producers' Monthly*, **22**:12–30.

Stephenson, M., and Stickland, L. H. 1933. *Biochem. J.*, **27**:1517–1527.

Stüven, K. 1960. *Arch. f. Mikrobiol.*, **35**:152–180.

Thayer, L. A. 1931. *Bull. Am. Assoc. Petroleum Geol.*, **15**:441–453.

Wieringa, K. T. 1936. *Ant. v. Leeuwenhoek*, **3**:1–11.

Wilson, L. G., and Bandurski, R. H. 1958. *J. Biol. Chem.*, **233**:975–981.

ZoBell, C. E. 1945. *Science*, **102**:364–369.

*ZoBell, C. E. 1946. *Oil Weekly*, Feb. 18, pp. 1–8.

Part Four

Growth and Synthesis

CHAPTER XIX

Growth and Protoplasm Formation

The amazing feature of growth, in a microbial culture as in living beings in general, lies in the fact that it involves the manufacture and orderly arrangement of the . . . components which characterize the organism, in such a way as to duplicate accurately an existing pattern.

C. B. van Niel (1949)

1. THE NORMAL GROWTH CURVE

Under ideal conditions a bacterial cell can divide in two every 15 to 20 minutes. At this rate any reasonably sized culture flask would be filled to overflowing in about 12 hours. If the rate continued undiminished for 36 hours, the progeny of a single cell would cover the whole earth with a layer of bacteria a foot deep.

Needless to say, what actually happens is that the growth rate changes rapidly with time. The study and interpretation of these changes are, therefore, of the highest importance.

If a few bacteria are inoculated into a new medium, and small samples taken out from time to time for counting, by the conventional method of pouring plates and enumerating the colonies, there is obtained all or part of a curve like Figure XIX–1. Such curves have been divided into eight phases:

(1) The *stationary phase*, in which no multiplication occurs.

(2) The phase of increasing growth rate. These first two phases together constitute the *lag phase*.

(3) The *"logarithmic"* or *exponential phase*, in which the log of the number of cells increases linearly with time. This means that each cell is dividing in two at a fixed time interval, i.e., the growth rate is constant and maximal.

(4) A phase of decreasing growth rate, with many cells dying off.

(5) A brief stationary phase, in which growth and death are just balanced, and the population is at the maximum the medium can support.

(6) The phase of increasing death rate.

(7) The "logarithmic" death phase; the inverse of phase 3. This is seldom studied at medium temperature and is mainly of interest in connection with heat sterilization.

(8) A phase, which may last a very long time, of decreasing death rate. Provided the medium does not dry up, a few survivors may be present almost indefinitely (cf. p. 186).

In interpreting the curve it may be objected that the plating method does not actually count the bacteria, but counts colonies derived from

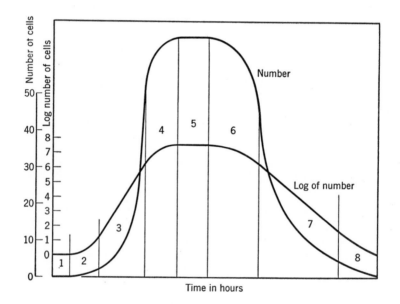

FIGURE XIX–1

Diagrammatic growth curves. The arithmetical and logarithmic scales are not in proportion.

them; i.e., it counts only those bacteria that could multiply to form colonies. Indeed, it is called the *viable count*. This difficulty (cf. also Chap. VI) can be avoided by actually counting all cells present (total count), which is done by pipetting a small volume of culture into a measured depression on a microscope slide and counting the visible cells, either under dark-field illumination or after staining. Generally these counts give results only a little higher than the viable count.

The difference, in a careful study with *S. cholerae-suis*, was about 25 per cent (Wilson, 1922). Hence the phenomena of the growth curve really do represent rates of change of the population. Much work has been done to explain the different phases.

2. THE LAG PHASE

The first and most obvious problem is: Why do not the organisms begin to multiply immediately? Why need there be any lag? Phases 1 and 2, the so-called "lag period," are not really to be expected a priori, considering that the medium is new.

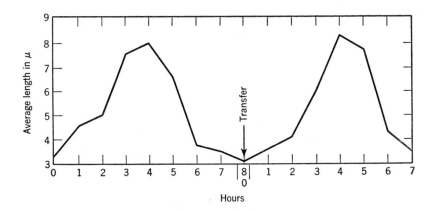

FIGURE XIX-2

Bacillus megaterium. Average length of cell as a function of time after transfer to new medium. (From A. T. Henrici, *Proc. Soc. for Exptl. Biol. and Med.,* **21**:215–227. By courtesy of the Soc. for Exptl. Biol. and Med.)

As a matter of fact, if we take for the inoculum cells from the actively dividing period, phase 3, they do not show any lag (Chesney, 1916). The lag is shown by inocula taken from phase 1 and also from phases 5 and 6. It is therefore a function of the state of the cells when transferred; nongrowing cells have to get into a growing or "embryonic" state before they can start dividing. The first clue to the nature of this growing state was obtained by carefully observing the cells. It then appeared that during the lag they grow to much greater size than normal, then decrease again during the logarithmic phase. Henrici's data for *Bac. megatherium* are shown in Figure XIX–2. Two cycles are given, a subculture being made at eight hours when the cells have come down to the initial size. The actual size reached depends some-

what on the concentration of the nutrient medium: when the medium
was reduced to a quarter of its original strength, the maximum size
fell from 8 μ to 6 μ (Henrici, 1923; cf. p. 636).

Since the cells grow larger instead of dividing, there is no lag in
the synthesis of protoplasm. If we follow, instead of cell numbers, the
total protein, the nucleic acid, or the cell phosphorus, we see that the
increase of cell material begins immediately. The total nitrogen, for
instance, increases linearly, on a logarithmic scale, from the start
(Hershey, 1938). Synchronized cultures (see below) show these relationships best. It is evident that many constituents must be increasing
on a per cell basis during the lag phase.

The oxygen uptake per cell also passes through a sharp maximum,
which is reached at about one and one-half hours with *E. coli*, i.e., after
the end of the lag phase, and corresponds exactly to the time when
the cells are at their largest (Fig. XIX–3). Again, if calculated per
unit of bacterial nitrogen, there is no maximum, but the rate remains
constant, i.e., oxygen uptake is a function of the amount of protoplasm
and not of the number of cells. However, respiration is increased by
growth (see below).

All these data, therefore, show that in young cultures the cells
increase at once in size and in materials, but without dividing; it is
only the division process that shows a lag. The lag phase should be
called the "phase of cell enlargement" (Hershey, 1938).

The reason for the lag in cell division is not known, and a special
cell division factor has been postulated (Lodge and Hinshelwood,
1943). Of its nature there are conflicting indications. Apparently Mg
ions promote cell division in *Cl. welchii*, and the cultures become
filamentous without Mg (Webb, 1948), but it is hard to see how this
could play a part in the "lag" phenomenon. In yeasts, cysteine and
glutathione promote cell division, while penicillin and also cobalt
inhibit it, producing long "mycelial" growths (Nickerson and van Rij,
1949). Thus, if there really is a division factor in these cells, it might
be a sulfhydryl compound. (Cobalt readily forms complexes with
sulfhydryl). Many bacteria growing in the presence of penicillin also
form filamentous growths because this antibiotic inhibits the formation
of the cell wall (Chap. XXV). In Bacilli the lag can be reduced or
prevented by adding glucose autoclaved with phosphate (Sargeant
et al., 1957). The effective compound is a hydroxyacid, and several
ordinary hydroxyacids have the same effect; possibly they act by
chelating a metal ion. In Aerobacter the lag is removed by adding
glutamic acid in concentrations of 5 to 10 parts per million. The
effect is not specific, since some other amino acids, and also succinate,
have a similar effect (Dagley *et al.*, 1949). (The bacteria can form

glutamate from succinate, however.) This suggests that the lag is concerned with amino acid formation. In some lactobacilli the lag is reduced by adding extra vitamins. Probably cell division is complexly interrelated with nitrogen metabolism.

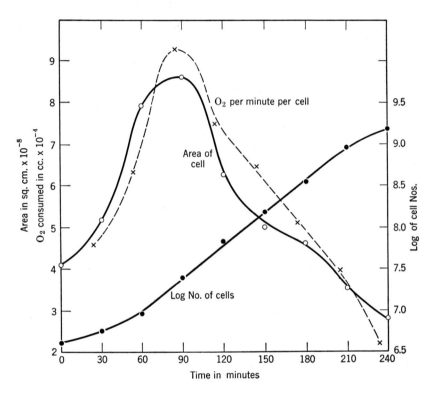

FIGURE XIX–3

Cell number compared with cell size and O_2 consumption per cell for young *E. coli* cultures in peptone. Cell size expressed as area of cell as seen in the microscope field. (Data of D. S. Martin, 1932, replotted.)

During the lag phase the cells are less sensitive to unfavorable conditions than later. Thus, cells of *E. coli* in the first hour after transfer from a one-week-old culture were resistant to a 5 per cent NaCl (= 0.9 M), but similar exposure a few hours later caused great mortality. The sensitivity began to increase before there was appreciable cell division (Sherman and Albus, 1923–1924). The resistance to heat treatment is also increased at first, then rapidly decreases as cell division begins (Elliker and Frazier, 1938). Part of this resistance of the nondividing cells may be simply due to their large size and consequent smaller relative surface.

3. SYNCHRONIZED CELL DIVISION

The time of emergence from the lag phase is evidently distributed statistically through the population. In recent years several means have been developed to minimize distribution and start all cells dividing at once.

One method depends on sudden changes in temperature. Many cultures, if chilled to 0° C in a nutrient medium and rapidly warmed, at

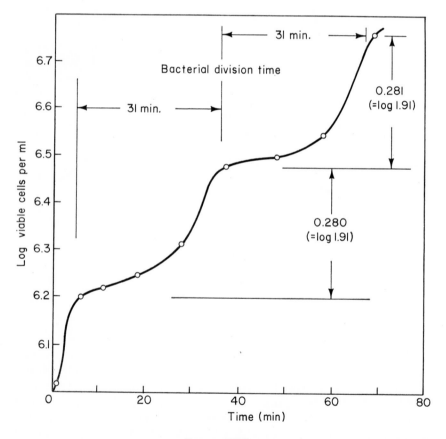

FIGURE XIX–4

Growth of pneumococci at 37° after 15 minutes at 25° C. The 31-minute generation time is calculated from the curve. (From R. D. Hotchkiss, 1954.)

once begin to divide. When Salmonella cultures are quickly raised from 25° to 37° C by adding a known volume of hot medium, the two deeply staining "nuclear" bodies each divide within about six minutes; within 20 minutes all the cells have divided once (Lark and Maaløe, 1954). This *synchronized division* can be repeated several times by cooling and reheating; the precise time intervals depend on the culture density and its growth phase. In Pneumococcus a similar rise to 37° C, after 15 minutes at 25° C, gave the viable counts in Figure XIX–4, in which synchronized doubling (log 2 = 0.3) is very obvious (Hotchkiss, 1954).

A method developed by Japanese workers depends on the observation that the smaller cells divide more rapidly than the larger ones. In *E. coli* strain B, synchronized division can be achieved by centrifuging into fractions of different cell size; on then being placed in fresh medium the small cells all divide in 30 to 40 minutes (at 37° C), while the large ones undergo two or three division cycles at 50-minute intervals (Maruyama and Yanagita, 1956). The separation can be made neatly by running the suspension through many layers of filter paper; the smallest cells come through first. While the cell numbers then go up in discrete steps, the rate of incorporation of leucine into protein, the rates of synthesis of DNA and of β-galactosidase, as well as the total amounts of DNA, RNA, and protein, all remain smoothly linear (Abbo and Pardee, 1960, see Fig. XIX–5). It is evident that syntheses in the cell go on independently of cell division.

A third method depends on the suppression of cell division exerted by very high cell densities. In *E. coli* all divisions cease at 5.10^9 cells per milliliter (Yanagita and Kaneko, 1961). Syntheses still go on, as noted above, DNA and protein increasing 40 to 50 per cent in 50 minutes at 37° C. Then, when the suspension is suddenly diluted 1:100, all the cells divide.

These procedures will have increasing use in the study of cell division.

4. THE "LOGARITHMIC" PHASE AND ITS CONTROL

In this phase cells are dividing at a constant rate. The growth rate, $\alpha, = \frac{1}{n} \cdot \frac{dn}{dt}$, where n is the number of cells at any time t. We can calculate the generation time, g, or time from one cell division to the next, simply from two counts. If there are n_1 cells at time t_1 and n_2 at time t_2, then the average growth rate is $\frac{\log n_2 - \log n_1}{(t_2 - t_1) \log 2}$, and the number of generations is $\frac{t_2 - t_1}{g}$. Since $\log_2 10 = 3.32$, this becomes $\log_2 \frac{n_2}{n_1} = 3.32$

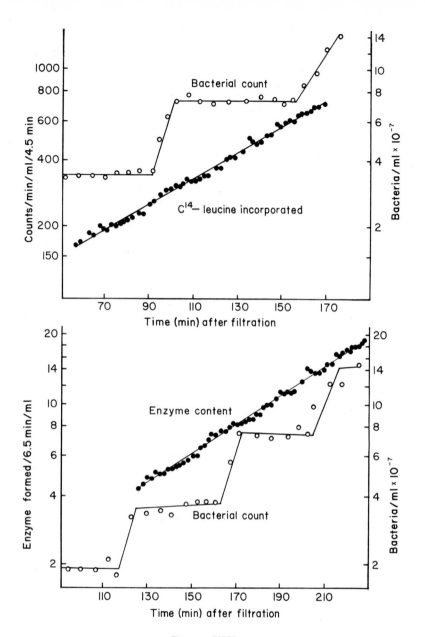

FIGURE XIX–5

While the bacterial divisions are synchronized, so that the counts go up stepwise, the incorporation of amino acid into protein and the synthesis of an enzyme (β-galactosidase) proceed linearly. (From Abbo and Pardee, 1960.)

$(\log_{10} n_2 - \log_{10} n_1)$. Hence the time for each generation is:

$$g = \frac{t_2 - t_1}{\log_2 \dfrac{n_2}{n_1}} = \frac{t_2 - t_1}{3.32(\log_{10} n_2 - \log_{10} n_1)}$$

Of course, if some of the cells do not divide, the division rate of those that do is a little greater. If we take Wilson's figure of 25 per cent for the nonviable cells (p. 625), the constant 3.32 would become 4.11.

As stated at the outset, the generation time can be less than 20 minutes—17 minutes has been recorded for *E. coli* (Barber, 1908), 20 minutes for *S. cholerae-suis* (Wilson, 1922). These high rates are not maintained for long; figures determined over a period of several hours are more commonly 30 to 40 minutes (Monod, 1942).

The rate of multiplication is controlled by the following factors.

A. Aeration

With the obvious exception of the anaerobes and microaerophiles, the growth of all microorganisms studied is highly dependent on oxygen.

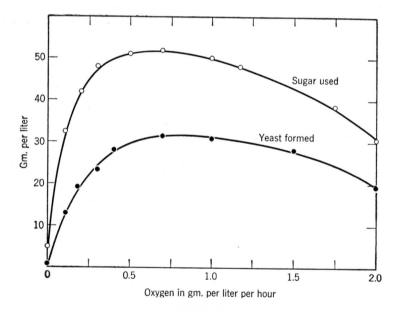

FIGURE XIX–6

Yeast formed and sugar consumed as a function of aeration. Inoculum, 300 mg fresh yeast per liter. Growth at 30° C in sucrose-salts-vitamins medium. (From J. White and D. J. Munns, *Wallerstein Lab. Comm.*, 14:199–218, 1951. By courtesy of Wallerstein Labs., New York.)

This is true for yeast (Chap. XI, sec. 11), ciliate protozoa (Phelps, 1936), and numerous bacteria (Monod, 1942; Rahn and Richardson, 1940–1942; van Niel, 1949). It is also true for fungi and higher plants. Some experiments with yeast are summarized in Figure. XIX–6. The curves show an enormous increase of growth with aeration.[1] The decrease of growth and of sugar consumption at excessively high aeration rates may be due to the cooling effect of the air. For bacteria an example can be taken from the work of Winslow's group with *E. coli* (Table XIX–1). Here the addition of glucose raises the number of

TABLE XIX–1. Multiplication, and CO_2 Production, of *E. coli* as Affected by Glucose and by Aeration

(Data from Walker *et al.*, 1934)

Gas Bubbled	Medium	NO. OF CELLS (IN MILLIONS)		Growth Period (hours)	Maximum CO_2 Production mg $\times 10^{-11}$ per Cell per Hour
		Inoculated	After Growth		
N_2	Peptone	11	38	6	68
N_2	Peptone-glucose	11	152	6	211
Air	Peptone	16	655	5	123
Air	Peptone-glucose	17	861	5	117

cells somewhat, but the effect of aeration is far greater. In peptone, the numbers increase only about three and one-half times when nitrogen is bubbled, but about 41 times with air. It may be noted, too, from the last column, that aeration decreases the output of CO_2 from glucose (Pasteur effect).

Not only does aeration increase the population density, but rapidly growing cells have a higher oxygen consumption than resting cells. Pirt (1957), for instance, found with Aerobacter in continuous culture that the respiration rate, per milligram of dry weight, varied linearly with the growth rate. Thus, the oxygen demand in growing cultures is increased even more, and to maintain maximum growth rate in a dense culture becomes very difficult.

B. Temperature

This was discussed in Chapter IV. The Q_{10} of cell multiplication is commonly 2 to 3, but it becomes very high at around 0° C. Above

---

[1] The fact that more sugar is used up in aerated cultures is not in contradiction to the Pasteur effect. The yeast population becomes so much greater that it is not comparable with that in the anaerobic cultures.

the optimum temperature the growth rate falls off very sharply, due to the excessively high Q_{10} of processes like enzyme destruction and protein denaturation. Temperature has very little influence on the total crop when other conditions are constant. With *E. coli* on a glucose medium, the total crop was almost constant from 23° to 33° C (Monod, 1942), while the generation time, g, would be about halved by the same 10° C rise. At much higher temperatures the yield does, of course, fall off, and very sharply (cf. Fig. IV–5).

C. Nutrients

Two types of control by nutrients must be considered. In the first place there are *specific* nutrients, essential for growth, like vitamins or, for some organisms, amino acids. Evidently one nutrient can easily be the limiting factor in an otherwise complete medium. This is the basis for microbiological assay of such compounds (cf. Chap. XII), in which the procedure is usually to determine the total crop after a fixed time. The relationship between yield and concentration of the factor is roughly linear over a certain concentration range and eventually flattens when some other factor becomes limiting. For each determination, an arbitrary "calibration curve" has to be constructed for the particular organism and the conditions of growth used (Fig. XII–4, p. 467). Sometimes the shape of this calibration curve changes very materially with time. This can be seen in a three-dimensional diagram like that for thiamine in the growth of Phycomyces (Fig. XIX–7).

In a different category from growth factors are the *general* nutrients like the sugars, which provide both the energy and the carbon for synthesis. With these, organisms whose growth is not limited by specific growth factors can also show a response over a considerable concentration range. Figure XIX–8 shows how the total yield of *E. coli* and *Bac. subtilis* (both of which synthesize all required vitamins) varies linearly with sugar concentration up to about M/1000. It is striking that two different bacteria, utilizing two different sugars, give the same straight line. Aerobacter shows similar variation in yield with concentration of medium (Dagley and Hinshelwood, 1938).

Although the total yield varies directly with the concentration of nutrient, the growth *rate* shows proportional response only at the lowest concentrations. Thus, the growth rate of *E. coli* increases up to a glucose concentration of about 40 mg per liter (M/4500) and then is absolutely constant (Monod, 1942); with strains that require tryptophan, the growth rate is proportional to tryptophan only up to 1 to 5 micrograms per liter, or about 10^{-8} M (Novick and Szilard, 1950). With phosphate, the independence of growth rate and concentration is striking; the generation time for *E. coli* on a synthetic medium was constant over the range from 0.1 to 50 mg phosphate per liter, i.e., over a range of 500 times (Caldwell and Hinshelwood, 1951).

The relation between growth rate and the concentration of a limiting factor has been utilized in an ingenious way to obtain a stationary

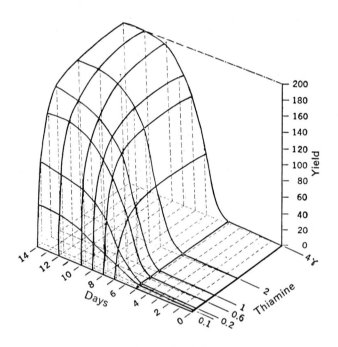

FIGURE XIX–7

Yield of Phycomyces as a function of time and thiamine. The origin is at the bottom front of the figure. Abscissa toward left, time in days; toward right, thiamine in milligrams per liter. Ordinate, yield in milligrams. Synthetic medium with asparagine 0.4%. (From W. H. Schopfer and A. Jung, *Compt. rend. 5th Cong. Int. Tech. chim. Ind. Agric.* (Scheveningen), 22–34, 1937.)

population (Novick and Szilard, 1950). Nutrient medium containing a very low concentration of tryptophan is supplied continuously to a culture vessel from which the excess is allowed to overflow with a constant level device. The culture, a tryptophan-requiring strain of *E. coli*, increases in density and thus withdraws tryptophan from solution, which in turn reduces growth. Finally a state is reached when the bacteria just divide once in the time it takes to renew the whole contents of the culture vessel, i.e., the population becomes constant. If the concentration of tryptophan (or other limiting factor) is a in the inflow tube and is reduced to c in the growth vessel, then the number of cells:

$$N = \frac{a - c}{Q}$$

where Q is the amount of the limiting factor needed to produce one cell. For tryptophan Q is only about six million molecules, for glucose

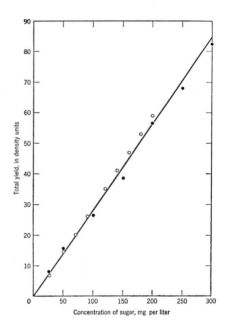

FIGURE XIX–8

Total yield of cultures in synthetic medium as a function of sugar concentration. Black points, *Bac. subtilis* on sucrose; circles, *E. coli* on glucose. (Data replotted from J. Monod, 1942.)

about 10^4 times greater. Any essential nutrient can be used as limiting factor in the same way. If a mutant should appear that uses the limiting factor more efficiently, i.e., can grow faster on the same concentration, it will replace the original form almost completely. Even a mutant that grows at the same rate as the original strain will be present in steadily increasing numbers, while one that grows more slowly will soon reach a constant number (Northrop and Kunitz, 1957). Thus, the apparatus is useful for the study of populations and evolution. Monod (1950) and Herbert *et al.* (1956) have used similar systems; in the latter case, with *Aerobacter cloacae*, mutations growing faster than the original strain were not encountered. An alternative control method is to maintain constant optical density with a photocell and adjust the flow rate accordingly, but this suffers from practical difficulties due to growth of cells on the walls or the optical window (Novick, 1955). These methods are increasingly important for large-scale cultures (see reviews of Novick, 1955, and James, 1961).

As noted above, the cell size is about constant during the logarithmic phase, but its absolute size varies with the medium. In *Salmonella typhimurium* the influence of the medium on cell size is much greater than that of the temperature; the smaller cells have less RNA, less DNA, and a smaller average number of nuclei (Schaechter *et al.*, 1958). Some of the Danish workers' data are shown in Table XIX–2; all figures refer to the logarithmic phase. In spite of the large differences, the rate of protein synthesis on the different media was calculated to be the same per unit of RNA.

TABLE XIX-2. Growth Rate, Cell Size, and Contents of S. *typhimurium* on Two Media at Two Temperatures

(From Schaechter *et al.*, 1958)

Medium	Temp. ° C	Growth Rate, Divisions per Hour	PER CELL			
			Total Mass	RNA	DNA	No. of Nuclei
Broth	25	1.06	5.8	1.64	0.130	2.85
	37	2.40	5.0	1.44	0.095	2.40
Glucose + salts	25	0.65	2.3	0.56	0.065	1.46
	37	1.20	1.9	0.44	0.048	1.38
Lactate	25	0.50	1.5	0.39	0.038	1.30
	37	0.90	1.6	0.39	0.039	1.35

When the cells were transferred to a richer medium, the RNA synthesis increased at once, but the DNA and the cell division rate increased only after 70 minutes (at 37° C). This delay is evidently analogous to the lag phenomenon.

5. DIAUXIC GROWTH CURVES

A curious type of growth curve was described by Monod (1942, 1947; van Niel, 1949). *Bac. subtilis* growing on a synthetic medium, with nitrogen and phosphorus in excess, gives a normal growth curve

(Fig. XIX–9A), and the total yield is linearly proportional to the carbohydrate supply. However, when *two* carbohydrates are present in the medium, an entirely different growth curve may be produced, with two successive growth cycles separated either by a lag or by a slight decrease (Fig. XIX–9B). Study of this phenomenon, "diauxic growth," showed that it occurred only with certain sugars. When the two carbohydrates were glucose, mannose, fructose, sucrose, or mannitol, any pair of these gave a normal curve (Fig. XIX–9A). When one of them belonged to this group and the other was maltose, arabinose,

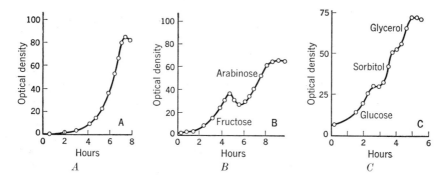

FIGURE XIX–9

A. Growth curve of *Bac. subtilis* on a single carbohydrate.

B. Diauxic curve on fructose and arabinose.

C. Triauxic curve on glucose, sorbitol, and glycerol.

Note that in B and C growth slows down, stops, or the number may even decrease somewhat, before the second carbohydrate is attacked. (From J. Monod, *Growth*, 11:(suppl.) 223–289, 1947.)

sorbitol, or inositol, then the two-peaked or diauxic curve was obtained. In such diauxic curves, the first cycle corresponds to utilization of the first-mentioned carbohydrate. Only when this substrate is all used up and the stationary or decreasing phase is reached can the second carbohydrate be attacked. The amount of growth at the end of the first cycle is proportional to the amount of the first carbohydrate.

This type of curve is due to the induced formation of the carbo-hydrate-attacking enzymes. The carbohydrates in the first group, whose combination in pairs yields normal curves, are evidently attacked by *constitutive* enzymes, so that the cell's enzyme content does not change during growth. The ones in the second group are those whose enzymes are not initially present and are formed *inductively* by presence of the substrate. This induced enzyme formation is *repressed* by presence of the first carbohydrate. Thus, fructose represses formation of "arabinozymase" (Fig. XIX–9*B*), and glucose that of sorbitol dehydrogenase (Fig. XIX–9*C*). It is indeed an old observation that adaptation of yeast to galactose is prevented by glucose, and the attack of starch by Penicillium is prevented by sucrose (see Monod, 1947).

In some cases the second carbohydrate inhibits the formation of enzyme for a third, and a *triauxic* curve results (Fig. XIX–9*C*).

6. THE UPTAKE OF SOLUTES

Although it seems clear from the above that growth is limited by the uptake of solutes, and perhaps also of water, our knowledge of the uptake process is not extensive.

For phosphate, uptake is known to be linked to metabolism. Yeast cells take up little phosphate in the absence of nutrient, and the inhibition of metabolism by cyanide, dinitrophenol, or azide leads to inhibition of phosphate uptake (Mullins, 1942; Hotchkiss, 1944). On the other hand, when riboflavin is added to yeast, it increases phosphate uptake without increasing the oxidation of carbohydrate; what *is* increased, however, is the conversion of glucose to cell substance, i.e., oxidative assimilation (Nickerson and Mullins, 1948). Hence the uptake of phosphate is increased by increasing its conversion to synthetic products. Unlike yeast, the bulk of the phosphate in *M. pyogenes* is in the inorganic (acid-soluble) form. By using P^{32} the uptake and loss of phosphate can be followed independently, and it is clear that there is rapid exchange (Mitchell and Moyle, 1953). The exchange mechanism is poisoned by mercury, silver, and other heavy metals (Mitchell, 1954). During respiration the uptake is not appreciably increased, but the outgo is abolished, so that the net accumulation increases.

The uptake of iron by *C. diphtheriae* differs from this picture in that it seems quite independent of the functions of the iron. Both Fe^{++} and Fe^{+++} are taken up rapidly, even if the iron level is high enough to inhibit toxin production completely; the shape and length of the growth curve are quite unaffected (Edwards and Seamer, 1960). Potassium, however, resembles phosphate in that its uptake depends on sugar metabolism, while sodium seems to pass in and out freely and not to be accumulated. With yeast the K taken up is strictly proportional to the sugar added, and it is excreted again as the sugar is used up (Pulver and Verzar, 1940). Once taken up, the intracellular K promotes the uptake of other solutes, especially glycine (Eddy and Indge, 1962). Since K plays a special role in fermentation (Chap. IV, sec. 2B), and since also iodoacetate, which inhibits fermentation, inhibits K uptake, one might conclude that the K is taken up only to the extent that it can function. However, the analogy with higher plants (Laties, 1959), in which sugar oxidation leads to the uptake and accumulation of both cations and anions, makes one very cautious about so simple an explanation. Indeed, in plants the uptake of water itself is linked to oxidative metabolism (Thimann and Leopold, 1955).

The uptake of sugar is also dependent, at least largely, on metabolism. With yeast it has been known for a long time that sugar is taken up faster than it can be metabolized, and after suspension in glucose solution, yeast becomes rich in glycogen (Stier and Stannard, 1936; cf. Brooks, 1947). The uptake can hardly be linked to glycogen formation, however, since it is too rapid. The speed of uptake is remarkable because glucose is not lipoid-soluble and, therefore, on classical views of permeability it would be expected to enter slowly. The same is true of amino acids, which are taken up rapidly, as shown below. Part of the explanation is that the classical concepts, according to which lipoid solubility and molecular size determine rates of entry, are largely founded on entry into the vacuole of plant cells, which is much slower than entry into the cytoplasm.

Some characteristics of glucose uptake by yeast are shown in Figure XIX–10, where uptake of glucose, measured by refractometer, is compared with its consumption by oxidation and fermentation, measured under the same conditions in the respirometer. The data show that over the whole temperature range the uptake is more than double the combined fermentative and oxidative breakdown. Nevertheless, uptake is entirely dependent on consumption, since it remains proportional throughout the temperature range (cf. the two upper curves), and it is about 90 per cent stopped by M/100 iodoacetate which inhibits both respiration and fermentation almost completely. Cyanide, which inhibits respiration but increases fermentation, does not prevent uptake and can even increase it. On the other hand, while metabolism virtually stops at $0°$ C, some glucose uptake persists, probably due to passive diffusion.

Amino acids can also be taken up both actively and passively, and the process is complicated by their incorporation into proteins. The active process depends on a source of energy; glucose promotes the uptake of glycine by yeast one-hundredfold (Eddy and Indge, 1962), while azide, iodoacetate, dinitrophenol, and fluoride all inhibit uptake of glutamate by both M. aureus and Sc. fecalis (Gale, 1951). In the first stages the uptake is partly reversible, i.e., the amino acid can be exchanged for another, both in E. coli (Cohen and Rickenberg, 1956) and in Candida (Cowie and McClure, 1959), but this happens only very slightly in yeast. However, if yeast that has taken up C^{14}-phenyl-alanine for 5 or 10 minutes is extracted with hot water, the amino acid is seen to be still free; if protein synthesis is depressed by ultra-violet irradiation (see p. 783), some of the phenylalanine can be displaced by other amino acids (Halvorsen and Cohen, 1958). Thus, the exchangeability varies with the organism and conditions.

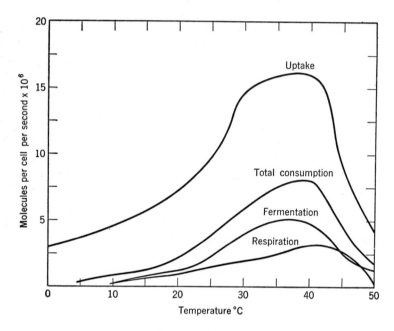

FIGURE XIX–10

Rates of uptake, fermentation, and respiration of glucose by baker's yeast (*Sacch. cerevisiae*). All reduced to the same units. (Data replotted from H. P. Rieder, *Ber. Schweiz. Bot. Ges.*, **61**:539–616, 1951.)

The uptake of phenylalanine by yeast is depressed by valine (and vice versa), although valine does not stop incorporation of phenyl-alanine into protein; it merely inhibits the uptake process proper. Tyrosine or phenylalanine similarly inhibits the uptake of tryptophan in *E. coli* (Scott and Happold, 1962). This interference by related amino acids doubtless explains certain specific effects on growth; those Neurospora mutants that require lysine are inhibited by arginine, which has no effect on growth of the wild type (Doermann, 1944), and similarly a mutant requiring leucine is inhibited, competitively, by δ-chloroleucine (Ryan, 1952). In *Cl. septicum* a pantothenate-requiring strain is inhibited by taurine (analogue of part of the pantothenate molecule), while the wild type is not (Ryan *et al.*, 1947). Such specificity indicates that amino acids are taken up by rather specific carrier mechanisms, perhaps like those for galactosides (sec. 7). In the special case in which glutamate uptake into *M. aureus* is inhibited by cysteine or alanine, the glutamate is combined with the cysteine or alanine into a peptide, which is excreted (Gale and van Halteren, 1951); this suggests that both are "activated" by the carrier mechanism and in this state combine *with one another* and therefore lose their hold on the carrier.

At a later stage, protein is formed (pp. 650–654 and 659 ff.). Even cells disrupted by supersonic vibration can still form proteins, although, having little "storage pool," they require other amino acids to be supplied as well (Gale and Folkes, 1955). A peculiar feature is that the most recently absorbed amino acids are converted to protein preferentially; when yeast is supplied with C^{14}-phenylalanine first, and then with C^{12}-phenylalanine, the radioactivity of the protein formed is lowered, although that of the free amino acid in the cell is sustained (Halvorsen and Cohen, 1958). The pool of absorbed amino acid, therefore, may not be on the direct pathway of protein synthesis, and it is thought that amino acid uptake follows the scheme:

$$\text{External AA} \rightleftharpoons \text{AA-X} \rightarrow \text{Protein}$$
$$\Updownarrow$$
$$\text{Pool AA}$$

where AA-X is the "activated" form in which entry occurs (perhaps an adenosyl-amino acid).

7. PERMEATION ENZYMES

The idea discussed above, that metabolism somehow enables the cell to bring certain organic compounds inside, must be set against the fact that some yeasts are unable to ferment specific sugars, although they contain the enzymes to do so. The autolyzates of many yeast strains contain maltase, invertase, etc.; yet the intact cells do not metabolize maltose or sucrose (see Leibowitz and Hestrin, 1945). Even stranger, a strain of *E. coli* could completely metabolize maltose but not glucose, although it contained hexokinase (Doudoroff, 1951). The only reasonable explanation for such phenomena is that there are highly specific permeation systems or carriers in the cell membrane, which, when activated by oxidative metabolism, take their particular substrates into the cell. In one case, that of the galactosides, this has been confirmed by Monod and his co-workers, and the system is called a "galactoside-permease."

The uptake phenomenon can be shown in *E. coli* by first growing the cells in presence of lactose or other galactoside, so that they have formed the galactosidase enzyme adaptively. (This "induction" is described in full in Chap. XX.) If to these induced cells is added a thiogalactoside (i.e., with S instead of O in the galactoside bridge), this compound is at once accumulated to perhaps 100 times the external concentration, as can be shown by using the compound labeled with S^{35}. If the cells are then extracted, the S^{35} is found to be mainly present as unchanged thiogalactoside, and furthermore if an unlabeled thiogalactoside is added, some of the S^{35} comes out again (Rickenberg *et al.*, 1956). Now these thiogalactosides are not hydrolyzed by β-galactosidase, and they are hardly likely to be bound in the cell, because the high internal concentrations reached (up to 5 per cent of the cell dry weight) would require an impossibly high content of the binding material. If neither bound nor metabolized, then the thiogalactoside must be free in the cell, and hence the uptake system must act catalytically. The same would be true for other substrates also. That the substrate is truly free and contributes to the cell's osmotic pressure was ingeniously shown by using wall-less protoplasts, i.e., cells that had been treated with lysozyme (cf. p. 110). Protoplasts were prepared from cells that had been induced to form permease by being grown in lactose. When these were suspended in dilute lactose solution, they burst, showing that their osmotic pressure had been increased by the further accumulation of lactose (Sistrom, 1958). Suspension in glucose of the same molarity did not cause bursting. Protoplasts from uninduced cells also did not burst.

As with the amino acids in section 6, azide or dinitrophenol inhibits the uptake, although they do not inhibit the actual hydrolysis of galactosides. Addition of the thiogalactoside even causes a very small *increase* in the endogenous respiration (Képès, 1957). Since the thiogalactosides are not hydrolyzed by galactosidase, the energy requirement must be to carry out the work of accumulating the compound against the concentration gradient.

The evidence that the "permease" is enzyme-like (see Cohen and Monod, 1957) is:

(1) Its formation, like that of the galactosidase, and indeed of many other enzymes, can be induced.

(2) Such induction has all the properties of a protein synthesis (see Chap. XX); specifically here it is inhibited by chloramphenicol, by amino acid deficiency, and by certain amino acid analogues.

(3) Like many other enzymes (cf. urease, p. 330), it depends on an SH group for its activity and is inhibited by mercury compounds and other SH reagents.

(4) Formation of the permease, like that of many other induced enzymes, is strongly inhibited by glucose (p. 666).

It is evident that formation of a specific permease can explain many quirks of metabolism such as the inability of intact cells to metabolize specific compounds for which they contain the enzymes (see above). This "cryptic" behavior can indeed be imitated in *E. coli*, because several "cryptic" mutants have been found that are able to form galactosidase, as shown by extracting the cells, but nevertheless metabolize galactosides only extremely slowly (due to passive entry) (Herzenberg, 1959). A second type of mutant, which does not form galactosidase but can still take up galactosides, obviously produces the permease but not the hydrolytic enzyme.

However, so far the evidence for permeases acting on other substrates is not extensive. They may participate in the uptake of some glucosides and glucuronides, and in one such instance, the accumulation of thiophenyl-β-glucuronide, which is not metabolized, the process is inhibited by several closely related compounds, as well as by azide and dinitrophenol. Also the accumulation can go on simultaneously with that of β-galactosides, or separately, so that two independent permeases must be present (Stoeber, 1957). Nevertheless, it must be remembered that permeases are not absolutely essential since, particularly at high concentrations, passive diffusion allows appreciable entry of galactosides (Holmes *et al.*, 1961). Indeed, in the case of α-galactosides, an enzyme for their hydrolysis is induced when the cells are exposed to melibiose or other α-galactosides, just as for β-galactosides; yet there was no evidence for the formation of a permease (Sheinin and Crocker, 1961). A group of permeases for organic acids appear to act in *Ps. aeruginosa*, for while these cells oxidized many acids only after a short lag period, their cell-free extracts showed no such lag in oxidation (Clarke and Meadow, 1959). The lag is thus interpreted as being the time required for the synthesis of the specific permease. Many of the observations with amino acids above may also be due to specific permeases, but they seem not to be inducible, and the situation may be more complex. In animal cells the postulated "carriers" for taking up solutes are generally thought not to be themselves enzymes, but rather products of enzymes forming parts of the cell membrane. The future will have to decide how far the action of permeases can be generalized to other solutes.

REFERENCES

Abbo, F. E., and Pardee, A. B. 1960. *Biochim. Biophys. Acta*, **39**:478–485.

Barber, M. A. 1908. *J. Inf. Dis.*, **5**:379–400.

*Brooks, S. C. 1947. Permeability and Enzyme Reactions. *Adv. in Enzymol.*, **7**:1–34.

Caldwell, P. C., and Hinshelwood, Sir C. N. 1951. *J. Chem. Soc.*, 158–166.

Chesney, A. M. 1916. *J. Exp. Med.*, **24**:387–418.

Clarke, P. H., and Meadow, P. M. 1959. *J. Gen. Microbiol.*, **20**:144–155.

*Cohen, G. N., and Monod, J. 1957. Bacterial Permeases. *Bact. Revs.*, **21**:169–194.

Cohen, G. N., and Rickenberg, H. U. 1956. *Ann. Inst. Pasteur*, **91**:693–700.

Cowie, D. B., and McClure, F. T. 1959. *Biochim. Biophys. Acta*, **31**:236–245.

Dagley, S.; Dawes, E. A.; and Morrison, G. A. 1949. *Nature*, **163**:532–533.

Dagley, S., and Hinshelwood, C. N. 1938. *J. Chem. Soc.*, pp. 1930–1936.

Doermann, A. H. 1944. *Arch. Biochem.*, **5**:373–383.

Doudoroff, M. 1951. In, Protein Metabolism, McCollum Pratt Symposium; Baltimore, Johns Hopkins Press, **1**:42–48.

Eddy, A. A., and Indge, K. J. 1962. *Biochem. J.*, **82**:15P–16P.

Edwards, D. C., and Seamer, D. A. 1960. *J. Gen. Microbiol.*, **22**:698–704, 705–712.

Elliker, P. R., and Frazier, W. C. 1938. *J. Bact.*, **35**:63–64; **36**:83–98.

Englesberg, E., and Baron, L. S. 1959. *J. Bact.*, **78**:675–686.

Gale, E. F. 1951. *Biochem. J.*, **48**:286–290 (and earlier papers cited therein).

Gale, E. F., and Folkes, J. P. 1955. *Biochem. J.*, **59**:661–675, 675–684.

Gale, E. F., and van Halteren, M. B. 1951. *Biochem. J.*, **50**:34–53.

Gale, E. F., and Paine, T. F. 1951. *Biochem. J.*, **48**:290–301.

Halvorsen, H. O., and Cohen, G. N. 1958. *Ann. Inst. Pasteur*, **95**:73–87.

Henrici, A. T. 1923. *Proc. Soc. Exp. Biol. Med.*, **21**:215–217, 343–345.

Herbert, D.; Ellsworth, R.; and Telling, R. C. 1956. *J. Gen. Microbiol.*, **14**:601–622.

Hershey, A. D. 1938. *Proc. Soc. Exp. Biol. Med.*, **38**:127–128.

Herzenberg, L. A. 1959. *Biochim. Biophys. Acta*, **31**:525–538.

Holmes, R.; Sheinin, R.; and Crocker, B. F. 1961. *Canad. J. Biochem. Physiol.*, **39**: 45–54.

*Hotchkiss, R. D. 1944. Gramicidin, Tyrocidine and Tyrothricin. *Adv. in Enzymol.*, **4**:153–199.

Hotchkiss, R. D. 1954. *Proc. Nat. Acad. Sci.*, **40**:49–55.

James, T. W. 1961. Continous Culture of Microorganisms. *Ann. Rev. Microbiol.*, **15**: 27–46.

Képès, A. 1957. *Compt. rend. Acad. Sci.*, **244**:1550–1553.

Lark, K. G., and Maaløe, O. 1954. *Biochim. Biophys. Acta*, **15**:345–356.

*Laties, G. G. 1959. Active Transport of Salt into Plant Tissue. *Ann. Rev. Plant Physiol.*, **10**:87–112.

Leibowitz, J., and Hestrin, S. 1945. Alcoholic Fermentation of the Oligosaccharides. *Adv. in Enzymol.*, **5**:87–127.

Lodge, R. M., and Hinshelwood, C. N. 1943. *Trans. Faraday Soc.*, **39**:420–423.

Martin, D. S. 1932. *J. Gen. Physiol.*, **15**:691–708.

Maruyama, Y., and Yanagita, T. 1956. *J. Bact.*, **71**:542–546.

Mitchell, P. 1954. In, Active Transport and Secretion; VIIIth Symp. Soc. Exp. Biol., pp. 254–261; *J. Gen. Microbiol.*, **11**:73–82.

Mitchell, P., and Moyle, J. M. 1953. *J. Gen. Microbiol.*, 9:257–272.

*Monod, J. 1942. La croissance des cultures Bacteriennes. Paris, Hermann et Cie.

*Monod, J. 1947. Enzymatic Adaptation and Its Bearing on Problems of Cell Physiology, Genetics, and Differentiation. *Growth*, 11:Suppl. (7th Growth Symp.), pp. 223–289.

Monod, J. 1950. *Ann. Inst. Pasteur*, 79:390–410.

Mullins, L. J. 1942. *Biol. Bull.*, 83:326–333.

Nickerson, W. J., and Mullins, L. J. 1948. *Nature*, 161:939–941.

Nickerson, W. J., and van Rij, N. J. W. 1949. *Biochim. Biophys. Acta*, 3:461–475.

*van Niel, C. B. 1949. The Kinetics of Growth of Microorganisms. In, The Chemistry and Physiology of Growth, ed. A. K. Parpart. Princeton Univ. Press.

Northrop, J. H., and Kunitz, M. 1957. *J. Gen. Physiol.*, 41:119–129.

Novick, A. 1955. Growth of Bacteria. *Ann. Revs. Microbiol.*, 9:99–110.

Novick, A., and Szilard, L., 1950–1952. *Proc. Nat. Acad. Sci.*, 36:708–719; 1951 Cold Spring Harbor Symp., 16:337; *Nature*, 170:926–927 (1952).

Phelps, A. 1936. *J. Exp. Zool.*, 72:479–496.

Pirt, J. G. 1957. *J. Gen. Microbiol.*, 16:59–75.

Pulver, R., and Verzar, F. 1940. *Helv. Chem. Acta*, 23:1087–1100.

Rahn, O., and Richardson, G. L. 1940–1942. *J. Bact.*, 41:225–249 (1940); 44:321–332 (1942).

Rickenberg, H. V.; Cohen, G. N.; Buttin, G.; and Monod, J. 1956. *Ann. Inst. Pasteur*, 91:829–857.

*Rieder, H. P. 1951. *Ber. schweiz. bot. Ges.*, 61:539–616.

Ryan, F. J. 1952. *Arch. Biochem. Biophys.*, 36:487–488.

Ryan, F. J.; Schneider, L. K.; and Ballantine, R. 1947. *J. Bact.*, 53:417–434.

Sargeant, T. P.; Lankford, C. E.; and Traxler, R. W. 1957. *J. Bact.*, 74:728–736.

Schaechter, M.; Maaløe, O.; and Kjeldgard, N. O. 1958. *J. Gen. Microbiol.*, 19:592–606, 607–616.

Scott, T. A., and Happold, F. C. 1962. *Biochem. J.*, 82:13P.

Sheinin, R., and Crocker, B. F. 1961. *Canad. J. Biochem. Physiol.*, 39:55–61, 63–71.

Sherman, J. M., and Albus, W. R. 1923–1924. *J. Bact.*, 8:127–139; 9:303–305 (1924).

Sistrom, W. R. 1958. *Biochim. Biophys. Acta*, 29:579–587.

Stier, T. J. B., and Stannard, J. N. 1936. *J. Gen. Physiol.*, 19:461–477.

Stoeber, F. 1957. *Compt. rend. Acad. Sci.*, 244:1091–1094.

*Thimann, K. V., and Leopold, A. C. 1955. In, The Hormones, ed. G. Pincus and K. V. Thimann. New York, Academic Press, III, 42–56.

Walker, H. H.; Winslow, C.-E. A.; and Mooney, M. G. 1934. *J. Gen. Physiol.*, 17:349–357.

Webb, M. 1948. *J. Gen. Microbiol.*, 2:275–287.

White, J., and Munns, D. J. 1951. *Wallerstein Communications*, 14:199–218.

Wilson, G. S. 1922. *J. Bact.*, 7:405–446.

Yanagita, J., and Kaneko, K. 1961. *Plant and Cell Physiol.*, 2:443–449.

Zabin, I.; Képès, A.; and Monod, J. 1959. *Biochem. Biophys. Res. Comms.*, 1:289–292.

CHAPTER XX

The Synthesis of the Major Polymers

It's a very odd thing,
As odd as can be,
That whatever Miss T. eats
Turns into Miss T.

WALTER DE LA MARE

1. THE LINKAGE BETWEEN SYNTHESIS AND BREAKDOWN

The growth of bacteria represents the synthesis of complex compounds from simpler materials. The uptake of these from the medium has been discussed in Chapter XIX. Bacterial syntheses of many smaller molecules have been discussed in several other chapters, and here we shall be concerned with general mechanisms of synthesis, primarily of polymers and storage materials, and especially with the crucially important special case of the synthesis of enzymes, on which all other metabolic processes of course depend.[1]

Hydrolysis of any large molecule to smaller units is a reversible reaction, and if the small molecules are in high enough concentration, some synthesis occurs. For example, fats are hydrolyzed by lipase to glycerol and fatty acid, but a concentrated mixture of glycerol and fatty acid, in presence of lipase, synthesizes some fat, and an equilibrium mixture is reached. Similarly a very concentrated mixture of amino acids in presence of chymotrypsin will synthesize true proteins (Tauber, 1951).

Few biological syntheses, however, are carried out in this way, because generally they go almost to completion in dilute intracellular solutions. In order to do this, since synthesis produces compounds

[1] A general presentation of current work on synthetic processes in bacteria is given in the Cold Spring Harbor Symposium, Volume 26, 1962.

of higher energy, another process must be coupled with it to supply the energy. This "exergonic" (= energy-yielding) reaction is usually a breakdown. One of the simplest examples, in which the bond broken is of the same type as the one formed, and the amounts of energy required are extremely small, is the synthesis of polysaccharides from disaccharides. In this case, if the disaccharide is represented as S_1S_2, the reaction is:

$$n\ S_1S_2 \rightarrow (S_1)_n + n\ S_2$$

The free energy $(-\Delta F_0)$ of the 1-2 linkage in sucrose is 6600 cal and that for the 1-4 or 2-6 linkage, whether in a disaccharide or a polysaccharide, is only 4000 cal (Hassid and Neufeld, 1962). Enzymes prepared from bacteria catalyze at least four such reactions:

Sucrose $\rightarrow \beta$2-6-Polyfructoside ("levan") + glucose
Sucrose $\rightarrow \alpha$1-6-Polyglucoside ("dextran") + fructose
Sucrose $\rightarrow \alpha$1-4-Polyglucoside (amylopectin[?]) + fructose
Maltose $\rightarrow \alpha$1-4-Polyglucoside (amylose [?]) + glucose

The first reaction is due to Bacilli and Aerobacter, and its enzyme, levan sucrase, also forms dextran from raffinose (Hestrin and Avineri-Shapiro, 1944). The second reaction is characteristic of Leuconostoc (Hehre, 1946) and of *Sc. bovis* (Bailey and Oxford, 1958); it is accompanied by formation of small amounts of a sucrose isomer, 5'-glucopyrosanyl-fructose, in both organisms (Bailey and Bourne, 1959). The third reaction is due to *Neisseria perflava* (Hehre, 1949), and the last to *E. coli* (Torriani and Monod, 1949; Monod and Torriani, 1950). In each case, the reaction is due to a single enzyme and does not involve phosphate. In the last instance, the reaction is partly reversible, glucose causing the starchlike product to depolymerize to a dextrin.

The formation of dextran is the most studied of these reactions, because of the medical applications of the dextrans. A chemical survey of the dextrans formed by 96 strains of Leuconostoc, Streptococcus, Acetobacter, etc., revealed that they all have 1, 6 linkages with up to 40 to 50 per cent of 1, 4 and 1, 3 linkages as well (Jeanes *et al.*, 1954).

All these are group-transfer reactions (cf. Chap. V, sec. 2) in which the transferred group is an entire glycoside, and the enzymes *transglycosidases*. The energy required for the linkage of one glycoside unit to another does not differ much whether there are 2 or 200 units in the molecule, so that the dissociation of the link in the small molecule furnishes enough energy to remake it in the large one. Formation of polysaccharide from monosaccharide is a quite different process.

The synthesis of polysaccharides is of special importance in the formation of capsules (Chap. III, sec. 2), particularly on account of their interrelation with pathogenic virulence. However, it must be noted that capsular materials are seldom pure polysaccharides.

2. "PHOSPHORYLATIVE SYNTHESIS"

A. Simple Cases

In more complex syntheses, the energy is produced by one reaction and utilized by another, e.g., in the synthesis of starch. When phosphorylase is added to glucose-1-phosphate (K salt), in presence of a little starch, starch is synthesized (Hanes, 1940). The synthesis proceeds in vitro, at room temperature and neutral pH. There is little energy change in this reaction, and indeed it is reversible.

However, the normal synthesis of starch entails additional steps whereby the glucose-phosphate first combines with ATP to produce adenosine diphosphoglucose, ADPG, eliminating pyrophosphate, and it is the ADPG which then, in presence of the enzyme starch synthetase, forms starch:

$$ATP + G\text{-}1\text{-}P \rightarrow ADPG + P\text{-}P$$
$$nADPG \qquad \rightarrow nADP + (G)_n$$

Both amylose and amylopectin are formed (Recondo and Leloir, 1961). Instead of ADPG, uridine diphosphoglucose (pp. 467, 581) also acts, but at only one-tenth the rate (Leloir et al., 1961).

To form glucose-1-phosphate from glucose requires ATP (Chap. XI), and to transfer it to starch requires a second molecule of ATP. If phosphorylase is used, only one ATP is required. In either case a continuous synthesis of polysaccharide can only occur if oxidation (or fermentation, or photosynthesis) continuously forms ATP. Thus, the over-all reaction comprises an oxidation *linked* to a synthesis by ATP transfer.

Synthesis of the disaccharide sucrose follows a similar pair of pathways: in *Ps. saccharophila*, sucrose phosphorylase combines glucose-1-phosphate and fructose into sucrose:

$$G\text{-}1\text{-}P + Enz \rightarrow P_i + G\text{-}1\text{-}Enz; \ G\text{-}1\text{-}Enz + Fr \rightarrow G\text{-}1\text{-}Fr + Enz$$

where G-1-Fr is sucrose (Doudoroff, 1943; Hassid et al., 1944, 1947). The glucose-enzymate, G-1-Enz, can also combine with other sugars to produce different disaccharides. In the longer pathway, G-1-P combines with uridine triphosphate to form UDPG, and this then reacts with fructose (Munch-Peterson et al., 1953; Cardini et al., 1955):

$$UTP + G\text{-}1\text{-}P \rightleftharpoons UDPG + P\text{-}P$$
$$UDPG + Fr \rightleftharpoons UDP + G\text{-}1\text{-}Fr$$

As with starch the over-all reaction requires an oxidation (as source of ATP, or ATP plus UTP) linked to the synthesis.

The pattern is not limited to carbohydrates. Amino acids can enter into a variety of reactions by being first converted to carboxyl phosphates, which are very reactive. For instance, glutamine is synthesized from glutamic acid and ammonia by enzymes from liver or disintegrating cells of *M. aureus*, but only in the presence of ATP (see Lipmann, 1949). The first step is formation of γ-glutamyl-phosphate, which reacts with NH_3 or NH_2OH, liberating the H_3PO_4. In the synthesis of thiamine from its pyrimidine and thiazole precursors, *both* have first to be phosphorylated, the pyrimidine forming a pyrophosphate (see Brown, 1960).

Pantothenic acid is synthesized from pantoic acid and β-alanine via a more complex intermediate; here the ATP does not form a phosphate but an adenylate (the type of linkage is shown below), and the adenylic acid is then displaced by the β-alanine (Maas and Novelli, 1953):

$$[Pa]COOH + AMP \cdot PP \rightarrow [Pa]CO \cdot AMP + PP_i$$
$$[Pa]CO \cdot AMP + NH_2CH_2CH_2COOH \rightarrow [Pa]CO \cdot NHCH_2CH_2COOH + AMP \cdot H,$$

where [Pa] is the pantoyl residue (see p. 434). A cell-free enzyme from *E. coli* carries this out.

B. Protein Synthesis

The synthesis of proteins involves a much higher degree of complexity, since many different amino acids must be linked in a particular order. The first stage is like that for pantothenic acid, namely, formation of the adenylate derivative, which is most probably bound to the enzyme (Hoagland *et al.*, 1956):

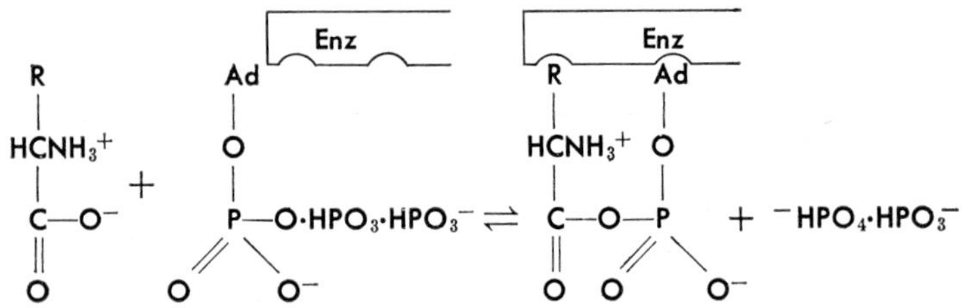

The enzymes forming these aminoacyl-adenylates are a related group, each of which is specific for one amino acid only. They can often react instead with an amino acid analogue, however, such as ethionine or parafluoro-phenylalanine, and these become incorporated into the final protein; *Bac. subtilis*, grown in presence of ethionine, produces a crystalline amylase which contains ethionine instead of methionine (Yoshida and Yamasaki, 1959).

The second step is transfer of the aminoacyl residues to soluble RNA. This transfer does not require a second series of enzymes, but the enzyme-bound aminoacyl-adenylate apparently reacts directly with the RNA (Berg, 1958; Wong et al., 1959). In bacteria this occurs very rapidly, since the binding of C^{14}-amino acids to the RNA of growing E. coli reaches a maximum in about five minutes (Lacks and Gros, 1959). The reaction takes place at an adenylic acid residue which is attached to the rest of the RNA by two cytidylic acid residues; i.e., at -AMP-CMP-CMP-RNA (Hecht et al., 1958–1959; Zachau et al., 1958). The linkage involves the 2' or 3' hydroxyl group of the ribose in the AMP, and if the RNA is hydrolyzed by ribonuclease, the amino acid is recovered as its adenosyl derivative (Preiss et al., 1959). Since the whole process thus takes place at one end of the RNA molecule, the specificity for particular amino acids must reside in the rest of this large molecule. In the RNA of E. coli there is only one terminal AMP residue for about 100 nucleotides, so that the whole subunit, of a molecular weight not less than 35,000, is used in attaching to one amino acid (see Cohen and Gros, 1960; Hoagland, 1960). It follows, therefore, that the rate of turnover must be very high, the soluble RNA cycling rapidly. Since each different amino acid must attach to a specific RNA, it follows too that an apparently pure preparation of soluble RNA really contains a large group of slightly different molecules. Work on separating these specific "amino acid acceptors" is going on actively (see Berg et al., 1961); in the case of threonine the partial composition (Nathans et al., 1962) is:

Thre-A-C-C-G-C-U-G......U-A-C-G

where A represents adenylic, C cytidylic, G guanylic, and U uridylic acid.

The third step is transfer of the soluble RNA-bound amino acids to the RNA-protein of the ribosome particles. It is in this step that protein is formed. Evidently the reaction goes best if most of the 20 amino acids required to form the protein are transferred together to the particles (see Hoagland, 1960). The transfer requires a single soluble enzyme, which is not specific for amino acids (unlike the RNA's), although it is specific for the organism, that from E. coli not functioning with the ribosomes from liver (Nathans and Lipmann, 1961). The soluble RNA, by contrast, is not specific for the organism at all; the mixture from E. coli, charged with amino acids, can react with the reticulocyte ribosomes of the rabbit to synthesize their normal product, hemoglobin! Besides the enzyme, guanosine-triphosphate, GTP,

Mg^{++}, and a phosphorylating system are needed (Nathans *et al.*, 1962). The released RNA is ready to take up a new charge of amino acids at once and is therefore a true catalyst. The reaction sequence is:

$$NH_2AA_1 \cdot COO \cdot (s\text{-}RNA_1) +$$
$$\downarrow NH_2AA_2 \cdot COO \cdot (s\text{-}RNA_2)$$
$$NH_2AA_1 \cdot CONH \cdot AA_2 \cdot COO \cdot (s\text{-}RNA_2) + s\text{-}RNA_1$$
$$\downarrow NH_2AA_3 \cdot COO \cdot (s\text{-}RNA_3)$$
$$NH_2AA_1 \cdot CONH \cdot AA_2 \cdot CONH \cdot AA_3 \cdot COO \cdot (s\text{-}RNA_3) + s\text{-}RNA_2, \text{ etc.}$$

where AA_1, AA_2, AA_3, etc. are the different amino acids.

Thus, in protein synthesis ATP is needed for the very first step (formation of adenosyl-amino acid), and in addition the synthesis of each individual amino acid generally involves several phosphorylations (e.g., arginine, pp. 325 ff, 663). GTP also participates in the synthesis in some way. Protein synthesis is thus highly dependent on energy supply.

The *type* of protein formed is determined, not by the ribosome protein, but by another RNA, the "messenger-RNA" (abbreviated m-RNA), an unstable form whose composition is determined by the DNA, whch acts as primer for its synthesis (see pp. 654, 679, and Fig. XX–2, p. 668). What the messenger-RNA does is to arrange the aminoacyl-RNA's in a specified order. This order corresponds to its own composition, and it is now probable that three particular nucleotides compose a "code" which corresponds to a given amino acid.

This fundamental conclusion was derived as follows: in the cell-free *E. coli* extract DNA-ase inhibits protein synthesis, because the m-RNA is then not formed (Tissières *et al.*, 1960). Only if messenger-RNA is added can protein synthesis now be reinstated, so that we have here an *assay* for m-RNA. Using pure polyuridylic acid ("poly-U") formed by the Azotobacter enzyme described below in section 2C, Nirenberg and Matthaei (1961) added various C^{14}-labeled amino acids in presence of ribosomes, ATP, GTP, Mg, substrate, and the enzyme. With phenylalanine, and with *no other* amino acid, the resulting protein was radioactive. About 1.5 moles of uridylic acid in a "poly-U" of molecular weight about 50,000 incorporated 1 mole of phenylalanine into protein. On the assumption that three nucleotides are needed, the code would be UUU.

Polyadenylic acid, "poly-A," alone in similar experiments formed no protein, but polymers containing two or three different nucleotides each caused incorporation of only one or two amino acids. Thus, poly-UA incorporates lysine and acts best when the A content is high; therefore, the code for lysine is probably UAA. Present data lead to the following tentative nucleotide combinations as codes for the amino acids (Matthaei *et al.*, 1962):

AMINO ACID	NUCLEOTIDES
phe	UUU
leu	UUC or UUG
val	UUG
ala	CAG or CCG
arg	UCG
cys	UGG or UUG
lys	UAA
his	UAC
ser	UUC or UGC
pro	CCC or CUC
meth and asp	UGA
glu	UAG?
tyr and isoleu	UUA
tryp and gly	UGG

Some of these overlap; some are uncertain. It has been objected that the proportion of uridylic acid in a nucleic acid that would synthesize normal protein would be impossibly high (Chargaff, 1962). However, some of the U's may be only acting as "spacers" to maintain the other two members of the triplet in the right positions (Jukes, 1963), and indeed Ochoa (1963) finds that poly-A can to some degree promote the incorporation of lysine, and poly-C of proline. Thus a firm basis for the coding system is clearly in sight. One important point, namely, that the code selects aminoacyl-RNA's and not free amino acids, has been rigidly confirmed. Since cysteine can be chemically hydrogenated to alanine, C^{14}-cysteyl-s-RNA was carefully hydrogenated to C^{14}-alanyl-s-RNA. This was added to a preparation of E. coli ribosomes in presence of poly-UG, which incorporates cysteine but not alanine. The resulting protein contained C^{14}, i.e., it had incorporated alanine; this means that because the alanine was attached to the RNA specific for cysteine, it was "mistaken" for cysteine by the coding system. Oxidation of cysteyl-s-RNA to the cysteic acid derivative similarly caused incorporation of cysteic acid into protein (Chapeville et al., 1962).

Another valuable confirmation comes from the nitrous acid experiments on virus (p. 93). For cytosine would be converted by HNO_2 to uracil, so that UUC would be replaced by UUU, and CUC by UUC. Correspondingly (see list above) one mutant formed by HNO_2 has its serine replaced by phenylalanine, and another has proline replaced by leucine (Martin et al., 1962). Similar changes have been detected in hemoglobins formed by cell-free systems (Smith, 1962).

The ribosomes are not the only site of protein synthesis, because fractions rich in phospholipid also incorporate C^{14}-amino acids (Schachtschabel and Zillig, 1959, with E. coli; Godson et al., 1961, Hill, 1962, with Bac. megaterium). These fractions derive from the cell membrane, since they can be prepared from washed isolated membranes, and in the Bacillus they become labeled 10 to 30 times as intensely as the ribosomes in the first few minutes. Thus, the soluble RNA may orient itself along more than one kind of receptor surface.

C. Synthesis of Nucleic Acids

This is a subject of very recent rapid growth in understanding. It stems from the finding of Ochoa and co-workers (1957) that cells of *Azotobacter vinelandii* yield an enzyme able to polymerize nucleotide-triphosphates to RNA-like macromolecules. The purified enzyme had the same activity for all the nucleotides tested and is therefore a single enzyme; nevertheless, it converts ATP to polyadenylic acid, GTP to polyguanylic acid, UTP to polyuridylic acid, and CTP to poly-cytidylic acid. The reaction lags at first, and the lag is removed by adding a small amount of polymer as primer; each polymer primes only for the formation of itself, except polycytidylic acid which acts as primer for all four. Mixed polymers can also be made. *M. lysodeikt-icus* gives a similar preparation (Beers, 1957), which is easier to extract (Boldingh and Veldstra, 1961). These preparations have played a crucial part in the experiments on "coding" mentioned above. The composition of the RNA made by the *E. coli* enzyme can be influenced by DNA used as primer (cf. Chap. XXI, sec. 2); if polymers of a single deoxyribonucleotide are used as primers, they cause synthesis of the corresponding ribonucleotide polymer, deoxyribo-thymidylate resulting in riboadenylate, etc. (Chamberlin and Berg, 1962). *Bac. megaterium* yields an even more striking preparation, since, when its protoplasts are lysed with detergent, a nuclear fraction, containing almost all its DNA, is obtained and this directly synthesizes RNA from a mixture of the four triphosphates (Godson and Butler, 1962). In reactions like this, one can see just how the nucleus controls the biochemistry of the cell.

A parallel system obtained from *E. coli* synthesizes DNA from a mixture of the four deoxynucleotide triphosphates (Lehman *et al.*, 1958, Aposhian *et al.*, 1962). Again a primer of a little DNA is needed; otherwise the reaction shows a marked lag. The DNA once formed evidently acts as a nucleus for autocatalytic replication (Radding and Kornberg, 1962). This system differs from that for RNA in that it needs all four nucleotides (thymine, cytosine, adenine, and guanine deoxyriboside triphosphates), and if one is omitted, the polymeriza-tion becomes exceedingly slow. However, it can, in the absence of a primer, form a co-polymer of adenine and thymine deoxyribosides only. This product then acts as primer in formation of itself, and its properties are like those of a modified DNA (Schachman *et al.*, 1960).

The above brief outline of our explosively growing knowledge of the synthesis of the proteins and nucleic acids will serve as background for the treatment of the formation of assimilate and of enzymes, and the transfer of genetic material, which follows.

3. OXIDATIVE ASSIMILATION

The over-all synthesis of polymers in intact bacteria of course comprises many of the individual processes summarized above. That it depends on oxidation for energy source was first brought out by Cook and Stephenson (1928) with *E. coli*. When various oxidizable substrates were added to the washed cells, the increased oxygen consumption ceased after a time, although only about two-thirds of the calculated amount of oxygen had been consumed. The enzymes appeared to be still intact, and no intermediate, unattackable by the bacteria, had seemed to accumulate in the medium. Evidently the rest of the substrate had been converted to polymer, or "assimilated." Cells whose power of multiplication had been largely reduced (by exposure to ultraviolet) behaved in nearly the same way.

Spirilla accumulate granules of "volutin," an assimilation product, when the cells (in the absence of nitrogen compounds and thus unable to grow) oxidize various substrates; Giesberger (1936) found that the oxygen taken up was never enough for complete oxidation of the substrate, so that part was oxidized and part "assimilated." Assuming the assimilate to be of the composition of a carbohydrate (CH_2O), the oxygen consumption indicated the following over-all reactions:

Acetic: $CH_3COOH + O_2 \rightarrow (CH_2O) + CO_2 + H_2O$
Propionic: $2\ C_2H_5COOH + 5\ O_2 \rightarrow 2(CH_2O) + 4\ CO_2 + 4\ H_2O$
Lactic: $CH_3CHOHCOOH + O_2 \rightarrow 2(CH_2O) + CO_2 + H_2O$
Pyruvic: $CH_3COCOOH + 1\frac{1}{2}\ O_2 \rightarrow (CH_2O) + 2\ CO_2 + H_2O$

Similar results with the colorless alga *Prototheca zopfii* (Barker, 1936) are shown in Table XX–1. They show that organic acids, as well as glycerol and ethanol, are assimilated by the cells, the product having the composition of a carbohydrate. The gas exchange measurements agree acceptably with the proposed equations, particularly since the assimilate may not be exactly of the composition (CH_2O). They also agree well with the assimilation processes of the spirilla. These data suggest that all the reactions proceed via acetate (Anderson, 1945). Acetate is no doubt utilized via the glyoxylic acid cycle (p. 251).

Other organisms assimilate with not quite the same relationships. For instance, *Ps. calcoacetica* and *E. coli*, respiring acetate, use $1\frac{1}{2}$ moles of oxygen (Cook and Stevenson, 1928; Clifton, 1946):

$$2 \ CH_3COOH + 3 \ O_2 \rightarrow (CH_2O) + 3 \ CO_2 + 3 \ H_2O$$

while the water mold *Leptomitus lacteus* uses only $\frac{2}{3}$ mole of oxygen (Schade and Thimann, 1940):

$$3 \ CH_3COOH + 2 \ O_2 \rightarrow 4(CH_2O) + 2 \ CO_2 + 2 \ H_2O$$

On glycerol, Mycobacteria use 1 to 1.5 moles of oxygen (cf. Table XX–1), and there is good evidence that the glycerol is converted to pyruvate (Hunter, 1953; see also Clifton, 1946).

Carbohydrate is also in part assimilated. With yeasts oxidizing glucose, only about one-third the theoretical amount of oxygen is taken up, the reaction being:

$$C_6H_{12}O_6 + 2 \ O_2 \rightarrow 4(CH_2O) + 2 \ CO_2 + 2 \ H_2O$$

Not all the (CH_2O) could be identified as actual carbohydrate, about half of it, in *Sacch. cereviseae*, being in the form of other compounds, probably fat (see Stier and Newton, 1939). Endomyces and Geotrichum in particular build up large amounts of fat. The assimilation product may vary with the substrate, some substrates giving rise predominantly to fat, others to protein. The amount of fat and sterol formed depends on the content of CoA and can be varied in yeast by varying the pantothenic acid in the medium (Klein and Lipmann, 1953). It can also be varied in algae by changes in growth conditions.

Much of the assimilate, in bacteria at least, is evidently a polymer of β-hydroxybutyric acid. This compound is also accumulated by photosynthetic bacteria (pp. 126, 730). When *Ps. saccharophila* assimilates C^{14}-labeled glucose, two-thirds of the C^{14} is found in this polymer (Doudoroff and Stanier, 1959). Assimilation on acetate and butyrate gave over 80 per cent conversion of their C^{14} to poly-β-hydroxybutyric.

Oxidative assimilation in presence of a nitrogen supply leads to protein synthesis. In the water mold *Leptomitus lacteus*, ammonia is absorbed from the medium when acetate or butyrate is being assimilated, and the product has about the over-all composition of alanine, $C_3H_7NO_2$ (Schade and Thimann, 1950). With leucine as substrate, no deamination could be detected, and the reaction approximated:

$$C_4H_9CHNH_2COOH + 4\frac{1}{2} \ O_2 \rightarrow (C_3H_7NO_2) + 3 \ H_2O + CO_2$$

If the product is really protein, it would mean that leucine (or acetate and ammonia) gives rise to all the amino acids. *Ps. aeruginosa* similarly

TABLE XX–1. Oxidative Assimilation by *Prototheca zopfii*

(From Barker, 1936)

Substrate	Over-all Equation	MOLES PER MOLE OF SUBSTRATE:			
		O_2 Consumed		CO_2 Produced	
		Expected	Found	Expected	Found
Glycerol	$2\ C_3H_8O_3 + 2\ O_2 \rightarrow 5(CH_2O) + CO_2 + 3\ H_2O$	1	1.01	0.5	0.61
Ethanol	$2\ C_2H_6O + 3\ O_2 \rightarrow 3(CH_2O) + CO_2 + 3\ H_2O$	1.5	1.37	0.5	0.49
Acetic acid	$C_2H_4O_2 + O_2 \rightarrow (CH_2O) + CO_2 + H_2O$	1	1.00	1	1.03
Propionic acid	$2\ C_3H_6O_2 + 4\ O_2 \rightarrow 3(CH_2O) + 3\ CO_2 + 2\ H_2O$	2	2.03	1.5	1.56
n-Butyric acid	$2\ C_4H_8O_2 + 5\ O_2 \rightarrow 5(CH_2O) + 3\ CO_2 + 3\ H_2O$	2.5	2.40	1.5	1.70
Isobutyric acid	$C_4H_8O_2 + 3\ O_2 \rightarrow 2(CH_2O) + 2\ CO_2 + 2\ H_2O$	3	2.90	2	1.94
Valeric acid	$2\ C_5H_{10}O_2 + 6\ O_2 \rightarrow 7(CH_2O) + 3\ CO_2 + 3\ H_2O$	3	2.14	1.5	1.63

takes up NH_3, while organic acids are being oxidized (Bernheim and de Turk, 1951).

In general, the rate at which an organism can grow is doubtless a function of the rate at which it can assimilate, and especially of the rate at which it produces enzymes (see sec. 5 below). Slow-growing mutants of Salmonella, especially *S. pullorum*, were found to oxidize alanine, serine, and glycine completely, without any assimilation (Stokes and Bayne, 1958, 1961); while on some other amino acids, oxygen uptake stopped when 70 to 80 per cent of the theoretical O_2 had been taken up, indicating slow assimilation. The normal fast-growing strains all stopped oxidizing alanine and serine when 50 to 60 per cent of the theoretical O_2 had been taken up, which about corresponds to the types of assimilation above.

Assimilation is readily prevented by poisons without poisoning the remainder of the respiration. Fluoride prevents yeast from converting glucose to glycogen, probably by poisoning the phosphoglucomutase that converts glucose-6-phosphate into glucose-1-phosphate (Nickerson and Chung, 1952). Iodoacetate, azide, and especially dinitrophenol, all prevent the assimilation of acetate by *Ps. calcoacetica* (Clifton, 1946); in their presence, therefore, the oxidation of acetate goes almost to completion. Since the nitrophenols are specifically known to inhibit phosphorylation (p. 455), this confirms the need for ATP in these processes. In *Mycob. ranae*, iodoacetate prevents the oxidative assimilation of pyruvate, which instead is oxidized to acetate and CO_2 (Lindsay *et al.*, 1950). On the other hand, arsenite prevents the oxidation of the pyruvate so that in its presence Mycobacteria convert pyruvate to glycerol (Hunter, 1953). As would be expected, all these assimilation inhibitors inhibit growth also.

Only in those cells which, because of metabolic imperfections or presence of poisons, are neither growing nor assimilating, can true respiration uncomplicated by synthesis be said to go on. In all other cases, respiration is only a partial aspect of the vital process; as Kluyver once put it, the CO_2 evolved resembles the chips scattered when the sculptor converts a shapeless block of granite to a desired form.

4. FERMENTATIVE ASSIMILATION

Assimilation can also, of course, occur anaerobically when microorganisms grow without oxygen. In yeast that is fermenting sugars (in the absence of oxygen), only about 70 per cent of the sugar is accounted for as CO_2 and alcohol, most of the rest being found as increased weight of cells (Meyerhof and Schulz, 1936; van Niel and Anderson, 1941).

Young yeast cells, even in air, ferment sugars and consume very little oxygen (Swanson and Clifton, 1948). As the sugar becomes used up, the assimilate, as well as the alcohol produced, begins to be oxidized, and the resulting energy of oxidation leads to further assimilation. Similarly *Propionibact. pentosaceum*, while fermenting dextrose, stores 10 per cent of the carbon as polysaccharides and ferments this again when the dextrose is all used (Wood and Werkman, 1934). Several bacteria store glycogen, both aerobically and anaerobically, and use it up again if starved (cf. p. 585).

On the other hand, *Sc. fecalis* shows no fermentative assimilation at all and gives an almost theoretical yield of lactic acid from glucose (van Niel and Anderson, 1941). This may be connected with the great need of the lactic bacteria for preformed amino acids and vitamins. The high yields of lactic acid often recorded in the literature (cf. Chap. XII) doubtless rest on similar absence of assimilation.

5. THE FORMATION OF ENZYMES

A. Basic Observations

It was shown in Chapter XVII that, when a medium containing a new substrate is inoculated, the growth of any mutant cells that can attack the new substrate is immediately favored. Similarly, if a required nutrient is missing, the growth of mutant cells that can synthesize this nutrient is favored. In this way a bacterial population can be continuously variable, since three factors favoring rapid change are present: high selection pressure exerted through essential nutrients, a high mutation rate, and enormous populations.

However, in addition to selection, there is a quite other factor operating, namely, the formation of specific enzymes *in response to the substrate* and independent of growth. The study of this phenomenon, called adaptation or induction, has shed a flood of light on the process of enzyme formation in bacteria.

The first clear instance of this process came from the work of Stephenson and Stickland (1933) with formic hydrogenlyase. This enzyme-complex (see p. 519) appears in *E. coli* when it is grown on a medium containing formate. If cells grown without formate are washed and suspended in formate, the enzyme is produced within two hours; the only requirement is the presence of broth, since adaptation occurs poorly in formate alone. However, no growth need occur. In experiments lasting three hours, the amount of enzyme, measured as the rate of H_2 evolution per milligram bacterial N per hour $(= Q_{H_2})$ rose from 0 to about 1000, while the number of cells (*ca.* 3×10^8 per milliliter) showed no increase at all. The formation of enzyme thus took place entirely in the lag phase. Instead of broth, the amino acids, serine, aspartic acid, and arginine, will suffice to supply whatever energy or nitrogen is needed (Pinsky and Stokes, 1952). Induction can even occur anaerobically, providing fumarate or nitrate is added, evidently to act as hydrogen acceptors for an energy-yielding reaction (Kushner and Quastel, 1953).

Tryptophanase, the enzyme that converts tryptophan to indole, is similarly formed when *E. coli*, grown without tryptophan, is suspended in this amino acid. No other substrate is required, and no growth occurs, although tryptophan itself is, of course, a potential energy source (Happold *et al.*, 1936, 1941). In yeasts the fermentation of galactose can be similarly induced; energy, if needed, is supplied by endogenous substrates, and on pure galactose alone the galactokinase that forms galactose-1-phosphate and is the limiting factor in galactose utilization appears in about an hour (Lindegren and Pelleroni, 1952; Sheffner and McClary, 1954). Another remarkable induction occurring in yeasts is the formation of cytochromes (Ephrussi and Slonimski, 1950). After growing anaerobically for 24 hours (six generations), yeast loses the ability to oxidize glucose, and the spectral bands of cytochromes a, b, and c disappear, a_1 and b_1 replacing them. Aeration in glucose-buffer brings back both the full cytochrome spectra and the respiration. The change begins immediately, although, if the cells are in the logarithmic phase, there is an hour's lag, probably due to the synthesis of the oxidase (Lindenmayer and Estabrook, 1958).

In the case of nitratase, i.e., the enzyme in *E. coli* needed for the reduction of nitrate by organic hydrogen donors, enzyme formation occurs in nitrate with any metabolizable substrate, such as formate or lactate, but is fastest with sugar, probably because it is the best energy source (Pollock, 1946). In presence of glucose the rate is further accelerated by adding amino acids and depends less on their *concentration* than on the number of different amino acids, which clearly indicates the need for protein synthesis. A similar case is formation of β-galactosidase by Aerobacter (induced by adding lactose); this proceeds for a few hours in buffer alone, but by 20 hours the enzyme can no longer be formed. If peptone is added with the lactose, the enzyme is formed at the full rate even after 68 hours' starvation, so that it is clearly amino acids that are needed (Strange, 1961). Such starved cells lose both protein and RNA to the medium.

In the above cases, formation of the enzyme is induced by its substrate: formate, nitrate, tryptophan, galactose, lactose, or, in the case of the cytochromes, oxygen. However, in *E. coli* the β-galactosidase can be induced not only by lactose but also by the unattackable compounds melibiose (an α-galactoside), several thio-β-galactosides, and even weakly by galactose. Conversely phenyl-β-galactoside, which *is* hydrolyzed, does not induce formation of the enzyme (see Cohn, 1957). In *Proteus vulgaris*, formation of leucine decarboxylase is induced by alanine, which is not attacked, almost as rapidly as by valine or leucine, which are substrates for the enzyme (Haughton and King, 1961). Also, some *E. coli* mutants are simultaneously induced to form a second protein (PZ), which is enzymatically inactive and was only detected by immunologic methods. In many cases the inducer also induces formation of the "permease" described above (p. 642), which may be a third protein. Thus, (1) the process of induction can be multiple, and (2) it has a different specificity from that relating the enzyme to its substrate.

Formation of an induced enzyme is actual *synthesis* of the enzyme protein and not merely unmasking or activation of some inactive precursor. This has been shown in several cases, but most clearly as follows (Rotman and Spiegelman, 1954; Hogness *et al.*, 1955): *E. coli* was grown in presence of C^{14}-lactate or S^{35}-sulfate, so that the cell proteins were all labeled to varying extents. The cells were then washed and transferred to isotope-free medium, to which an inducer for β-galactosidase was added. After an interval, the β-galactosidase formed was extracted and purified; in both cases it was virtually free from radioactivity. Hence it must have been formed anew from the *unlabeled* constituents of the second medium.

In growing cells the enzymes once formed are not appreciably broken down again. During the lag phase, or in nongrowing cultures, however, there is appreciable breakdown with resynthesis of protein, amounting to about 5 per cent of the cell proteins per hour (Mandelstam, 1958). Essentially the same is true for nucleic acids, both RNA and DNA being very stable in growing cells; while in starved *E. coli* the rate of turnover of RNA is around twice as fast as that of protein. Such slow turnover accounts for the occasional formation of induced enzymes by nitrogen-starved cells (Wainwright and Nevill, 1956).

The power to form an enzyme in response to an inducer is inherited as a normal genetic character. The earliest genetic work, e.g., on β-galactosidase of *E. coli*, distinguished only ability and inability to use lactose, inherited as lac⁻ and lac⁺, respectively. Later the gene i⁺, for inducible galactosidase, could be distinguished from z⁺, which controls the enzyme synthesis itself (see sec. 5C below). With z⁻ no enzyme can be formed; with z⁺ it can be either inducible (that is, genetically *i*⁺), or constitutive, *i*⁻.

B. Inhibition and Repression

The diauxic curves in Chapter XIX indicated the inhibition of the arabinose-attacking enzyme by glucose, etc. Clearer evidence that enzyme synthesis can be specifically inhibited was given first for tryptophan-synthetase, which combines indole and serine to form tryptophan (Monod and Cohen-Bazire, 1953); formation of this enzyme is inhibited by tryptophan and some of its analogues. Many such cases have now been studied. Sometimes it is the direct products of the reaction that inhibit, but in others it is the *end products* of the resulting entire sequence of enzymatic reactions. As examples, *valine* and *isoleucine* are formed by transamination between their keto-derivatives and phenyl-alanine or alanine; the keto acids in turn are derived from pyruvate and α-ketobutyrate, respectively. Now α-ketobutyrate is formed by deamination of threonine (pp. 319, 347), and this deamination is inhibited competitively by isoleucine (Umbarger and Brown, 1958). Thus the end product, isoleucine, powerfully inhibits the very first reaction in the sequence, a process called "feedback inhibition." Similarly, *proline* is formed by the sequence:

$$\text{Glutamic acid} \xrightarrow{1} \underset{\substack{\text{semi-alde-}\\\text{hyde}}}{\text{Glutamic}} \xrightarrow{2} \underset{\substack{\text{5-carbox-}\\\text{ylic acid}}}{\Delta'\text{-Pyrrolene}} \xrightarrow[3]{\text{DPNH}} \text{Proline}$$

Reaction 2 is spontaneous, but reaction 1, which is probably complex, is strongly inhibited by proline (Strecker, 1957). Again, *threonine* comes from aspartate via its semi-aldehyde (Chap. VIII, sec. 7), and this is formed by the phosphorylation of one carboxyl. The enzyme for this, β-aspartokinase, is competitively inhibited by threonine (Wormser and Pardee, 1958). In these three cases the control is thus by inhibition of the *enzyme activity*.

In several cases the control system is more complex, acting by preventing *formation* of the enzyme. The two types of control are shown as I and II in Figure XX–1. The second type, which is probably more important, is exemplified by the synthesis of uracil; here Yates and Pardee (1957) studied the enzymes that catalyze three of the four synthetic reactions:

$$
\begin{array}{l}
\text{Aspartic} \\
\quad + \\
\text{Carbamyl} \\
\text{phosphate}
\end{array}
\underset{1}{\overset{-Pi}{\rightleftharpoons}}
\begin{array}{ccc}
NH_2 & COOH \\
| & | \\
CO & CH_2 \\
| & | \\
NH\!\!-\!\!CH \\
& | \\
& COOH
\end{array}
\underset{2}{\overset{-H_2O}{\rightleftharpoons}}
\begin{array}{ccc}
NH\!\!-\!\!CO \\
| & | \\
CO & CH_2 \\
| & | \\
NH\!\!-\!\!CH \\
& | \\
& COOH
\end{array}
\underset{3}{\overset{-2\,H}{\rightleftharpoons}}
\begin{array}{ccc}
NH\!\!-\!\!CO \\
| & | \\
CO & CH \\
| & || \\
NH\!\!-\!\!C \\
& | \\
& COOH
\end{array}
\underset{4}{\overset{+Ribose\text{-}5\text{-}P}{\rightleftharpoons}}
\begin{array}{l}
\text{Orotidylic acid,} \\
\text{uridylic acid,} \\
\text{and uracil}
\end{array}
$$

These are the reverse of the breakdown series in Chapter VIII, section 9. In *Zymob. oroticum* two of the enzymes are inducible; in *E. coli* strain 6386, which requires pyrimidines for growth, all three are very weakly present, but when the cells are washed and aerated *without* uracil, No. 1 increases 150 to 500 times, No. 2, 10 to 40 times, and No. 3, 4 to 10 times. At the same time the total protein synthesis stops. Now chloramphenicol also stops total protein synthesis (p. 822), but since it does not *cause* formation of these enzymes, their formation cannot be the result of stopping protein synthesis but must

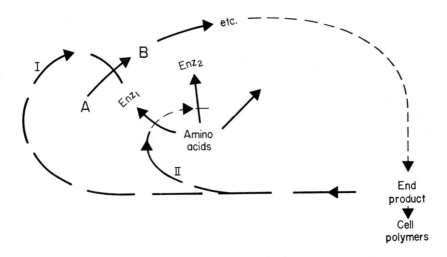

FIGURE XX–1

Control of a series of biosynthetic enzymes by the end product.

I. Inhibition of the action of the enzyme at one of the first steps in the series.

II. Inhibition of the synthesis of one or more of the enzymes.

be the result of *absence of uracil.* If the cells are suspended in C^{14} leucine and then the proteins separated, high C^{14} activity is found in enzyme No. 1, showing that it has been actively synthesized. Hence uracil (or its products) inhibits formation of these enzymes.

Another well-studied case is that of acetylornithinase (A-O-ase) which converts acetylornithine to ornithine and thus, in *E. coli,* lies on the path of synthesis of arginine (Chap. VIII, sec. 5B). Mutant arginine-requiring or acetylornithine-requiring cells, when grown on arginine and transferred to an acetylornithine medium, grow only after a lag of some hours (Vogel, 1957). Such behavior might appear to be due to induction of the A-O-ase by its substrate, but no evidence for such induction could be found. Instead, presence of arginine in the cells (also in wild-type cells) *lowered* the amount of the A-O-ase. It was deduced that arginine, end product of the sequence, *represses* formation of the A-O-ase which acts at an earlier stage.

Such repression has obvious value in economizing on protein, and Vogel concluded that "a cell in an environment that supplies arginine will utilize this exogenous arginine, and . . . conserve its resources by sharply curtailing the *now unnecessary* synthesis of A-O-ase." Looking at it the other way round, the formation of an enzyme that helps synthesize a necessary food, when that food is scarce or absent, makes growth possible on otherwise inadequate media.

Thus induction and repression are two comparable ways in which synthesis of enzymes is controlled by their products.

In at least two cases, the histidine- and tryptophan-forming sequences, the control extends to a whole group of enzymes. In *Salmonella typhimurium*, six enzymes function in the histidine series, and the activities of at least the last four bear a constant ratio to one another, irrespective of the type of mutant. Some 40 mutations in different locations give rise to cells with the same ratios of these

$$
\begin{array}{l}
\text{Phospho-} \underset{1}{\rightleftharpoons} \text{"cpd. III"} \underset{2}{\rightleftharpoons} \text{Imidazole-} \overset{-2\,H}{\underset{3}{\rightleftharpoons}} \text{Imidazole-} \overset{-RNH_2}{\underset{4}{\rightleftharpoons}} \text{Histidinol} \overset{-(P)}{\underset{5}{\longrightarrow}} \\
\text{ribosyl} \qquad\qquad\qquad \text{glycerol} \qquad\quad \text{acetol} \qquad\qquad \text{phosphate} \\
\text{pyro-} \qquad\qquad\qquad\quad \text{phosphate} \qquad \text{phosphate} \\
\text{phosphate} \\
\qquad + \qquad\qquad\qquad\qquad\qquad\qquad\qquad\qquad\qquad\qquad\qquad \overset{-2\,H}{\longrightarrow} \\
\qquad \text{AMP} \qquad\qquad\qquad\qquad\qquad\qquad\qquad\quad \rightarrow \text{Histidinol} \underset{6}{\longrightarrow} \text{Histidine}
\end{array}
$$

enzymes. Furthermore, it is possible to grow a histidine-requiring mutant without adding histidine, by the device of supplying formyl-histidine, which is hydrolyzed so slowly that (at any one time) very little free histidine is present in the cell. This minimizes the repression, and it is then found that the concentrations of *all four* of the enzymes studied (Nos. 3, 4, 5, and 6 above) increase by some 15 times (Ames and Garry, 1959; Ames *et al.*, 1960). Evidently, therefore, their formation has been repressed by histidine. What makes this particularly interesting is that genetic evidence, from recombination, shows that the genes controlling formation of the series of enzymes are located very close together on the chromosome, and indeed their order along the gene-string is almost *the same as the biochemical order* in which the enzymes have to function (Hartman *et al.*, 1960). This holds for five of the mutant groups, controlling, respectively, five of the enzymes and has been verified for over 200 individual histidine mutants of Salmonella.

A comparable sequence functions in the synthesis of tryptophan by *E. coli* and *S. typhimurium* (Smith and Yanofsky, 1960). The first enzyme forms anthranilic acid, the second links a phosphoribulose group to it, the third (probably dual) closes the ring to form indole-3-glycerol phosphate, and the fourth (doubtless multiple) reduces and aminates this to tryptophan. An alternative (fifth) enzyme splits off the side-chain to form indole, which combines with serine to form tryptophan also:

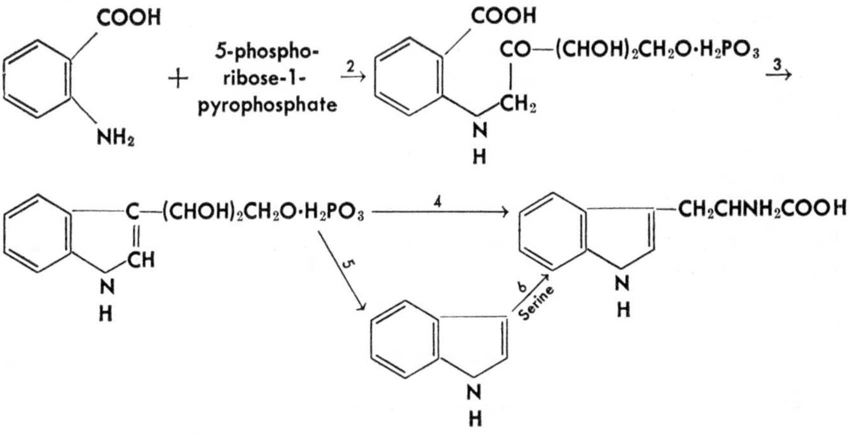

Here, in *Salmonella, E. coli,* and *Bac. subtilis,* all the effective genes are closely linked and lie approximately in order of the biochemical sequence of their enzymes. An odd exception is the fact that in *Bac. subtilis* (where the gene order was determined by using transforming substances), the order of enzymes 2 and 3 is reversed (Anagnostopoulos and Crawford, 1961).

An instance from another field is the fermentation of galactose: three enzymes are required to phosphorylate the galactose, combine it with UDPG, and reverse the spatial arrangement at carbon 4 (p. 467). Yet a single-step mutation, occurring both in *E. coli* K12 and in a Salmonella strain, can inhibit synthesis of all three (Kalckar *et al.,* 1959; Nikaido and Fukasawa, 1961). Rhamnose offers a comparable example, with only two enzymes (Englesberg and Baron, 1959).

Thus the "single mechanism," sometimes at least, controls a whole group of enzymes, which are closely related both in their substrates and in their spatial positions.

Finally, it is important that enzyme repression is common in synthetic *sequences.* It has now been found in nine bacterial syntheses, namely, of ornithine, citrulline, histidine, proline, methionine, valine, tryptophan, pyrimidines, and purines.

A number of enzyme inductions are strongly affected by glucose.

Formation of proteinases, amino acid oxidases, histidinase, and many other deaminating enzymes is suppressed by glucose, while formation of amino acid decarboxylases, tryptophan-synthetase, and several other synthetic enzymes is promoted by glucose. The phenomenon of enzyme repression has been invoked to explain these glucose effects as follows (Neidhart and Magasanik, 1956). Enzymes whose formation is *repressed* by glucose would be those whose products can be readily formed by the cell by alternative routes directly from glucose, e.g., urocanic acid and the α-keto acids. Glucose would be metabolized so fast that these products would accumulate and repress the deaminases, etc., that produce them. Enzymes whose formation is *promoted* by glucose would be those whose products are removed by reacting with the glucose breakdown products (e.g., amines, or compounds which can enter a synthetic reaction if energy is supplied). In this case the removal of the products would lift the repressive influence that these compounds normally exert. The theory remains unproven, though attractive.

C. Are Enzyme Induction and Repression Really Different?

For some time the feeling has been growing that induction and repression are not two "comparable ways" of controlling enzyme synthesis, but that they are really the same, i.e., that induction is *the lifting of a repression*. The best evidence for this is the following. The synthesis of β-galactosidase in *E. coli*, which is inducible in some strains, is constitutive in others, and the control resides in a pair of genes, i^+ and i^-, respectively. The conjugation phenomenon (Chap. III, sec. 5C) has been used to study inheritance here and has revealed two other factors besides the i gene; y, which makes a "permease," or factor allowing β-galactosides to enter the cell, and z, which controls synthesis of the enzyme itself; z^- cells cannot make the enzyme under any conditions.

Thus:

z^+ allows enzyme synthesis, z^- prevents it;

y^+ allows permease synthesis, y^- prevents it;

i^+ requires inducer for the formation of both galactosidase and permease ("inducible");

i^- allows synthesis of these in the absence of inducer ("constitutive").

The galactosidase and permease are in most cases made together, and in over 100 i^- mutants both enzyme and permease are formed (Jacob and Monod, 1961). All occurrences of z^-, y^-, and i^+ are found by crossing over to be located near together on the chromosome (see diagram p. 682).

Suggestively, in cells diploid for the i gene, when i^+ and i^- occur in the same cell, the cell is not constitutive for the enzyme, but requires inducer, i.e., *inducibility is dominant*. This means that the inducible is the active form, which does not fit with the idea that inducible cells are missing something needed to make the enzyme; instead, it suggests that they actively *produce* something that prevents enzyme formation. Only an inducing substance (on this concept) can stop this and hence allow the enzyme to be formed.

Ingenious proof that this is the case, i.e., that the inducer removes a repression, has been given by timing the transfer of the male characters into the female during conjugation (Pardee *et al.*, 1959). Three characters were concerned, z, i, and one controlling sensitivity or resistance to streptomycin, designated Sm^s and Sm^r, respectively. The mating was between: male, $z^+i^+Sm^s$, and female, $z^-i^-Sm^r$. The addition of the antibiotic streptomycin to the medium prevents the male cells from multiplying, but they can still conjugate.[2] The female cells make no enzyme anyway. Thus, any increase in the enzyme in the culture must be due to *zygotes* that have received the z^+ gene. The two cultures are mixed, and samples taken from time to time for β-galactosidase assay. In 20 minutes z^+ enters the females, as shown by formation of enzyme at once. Since no lactose is present, the enzyme is being made constitutively (i^-). But 60 minutes later, its formation stops; now it will resume only on addition of lactose (or other inducer); evidently i^+ has now entered. Hence the i^+ gene has *stopped* the formation of the enzyme which was proceeding normally; i^+, therefore, causes formation of a *repressor*. Inducing substances prevent the repression.

D. Nature of the Repressor[3]

Since mutations of the i gene do not affect other enzyme systems, it follows that the repressor is highly specific. On the other hand, it can control more than one gene at a time; e.g., those for β-galactosidase and permease, in the above instance. In the case of histidine synthesis all the eight sequential enzymes concerned can be prevented from forming by a *single* mutation. Hence the repressor does not act upon a gene but upon something else which may control a group of genes located close together—an "operator."

In the above conjugation experiment, if methyl-tryptophan is added

---

[2] In this organism, formation of β-galactosidase is dependent on growth.

[3] A full review of this material is given by Jacob and Monod (1961).

before z^+ enters, the synthesis of tryptophan is inhibited, and therefore proteins, including β-galactosidase, are not formed. However, repressor is still formed, because if tryptophan is added 60 minutes after the methyl-tryptophan, to reinstate synthesis of the enzyme, the synthesis *will not start* without inducer. Thus the repressor is not a protein and therefore not an enzyme. This rules out one possible explanation of repression, namely, that the repressor is an enzyme destroying the inducer.

The picture of the system developed so far is shown in Figure XX–2. The operator lies on the chromosome and controls the activity of the string of functionally related genes, which are close together.

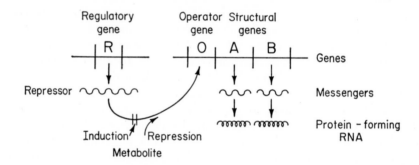

FIGURE XX–2

Mode of regulation of gene action by a repressor-operator system, as envisaged by Jacob and Monod (1961). The repressor can be prevented from operating by becoming combined with an inducing metabolite.

Each gene forms a specific ribonucleic acid molecule which migrates into the cytoplasm—doubtless to the ribosomes which are the seat of protein synthesis—and there forms a specific enzyme. That the step from gene to enzyme is mediated by a ribonucleic acid is to be expected, since RNA controls protein synthesis (pp. 650, 680). Also cells which have been x-rayed sometimes fail to form enzyme, and the most effective wavelengths are those absorbed by nucleic acids (Pauly, 1959; and see Chap. XXIV, sec. 6). From the x-ray dosage needed to inactivate the synthesis, the calculated size of the "target," both for lysine decarboxylase and for β-galactosidase, gives a molecular weight of 20 millions, which compares well with that of the DNA of bacteriophage (see p. 97).

The operator may combine with a repressor (probably a nucleic acid too) and thus be incapacitated. But an inducing substance, which is biochemically similar to the enzyme substrate, can combine with the repressor and prevent its attachment to the operator. The constitutive gene, i^-, which is recessive, fails to confer the power of making repressor; it is because of this, perhaps, that constitutive cells have about 50 per cent more galactosidase than the maximum inducible amount. As Vogel first suggested (1957): "Inducers or repressers have affinity for the very portions of the genome that control the formation of the corresponding enzymes." The evidence of Pardee et al. (1959) seems to make a mechanism of this type extremely general in bacteria.

E. Some Additional Points

(1) Repression of formation of a related group of enzymes, although a striking phenomenon when it does occur, is not necessarily the rule. In some sequences, as in that for uracil above, formation of each enzyme appears to be repressible separately. An operator must in that case be assumed for each gene, which makes the above picture more complex.

(2) The repression of enzyme *formation* must be clearly distinguished from the inhibition of enzyme *activity*. For instance, in the uracil-forming sequence described above, the first reaction is the linkage of carbamyl phosphate to aspartic acid; this reaction is inhibited by cytidylic acid (Pardee and Yates, 1956). Since cytidylic acid is formed from uracil, this means that the last product of a sequence inhibits the first step, another instance of the "feedback inhibition" discussed above. Yet this does not concern enzyme synthesis, but only enzyme activity.

(3) A controversial point concerns the relation between induced enzyme formation and growth. In *E. coli* the formation of β-galactosidase was first found to be strictly dependent on growth, and the enzyme represented a constant fraction of the total protein formed (Monod et al., 1952). Later the enzyme was found to appear in a disproportionately large amount during the early phase of growth, so that, although protein was being synthesized, the enzyme was being formed preferentially (Løvtrup, 1956). As was shown in section A, an external energy source, rather than an external nitrogen source, is necessary, i.e., the enzyme can be formed from reserve free amino acids. For example, *Ps. saccharophila* forms amylase well within an hour when suspended in buffer with starch, although S^{35}-sulfate was not incorporated detectably into protein in that time (Schiff et al., 1959). There is, in fact, a small pool of free amino acids in *E. coli*, and this increases when the cells are nitrogen-starved, presumably by proteolysis (Mandelstam, 1958). A rate of protein "turnover" scarcely

detectable by chemical means may suffice for formation of appreciable enzyme. Hence neither growth nor net protein synthesis really needs to be a prerequisite for enzyme formation.

(4) Correspondingly a very small amount of inducer can be effective. *Bac. cereus* makes penicillinase, the enzyme that hydrolyzes penicillin, inductively, and by using S^{35}-labeled penicillin it was shown that the isotope is fixed in the cells and that each molecule of penicillin fixed causes the formation of at least 10 molecules of enzyme (Pollock and Peret, 1951; Pollock and Torriani, 1953). However, if after a few minutes the cells are washed free of penicillin, the enzyme continues to be formed. This is no doubt because the cells fix and retain some penicillin (i.e., inducer) irreversibly. By contrast, with the β-galactosidase of *E. coli*, removal of the inducer stops enzyme formation in a few minutes (see Cohn, 1957), and some other systems behave similarly.

(5) So far, clear evidence for repression is limited to bacteria, although *induction* certainly occurs in yeast, Neurospora, and even in mammals (see Knox *et al.*, 1956).

(6) Lastly, a striking recent development is the synthesis of β-galactosidase in an entirely cell-free system (Novelli *et al.*, 1961). This was discovered via studies of the effect of radiation on enzyme formation (Chap. XXIV, sec. 6). The synthesis requires both particles and supernatant fraction from *E. coli* cells previously induced with thiomethyl-galactoside (sec. 5A above); amino acids, ATP, and several nucleotides are also needed. Within an hour the enzyme activity was more than doubled, and C^{14}-leucine was generously incorporated. The reaction is inhibited by x-rays and ultraviolet, and then reinstated by adding DNA from untreated cells. Doubtless many other such systems will soon be elaborated.

REFERENCES

Ames, B. N., and Garry, B. 1959. *Proc. Nat. Acad. Sci.*, **45**:1453–1460.
Ames, B. N.; Garry, B.; and Herzenberg, L. A. 1960. *J. Gen. Microbiol.*, **22**:369–378.
Anagnostopoulos, C., and Crawford, I. P. 1961. *Proc. Nat. Acad. Sci.*, **47**:378–389.
Anderson, E. H. 1945. *J. Gen. Physiol.*, **28**:287–327.
Aposhian, H. V.; Richardson, C. C.; and Schildkraut, C. 1962. *Fed. Proc.*, **21**:381.
Bailey, R. W., and Bourne, E. J. 1959. *Nature*, **184** (Suppl. 12): 904–905.
Bailey, R. W., and Oxford, A. E. 1958. *J. Gen. Microbiol.*, **19**:130–145.
Barker, H. A. 1936. *J. Cell. Comp. Physiol.*, **8**:231–250.
Beers, R. F. 1957. *Biochem. J.*, **66**:686–693.
Berg, P. 1958. *Proc. Nat. Acad. Sci.*, **44**:78–86.
Berg, P.; Bergmann, F. H.; Ofengaud, E. J.; and Dieckmann, M. 1961. *J. Biol. Chem.*, **236**:1726–1734, 1735–1740, 1741–1747, 1748–1757.

Bernheim, F., and de Turk, W. E. 1951. *J. Pharmacol.*, **103**:107–111.

Boldingh, W. H., and Veldstra, H. 1961. *Rec. trav. chim. Pays. Bas.*, **80**:1357–1371.

*Brown, G. 1960. Biosynthesis of Water-soluble Vitamins and Co-enzymes. *Physiol. Revs.*, **40**:331–368.

Cardini, C. E.; Leloir, L. F.; and Chiriboga, J. 1955. *J. Bicl. Chem.*, **214**:149–155.

Chamberlin, M., and Berg, P. 1962. *Fed. Proc.*, **21**:385.

Chapeville, F.; Lipman, E.; Ehrenstein, G.; Weisblum, B.; Ray, W. J.; and Benzer, S. 1962. *Proc. Nat. Acad. Sci.*, **48**:1086–1096.

Chargaff, E. 1962. *Nature*, **194**:86–87.

*Clifton, C. E. 1946. Microbial Assimilations. *Adv. in Enzymol.*, **6**:269–308.

*Cohen, G. N., and Gros, F. 1960. Protein Biosynthesis. *Ann. Revs. Biochem.*, **29**: 525–546.

Cohn, M. 1957. Contributions of Studies on the β-Galactosidase of *Escherichia coli* to Our Understanding of Enzyme Synthesis. *Bact. Revs.*, **21**:140–168.

Cook, R. P., and Stephenson, M. 1928. *Biochem. J.*, **23**:1368–1386.

Doudoroff, M. 1943. *J. Biol. Chem.*, **151**:351–361.

Doudoroff, M., and Stanier, R. Y. 1959. *Nature*, **183**:1440–1442.

Englesberg, E., and Baron, L. S. 1959. *J. Bact.*, **78**:675–686.

Ephrussi, B., and Slonimski, P. P. 1950. *Compt. rend. Acad. Sci.*, **231**:375–376; *Biochim. Biophys. Acta*, **6**:256–257.

Giesberger, G. 1936. Beiträge zur Kenntniss der Gattung *Spirillum* Ehbg. Dissertation, Utrecht.

Godson, G. N., and Butler, J. A. V. 1962. *Nature*, **193**:655–656.

Godson, G. N.; Hunter, G. D.; and Butler, J. A. V. 1961. *Biochem. J.*, **81**:59–68; Hunter, G. D., and Godson, G. N., *Nature*, **189**:140–141; *J. Gen. Microbiol.*, **29**: 65–68 (1962).

Hanes, C. S. 1940. *Proc. Roy. Soc.*, B **128**:421–450.

Happold, F. C., and Hoyle, L. 1936. *Brit. J. Exp. Path.*, **17**:136–145; Evans, W. C.; Handley, W. R. C.; and Happold, F. C. 1941. *Biochem. J.*, **35**:207–212.

Hartman, P. E.; Loper, J. C.; and Šerman, D. 1960. *J. Gen. Microbiol.*, **22**:323–353.

Hassid, W. Z.; Doudoroff, M.; and Barker, H. A. 1944–1947. *J. Am. Chem. Soc.*, **66**: 1416–1419; *Arch. Biochem.*, **14**:29–37 (1947).

Hassid, W. Z., and Neufeld, E. F. 1962. In, The Enzymes, ed. P. Boyer, A. Lardy, and K. Myrbäck. New York, Academic Press, Vol. 6, Chap. 18.

Haughton, B. G., and King, H. K. 1961. *Biochem. J.*, **80**:268–277.

Hecht, L. I.; Stephenson, M. L.; and Zamecnik, P. C. 1958–1959. *Biochim. Biophys. Acta*, **29**:460–461; *Proc. Nat. Acad. Sci.*, **45**:505–518 (1959).

Hehre, E. J. 1946–1949. *J. Biol. Chem.*, **163**:221–223; **177**:267–279 (1949).

Hestrin, S., and Avineri-Shapiro, S. 1944. *Biochem. J.*, **38**:2–10.

Hill, P. B. 1962. *Can. J. Biochem. Physiol.*, **40**:709–716.

*Hoagland, M. B. 1960. The relationship of nucleic acid and protein synthesis as revealed by studies in cell-free systems. In: The Nucleic Acids, ed. Chargaff and Davidson, **3**:349–408. New York, Academic Press.

Hoagland, M. B.; Keller, E. B.; and Zamecnik, P. C. 1956. *J. Biol. Chem.*, **218**: 345–358.

Hogness, D. S.; Cohn, M.; and Monod, J. 1955. *Biochim. Biophys. Acta*, **16**:99–109.

Hunter, G. J. E. 1953. *Biochem. J.*, **55**:320–328.

Jacob, F., and Monod, J. 1961. *J. Mol. Biol.*, **3**:318–356.

Jeanes, A. R.; Hanes, W. C.; Wilham, C. A.; Rankin, J. C.; Melvin, E. H.; Austin, M. J.; Cluskey, J. E.; Fisher, B. E.; Tsuchiya, H. M.; and Rist, C. H. 1954. *J. Am. Chem. Soc.*, **76**:5041–5042.

Jukes, T. H. 1963. *Biochem. Biophys. Res. Comms.*, **10**:155–159.

Kalckar, H. M.; Kurahashi, K.; and Jordan, E. 1959. *Proc. Nat. Acad. Sci.*, **45**:1776–1786.

Klein, H. P., and Lipmann, F. 1953. *J. Biol. Chem.*, **203**:95–99.

*Knox, W. E.; Auerbach, V. H.; and Lin, E. C. C. 1956. Enzymatic and Metabolic Adaptations in Animals. *Physiol. Revs.*, **36**:164–254.

Kushner, D. J., and Quastel, J. H. 1953. *Proc. Soc. Exp. Biol. Med.*, **82**:388–392.

Lacks, S., and Gros, F. 1959. *J. Mol. Biol.*, **1**:301–320.

Lehman, I. R.; Bessman, M. J.; Simms, E. S.; and Kornberg, A. 1958. *J. Biol. Chem.*, **233**:163–170, 171–177; Bessman, M. J.; Lehman, I. R.; Adler, J.; Zimmerman, S. B.; Simms, E. S.; and Kornberg, A. *Proc. Nat. Acad. Sci.*, **44**:633–640, 641–647.

Leloir, L. F.; de Fekete, M. A. R.; and Cardini, C. E. 1961. *J. Biol. Chem.*, **236**:636–641.

Lindegren, C. C., and Pelleroni, N. J. 1952. *Nature*, **169**:879.

Lindenmayer, A., and Estabrook, R. W. 1958. *Arch. Biochem. Biophys.*, **78**:66–82.

Lindsay, M.; O'Donnell, T. V.; and Edson, N. L. 1950. *Biochem. J.*, **46**:248–257.

Lipmann, F. 1949. Mechanism of Peptide Bond Formation. *Fed. Proc.*, **8**:597–602.

Løvtrup, S. 1956. *Biochim. Biophys. Acta*, **19**:247–255, 433–439.

Maas, W. K., and Novelli, G. D. 1953. *Arch. Biochem. Biophys.*, **43**:236–238.

Mandelstam, J. 1958. *Biochem. J.*, **69**:110–119; Mandelstam, J., and Halvorson, H., *Biochim. Biophys. Acta*, **40**:43–49 (1960).

Martin, R. G.; Matthaei, J. H.; Jones, O. W.; and Nirenberg, M. W. 1962. *Biochem. Biophys. Res. Comms.*, **6**:410–414; cf. Wittmann, H. G. *Z. Vererbungslehre*, **90**:463–475 (1959); Tsugita, A., and Fraenkel-Conrat, H. *Proc. Nat. Acad. Sci.*, **46**:636–642 (1960).

Matthaei, J. H.; Jones, O. W.; Martin, R. G.; and Nirenberg, M. W. 1962. *Proc. Nat. Acad. Sci.*, **48**:666–677.

Meyerhof, O., and Schulz, W. 1936. *Biochem. Z.*, **287**:206–211.

Monod, J., and Cohen-Bazire, G. 1953. *Compt. rend. Acad. Sci.*, **236**:530–532.

Monod, J.; Pappenheimer, A. M., Jr.; and Cohen-Bazire, G. 1952. *Biochim. Biophys. Acta*, **9**:638–660.

Monod, J., and Torriani, A. M. 1950. *Ann. Inst. Pasteur*, **78**:65–82.

Munch-Peterson, A.; Kalckar, H. M.; Cutolo, E.; and Smith, E. E. B. 1953. *Nature*, **172**:1036–1037.

Nathans, D.; Ehrenstein, G. von; Monro, R.; and Lipmann, F. 1962. *Fed. Proc.*, **21**:127–133.

Nathans, D., and Lipmann, F. 1961. *Proc. Nat. Acad. Sci.*, **47**:497–504.

Neidhart, F. C., and Magasanik, B. 1956. *Nature*, **178**:801–802.

Nickerson, W. J., and Chung, C. W. 1952. *Am. J. Bot.*, **39**:669–678.

van Niel, C. B., and Anderson, E. H. 1941. *J. Cell. Comp. Physiol.*, **17**:49–56.

Nikaido, H., and Fukasawa, T. 1961. *Biochem. Biophys. Res. Comms.*, **4**:338–342.

Nirenberg, M. W., and Matthaei, J. H. 1961. *Proc. Nat. Acad. Sci.*, **47**:1588–1602.

Novelli, G. D.; Kameyama, T.; and Eisenstadt, J. M. 1961. *J. Cell. Comp. Physiol.*, **58** (suppl.):225–244.

Ochoa, S. 1957, *Spec. Publ. N. Y. Acad. Sci.*, **5**:191–205.

*Ochoa, S. 1963. *Fed. Proc.*, **22**:62–74.

Pardee, A. B.; Jacob, F.; and Monod, J. 1959. *J. Mol. Biol.*, **1**:165–178.

Pardee, A. B., and Yates, R. A. 1956. *J. Biol. Chem.*, **221**:757–770.

Pauly, H. 1959. *Nature*, **184**:1570.

Pinsky, M. J., and Stokes, J. L. 1952. *J. Bact.*, **64**:151–161.

Pollock, M. R. 1946. *Brit. J. Exp. Path.*, **27**:419–432.

Pollock, M. R., and Perret, C. J. 1951. *Brit. J. Exp. Path.*, **32**:387–396.

Pollock, M. R., and Torriani, A. M. 1953. In, Symposium on Adaptation, Soc. Gen. Microbiol. Cambridge, University Press.

Preiss, J.; Berg, P.; Ofengand, E. J.; Bergmann, F. H.; and Dieckmann, M. 1959. *Proc. Nat. Acad. Sci.*, **45**:319–328.

Radding, C. M., and Kornberg, A. 1962. *Fed. Proc.*, **21**:382.

Recondo, E., and Leloir, L. F. 1961. *Biochem. Biophys. Res. Comms.*, **6**:85–88.

Rotman, B., and Spiegelman, S. 1954. *J. Bact.*, **68**:419–429.

Schachman, H. K.; Adler, J.; Radding, C. M.; Lehman, I. R.; and Kornberg, A. 1960. *J. Biol. Chem.*, **235**:3242–3249.

Schachtschabel, D., and Zillig, W. 1959. *Z. physiol. Chem.*, **314**:262–275; McCorquodale, D. J., and Zillig, W. *Ibid.*, **315**:86–89.

Schade, A. L., and Thimann, K. V. 1940. *Am. J. Bot.*, **27**:659–670.

Schiff, J. A.; Eisenstedt, J. M.; and Klein, H. P. 1959. *J. Bact.*, **78**:124–129.

Sheffner, A. L., and McClary, D. O. 1954. *Arch. Biochem. Biophys.*, **52**:74–82.

Smith, E. L. 1962. *Proc. Nat. Acad. Sci.*, **48**:859–864.

Smith, O. H., and Yanofsky, C. 1960. *J. Biol. Chem.*, **235**:2051–2057.

Stephenson, M., and Stickland, L. H. 1933. *Biochem. J.*, **27**:1528–1532.

Stier, T. J. B., and Newton, M. I. 1939. *J. Cell. Comp. Physiol.*, **13**:345–351.

Stokes, J. L., and Bayne, H. G. 1958, 1961. *J. Bact.*, **76**:136–141; **81**:118–125 (1961).

Strange, R. E. 1961. *Nature*, **191**:1272–1273.

Strecker, M. J. 1957. *J. Biol. Chem.*, **225**:825–834.

Swanson, W. H., and Clifton, C. E. 1948. *J. Bact.*, **56**:115–123.

Tauber, H. 1951. *J. Am. Chem. Soc.*, **73**:1288–1290, 4965–4966.

Tissières, A.; Schlesinger, D.; and Gros, F. 1960. *Proc. Nat. Acad. Sci.*, **46**:1450.

Torriani, A. M., and Monod, J. 1949. *Compt. rend. Acad. Sci.*, **227**:240–242; **228**:718–720.

Umbarger, H. E., and Brown, B. 1958. *J. Biol. Chem.*, **233**:415–420.

Vogel, H. J. 1957. In, The Chemical Basis of Heredity, ed. W. B. McElroy and B. Glass. Baltimore, Johns Hopkins Press, pp. 276–289; *Proc. Nat. Acad. Sci.*, **43**:491–496.

Wainwright, S. D., and Nevill, A. 1956. *J. Gen. Microbiol.*, **14**:47–56.

Wood, H. G., and Werkman, C. H. 1934. *J. Biol. Chem.*, **105**:63–72.

Wong, K. K.; Meister, A.; and Moldave, K. 1959. *Biochim. Biophys. Acta*, **36**:531–533.

Wormser, E. H., and Pardee, A. B. 1958. *Arch. Biochem. Biophys.*, **78**:416–432.

Yates, R. A., and Pardee, A. B. 1957. *J. Biol. Chem.*, **227**:677–692.

Yoshida, A., and Yamasaki, M. 1959. *Biochim. Biophys. Acta*, **34**:158–165.

Zachau, H. G.; Acs, G.; and Lipmann, F. 1958. *Proc. Nat. Acad. Sci.*, **44**:885–889.

CHAPTER XXI

The Transmission of Characters

The gene is like nothing known to the inorganic world. It possesses the unique property of being able to direct the synthesis of replicas of itself from a large array of building blocks. The message that is coded within it is capable of being translated into the complex processes that are development and function. . . . It is the occasional mistakes that presumably occur in the replication of genes that provide the genetic variability from which all organic evolution is believed to come.

GEORGE W. BEADLE (1955)

The heredity of bacteria plays such an all-inclusive role in their life that its study ramifies into almost all the areas treated in this book. For this reason no attempt will be made to present the whole of bacterial genetics in this chapter, and indeed the use of genetic methods and the production and study of mutants have been discussed already many times in other parts of the book. Instead, the aims of the present chapter will be more limited, namely, to provide a nucleus of basic fact around which much of the other work can be centered, and to present certain special aspects of heredity, peculiar to bacteria, which have not been treated extensively elsewhere.

1. MUTATIONS

It was in 1912 that M. W. Beijerinck, plating out *B. prodigiosum* (=*Serratia marcescens*), noticed that a single small red[1] colony when plated out gave rise to a few orange or yellow, or even deeper red ones, and to viscous forms. All these on subsequent transfers bred true, and some of the changes were found reversible. Where two successive changes had occurred (e.g., normal red → viscous red → viscous white), reversal occurred one step at a time. Often the same type of change appeared repeatedly. After taking careful precautions against contamination,

[1] For chemistry of the pigment see Chapter VIII, section 6B.

Beijerinck concluded that the bacteria were mutating. (His country-man de Vries had introduced the idea of mutations from studies of higher plants some 10 years earlier). Since that time mutant forms and strains of almost every known bacterium have been recognized. They include changes in cytology, flagellation and motility, pigments, colony type, respiration system, resistance to antibiotics, and, above all, changes in the complement of enzymes. The latter often lead to changes in nutrient requirements, which provide one of the most useful groups of "markers" for genetic experiments.

Mutants are distinguished by three characteristics, their sudden appearance, their usual lack of direct relation to the external en-vironment (i.e., "undirectedness") and their inheritance. Commonly a mutation occurs once in about 10^8 cell divisions; however, the incidence can be readily increased by ultraviolet or x-radiation (see Chap. XXIV). The mutation rate can also be raised by certain chem-icals, especially Mn ions (Demerec and Hanson, 1951) and compounds reacting with SH groups (p. 759 ff), also by some internal factors, such as the intracellular mutagen of *E. coli* (Bryson, 1961) which increases by 1000 times the rate at which mutants resistant to antibiotics appear. Until recently both external and internal treatments always produced strictly random mutations, but a beginning has now been made toward breaking this limitation by the use of nitrous acid (pp. 93, 653).

That normally mutations are independent of the substrate was given rigid proof for the case of resistance to bacteriophage (Newcombe, 1949). Pairs of plates with growing colonies of a strain of *E. coli* very susceptible to bacteriophage were prepared. One in each pair was smeared with saline so that all colonies were broken up and redis-tributed. All plates were then sprayed with the phage. After further incubation, the remaining colonies, which must be phage-resistant mutants, were counted. Now if the resistance arose as a response to exposure to the phage, all bacteria before spraying would be equally susceptible, and hence spreading would make no difference. But if it were due to chance mutation, some resistant cells would be already present, as colonies, subcolonies, or little groups (depending on how soon the mutation occurred). Hence, if not disturbed, each such group would form one visible colony; if spread, each *individual* would form a colony. Thus spreading should greatly increase the number of resist-ant colonies. Spreading *did* increase the number, by a factor of up to 50 times. Phage-resistant mutants were therefore present among cells *which had never been exposed to the phage*. Similarly, mutants conferring resistance to antibiotics, notably penicillin and streptomycin, occur among bacteria that have never been subjected to the drugs (Chap. XXV). In another example with yeast, the mutation conferring ability to synthesize pantothenate was shown to appear by chance both in the presence and absence of pantothenate, and to behave genetically like a single-gene mutation (Raut, 1950). With pantothenate in the medium, however, the mutant cells regularly become overgrown by the others.

Besides occurring during division, a few mutations occur in cultures that are in the stationary phase (e.g., histidine-requiring *E. coli* in a histidine-free medium). It appears that the DNA content per cell may increase by some 30 per cent in such nondividing cells in the first few hours of starvation, but later it decreases again; yet mutation continued at a constant rate for 429 hours (Nakada and Ryan, 1961; Ryan *et al.*, 1961). The interpretation of this behavior must await the discussion of the mechanism of mutation (below). Certainly cell division and DNA duplication are normally necessary for mutation to occur.

It was the systematic study of biochemical mutants in Neurospora that led Beadle and Tatum (see Beadle, 1947) to the celebrated concept that each gene controls the formation of one enzyme. Examples of this have been noted throughout the book. However, closer examination of the appearance of known mutants has modified this simple view, since, when a large number of separate isolations are made of bacteria with apparently the same mutant character, it develops that many of the mutations are not really identical. The manner in which this was established (first for bacteriophages by Benzer [1955], then for Salmonella by Demerec *et al.* [1956]) will be discussed below; here the point is only that within one gene many different mutations having the same visible effect can occur. Most of these complement one another, in that when both are present, the wild-type character reappears. Mutants that do not so complement one another evidently fall within the same functional group or subunit, called a "cistron."

2. THE COPYING OF NUCLEAR MATERIAL AND ITS ACTION ON THE CYTOPLASM

In the absence of sexuality, inheritance in a microorganism is simple; the progeny produced by cell division are identical with the parent, except for the rare occurrence of mutations, which are thought of as imperfect copying of the parental genes.

The copying of genes for inheritance and the transmission of genetic information to the cytoplasm are closely interrelated. The essential steps are as follows:

(1) The DNA, which is the genetic material itself, consists of a pair of helical strands in which the purine bases of one strand are linked (by hydrogen bonds) to the pyrimidine bases of the other: adenine to thymine, and guanine to cytosine (Fig. XXI–1). This concept was developed partly as an interpretation of x-ray diagrams of

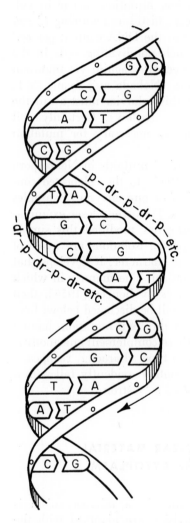

FIGURE XXI–1

Diagram of the DNA molecule showing the bases (A, adenine; G, guanine; C, cytosine; T, thymine) paired within the helix. (dr, deoxyribose; p, phosphate) (Modified from Watson and Crick, 1953.)

purified DNA (Watson and Crick, 1953), but is supported by the analyses of DNA from various sources, which show the amount of adenine always equal to the amount of thymine, and the amount of guanine (which may be more or less than that of adenine) always equal to the amount of cytosine (Chargaff, 1955). Thus, A = T and G = C, but A + T/G + C varies from one nucleic acid to another.

At a certain moment the two strands unwind and separate. Each single strand then produces, from smaller nucleotides in the vicinity, the strand complementary to it, i.e., bearing a thymine opposite the parent strand's adenine and a guanine opposite its cytosine.

At the chromosomal level, this strand duplication can be neatly shown. Cells exposed briefly to thymidine labeled with tritium (H^3) incorporate this into the DNA of their chromosomes; on subsequent division, in absence of H^3, radioautographs show that one of the daughter chromosomes is labeled, the other not; hence the latter has been newly synthesized, and DNA is not simply divided equally between the two (Taylor et al., 1957; Taylor, 1958). A corresponding observation has been made at the molecular level, by growing E. coli on $N^{15}H_4Cl$ so that the bases of their DNA are heavily labeled with N^{15}. The cells are then transferred to $N^{14}H_4Cl$ medium, left there just long enough for the DNA to be replicated once, then quickly frozen and extracted. The nitrogen content of nucleic acid is so high that the DNA labeled with N^{15} is appreciably heavier than normal; Meselson and Stahl (1958) showed that by centrifuging in a graded series of layers of concentrated caesium chloride solution, the N^{15}-DNA could be separated from N^{14}-DNA; ultraviolet photographs clearly revealed two layers. But—and this is the critical observation—there was also an intermediate layer, halfway between the two, which must consist of hybrid DNA, one strand containing N^{15}, the other N^{14}. Thus, the material of the second strand had been produced from the $N^{14}H_4Cl$ to which the cells had been transferred; yet it was attached to N^{15}-DNA formed previously in the $N^{15}H_4Cl$ medium. This is clear evidence that the new strand is formed from the new substrates but laid on the old, and only later becomes separated.

Recently an interesting parallel has been observed in DNA solution in vitro: the helical macromolecules of DNA are found to form two-stranded complexes spontaneously at particular ranges of pH and ionic strength; in this way even hybrid DNA's can be formed with two strands differing slightly from one another. The stability of these depends on the pairing between bases, mentioned above (Doty, 1961).

(2) Similar helical strands of the other type of nucleic acid, namely, RNA, are formed by the enzymatic polymerization of nucleotides, when in close association with the helices of the DNA. Such association can occur, at least over short distances along the helix, in vitro. Thus, the RNA-synthesizing enzyme from E. coli, which converts a mixture of the triphosphates of the four bases into RNA (p. 654), is dependent on the presence of a small amount of "primer" DNA. In

consequence, the base composition of the resulting RNA closely follows that of the type of DNA used (Table XXI–1).

TABLE XXI–1. Relation between the Composition of RNA Synthesized by the Enzyme of Furth *et al.* (1961) and the Composition of the DNA Supplied to It

Source of DNA	RATIO: $\dfrac{\text{Adenine} + \text{Thymine}}{\text{Cytosine} + \text{Guanine}}$ $\left\{\begin{array}{l}\text{in DNA}\\\text{Supplied}\end{array}\right.$	RATIO: $\dfrac{\text{Adenine} + \text{Uracil}}{\text{Cytosine} + \text{Guanine}}$ $\left\{\begin{array}{l}\text{in RNA}\\\text{Formed}\end{array}\right.$
Phage T_2	1.86	1.85
Thymus gland	1.35	1.52
E. coli	1.0	0.93
M. lysodeikticus	0.40	0.48

(3) The resulting specific RNA is presumably now released from its association and transported to the ribosomes which are the seat of synthesis of the protein enzymes (Chap. XX). Here its function is to modify the RNA of the ribosomes so that the latter will synthesize only those specific proteins called for by the DNA. Since enzyme induction can begin within three minutes of exposure to an inducer and cease a few minutes after the inducer has been removed, this so-called "messenger-RNA" must be highly unstable. Just how it modifies or controls the ribosomal RNA is not yet clear; it may actually enter the ribosomes.

(4) A different type of soluble RNA combines with amino acids, to form the aminoacyl nucleotides discussed in Chapter XX—one nucleic acid for each different amino acid. It then carries them to the ribosomal RNA. By this substance they are combined into specific proteins, and the soluble RNA released. The sequence of amino acids in the protein is determined by the sequence of the bases in the ribosomal RNA, which, in turn, has been modified by the DNA as above. It was seen on pages 653 and 668 that the amino acids are selected and ordered by the messenger RNA in the form of amino-acyl RNA's.

In this manner the gene controls the formation of the proteins, especially enzyme proteins, which are thus essentially *the expression of the gene's presence*. Mutations modify the DNA so that (1) it perpetuates the mutation, and (2) it gives rise to altered RNA's so that they produce modified enzymes.

The actual chemical changes constituting mutations can be of two kinds:

(1) Errors in base pairing, so that, e.g., adenine is replaced by guanine, or cytosine by hypoxanthine. Such changes can be induced

by the base analogues (e.g., diaminopurine, bromodeoxyuridine, etc.) which become incorporated into the nucleic acid and may then pair with the "wrong" base. As an example (see Strelzoff, 1962), 5-bromo-uracil (B) may take the place of thymine (T) and thus pair with adenine (A). As this is replicated, in the absence of any further supply of 5-bromo-uracil, usually thymine will replace it again, but very occasionally the B will pair with guanosine (G) instead of A. The guanosine will in the next replication call for a cytosine, and thus a mutation will have occurred:

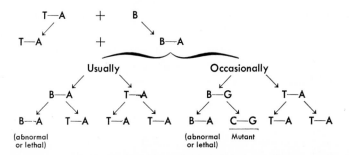

In treatment with nitrous acid (Chap. II, sec. 10) adenine is converted to hypoxanthine, guanine to xanthine, and cytosine to uracil; the results, when replication occurs, are similar to the above.

(2) Replacement or "transversion," a purine becoming replaced by a pyrimidine (or vice versa) (Freese, 1959). In the next replication each pyrimidine (Py) becomes paired with a purine (Pu), one thus forming a normal DNA chain and the other a mutant:

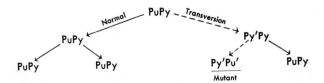

Freese's study of phage with base analogues suggests that spontaneous mutations probably are of this second type. A fuller discussion is given by Sager and Ryan (1961).

3. SEXUALITY

The major value of sex to the life of the organism is, of course, that it allows the *recombination* of genetic characters. The sexual process itself as it occurs in bacteria has been described in Chapter III, sec. 5. Discovered as recently as 1947, it still has been observed only in very few organisms. The process consists simply of the transfer of a linear array of genes from the donor (or male) to the receiver (or female) cell. There is no cell fusion as there is in the sex cells of higher organisms; the transfer is one way only. The resulting zygote is diploid for the genes transferred and can show the typical phenomena of genetic diploids; *dominance* in inducibility of enzymes was mentioned on page 667; *segregation* can be visually observed by growing a diploid strain of *E. coli mutabile* on lactose-indicator medium, when the resulting colonies are variegated, some zones fermenting the lactose and some not, i.e., they have segregated during growth (Lederberg *et al.*, 1951). The recessive gene giving resistance to phage T_1 also begins to appear soon after conjugation, showing that segregation is rapid (Hayes, 1957). So far as is known, there is nothing in bacteria akin to the thick-walled or resting zygote which so often occurs in algae and fungi; division begins soon after conjugation is complete.

Top Line. Genetic characters
Bottom Line. Time at which transferred (in minutes)
(lys λ, lys 21, and lys 424 are three genes conferring lysogeny)

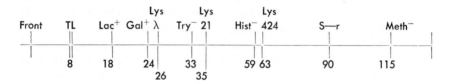

FIGURE XXI–2

Gene order and timing in *E. coli* K12. For meaning of gene name abbreviations, see footnote 2.

If conjugation is interrupted by mechanical stirring, those genes that have already entered the female cell remain fully effective and appear normally in the zygote's progeny. Thus, by interrupting at different times after conjugation begins, the order in which the genes go in has been established (p. 148). An example is shown in Figure XXI–2. The process can also be interrupted by inhibiting the metabolic energy supply to the male, since the donation process requires energy; subsequent washing out of the inhibitor allows it to go on again (Wollman *et al.*, 1956; Fisher, 1957).

The Hfr (high frequency recombination) mutants, with which the earlier conjugation work was done (Chap. III), transfer only a *part* of the genetic material at high frequency; the remainder goes in more rarely. Hence, when the conjugation is interrupted, one can only trace the linear order of a part of the genes. Later a Vhf strain was discovered in which transference goes all the way (Taylor and Adelberg, 1960). This has allowed confirmation of the conclusions drawn from more extensive work with Hfr, in which the difficulty of partial transfer was surmounted by analyzing five different Hfr mutants; between them, these covered 18 genetic characters. The order of these was determined by shaking or stirring the conjugation pairs and then, by plating out on different media, finding which genes had been transferred (see Fig. XXI–2). The use of five different mutants brought out the important conclusion that although the linear order was the same in each, the gene-string may be inserted into the receptor cell *forward or backward*. For instance, in one Hfr mutant the order is[2]

$$\text{T6-r } lac^+ \text{ Tl-r Az-r } leu^- \; thr^- \; thi^- \; meth^- \; mtol^+ \; mal^+ \text{ S-r}$$

in another it is

$$meth^- \; thi^- \; thr^- \; leu^- \text{ Az-r Tl-r } lac^+ \text{ T6-r } gal^+ \; \lambda$$

Wollman and Jacob (1958), therefore, deduced that in the bacterium the genes are arranged linearly *in* a *ring*, but that the ring can be broken at almost any point, by insertion of the Hfr character. "The properties of the different Hfr strains could thus be accounted for by the single hypothesis that the insertion of a specific factor at the proper place in the circular linkage group would determine the rupture of the circle." The resulting linear structure is then transferred in conjugation. This interpretation is confirmed in the work with Vhf strains and very recently by direct microscopy (Cairns, 1963, cf. p. 148).

As stated, the formation of a zygote allows *recombination* of characters to occur. This process, in the chromosomes of higher organisms, is ascribed to the simultaneous breaking and refusion of two complementary strands, during meiosis (Fig. XXI–3). As a result, two genes formerly located in separate chromosomes are now found on the same one and thus inherited in the same linkage group. Now if the two genes are nearly at opposite ends of their chromosomes, as *A* and *B*, they will come together irrespective of where the crossover point occurs, because all such points will lie between these two genes. But if they are very close, as *C* and *D*, they will only come together in the few cases when the crossover point falls between *C* and *D*, and for the majority of locations of the crossover (e.g., between *A* and *C*), *C* and *D*

[2] Tl-r and T6-r confer resistance to the designated bacteriophages; Az-r and S-r, resistance to azide and streptomycin; λ carries the lysogenic phage; lac^+, gal^+, $mtol^+$, and mal^+ confer the ability to ferment lactose, galactose, mannitol, and maltose, respectively; while leu^-, thr^-, thi^-, and $meth^-$ give requirements for leucine, threonine, thiamine, and methionine.

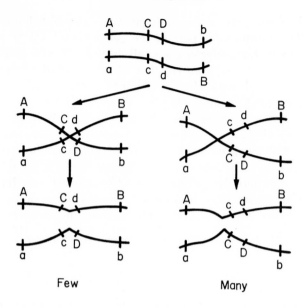

FIGURE XXI–3

Changes in the linkage of specific genes due to crossing-over, and the influence of the exact location of the crossover.

will remain on separate chromosomes. The crucially important result of this is that by observing the frequency with which any two genes recombine, i.e., come together into the same linkage group, we determine how far apart on the chromosome they lie. In this way, crossover frequencies have been used to produce detailed "maps" of the positions of the genes on the chromosomes, first of Drosophila by Morgan, Sturtevant, and Bridges in the 1920's, then of maize and many other genetically useful organisms, including Neurospora.

Now the phenomenon of conjugation in *E. coli* allows a similar approach to the location of genes in this bacterium, at least within that part of the genetic constitution that is transferred. Using the nutritional mutants mentioned above and in Chapter III, along with phage-resistance and the fermentation of lactose, Lederberg (1947) concluded that there was only one linkage group or "chromosome," and that the genes were probably in linear order on it.

When it was discovered that conjugation could be interrupted and that then a smaller part of the genetic material was transferred, it became possible to determine the order of genes and the distance between them by comparing the length of time conjugation had proceeded with the genetic constitution of the zygote and its progeny. This time-based gene map is quite independent from the crossover-based map; yet the two agree excellently (Wollman and Jacob, 1957); the order listed above is the same for both methods, and only the distance apart is uncertain by the conjugation method, and relatively reliable by recombination frequency. This agreement not only validates both the methods, but gives confidence in the whole conception of a "normal" genetics in bacteria.

The straight-line arrangement of hereditary characters in all organisms is remarkable. As Gierer put it: "The nucleic acids contain a great deal of information which is stored in a 1-dimensional static form *analogous to writing.*"

4. HETEROKARYOSIS

In *Streptomyces* sexuality is indicated, just as in *E. coli*, when two strains, each defective in synthesizing a different amino acid, are grown side by side; strains able to synthesize all amino acids, i.e., *prototrophs*, result. This is due to the fusion of hyphae, followed by the intermixing of nuclei (see Fig. XXI–4). In the resulting *hetero-karyotic mycelium*, fragments that are not too small contain nuclei of both types and are thus prototrophs. This phenomenon was discovered almost simultaneously by three groups of workers (Bradley and Leder-berg, 1956; Sermonti and Spada-Sermonti, 1955–1956; and Braendle and Szybalski, 1957). That the mycelium is indeed heterokaryotic is shown by the fact that occasionally a hyphal fragment can only grow on a medium *partially* supplemented with one of the amino acids; evidently one of the nuclear types is then present in insufficient numbers to allow of the full rate of synthesis (Braendle and Szybalski, 1959). Thus heterokaryosis clearly differs from nuclear fusion.

The formation of conidia (see Chap. II, sec. 4) results from breaking up of the aerial mycelium into uninuclear sections (Fig. XXI–4). The conidia, therefore, should only be of the two parental types, requiring one or the other amino acid for growth. This is indeed the case in *Str. griseus*, but in *Str. coelicolor* some of the conidia are prototrophic, like the hyphae, indicating that recombination has occurred (Sermonti and Spada-Sermonti, 1955–1956; Bradley, 1957–1958; Saito and Ikeda, 1959). While this may indicate true nuclear fusion, it may only be due to presence of two nuclei in some conidia. Cytological study supports the occasional occurrence of such conidia (Kinoshita and Itagaki, 1959). Whether they are diploid or only "bipartite" is not clear.

Heterokaryosis, with the conidia yielding only parental-type colonies, occurs in *Str. griseoflavus, venezuelae, albus,* and *spheroides,*
while recombination as well, with production of prototrophic conidia,
occurs in *Str. coelicolor, fradiae, rimosus, griseoflavus,* and *scabies*
(Braendle and Szybalski, 1959). From *Str. aureofaciens* a number of
arginine-requiring mutants have been obtained, which could be crossed
to yield prototrophs (Alikhanian and Borisova, 1961). These prototrophs did not have the ability to produce antibiotic, as did the

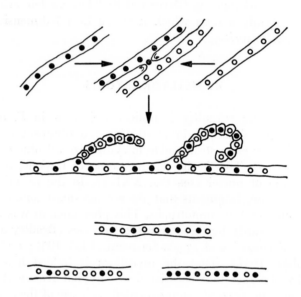

FIGURE XXI-4

Fusion of hyphae of *Str. griseus* to produce a heterokaryon; the conidia are, however, uninucleate and hence of the parental types. *Below.* Unequal distribution of
nuclei in the hyphae causes short hyphal fragments to be only imperfectly prototrophic.
(After Braendle and Szybalski, 1959.)

parental cultures. Since these and most of the other Streptomyces mentioned are major producers of antibiotics, the potential importance of
these phenomena for the drug industry are great.

5. TRANSDUCTION

In contrast to these "normal" hereditary phenomena, which closely
parallel those in higher organisms, two strikingly "abnormal" kinds

of hereditary transfer have been discovered, which so far are limited to the bacteria. In these, genes are not transferred *in situ* on the chromosome (and therefore as whole genomes) but are transferred singly or in very small groups. In the first such system the transfer is carried out by a bacteriophage. Because it does not immediately lyse the bacteria (cf. p. 102) but can grow internally as a kind of symbiont, this type is referred to as a *temperate phage*.

A. Transduction in Salmonella

The occurrence of this phenomenon was brought to light by Zinder and Lederberg (1952) from study of physiological characters, such as ability to grow without added amino acids (*prototrophism*), ability to ferment specific sugars, or resistance to antibiotics. Strains of *S. typhimurium* can be had which are positive or negative for all these characters. If to a strain that will *not* grow on minimal medium or in the presence of streptomycin, and will *not* ferment galactose or xylose, is added a cell-free filtrate from a strain that *will* do these four things, a few colonies will subsequently grow on minimal medium, in a streptomycin medium, and in media containing galactose or xylose. Of 10^8 to 10^9 cells transferred, some 50 will grow, i.e., more than one in ten millions have received the new gene. However, in each case only the one character has been transferred or *transduced;* for example, the galactose-fermenting cells will not ferment xylose and vice versa. In this respect, the phenomena differ from those of sexuality, because there several characters are transferred at once, and cell-free filtrates are always inactive.

The filterable agent in Salmonella has been identified as a bacteriophage active against a considerable group of Salmonellae; all those that contain the antigen XII_2 (see below) are susceptible to it, and hence the antigen XII_2 is probably the receptor of the phage. The identification was made from the observations that (1) when the phage is adsorbed on boiled cells, the filterable agent is removed from solution to about the same degree as on live cells (as shown by counting the number of transduced colonies); (2) both phage and filterable agent can be precipitated by cold alcohol without inactivation; (3) when the phage is inactivated by heat, the filterable agent is inactivated too. Zinder and Lederberg (1952) explain the transference of genetic characters by the phage as follows: the phage particles multiply in the cell by conversion of the nucleoproteins of the cell into nucleoproteins of the phage; in doing this, some whole genes become transferred to phage particles. When the cell is lysed, these phage particles are set free and enter a new host cell, where they attach to the dividing

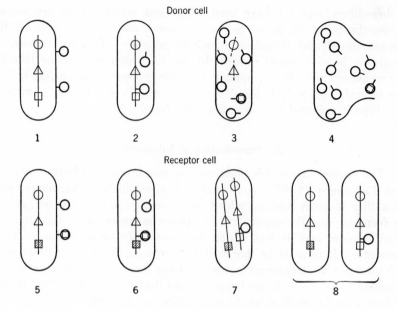

FIGURE XXI–5

The stages of transduction (modified from Morse *et al.*, 1956).

1. Bacterium with three genes in the nucleus being attacked by phage.

2. Two phage particles enter the cell, one becoming attached to the genes.

3. As the phage particles multiply, the nucleus is broken up, and one of the genes becomes incorporated into the phage particle that was attached to it.

4. The cell is lysed, and the phage particle carrying a gene is released along with the others.

5. New bacterium with three genes, one of which differs from that in the first cell, though homologous with it.

6. The phage particle enters and attaches to the homologous gene.

7. The nucleus divides, and in some way the gene introduced by the phage particle becomes substituted for the one which would normally be duplicated.

8. One of the resulting cells contains the transduced gene.

nucleus; the introduced gene thus becomes substituted for the one homologous to it. The process is shown diagrammatically in Figure XXI–5 (Morse *et al.*, 1956).

B. The Antigens of the Genus Salmonella

The transduction phenomenon helps greatly to understand the complexities of the antigens and the interrelations of the "species" within the genus Salmonella.

Long ago it was noticed that motile Proteus cultures produce on agar a thin, spreading film described in German as *Hauch*, while nonmotile cultures are *ohne Hauch*. Injection into animals showed that the motile and nonmotile forms contained different antigens, named by Weil and Felix (1917) H and O, respectively. H is ascribed to the flagella and O to the body of the bacterium; this is supported by the fact that when the serum prepared against a motile strain, and therefore containing antibody to both H and O, is mixed with the nonmotile cells, it loses its ability to agglutinate nonmotile cells (i.e., its antibody against them is absorbed), while it can still agglutinate a motile strain. Similar antigens are found in many of the gram-negative rods, and especially in Salmonella. Here the flagellar (or H) antigens are sometimes multiple, and the somatic (or O) antigens usually so, most organisms containing from two to four. (These are given Roman numerals.) Many of the antigens, both H and O, are common to different organisms, so that sera prepared from one strain or species will agglutinate a different one ("cross-agglutination"). For example, the three Salmonellae, *S. typhimurium*, *S. paratyphi B*, and *S. typhosa*, all have somatic antigen No. XII in common, while they have different flagellar (H) antigens.

The O antigens are connected with a surface polysaccharide, which makes the cultures form smooth colonies; rough forms do not contain this antigen, but instead contain a less specific R antigen. Smooth forms of Salmonella, Escherichia, and Aerobacter, after oxidation with periodate and treatment with Feulgen's stain (p. 136 ff.), show stained polar or bipolar bodies, while rough variants give no such stain. (Lankford *et al.* [1951] therefore proposed that the polar bodies are themselves the O antigens.) The Feulgen staining is due to the presence in these antigens of di-deoxyhexoses. Purification studies indicate that, for instance, antigen IX is a disaccharide of mannose and di-deoxymannose. Others contain the di-deoxy derivatives of glucose and galactose and up to four or five hexose residues per molecule (Staub and co-workers, 1959–1960). At least four other types of antigen are known: Vi, M, Q, and T.

Study of all these antigens has led to the classification of the genus on the basis of its antigens—the so-called "Kauffmann-White system" (see Bergey *et al.*, 1957). Of the somatic antigens, about 12 have been distinguished, while the group associated with the flagella contains over 30. These are now regarded as "serological types," differing only in the sugars and other components of their antigens, while the number of true species may be as few as three (Borman *et al.*, 1944) or perhaps 10 (Bergey *et al.*, 1957). But transduction casts a different light on these.

The O, H, and R antigens can all be transduced. Nonmotile or O strains, which do not have the O antigen, can be "mobilized," i.e., made motile, by the phage from an H strain. This confers *both* flagella *and* the H antigen (Stocker, 1956). Among other antigens that can be transduced are some which alternate from time to time in two "phases."

What does transduction mean for the systematist? Is it feasible to retain the fiction of "species" for a form that is readily convertible to another, *and back*, by a parasite? These problems are not limited to Salmonella, since transduction is now known to occur widely, and indeed characters can be transduced from Salmonella into *E. coli*.

C. Transduction in Other Organisms

Outside of Salmonella, the transduction phenomenon has been found in several gram-negative forms, notably Escherichia, Shigella (Lennox, 1955), and *Ps. aeruginosa* (Holloway and Monk, 1959). It has recently also come to light in the gram-positive forms *M.* (*"Staph."*) *aureus* (Morse, 1959), *Bac. subtilis* (Takahashi, 1961), and an Actinomyces (Alikhanian *et al.*, 1960). In *M. aureus*, genes for resistance to streptomycin and novobiocin were transduced by growing bacteriophage on the resistant strains, then purifying it and mixing it with sensitive cells. Between 1 and 10 phage particles in 10^8 transfer genes in the Micrococcus, up to 1 in 10^6 in *Bac. subtilis*. Among the genes transduced in *Bac. subtilis* was the ability to form spores, which a stable "asporogenous" strain had lost (Takahashi, 1961). The strains of bacteria showing transduction were in most cases those that show no sexuality. However, the distinction is often difficult to make, because the phage infection occurs about as fast as sexual transfer. Hayes (1952) found that two *E. coli* strains when mixed gave rise to prototrophs even when one strain was dead (freshly killed by irradiation or by streptomycin). In fact, the recombination was more frequent than when both strains were alive! The apparent sexual activity of the corpse was traced to its containing a latent phage, so that in this case the recombination was evidently due to transduction. Phages occur so widely that transduction is probably of general importance in bacterial evolution.

A phenomenon perhaps akin to transduction, though not as well understood, is the transference of the property of producing colicines. These are toxic compounds of high molecular weight, discovered by Fredericq in 1946, which adsorb to cells of the Enterobacteriaceae and kill them; the recipient cells are not lysed, and the effect is more like that of an antibiotic than of a phage (see Fredericq, 1957). Colicines are produced by specific "colicinogenic" strains and kill only specific sensitive strains. However, if a nonproducer and a producer are mixed together for a few minutes, the former may become colicinogenic. No other property is transferred, e.g., a strain of *E. coli* made colicinogenic by mixture with a colicinogenic *Shigella sonnei* retained the biochemical properties of *E. coli* (Fredericq, 1956–58). Similar genetic transfer of nothing but colicinogenesis took place between several other members of the Enterobacteriaceae (Hamon, 1956), although the property is not transferable in every case. Since the transformed or transduced strains continue to produce colicines indefinitely and can even transfer this property to a third strain, a specific hereditary character has been transmitted. Whether the transfer is accomplished by a phage, as transduction, is not yet clear.

Another transduction-like phenomenon is that of the F^+ character or "sex factor" in *E. coli*, which confers conjugating ability (Cavalli *et al.*, 1953; Hayes, 1953). It will be remembered (see sec. 3) that the Hfr strains are mutants of F^+ in which the character has become incorporated into the heredity, it becoming localized on the chromosome at different places in different Hfr strains (Jacob and Wollman, 1956–1957). The F^- strains are sterile among themselves, while matings of F^+ with F^- give maximum fertility. But F^- is converted to F^+ by growing in mixed cultures. For example, F^+ Lac^+ and F^- Lac^- strains were mixed, and samples withdrawn and plated on lactose-indicator medium. Those *not* fermenting were then tested for their F^+ capacity; about half the initially F^- cells had become F^+ in two hours. Since this procedure eliminates sexual recombinants, F^+ must evidently be transduced ("F-duction").

In general, for heredity-carrying bodies like lysogenic phages, transducing phages, colicines, F^+, or the transforming substances described below, all of which in one phase are free in the cytoplasm and in the other phase are incorporated into genetic material, Jacob *et al.* (1960) propose the term "episomes." The *epi*, as in epiphyte (= plants growing on the outside of others), means outside (i.e., outside the nucleus).

6. TRANSFORMATION

It has been seen above that in sexuality of higher organisms there is transferred from male to female an entire nucleus; in the sexuality of bacteria what is transferred is essentially a group of characters on a single chromosome. In transduction the transferred material is still further decreased to a single gene, or a very small group of linked genes, encased in a phage structure. Logically the ultimate term in this decreasing series would be the transfer of a single inheritable character by a single DNA molecule, and this is close to what happens in the transformation process.

Transformation was discovered through the relatively common observation that Pneumococcus cultures occasionally mutate to produce strains that have lost the power of synthesizing their capsular polysaccharide and have therefore become rough or R strains. The parent cultures are smooth (S) types (Chap. III, sec. 2). As with Salmonella, the R cultures are precipitated by antibodies formed against any of the types, i.e., by antibodies that are not type-specific and react only with the protein.

The critical observation is that rough colonies can be artificially reconverted to smooth. If rough cells are injected into mice together with heat-killed smooth cells, a culture of smooth cells can afterward be isolated, i.e., the ability to form capsular polysaccharide has been conferred on the cells. Not only that, but the specificity also has been conferred; heat-killed Type II cells convert rough cells (which have been derived from any type) to smooth Type II. The transformed cells breed true. This observation, made first by Griffith in 1928, means that the smooth cells contain a "transforming principle" which confers on the rough forms a new synthetic activity. This principle is not destroyed when the cells are heat-killed. It is not necessary to use whole heat-killed smooth cells, since extracts also have transforming action (Avery et al., 1944), and these extracts can be purified free of protein or polysaccharide; they are fully effective when they consist only of DNA. One part of the DNA in 600 millions, or 3×10^{-5} mg per liter, will bring about transformation, and the specific enzyme deoxyribonuclease (DNase) inactivates it.

Many heritable characters other than polysaccharide formation can be transferred by DNA preparations. They include resistance to streptomycin (S-r) and to penicillin, sulfonamides, and other drugs; the power to metabolize salicin, mannitol, mannose, and other carbohydrates; and even the ability to form some inducible enzymes (Hotchkiss and Marmur, 1954). Although these often act as single "transforming factors," in some cases, e.g., S-r with mannitol dehydrogenase, or two different degrees of sulfonamide-resistance, two or more factors can be transformed at once and are probably linked in a single DNA molecule (Hotchkiss and Evans, 1958). The presence of groups of closely related characters indicates that the transforming DNA can also mutate. For example, "extra rough" (ER) strains are transformed to rough (R) by a preparation from the R (also obtainable from S), while conversely R is transformed to ER by a preparation from ER

(Ephrussi-Taylor, 1950). Strains intermediate between R and S, with specific transforming factors for them, also exist.

More remarkable is the fact that bacteria other than Pneumococcus can be transformed. The list at the time of writing includes *Neisseria meningitidis*, a strain of *E. coli*, *Bac. subtilis*, three strains of *Hemophilus influenzae* and *H. para-influenzae*. Generally the experiments only work well on complex media, which apparently act by promoting combination of the DNA with the cell; serum albumin is particularly effective. Nevertheless, clear-cut transformation on chemically defined media has been obtained with *Bac. subtilis* (Spizizen, 1959) and *H. influenzae* (Talmadge and Herriott, 1960).

It might be thought that the ability to introduce new hereditary characters by the uptake of DNA molecules alone would provide an easy approach to the study of the genetic mechanism. But there are many complications. In the first place, all the transforming DNA molecules from a pure culture, even if they are carrying a single "marker" character, are not the same. Thus, Ephrussi-Taylor (1955) purified the Pneumococcus DNA that transformed the recipient cells to streptomycin-resistance (i.e., carried S-r), and then fractionated it on columns; some of the fractions were up to five times as active as the original preparation. Activity is, in fact, present in several fractions of differing properties (Beiser *et al.*, 1959).

In the second place, the transforming process has several stages; the DNA must first adsorb on the host cell, then penetrate the membrane, then attach to the host cell's genetic material, and finally interact with it and become substituted for the corresponding piece of host DNA. It might fail in any one of these steps, and thus the kinetic and mathematical analysis of transformation leads to complex results (see e.g., Rosenberg *et al.*, 1959). Time studies, in which the recipient cells are briefly exposed to transforming DNA and then treated with DNase to destroy the unadsorbed DNA, show that, with cells in the logarithmic growth phase, the new character is integrated into the host genetic material within a few minutes after the DNA is fixed onto the cell. At first, the adsorbed DNA appears to be inactivated, since it cannot be re-extracted, but in a few minutes its activity recovers (Fox and Hotchkiss, 1960). Little or no new synthesis of DNA need take place, although gene duplication may occur an hour or so later.

A number of experiments have been made in which the transforming DNA is exposed to heat, ultraviolet, x-rays, mechanical shearing, or hydrolysis with DNase, and the effects on the transforming ability determined. These show that transforming ability is destroyed (by ultraviolet) some five times as fast as adsorption; by using DNA labeled with P^{32}, it is clear that ultraviolet-inactivated DNA can be incorporated into the host cell (Lerman and Tolmach, 1957). Two marker characters can be inactivated at different rates by ultraviolet, but at the same rate by x-rays or DNase, so that they behave to some extent independently. Mechanical breakage, reducing the average molecular weight by one-half, reduces the transforming activity drastically—to 10 per cent of the control, or even to zero, depending on the character concerned (Rosenberg et al., 1959). Most of the effect appears to be on the adsorption process, and it is curious that intact molecules, with a molecular weight in millions, should be adsorbed better than fractional parts of them.

In spite of these complications, transformation can provide valuable genetic analysis of DNA. An example is the transformation of maltase-negative pneumococcus mutants to maltase-positive strains; this can be done with DNA from a maltase-positive wild-type, but also, in some cases, with DNA *from other maltase-negative mutants* (Lacks and Hotchkiss, 1960). In these cases recombination has therefore taken place, the pair evidently having mutated regions in common. In other words, the deficiencies behave as nonidentical alleles (cf. sec. 1 above), and their recombination frequencies can be determined. With a series of mutants, *c d e f g h i j*, the following genetic map was obtained, the numbers being the recombination frequencies:

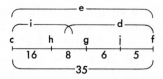

Thus, the maltase locus is linear, a straight subsection of a DNA molecule; single mutations alter regions on it of different sizes, and some of the regions altered can include several mutations. If the wild-type DNA is heated and the rate of inactivation of transforming ability followed, the largest regions like *e* are seen to be inactivated faster than the small regions, *c*, *f*, *g*, and *h*, while *d* and *i* behave intermediately. It is concluded that a DNA molecule can be partly denatured and yet retain activity largely unchanged in another part.

Transformation is not solely a phenomenon of killed cells or extracted DNA, since the transforming DNA can be excreted into the medium by live, growing Pneumococci (Ottolenghi and Hotchkiss, 1960). The maximum excretion occurs at the middle of the logarithmic growth phase, which is also the time when the cells are most responsive to added transforming DNA. Thus, two live cultures, on mixing, can produce recombinants, so that this must be a mechanism for genetic recombination *under natural conditions*. The implications of this are far-reaching.

The fact that transforming factors contain only DNA points up the earlier conclusion that heredity-transferring power resides in DNA alone, and hence that in genetic bodies of higher complexity (viruses and chromosomes), the protein part must play only a secondary role.

Lastly, biochemical and genetic details apart, the fact remains that here are organisms that have their heredity modified by the transfer of characters *through the solution*. This behavior is so radically different from that of other organisms as to suggest that the gulf between the bacteria and the other orders is wider than the differences separating any of the higher groups from one another. How fortunate that when we visit our communal swimming pool we do not need to fear a change of character in our unborn children!

REFERENCES

Alikhanian, S. I., and Borisova, L. N. 1961. *J. Gen. Microbiol.*, **26**:19–28.

Alikhanian, S. I.; Iljina, T. S.; and Lomooskaya, N. D. 1960. *Nature*, **188**:245–246.

Avery, O. T.; MacLeod, C. M.; and McCarty, M. 1944. *J. Exp. Med.*, **79**:137–158.

Beadle, G. 1947. Genes and the Chemistry of the Organism. In, *Science in Progress*, **5**:166–196.

Beijerinck, M. W. 1912. Mutation bei Mikroben. *Folia Microbiologica*, **1**:1–97.

Beiser, S. M.; Pahl, H. E.; Rosenkrantz, H. S.; and Bendich, A. 1959. *Biochim. Biophys. Acta*, **34**:497–502.

Benzer, S. 1955. *Proc. Nat. Acad. Sci.*, **41**:344–354.

Bergey, D. H. 1957. Manual of Determinative Bacteriology by R. S. Breed, E. G. D. Murray, and N. R. Smith, 7th ed., Baltimore, Williams and Wilkins, 368–383.

Borman, E. K.; Stuart, C. A.; and Wheeler, K. M. 1944. *J. Bact.*, **48**:351–367.

Bradley, S. G. 1957–1958. *J. Bact.*, **73**:581–582; **76**:464–470 (1958).

Bradley, S. G. 1962. *Ann. Revs. Microbiol.*, **16**:35–52.

Bradley, S. G., and Lederberg, J. 1956. *J. Bact.*, **72**:219–225.

Braendle, D. H., and Szybalski, W. 1957. *Proc. Nat. Acad. Sci.*, **43**:947–955.

Braendle, D. H., and Szybalski, W. 1959. *Ann. N. Y. Acad. Sci.*, **81**:824–853.

Bryson, V. 1961. Antibiotics: Practical and Experimental Aspects. *Survey of Biol. Progress*, **4**:345–440.

Cairns, J. 1963. *J. Mol. Biol.*, **6**:208–213.

Cavalli, L. L.; Lederberg, J.; and Lederberg, E. M. 1953. *J. Gen. Microbiol.*, **8**:89–103.

*Chargaff, E. 1955. In, The Nucleic Acids, Ed. E. Chargaff and J. N. Davidson. Vol. I, Chap. 10. New York, Academic Press.

Demerec, M., and Hanson, J. 1951. *Cold Spr. Harb. Symp. Quant. Biology*, **16**:215–228.

Demerec, M.; Hartman, Z.; Hartman, P. E.; Gotz, J. S.; and Yura, T. 1956. Carnegie Inst., Washington, Publ. No. 612, pp. 1–120 (7 papers).

Doty, P. 1961. *Biochem. J.*, **79**:(3), 15P; Doty, P.; Marmur, J.; Eigner, I.; and Schildkraut, C. 1960. *Proc. Nat. Acad. Sci.*, **46**:461–476.

Doudney, C. O., and Haas, F. L. 1959. *Proc. Nat. Acad. Sci.*, **45**:709–722, 1620–1624.

Ephrussi-Taylor, H. 1950. Biological Significance of the Transforming Principles of Pneumococcus. *Publ. Sta. Zool. Napoli* (Naples), **22**:Suppl. 1–14; *Endeavour*, April, 1950.

*Ephrussi-Taylor, H. 1955. Current Status of Bacterial Transformations. *Adv. Vir. Res.*, **3**:275–307.

Ephrussi-Taylor, H., and Latarjet, R. 1955. *Biochim. Biophys. Acta*, **16**:183–197.

Fisher, K. 1957. *J. Gen. Microbiol.*, **16**:136–145.

Fox, M. S., and Hotchkiss, R. D. 1960. *Nature*, **187**:1002–1006.

Fredericq, P. 1954. *Compt. rend. soc. biol.*, **148**:399–402.

*Fredericq, P. 1957. The Colicines. *Ann. Revs. Microbiol.*, **11**:7–21.

Fredericq, P. 1956–1958. *Compt. rend. Soc. Biol.*, **150**:1036–1039, 1514–1518; *J. Gen. Microbiol.*, **18**:527–528 (1958).

Freese, E. 1959. *Proc. Nat. Acad. Sci.*, **45**:622–633; *J. Mol. Biol.*, **1**:87–110.

Furth, J. J.; Hurwitz, J.; and Goldmann, M. 1961. *Biochem. Biophys. Res. Communs.*, **4**:362–367.

Hamon, Y. 1956. *Compt. rend. Acad. Sci.*, **242**:1240–1242, 2064–2066.

Hayes, W. 1952. *Nature*, **169**:118–119, 1017–1018.

Hayes, W. 1953. *Cold Spring Harbor Symp. Quant. Biol.*, **18**:75–93.

Hayes, W. 1957. *J. Gen. Microbiol.*, **16**:97–119.

Holloway, B. W., and Monk, M. 1959. *Nature*, **184**:1426.

Hotchkiss, R. D., and Evans, A. H. 1958. *Cold Spring Harbor Symp. Quant. Biol.*, **23**:85–97.

Hotchkiss, R. D., and Marmur, J. 1954. *Proc. Nat. Acad. Sci.*, **40**:55–60.

Jacob, F.; Schaeffer, P.; and Wollman, J. 1960. In, Microbial Genetics, ed. W. Hayes and J. Clowes, Cambridge Univ. Press.

Jacob, F., and Wollman, E. L. 1956–1957. *Compt. rend. Acad. Sci.*, **242**:303–306; **245**:1840–1843 (1957).

Kinoshita, S., and Itagaki, S. 1959. *Botan. Mag. (Tokyo)*, **72**:1–9.

Lacks, S., and Hotchkiss, R. D. 1960. *Biochim. Biophys. Acta*, **39**:508–518.

Lankford, C. E.; Hoyo, H.; and Lutteringer, J. R. 1951. *J. Bact.*, **62**:621–626; cf. Pennington, D. 1949. *J. Bact.*, **57**:163–167.

Lederberg, J. 1947. *Genetics*, **32**:505–525.

Lederberg, J.; Lederberg, E. M.; Zinder, N.; and Lively, E. R. 1951. *Cold Spring Harbor Symp. Quant. Biol.*, **16**:413–443.

Lennox, E. S. 1955. *Virology*, **1**:190–206.

Lerman, L. S., and Tolmach, L. J. 1957. *Biochim. Biophys. Acta*, **26**:68–82.

Meselson, M., and Stahl, F. W. 1958. *Proc. Nat. Acad. Sci.*, **44**:671–682.

Morse, M. L. 1959. *Proc. Nat. Acad. Sci.*, **45**:722–727.

Morse, M. L.; Lederberg, E. M.; and Lederberg, J. 1956. *Genetics*, **41**:142–15; cf. W. Arber; G. Kellenberger; and J. Weigle. *Schweiz. Zeit. f. allgem. Path. u. Bakt.*, **20**: 659–665, 1957.

Mundry, K. W., and Gierer, A. 1958. *Zeit. f. Vererbungslehre*, **89**:614–630.

Nakada, D., and Ryan, F. J. 1961. *Nature*, **189**:398–399; cf. F. J. Ryan. 1955. *Genetics*, **40**:726–738.

Newcombe, J. 1949. *Nature*, **164**:150–151.

Ottolenghi, E., and Hotchkiss, R. D. 1960. *Science*, **132**:1257–1258.

Raut, C. 1950. *Genetics*, **35**:381–395.

Rosenberg, B. H.; Sirotnak, F. M.; and Cavalieri, L. F. 1959. *Proc. Nat. Acad. Sci.*, **45**:144–156.

Ryan, F. J.; Nakada, D.; and Schneider, M. J. 1961. *Zeit. f. Vererbungslehre*, **92**:38–41.

Sager, R., and Ryan, F. J. 1961. Cell Heredity. New York, John Wiley & Sons.

Saito, H., and Ikeda, Y. 1959. *Ann. N. Y. Acad. Sci.*, **81**:862–878.

Sermonti, G., and Spada-Sermonti, I. 1955–1956. *Nature*, **176**:121; *J. Gen. Microbiol.*, **15**:609–616 (1956).

Spizizen, J. S. 1959. *Fed. Proc.* **18**: 957–965.

Staub, A. M.; Tinelli, R.; Lüderitz, O.; and Westphal, O. 1959. *Ann. Inst. Pasteur*, **96**:303–332; Stocker, B. A. D.; Staub, A. M.; Tinelli, R.; and Kopacka, B. *Ibid.*, **98**:505–523, 1960; Staub, A. M. (review). *Ibid.*, **98**:814–828, 1960.

Stocker, B. A. D. 1956. Bacterial Flagella: Morphology, Constitution and Inheritance. *Symp. Soc. Gen. Microbiol.*, **6**:19–30.

Stocker, B. A.; Zinder, N. D.; and Lederberg, J. 1953. *J. Gen. Microbiol.*, **9**:410–433.

Strelzoff, E. 1962. *Zeit. f. Vererbungslehre*, **93**:287–300, 301–318.

Takahashi, I. 1961. *Biochem. Biophys. Res. Communs.*, **5**:171–175.

Talmadge, M. B., and Herriott, R. M. 1960. *Biochem. Biophys. Res. Communs.*, **2**: 203–206.

Taylor, A. L., and Adelberg, E. A. 1960. *Genetics*, **45**:1233–1243.

Taylor, J. H. 1958. *Genetics*, **43**:515–529.

Taylor, J. H.; Woods, P. S.; and Hughes, W. L. 1957. *Proc. Nat. Acad. Sci.*, **43**:122–128.

Watson, J. D., and Crick, F. C. 1953. *Cold Spring Harbor Symp. Quant. Piol.*, **18**: 123–131.

Weil, E., and Felix, A. 1917. *Wiener Klin. Wochenschrift*, **30**: pt. 1, 393–399, pt. 2, 1509–1511.

Wollman, E. L., and Jacob, F. 1957. *Ann. Inst. Pasteur*, **93**:323–339.

Wollman, E. L., and Jacob, F. 1958. *Symp. Soc. Exp. Biol.*, **12**:75–92.

Wollman, J.; Jacob, F.; and Hayes, W. 1956. *Cold Spring Harbor Symp. Quant. Biol.*, **21**:141–162.

*Zinder, N. D. and Lederberg, J. 1952. *J. Bact.*, **64**:679–699.

CHAPTER XXII

The Autotrophic Mode of Life

The sulfur bacteria thus form a sharply characterized physiological group, a *physiological type*, which differs fundamentally from the usual one. Their life processes are played out according to a much simpler scheme; all their activities are maintained by a purely inorganic chemical process, that of sulfur oxidation.

S. WINOGRADSKY (1887)

1. THE CONCEPT OF AUTOTROPHY

A more extreme type of synthesis than those described in Chapters XIX and XX is the formation of all the organic matter of a cell directly from CO_2 and water, i.e., autotrophy. Since CO_2 and water are the end products of the oxidations that have yielded all the energy needed by the cell for chemical and physical work, it is obvious that considerable energy must be provided for their conversion back to organic matter. This energy is needed in two forms, namely, electrons or reactive hydrogen for reduction, and ATP or other reactive phosphate for phosphorylation. When sugars are synthesized from simple organic compounds like acetate, the energy, as we have seen, is obtained by the concomitant oxidation of other molecules of the simple compound. Hence, when synthesis of cellular material takes place from CO_2 and H_2O, one way in which the energy can be supplied is by oxidations.[1] But because CO_2 and H_2O cannot be themselves oxidized, some other oxidizable substrate has to be supplied. If this substrate is inorganic, the organism are autotrophic and *chemosynthetic*. This mode of life has so far only been discovered in bacteria.

There is, of course, no reason why oxidation should be the only chemical means of supplying energy. Hydrolysis and fermentation could perfectly well do so, except that they supply so much less.

[1] Another is by light; see the next chapter.

Hydrolytic reactions notoriously yield so little energy that they are largely reversible by increasing the concentration of the products. Besides, even if a hydrolysis did yield enough energy, it is not clear how it could furnish hydrogen for CO_2 reduction. Fermentation is better in that it certainly provides reducing power and does yield a little ATP; fermentation of 1 mole of hexose yields 4 ATP, while its oxidation yields about 36 (p. 203). Correspondingly, fermentation appears to support enough CO_2 reduction for growth, in three cases: (1) the reduction of CO_2 to CH_4 by the methane bacteria, which are strict anaerobes (p. 613), but are scarcely considered to be auto-trophs because organic matter must be supplied to them; (2) the autotrophic growth of sulfate-reducing bacteria in hydrogen gas; in this case hydrogen does indeed become combined with oxygen, but the oxygen is that of sulfate and hence the organisms are anaerobic; (3) the growth of methane bacteria using hydrogen instead of organic matter.

The concept of autotrophy involves the use of CO_2 as *sole* carbon source. The mere ability to form *some* organic compounds from CO_2 is not autotrophy. Thus, CO_2 furnishes one of the carbons of purines and pyrimidines, and the guanidine carbon of arginine, in most or all organisms. Most microorganisms can convert CO_2 also to carboxyl groups, particularly in formic and oxalacetic acids, and several can directly reduce such carboxyl groups (Chaps. XI, XII, and XV). Those bacteria that, like the *Athiorhodaceae* (Chap. XXIII) or perhaps also the sulfate-reducing and methane-forming anaerobes, regularly reduce CO_2 to cell substance, but normally grow in the presence of organic matter, constitute borderline cases which show up the imperfection of our terminology. Truly chemosynthetic autotrophs are considered to be only *those organisms that grow on CO_2 and H_2O together with an oxidizable compound or element.*[2] This latter can be one of the following:

Ammonium ⎫ see Chapter X
Nitrite ⎭
Hydrogen gas
Carbon monoxide or formaldehyde, formate or methanol
Methane or other simple hydrocarbons
Ferrous and manganous salts
Hydrogen sulfide or sulfur or thiosulfate

[2] A very few bacteria can grow autotrophically except for the ability to synthesize a single vitamin. The Athiorhodaceae which require biotin present an analogy among the photosynthetic forms. Not only does such a way of life strain our terminology (see Woods and Lascelles, 1954), but it also discourages facile generalization about selective advantage and evolution.

Since the autotrophs include some of the most unusual modes of life, detailed treatment is justified in spite of the relatively small amount of work done on them.

2. HYDROGEN BACTERIA

If moist soil is incubated with a mixture of hydrogen and oxygen, much of the gas disappears in a few days. Both Kaserer (1906) and Niklewski (1910) set up enrichment cultures in mineral solutions containing bicarbonate in closed flasks with a mixture of hydrogen, oxygen, and CO_2. The hydrogen and oxygen both largely disappeared within a very few days. In the absence of H_2 no growth occurred. Cultures made from the pellicle on the surface of the solution gave colonies on ordinary sugar medium, which when subcultured in the inorganic medium again oxidized hydrogen. Evidently these organisms are facultatively autotrophic, growing either in CO_2 and H_2 or on organic substrates. On continued culture with organic acids, however, H_2 utilization was reduced. Doubtless heterotrophic conditions lead to the continued selection of forms in which the hydrogen-oxidizing ability is weak (Kluyver and Manten, 1942). Kaserer's organism was motile, but Niklewski isolated two nonmotile rods, oddly named[3] *Hydrogenomonas;* later several "species" of this have been obtained, both motile and nonmotile (e.g., Schatz, 1952; Schlegel *et al.*, 1961), as well as the sporeformer, *Bac. pycnoticus* (Ruhland, 1924)), and a Streptomyces, *Str. autotrophicus* (Takamiya and Tubaki, 1956). Since several hydrocarbon-oxidizing bacteria and some Mycobacteria can also use H_2 for growth, the name Hydrogenomonas should probably be dropped (Dworkin and Foster, 1958).

The development of hydrogen bacteria apparently involves two major reactions: the combination of oxygen and hydrogen, and the reduction of CO_2 by hydrogen to form cell substance. In growth of *Bac. pycnoticus*, the ratio H_2/O_2 consumed was found to be 2.3 to 2.6, and the extra H_2 above the value 2.0 corresponded exactly to half the CO_2 absorbed, as follows (Ruhland, 1924):

$$2 \ H_2 + O_2 \rightarrow 2 \ H_2O + 112{,}000 \ cal. \tag{1}$$
$$(0.15 - 0.3) \times [2 \ H_2 + CO_2 \rightarrow (CH_2O) + H_2O] \tag{2}$$

When washed organisms were suspended in a medium without CO_2, on the other hand, the ratio H_2/O_2 was 1.8, i.e., the oxy-hydrogen reaction ($H_2/O_2 = 2.0$) was occurring along with some endogenous

[3] Oddly, because the ending "-omonas" should mean having polar monotrichous flagella.

respiration. With *Hydrogenomonas facilis*, Schatz (1952) obtained the equation:

$$6 \; H_2 + 2 \; O_2 + CO_2 \rightarrow (CH_2O) + 5 \; H_2O \tag{3}$$

This agrees with (1) and (2) above, except that the factor by which equation (2) is multiplied would be 0.5. Packer and Vishniac (1955), with *H. ruhlandii* which they isolated from soil, found that the factor for equation (2) could be 1, giving an over-all ratio of H_2/O_2 of 4. But with old cultures or other suboptimal conditions, the efficiency was less, i.e., more H_2 was oxidized per mole of CO_2 reduced. With *Str. autotrophicus*, whose CO_2 fixation is slow, the ratio H_2/CO_2 is 11, and hence the factor is 0.22 (Kanai *et al.*, 1960).

Actually the cell substance is not (CH_2O) but mainly poly-β-hydroxybutyric acid, $(C_4H_6O_2)_n$, which is accumulated in amounts up to 65 per cent of the cell weight (Schlegel *et al.*, 1961). This requires the equation:

$$25 \; H_2 + 8 \; O_2 + 4 \; CO_2 \rightarrow (C_4H_6O_2) + 22 \; H_2O$$

giving a ratio H_2/O_2 of about 3, and H_2/CO_2 about 6, as in equation (3).

Without O_2, no H_2 is consumed, because the H_2-CO_2 reaction is slightly endergonic (Kluyver and Manten, 1942). On the other hand, CO_2 uptake can be inhibited by poisons, with little or no effect on H_2 oxidation (McFadden and Atkinson, 1957); arsenite, for instance, at M/1000, inhibits CO_2 uptake 74 per cent but H_2 oxidation only 3 per cent. Without CO_2, the stored poly-β-hydroxybutyrate is respired away or, if ammonium is supplied, converted into cell protein (Schlegel *et al.*, 1961).

Hydrogen can also be oxidized anaerobically using nitrate instead of O_2 (Lebedeff, 1910; Kluyver, 1953). Equal volumes of CO_2 and H_2 are consumed, and one-half volume of N_2 liberated. The necessary enzymes, hydrogenase and nitratase, are both inducible in Kluyver's *Micrococcus denitrificans*, the hydrogenase being repressed by organic nutrition. These bacteria need traces of organic matter for growth and are thus not strict autotrophs.

Not only are hydrogen bacteria capable of heterotrophic growth, but the enzymes involved are also strictly independent from those used in autotrophy. Bacteria oxidizing H_2 can still oxidize lactate, and do it just as fast as when hydrogen is absent (Kluyver and Manten, 1942). Growth occurs on pyruvate without CO_2 and H_2 (Schatz, 1952), while on crotonate or β-hydroxybutyrate the polymeric reserve material is formed almost as fast with hydrogen as without (Schlegel *et al.*, 1961).

Hydrogen is also taken up by purple bacteria using, instead of the oxy-hydrogen reaction, the energy of light (Chap. XXIII). Again the major product is poly-β-hydroxybutyric acid, giving the approximate equation:

$$4 \; CO_2 + 9 \; H_2 \xrightarrow{\text{light}} C_4H_6O_2 + 6 \; H_2O$$

The ratio H_2/CO_2 would thus be 2·3, and actually 2·6 was found (Wessler and French, 1939).

Anaerobic autotrophy with hydrogen is also shown by sulfate-reducing bacteria. These organisms (see p. 611) are facultatively autotrophic too. Anaerobic cultures, growing with H_2 and 5 per cent CO_2, can reduce sulfate, sulfite, thiosulfate, or sulfur to H_2S (Starkey and Wight, 1945; Butlin et al., 1949). The growth is "not nearly as abundant as in heterotrophic conditions," probably because the organic compound is relatively easily converted to cell substance, since its reaction path is doubtless shorter than that from CO_2.

Lastly there are the methane bacteria and *Cl. aceticum*, which, as described in Chapter XVIII, can combine H_2 and CO_2 to form CH_4 or CH_3COOH, respectively. Like Nitrosomonas, *Cl. aceticum* responds to an organic growth-promoting factor, present in mud extract (Wieringa, 1940). This somewhat impairs its claim to be regarded as strictly autotrophic; Nitrosomonas can develop in purely mineral medium, but it is not certain that *Cl. aceticum* can.

3. ORGANISMS OXIDIZING THE SIMPLEST CARBON COMPOUNDS

This is one of the most peculiar chapters in a science rich with peculiarities. On a purely mineral medium, suitable for the growth of algae but alkaline instead of acid, Beijerinck observed a very thin, dry film of colorless or pink bacteria growing slowly over a period of months (Beijerinck and van Delden, 1903). Growth was limited to the surface and was dependent on a source of nitrogen, but the source of carbon remained obscure. It was clearly not CO_2. Yet on 100 ml of medium some 4 to 10 mg dry weight of bacteria were produced per month, depending on the composition of the mineral solution. Evidently some "atmospheric carbon compound" was being assimilated, and because cultures grew more poorly in the greenhouse than in the laboratory, this was considered to be an atmospheric impurity. Beijerinck called the organism *Bacillus oligocarbophilus* (= little-carbon-loving, cf. the "oligonitrophilic" bacteria). He noted also that sometimes an Actinomycete with similar properties appeared. Kaserer

(1906) found a similar organism and concluded, without proof, that its substrate was CO, which is known to be often present in air. Later, Lantzsch (1922) described an organism able to grow on formate (which in dilute solution probably decomposes to CO and H_2O) and on other simple compounds, and believed that it too grew on CO. Since this organism existed in a coccoid and a hyphal form, both nonmotile, gram-positive, and acid-fast, he renamed it *Actinomyces oligocarbophilus*. Lantzsch's cultures with CO gave the thead-form, which produces a thin unwettable film (due to high-fat content); those with acetone vapor, acetic acid, or formalin as carbon source were coccoid and encapsulated. The change of morphology thus mirrors a change of physiology.

Another Actinomyces-like organism was later shown (Hasemann, 1927) definitely to oxidize CO while growing in a mineral medium. However, a subsequent study (Kistner, 1953) resulted in the isolation from sewage sludge of a CO-oxidizing bacterium which is clearly a Pseudomonad. This could grow in a very dilute organic medium with a $CO:O_2$ mixture as high as 80 per cent CO. Twice as much CO as O_2 was consumed, indicating that the organism catalyzes the reaction:

$$CO + \tfrac{1}{2}\, O_2 \rightarrow CO_2\ (-\Delta F = +66{,}000\ cal.)$$

Probably it is not fully autotrophic, since some peptone is needed for growth. Because it also oxidizes hydrogen gas, Kistner regards it as a hydrogen bacterium. A similar organism, which can oxidize HCHO or HCOOH, only *grows* on methane or methanol (Dworkin and Foster, 1956). *Str. autotrophicus* (Takamiya and Tubaki, 1956) is also related, especially because, when growing on inorganic medium, it forms a thin unwettable film like that noted by Lantzsch. Thus, there are several physiologically similar organisms, morphologically dissimilar, and varying slightly in their substrates. Since CO powerfully inhibits cytochrome oxidase, the enzyme oxidizing CO here should be worth studying.

Since methane is continuously being produced in nature by fermentation, it must be continuously removed. With this in mind, Söhngen (1906) set up enrichment cultures and obtained a short pink-colored rod, "*Bac. methanicus*" or Methanomonas,[4] which grew autotrophically on a mineral-NH_4^+ medium, oxidizing methane:[5]

$$CH_4 + 2\ O_2 \rightarrow CO_2 + 2\ H_2O\ (-\Delta F_{298} = +195{,}000\ cal.)$$

[4] Again the name is unfortunate, since Söhngen says: "At first I thought this bacterium was motile in young cultures, later I have not been able to confirm this."

[5] Russian workers (Yurovskii *et al.*, 1939) made the interesting suggestion that Methanomonas cultures, in the form of a paste, could be introduced into crevices in coal mines to remove methane from the air and thus obviate the risk of explosions!

Organic matter equal to about half the carbon was formed in 14 days. Since Söhngen's time, many isolations of such organisms have been reported (see, e.g., Davis and Updegraff, 1954); often the cultures have been able to oxidize hydrogen as well, perhaps by a closely related enzyme system (Tausz and Donath, 1930). In one case, enrichments similar to Söhngen's yielded a similar pink gram-negative rod, but motile, and named *Ps. methanica* (Leadbetter and Foster, 1958). If soil inocula were used, grayish to colorless organisms grew; soil particles on Petri plates yielded yellow organisms, and incubation at 37° C yielded brown organisms. All are considered varieties of *Ps. methanica,* differing only in pigments, which are carotenoids; the yellow cultures in liquid media, indeed, regularly gave rise to pink mutants. The organisms could oxidize methanol and several other alcohols, but not H_2 and no other hydrocarbons but CH_4. A *Pseudomonas* species from soil which can grow on methanol as sole carbon source (Kaneda and Roxburgh, 1959) is similar but requires biotin for growth. It assimilates formate, formaldehyde, and even CO_2, as shown by C^{14} uptake, but not CH_4. A cell-free extract could use methanol or formate to reduce DPN.

The metabolism of these bacteria is not necessarily autotrophic. Söhngen and many others assumed that the methane oxidation yielded energy which was used to reduce CO_2 to cell substance. But Leadbetter and Foster (1958), supplying $C^{14}O_2$ and analyzing the C^{14} of the cell substance, found that the pink and yellow variants assimilated no more $C^{14}O_2$ than did *E. coli* and *Ps. fluorescens* under the same conditions; the specific activity of the cell carbon averaged 27 per cent of that of the $C^{14}O_2$ supplied in each case. The brown and colorless variants, however, had cell carbon 68 per cent as active as the $C^{14}O_2$, indicating that the cells used relatively large amounts of CO_2, but *did not use it exclusively*. Kaneda and Roxburgh (1959) also consider that the 1-C compounds are directly incorporated by their pseudomonad. The cell substance is thus formed from *both* CH_4 and CO_2. Indeed, all the organisms in this group lie on the border line between autotrophy and heterotrophy.

Another type of hydrocarbon bacterium was obtained by enrichment cultures with natural gas; these utilized ethane and not methane (Bokova, 1954; Dostalek and Knobl, 1956; Dworkin and Foster, 1958). Some of these were heterotrophic, but two of Foster's, both Mycobacteria, seemed limited to hydrocarbons, while Dostalek's, *Ps. ethanica,* used lower hydrocarbons, ethanol, and some fatty acids. As above, many of them could grow on H_2 and CO_2, which may well be a widely distributed property. A more unusual organism, isolated from soil near petroleum deposits, grows on propane and higher hydrocarbons, but not methane or ethane (Dostalek, 1954). It can also grow hetero-trophically. Being gram-negative and motile, it is called *Ps. propanica*.

Perhaps the most curious of all organisms in this group is the stalked bacterium, *Hyphomicrobium* (see p. 82). First found in nitri-fying cultures, though it does not itself nitrify (Stutzer and Hartleb, 1897–1899), *Hyphomicrobium* needs little carbon and grows in a tap water-salts medium. However, neither CO_2 nor carbonate promotes its growth. It will grow on 0.1 per cent formate or acetate with NH_4^+ or nitrate as nitrogen source, and thus resembles *Act. oligocarbophilus* (Kingma Boltjes, 1936). On more complex carbon compounds, such as dextrose or asparagine, it grows only when the air is unpurified; this growth is therefore, at the expense of an impurity which, by analogy, is probably CO.

4. IRON BACTERIA

These organisms are included here in spite of the fact that it has not really been proved that they are autotrophic. They deposit ferric hydroxide from ferrous salt solutions, and the most that can be said is that in some instances their life appears to be linked to this process. A great many algae, especially among the blue-greens and the desmids, also precipitate iron from ferruginous waters, but there is no reason to believe the process is important for their metabolism.

The iron bacteria are of two types, unicellular and multicellular. Both have morphological peculiarities which have given rise to much confusion. It will be convenient to consider them separately.

A. The Gallionellas and Other Unicellular Forms

Like the coral animals, the Gallionellas are more notable for their excreta than for themselves. They are small curved rods, widely dis-tributed in streams and springs wherever iron is in solution. From the concave side of the cell issues a flat twisted ribbon of iron oxide $(Fe[OH]_3)$ held together by some cement (Fig. XXII–1A and B). Apparently the cell excretes this material from pores on the concave side, twisting slowly as it does so. When the cell divides, twin ribbons, gradually separating, are formed; sometimes, however, the divided pair do not separate and continue to make a single ribbon of double width (see Fig. XXII–1C). The ribbons are so characteristic that for 90 years after Ehrenberg's first description of them (in 1836) they were mis-taken for the organism itself. Only by suspending glass slides in the spring water could Cholodny (1926) observe the complete growth and

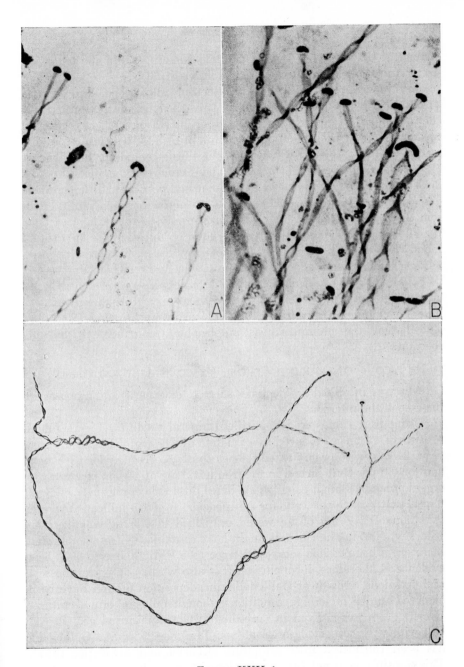

FIGURE XXII–1

A. Gallionella minor, 1100 ×. *B. Gallionella major*, 1100 ×. *C. Gallionella ferruginea*. 650 ×. (All from N. Cholodny, 1929. Reproduced by R. L. Starkey.)

distinguish between the small, stainable bacterium and the extensive excretion, partly organic and partly soluble in HCl.

In preparing material for the electron microscope, van Iterson (1958) found the ferruginous ribbons so often without end-cells that she concluded, like the older workers, that the ribbon itself has "properties of a form of presumably autotrophic life." This was felt to be supported by (1) a regular waviness in the fibrils composing the ribbons, (2) evidence that the fibrils grow and branch in the medium, (3) development of the ribbons in media that had been Seitz-filtered. Such observations, though inconclusive, do raise the bare possibility that something much smaller than a bacterium may be the unit.

The physiology of Gallionella is equally unclear. Lieske (1911) found that enrichment cultures did not grow unless ferrous salts (usually carbonate) were added, but as he saw only the ribbon, this was to be expected; iron could not be deposited unless it were present. Lieske observed no growth without CO_2, or without air, while there was definite development in purified mineral medium; he, therefore, concluded that the organism was autotrophic, reducing CO_2 by the reaction:

$$4\ FeCO_3 + O_2 + 6\ H_2O \rightarrow 4\ Fe(OH)_3 + 4\ CO_2\ (-\Delta F = +40,000\ cal.)$$

Growth was inhibited by peptone, sucrose, or asparagine, much as in the case of the nitrifiers.

Using iron filings and a purified mineral medium, Lieske found 496 mg of bacteria produced by oxidation of 217 mg of Fe. Of the bacteria, 21 mg were organic (only 4 per cent!); correction for carbonate and for 0.6 per cent carbon in the iron left 3 mg of carbon converted to organic matter. Rough calculations based on a free-energy efficiency of 8 per cent (cf. 9 per cent for Nitrobacter, p. 410) indicate that the oxidation of 217 mg of Fe would only lead to 0.3 mg cell material (Starkey, 1945). The cultures might have contained Nitrosomonas, and there are other possible sources of error (see Pringsheim, 1949a). The evidence is, therefore, inconclusive. It is also worth noting that on several occasions, growth of Gallionella and deposition of iron have been observed under anaerobic conditions, though only in crude cultures (Dorff, 1934, p. 5). Even in (presumably) pure cultures, growth was best with very restricted aeration (van Iterson, 1958), and Gallionella has been considered microaerophilic (Charlet and Schwartz, 1954). This certainly does not suggest simple oxidative autotrophy.

A different kind of unicellular iron bacterium, of simple rod shape, is *Ferrobac. ferro-oxidans* (Leathem et al., 1956) which oxidizes Fe^{++} to Fe^{+++} vigorously at pH 3 to 3.6 and 37°C. For 50 μM of Fe^{++} oxidized, about 1 μM of CO_2 is assimilated, which indicates some 20 per cent efficiency. Mn, Co, and Ni salts are not oxidized, but free sulfur is (Silverman and Lundgren, 1959), and a very similar organism oxidizing thiosulfate vigorously has been isolated from coal-mine drainage waters as "Thiobacillus ferro-oxidans" (Colmer et al., 1950–1951). This organism needs a high ratio of sulfate to chloride in order to oxidize iron; it cannot oxidize $FeCl_2$ (Lazaroff, 1963). It has been proposed to use it to remove sulfur from iron ore. Apparently both these forms, though incompletely studied as yet, are true iron-oxidizing autotrophs.

Several other unicellular iron bacteria have been described, particularly Siderocapsa, a coccoid form, embedded in a gelatinous capsule which becomes heavily encrusted with iron oxide (Dorff, 1934). However, their nature is unclear, and they may not be bacteria at all.

B. The "Chlamydobacteria"

The second kind of iron bacteria comprises sheathed filaments of a variety of types. The sheath becomes impregnated to varying degrees with $Fe(OH)_3$ and sometimes with $Mn(OH)_3$. Most of these seem to be forms of *Sphaerotilus natans* or *Sphaerotilus discophora* (Pringsheim, 1949b). The former is widely encountered as a pest in sewage disposal plants, where its filamentous nature prevents the activated sludge from settling (Smit, 1934; Lackey and Wattie, 1940). Modified forms, described earlier as Cladothrix and Leptothrix, can be obtained from pure cultures of *S. natans,* the former in dilute media such as extract of dead leaves or soil water, the latter as "the accumulated remains of an aged vegetation" after prolonged growth in organic media containing a ferrous salt (Pringsheim, 1949b). Both have $Fe(OH)_3$ deposited around the filaments.

The growth of Sphaerotilus is characteristic. Its mature filaments give rise to motile, polarly flagellated, single cells (Fig. XXII–2C) which settle on the sides of the old growth and develop into new filaments, thus producing "false branching" (Fig. XXII–2A). Mechanical fragmentation also leads to new filaments growing from the immotile cells. The motile cells have a tuft of closely twined flagella inserted polarly (Fig. XXII–2C), subpolarly, or even in the middle of the long side (Stokes, 1954). *Sphaerotilus discophorus* is somewhat similar and also has a variety of growth types.

Crenothrix polyspora, the *Brunnenfaden* of Cohn (1870), differs from the above in forming broader filaments, at the apex of which the large cells break up into small coccoids of 1 to 2 μ in diameter; these grow into new filaments. Cohn's original drawing is shown in Fig. XXII–3. Under some circumstances Crenothrix grows enormously in iron water pipes and reservoirs, causing the "water-calamities" experienced in many European cities, especially Berlin and Lille. It probably requires organic matter for growth (Dorff, 1934).

It was Winogradsky (1888) who first regarded "Leptothrix" (i.e., *Sphaerotilus natans*) as autotrophic when he found that its growth in hay infusion was aerobic and strictly dependent on the presence of ferrous carbonate, which was deposited as ferric hydroxide in the sheath.[6] The addition of traces of butyrate or acetate to iron-containing waters was sufficient to produce vigorous growth and iron deposition.

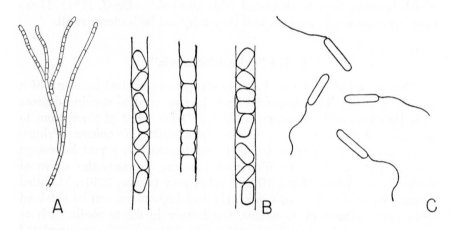

FIGURE XXII–2

Sphaerotilus natans.

A. The cladothrix form showing false branching. 600 ×.

B. Cells within the primary sheath beginning to separate. 1500 ×.

C. Motile stages from four-day-old culture on 0.2 per cent yeast-extract agar. 1200 ×.

(From E. G. Pringsheim, *Trans. Roy. Soc.*, **B233**:453–482, 1949.)

Pure cultures grow well enough on dilute organic media, oxidizing sugars, sugar alcohols, etc., and using ammonium, nitrate, or amino acid for nitrogen source (Stokes, 1954). Amino acids alone also suffice (Höhnl, 1955). No growth factors are required, and growth occurs from 15° to 40° C and from pH 5.8 to 8.1. Some iron is essential, although organic media containing too little iron to show as a visible

[6] On this critical point Winogradsky says that if the $FeCO_3$ solution were first oxidized in air till free of ferrous ions, then, "in spite of repeated renewal of the solution, the state of the threads remains absolutely stationary, as long as one does not add $FeCO_3$-containing water. Then, however, growth begins at once and again comes to a standstill after removal of the $FeCO_3$, and so on."

sheath will still support growth, and the optimal concentration is around 5 mg per liter (Präve, 1957). The organism can deposit Mn instead of Fe, although higher Mn concentrations are needed, and pure cultures have been grown on Mn acetate agar (*S. discophorus*

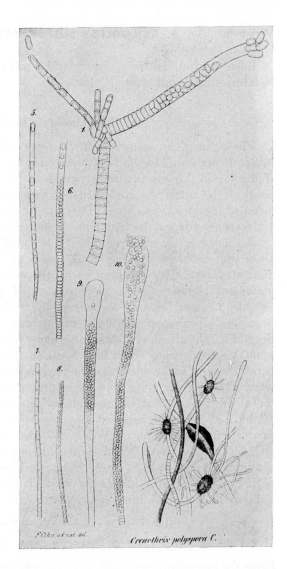

FIGURE XXII–3
Crenothrix polyspora.
Cohn's original drawings. Filaments showing various types of division and "gonidia" emerging. At right a mass of filaments showing incrustation by ferric hydroxide. (From F. Cohn, *Beitr. Biol. Pflanzen*, 1:108–131, 1870.)

by Lieske, 1919), or Mn-glucose-asparagine solution ("*Leptothrix ochracea*" by Präve, 1957). As the pure culture studies show, the growth conditions are not very demanding, and the remains of Sphaerotilus can often be seen in iron ores or in ferruginous salt deposits such as carnallite, where presumably it must have been growing in saturated salt solutions (Müller and Schwartz, 1953).

It is safe to conclude that the life of the iron bacteria as autotrophs is by no means clear.

5. COLORLESS SULFUR BACTERIA

Like the iron bacteria, the colorless sulfur-oxidizing forms are of both unicellular and multicellular types.

A. The Filamentous Forms

These organisms occur in sulfur springs and in natural waters where sulfide is present. The walls of sewage channels, just above the surface of the liquid, almost invariably yield one or more types. Their relationships are uncertain, and probably most of them are really colorless forms of the blue-green algae. They are relatively large, the cells being 1 to 5 μ in width and the filaments of indefinite length.

Beggiatoa alba, whose similarity to Oscillatoria of the blue-green algae was discussed in Chapter II, consists of unattached, unsheathed filaments, motile by creeping or gently waving. It is notable for its prominent globules. These were recognized as sulfur as long ago as 1870 by Cramer, because of their solubility in CS_2. The globules give Beggiatoa cultures a peculiarly milk-white appearance. It was with Beggiatoa that chemosynthetic autotrophy was first discovered. Winogradsky (1887) grew them in a moist chamber on a microscope slide, with inlet and outlet tubes for passing gas over them, and showed that when H_2S and air were supplied, sulfur globules were deposited. On the other hand, added sulfate did not cause deposition of any sulfur. (Cohn had formerly believed that Beggiatoa was responsible for H_2S production from sulfate.) When the H_2S supply was stopped, the globules slowly disappeared, and, instead, sulfate appeared in the medium. Too much H_2S, or too little, inhibited growth. In the absence of H_2S the Beggiatoa invariably died. This indicated that Beggiatoa not only oxidizes H_2S, but lives by the process:

$$H_2S + \tfrac{1}{2}\,O_2 \rightarrow S + H_2O\;(-\Delta F = +41{,}500\ \text{cal.})$$

$$S + H_2O + 1\tfrac{1}{2}\,O_2 \rightarrow H_2SO_4\;(-\Delta F = +118{,}000\ \text{cal.})$$

Since the organism grew well in media extremely low in organic compounds and occurred in sulfur springs with only 0.005 ppm organic matter, Winogradsky concluded that organic carbon was not needed as an energy source at all, the H_2S oxidation being the sole energy

FIGURE XXII–4

Radiating microcolony of Thiothrix on glass slide immersed in a sulfur spring. 1400 ✕. Note sulfur globules. (Photograph provided by F. E. Palmer and E. J. Ordal.)

source. In other words, sulfur for Beggiatoa "plays the same role as carbohydrates in other organisms." He deduced that the only carbon it needed was for cell substance, which would be a very small amount, and since this did not have to supply energy, it could be in the form of a compound (such as formate) unavailable to other organisms. Later, from studying the nitrifying bacteria (Chap. X), he concluded that the carbon source for such organisms was CO_2 and demonstrated this conclusively. It could not be shown for Beggiatoa because: (1) the cultures were not pure, (2) the best growth was obtained in solutions containing a few decaying leaves or other traces of organic matter, and (3) Winogradsky had not quite (in his writing at least) distinguished between organic compounds "of low energy," like formate or propionate, and CO_2 itself. The concept of autotrophy may be said to have been born, but not matured, with Beggiatoa. It was a quarter of a century before the truly autotrophic nature of Beggiatoa was proved (Keil, 1912). The organism was grown in a purely mineral medium and in pure culture, H_2S with oxygen and some CO_2 being necessary. Ammonium was used as nitrogen source. Organic substances had no effect on growth, and CO_2 was the sole usable carbon source. Only low H_2S concentrations were tolerated, the optimum being about 1 part H_2S in 900 of air. Keil's work was in part repeated by Bavendamm (1924), especially as to the occurrence of good growth in the complete absence of organic matter. The organism is thus autotrophic, and the oxidation of sulfur or H_2S is its source of energy.

Thiothrix differs from Beggiatoa in being usually attached at one end by gummy material; at the other end the terminal part separates off and glides away (Winogradsky, 1888). After a few hours it comes to rest at a distance of 100 μ or so. In nature it forms beautiful radial microcolonies (Fig. XXII–4); Harold and Stanier (1955) ascribe these to aggregation of the gliding motile cells, by analogy with the colorless heterotroph, Leucothrix, which it resembles. Keil (1912), who obtained probably the only pure cultures on record, found it autotrophic, and indeed it grows better in synthetic (inorganic) media than does Beggiatoa (Bavendamm, 1924).

Thioploca filaments are ensheathed in a gelatinous matrix, and several filaments are found embedded together. Its metabolism is little known.

B. The Unicellular Forms

Apart from two very large single cells, *Achromatium* and *Hillhousia* (the latter being up to 26×60 μ in size!), the unicellular sulfur bacteria are small and motile. Like most other autotrophs, they are short, gram-negative rods, of mesophilic temperature requirements. Although nonsporeformers, they have been given the unfortunate name of Thiobacillus. They do not contain sulfur globules, but this may be simply because the cells are too small (0.5×1 to 2.5 μ). All members of the group oxidize H_2S and usually thiosulfate or sulfur. They are autotrophic, needing no organic growth factors, and *T. thioöxidans,* on a mineral medium, was shown to form at least six vitamins (O'Kane, 1942). Five species have been so far described (cf. Peck, 1962):

T. novellus, perhaps a facultative autotroph (Starkey, 1934);

T. thioparus, depositing sulfur from thiosulfate;

T. thioöxidans, growing in acid media down to pH 1, although its optimum for sulfur oxidation is pH 3 to 6 (Iwatsuka and Mori, 1960);

T. ferroöxidans, which oxidizes ferrous salts and was treated in section 4B; and

T. denitrificans, a facultative anaerobe, able to use nitrate instead of O_2 as hydrogen acceptor, although it requires ammonium as nitrogen source (Baalsrud and Baalsrud, 1954).

The oxidations that these bacteria carry out can be expressed:

$$\text{(a)} \quad 2\ H_2S + O_2 \rightarrow 2\ S + 2\ H_2O$$
$$\text{(b)} \quad S(H_2O) + 1\tfrac{1}{2}\ O_2 \rightarrow (H_2SO_3 \rightarrow)H_2SO_4$$
$$\text{(c)} \quad {}^=S_2O_3 + H_2O + 2\ O_2 \rightarrow 2\ {}^-HSO_4$$

As an alternative to (c), the reaction with *T. thioparus* is:

$$\text{(d)} \quad 5\ {}^=S_2O_3 + H_2O + 4\ O_2 \rightarrow 6\ {}^=SO_4 + 4\ S + 2\ H^+$$

the sulfur being then subject to slower oxidation by equation (b). The precipitation may be a purely chemical reaction (see Starkey, 1956). Reaction (c) probably goes via tetrathionate, because in media low in K^+, both tetrathionate and trithionate accumulate (Jones and Happold, 1961).

In addition to the above, "thionic acid bacteria," i.e., organisms oxidizing thiosulfate to tetrathionate, have been described, but these are heterotrophs, and many bacteria, actinomycetes, and even fungi can carry out this oxidation while growing on organic media (Starkey, 1934, 1956; contrast the reduction of tetrathionate, p. 612).

Obligate halophilic forms of Thiobacillus have been isolated from salt water on several occasions (e.g., by Jacobsen, 1912–1914; Saslavsky, 1927). They are probably forms of *T. thioparus,* since they oxidize thiosulfate to a mixture of sulfate and sulfur. Saslavsky's organism needs a minimum of 2 per cent NaCl for growth and can live in 22 per cent NaCl (= about 4 M). Presumably it is a salt-adapted modification like that described for Desulfovibrio (Chap. IV, sec. 1). The oxidizing activity of the pure culture in 3 per cent NaCl medium is somewhat greater than that of the fresh-water form (Jacobsen, 1912).

The denitrifying organism, *T. denitrificans*, was obtained in pure culture through its producing an opalescent zone of finely divided sulfur far below the surface of a thiosulfate medium containing a little nitrate (Lieske, 1912). From this zone the organisms were cultured under anaerobic conditions. H_2S, sulfur, or thiosulfate is oxidized to sulfate, the nitrate being completely reduced to N_2. With sulfur, the reaction goes via the lower thio acids and is relatively slow. Sulfur or an oxidizable sulfur compound is essential for growth. Lieske found 1.09 mg of carbon assimilated for 100 mg thiosulfate oxidized, which corresponds to 7 molecules of thiosulfate to 1 atom of carbon, i.e., some 10 per cent of the free energy liberated is used for synthesis.

A significant observation, made with aerobic Thiobacilli, is that the presence of CO_2 reduces the oxygen consumption slightly (Baalsrud and Baalsrud, 1952). With 25 micromoles of thiosulfate in the absence of CO_2, about 1.120 ml of O_2 were consumed, which is the theoretical requirement for equation (c). In the presence of CO_2, 0.12 ml of CO_2 was absorbed and only 1.025 ml of O_2. Hence CO_2 substitutes for oxygen as hydrogen acceptor (cf. the equations for Nitrosomonas, p. 410). For *T. thioparus* the older data, though somewhat variable (Jacobsen, 1912), indicate a ratio of 14 atoms of sulfur oxidized per atom of carbon assimilated. Baalsrud and Baalsrud (1952) found values with nongrowing cultures of from 8 to 25 atoms of S. These figures agree with the 7 molecules of $^=S_2O_3$ mentioned above for *T. denitrificans*, so that the free-energy efficiency is not very different in the two organisms.

T. thioöxidans was first isolated from soil containing sulfur as fertilizer, and it is notable for the rate at which it oxidizes elementary sulfur (Waksman and Joffe, 1922). Other Thiobacilli have been reported to oxidize sulfur only slowly. Since sulfur is very insoluble, the manner in which the cells could absorb it seemed to warrant special study. At each end of the cell is a rather large globule of highly unsaturated fat (Umbreit et al., 1942), which apparently accounts for the "bipolar" type of staining; the fat content may reach 12 per cent of the dry weight. Apparently, the bacteria resting on the sulfur particles are oriented with one end of the cell in direct contact with the sulfur. It was suggested that the sulfur is absorbed by dissolving in the fat globule and thus oxidized within the cell. Cells resting on the sulfur crystals do erode them (Schaeffer et al., 1963). The fact that when Beggiatoa filaments are free from S, they also become virtually free from lipid supports this idea too (Drawert and Küster, 1958). Against this is the fact that a cell-free extract of *T. thioöxidans* has been found to reduce sulfur. It acts only in presence of glutathione, which is oxidized (Suzuki and Werkman, 1960):

$$S + 2 \; GSH \rightarrow H_2S + GSSG$$

The H_2S is then rapidly oxidized, while the glutathione is reduced again by a dehydrogenase with TPN:

$$GSSG + TPNH + H^+ \rightarrow 2 \; GSH + TPN^+$$

Another remarkable character of *T. thioöxidans* is its extreme acid tolerance. Most other acid-producing organisms, Lactobacillus, for instance, or Nitrosomonas, need to have the acid formed constantly neutralized, in order to maintain a pH suitable for growth. Not so *Thiobacillus thioöxidans*, which goes on oxidizing sulfur until the sulfuric acid formed reaches 1 N, a pH of about 0. The basis for this acid tolerance—the greatest known among microorganisms—is not known; it has been ascribed to the fat content, but Mycobacteria with at least as high a fat content show no such resistance to acid.

C. The Probable Mechanism of Autotrophy

The fundamental problem of chemo-autotrophic growth is how the energy made available by the oxidation reaction is transferred to the synthetic process and results in assimilation. On this important question there have been many developments in recent years, mainly because of improved methods of cultivation. An early claim that *T. thioöxidans* could assimilate some CO_2 *after* sulfur oxidation had stopped has not been confirmed (Baalsrud and Baalsrud, 1952). This would have meant that a stable oxidation product is responsible for CO_2 assimilation. It was found, however, that if the cells oxidized sulfur in absence of CO_2, a *very* small amount of CO_2 could be fixed afterward, the amount fixed being proportional to the amount of sulfur previously oxidized (Umbreit, 1953; Newburgh, 1954). Hydrogenomonas, if allowed to oxidize H_2 alone and then exposed to CO_2, did not assimilate CO_2 (Schlegel, 1954). Nitrobacter behaves similarly (Remer, 1957). Evidently, therefore, any oxidation product taking part in CO_2 assimilation is unstable. The experiments did lead to the idea that the important product might be ATP, however, and this has been indirectly confirmed by the remarkable parallels with the chemistry of photosynthesis (cf. Vishniac and Trudinger, 1962).

From *T. thioparus* and *T. denitrificans* cell-free extracts have been prepared that fix CO_2; $C^{14}O_2$ produces isotope in the carboxyl group of 3-phosphoglyceric acid (Santer and Vishniac, 1955; Trudinger, 1956; Aubert et al., 1957–1958). In the latter two cases the addition of ribulose-1, 5-diphosphate, or the monophosphate plus ATP, increased the fixation. The cells, therefore, probably have the same CO_2-fixing system as green plants and purple bacteria (p. 752). Furthermore the extracts contain all the enzymes needed to convert phosphoglyceric acid to hexose phosphate and thence to pentose, heptulose, and tetrose phosphates. They also fixed CO_2 by a second pathway with phospho-enol-pyruvate to oxalacetate (cf. Fig. XXIII–8).

Similarly, whole cells of *Hydrogenomonas facilis*, supplied with $C^{14}O_2$ for only 45 seconds, fixed isotope in phosphoglyceric acid, fructose-diphosphate, sedoheptulose-7-phosphate, and ribulose-1,5-di-phosphate (McFadden, 1959). After one minute, amino acids began to be labeled. It follows that *the whole mechanism of formation of cell materials from CO_2 is the same in colorless autotrophs as in photosynthetic forms.*

The first step is, therefore, to oxidize the substrate. This requires specific enzymes such as (presumably) thiosulfate dehydrogenase for Thiobacillus, ammonia dehydrogenase for Nitrosomonas, etc., e.g.:

$$NH_3 + R + O_2 \rightarrow HNO_2 + RH_2$$

The sensitivity of CO_2 fixation to iodoacetate and arsenite indicates that this may involve a sulfhydryl enzyme. In hydrogen bacteria the presence of hydrogenase is well established by numerous workers, e.g., Packer and Vishniac (1955), who found the enzyme to be suppressed by growth on organic media.

The next step is to oxidize most of the reduced coenzyme, RH_2, and produce ATP in the process. This is doubtless done by a cytochrome system, since growth and sulfur oxidation by *T. thioöxidans* are inhibited by cyanide, azide, and dinitrophenol (Vogler et al., 1942; Iwatsuka and Mori, 1960). Still stronger evidence is the fact that in Nitrobacter the cell-free nitrite oxidase is present in particles that contain the cytochrome (Aleem and Nason, 1960). Unfortunately the most typical cytochrome oxidase reaction, namely, inhibition by CO and its reversal by light, could not yet be detected (Iwatsuka and Mori, 1960). Both Hydrogenomonas and Nitrobacter are known to convert inorganic phosphate to organic phosphates during their oxidations. In Hydrogenomonas not only H_2 and O_2, but also CO_2, are essential for this (Schlegel, 1955).

The third step is usage of the ATP (a) to form ribulose diphosphate, which acts as CO_2 acceptor, and again (b) to phosphorylate phosphoglyceric acid (see p. 445).

Fourth, some of the RH_2 formed in the first step is probably used to reduce phosphoglyceryl phosphate to phosphoglyceraldehyde, from which sugar phosphates, etc., are formed. In a cyclic series of reactions described in Chapter XXIII, ribose-5-phosphate is thence produced, to act as CO_2 acceptor again.

Lastly, additional CO_2 molecules are fixed in oxalacetate to produce Krebs' cycle acids and the related amino acids.

The bulk of the energy of oxidation is thus invested in the energy of the ATP and thence in the phosphoglyceryl phosphate; the energy exchange in its reduction completes the balance. In most autotrophs, only a small part of the (H) of the substrate finds its way into cell substance, most being oxidized to water in the formation of ATP and perhaps other high-energy phosphates. However, hydrogen bacteria have more favorable energy relations.

If the main reaction is merely accumulation of poly-β-hydroxy-butyrate as in Hydrogenomonas (Schlegel et al., 1961), the ATP may be the only essential product, because the cells can grow on the monomer, β-hydroxybutyrate, polymerizing it via β-hydroxybutyryl-phosphate. The H_2 is then only the energy source.

This over-all picture, while very satisfying, leaves unexplained why autotrophic bacteria so often cannot use organic compounds for growth. Obviously they metabolize many organic compounds in their life processes. The fact that sulfur oxidation by Thiobacillus is inhibited by long-chain alcohols and some fatty acids (Iwatsuka and Mori, 1960) shows that these organic compounds readily enter the cell. Perhaps the required enzymes are repressed or masked in some way, like those in spores.

REFERENCES

Aleem, M. I. H., and Nason, A. 1960. *Proc. Nat. Acad. Sci.*, **46**:763–768.

Aubert, J. P.; Milhaud, G.; Millet, L. 1957–1958. *Ann. Inst. Pasteur*, **92**:516; Aubert, J. P.; Milhaud, G.; Moncel, C.; and Millet, J. *Compt. rend.*, **246**:1616–1617 (1958).

Baalsrud, K., and Baalsrud, K. S. 1952. The Role of Phosphate in CO_2 Assimilation of Thiobacilli. In, Phosphorus Metabolism, ed. W. D. McElroy. Vol. 2, 544–576, Baltimore, Johns Hopkins Press.

Baalsrud, K., and Baalsrud, K. S. 1954. *Arch. f. Mikrobiol.*, **20**:34–62.

Baas-Becking, L. G. M., and Parks, G. S. 1927. Energy Relations in the Metabolism of Autotrophic Bacteria. *Physiol. Revs.*, **7**:85–106.

*Bavendamm, W. 1924. Die farblosen und roten Schwefelbakterien des Süss- and Salz-wassers. Jena, G. Fischer. 156 pp.

Beijerinck, M. W., and van Delden, A. 1903. *Proc. Kon. Akad. Amsterdam*, pp. 398–413.

Bokova, E. N. 1954. *Mikrobiologia (U.S.S.R.)*, **23**:15–21.

Butlin, K. R.; Adams, M. E.; and Thomas, M. 1949. *J. Gen. Microbiol.*, **3**:46–59.

Charlet, E., and Schwartz, W. 1954. *Schweiz. Zeit. f. Hydrol.*, **16**:318–341.

*Cholodny, N. 1926. Die Eisenbakterien. Beiträg zu einer Monographie. Pflanzenforschung, ed. R. Kolkwitz. Jena, G. Fischer.

Cohn, F. 1870. (Cohn's) *Beitr. Biol. Pflanzen*, **1**:108–131.

Colmer, A. R.; Temple, K. L.; and Hinkle, M. E. 1950–1951. *J. Bact.*, **59**:317–328; Temple, K. L., and Colmer, A. R. *ibid.*, **62**:605–611 (1951).

*Davis, J. B., and Updegraff, D. M. 1954. Microbiology in the Petroleum Industry. *Bact. Revs.*, **18**:215–238.

*Dorff, P. 1934. Die Eisenorganismen. Systematik und Morphologie. Pflanzenforschung, ed. R. Kolkwitz. Jena, G. Fischer.

Dostalek, M. 1954. *Ceskoslov. Biol.*, **3**:162–169.

Dostalek, M., and Knobl, J. 1956. Prácé Ustavu pro Naftovy Vyzkum, E. No. 14–16, 21–37; *Chem. Abstr.*, **50**:15716.

Drawert, H., and Kuster, M. 1958. *Arch. f. Mikrobiol.*, **31**:422–434.

Dworkin, M., and Foster, J. W. 1958. *J. Bact.*, **75**:592–603.

Hasemann, W. 1927. *Biochem. Zeit.*, **184**:147–171.

Höhnl, G. 1955. *Arch. f. Mikrobiol.*, **23**:207–250.

Howard, R., and Stanier, R. Y. 1955. *Bact. Revs.*, **19**:49–58.

van Iterson, W. 1958. Verhandl. Kon. Nederl. Akad. Wetensch., Amsterdam, Ser. 2, **52**: No. 2, 185 pp.

Iwatsuka, H., and Mori, T. 1960. *Plant and Cell Physiol.*, **1**:163–172.

Jacobsen, H. C. 1912–1914. *Folia Microbiologica*, **1**:487–502; **3**:155–162.

Jones, G. L., and Happold, F. C. 1961. *J. Gen. Microbiol.*, **26**:361–366.

Kanai, R.; Miyachi, S.; and Takamiya, A. 1960. *Nature*, **188**:873–875.

Kaneda, T., and Roxburgh, J. M. 1959. *Canad. J. Microbiol.*, **5**:87–98.

Kaserer, H. 1906. *Zentr. Bakt.* II, **16**:681–696.

Keil, F. 1912. (Cohn's) *Beitr. Biol. Pflanzen*, **11**:335–372.

Kingma Boltjes, T. Y. 1936. *Arch. Mikrobiol.*, **7**:188–205.

Kistner, A. 1953. *Proc. Kon. Akad. Wetensch. Amsterdam*, **C56**:443–450.

Kluyver, A. J. 1953. *Symp. Microbiol. Metabolism, Rome* (Inst. Sup. di Sanita), pp. 71–91.

Kluyver, A. J., and Manten, A. 1942. *Ant. v. Leeuwenhoek*, **8**:71–85.

Lackey, J. B., and Wattie, E. 1940. *U. S. Pub. Health Rep.* (Washington), **55**:975–987; cf. also Littman, M. L. 1940. *Sewage Works J.*, **12**:685–693.

Lantzsch, K. 1922. *Zentr. Bakt.* II, **57**:309–319.

Lazaroff, N. 1963. *J. Bact.*, **85**:78–83.

*Leadbetter, E. R., and Foster, J. W. 1958. *Arch. f. Mikrobiol.*, **30**:91–118.

Leathem, W. W.; Kensel, N. A.; and Braley, S. A. 1956. *J. Bact.*, **72**:700–704.

Lebedeff, A. J. 1910. *Ber. deut. bot. Ges.*, **27**:598–602.

Lieske, R. 1911. *Jahrb. wiss. Bot.*, **49**:91–127.

Lieske, R. 1912. *Ber. deut. bot. Ges.*, **30**:(12)–(22).

Lieske, R. 1919. *Zentr. Bakt.* II, **49**:413–415.

McFadden, B. A. 1959. *J. Bact.*, **77**:339–343.

McFadden, B. A., and Atkinson, D. E. 1957. *Arch. Biochem. Biophys.*, **66**:16–22.

Molisch, H. 1910. Die Eisenbakterien. Jena, G. Fischer.

Müller, A., and Schwartz, W. 1953. *Z. deutsch. geol. Ges.*, **105**:789–802.

Newburgh, P. W. 1954. *J. Bact.*, **68**:93–97.

Niklewski, B. 1910. *Jahrb. wiss. Bot.*, **105**:111–142.

O'Kane, D. J. 1942. *J. Bact.*, **43**:7.

Packer, L., and Vishniac, W. 1955. *J. Bact.*, **70**:216–223.

* Peck, H. D., Jr. 1962. Comparative Metabolism of Inorganic Sulfur Compounds in Microorganisms. *Bact. Revs.*, **26**:67–94.

Präve, P. 1957. *Arch. f. Mikrobiol.*, **27**:33–62.

*Pringsheim, H. 1949a. Iron Bacteria. *Biol. Revs.*, **24**:200–245.

Pringsheim, H. 1949b. *Phil. Trans. Roy. Soc.*, **B233**:453–482.

Remer, E. 1957. *Arch. f. Mikrobiol.*, **27**:125–145.

*Ruhland, W. 1924. *Jahrb. wiss. Bot.*, **63**:321–389.

Santer, M., and Vishniac, W. 1955. *Biochim. Biophys. Acta*, **18**:157–158.

Saslavsky, A. 1927. *Zentr. Bakt.* II, **72**:236–242.

Schaeffer, W. I.; Holbert, P. E.; and Umbreit, W. W. 1963. *J. Bact.*, **85**:137–140.

Schatz, A. 1952. *J. Gen. Microbiol.*, **6**:329–335.

Schlegel, H. G. 1954. *Arch. f. Mikrobiol.*, **21**:127–155.

Schlegel, H. G. 1955. *Arch. f. Mikrobiol.*, **23**:195–206.

Schlegel, H. G.; Kaltwasser, H.; and Gottschalk, G. 1961. *Arch. Mikrobiol.*, **38**:209–222; Schlegel, H. G.; Gottschalk, G.; and v. Bartha, R. *Nature*, **191**:463–465.

Silverman, M. P., and Lundgren, D. G. 1959. *J. Bact.*, **77**:642–647; **78**:326–331.

Smit, J. 1934. *Arch. Mikrobiol.*, **5**:550–560.

Söhngen, N. L. 1906. *Zentr. Bakt.* II, **15**:513–517. Het onstaan en verdwijnen van Waterstof en Methaan onder den invloed van het organische Leven. Dissertation, Delft.

*Starkey, R. L. 1934. *J. Bact.*, **28**:365–386, 387–400.

Starkey, R. L. 1945. *Science*, **102**:532.

*Starkey, R. L. 1956. Transformations of Sulfur by Microorganisms. *Ind. Eng. Chem.*, **48**:1429–1437.

Starkey, R. L., and Wight, K. M. 1945. *Bull. Am. Gas Assoc., N. Y.* Cited by Starkey, R. L. 1947. *Ant. v. Leeuwenhoek*, **12**:193–203.

Stokes, J. L. 1954. *J. Bact.*, **67**:278–291.

Stutzer, A., and Hartleb, R. 1897–1899. *Zentr. Bakt.* II, **3**:621–622; **5**:678–682 (abstr. from Mitt. landw. Inst. Kgl. Univ. Breslau, 1898).

Suzuki, I., and Werkman, C. H. 1960. *Biochem. J.*, **74**:359–362.

Takamiya, A., and Tubaki, K. 1956. *Arch. f. Mikrobiol.*, **25**:58–64.

Tausz, J., and Donath, P. 1930. *Zeit. physiol. Chem.*, **190**:141–168.

Trudinger, P. A. 1956. *Biochem. J.*, **64**:274–286.

Trudinger, P. A. 1958. *Biochim. Biophys. Acta*, **30**:211–212.

Umbreit, W. W. 1953. *J. Bact.*, **67**:387–393.

Umbreit, W. W.; Vogel, H. R.; and Vogler, K. G. 1942. *J. Bact.*, **43**:141–148.

Vishniac, W., and Trudinger, P. A. 1962. *Bact. Revs.*, **26**:168–175.

Vogler, K. G.; LePage, C. A.; and Umbreit, W. W. 1942. *J. Gen. Physiol.*, **26**:89–102.

Waksman, S. A., and Joffe, J. S. 1922. *J. Bact.*, **7**:239–256.

Wessler, S., and French, C. S. 1939. *J. Cell Comp. Physiol.*, **13**:327–334.

Wieringa, K. T. 1940. *Ant. v. Leeuwenhoek*, **6**:257–262.

Winogradsky, S. 1887. *Bot. Ztg.*, **45**:489–610 (with breaks). See also long abstr. in *Bot. Centr.*, **33**:292–300 (1888).

Winogradsky, S. 1888. *Bot. Ztg.*, **46**:262–270.

Woods, D. D., and Lascelles, J. 1954. *Symp. Soc. Gen. Microbiol.*, **3**:1–27.

Yurovskii, A. Z.; Kapilash, G. P.; and Mangubi, B. V. 1939. Ugol No. 7, pp. 48–53 (from *Chem. Abstr.*, **34**:7322).

CHAPTER XXIII

Bacterial Photosynthesis

. . . for the photosynthetic CO_2-reduction only those hydrogen compounds can serve as H-donors in which the hydrogen can be sufficiently activated by the organisms. Then, it is quite conceivable that organisms exist which cannot use H_2O as a H-donor, because they cannot activate the H in this compound sufficiently. These organisms might, however, be typically photosynthetic—i.e., reduce CO_2 with the supply of radiant energy—in case some other H compound is present containing the hydrogen in a form in which these organisms can bring about a sufficient activation. Consequently *those organisms are capable of reducing CO_2 photosynthetically without the liberation of oxygen, because O_2 is the dehydrogenation product of the H-donor only in case this latter is H_2O (or H_2O_2).*

C. B. VAN NIEL (1931)

1. THE PURPLE, BROWN, AND GREEN BACTERIA

The *Rhodobacteriineae* are a large and varied group, occurring in mud, sulfur springs, soil, sewage, and natural waters where exposure to light occurs. Their morphology is simple, like that of the Eubacteria, and comprises the forms of Pseudomonas, Vibrio, Streptococcus, and Spirillum. Roughly they can be subdivided as follows (van Niel, 1941, 1944):

Chlorobacteriaceae. Green bacteria, occurring in H_2S media. Not using organic compounds and not requiring organic growth factors.

Thiorhodaceae. Purple (to red) sulfur bacteria, occurring primarily in H_2S media; capable of oxidizing various inorganic sulfur compounds as well as some organic acids and, in some cases, hydrogen. Not requiring organic growth factors.

Athiorhodaceae. Purple (or red or brown) nonsulfur bacteria occurring mainly in media containing organic compounds, although a few species can oxidize sulfide and thiosulfate. Organic growth factors essential, principally biotin, needed by most strains, generally with one or more additional vitamins.

The distinction between the two groups of purples—the sulfur and nonsulfur forms—is not as clear-cut as used to be thought, but remains convenient. The principal difference is the need for biotin and other

TABLE XXIII-1. The Athiorhodaceae

	Cell Shape	Cell Size	Color	GROWTH WITH:		Other Characteristics
				Na$_2$S$_2$O$_3$ as Oxidizable Material	Propionate 0.2%	
Rhodospirillum:						
rubrum	Spiral	1–1.2 × 2–50 μ	Dark red; (reddish gray in dark)	–	–	Cannot attack sugars; require biotin
fulvum	Small spiral	0.5 μ or less × 2.5 μ or less	Brown to orange, spirilloxanthin (abs. max 550 mμ) absent	–	+	Strict anaerobe; can utilize glucose
molischianum	Spiral	0.8 × 5–10 μ	Reddish brown, spirilloxanthin absent	–	+	Can utilize citrate, but not glucose; strict anaerobe
photometricum	Large spiral	4–6 × 7–10 μ	Reddish brown	–	+	Can utilize citrate, microaerophilic to anaerobic
Rhodopseudomonas:						
palustris	Rod	0.8 × 1.2–2 μ (tendency to long, immotile forms)	Red to dark brown-red	+	+	Cannot attack sugars; require p-aminobenzoic acid
gelatinosa	Rod	0.5 × 1.2	Pale brown to peach	–	–	Liquefy gelatin; mucus formed
capsulata (formerly *Sc. varians*)	Sphere at pH < 7 Rod at pH > 7 Zigzag chains	1 × 1–2.5 μ (pH > 7)	Brown when anaerobic, reddish in air	–	+	Mucus formed at pH > 8; require thiamine
spheroides	Sphere or almost so	0.7–4 μ in diam., single	Brown when anaerobic, reddish in air	–	–	Mucus formed at pH > 7

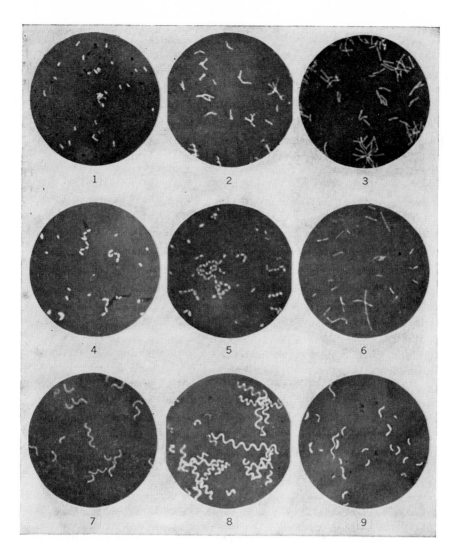

FIGURE XXIII–1

Some growth types of *Athiorhodaceae*

Top Row. Rhodopseudomonas palustris. 1. With 0.1% leucine, 48-hr culture. *2.* With 0.2% crotonate, 7 days. *3.* With 0.2% glycerol, 10 days.

Second Row. Rhodopseudomonas capsulatus (= *Sc. varians*). *4.* With 0.2% isobutyrate, 3 days. *5.* With 0.2% glutamate, 5 days. *6.* In yeast-extract medium, 6 days.

Third Row. Rhodospirillum rubrum. 7. With 0.2% acetate, 7 days. *8.* With 0.2% propionate, 7 days. *9.* With 0.2% butyrate, 7 days.

All cultures but No. 6 have basal medium added in addition. All cultures anaerobic· 800 ×.

(From C. B. van Niel, *Bact. Revs.*, **8**:118. Copyright 1944 by the Williams & Wilkins Co., Baltimore, Md.)

vitamins by the *Athiorhodaceae* (Hutner, 1946, 1950). According to van Niel (1944) the *Athiorhodaceae* comprise two genera, Rhodopseudomonas and Rhodospirillum, with eight species or groups. All are motile, with polar flagella. Their main characters are shown in Table XXIII–1, and examples are seen in Figure XXIII–1. In addition a curious form—somewhat resembling Hyphomicrobium or perhaps Micromonospora—which produces ellipsoidal cells on the ends of filaments and is called *Rhodomicrobium vannielli* falls in the *Athiorhodaceae* (Murray and Douglas, 1950; Boatman and Douglas, 1961); however, it does not require growth factors.

The *Thiorhodaceae* have not been critically monographed, and the types given in Bergey are still based on observations of the shapes of cell masses. Morphologically there are three main groups (van Niel, 1931):

Chromatium. Relatively large ellipsoidal to cylindrical cells containing sulfur droplets (if the medium is not depleted of H_2S); motile with polar flagella (see Chap. II, Fig. 10). They range in size up to 6 by 20 μ.

Thiocystis. Spherical or nearly so, often in pairs, also containing sulfur droplets; some motile with polar flagella, some apparently not.

Pseudomonas type. Small rod-shaped cells, not storing sulfur within them; motile with polar flagella.

To these must be added two others less common:

Thiospirillum. Large C- or S-shaped cells with sulfur granules. Their size—up to 4 by 40 μ—makes them "giants among bacteria" (Schlegel and Pfennig, 1961). Orange-brown in color.

Amoebobacter. Small cells, about 3 by 5 μ, nonmotile, and with a heavy capsule.

The shape and size of the first two types vary with the sulfide concentration and pH.

Of the green bacteria, only *Chlorobium limicola* and *Chl. thiosulfatophilum* have been extensively studied. They are streptococcal in form, but with a tendency to form long, fine, tightly wound spirals in alkaline media. Both are strict anaerobes. Several other genera of green bacteria have been described but are imperfectly known.

2. GENERAL METABOLISM OF THE THIORHODACEAE

The mode of life of these organisms was elucidated only after considerable confusion. Winogradsky, in the 1880's, following his work on the colorless sulfur bacteria (cf. p. 712), studied the purple bacteria briefly and found that:

(1) They contain sulfur globules;

(2) They need H_2S in order to form these globules;

(3) They gradually convert the S to sulfate, which appears in the medium; and

(4) They die after a prolonged stay in H_2S-free waters. He, therefore, and naturally, concluded that they are chemosynthetic autotrophic bacteria, just like the colorless forms. Their morphology was, however, more varied.

On the other hand, Engelmann (1882–1888) formed the idea that they are photosynthetic. This was based on the following experiment: if one projects a bright spot of light on a thick suspension of motile algae (Euglena), the algae assemble in the light, and if accidentally they swim into the dark, they will reverse and come back to the light. In a small spectrum they will assemble at a point in the blue, of wavelength 470 to 490 mμ. The part of the cell responsible for this movement (*phototaxis*) is the forward part which contains a reddish (carotenoid) spot of pigment (1882). The phototaxis is thus mediated by a particular pigment, and one which may be connected with the photosynthetic system. If now one does the same with a suspension of purple bacteria, they assemble mainly in the infrared, in a band between 800 and 900 mμ and in less marked bands in the yellow (590 mμ) and green (520 to 550 mμ). In a later study, bands of phototaxis at 530, 490, and 470 mμ were also observed (Buder, 1919). The absorption spectrum of the bacteria had bands at 850 (very sharp), 590, 520 to 540, and 490 mμ (Engelmann, 1888). Since the "forms and individuals richer in pigment appeared to react more strongly," and the bacteria could be grown only in light, Engelmann concluded that they are photosynthetic, using parts of the visible spectrum, and to a larger extent the infrared light, for this purpose. He also attempted to show the evolution of oxygen in light, using as indicator the movement of colorless spirilla toward low-oxygen tensions and that of a Pseudomonas which becomes immotile in absence of oxygen. However, these experiments do not convincingly show oxygen evolution by the purple bacteria, and one of them (1883) gave a clearly negative result.

The picture was complicated by Molisch's finding (1907) that purple bacteria need organic matter in order to grow, but as it turned out (Buder, 1919), Molisch was working with *Athiorhodaceae*, and thus his data did not bear on the sulfur forms.

In spite of Engelmann's claim to have shown oxygen evolution,

Buder made clear that the *Thiorhodaceae* are anaerobic. He also established that they need *both* H_2S *and* light for growth, and this was confirmed with the first pure cultures in this group by Bavendamm (1924). Both these men believed that O_2 was formed in photosynthesis, but that it at once reacted with H_2S to produce the observed sulfur or sulfate.

If this were so, then when the H_2S is all used up, the O_2 should be set free; yet none can be found, even using the excessively sensitive luminous bacteria as a test for oxygen (van Niel, 1941; cf. p. 748). The puzzle of apparently photosynthetic organisms that yield no oxygen, and indeed are anaerobic, but yet oxidize H_2S, was cleared up by van Niel (1931) whose brilliant and extensive researches, with pure cultures, established that:

(1) H_2S is converted to S, and S later to sulfate (as claimed by Winogradsky), but these processes are strictly anaerobic.

(2) The bacteria will develop in a mineral medium, in light, and in so doing consume CO_2.

(3) CO_2 consumption and growth stop when all the S has been oxidized.

(4) Unlike the chemosynthetic forms, the ratio of H_2S oxidized to CO_2 consumed is simple and constant. With chemosynthetic organisms, ratios of 40:1 are common, but with purple bacteria the following experiment is typical:

9.14 mg H_2S oxidized to 25.87 mg H_2SO_4, and 22.2 mg CO_2 consumed.

Converting to moles we have: 0.269 mM H_2S, 0.264 mM H_2SO_4, and 0.505 mM CO_2, or (almost exactly) 1:1:2, and assuming that the bacteria have about the composition of carbohydrate we should have:

$$H_2S + 2\ CO_2 + 2\ H_2O \xrightarrow{\text{light}} H_2SO_4 + 2(CH_2O) \tag{1}$$

This means that CO_2 has been reduced to organic matter by the hydrogen of H_2S. This reaction explains how the process can be both photosynthetic and anaerobic.

The green bacteria were also found to be anaerobic, and in this case the metabolism was simpler, since the H_2S was oxidized only to sulfur, and the analyses showed that:

$$CO_2 + 2\ H_2S \xrightarrow{\text{light}} (CH_2O) + H_2O + 2\ S \tag{2}$$

The sulfur accumulates in the growing culture as refractile globules.

Van Niel showed that equation (2) corresponds to the first phase of development of the purple bacteria too. The second phase, considered by itself, is formulated:

$$3\ CO_2 + 2\ S + 5\ H_2O \xrightarrow{\text{light}} 3(CH_2O) + 2\ H_2SO_4 \tag{3}$$

Equation (1) is thus the sum of equations (2) and (3).

Now the photosynthesis of green plants can be represented:

$$CO_2 + H_2O \xrightarrow{\text{light}} (CH_2O) + O_2$$

By adding H_2O to both sides, we get (cf. equation [2]):

$$CO_2 + 2\ H_2O \xrightarrow{\text{light}} (CH_2O) + H_2O + O_2 \tag{4}$$

It appears, therefore, that the photosynthesis both of green plants and of sulfur bacteria can be expressed as a general photosynthetic reaction:

$$CO_2 + 2\ H_2A \xrightarrow{\text{light}} (CH_2O) + H_2O + 2A \tag{5}$$

Viewed in this light, the compound H_2A is seen to be a hydrogen donor, or (since the water is in equilibrium with H^+ and ^-OH) an electron donor. Other hydrogen or electron donors functioning with purple bacteria are sulfite, selenium, and thiosulfate. With this last we have (van Niel, 1936):

$$CO_2 + 4\ Na_2S_2O_3 + 3\ H_2O \xrightarrow{\text{light}} (CH_2O) + 2\ Na_2S_4O_6 + 4\ NaOH$$

or in the case of the green bacterium *Chlorobium thiosulfatophilum* (Larsen *et al.*, 1952):

$$2\ CO_2 + Na_2S_2O_3 + 3\ H_2O \xrightarrow{\text{light}} 2(CH_2O) + 2\ NaHSO_4 \tag{6}$$

A striking variant occurs with hydrogen gas (Roelofsen, 1935):

$$CO_2 + 2\ H_2 \xrightarrow{\text{light}} (CH_2O) + H_2O \tag{7}$$

In this case the A of equation (5) is absent altogether. Here it is to be noted that the oxidation of the hydrogen yields so much energy that the reaction goes from left to right with the aid of only 1700 cal. $(-\Delta F_{298})$. This point is important in connection with the photosynthetic mechanism (sec. 8).

A number of organic compounds can also act as hydrogen donors, being commonly converted to acetate, which then makes possible a combination of photosynthesis with organic acid metabolism, discussed below. They do not, however, allow growth in the dark.

3. METABOLISM OF THE ATHIORHODACEAE

A. Photosynthesis with Organic Compounds as Hydrogen Donors

Molisch's conclusion that purple bacteria require organic matter was referred to above. Because these bacteria grow much better in light than in dark (particularly in liquid cultures), however, he concluded that they cannot "assimilate" CO_2, i.e., they cannot photosynthesize cell material from CO_2, but can do so from organic matter. This concept was very close to the truth. Still closer was the suggestion, unnoticed at the time, that these organisms can assimilate CO_2 but need organic matter for respiration (Lebedev, 1921).

The fact is that the *Athiorhodaceae* do assimilate CO_2 in light, but only in the presence of certain organic (or a few inorganic) compounds. Fatty acids are the best substrate (Gaffron, 1933–1935); the amount of CO_2 taken up increases with the number of methylene groups in the fatty acid, and from 2 to 3 "moles" of (CH_2) are needed for the uptake of 1 mole of CO_2. If the ratio were 2, one could write:

$$CO_2 + 2(CH_2) + H_2O \xrightarrow{\text{light}} 3 \ CH_2O \tag{8}$$

and this would be in line with equations (4) to (7). However, the composition of the organisms is not that of (CH_2O) but is more reduced. Gaffron prepared from Rhodovibrio a fatty material of the composition $(C_4H_6O_2)$, which much later was identified by Stanier *et al.* (1959) as a polymer of β-hydroxybutyric acid, $CH_3CHOHCH_2COOH$:

$$
\begin{array}{ccccc}
CH_3 & & CH_3 & & CH_3 \\
| & & | & & | \\
-O-CH\cdot CH_2CO- & O- & CH\cdot CH_2CO- & O- & CH\cdot \text{etc.}
\end{array}
$$

It is the major reserve material of these cells and is found also in many colorless bacteria (p. 656). To form this polymer from free β-hydroxybutyric acid requires ATP, which is now known to be produced in quantity in photosynthesis (see sec. 8). Thus, for organisms photosynthesizing on this acid no CO_2 would be required, and the main contribution of the light would be to form ATP. A near approach to this is given by growth on acetate in presence of H_2, when poly-β-hydroxybutyrate is formed via acetoacetyl-CoA as in the butyric acid Clostridia discussed in Chapter XV (Stanier *et al.*, 1959):

$$
\begin{array}{c}
\overset{\text{Light}}{\underset{\text{ATP}}{\downarrow}} \\
\text{Acetate} \xrightarrow{} CH_3CO\cdot CoA \rightarrow CH_3COCH_2CO\cdot CoA \xrightarrow{\overset{H_2}{\downarrow}} CH_3CHOHCH_2CO\cdot CoA \\
\downarrow \\
\text{polymer}
\end{array}
$$

However, other reaction sequences would be needed for the formation of the other cell compounds. *Rhodo-sp. rubrum* forms some polysaccharide, which stains brown with iodine and is similar to glycogen (cf. Fig. XXIII–8), and in addition amino acids appear to be major photosynthetic products. For such reactions the organic compound could act as hydrogen donor.

While a variety of compounds act in this way (van Niel, 1944), a particularly clear example of the reducing role of an organic compound is shown by growth in light on isopropyl alcohol (Foster, 1940). Here the dehydrogenated product, acetone, is left in the medium:

$$CO_2 + 2\ CH_3CHOHCH_3 \xrightarrow{\text{light}} (CH_2O) + H_2O + 2\ CH_3COCH_3 \tag{9}$$

Although this reaction is relatively slow, it is quantitative, and the ratio—isopropanol disappeared/CO_2 absorbed—averages 2.05. Acetone itself can also be used, after a period of adaptation, by *Rhodo-ps. gelatinosa*, and it is converted quantitatively (in light) to cell material (Siegel, 1950).

In other cases, as with pyruvate or malate, some CO_2 is given off. When $C^{14}O_2$ is supplied, some is taken up, but the evolved CO_2 comes from the C^{12}-organic acids (van Niel, 1949, Ormerod, 1956). Acetate, however, appears to inhibit the $C^{14}O_2$ uptake (Ormerod, 1956).

Thus, whereas in green plants photosynthesis produces both ATP and "reducing power" in the form of TPNH, the Athiorhodaceae are evidently limited in formation of the latter and need a supply of organically bound (H) to reduce the CO_2 taken up. However, CO_2 incorporation is quantitatively less important than organic acid assimilation, and it seems, especially from the work of Stanier *et al.* (1959), that the main role of light is to form ATP (see sec. 8).

B. Similarities with the Thiorhodaceae

The *Athiorhodaceae* can grow also on H_2 like the sulfur organisms (equation [7]). However, the ratio H_2/CO_2 is really not 2 but averages 2.6 (Wessler and French, 1939), as would be expected from the relatively reduced composition of the cell material. Still closer similarity with the sulfur organisms is shown by the fact that *Rhodo-ps. palustris* can photosynthesize with thiosulfate (though not with H_2S). However, so far *Athiorhodaceae* have not been grown in a purely mineral medium. The *Thiorhodaceae*, in their turn, approach the non-sulfur forms in that they can absorb CO_2 in light in the presence of some organic acids, especially malate, acetate, and butyrate (Muller, 1933). Again the organic acid evidently supplies reducing power, while photosynthesis forms ATP and phosphoglyceric acid in the same way as with green plants. In presence of organic acids, indeed, *Athiorhodaceae* even evolve H_2 in light (Gest *et al.*, 1950), showing that there is no shortage of reducing power if adequate substrate is present. *Thiorhodaceae* will do the same in presence of thiosulfate, which is converted to sulfate (Losada *et al.*, 1961). Fuller and co-workers (1961) have shown that Chromatium, a typical sulfur organism, possesses all the enzymes for the conversion of CO_2 to sugars and even to uridine-diphosphate-glucose, as well as for conversion of acetate via acetyl-CoA to the acids of the glyoxalate cycle (p. 746), and thence to aspartate and glutamate. Even the colorless *Beggiatoa* grows well on acetate (Pringsheim and Wiessner, 1963). Thus the organic metabolism of the sulfur and nonsulfur bacteria differs only in detail.

The one important difference is that some Athiorhodaceae can grow purely heterotrophically, in air, on organic media, while such typical Thiorhodaceae as Chromatium are *obligately* photosynthetic.

4. THE PIGMENT SYSTEM

A. The Pigments Themselves

The pigments of the purple bacteria, like those of the algae and higher plants, comprise chlorophyll and carotenoids. The latter, which give the characteristic purple and red colors, are all relatives of lycopene, the red pigment of tomatoes, containing 13 double bonds (*A* below) and no rings (unlike the carotenes of green plants). The pigments fall into two groups: (1) those that can be considered as having one or two molecules of water directly added to lycopene, followed by methylation of (either or both) the HO groups; (2) those similarly derived from a related structure, *B* below, mostly with only 12 double bonds, (Jensen *et al.*, 1961):

A: *Lycopene*
  H·OH added at (1): Rhodopin
  CH_3O· and H added at (1): Anhydro-rhodovibrin
  CH_3O· and H added at (1) and HOH added at (2): Rhodovibrin
  CH_3O· and H added at (1) and (2), plus double bond at (3):
    Spirilloxanthin
B: *Second parental type*
  CH_3O· and H added at (1): "Pigment Y"
  HOH added at (1): "Hydroxy-Y"
  CH_3O· and H added at (1); C=O at (2): Spheroidenone

The pigments of the first group occur in Rhodospirillum, Chromatium, and *Rhodo-ps. palustris*, while the other three Rhodopseudomonads contain only pigments of the second group. Most species have 5 to 10 related carotenoids, but spirilloxanthin and rhodopin are the commonest (van Niel and Smith, 1935; van Niel, 1947; Goodwin and Land, 1956; Jensen, 1959–1961). Rhodomicrobium contains pigments of group (1) together with some β-carotene.

Some Athiorhodaceae are brown in anaerobic culture, but turn red in air. This is an enzymatic change in which the yellow pigment decreases and the red one increases, probably by interconversion (van Niel, 1947). Formation of all the pigments is inhibited by adding diphenylamine to the medium (Goodwin and Land, 1956). More saturated precursors then appear instead, i.e., it prevents dehydrogenation.

The green pigment remaining in the cells after the carotenoids have been extracted is bacteriochlorophyll *a*. It is apparently the same in all purple bacteria. It differs from chlorophyll *a* of green plants only in two points: (1) the acetyl group in place of a vinyl group on ring A, and (2) one less double bond (see formulae on p. 735). The formula shown for chlorophyll *a* has recently been confirmed by synthesis (Woodward *et al.*, 1960); that for the bacterial pigment is only probable (Fischer and Stern, 1940). These small chemical differences, as well as some differences in the conjugation with protein, cause very large differences in color, since the main absorption peak of chlorophyll *a* in vivo is in the red at 670 mμ, while that for bacteriochlorophyll is well into the infrared, which means that the purple bacteria can photosynthesize at these invisible wavelengths. The two infrared peaks in Rhodospirillum at *ca.* 800 and 880 mμ are ascribed to different combined forms of the same bacteriochlorophyll.

The green bacteria contain a quite different chlorophyll, superficially resembling chlorophyll *a* of green plants; its main peaks in vivo lie at 730 and 460 mμ, but in ether they fall at 660 (red) and 432 mμ (blue), with secondary ones at 622 and 412. Chlorophyll *a*

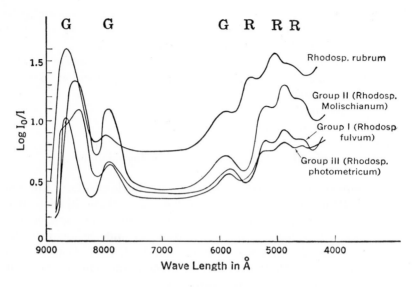

FIGURE XXIII–2

Absorption curves of living nonsulfur bacteria (four Rhodospirillum species) in the infrared and visible. The peaks marked *G* are due to green pigments, those marked *R* to red ones. (From C. Giesberger; Beitr. zur Kenntniss der Gattung Spirillum Ehbg. Thesis, Delft, 1947.)

shows 622 and 430, 615 and 410. Seven strains (Stanier and Smith, 1960) of *Chlorobium limicola* and *thiosulfatophilum* contained this pigment, while one other showed the main peak at 650 mμ, and the others shifted correspondingly toward the blue. This is remarkable, since in the algae the chlorophylls do not differ within a major taxonomic grouping. The optical similarity to chlorophyll *a* is misleading, because the Chlorobium chlorophyll does not contain the fifth ring adjacent to

TABLE XXIII–2. Absorption Peaks of Some Living Sulfur Bacteria

(Data of Schlegel and Pfennig, 1961)

Organism	Visible Color	Wavelengths of Peaks (mμ)				
Chr. okenii	Purple-red	380	510		(800)	830–840
Chr. vinosum	Purple	380	490	595	800	850
Chr. warmingii	Pale red	380	510–520	590	800	845
Thiosp. jenense	Orange-brown	380	490, 510	595	800	845
Amoebobacter	Purple	380	520	590	805	840
Chlorobium	Green	460		740		

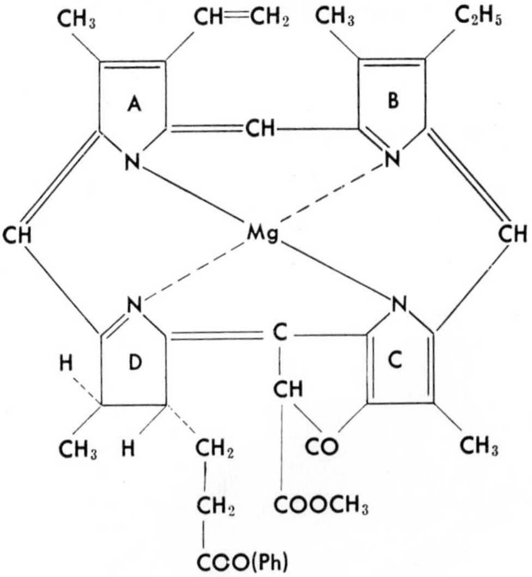

Chlorophyll a

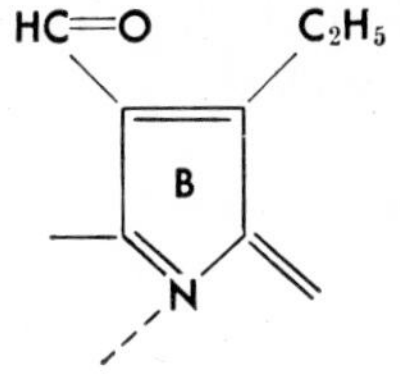

Chlorophyll b

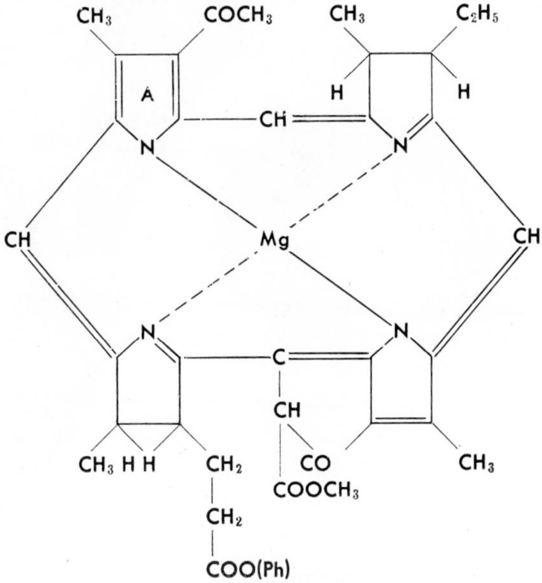

Bacteriochlorophyll a
(Ph) = Phytol

ring C (Holt and Morley, 1960), and the long chain is not Phytyl but Farnesyl, $C_{15}H_{26}$ (Rapaport and Hamilton, 1961).

Typical absorption curves of living Athiorhodaceae are shown in Figure XXIII–2, and the absorption peaks of some Thiorhodaceae and Chlorobium are listed in Table XXIII–2. The general correspondence, particularly for the chlorophyll bands at 590, 800, and 850 or 880 mμ, is very clear.

B. The Chromatophores

The pigments of green algae and higher plants are not free but are deposited in fine layers or lamellae within the (usually disc-

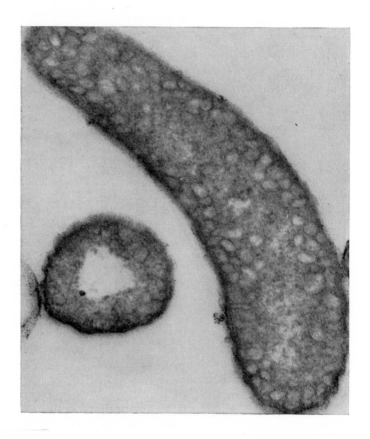

shaped) plastids. Similarly the pigments of purple bacteria are contained within small disc-shaped "chromatophores," which can be prepared from broken cell suspensions by centrifuging (Schachman *et al.*, 1952) and can carry out the formation of ATP in light, i.e., "photophosphorylation" (Frenkel, 1954–1956, for Rhodo-spirillum; Williams, 1956, and Anderson and Fuller, 1958, for Chromatium). The particles vary in size from 70 to 300 mμ in diameter depending on species and age; in 12-hour cultures of *Rhodo-sp. rubrum*, smaller particles only 25 mμ in diameter are present, but these act in the same way and at the same rate (Hickman and Frenkel, 1959). The chromatophores show a finely layered lamellar structure (Drews, 1960), and in Chromatium each contains about 200 molecules of chlorophyll, 100 of carotenoid, and 20 of cytochrome, together with protein, lipids, and polysaccharide (Newton and Newton, 1957; Newton and Levine, 1959). This last suggests relationship with the cell

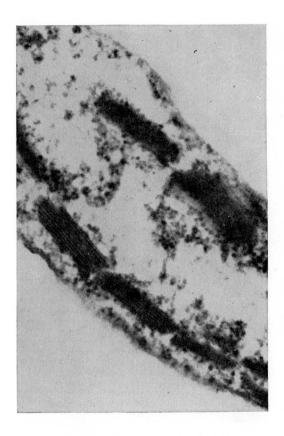

FIGURE XXIII–3
Chromatophores of purple bacteria in thin section. *Left. Rhodo-sp. rubrum* grown anaerobically in light, longitudinal and transverse sections. 85,000 ×. (Photo by D. D. Hickman, 1959; cf. Hickman and Frenkel, *J. Biophys. Biochem. Cytol.,* **6**: 277, 1959.)

Right. Rhodo-sp. molischianum, showing lamellated structure of the chromatophores. 100,000 ×. (From G. Drews, *Arch. Mikrobiol.,* **36**:99, 1960.)

wall, and indeed electron microscopy shows the chromatophores to lie often near the edge of the cell (see Fig. XXIII–3). In *Rhodomicrobium vanniellii* (Vatter *et al.,* 1959; Boatman and Douglas, 1961), as well as in the blue-green algae, which as noted in Chapter II may be the bacteria's nearest relatives, no chromatophores are present, but the characteristic layered structure of the photosynthetic pigments is seen lying close to the wall, or occasionally folded into the cytoplasm (Fig. XXIII–4). Thus, both here and in the bacteria, the pigmented lamellae are attached either to the cell membrane or to "a reticulum of membranous extensions penetrating the cytoplasm" (Tuttle and Gest, 1959).

The significance of these various features is understood to be as follows:

The layering is a device to spread the pigments out for optimum light absorption and yet keep them in a rigid framework so that energy

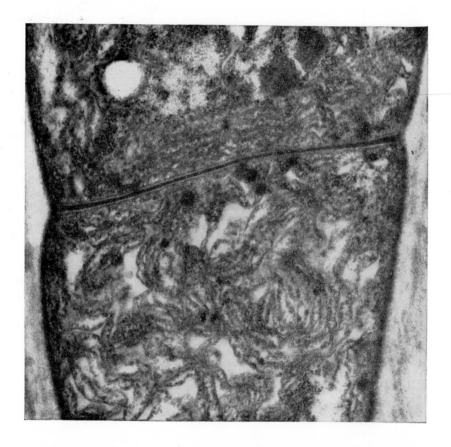

can be transferred from one pigment molecule to another. That energy is indeed transferred is shown in three ways: (1) Light absorbed by the carotenoids, i.e., in the blue, can cause photosynthesis. The effectiveness of different wavelengths in the visible (Thomas, 1950) is shown in Figure XXIII–5. Only the peak at 590 mμ can be due to chlorophyll, the other peaks being due to light absorption by carotenoids. Apparently the spirilloxanthin takes no part, since its maximum is at 550 mμ, but the other carotenoids are active. The photosynthetic efficiency achieved when the carotenoids are absorbing is evidently comparable with that found when chlorophyll is absorbing. (2) When Rhodospirilla are illuminated with red or infrared, the absorption in the region of the three peaks at 400 to 520 mμ changes markedly. Because similar changes occur on aeration, they probably mean the carotenoids are being oxidized (Smith and Ramirez,

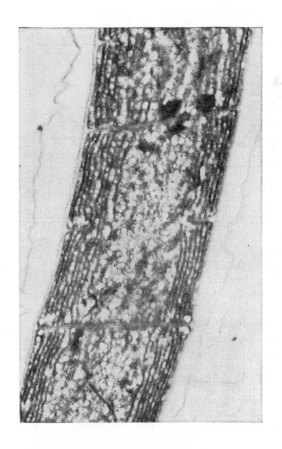

FIGURE XXIII–4
Photosynthetic structures of blue-green algae. *Left. Calothrix* sp.; in the upper cell the lamellae parallel the wall; in the lower one they are folded throughout the cytoplasm. 56,000 ×. (Photo, Professor H. Ris and R. N. Singh., 1959.)

Right. Phormidium uncinatum; lamellae parallel the longitudinal walls throughout the filament. Compare cross-wall forming with that in Fig. III–12. 30,000 ×. (Photo, courtesy Dr. Sarah Gibbs, 1962.)

1959). The cytochrome band at 418 mμ also shows oxidation in light. (3) Light absorbed by one form of chlorophyll (at 590 mμ) causes the other forms, absorbing at 850 and 880 mμ, to fluoresce (Bril, 1960). Energy has, therefore, been passed from one chlorophyll type to another. If the chromatophores are treated with a detergent, which fragments them, the transfer of energy is interfered with. A similar thing happens in the green bacteria, light of wavelengths absorbed only by the carotenoids causing the chlorophyll to fluoresce (Sybesma and Olson, 1963).

It is remarkable that Engelmann in 1888 concluded that "bacteriopurpurin is a true chromophyll, in that the energy of light absorbed by it is converted into potential chemical energy." The participation of carotenoids in bacterial photosynthesis parallels their

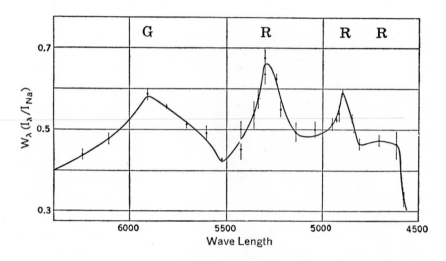

FIGURE XXIII–5

The action spectrum of photosynthesis of *Rhodospirillum rubrum*. The values plotted are the relative rates of CO_2 uptake, at each wave length, in a butyrate medium. The peak marked G is to be ascribed to a green pigment, those marked R to red ones. The peaks fall at 5900, 5250, 4900, and about 4600 AU. (Reproduced from Fig. 5 of J. B. Thomas, *Biochim. Biophys. Acta*, 5:186–196, 1950. Elsevier Publishing Co., New York and Amsterdam.)

action in the diatom Nitzschia (Dutton and Manning, 1941) and the blue-green alga Chroöcoccus (Emerson and Lewis, 1942–1943).

The protein, together with a phospholipid, provides the stable framework, holding the pigment in essentially solid, very concentrated state. Combination with protein drastically alters the position of the absorption peaks of the pigments; bacteriochlorophyll has its peak at 770 mμ in methanol and is the same in all purple forms studied; yet the cells, or the chromatophores, show peaks at about 880 and 800 mμ, whose positions differ slightly in different species. Chlorobium chlorophyll, with peak in ether at 660 mμ, absorbs at 720 mμ in the cell—a smaller shift, perhaps related to the absence of true chromatophores in these green cells. Chlorophyll *a* shows a similar but still smaller shift between the absorption peaks in organic solvents and in the plastid. The nature of the combination with protein is doubtless of crucial importance for photosynthesis; Fuller calculates that one protein of molecular weight 67,000 is combined with 600 molecules of chlorophyll, 300 of carotenoid, and 3000 of phospholipid.

The carotenoids, besides absorbing and transferring energy to chlorophyll for photosynthesis, have another function: they protect the cells from damage due to photo-oxidation and protect the chlorophyll from bleaching. In methanol extracts, bacteriochlorophyll bleaches more than 1000 times faster than in the chromatophores (Goedheer, 1960). In a blue-green mutant of *Rhodo-ps. spheroides*, which contains none of the purple carotenoids, synthesis of pigment stops at once in air (in light), and in two hours most of the cells are dead; the chlorophyll is also slowly bleached (Cohen-Bazire *et al.* 1957). Cells kept in the dark are not killed in air, but, of course, they do not form bacteriochlorophyll in the dark; thus the chlorophyll must *sensitize* a photo-oxidation in air. Evidently the carotenoid protects against this reaction. By treating *Rhodo-sp. rubrum* with diphenylamine, which inhibits carotenoid formation, cells like the above mutant were obtained, and some of these too are killed in air and light, although this is controversial (Wassink and Kronenberg, 1962). Carotenoids even protect ordinary bacteria against light damage, since a colorless mutant of *Sarcina lutea* is killed in sunlight while the yellow wild type survives (Mathews and Sistrom, 1960).

C. Associated Compounds

Besides these highly colored substances there are probably three other compounds of great physiological importance, although only one is yet known for certain. First, all photosynthetic bacteria, like their green-plant relatives, contain cytochromes; *Rhodo-sp. rubrum* contains more cytochrome *c* than rat liver (Vernon, 1953). Both in this and in *Chromatium* the cytochrome is c_2 (see Table V–2), having bands in the reduced form at 552, 522, and 418 mμ, and it has been extracted, purified, and crystallized (Bartsch and Kamen, 1960; Morita, 1960). The cytochrome of the green bacterium, *Chl. thiosulfatophilum*, is very similar and comprises some 0.2 per cent of the cell weight (Gibson and Larsen, 1955). Like the cytochrome *f* of green plants, the cytochrome of purple bacteria is rapidly oxidized in light (sec. 8).

In green plants the critical reducing step in photosynthesis, reduction of phosphoglyceric acid to phosphoglyceraldehyde, is mediated by TPN, which is directly reduced by the chlorophyll via TPN reductase, a pinkish-brown enzyme which may be a hemin-protein (Hill and Bendall, 1961). In Chromatium and Rhodospirillum this reduction is done by DPNH, so that by analogy a DPN reductase is no doubt present.

Third, the photosynthetic formation of ATP, which is known to occur in chromatophores just as in chloroplasts, is associated in spinach chloroplasts with a reducible benzoquinone derivative, "plastoquinone." In purple bacteria this is replaced by the closely related coenzyme Q_7 or Q_9 (identical except for having 7 or 9 isoprene units in the side-chain); 1 mole of this coenzyme is present for 5 of chlorophyll (Lester and Crane, 1959; Fuller *et al.*, 1961). Vitamin K is also present.

Coenzyme Q_7 or Q_9

The pigment particles of Chlorobium appear to contain two quinones similar to plastoquinone.

D. Pigment Formation

It was shown with red corpuscles of birds in the early 1950's, mainly by Shemin and Rittenberg (1951; see Shemin, 1955), that the synthesis of the porphyrin nucleus takes place from glycine and succinyl-CoA via δ-aminolevulinic acid, of which two molecules condense to form the basic unit, porphobilinogen; four molecules of this, with a series of changes, yield protoporphyrin IX, see formula on page 743. From this the cytochromes and chlorophylls are derived. There is good evidence that bacteria follow the same route. If *Rhodo-ps. spheroides* is grown in a medium low in Fe, and the washed cells incubated in light with glycine and succinate, large amounts of coproporphyrin (one of the last intermediates) are excreted (Lascelles, 1956). A soluble enzyme for the first step, δ-aminolevulinic synthetase, has been extensively purified from these organisms, and various extracts that carry out subsequent steps have also been prepared (Hoare and Heath, 1959; see Lascelles, 1961). The porphyrin excretion is due to iron deficiency, and if 10^{-5}M Fe is added, the excretion stops, and instead bacteriochlorophyll is formed in the cells.

The chlorophyll synthesis is inhibited by chloramphenicol, which is known to prevent synthesis of proteins (see p. 822), and also

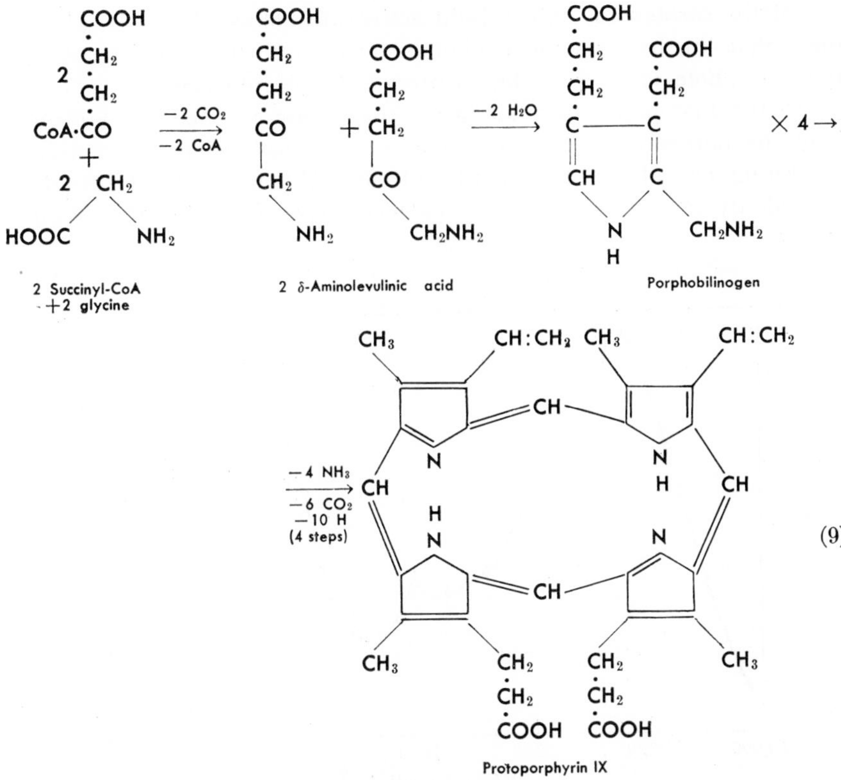

$$2 \begin{array}{c} \text{COOH} \\ | \\ \text{CH}_2 \\ | \\ \text{CH}_2 \\ | \\ \text{CoA·CO} \\ + \\ \text{CH}_2 \\ \diagup \quad \diagdown \\ \text{HOOC} \quad \text{NH}_2 \end{array} \xrightarrow[-2\,\text{CoA}]{-2\,\text{CO}_2} \begin{array}{c} \text{COOH} \\ | \\ \text{CH}_2 \\ | \\ \text{CH}_2 \\ | \\ \text{CO} \\ | \\ \text{CH}_2 \\ | \\ \text{NH}_2 \end{array} + \begin{array}{c} \text{COOH} \\ | \\ \text{CH}_2 \\ | \\ \text{CO} \\ | \\ \text{CH}_2\text{NH}_2 \end{array} \xrightarrow{-2\,\text{H}_2\text{O}} \begin{array}{c} \text{COOH} \\ | \\ \text{CH}_2 \\ | \\ \text{CH}_2 \\ | \\ \text{C}\!-\!\!-\!\text{C} \\ \| \quad \| \\ \text{CH} \quad \text{C} \\ \diagup \quad \diagdown \\ \text{N} \quad \text{CH}_2\text{NH}_2 \\ | \\ \text{H} \end{array} + \begin{array}{c} \text{COOH} \\ | \\ \text{CH}_2 \\ | \\ \text{CH}_2 \end{array} \quad \times 4 \rightarrow$$

2 Succinyl-CoA ·+2 glycine   2 δ-Aminolevulinic acid   Porphobilinogen

$$\xrightarrow[\substack{-6\ \text{CO}_2 \\ -10\ \text{H} \\ (4\ \text{steps})}]{-4\ \text{NH}_3}$$

(9)

Protoporphyrin IX

by analogues of purines and pyrimidines (Lascelles and Bull, 1963). Incorporation of C^{14}-labeled phenylalanine into the chromatophore also parallels chlorophyll formation. It appears, therefore, that synthesis of chlorophyll and of protein are tightly interrelated, and hence probably that chlorophyll is formed only to the extent that chromatophores are formed. The linkage is not absolute, though, for when *Rh-ps. spheroides* is transferred from bright to dim light, the pigments are formed preferentially to the protein (Sistrom, 1962). Thus dimmer light leads to more pigment and hence to faster photosynthetic rate: a remarkable control system.

5. PHOTOTAXIS OF PURPLE BACTERIA

As stated at the outset, Engelmann saw the purple bacteria accumulate in the infrared, where bacteriochlorophyll absorbs, and in the blue-green, where the carotenoids absorb. The accumulation in the latter region was determined more carefully by Buder (1919) as at 530, 490, and 470 mμ. We have seen above that the chlorophyll and one of the carotenoids absorb light active in photosynthesis. It follows, then, that the bacteria move phototactically into those regions where they can photosynthesize. The meaning of this is important.

In the first place the phototaxis, in the case of *Rhodo-sp. rubrum*, is of the nature of a shock reaction. Engelmann's term was *Schreck-bewegung* or "alarm movement" (1888). When the light intensity is suddenly reduced, or when the bacteria move suddenly into a region

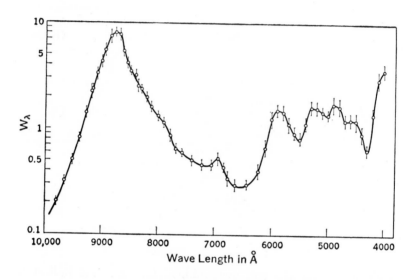

FIGURE XXIII-6

Action spectrum of phototactic movement in *Rhodospirillum rubrum*. The values plotted, W_λ, are the relative effectiveness of each wave length compared to that of a yellow-green standard. In addition to the peak at 8800 AU, which corresponds to that of the bacteriochlorophyll, peaks fall in the visible at 5900, 5250, 4900, and about 4600 AU. These correspond closely with those in Figure XXIII-5. (From A. Manten, Dissertation, Utrecht, 1948.)

of decreased light intensity, they stop and reverse their motion by reversing the flagella (cf. Fig. II–9). The time this reaction takes is one to several seconds, depending on the difference in intensity. In Manten's later study (1948; cf. Milatz and Manten, 1953), a pair of adjacent light fields was set up under a microscope with a sharp boundary between, and the spirilla introduced. By holding one light constant and varying the other, both in intensity and wave-length, the two fields can be adjusted so that the bacteria show no reaction at the boundary and become evenly distributed over the whole field. The two light fields are then phototactically equivalent. The ratio of their intensities, or "phototactic action" of the variable field, is shown over the whole spectrum in Figure XXIII–6. If we compare it with Figure XXIII–5, it is clear that the action spectrum is the same as for photosynthesis. All the photosynthetic pigments must, therefore, function in phototaxis.

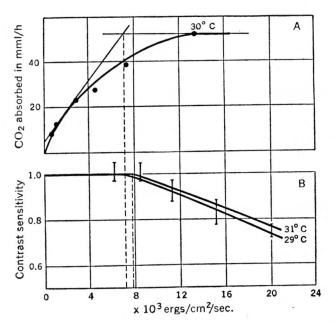

FIGURE XXIII–7

Comparison of the light intensities causing (A) saturation of photosynthesis, and (B) decrease in phototactic sensitivity. At about 7500 ergs/cm²/sec photosynthesis is just saturated (by extrapolation), and the phototactic sensitivity begins to go down. Measurements made in sodium light on *Rhodospirillum* sp. (Reproduced from Figure 7 of J. B. Thomas and L. E. Nijenhuis, *Biochim. Biophys. Acta*, **6**:317–324, 1950. Elsevier Publishing Co., New York and Amsterdam.)

The mode of their action has been largely elucidated by intensity measurements. The minimum light intensity difference needed to cause phototaxis (at any one wavelength) goes up very sharply when the absolute intensity becomes high, i.e., the bacteria become phototactically less sensitive. The intensity at which this occurs is precisely the intensity at which photosynthesis begins to be saturated with light (Thomas and Nijenhuis, 1950; see Fig. XXIII–7). Data with inhibitors also show a close relation with photosynthesis, and it is concluded that the phototactic reaction is due to "a sudden change in the photosynthetic rate" (Milatz and Manten, 1953). Such a reaction is of obvious survival value for the purple bacteria, although just how photosynthetic rate controls the *directional* movement of the flagella is obscure. A similar problem is that of *chemotaxis*, i.e., the swimming of organisms toward a dissolved substance. Nonmotile blue-green algae bend toward the spectral region absorbed by chlorophylls, which is probably a similar mechanism (Manten, 1948), but the movement of motile green algae is controlled only by blue light and evidently has a different basis (see Thimann and Curry, 1960).

6. GROWTH AND METABOLISM ON ORGANIC MEDIA

Although photosynthesis in the purple bacteria is anaerobic, some of the Athiorhodaceae are capable of aerobic growth on organic media. *Rhodo-sp. rubrum* has indeed been carried for years as a stock culture on yeast agar slants. Several other species will gradually become oxygen-tolerant on continued transfers, and grow independent of light, although the pigment does appear somewhat deepened when the slant is illuminated (Table XXIII–1). Evidently growth is now hetero-trophic and dependent on oxidation. As substrates, simple organic acids and hydrogen seem to be the best (Gaffron, 1935, Glover *et al.*, 1952). Even Chromatium, a sulfur form, will oxidize acetate in the dark and take up some CO_2 as well, forming mainly phosphoglyceric acid, as in photosynthesis, although it does not grow. Thus, the oxidative assimilation has much in common with photosynthetic assimilation, and many enzymes evidently function in both processes. In some respects the dark metabolism may compete with that in light, since light inhibits oxygen uptake (on butyrate) by 60 to 80 per cent (Johnston and Brown, 1954). It also inhibits the small amount of fermentation that occurs anaerobically. Some interrelation with the metabolism of Desulfovibrio is seen in the fact that Rhodospirillum chromatophores can reduce sulfate to sulfide, using ATP formed in the light (Ibanez and Lindstrom, 1962).

A very complete survey of the enzymes of Chromatium shows that not only can it fix CO_2 photosynthetically into phosphoglyceric acid and thence sugars, but it also carries out a *second* fixation of CO_2 to convert pyruvate to oxalacetate and thence to aspartate, which accumulates. In addition, it readily forms the enzymes of the Krebs-Kornberg glyoxalate cycle (Fuller *et al.*, 1961). These reactions are summarized in Figure XXIII–8.

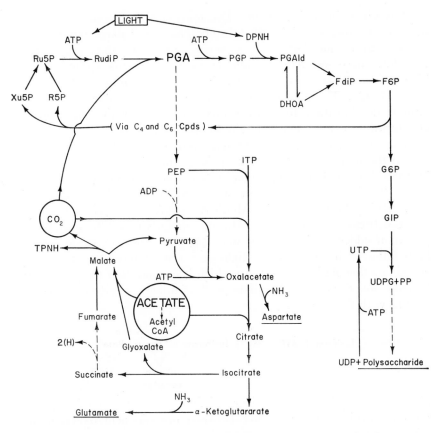

FIGURE XXIII–8

Diagram of the biochemical reactions of *Chromatium*, strain D, in light and in dark. (Modified from Fuller *et al.*, *J. Biol. Chem.*, **236**:2140, 1961.) Major end-products are underlined; major raw materials, encircled.

Abbreviations: *F*, fructose; *G*, glucose; *R*, ribose; *Ru*, ribulose; *Xu*, xylulose; *I*, inosine; *A*, adenine; *U*, uridine.

7. EMISSION OF LIGHT (LUMINESCENCE)

In photosynthesis, the energy of light is converted to that of chemical bonds. Some organisms, however, use chemical energy to emit light. Although the bacteria that do this are quite different from the photosynthetic bacteria, the process is near enough to the *converse of photosynthesis* to merit brief discussion here.

The luminescent bacteria are mainly pseudomonads and are grouped in the genus *Photobacterium* (Breed and Lessel, 1954). Some Vibrios also luminesce. Several species are marine, and decaying fish often

glow brightly in a dark room. The optimum temperature for luminescence is low, 19° C in *Photob. phosphoreum;* above the optimum
the system is not destroyed, however, since on subsequent cooling
the glow increases. Also, at temperatures above the optimum, very
high pressures (*ca.* 100 atm.) will increase the luminescence (Brown
et al., 1942). These facts are interpreted as indicating a *reversible*
protein denaturation by temperature, because certain other protein
denaturations can be retarded by high pressure.

The system that yields light has been more studied in the firefly
and in the marine invertebrate Cypridina than in the bacteria. Dubois
in 1885 separated the Cypridina system into two components, a substrate, "luciferin," and an enzyme, "luciferase," which oxidizes it.
In purifying firefly luciferin, McElroy (1947, 1951) found that ATP
is a constituent of the system. Minute amounts of ATP (around $\frac{1}{100}$
γ), when added to the enzyme with Mg and substrate, cause a bright
flash followed by a long slow light emission. If more enzyme is now
added, another flash occurs, from which it appears that the enzyme has
become inactive. Pyrophosphate will similarly elicit a flash. The
data fit with the scheme:

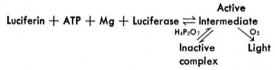

Since pyrophosphate can be liberated by the acetate-oxidizing enzyme
(p. 245), this provides a link between organic acid oxidation and
luminescence.

Since oxidation is involved, luminescence can be used as a delicate
test for oxygen. Beijerinck (1901) showed that when *Photob. fischeri*
and algae were mixed and left sealed up in gelatin in the dark,
luminescence was gradually extinguished as conditions became anaerobic. A brief flash of light gave rise to enough oxygen to re-establish
luminescence. The minimum oxygen pressure for light emission was
subsequently found to be 0.005 mm Hg (Harvey and Morrison, 1923).

The great sensitivity of the system also makes it a delicate test
for ATP, and this in turn allows one to test whether high-energy
phosphate is formed in photosynthesis. When Chlorella cells are kept
in the dark for two hours and then illuminated, ATP does appear and
at once (Strehler and Totter, 1952). One cubic millimeter of cells
produces, per second, 3.6×10^{-11} moles of ATP and 2.1×10^{-10} moles
of oxygen, i.e., a ratio of about 6 to 1 (Strehler, 1953). At high-light
intensity the yield of ATP is lower, but after the light is off, it rises
again. Ths indicates that ATP is *both made and utilized* in photochemical reactions; evidently it reacts with something which is itself a

light product. We now know that this comprises two different compounds, ribulose-phosphate and phosphoglyceric acid (see sec. 8).

As far as bacterial luminescence is concerned, the light-emitting substrate is not luciferin, but appears to be a long-chain aldehyde. Dodecanal, $C_{11}H_{23}CHO$, or decanal, $C_9H_{19}CHO$, will function, and flavin mononucleotide, FMN, is an essential participant (McElroy and Green, 1955). Extracts from *Photob. fischeri* are thought to cause the peroxidation of the aldehyde by an FMN-peroxide; the FMN is regenerated, but the aldehyde appears to be used up (Cormier and Totter, 1957) although this last point is doubtful. Reduced FMN is formed via DPNH through dehydrogenation of various substrates:

$$DPNH + H^+ + FMN \rightarrow FMNH_2 + DPN^+$$
$$FMNH_2 + O_2 \rightarrow (peroxide)$$
$$RCHO + (peroxide) \rightarrow RCOOH + H_2O + light$$

Divalent ions increase the flash intensity (Terpstra and van Eijk, 1961). A possible link with photosynthesis is seen in the fact that naphthoquinones inhibit luminescence by competing for reducing power (McElroy and Green, 1955). The system is complicated by the presence of a luciferase inhibitor in the enzyme preparation, at least from *Photob. phosphoreum* (Terpstra, 1960), and by the simultaneous presence of an ordinary dehydrogenase to which the dodecyl aldehyde is susceptible.

8. THE MECHANISM OF BACTERIAL PHOTOSYNTHESIS

Although the pigment system of the purple bacteria shows a basic similarity to that of green plants, in that it contains both chlorophyll and carotenoids, both are very different from those in green plants. The photosynthetic process is different too; it can be regarded as a major variation on the theme that nature has pursued with minor variations through the algae and higher plants. Biochemically, the difference is that in purple bacteria organic compounds or reduced S compounds are needed, evidently as hydrogen (or electron) donors. In the algae, water acts as the corresponding hydrogen donor.

There is good reason to consider that the photoreaction is the same in all cases. The best evidence for this is the fact that the same amount of energy, in the form of light quanta, is needed, however much chemical energy may be contributed by oxidation of the hydrogen donor. Thus:

(1) When hydrogen gas is hydrogen donor (equation [7]), the reduction of CO_2 theoretically should require very little additional energy (about 0.04 quantum per mole of CO_2); yet 5 quanta are

still absorbed by Rhodopseudomonas, 8 to 16 by Chromatium, and 9 by Chlorobium, for each molecule of CO_2 reduced (Wessler and French, 1939; Wassink et al., 1942; Larsen et al., 1952).

(2) Again, when thiosulfate is hydrogen donor (equation [6]), the reaction requires about one-fourth as much light energy as when H_2O is used (29,000 cal. per mole of CO_2, compared to 112,000 with H_2O). Nevertheless, with Chlorobium, 9 to 10 quanta are required (Larsen et al., 1952). This agrees closely with the requirement for green algae, in which the figure usually found is about 10 quanta.

The second major point is that when the cells are illuminated, the cytochrome c_2 is instantly oxidized from the Fe^{++} to the Fe^{+++} state. In the dark it is slowly reduced again. This change, first observed with green chloroplasts, takes place also in whole Chromatium cells (Duysens, 1954–1955) and in Chromatophores of Rhodo-sp. rubrum (Smith et al., 1958–1959, 1961). Chance and Nishimura (1960) have added the remarkable discovery that the oxidation goes nearly as fast in liquid nitrogen as it does at 25° C. This shows that the cytochrome and chlorophyll must be in most intimate spatial relationship (cf. the relation between chlorophyll and protein shown by Lascelles' work above).

Third, ATP is formed in light. Again this was first shown in chloroplasts (Strehler and Trotter, 1952) but soon demonstrated in a macerate of Rhodo.-sp. rubrum (Frenkel, 1954) and in particles from Chromatium and Chlorobium (Williams, 1956). Since these last are strict anaerobes, it is clear that photosynthetic ATP formation is not related to oxygen. Unlike oxidative phosphorylation, photosynthetic phosphorylation is not inhibited by dinitrophenol (see Arnon, 1961). The process is somehow mediated by the quinones, coenzyme Q_7 and vitamin K.

That ATP formation is a normal and essential part of photosynthesis is shown by the fact that Chromatium chromatophores, supplied with ATP in the dark, fix CO_2 into soluble products, especially malate, aspartate, and glutamate, just as without ATP in the light (Losada et al., 1961; Arnon, 1961). The fixation was about one-half as much as in the light. If the ATP were removed from the system by adding hexokinase and glucose (which uses ATP to form hexosephosphate), CO_2 fixation stopped.

Putting these three facts together, namely, that the energy used is the same as in green plants, that cytochrome becomes oxidized, and that ATP is formed, we arrive at the following picture of bacterial photosynthesis:

Light activates the chlorophyll, which loses an electron (see Arnon, 1961): $Chl + h\nu \rightarrow Chl^*$; $Chl^* \rightarrow Chl^+ + e$. The cytochrome, being closely adjacent, at once supplies an electron in replacement: Chl^+ $+ Cyt^{++} \rightarrow Chl + Cyt^{+++}$. The electron ejected by chlorophyll has two alternative paths:

In *one*, it reduces the quinone, which then passes it back to the cytochrome, at the same time forming ATP:

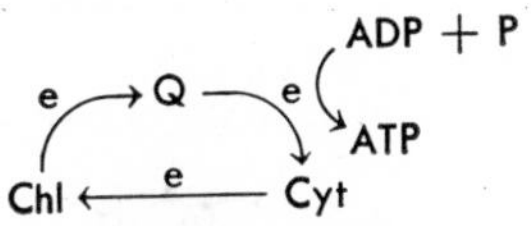

Thus, in this process, called by Arnon *et al.* (1959) "cyclic photophosphorylation," ATP is the only product.

In the more complex *second* alternative, the electron is accepted by a special reductase, which reduces a pyridine nucleotide, probably DPN; in these reactions a molecule of ATP is formed. The DPNH, in turn, reduces the carboxyl group of phosphoglyceric acid (PGA), which has been formed in the primary (dark) uptake of CO_2. In order to be reduced, the PGA must be phosphorylated to phosphoglyceryl phosphate, PGP, and the reduction is the exact reversal of the phosphorylative oxidation shown on page 445:

$$
\begin{array}{l}
H_2CO\cdot H_2PO_3 \\
\quad | \\
HCOH \\
\quad | \\
O:CO \sim H_2PO_3 \\
\quad \text{PGP}
\end{array}
+ DPNH + H^+ \rightarrow
\begin{array}{l}
H_2CO\cdot H_2PO_3 \\
\quad | \\
HCOH \\
\quad | \\
O:CH \\
\quad \text{PGAld.}
\end{array}
+ H_3PO_4 + DPN^+ \tag{10}
$$

Because the electron has been carried away to DPN, the oxidized cytochrome takes an electron from a convenient donor, H_2S or thiosulfate, alcohol, or butyrate, etc. This may require a second cytochrome (Hill and Bendall, 1961). The hydrogen from these donors joins with the electron to reduce the DPN:

$$DPN^+ + 2\ H^+ + 2\ e \rightarrow DPNH + H^+$$

The second electron path and its results can then be represented:

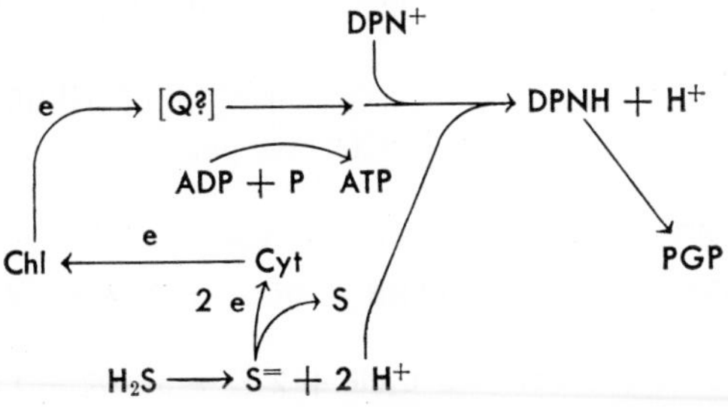

The exact location of the phosphorylation is not clear.

For CO_2, the first step is combination with ribulose diphosphate as in green plants; the resulting branched chain acid is thought to split into two molecules of phosphoglyceric acid, PGA (Calvin, 1956):

$$
\begin{array}{ccccc}
\text{H}_2\text{CO·}\textcircled{P} & \text{H}_2\text{CO·}\textcircled{P} & & \text{H}_2\text{CO·}\textcircled{P} & \text{H}_2\text{CO·}\textcircled{P} \\
| & | & & | & | \\
\text{C}=\text{O} & \text{C}-\text{OH} & ^-\text{OCC·C}-\text{OH} & \text{HOOC·C}-\text{OH} \\
| & \| & & | & \text{H} \\
\text{HCOH} \rightleftharpoons & \text{C}-\text{OH} \xrightarrow{CO_2} & \oplus\text{C}-\text{OH} \xrightarrow{H_2O} & + \\
| & | & | & \text{COOH} \\
\text{HCOH} & \text{HCOH} & \text{HCOH} & | \\
| & | & | & \text{HCOH} \\
\text{H}_2\text{CO·}\textcircled{P} & \text{H}_2\text{CO·}\textcircled{P} & \text{H}_2\text{CO·}\textcircled{P} & | \\
& & & \text{H}_2\text{CO·}\textcircled{P}
\end{array}
\qquad (11)
$$

Ribulose 1:5-diphosphate   2 PGA

The PGA is then phosphorylated to PGP and reduced to phosphogly-ceraldehyde, PGAld, as in equation (10). The supply of ribulose diphosphate comes no doubt, as in green plants, from a cyclic series of reactions elucidated by Calvin, Horecker, and others (see Goodwin 1960), in which five phosphoglyceraldehyde molecules give rise, via phospho-tetrose and phospho-heptose, to three phospho-ribulose molecules, thus (P_i = inorganic phosphate):

$$
\begin{aligned}
2\ \text{C}_3\text{P} &\rightarrow \text{C}_6\text{diP (fructose)} \\
\text{C}_6\text{diP} + \text{C}_3\text{P} &\rightarrow \text{C}_4\text{P (erythrose)} + \text{C}_5\text{P (ribose)} + \text{P}_i \\
\text{C}_4\text{P} + \text{C}_3\text{P} &\rightarrow \text{C}_7\text{P (sedoheptulose)} + \text{P}_i \\
\text{C}_7\text{P} + \text{C}_3\text{P} &\rightarrow \text{C}_5\text{P (ribose)} + \text{C}_5\text{P (xylulose)}
\end{aligned}
$$

$$
\left.
\begin{array}{c}
\text{C}_5\text{P (xylulose)} \\
+ \\
\text{C}_5\text{P (ribose)}
\end{array}
\right\} \rightarrow 2\ \text{C}_5\text{P (ribulose)}
$$

In sum, $5\ \text{C}_3\text{P} \rightarrow 3\ \text{C}_5\text{P} + 2\ \text{P}_i$

Then, $3\ \text{C}_5\text{P} + 3\ \text{ATP} \rightarrow 3\ \text{C}_5\text{diP (ribulose1:5 diphosphate)} + 3\ \text{ADP}$

The requirement for ATP is, for each CO_2 reduced, two ATP to phosphorylate the two phosphoglyceric acids formed, plus one ATP to form the acceptor ribulose diphosphate from its monophosphate produced in the above cycle. Since the DPN reduction yields only one ATP, the first electron pathway is needed in addition to supply extra ATP.

Combining the above cyclic regeneration of ribulose diphosphate with the fixation and reduction of CO_2, we get:

Fixation: $3\ \text{C}_5\text{diP} + 3\ CO_2 + 3\ H_2O \rightarrow 6\ \text{PGA}$

Reduction: $6\ \text{PGA} + 6\ \text{ATP} + 6\ \text{DPNH} + 6\text{H}^+ \rightarrow 6\ \text{PGAld} + 6\ \text{P}_i + 6\ \text{ADP}$
                                                      $+ 6\ \text{DPN}^+ + 6\ H_2O$

Regeneration: $6\ \text{PGAld} + 3\ \text{ATP} \rightarrow 3\ \text{C}_5\text{diP} + 2\ \text{P}_i + 3\ \text{ADP} + 1\ \text{PGAld}$

The path of carbon is underlined; only half of the six PGA molecules contain the C of the CO_2 (equation [11]). Each CO_2 requires three ATP and two DPNH. From three CO_2 molecules the cell ultimately derives one molecule of phosphoglyceraldehyde, which it then uses for all its other syntheses.

If the primary light process is the ejection of electrons from chlorophyll and their replacement by cytochrome, then the carriage of the electrons to DPN and thence to phosphoglyceric acid is only secondary and not an essential part of the reaction. Several alternative acceptors of the electrons have been shown to function.

Organic acids, especially malate, are converted by Athiorhodaceae to oxidized products and H_2 gas in the light (Gest et al., 1950; Morita et al., 1951):

$$\text{Malate} \rightarrow \text{Pyruvate} + CO_2 + H_2$$

This can now be regarded as depending on electron acceptance, i.e.,

$$2 \; Cyt^{++} \rightarrow 2 \; Cyt^{+++} + 2 \; e$$
$$2 \; e + 2 \; H^+ \rightarrow H_2 \text{ gas}$$

To reduce the cytochrome again:

$$\text{Malate} \rightarrow \text{Pyruvate} + CO_2 + 2 \; H^+ + 2 \; e$$
$$2 \; Cyt^{+++} + 2 \; e \rightarrow 2 \; Cyt^{++}$$

Thiosulfate functions similarly with Chromatium, causing the evolution of H_2 only in the light (Losada et al., 1961). Direct observation showed that the cytochrome is reduced by thiosulfate. In four-day experiments sulfate appeared, which Losada et al. formulate as:

$$^=S_2O_3 + 5 \; H_2O \xrightarrow{\text{light}} 2 \; ^=SO_4 + 2 \; H^+ + 4 \; H_2$$

However, the yield of hydrogen shown is only about $\frac{1}{2} H_2$ for each thiosulfate molecule decomposed, which rather suggests:

$$2 \; ^=S_2O_3 + 2 \; H_2O \rightarrow \; ^=S_4O_6 + 2 \; ^-OH + H_2$$

With both these types of electron acceptors, photoproduction of H_2 was inhibited by nitrogen gas. This can now be interpreted as competition for electrons by nitrogen:

$$N_2 + 6 \; H_2O + 6 \; e \rightarrow 2 \; NH_3 + 6 \; OH^-$$

resulting in *nitrogen fixation*. It was through this phenomenon that the fixation of nitrogen by purple bacteria was discovered (p. 386). In green or blue-green algae the OH^- reduces the cytochrome, and O_2 is evolved. In purple bacteria organic acids are metabolized instead.

Finally, the concept of electron ejection by light and its return via cytochrome helps to explain the early oxidation-reduction potential measurements of Roelofsen (1935) and Wassink (1947). If the cells are placed in a closed vessel with a platinum electrode, the potential becomes very reducing. If CO_2 alone is present, light makes the potential rise sharply, i.e., the system is becoming oxidized, but no reducing agent is supplied. If H_2 alone is present, light makes the potential fall, because now the cytochrome and other acceptors are being reduced, and no further electron acceptor is supplied. In presence of CO_2 plus H_2 the potential keeps nearly constant.

Our knowledge of the life of the purple bacteria has deepened greatly in the last few years. Much of this has been made possible by parallel researches with algae and chloroplasts of higher plants. But the underlying reason for the rapid development of a difficult field has been the bringing to bear of a wide variety of techniques, including optical measurements, use of isotopes, controlled breakage of cells, chromatography, and much cultural and biological sophistication. The next few years should see a great deal of the remaining mystery dispelled.

REFERENCES

Anderson, I. C., and Fuller, R. C. 1958. *Arch. Biochem. Biophys.*, **76**:168–179.
*Arnon, D. I. 1961. In, Light and Life, ed. McElroy and Glass. Baltimore, Johns Hopkins Press, pp. 489–565.
Arnon, D. I.; Whatley, F. R.; and Allen, M. B. 1959. *Biochem. Biophys. Acta*, **32**: 47–57.
Bartsch, R. G., and Kamen, M. D. 1960. *J. Biol. Chem.*, **235**:825–831.
*Bavendamm, W. 1924. Die farblose und roten Schwefelbakterien der Süss- und Salzwassers. Jena, G. Fischer, 156 pp.
Beijerinck, M. W. 1901. *Proc. Kon. Akad. Wetensch., Amsterdam*, pp. 45–49.
Boatman, E. S., and Douglas, H. C. 1961. *J. Biochem. Biophys. Cytol.*, **11**:469–480.
Breed, R. S., and Lessel, E. F., Jr. 1954. *Ant. v. Leeuwenhoek*, **20**:58–64.
Bril, C. 1960. *Biochim. Biophys. Acta*, **39**:296–303.
Brown, D. E.; Johnson, F. H.; and Marsland, D. A. 1942. *J. Cell. Comp. Physiol.*, **20**:151–168.
Buder, H. 1919. *Jahrb. wiss. Bot.*, **58**:525–628.
Calvin, M. 1956. *Bull. Soc. Chim. Biol.*, **38**:1233–1244; also in *Proc. 2nd Int. Conf. Peaceful Uses of Atomic Energy, Geneva*, **24**:24–32 (1958).
Chance, B., and Nishimura, M. 1960. *Proc. Nat. Acad. Sci.*, **46**:19–24.
Cohen-Bazire, G.; Sistrom, W. R.; and Stanier, R. Y. 1957. *J. Cell Comp. Physiol.*, **49**:25–68; see also Cohen-Bazire, G., and Stanier, R. Y. *Nature*, **181**:250–252 (1958); Fuller, R. C., and Anderson, I. C. *Ibid.*, pp. 252–254.
Cormier, M. J., and Totter, J. R. 1957. *Biochim. Biophys. Acta*, **25**:229–237.
Drews, G. 1960. *Arch. f. Mikrobiol.*, **36**:99–108.
Dutton, H. J., and Manning, W. M. 1941. *Am. J. Bot.*, **28**:516–526.
Duysens, L. M. N. 1954–1955. *Nature*, **173**:692; *Science*, **121**:210–211 (1955).
Emerson, R., and Lewis, C. M. 1942. *J. Gen. Physiol.*, **25**:579–595; *Am. J. Bot.*, **30**: 165–178 (1943).

Engelmann, Th. W. 1882–1888. *Arch. ges. Physiol.* (Pfluger's), **29**:387–400 (1882); **30**:95–124 (1883); **42**:183–188; *Bot. Ztg.*, **46**:661–669, 677–689, 693–701, 709–720 (1888).

*Fischer, H., and Stern, A. 1940. Chemie des Pyrrols. Berlin, Springer. Vol. II-2 Hälfte, pp. 23 and 313.

Foster, J. W. 1940. *J. Gen. Physiol.*, **23**:123–134.

French, C. S. 1937–1940. *J. Gen. Physiol.*, **21**:71–87 (1937), **23**:469–481 (1940).

Frenkel, A. W. 1954–1956. *J. Am. Chem. Soc.*, **76**:5568–5569; *J. Biol. Chem.*, **222**: 823–834 (1956).

Fuller, R. C.; Smillie, R. M.; Rigopoulos, N.; and Yount, V. 1961. *Arch. Biochem. Biophys.*, **95**:197–202.

Fuller, R. C.; Smillie, R. M.; Sisler, E. C.; and Kornberg. H. L. 1961. *J. Biol. Chem.*, **236**:2140–2149.

*Gaffron, H. 1933–1935. *Biochem. Z.*, **260**:1–17 (1933); **275**:301–319 (1935).

Gest, H.; Kamen, M. D.; and Bregoff, H. M. 1950. *J. Biol. Chem.*, **182**:153–170.

Gibson, J., and Larsen, H. 1955. *Biochem. J.*, **60**:xxvii.

Giesberger, C. 1947. *Ant. v. Leeuwenhoek*, **13**:135–148.

Goedheer, J. C. 1960. *Biochim. Biophys. Acta*, **38**:389–399.

Glover, J.; Kamen, M. D.; and van Genderen, H. 1952. *Arch. Biochem. Biophys.*, **35**: 384–408.

Goodwin, T. W. 1960. Recent Advances in Biochemistry. London, J. and A. Churchill. Chapter 2.

Goodwin, T. W., and Land, D. G. 1956. *Arch. Mikrobiol.*, **24**:305–312; Goodwin, T. W. *Ibid.*, pp. 313–322.

Harvey, W. D., and Morrison, T. D. 1923. *J. Gen. Physiol.*, **6**:13–19.

Hickman, D. D., and Frenkel, A. W. 1959. *J. Biophys. Biochem. Cyt.*, **6**:277–284, 285–290.

Hill, R., and Bendall, F. 1961. *Nature*, **187**:417.

Hoare, D. S., and Heath, H. 1959. *Biochem. J.*, **73**:679–690.

Holt, A. S., and Morley, H. V. 1960. *J. Am. Chem. Soc.*, **82**:500.

Hutner, S. H. 1946. *J. Bact.*, **52**:213, 221.

Hutner, S. H. 1950. *J. Gen. Microbiol.*, **4**:286–293.

Ibanez, M. L., and Lindstrom, E. S. 1962. *J. Bact.*, **84**:451–455.

Jensen, S. L. 1959–1961. *Acta Chem. Scand.*, **13**:381–383, 842–845, 2142–2144; **14**: 952(1960); **15**:1182–1185 (1961).

Jensen, S. L.; Cohen-Bazire, G.; and Stanier, R. Y. 1961. *Nature*, **192**:1168–1172.

Johnston, J. A., and Brown, A. H. 1954. *Plant Physiol.*, **29**:177–182.

Kamen, M. D. 1955. Bacterial Heme Proteins. *Bacteriol. Revs.*, **19**:250–262.

Karrer, P., and Solmssen, V. 1935–1940. *Helv. Chim. Acta*, **18**:1306–1315; **19**:3–5, 1019–1024; **23**:460–463.

Larsen, H.; Yocum, C. S.; and van Niel, C. B. 1952. *J. Gen. Physiol.*, **36**:161–171.

Lascelles, J. 1956. *Biochem. J.*, **62**:78–93.

*Lascelles, J. 1961. Synthesis of Tetrapyrroles by Microorganisms. *Physiol. Revs.*, **41**:417–441.

Lascelles, J., and Bull, M. J. 1963. *Biochem. J.*, **87**:15–28.

Lebedev, A. F. 1921. Quoted in *Amer. Rev. Soviet Med.*, **5**:17–27, 1947–1948.

Lester, R. L., and Crane, F. L. 1959. *J. Biol. Chem.*, **234**:2169–2175.

Losada, M.; Nozaki, M.; and Arnon, D. I. 1961. In, Light and Life, ed. McElroy and Glass. Baltimore, Johns Hopkins Press, pp. 570–575.

McElroy, W. D. 1947. *Proc. Nat. Acad. Sci.*, **33**:342–345.

McElroy, W. D. 1951. *J. Biol. Chem.*, **191**:547–557.

McElroy, W. D., and Green, A. A. 1955. *Arch. Biochem. Biophys.*, **56**:240–255.

*Manten, A. 1948. Phototaxis, Phototropism and Photosynthesis in Purple Bacteria and Blue-green Algae. Dissertation, Utrecht.

Mathews, M. M., and Sistrom, W. R. 1960. *Archiv. f. Mikrobiol.*, **35**:139–146.

Milatz, J. M. W., and Manten, A. 1953. *Biochim. Biophys. Acta*, **11**:17–27.

Molisch, H. 1907. Die Purpurbakterien nach neuen Untersuchungen. Jena.

Morita, S. 1960. *J. Biochem* (Tokyo), **48**:870–873.

Morita, S.; Suzuki, K.; and Takashima, S. 1951. *J. Biochem.* (Japan), **38**:255–262.

Muller, F. M. 1933. *Arch. Mikrobiol.*, **4**:131–166.

Murray, R. G., and Douglas, H. C. 1950. *J. Bact.*, **59**:157–167.

Newton, J. W., and Levine, L. 1959. *Arch. Biochem. Biophys.*, **83**:456–471.

Newton, J. W., and Newton, G. A. 1957. *Arch. Biochem. Biophys.*, **71**:250–265.

*van Niel, C. B. 1931. *Arch. Mikrobiol.*, **3**:1–112.

van Niel, C. B. 1936. *Arch. Mikrobiol.*, **7**:323–358.

*van Niel, C. B. 1941. The Bacterial Photosyntheses and Their Importance for the General Problem of Photosynthesis. *Adv. in Enzymol.*, **1**:263–328.

*van Niel, C. B. 1944. The Culture, General Physiology, Morphology and Classification of the Non-sulfur Purple and Brown Bacteria. *Bact. Revs.*, **8**:1–118.

van Niel, C. B. 1947. *Ant. v. Leeuwenhoek*, **12**:156–166.

van Niel, C. B. 1949. *Am. Scientist*, **37**:371–385.

van Niel, C. B., and Smith, J. H. C. 1935. *Arch. Mikrobiol.*, **6**:219–229.

Ormerod, J. G. 1956. *Biochem. J.*, **64**:373–380.

Pringsheim, E. G., and Wiessner, W. 1963. *Nature*, **197**:102.

Rapaport, H., and Hamilton, H. P. 1961. *Biochem. Biophys. Res. Communs.*, **6**:134–137.

Roelofsen, P. A. 1935. On Photosynthesis of the Thiorhodaceae. Dissertation, Utrecht; cf. *Proc. Kon. Akad. Wetensch. Amsterdam*, **37**:660–669 (1934).

Schachman, H. K.; Pardee, A. B.; and Stanier, R. Y. 1952. *Arch. Biochem. Biophys.*, **38**:345–360.

Schlegel, H. G., and Pfennig, N. 1961. *Archiv. f. Mikrobiol.*, **38**:1–39; Pfennig, N. *Naturwiss.*, **5**:136–137.

Shemin, D. 1955. In, Ciba Foundn. Symp. on Porphyrin Biosynthesis and Metabolism, ed. Wolstenholme and Millar. London, J. and A. Churchill.

Shemin, D., and Wittenberg, J. 1951. *J. Biol. Chem.*, **192**:315–334.

Siegel, J. M. 1950. *J. Bact.*, **60**:595–606.

Sistrom, W. R. 1962. *J. Gen. Microbiol.*, **28**:607–616.

Smith, L. 1961. In, Light and Life, ed. McElroy and Glass, Baltimore, Johns Hopkins, Press, pp. 436–443.

Smith, L., and Ramirez, J. 1958. *Brookhaven Symp. in Biol.*, **11**:310–315; Smith, L., and Baltscheffsky, M. *J. Biol. Chem.*, **234**:1575–1579 (1959); Smith, L., and Ramirez, J. *Arch. Biochem. Biophys.*, **79**:233–244 (1959)

Stanier, R. Y.; Doudoroff, M.; Kunisawa, R.; and Contopoulos, R. 1959. *Proc. Nat. Acad. Sci.*, **45**:1246–1260.

Stanier, R. Y., and Smith, J. H. C. 1960. *Biochim. Biophys. Acta*, **41**:478–484.

Strehler, B. L. 1953. In, Phosphorus Metabolism, ed. W. D. McElroy and B. Glass. Baltimore, Johns Hopkins Press, pp. 491–502.

Strehler, B. L., and Totter, J. R. 1952. *Arch. Biochem. Biophys.*, **46**:28–41.

Sybesma, C., and Olson, J. M. 1963. *Proc. Nat. Acad. Sci.*, **49**:248–253.

Terpstra, W. 1960. *Biochim. Biophys. Acta*, **41**:55–67.

Terpstra, W., and van Eijk, H. G. 1961. *Biochim. Biophys. Acta*, **51**:473–481.

*Thimann, K. V., and Curry, G. M. 1960. Phototropism and Phototaxis. In, Comparative Biochemistry, ed. Mason and Florkin. New York, Academic Press, pp. 243–309.

Thomas, J. B. 1950. *Biochim. Biophys. Acta*, **5**:186–196.

Thomas, J. B., and Nijenhuis, L. E. 1950. *Biochim. Biophys. Acta,* **6**:317–324.

Tuttle, A. L., and Gest, H. M. 1959. *Proc. Nat. Acad. Sci.,* **45**:1261–1269.

Vatter, A. E.: Douglas, H. C.; and Wolfe, R. S. 1959. *J. Bact.,* **77**:812–813.

Vernon, L. P. 1953. *Arch. Biochem. Biophys.,* **43**:492–493.

Wassink, E. C. 1947. *Ant. v. Leeuwenhoek,* **12**:281–293.

Wassink, E. C.; Katz, E.; and Dorrestein, R. 1942. *Enzymologia,* **10**:285–354 (esp. Table VII, p. 319).

Wassink, E. C., and Kronenberg, G. H. M. 1962. *Nature,* **194**:553–554.

Wessler, S., and French, C. S. 1939. *J. Cell. Comp. Physiol.,* **13**:327–334.

Williams, A. M. 1956. *Biochim. Biophys. Acta,* **19**:570.

Woodward, R. B., and 17 collaborators (!). 1960. *J. Amer. Chem. Soc.,* **82**:3800–3801.

The Inhibition of Growth: General

Only those substances can be anchored at any particular part of the organism which fit into the molecule of the recipient combination as a piece of mosaic fits into a certain pattern.

PAUL EHRLICH

W e have seen in the preceding chapters that growth depends on synthesis, and that synthesis requires both materials and energy. It follows that growth can be inhibited: (1) by interfering with the energy supply, as by poisoning oxidations; (2) by reducing the supply of materials, especially of the most critical materials such as vitamins, needed in small amounts and not replaceable; (3) by interfering with the synthetic process itself, especially with its most vulnerable participants, the nucleic acids. Growth can also be inhibited less specifically by damaging the cell wall or the membrane, so that both cell enlargement and the mechanism for taking up solutes are impaired.

Each of these types of growth inhibition has been extensively explored, and in this chapter we shall try not so much to summarize the vast literature as to present some of its guiding ideas. Detailed treatment can be found in numerous reviews and in the books by Albert (1951), Martin (1951), and Woolley (1952).

1. SULFHYDRYL POISONS

Many enzymes, as well as coenzyme A and lipoic acid, depend for their activity on the group —C—SH. They are, therefore, inactivated when the —SH is combined with other groupings. Numerous metal ions, especially those that form insoluble sulfides, such as silver, mercury, arsenic, antimony, copper, cadmium, and lead, can combine with —SH groups and in so doing cause inactivation of enzymes. The list of SH-enzymes includes alcohol dehydrogenase, succinic dehydrogenase, and phosphoglyceraldehyde dehydrogenase, all of fundamental importance in carbohydrate metabolism (cf. Chaps. V and XI). Correspondingly, the above metals are all toxic to microorganisms and strongly inhibit growth. Copper in the form of Bordeaux mixture ($CuSO_4$ and lime) has been used to spray plants against fungi for over 100 years, the effect against the mildew of grapes having been discovered by Millardet at Bordeaux in 1882. Algae are also highly sensitive to copper. In the case of bacteria, the effect is usually to inhibit growth rather than to kill the cells (Seuderling, 1933). It is very easily demonstrated by pouring inoculated agar into a Petri dish with a copper or silver coin in the center. If the metal is carefully cleaned so as to be free of oxide, the effects are greatly decreased.

The mechanism of this action was elucidated by Fildes (1940) for the case of mercury. The growth of *E. coli* on an ammonium lactate medium was shown to be completely stopped by $HgCl_2$ at 8×10^{-6} M; if now thioglycollic acid, cysteine, or glutathione (all containing the —C—SH group) were added, growth was at once reinstated. Even after four days' exposure to the mercury, addition of an excess of one of the —SH compounds allowed immediate growth. Hence the action of mercury is probably exerted by combining with (one or more) —SH compounds essential for growth. Since higher concentrations of mercury salts actually kill, it appears that the integrity of —SH enzymes or coenzymes is essential not only for growth but for life.[1]

Many organic compounds of mercury have been prepared in the hope of finding a perfect antiseptic. Some, like "Mercurochrome" (dibromohydroxymercurifluorescein), are much less effective than $HgCl_2$, but others, particularly Metaphen (nitromersol) and phenylmercuric nitrate, are 5 to 10 times as active as $HgCl_2$. The gram-positive cocci are about twice as sensitive to these mercurials as other bacteria (for systematic comparisons of these compounds see Birkhaug, 1933).

[1] The bactericidal action of mercury seems to have been known to the ancients. The sensitivity of the syphilis spirochete, *Treponema pallida*, is hinted at in Fracastor's famous poem (1530); "Syphilis sive Morbus Gallicus." This poem, from which the disease gets its name, deals with "a certain shepherd of ancient times by the name of Syphilis, who had aroused the ire of the god of the sun with his mockeries; the god did punish him with a malady, which would not yield to any treatment until the nymph America did initiate him into her mysteries and lead him to a grove of the healing Guaiacum trees, a sulfur spring, and a lake of mercury." (Merejkovski, *The Romance of Leonardo da Vinci.*)

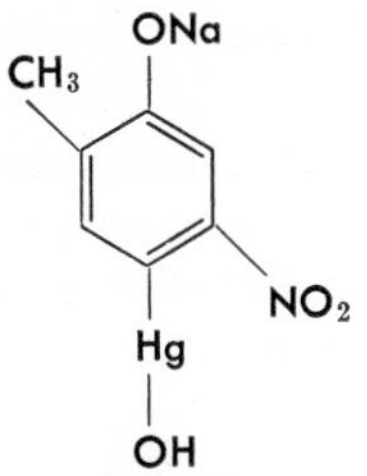

Nitromersol
(Metaphen)

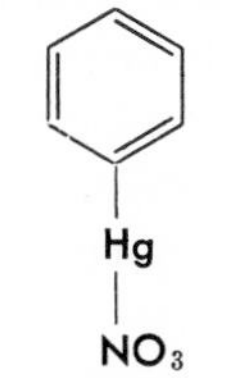

Phenylmercuric
nitrate

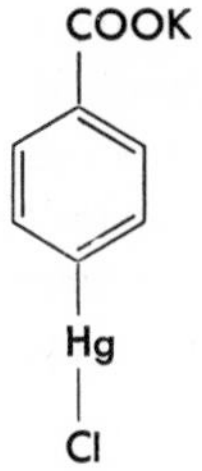

Parachloromercuri-
benzoate (PCMBA)

Parachloromercuribenzoate was subjected to a particularly critical study (Benesch and Benesch, 1948) which proved that its action is indeed limited to —SH groups and that it has no affinity for amino, imino, or guanido groups.

One of the most sensitive —SH enzymes is urease, which hydrolyzes urea to NH_3 and CO_2. One might expect, therefore, that bacterial hydrolysis of urea (cf. Chap. VIII, sec. 4) would be sensitive to —SH poisons. Figure VIII–3 (p. 329) shows the course of urea hydrolysis by a Urobacillus species. It is evident that cupric ions, as well as the Hg compound, powerfully inhibit urea hydrolysis and also the growth of the Urobacilli.

Arsenic compounds have also been used a good deal against specific microorganisms. Arsenite and trivalent As compounds are generally more effective than arsenate. Organic compounds of trivalent As were introduced by Ehrlich and co-workers in 1907 because, although of very slight toxicity to man and higher animals, they are toxic to parasites in the animal body, especially spirochetes and some

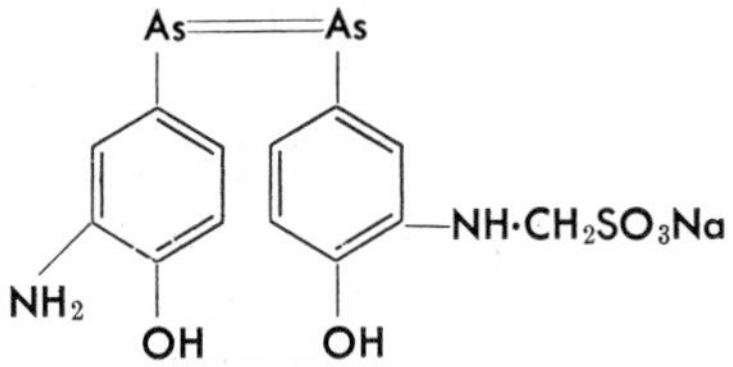

Neosalvarsan or neoarsphenamine

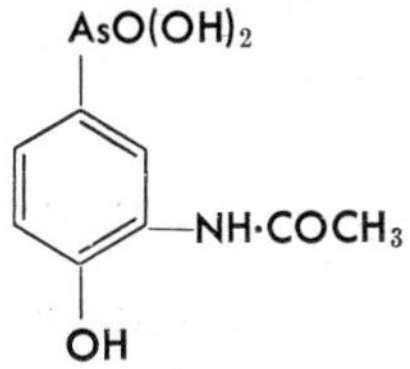

Acetarsone
(Stovarsol)

protozoa. Pentavalent As compounds, when effective, are probably reduced to the trivalent form. Neosalvarsan or neoarsphenamine, effective on injection, and Stovarsol (acetarsone), effective by mouth but less so than by injection, were used against syphilis (*Treponema pallida*) for over 30 years, until they were replaced by the newer antibiotics. These compounds have very little effect on the organisms in vitro, and it is most likely that they do not enter the bacterial cell as such, but are metabolized by the host so as slowly to release the arsenic in the form of a small, permeable molecule.

Several other As compounds are widely used in medicine. Against African sleeping sickness (caused by the flagellate *Trypanosoma gambiense*), especially in its late stages, tryparsamide is effective. Mapharsen (oxophenarsine hydrochloride) is used somewhat in dentistry.

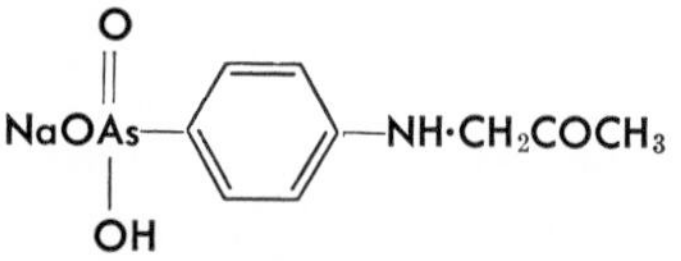

Tryparsamide

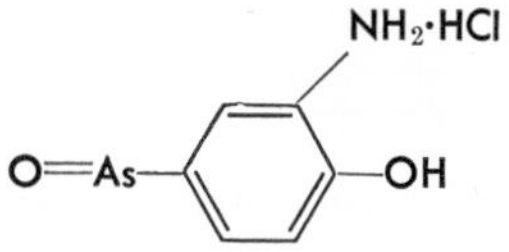

Oxophenarsine hydrochloride
(Mapharsen)

Similar antimony compounds are active against kala-azar (caused by another flagellate, *Leishmania donovani*) and other tropical diseases.

Iodoacetate is another reagent for SH groups, forming a thioether with the elimination of HI:

$$RSH + ICH_2COOH \rightarrow RSCH_2COOH + HI$$

However, although it inhibits the growth of higher plants strongly, its action on the growth of microorganisms seems to have been little studied. It inhibits a number of enzymes (cf., e.g., Barron and Singer, 1945).

Mustard gases owe their action on the skin to their ability to combine with the —SH groups of keratin, the skin protein. Both kinds, the sulfur mustards and the nitrogen mustards, have a pair of reactive halogen atoms, comparable to the iodine of iodoacetate, and these doubtless are eliminated when combination with —SH takes place. The commonest representatives of each group are:

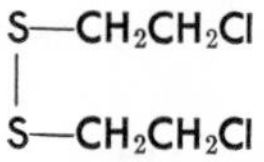

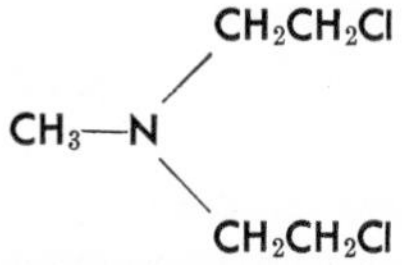

ββ-Dichlorodiethyl disulfide   and   ββ-Dichlorodiethylmethylamine
("mustard gas" or sulfur mustard)   ("nitrogen mustard" or HN₂)

Mustards have two types of action on bacteria; they inhibit growth powerfully, but perhaps a more striking effect is that they promote mutations. This was first found in Drosophila by Auerbach, but soon afterward was observed in *E. coli* (Tatum, 1946) as well as in fungi. Since x-radiation has similar effects, these compounds have been called *radiomimetic* (i.e., radiation-imitating). As seen in section 6, some of the effects of mustards must be ascribed to action on groups other than —SH. As an example, the biological activity on animals is dependent on the presence of *two* halogeno-alkyl groups, and for this reason it has been suggested that these substances act by introducing cross-links between two parts of the protein molecule. Indeed, many large molecules, including nucleic acid, alginic acid, and serum albumin, are cross-linked by mustards and also by related compounds such as epoxides and ethylene-imino derivatives (Alexander *et al.*, 1952). Although there is little correlation between ability to cause cross-linking in proteins and biological activity, cross-linking in nucleic acids may well be very important (sec. 3).

2. "SURFACE-ACTIVE" SUBSTANCES

A large group of substances have bacteriostatic or toxic effects of a more general nature than those discussed above. The action does not come under the head of "growth inhibition" properly speaking, since it is generally measured by killing,[2] but it is seldom that a clear distinction is made. Actually, bacteria apparently killed by phenol may be only inhibited and can sometimes be made to grow again by removing the last traces of phenol with absorbent charcoal or with ferric chloride (Flett *et al.*, 1945).

The group includes phenol and its congeners, the soaps and detergents, the salts of some organic acids, and a small group of basic peptides and amines.

For convenience the bactericidal action of substances of this group is expressed in comparison with that of phenol. Suppose the minimum concentration of phenol needed to kill a culture of a given organism under given (standard) conditions is a gram per liter and the minimum concentration of another substance is b gram per liter (under the same conditions); then the substance is said to have a "phenol coefficient" (or Rideal-Walker coefficient) of a/b. The procedure is to add to 5 ml of the test solution a small quantity (say 0.1 ml) of a standard broth culture of the bacterium. After 5 or 10 minutes, a subculture is made into fresh broth and incubated. By making a series of dilutions, the lowest concentration that prevents growth in the subculture is determined. *M. aureus* is generally used, with *S. typhosa* an alternative. Obviously a sporeformer would be unsuitable, and an anaerobe inconvenient. Since the results are often intended for application to medicine, the choice of a human pathogen is a natural one.

The action of these substances is often ascribed to their lowering of the interfacial tension at the surface of the organism. Thus, the sur-

---

[2] Note that the distinctive terms *bacteriostatic* and *fungistatic* apply to growth-inhibiting action, as opposed to *bactericidal* and *fungicidal* which apply to killing.

face energy of a paraffin-water interface is about 50 ergs/cm², and addition of 0.25 per cent sodium oleate brings it down to 3 ergs/cm². Table XXIV–1 gives an example of the parallelism between bactericidal activity and the effect on surface tension. The substituted resorcinols, where R is an alkyl group, show a steady decrease in surface tension

TABLE XXIV–1. Phenol Coefficient and Surface Tension in the Resorcinol Series

(Data of Frobisher, 1927, and Albert, 1942)

| Substance | PHENOL COEFFICIENTS WITH: | | Surface Tension of a 0.01% Solution |
	M. aureus	*S. typhosa*	
Resorcinol	0.3	0.3	76
4-Propyl resorcinol	3.7	5.0	73
4-Butyl resorcinol	10	22	66
4-Amyl resorcinol	30	33	60
4-Hexyl resorcinol	98	50+	54
4-Heptyl resorcinol	280	30	43
4-Nonyl resorcinol	960	....	(not soluble)

with increasing length of the side-chain, and there is a corresponding increase in phenol coefficient with the first of the two test organisms.

Roughly, the coefficient goes up about three times for each additional C atom. The other organism shows a less systematic response. However, in other groups of compounds, such as the phenyl-substituted fatty acids, there is no such simple relation. The surface-active compounds do lower surface tension, as shown by their ability to act as wetting and foaming agents, but the specificity of their action indicates that details of chemical structure are critical.

The bacterial cell wall (Chap. III) contains carboxyl and phosphate groups and is, therefore, negatively charged at ordinary pH; the iso-electric point of several bacteria lies between pH 1.8 and 3.8 (Yamaha and Abe, 1934). For this reason surface-active compounds that are anionic, such as Duponol, Drene, Dreft, etc., with the typical structure $C_{14}H_{28}SO_3O^-\cdot Na^+$, are only weakly bactericidal, and like the phenols, which are much weaker acids, they act best against gram-positive bacteria. However, they become more effective at highly acid pH, where the negative charge is reduced. Much more active are basic, cationic compounds like the antibiotic polymyxin, or cetyltrimethylammonium-bromide (CTAB) or cetylpyridinium chloride (CPC):

$$C_{16}H_{33}N^+(CH_3)_3\cdot Br^- \qquad C_{16}H_{33}-N^+\langle\text{⬡}\rangle Cl^-$$

CTAB   CPC

Again structure is critical, since the highly basic polypeptides of lysine have only weak activity (Burger and Stahmann, 1952). That basic properties do favor activity is shown, however, by work with the basic bactericidal peptide gramicidin S, which has two free amino groups; when these are substituted with the acidic group p-toluene-sulfonyl, it becomes inactive (Erlanger et al., 1954). Acetylation of the amino groups in other bactericidal peptides also largely reduces their activity.

For a given group of compounds the activity increases with increasing aliphatic chain-length: generally 12 to 16 C atoms constitute the optimum, e.g., lauryl-glycine $C_{12}H_{25}\cdot NH\cdot CH_2COOH$. With the amidines,

$$RC\!\!\begin{array}{c}\nearrow NH\\\searrow NH_2\end{array}, \quad C_{14}$$

is optimal (Schulman and Armstrong, 1949). With the

diamidines,

$$\begin{array}{c}NH\\\nwarrow\\C\cdot R\cdot C\\\diagup\quad\searrow\\NH_2\qquad NH_2\end{array}\!\!\!\!\begin{array}{c}NH\\\nearrow\end{array}, \quad\text{it is } C_{18}$$

(Fuller, 1942); with dialkyl-methylbenzylammonium chlorides, it is C_{12} to C_{16}, and with the sulfonium iodides, C_{16} is best against E. coli and C_{12} against M. aureus (Kuhn and co-workers, 1940).

The diamidines, which are strongly basic, are very effective against the malaria Protozoan, Plasmodium vivax. Paludrine (chlorguanide), the most widely used, has the structure (Curd and Rose, 1946):

$$Cl\langle\text{⬡}\rangle\!\!-NH\cdot C\cdot NH\cdot C\cdot NH\cdot CH\begin{array}{c}\diagup CH_3\\\\\searrow CH_3\end{array}$$
$$\qquad\qquad\overset{\cdot\cdot}{NH}\quad\overset{\cdot\cdot}{NH}$$

In this case the long alkyl chain has been replaced by C_3 at one end and a cyclic C_6 at the other. Longer chains as in the bisdiguanides, e.g.,

$$\left[Cl\text{—}C_6H_4\text{—}NH\cdot C\cdot NH\cdot C\cdot NH \atop \qquad\qquad\quad NH \quad NH \right]_2 \text{—}(CH_2)_5$$

confer a more general antibacterial action (Rose and Swain, 1956). The related propamidine salts:

$$NH_2\text{—}C\cdot C_6H_4OCH_2CH_2CH_2O\cdot C_6H_4\cdot C\text{—}NH_2\cdot HCl \atop \quad\ NH \qquad\qquad\qquad\qquad\qquad\qquad\ NH$$

are highly toxic to trypanosomes. The diguanide structure of streptomycin (p. 808) should also be noted.

The mechanism of action of the surface-active compounds, especially the bases, is at least partly understood (see Newton, 1958). In the first place, the active compounds are strongly adsorbed. The sensitive *M. aureus* takes up 300 to 400 mg of CTAB per gram dry weight of cells, and organisms sensitive to polymyxin take up similar amounts of this peptide, while resistant ones (*Sc. fecalis* and *Proteus*) take up only 25 per cent as much. The adsorption is decreased by acid *p*H and reverses the negative charge of the bacteria. Pretreatment with cations (to neutralize the negative charges) prevents the adsorption.

Evidently the adsorption occurs either on the cell wall or the membrane. Isolated wall material (p. 112) of polymyxin-sensitive species adsorbs five times as much polymyxin as walls of resistant species (Few and Schulman, 1953), but when a fluorescent derivative of polymyxin was used so that its localization could be seen, it was found to be mainly associated with the membrane (Newton, 1955, 1958). With CTAB, adsorption on isolated walls does not vary with sensitivity, and here too it is the membrane that is mainly affected. For if isolated (wall-less) protoplasts are treated with CTAB, or indeed other detergents, they are quickly lysed (Gilby and Few, 1960). Cations, especially uranyl, protect against the lysis.

In the second place, detergents cause the cells to "leak" solutes into the medium. With CPC and CTAB, purines and pyrimidines could be identified in solution (Salton, 1951). Desulfovibrio (see p. 611) even released some of its cytochrome (Postgate, 1956). This shows that the basic detergents open up pores in the membrane. Probably the lipids, which make up 28 per cent of the membrane of *M. lysodeikticus*, provide the point of attack. Isolated membranes are not dissolved, so that it is only specific areas that are opened up.

Anionic detergents, on the other hand, actually dissolve the isolated membranes of *M. lysodeikticus*, and they also dissolve cell walls isolated from several gram-negative species (Shafa and Salton, 1960). This reaction seems to have no simple relationship to charge, since it proceeds best at $_\rho$H 3 and 8. Pseudomonads are particularly sensitive to the anionic compounds. Evidently the mode of action differs from that of the cationics.

The effectiveness of surface-active materials brings up some curious secondary points. Many bacteria and fungi produce surface-tension-lowering substances; *Bac. subtilis* is very active, reducing the surface tension of a glycerol medium by half in five days (La Riviere, 1955). These substances may help to account for the autolysis and death of old cultures (pp. 299, 624), and they probably act to modify the form of colonies as do traces of "Tweens," etc. (Rook and Bruckman, 1953). These natural products are no doubt decomposed by other bacteria, leading to complex interactions in natural cultures.

The synthetic surface-active materials, however, are not readily decomposed, probably because they are so universally bactericidal. Their extensive introduction for laundering, especially in America and England, poses a serious problem in sewage disposal, and many sewage plants are plagued with mountains of white foam which cannot be disposed of. Fortunately, most commercial compounds of this type are anionic and hence not the most bactericidal; they are slowly attacked in enrichment cultures (McKinney and Symons, 1959), but the problem is a difficult one and likely to become more so.

3. DYES

A number of dyes inhibit growth of bacteria. The majority of gram-positive bacteria, with the exception of Mycobacteria, are strongly inhibited by gentian violet (= crystal violet) (Churchman, 1912, 1923). Gram-negative bacteria are much less affected. This principle is used for enrichment of gram-negative forms in public health bacteriology; gentian violet added to an agar medium inhibits sporeformers and most fungi, but allows the unhindered growth of *E. coli* and hence the detection of contamination of water by feces. Related dyes have similar action; brilliant green inhibits *M. aureus* at $\frac{1}{10}$ part per million, while concentrations 50 times as high are needed to affect *E. coli* (Browning, 1930). The corresponding ratio with malachite green and crystal violet is 500. These and other dyes, especially derivatives of acridine, have had some application in medicine. For example, crystal violet is mildly active against the skin fungi, especially athlete's foot, and against the asporogenous yeast *Candida albicans*, which grows in the throats of infants to produce thrush. Acriflavine is used in dentistry against fusiform bacteria associated with Vincent's angina of the gums. Most im-

portant is quinacrine (Atabrine), used internally against the protozoa
(*Plasmodium vivax*) causing malaria.

Gentian violet = crystal violet

Acriflavine
(methochloride of 2:8-diaminoacridine)

Quinacrine
(Atabrine)

The acridine dyes are strongly bactericidal as well as bacteriostatic;
a small sample of the extensive data of Browning and co-workers

**TABLE XXIV–2. Bacteriostatic and Bactericidal Effect of Acridines (Dissolved
in 0.7% Peptone Water at *p*H 7.2 to 7.8)**

(From Browning *et al.*, 1922)

	M. aureus (Gram +)		*E. coli* (Gram −)	
	CONCENTRATIONS IN PARTS PER MILLION:			
	To Inhibit	To Sterilize	To Inhibit	To Sterilize
(1) Acridine-HCl	50	500	500	1,000
Substituted acridines (hydro-chlorides):				
(2) 2,8-Diamino (proflavine)	2.5	5	25	50
(3) 3,7-Dimethyl	1,000	?	1,000	?
(4) 2,8-Diamino-3,7-dimethyl (acridine yellow)	2.5	50	1,000	?
(5) 2,8-Diamino-3,7-dimethyl 5-phenyl (benzoflavine)	2.5	5	1,000	?
(6) 2,8-Di-dimethylamino (acridine orange)	5	10	100	250

(1922; recalculated) is given in Table XXIV–2. They show that (a) the sensitivity of *M. aureus* is far greater than that of *E. coli;* (b) a concentration 2 to 20 times higher than that necessary to inhibit growth will sterilize the culture; (c) the introduction of amino groups greatly increases the potency, as shown by comparing (1) with (2), or (3) with (4). Other data show that replacement of the amino groups by hydroxyls practically abolishes the potency, and that higher concentrations are needed for a given effect when in serum than in peptone water, due to the adsorption of part of the dye on the serum proteins; the same effect of serum is shown on $HgCl_2$ and on some detergents. All the effective dyes stain bacteria strongly, especially the

TABLE XXIV–3. Parallelism between the Bacteriostatic Power of the Acridines and Their Basic Dissociation Constants

(Data of Albert, Rubbo, and Goldacre, 1941)

Compound	Bacteriostatic Index	Dissociation Constant (at 25° C) $\times 10^{-7} = D$	$4 \times \log$ (10^{11} D)
1-Aminoacridine	4	0.001	4
Acridine	6	0.002	5.2
3-Aminoacridine	8	0.01	8
4-Aminoacridine	9	0.03	10
2-Aminoacridine	21	12	20.4
2,8-Diaminoacridine (proflavine)	21	120	24.4
5-Aminoacridine	23	300	26

gram-positive forms, and they are all strong bases, i.e., in neutral *p*H the dye molecule would be a cation:

$$RNH_2 \cdot HCl \rightleftharpoons R \cdot NH_3^+ + Cl^-$$

The effect of amino groups, which would increase the basic strength, was noted above. Thus, the dyes are exactly like the cationic detergents, and it was therefore a natural suggestion—made very early—that they combine with the proteins of the bacterial cell (Stearn and Stearn, 1924[3]; Albert, 1942). Albert and co-workers have shown (1941) that

[3] It is interesting to note how long such an idea can be "in the air" without its being definitely established. Stearn and Stearn themselves ascribe the original idea of "acid groups in the structure of the organism, with which basic groups would tend to unite" to Simon and Wood in 1914. Actually the ideas of Stearn and Stearn also lay fallow until the work of Albert, though the activities of the dyes were published in detail by Browning *et al.* in 1922 and earlier.

the bacteriostatic potency of a series of acridine derivatives is in the same order as their basic dissociation constants (Table XXIV–3). In this table the "bacteriostatic index" is a measure of the dilution at which growth is stopped (a larger number means higher dilution and therefore higher potency) and is determined on *Cl. welchii, Strep. hemolyticus* A, *M. aureus, E. coli,* and *Proteus vulgaris;* the last two are, of course, much less susceptible than the three gram-positive forms. The much stronger basicity of the 2- and 5- substituted amines is ascribed to the possibility of resonance in them, to give a highly charged ion:

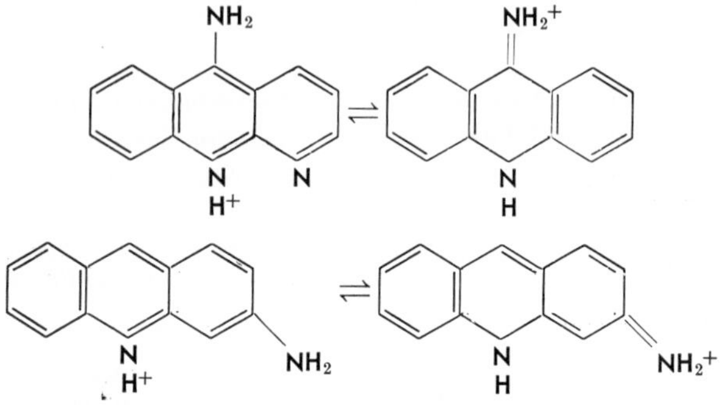

The comparison is simplified here by multiplying the dissociation constants by 10^{11} and listing four times their logarithms. The correlation between growth-inhibiting power and basic strength is then very striking. Evidently the dyes combine with something in the cell that is strongly acidic.

This conclusion makes the much greater effectiveness of basic dyes against gram-positive than gram-negative organisms fall into line at once. Gram-positive bacteria owe their staining to their possession of a layer of magnesium ribonucleate and protein around the periphery of the cell (see p. 127). This contains many phosphoric acid radicals, which are strong acids, and would therefore have more affinity for bases than the ordinary cytoplasm. The teichoic acids (ribitol phosphates) contain additional acid groups. Gram-positive cells would therefore take up more basic dye than gram-negative cells and hence be affected more strongly.

There are parallel phenomena with other organisms. Among the Trypanosomes, dye-sensitive strains accumulate acriflavine up to 8000 times the external concentration, while in resistant strains the concentration reaches only 60 times the external (Hawking, 1942). The ascospores of Neurospora rapidly take up the basic dye methylene blue, but scarcely adsorb acid dyes at all; both polymyxin (a basic antibiotic) and metallic cations prevent the uptake, or cause the elution of dye already adsorbed (Sussman and Lowry, 1955–1956). Cell fragments also take up the dye, and again polymyxin prevents it.

The view that nucleic acids, rather than proteins, are the main site for combination with basic dyes is supported by the fact that bacterial growth, when inhibited by acriflavine, is reinstated by adding nucleic acid or nucleotides (McIlwain, 1941). These compounds combine with the dye, extinguishing its fluorescence and forming brown crystals. More important is the fact that several dyes, the acridines especially, not only inhibit but also *cause mutations*. This was first observed by Ephrussi (1949–1950) when yeast after treatment with proflavine gave rise to a slow-growing "petite" form with modified cytochromes. More recently proflavine and other acridines have been found to cause many mutations in bacteriophage T_4. When the DNA was prepared from this treated phage, it was found to have greatly increased viscosity, but decreased sedimentation rate (Lerman, 1961). It had, therefore, not been aggregated by the dye, but the particles had been made lighter. It was deduced that the acridine molecule had been *intercalated* into the DNA spiral, by partly unwinding the (positively charged) ribose-phosphate backbone, and forcing the base-pairs 6.8 AU apart (instead of 3.4 AU). This makes the DNA helix longer and lighter. Now when the helix reduplicates, the space filled with proflavine will cause a gap in the new helix, which may be filled by insertion of a new base-pair and thus give rise to a mutation. Evidently the ability of a dye to act in this way depends not only on its negative charge but also critically on molecular size and shape; the acridine molecule owes its particular effectiveness to its occupying a space very similar to that of a base-pair:

Adenine . . . . Thymine   Proflavine

4. SULFONAMIDES

The work described in the preceding section led, especially in industrial laboratories, to a study of many dyes as possible antibacterials for clinical use. From this work there emerged a red dye named prontosil, patented in 1932, which Domagk[4] found an extremely effective growth

Domagk received the Nobel prize in medicine for this work.

inhibitor in vivo for gram-positive bacteria. Its structure is:

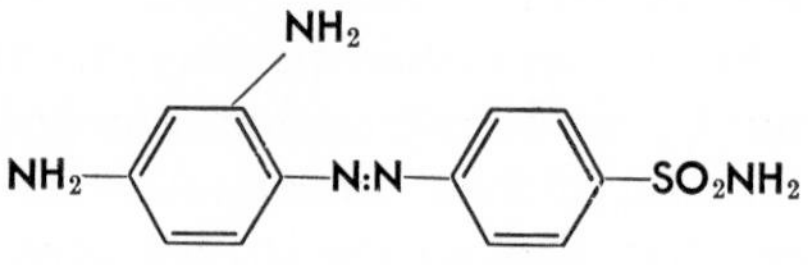

Further study of this dye revealed, however, that it was converted in animal bodies into *p*-aminobenzenesulfonamide or "sulfanilamide":

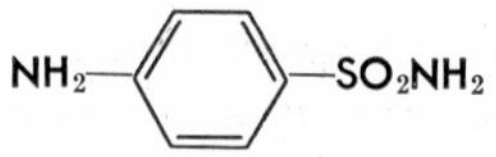

It is in this part of the molecule that the activity resides. Sulfanilamide inhibits the growth of many bacteria, both gram-positive and gram-negative. What is more important, it can protect animals against experimental infection with streptococci (Tréfouél *et al.*, 1935). Since 1935 several derivatives of sulfanilamide have been widely used in medicine, especially against streptococci and pneumococci, which are gram-positive, and gonococci and *B. dysenteriae* (Shigella) which are gram-negative. The most useful of the sulfonamides are:

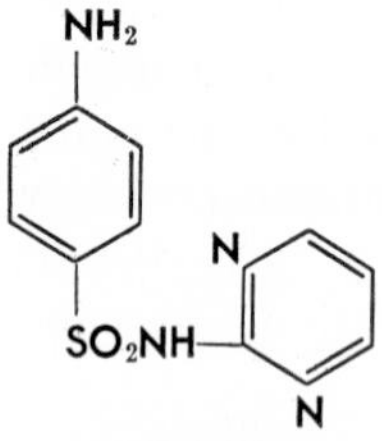

Sulfadiazine 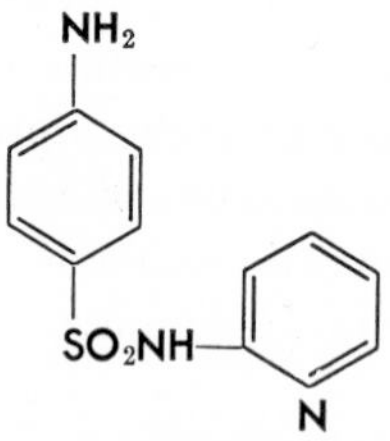   Sulfapyridine 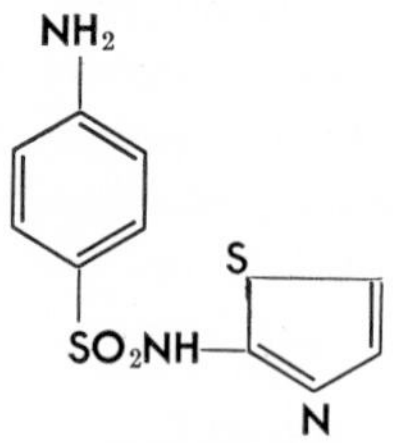   Sulfathiazole 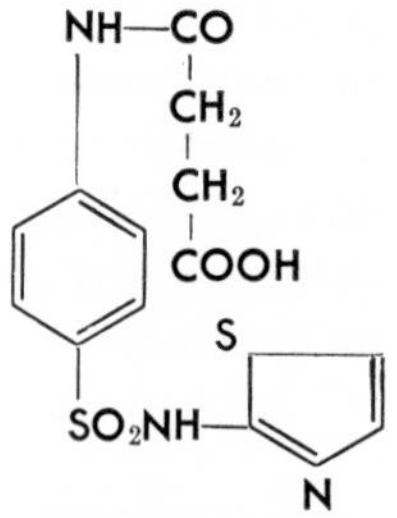   Sulfasuxidine, or succinylsulfathiazole

Evidently we are concerned here with a different mechanism from that of the nucleic acid-combining dyes. The way to understanding this was opened by Woods (1940), who found that yeast contains a substance that can protect streptococci against the growth inhibition caused by sulfanilamide; it was shown that the active factor is *p*-aminobenzoic acid (PAB):

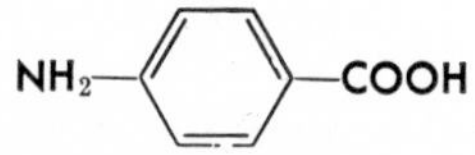

Woods thereupon proposed that PAB is an essential metabolite for the growth of all the susceptible organisms, being "normally associated in some way with an enzyme," and that the sulfonamides inhibit growth by inhibiting the metabolism of PAB. Proof that PAB is indeed essential for the growth of bacteria followed first for *Cl. acetobutyli-*

cum, for which the incredibly low concentration of 2×10^{-5} mg per liter (1 part in 500 billion) sufficed to allow growth (Rubbo and Gillespie, 1940). PAB is also either essential for growth, or growth-promoting, for several Lactobacilli and a Neurospora mutant. Many other bacteria synthesize PAB in considerable amounts. In all of 30 cultures which would grow in a medium not containing it, PAB was found to be formed and excreted into the medium (Landy *et al.,* 1943). Yeasts do the same (Lampen *et al.,* 1945).

The antagonism between sulfonamides and PAB presents some curious features. For example, the Neurospora mutant mentioned above requires 15,000 mg of sulfanilamide to prevent growth in presence of only 1 mg of PAB in the medium. On the other hand, *Lactob. arabinosus* is inhibited by only 6 mg of sulfanilamide per milligram of PAB. Still more remarkable, the "sfo" mutant of Neurospora cannot grow (under ordinary conditions) unless sulfanilamide is added, and PAB actually inhibits its growth (Emerson, 1947). The explanation is that it normally produces too much PAB and is inhibited by the excess. If it is prevented from producing PAB by introducing another mutation ("pag"), which blocks PAB synthesis, then it requires PAB to be added to the medium (Zalokar, 1948). The PAB is, therefore, in spite of appearances, an essential metabolite. Too much of it, however, as with many metabolites, is inhibitory.

The above two ideas, namely, that PAB acts as an essential metabolite, and that it may be present in bound form, were brilliantly vindicated by the discovery of folic acid in 1945. This substance, whose structure is:

contains three parts: glutamic acid (1), *p*-aminobenzoic acid (2), and a purine-like nucleus called pteridine (3).

Obviously PAB is needed for the synthesis of folic acid. Now folic acid is a vitamin for animals and a growth factor for some microorganisms, especially lactobacilli and streptococci.

The vitamin occurs in several forms: (1) as shown above, i.e., N-6-pteridylmethyl-p-aminobenzoyl-glutamic acid; (2) as the tetrahydro or N^{10}-formyl tetrahydro-derivatives; (3) as pteroic acid or pteridyl-p-aminobenzoic acid, i.e., without the glutamic acid residue; (4) as pteroyl-tri-glutamic acid, i.e., the peptide of folic acid with two additional glutamic residues; and (5) as pteroyl-heptaglutamic acid, a similar peptide with six additional glutamic residues. The peptides (4) and (5) are hydrolyzed by a carboxy-peptidase present in many bacteria, especially *Bac. subtilis*, *Bac. vulgatus*, and *Serratia marcescens*. The tetrahydro derivative of (4) is probably the major natural form.

The majority of bacteria and fungi can synthesize folic acid in one or another form (Burkholder *et al.*, 1945; van Lanen and Tanner, 1948). The cells of various bacteria, especially the bacilli, contain up to 4 mg folic acid per gram dry weight, and yeasts may contain up to 20 times as much. Addition of PAB to the medium generally increases the yield of folic acid, and *Lactob. arabinosus*, for the growth of which PAB is essential, clearly converts PAB to folic acid. *Lactob. casei*, which needs preformed folic acid, cannot make it from PAB.

The above considerations lead to the conclusion that the mode of action of sulfonamides is essentially to substitute for PAB at the surface of the enzyme that combines PAB with pteridine and glutamic acid. This conclusion has recently received full confirmation by isolation from *E. coli* of an enzyme that condenses PAB with 2-amino-4-hydroxy-6-hydroxymethyl-dihydro-pteridine, in presence of ATP and Mg ions (Brown, 1962). The product is dihydrofolic acid. This enzyme is inhibited by all sulfonamides, even more strongly than they inhibit growth, and the inhibition is relieved by PAB. *Sc. fecalis* has a similar system, using PAB and strongly inhibited by sulfonamides (Wolf and Hotchkiss, 1963). Evidently this process is the site of sulfonamide action.

The function of folic acid is to transfer formyl, formimino, and hydroxymethyl groups, the so-called "C_1-transfers" (see Hutner *et al.*, 1959; Rabinowitz, 1960). Formyl is transferred in purine synthesis, formimino in the breakdown of purines and histidine, and hydroxymethyl in the reversible conversion of glycine to serine, of homocysteine to methionine, of uridylic to thymidylic acid, and of cytidylic to hydroxymethylcytidylic acid. Tetrahydrofolic acid, FH_4, is the active form; this readily adds a formyl group either to the NH of the reduced ring (N_5) or to the NH of the p-aminobenzoic acid (N_{10}). The reaction requires ATP and Mg^{++} and is reversible, yielding ATP and formic acid. The bacterial breakdown of xanthine via formimino-glycine by extracts from *Cl. cylindrosporum* and *Cl. acidi-urici* (see p. 357) is an example of formimino transfer (Rabinowitz and Price, 1956–1958; tetrahydrofolic acid = FH_4):

$$Xanthine \rightarrow NH:CH \cdot NHCH_2COOH \xrightarrow{FH_4} (N_5)NH:CH \cdot FH_3 + Glycine$$
$$(N_5)NH:CH \cdot FH_3 \rightarrow (N_{10})CHO \cdot FH_3 + NH_3$$
$$(N_{10})CHO \cdot FH_3 + ADP + P_i \rightarrow HCOOH + FH_4 + ATP$$

The enzymes for each step were purified from the Clostridia. Histidine yields parallel reactions in which the ring is opened by Pseudomonads to yield formimino-glutamic or formimino-aspartic acids (Magasanik and Bowser, 1955; Hayaishi *et al.*, 1957). These correspond to the formimino-glycine produced from xanthine (above). The formimino or formyl groups are then converted to NH_3 and CO_2 via combination with folic acid.

Two formyl groups are transferred in the synthesis of purines (Warren *et al.*, 1957):

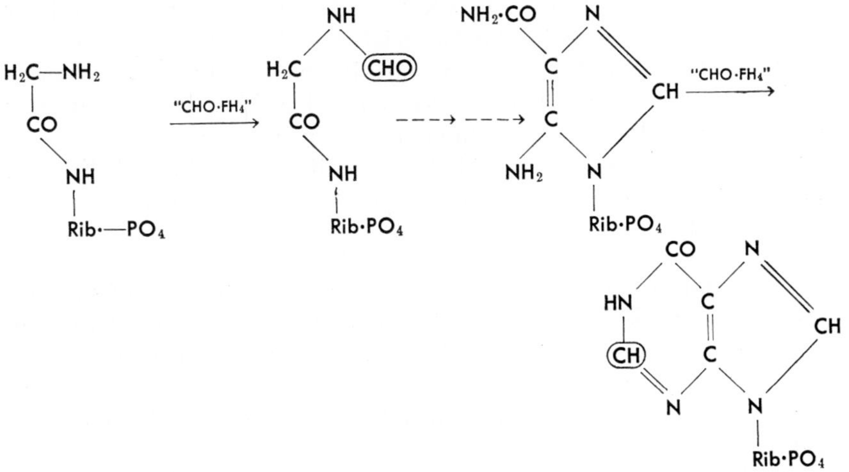

Thus, antagonists not only of PAB but also of folic acid inhibit growth through a variety of one-carbon transfers. Some of the inhibitions are reversed by adding purines (*Bac. subtilis*), or adenine and thymine (*Sc. fecalis*), or xanthine, thymine, methionine, and valine (*E. coli*). Often, however, complete reversal is not possible, probably because sulfanilamide is slowly converted to another, more toxic, compound (Melchior and Teune, 1962). Lack of PAB or of folic acid can sometimes be made up for by similar mixtures (cf. Chap. XI, sec. 3); thymine or thymidine allows growth of *Sc. fecalis* without PAB;

adenine + methionine + histidine + pantothenate act in the same way for some yeasts, and methionine *or* valine *or* B_{12} for *E. coli* mutants (see Hutner *et al.*, 1959). The interactions are almost endless, and we have indeed come a long way from prontosil.

It must be noted that the antagonists of PAB owe their great effectiveness to the fact that it has to be *converted* to folic acid. It is this that gives the sulfonamides their clinical value, since the mammalian host takes in preformed folic acid and hence is less susceptible to the sulfonamides than the bacterial parasite which has to synthesize it.

5. OTHER ANTAGONISTS OF ESSENTIAL METABOLITES

The case of the sulfonamides has been described in such detail not only because it is most important in itself, but also because it has led to a series of other growth inhibitors based on the same principle. These other inhibitors are derivatives, or structural analogues, of other essential metabolites, mostly in the vitamin B group. Major examples of these are summarized in Table XXIV–4. All the substances listed have actually been shown to inhibit bacterial growth, although the reversal of this inhibition by the specific metabolite may not have been demonstrated in all cases. Most of the references for this table are given in Woolley (1946, 1952), and Richmond (1962).

It will be seen that many kinds of modifications of metabolites are effective. Insofar as they can be grouped by types, seven types can be distinguished:

(1) Substitution of sulfonic for carboxyl (as in the case of sulfanilamide and PAB): the corresponding pantothenic acid derivative, pantoyl taurine, is a very effective inhibitor. Similar derivatives of nicotinic acid and of some amino acids have inhibiting properties. In this class also is the substitution of benzoyl for the carboxyl of pantothenic acid.

(2) Simple formation of homologues, as with β-alanine: this is not highly effective, and the homologues of pantothenic acid are quite weak inhibitors. However, in the case of tryptophan, mere esterification of the carboxyl suffices to make it an inhibitor; the C_8-alkyl esters are the most effective (Perri *et al.*, 1959). Methylation of histidine also makes it an inhibitor.

(3) Substitution of side-chains or radicals: this class includes the substitution of chlorine for the methyl groups of riboflavin, or for the methyl and phytyl groups of vitamin K; hydroxyl instead of the NH_2 of thiamine; oxygen instead of sulfur in methionine, and the nitro

Metabolite	Analogue	Notes
Nicotinic acid (pyridine ring)—COOH	Pyridine-3-sulfonic acid (pyridine ring)—SO₃H	The corresponding 3-acetyl-pyridine is an antivitamin in animals, but has no effect on bacteria
	Pyrazinoic acid amide N (pyrazine ring)—CONH₂	Powerfully inhibitory on *Mycob. tuberculosis* (Rogers *et al.*, 1952)
Thiamine CH—S [Pyr]—N⁺ | C==C·CH₂CH₂OH | CH₃ or N==C—NH₂ | | CH₃—C C—CH₂—[Thi] ‖ ‖ N—CH	Pyrithiamine CH—CH [Pyr]—N⁺ CH C==C—CH₂CH₂OH | CH₃ Oxithiamine N==C—OH | | CH₃—C C—CH₂—[Thi] ‖ ‖ N—CH	Only inhibits those species that require thiamine (or its component parts) for growth [Pyr] = 2-Me, 4-NH₂-pyrimidyl-methyl [Thi] = 4-Me, 5-hydroxyethyl-thiazole
Riboflavin CH₃ CH₃ (flavin ring system with [Rib], CO, NH, CO)	Dichloroflavin Cl Cl (flavin ring system with [Rib], CO, NH, CO) Isoriboflavin CH₃ CH₃ (flavin ring system with [Rib], CO, NH, CO)	[Rib] = D-ribityl

Metabolite	Analogue	Notes
Folic acid	Aminopterin (4 aminofolic acid)	[PAB-G] = N-p-amino-benzoyl-glutamic acid
(structure)	(structure)	Reversed also by thymidine and vitamin B_{12} (cf. Chap. XII), but high concentrations not reversible
	Also: Methopterin (N^{10} methyl folic acid)	
	Amethopterin (4-amino-N^{10}-methyl folic acid) etc.	
PAB (structure, COOH, NH₂) POB (structure, COOH, OH)	PNB (structure, COOH, NO₂) PAS (structure, COOH, OH, NH₂)	Both PAB and POB are essential metabolites for certain *E. coli* strains, and PNB competitively interferes with both. Mutant strains resistant to one of the inhibitors remain sensitive to the other (Davis and Maas, 1952)
Pantothenic acid (structure: $HOCH_2$—C(CH₃)₂—CHOHCO— ... —NHCH₂CH₂COOH)	Pantoyl taurine [Poy]—NH·CH₂CH₂SO₃H	[Poy] = 1,3-dihydroxy, 2,2-dimethyl-butyryl-group in brackets
		Also reversed by β-alanine
	[Poy]-NH-alkyl or [Poy]-NH-hydroxy-alkyl [Poy]-NH·CH₂CH₂COC₆H₅	Group of compounds inhibited *all* bacteria tested

Metabolite	Analogue	Notes
Biotin $$\begin{array}{c} O \\ \parallel \\ C \\ \diagup \quad \diagdown \\ NH \qquad NH \\ \mid \qquad \mid \\ CH\text{---}CH \\ \mid \qquad \mid \\ CH_2 \quad CH\cdot(CH_2)_4COOH \\ \diagdown \quad \diagup \\ S \end{array}$$	Desthiobiotin $$\begin{array}{c} CO \\ \diagup \quad \diagdown \\ NH \qquad NH \\ \mid \qquad \mid \\ CH\text{------}CH \\ \mid \qquad \mid \\ CH_3 \quad CH_2\cdot(CH_2)_4COOH \end{array}$$	Promotes growth of yeast, which converts it into biotin by adding sulfur; inhibits *L. casei*, however
	Biotin sulfone $$\begin{array}{c} CO \\ \diagup \quad \diagdown \\ NH \qquad NH \\ \mid \qquad \mid \\ CH\text{------}CH \\ \mid \qquad \mid \\ CH_2 \quad CH\cdot(CH_2)_4COOH \\ \diagdown \quad \diagup \\ SO_2 \end{array}$$	Inhibits Lactobacilli and *M. aureus* but somewhat promotes growth of yeast. Competitively inhibits *L. arabinosus* from forming aspartic and oleic acids (Ravel and Shive, 1955)
	Ureylene derivatives $$\begin{array}{c} CO \\ \diagup \quad \diagdown \\ NH \qquad NH \end{array}$$ (benzene ring)—$(CH_2)_nCOOH$ $$\begin{array}{c} CO \\ \diagup \quad \diagdown \\ NH \qquad NH \end{array}$$ (cyclohexane ring) $(CH_2)_nCOOH$	The ring may be benzene or cyclohexane. n = 3 or 4; no inhibition occurs if n = 0 (English *et al.*, 1945)

Metabolite	Analogue	Notes
Vitamin K or coenzyme Q (Chap. V, sec. 4c)	2,3-Dichloronaphthoquinone	[Phy] = Phytyl. Powerfully fungistatic
	Iodinin	Reversed by vitamin K, also by 2-methyl,1,4-naphthoquinone, and various anthraquinones (McIlwain, 1943)
	Bishydroxy coumarin	(An antivitamin in animals)
Adenine	Benzimidazole	Reversed by yeast nucleic acid (Klotz and Mellody, 1948)
	7-Amino-1-v-triazolopyrimidine = 8-aza-adenine	Reversible by adenine or hypoxanthine, not by any other purine or pyrimidine; inhibition ratio (to adenine) = 640

TABLE XXIV-4. Some Growth-Inhibiting Antagonists of Normal Metabolites of Bacteria (*Continued*)

Metabolite	Analogue	Notes
Guanine	5-Amino,7-hydroxy-1-v-triazolopyrimidine	Reversible by guanine or, less actively, by xanthine. Becomes incorporated into nucleic acids (Smith and Matthews, 1957)
Adenine and Guanine	6-mercapto and 6-chloropurine and 6-mercapto, 2-amino-purine (thioguanine)	Mainly used in leukemia and sarcoma Clarke *et al.*, (1953; Burchenal *et al.*, 1956)
Tryptophan [Ind]—CH$_2$—CHNH$_2$COOH	Indole-acrylic acid [Ind]—CH$\doteq$CH·COOH	[Ind] = Indolyl-3-; reversed also by nicotinic acid (Raoul and Marnay, 1948)
	4-Methyl-tryptophan	Inhibition ratio, 1000 (Roblin *et al.*, 1945); reversed also by certain dipeptides of tryptophan (Marshall and Woods, 1952)
Methionine CH$_3$—S—CH$_2$CH$_2$CHNH$_2$COOH	Methoxinine CH$_3$—O—CH$_2$CH$_2$CHNH$_2$COOH Ethionine C$_2$H$_5$—S—CH$_2$CH$_2$CHNH$_2$COOH	
Amino acids R—CH·COOH ⋮ NH$_2$	Amino-sulfonic acids R—CH·SO$_3$H ⋮ NH$_2$	Generally weak inhibitors
Glutamine	O-diazoacetyl-L-serine ("aza-serine")	Inhibits some tumors
Phenylalanine	Cyclohexyl-alanine Parafluorophenylalanine	Effective on many bacteria (See Richmond, 1962)

For the Guanine structure:

OH
|
C
/ \
N   C—NH
| \
NH$_2$—C   C—N   CH
\\   //
C   N
|
N

For the analogue (5-Amino,7-hydroxy-1-v-triazolopyrimidine) structure:

OH
|
C
/ \
N   C—NH
| \
NH$_2$—C   C—N   N
\\   //
C
|
N

781

group instead of *both* the NH_2 of PAB and the hydroxyl of p-hydroxy-benzoic acid; e.g., in p-nitroaniline (Wolf and Hotchkiss, 1963).

(4) Simple loss or removal of a group, as the removal of NH_3 from tryptophan, or of CO_2 from pantothenic acid: this can be accompanied by the formation of a homologue as well.

(5) Substitution of fluorine for hydrogen, especially in rings. Fluoro-derivatives both of amino acids (especially of phenylalanine and tryptophan) and of the nucleic bases, notably 5-fluoro-uracil, are strong inhibitors.

(6) Change of the constituents of a ring, as with adenine or guanine antagonized by benzimidazole or the triazolo-pyrimidines, with pyrazine antagonizing pyridine in the antitubercular substances, and with biotin.

(7) Changes in the shape and structure of rings: some of the best inhibitors belong to this type. It includes conversion of a 5-membered ring to a 6-membered ring, in the cases of thiamine (to pyrithiamin) and biotin (to the ureylene derivatives). In pyrithiamin and iodinin the ring constituents are changed at the same time as the ring structure is changed. In biotin the ring has been opened to form desthio-biotin, but some organisms apparently can reverse this process. In histidine, change of the imidazole ring to thiazole gives an antagonist which is still able to prevent biosynthesis of histidine by feedback inhibition (Moyed, 1961).

Many antimetabolites have found uses in medicine. Folic acid antagonists are effective in inhibiting the growth of white corpuscles in leukemia, although many of them are highly toxic. The nicotinic acid group, especially nicotinic acid hydrazide and pyrazinoic acid amide, are highly effective against clinical tuberculosis (Rogers *et al.*, 1952). In this case the antagonism is less obvious because nicotinic acid amide itself has some antitubercular effect; hence, the antagonism must be directed, not against nicotinic acid, but against something that is a derivative of it (cf. the action of excess PAB discussed in sec. 4). This could, of course, be a coenzyme.

In the case of the adenine and guanine antagonists (and also the comparable 6-aza-uracil), the antagonist is directly incorporated into the bacterial RNA (Smith and Matthews, 1957, for *E. coli*; Mandel, 1957, for *Bac. cereus*). The incorporation is prevented by the corresponding natural purine. Thus, this inhibition is not *exactly* like that due to the sulfonamides, since the synthesis (of RNA) is not prevented, but the product is modified. Similarly 5-bromo-uracil is incorporated into DNA (p. 681). There are other variations too; the amino-acid analogues act mainly by competing with the amino acid for uptake at the cell surface. In sequential syntheses where presence of the final product represses formation of one of the early-acting enzymes (p. 662), analogues can sometimes act like the normal product and repress enzyme formation.

6. RADIATION

Powerful growth-inhibiting, toxic, and other effects are exerted by irradiation with ultraviolet or x-rays. Practically all microorganisms, including bacteria, algae, many protozoa, and fungi are affected. There is reason to believe that the mechanism of the action is basically similar in many of these organisms.

A. Methods of Study

The lethal or growth-inhibiting effect is easily studied by irradiating on plates or in solution under fixed conditions and counting the survivors by plating after a measured exposure. The effect is dependent on the product of radiation intensity and time, $I \times t$. This holds over a fairly wide range of exposures, although with times longer than 10 or 20 minutes, secondary factors like multiplication and aging enter in.

For a given light quality and intensity the log of the percentage surviving decreases almost linearly with time of exposure, or

$$\log \frac{n_t}{n_o} = kt$$

where n_t is the number of survivors after a population, initially of n_o, is irradiated for a time t. The constant k includes characteristics of the organism and of the light. This straightforward relationship makes quantitative studies readily possible, and many have been made.

B. Ultraviolet Irradiation

The influence of ultraviolet irradiation is strikingly dependent on the wavelength. If the light exposures needed to produce the same effect (say 50 per cent inactivation) are compared for different wavelengths, using monochromatic or narrow-band ultraviolet, the wavelength region around 2650 AU is found to be by far the most effective. This holds for bacteria, dermatophyte fungi, and several viruses (Fig. XXIV–1). (Exceptions are tobacco mosaic and Rous sarcoma virus, which show maximal sensitivity at about 2300 AU.) It so happens that the wavelength 2537 AU, which is not far from the peak, is the

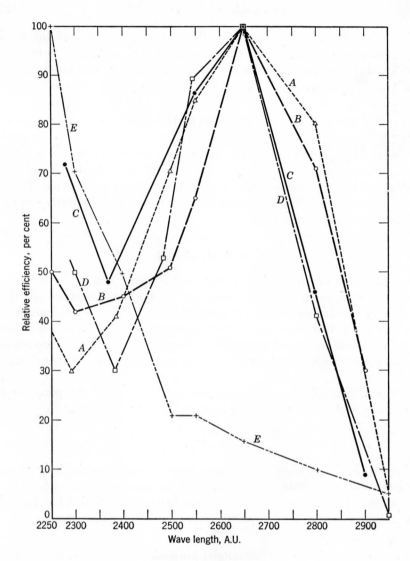

FIGURE XXIV–1

Relative sensitivity to ultraviolet wave lengths of:

A. Influenza A virus. *B. E. coli. C.* Fungus spores. *D.* Bacteriophage. *E.* Tobacco mosaic virus. (From A. Hollaender, A.A.A.S. Pub. No. 17, 156–165, 1942, and *Ann. Mo. Bot. Garden,* **32**:165–178, 1945.)

one emitted most intensely by ordinary low-pressure mercury-vapor lamps, and therefore their "germicidal" power is largely due to this wavelength. Hollaender (1942) has assembled data to show that the energy required to inactivate 90 per cent of the bacterial population with wavelength 2537 AU varies from 11,000 to 197,000 ergs per cm² for different bacteria, with most of the organisms requiring about 40,000 ergs per cm.² A 30-watt, low-pressure mercury-vapor lamp gives about 800 ergs per cm² per second, measured at a meter's distance; since most of this is at 2537 AU, an exposure of a minute or two should suffice to kill the large majority of vegetative bacterial cells. At the long wavelengths of 3500 to 4500 AU, almost a million times as much energy is needed.

The significance of the wavelength 2650 AU for the peak of sensitivity lies in its correspondence with the peak in the absorption spectra of nucleic acids; deoxyribonucleic acid has its maximum of absorption near 2600 AU, and living nuclei (hair cells of the tobacco leaf) show a sharp absorption peak at 2650 AU (Commoner, 1950). Thus, the growth-inhibiting or lethal effect of ultraviolet irradiation is due to action on the nucleus.

The sensitivity of the nucleus is also shown by the fact that survivors from irradiation show a very high rate of mutation. If conidia of dermatophyte fungi are heavily irradiated so that 90 to 99 per cent are killed, the surviving conidia give rise to as many as 40 per cent of mutant forms (Hollaender and Emmons, 1946). Similar high rates of mutation appear in bacteria and in Aspergillus and Penicillium spores, and indeed ultraviolet irradiation has long been one of the principal means of inducing mutation. The yield of penicillin from *Pen. notatum*, for instance, was enormously increased by using mutants (see p. 799). Furthermore, the greatest relative efficiency in the production of mutants (for fungi and *E. coli*) is also 2650 AU, and the shape of the wavelength curve for mutation is very similar to that for growth inhibition in Figure XXIV–1 (cf. Zelle *et al.*, 1958). If the DNA formation is carefully followed, it is found almost to stop within a few minutes after irradiation (Kelner, 1953; Kanazir and Errera, 1956). After 30 to 60 minutes it resumes in the surviving bacteria, but the DNA produced, at least in *Salmonella typhimurium*, is now slightly modified in its composition and properties (Hudnik-Plevnik and Stocken, 1961). In the nonsurvivors it never resumes; they may divide once more, and their respiration shows little change for some time. How long such cells stay alive without reproducing is not clear, since the usual criteria for "life" are growth and colony formation; however, for several hours they can still be "brought back to life" as described below.

The change caused by ultraviolet has been studied in vitro by using the "transforming activity" (Chap. XXI, sec. 6) as criterion. DNA from, for example, a streptomycin-resistant strain of *Bac. subtilis* is extracted, purified, irradiated with ultraviolet of 2537 AU wavelength; then its ability to "transform" a sensitive strain to streptomycin resistance is determined. Other transformable characters, such as ability to synthesize specific growth factors, are also used for comparison (Marmur *et al.*, 1961). The isolated DNA is not nearly as sensitive as intact cells, or even bacteriophages, but it is steadily inactivated by the ultraviolet. The rate of inactivation is not the same for different genetic characters; it increases also with the molecular weight of the DNA. Thus it is to some degree localized within the DNA molecule. Since some of the thymine of ultraviolet-treated DNA can be isolated in the form of a dimer (Wacker *et al.*, 1961), it is suggested that the ultraviolet introduces cross-linkages between the strands. The changes in properties of the "transforming factor" DNA also indicate cross-linkages (Marmur *et al.*, 1961). Such linkages would interfere with proper replication. This dimerization of DNA thymine probably explains at least half the UV effect (Setlow, 1962).

In 1949 a remarkable phenomenon was discovered. Irradiating *Streptomyces griseus* cultures in order to produce mutations, Kelner (1949) obtained on some occasions an unexpectedly high rate of survival. This apparent ineffectiveness of the ultraviolet was traced, not to any weakness of the light source, but to the fact that the irradiated cultures were being exposed to visible light. Further study showed that after irradiation with ultraviolet of wavelength 2537 AU, exposure to long wavelength ultraviolet or to visible light enables the irradiated ("killed") cells to recover. The survival rate may be increased by as much as 10,000 times. The exposure to visible light must occur fairly soon after irradiation, or else recovery does not take place. The phenomenon was called *photoreactivation*. With 2 out of 10 *E. coli* strains, reactivation also occurs on raising the temperature 10° C, in the dark (Anderson, 1951), but this "heat-reactivation" seems to be rare.

Almost all other organisms tested, including bacteria, fungi, ciliates, leaves, insects, and even the eggs and sperm of sea urchins and embryos of frogs and salamanders, show photoreactivation (see Jagger, 1958). Bacteriophage can also be photoreactivated, although this occurs only when the phage is attached to the host cells (Dulbecco, 1952). This may mean that the phage must be growing, for although its photoreactivation can occur at 6° C, and that of *E. coli* at 5° C, still, resting spores of *Bac. cereus* could not be photoreactivated until they were transferred to a nutrient medium on which they could germinate (Stuy, 1956).

The effective wavelengths are not always the same, although they nearly all lie in the violet or the near ultraviolet. *Str. griseus* spores show a sharp peak of response at 4358 AU (= 436 mμ), while *E. coli* strain B/r shows a less marked peak at 3750 AU (Fig. XXIV–2).

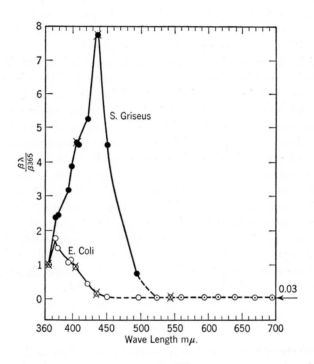

FIGURE XXIV-2
Action spectra for the photoreactivation of *Str. griseus* and *E. coli* (cf. Figs. XXIII-5 and 6, and Fig. V-1).

The ordinate is the photoactivity at each wave length relative to that at 365 mμ, which is put equal to 1. Dotted lines show the region where the maximum light intensity possible caused no photoreactivation. The crosses represent monochromatic mercury lines; the other points are narrow spectral bands. (From A. Kelner, *J. Gen. Physiol.*, **34**:835–852, 1951.)

For *Bac. subtilis* and *cereus* 4047 AU showed the highest activity (Stuy, 1955). For bacteriophage attached to *E. coli* the peak was at 3650 (Dulbecco, 1952) or 3850 (Jagger and Latarjet, 1956). Only with the ciliate Colpidium are wavelengths in the green effective (Giese et al., 1953). Mutations in *E. coli* are photoreactivated, i.e., reversed to normal, by wavelengths in the ultraviolet above 3200 AU (Zelle et al., 1958), and in the DNA of Hemophilus even by 2390 AU (Setlow, 1962).

Photoreactivation is not usually complete, and the ability of ultraviolet-treated cells to respond to the light dies out with time. In E. coli it lasts three to four hours, although longer at low temperature, and some viruses have been photoreactivated after 14 days (Bawden and Kleczkowski, 1953). Metabolism thus appears to reduce the response, and indeed photoreactivation itself must involve some metabolism, since it has a Q_{10} around 2 (see Jagger, 1958).

As with the ultraviolet effect, photoreactivation has been effectively studied in vitro by using transforming DNA. When this has been 90 per cent inactivated by ultraviolet, it can be brought back to within 10 per cent of its original activity by adding an enzyme preparation from unirradiated cells and exposing to visible light (Rupert and co-workers, 1958, 1960). The enzyme must come from cells that can show photoreactivation themselves, such as E. coli and Sacch. cereviseae, not from Hemophilus influenzae which is not subject to photoreactivation. The enzyme combines with the DNA, as shown by centrifuging down with it, adsorbing on columns with it (Porath, 1960) and being protected from heat-inactivation by it (Rupert, 1961). Such combination can be prevented by adding other, nontransforming, DNA's. No doubt all DNA's are thus photoreactivatable. It is a likely guess that the enzyme, after activation by light, breaks down the cross-linkages that ultraviolet has established in the DNA.

C. X-rays

The effects of x-rays differ in several respects from those of ultraviolet. X-irradiated cells are not subject to photoreactivation with any kind of light yet studied. They do show a slight recovery if kept at suboptimal temperatures after irradiation; E. coli, for instance, kept for 24 hours at 18° C, gave 100 times greater survival than cells kept at 37° C (Stapleton et al., 1952). As with ultraviolet, the immediate effect of x-rays on E. coli is not necessarily detectable by any change in respiration, but after a few hours the respiratory rate does fall drastically. Also, as with ultraviolet, the effects on growth are closely paralleled by effects on mutation. However, in higher organisms, ultraviolet produces mainly gene mutations, while x-rays mainly produce aberrations and breaks in the chromosomes. There is an enormous genetic literature on x-ray–induced mutations in all organisms from viruses to man (see Lea, 1947).

Comparable to a mutation is the induction of lysogeny in bacteria carrying temperate phages. This was discovered first for ultraviolet (Lwoff *et al.*, 1950), but is also caused by x-rays (Marcovich, 1956). The evidence indicates it is due to single hits on a target of 90 to 100 mμ diameter, doubtless the bacterial nucleus.

Among the specific processes inhibited by x-irradiation is the formation of inducible enzymes. In the case of the β-galactosidase of *E. coli*, synthesis of the enzyme is inhibited by an x-ray dose only $\frac{1}{100}$ of that which is needed to inactivate the preformed enzyme (Pollard *et al.*, 1959, 1961). Synthesis of diamine oxidase by Pseudomonas species is similarly x-ray–sensitive, and, like growth, the effect is largely prevented by irradiating in nitrogen or by adding glycerol (Dewey, 1962, and see below).

For a long while it has been considered that x-rays bring about their effects through the ionization they produce. These ions form, in water, free radicals which give rise to hydrogen peroxide and to organic peroxides, and it is these products that primarily cause the inhibitory, lethal, or mutagenic effects (cf. the reviews of Dale, 1956, and Weiss, 1959). Recent evidence has confirmed this view.

Most notable is the influence of oxidation and aerobic conditions on sensitivity to x-rays. It was first discovered by English workers, with bean roots, that when they were irradiated in low-oxygen tensions, their sensitivity was reduced. Extension of the experiments to bacteria showed that when cultures were irradiated in nitrogen, the exposure required to inactivate a given percentage of the population was about tripled (see Fig. XXIV–3). If the bacteria (*E. coli*) had been cultured under anaerobic conditions, then, even if they were irradiated in oxygenated buffer solution, they still showed a small but real decrease in sensitivity. Apparently, therefore, it is not the oxygen alone but the presence or absence of reducing materials in the cells that determines sensitivity. This led to treatment of bacteria with various reducing compounds, and to the finding that hydrosulfite ($Na_2S_2O_4$), cysteine, and other sulfhydryl compounds give considerable protection against x-rays (Burnett *et al.*, 1951). The effect was as great as that of irradiation in nitrogen, or even somewhat more (Fig. XXIV–3). Furthermore, a number of hydrogen donors, especially glycols and alcohols in high concentrations, as well as formate and succinate, have a similar effect. Presumably these substances, under the action of x-rays, or perhaps simply through their dehydrogenases, furnish reducing radicals that react with and destroy the oxidizing radicals responsible for the primary x-ray effect. Cyanide, which reacts with peroxy radicals, also protects (Schubert and Markley, 1963). It is of great practical interest that this phenomenon furnishes a basis for protecting

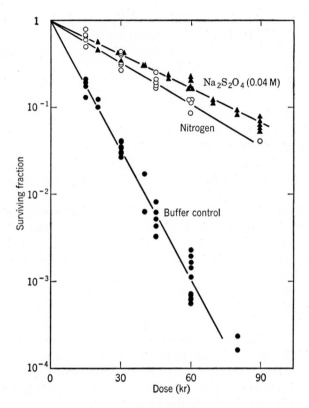

FIGURE XXIV-3
The protection against x-irradiation furnished by hydrosulfite or by nitrogen gas.
Ordinate (log scale). The fraction of bacteria (*E. coli*) that survive. *Abscissa*. Dose in
thousands of roentgens (kr). (From W. T. Burnett, G. E. Stapleton, M. L. Morse, and
A. Hollaender, *Proc. Soc. Exp. Biol. Med.*, **77**:636–638, 1951.)

man against radiation damage (see Hollaender and Stapleton, 1953).

The oxidizing radicals are usually considered to be uncharged
H and OH:

$$H_2O \rightarrow H_2O^+ + e; \quad H_2O + e \rightarrow H_2O^-$$

then:

$$H_2O^+ \rightarrow H^+ + OH; \quad H_2O^- \rightarrow OH^- + H$$

The OH radicals could combine to form H_2O_2, and the H can form
HO_2 (see Weiss, 1959; Siegel *et al.*, 1960). Indeed, with ultraviolet
there is direct evidence that H_2O_2 is formed, since if catalase is added
to broth during its irradiation, oxygen is evolved (Wyss *et al.*, 1948).
With x-rays the evidence is indirect, but there is some parallel between

the catalase content of different bacteria and their x-ray sensitivity. Table XXIV–5 shows that, with three strains of E. coli, decreasing catalase content parallels increasing sensitivity both to x-rays and to H_2O_2. (The fourth strain, H_7, is Beljanski's mutant [1955], which synthesizes no catalase or other hemin compounds and hence requires them in the medium; it apparently develops some other protective mechanism against x-rays.) Added catalase gives partial protection to cells grown aerobically. In most E. coli strains the x-ray resistance also increases parallel to the acidity produced in the medium; the per cent of cells surviving a 30-hour dose increases from 0.3 per cent at pH 8.4 to 20 per cent at pH 5 (Stapleton and Engel, 1960). Again the hemin-less mutant, although it similarly produces acid, shows no such pH-dependence, and Adler and Engel (1961) believe that bacteria produce more than one "protective system."

TABLE XXIV–5. Catalase of E. coli Strains and Resistance to X-rays and H_2O_2

(From Engel and Adler, 1961)
(cells grown in air on peptone-glucose)

E. coli Strain	Catalase Activity	PER CENT OF CELLS SURVIVING:	
		20 kr Dose X-rays	20 Min. in 6% H_2O_2
B/r	71	55	70
B	33	2.4	45
B_s	24	0.008	8
H_7	7	0.25	—

The increased sensitivity due to oxygen can be countered by adding methane, cyclopropane, nitrogen, or even argon. Such action can hardly be due to reducing power and is ascribed to the displacement of O_2 from solution in some lipids of the cell (Ebert et al., 1958; Chang et al., 1959). CO and CO_2, on the other hand, increase the sensitivity. If dry spores of Bac. megaterium are irradiated in N_2, then exposed to O_2, the sensitivity is less, showing that the radiation-induced radicals must react with O_2 at once to be effective, i.e., they are very short-lived. If before admitting O_2 the spores are heated to 80° C or exposed to NO or H_2S, the sensitivity is further lowered (Powers et al., 1960). This indicates a second type of oxidizing radicals with a longer life (Powers, 1961). Thus, there is no one type of radiation product that accounts for all the effects.

What is the sensitive site that is attacked by the peroxide radicals? This brings us back full circle to the opening of this chapter, because often the site is a sulfhydryl group. Many sulfhydryl enzymes are directly inactivated by x-rays. Three of them—phosphoglyceraldehyde dehydrogenase, ATP-ase, and succinoxidase—have been shown to be sensitive to the x-ray doses that are effective on cells, i.e., below 1 kr (Barron *et al.*, 1949). When the inactivation was not too extreme, the enzymes were reactivated by reduced glutathione, GSH. Non-sulfhydryl enzymes, like lysozyme and catalase, on the other hand, are very resistant to x-rays (Barron, 1954). The oxidizing radicals can be produced without water, since some enzymes are inactivated in the dry state, although with a sensitivity 2 to 100 times less than in water (Hutchinson, 1960). This may explain the fact that several —SH enzymes can be inactivated in nitrogen (Romani and Tappel, 1959). In the thought that the sensitivity of cells to x-rays depends on their —SH content, Alexander (1961) added iodoacetate or iodacetamide for an hour before irradiation; the sensitivity of *Ps. fluorescens* was doubled and that of a Micrococcus increased seven times.

The mutagenic action of x-rays, however, cannot be wholly explained by —SH effects, because nucleic acids contain no —SH groups. Even the transforming factor of Pneumococcus, which is solely DNA (pp. 691 ff), is rapidly inactivated by x-rays and was affected in complete dryness about 25 per cent as fast as in water (Hutchinson, 1960). A direct effect of x-rays on enzyme synthesis, via DNA, was described in Chapter XX, section 5E; when the cell-free preparation was inactivated by ultraviolet or x-rays, enzyme synthesis was wholly reinstated by adding DNA from untreated cells. DNA from uninduced cells, or from cells genetically deficient in ability to make the enzyme (Lac⁻), was inactive. Thus, the radiation must have acted on the DNA itself.

Another crucial case is that of a very small pleuropneumonia-like organism isolated from chicks, PPLO 5969. This sphere of 0.25-μ diameter contains DNA equivalent to a molecular weight of 50 million (Morowitz and Cleverdon, 1959–1960). Its sensitivity to γ-rays is like that of bacteria. From the relation:

$$\text{Mol. wt. of target} \times \text{dose for } 1/e \text{ decrease} = 72 \times 10^{10}$$

the molecular weight of the target is found to be 30 million, i.e., probably half the DNA content of the cell.

X-ray mutations are of two kinds; in one the mutation frequently varies linearly with the dose, and in the other it varies exponentially. Only the second is increased by O_2 (Anderson, 1951). Some of the effects may be chromosome breaks rather than true mutations. In *E. coli* K 12, which shows sexuality, the transfer of genes from the donor Hfr to the recipient F⁻ is inhibited by x-rays, and the further the character is from the origin, or point of entry of the chromosome, the greater the inhibition. Marcovich (1961) concludes that x-radiation causes breaks in the chromosome, but since there is no evidence of rejoining (i.e., no translocations), the x-rays must only make a "point of frailty," and the break occurs during conjugation.

The mutagenic effects of x-rays can be imitated by nitrogen mustards (see Auerbach, 1949), organic peroxides like $(CH_3)_3C \cdot OOH$ (Dickey et al., 1949), and epoxides of the form $R—CH_2—CH_2$ (Alex-

$$R—CH_2—CH_2 \overset{\diagdown \diagup}{O}$$

ander et al., 1952). All are classed as *radiomimetic*. Like radiation, they cause growth inhibition, mutations, and toxicity. *E. coli* strains selected for resistance to radiation also resist mustards and vice versa (Bryson, 1948). Most radiomimetic compounds are so reactive that they combine not only with —SH groups but also with others, attaching alkyl groups. It is possible, therefore, that they cause cross-linking in nucleic acids, as suggested above for ultraviolet. Other agents such as phenols, urethane, Fe and Mn ions (Demerec and Hanson, 1951), which have weakly mutagenic action on *E. coli*, perhaps promote the same kind of reaction indirectly.

Thus, the two actions of oxidizing radicals, inactivation of —SH groups and cross-linking in nucleic acids, will explain a divergent mass of radiation effects. Whether there are still more complexities remains to be seen.

REFERENCES

Adler, H. I., and Engel, M. S. 1961. *J. Cell Comp. Physiol.*, **58**: Suppl., pp. 95–105.

Albert, A. A. 1942. *Lancet*, Nov. 28, pp. 633–636.

*Albert, A. A. 1951. Selective Toxicity. London, Methuen; New York, Wiley and Sons, 228 pp.

Albert, A. A.; Rubbo, S. D.; and Goldacre, R. 1941. *Nature*, 147:332–333, 709.

Alexander, P.; Fox, M.; Stacey, K.; and Smith, L. F. 1952. *Biochem. J.*, **52**:177–187.

Anderson, E. H. 1951. *J. Bact.*, **61**:389–394.

*Auerbach, C. 1949. Chemical Mutagenesis. *Biol. Revs.*, **24**:335–391.

Barron, E. S. G. 1954. *Radiation Res.*, **1**:109–124.

Barron, E. S. G.; Dickman, S.; Muntz, J. A.; and Singer, T. P. 1949. *J. Gen. Physiol.*, **37**:537–552.

Barron, E. S. G., and Singer, T. P. 1945. *J. Biol. Chem.*, **157**:221–240, 241–253.

Bawden, F. C., and Kleczkowski, A. 1953. *J. Gen. Microbiol.*, **8**:145–156.

Beljanski, M. 1955. *Compt. rend. Acad. Sci.*, **240**:374–377.

Benesch, R., and Benesch, R. E. 1948. *Arch. Biochem.*, **19**:35–45.

Birkhaug, K. E. 1933. *J. Inf. Dis.*, **53**:250–261.

Brown, G. M. 1962. *J. Biol. Chem.*, **237**:536–540.

Browning, C. H. 1930. In, A System of Bacteriology in Relation to Medicine, Medical Research Council London I, pp. 202–207.

Browning, C. H.; Cohen, J. B.; Gaunt, R.; and Gulbransen, R. 1922. *Proc. Roy. Soc.*, **B93**:329–366.

Bryson, V. 1948. *Genetics*, **33**:99.

Burchenal, J. H.; Murphy, M. L.; and Tan, C. T. 1956. *Pediatrics*, **18**:643–660.

Burger, W. C., and Stahmann, M. 1952. *Arch. Biochem. Biophys.*, **39**:27–35.

Burkholder, P. R.; McVeigh, I.; and Wilson, K. 1945. *Arch. Biochem.*, **7**:287–303.

Burnett, W. T.; Stapleton, G. E.; Morse, M. L.; and Hollaender, A. 1951. *Proc. Soc. Exp. Biol. Med.*, **77**:636–638.

Chang, T. H.; Wilson, F. D.; and Stone, W. S. 1959. *Proc. Nat. Acad. Sci.*, **45**:1397–1404.

Churchman, J. W. 1912, 1923. *J. Exp. Med.*, **16**:221–247; **37**:543–551.

Clarke, D. A.; Philips, F. S.; Sternberg, S. S.; Stock, C. C.; Elion, G. B.; and Hitchings, G. H. 1953. *Cancer Res.*, **13**:593–604.

Commoner, B. 1950. *Faraday Soc. Discussion*, **9**:449–460.

Curd, F. H. S., and Rose, F. L. 1946. *J. Chem. Soc.*, pp. 729–737.

Dale, W. M. 1956. In, Ciba Foundation Symposium on Ionizing Radiations and Cell Metabolism, pp. 25–34.

Davis, B. D. and Maas, W. K. 1952. *Proc. Nat. Acad. Sci.*, **38**:775–785.

Demerec, M., and Hanson, J. 1951. *Cold Spring Harbor Symp. Quant. Biol.*, **16**: 215–228.

Dewey, D. L. 1962. *Nature*, **194**:158–160.

Dickey, F. H.; Cleland, G. H.; and Lotz, C. 1949. *Proc. Nat. Acad. Sci.*, **35**:581–586.

Dulbecco, R. 1952. *J. Cell. Comp. Physiol.*, **39** (Suppl. 1): 125–128.

Ebert, M. E.; Hornsey, S.; and Howard, A. 1958. *Radiation Res.*, **9**:109; *Nature*, **182**: 1240; *Act. chim. et biol. rad.*, **4**:113–116.

Emerson, S. H. 1947. *J. Bact.*, **54**:195–207.

Engel, M. S., and Adler, H. I. 1961. *Radiation Res.*, **15**:269–275.

English, J. P.; Clapp, R. C.; Cole, Q. P.; Halverstadt, I. F.; Lampen, J. O.; and Roblin, R. O., Jr. 1945. *J. Am. Chem. Soc.*, **67**:295–302.

*Ephrussi, B.; L'Heritier, Ph.; and Hottinguer, H. 1949. *Ann. Inst. Pasteur*, **77**:64–83; Ephrussi, B. *Pubbl. Sta. Zool. Napoli*, **22**:suppl. 1–15, and literature there cited.

Erlanger, B. F.; Sachs, H.; and Brand, E. 1954. *J. Am. Chem. Soc.*, **76**:1806–1810.

Few, A. V., and Schulman, J. H. 1953. *J. Gen. Microbiol.*, **9**:454–466.

Fildes, P. 1940. *Brit. J. Exp. Path.*, **21**:67–73; *Lancet*, **1**:955–957.

Flett, L. H.; Haring, R. C.; Guiteras, A. F.; and Shapiro, R. L. 1945. *J. Bact.*, **50**: 591–595.

Frobisher, M. 1927. *J. Bact.*, **13**:163–182.

Fuller, A. T. 1942. *Biochem. J.*, **36**:548–558.

Giese, A. C.; Iverson, R. M.; Shepard, D. C.; Jacobson, C.; and Brandt, C. L. 1953. *J. Gen. Physiol.*, **37**:249–258.

Gilby, A. R., and Few. A. V. 1960. *J. Gen. Microbiol.*, **23**:19–26, 27–33.

Hawking, F. 1942. *Biochem. J.*, **36**:2–3.

Hayaishi, O.; Tabor, H.; and Hayaishi, T. 1957. *J. Biol. Chem.*, **227**:161–180; Ohmura, E., and Hayaishi, O. *Ibid.* **227**:181–190.

Hine, G. J., and Brownell, G. L. (ed.). 1956. Radiation Dosimetry. New York, Academic Press.

Hollaender, A. 1942. A.A.A.S. Publ. No. 17, New York, 150–165.

Hollaender, A. 1945. *Ann. Missouri Bot. Gard.*, **32**:165–178.

Hollaender, A., and Emmons, C. W. 1946. Induced Mutations and Speciation in Fungi. *Cold Spring Harbor Symp. Quant. Biol.*, **11**:78–84.

Hollaender, A., and Stapleton, G. E. 1953. Fundamental Aspects of Radiation Protection from a Microbiological Point of View. *Physiol. Revs.*, **33**:77–84; *cf. Brit. J. Radiol.*, **27**:117–121 (1954).

Hudnik-Plevnik, T., and Stocken, L. A. 1961. *Nature*, **192**:5545.

Hutchinson, F. 1960. *Amer. Naturalist*, **94**:59–70.

*Hutner, S. H.; Nathan, H. A.; and Baker, H. 1959. Metabolism of Folic Acid and Other Pterin-Pteridine Vitamins. *Vitamins and Hormones*, **17**:1–52.

*Jagger, J. 1958. Photoreactivation. *Bact. Revs.*, **22**:99–142.

Jagger, J., and Latarjet, R. 1956. *Ann. Inst. Pasteur*, **91**:858–893.

Kanazir, D., and Errera, M. 1956. *Cold Spring Harbor Symp. Quant. Biol.*, **21**:19–29.

Kelner, A. B. 1949. *Proc. Nat. Acad. Sci.*, **35**:73–79; *J. Bact.*, **58**:511–522.

Kelner, A. B. 1953. *J. Bact.*, **65**:252–262.

Klotz, I. M., and Mellody, M. 1948. *J. Bact.*, **56**:253–255.

Kuhn, R., and Dann, O. 1940. *Ber. deut. chem. Ges.*, **73**:1092–1094; Kuhn, R.; Jerchel, D.; Westphal, O.; Möller, E. F.; and Czernucki, M. *Ibid.*, **73**:1095–1100.

Lampen, J. O.; Baldwin, H. L.; and Peterson, W. H. 1945. *Arch. Biochem.*, **7**:277–286.

Landy, M.; Larkum, N. W.; and Oswald, E. J. 1943. *Proc. Soc. Exp. Biol. Med.*, **52**: 338–341.

*van Lanen, J. M., and Tanner, F. W., Jr. 1948. Vitamins in Microorganisms—Distribution and Quantitative Synthesis. *Vitamins and Hormones*, **6**:164–224.

La Riviere, J. W. M. 1955. *Ant. v. Leeuwenhoek*, **21**:1–8.

*Lea, D. E. 1947. Action of Radiations on Living Cells. New York, Macmillan.

Lerman, L. S. 1961. *J. Mol. Biol.*, **3**:18–30; Luzzati, V.; Masson, F.; and Lerman, L. S. *Ibid.*, pp. 634–639.

Lwoff, A.; Siminovitch, L.; and Kjeldgaard, N. 1950. *Ann. Inst. Pasteur*, **79**:815–859.

McIlwain, H. 1941. *Biochem. J.*, **35**:1311–1319.

McIlwain, H. 1943. *Biochem. J.*, **37**:265–271.

McKinney, R. E., and Symons, J. M. 1959. *Sewage and Industrial Wastes*, **31**:549–556; McKinney, R. E., and Donovan, E. J. *Ibid.*, **31**:690–696.

Magasanik, B., and Bowser, H. R. 1955. *J. Biol. Chem.*, **213**:571–580.

Mandel, H. G. 1957. *J. Biol. Chem.*, **225**:137–150.

Marcovich, H. 1956. *Ann. Inst. Pasteur*, **90**:458–480.

Marcovich, H. 1961. *J. Cell Comp. Physiol.*, **58**: Suppl. 107–112.

Marmur, J.; Anderson, W. F.; Matthews, L.; Berns, K.; Gajewska, E.; Lane, D.; and Doty, P. 1961. *J. Cell Comp. Physiol.*, **58**:Suppl. 33–55.

Marshall, J. H., and Woods, D. D. 1952. *Biochem. J.*, **51**:(Proc.) ii.

*Martin, G. J. 1951. Biological Antagonisms. Philadelphia, Blakiston Co., 516 pp.

Melchior, J. B., and Teune, P. 1962. *Fed. Proc.*, **21**:176 (abstr.).

Morowitz, H. J., and Cleverdon, R. C. 1959–1960. *Biochim. Biophys. Acta*, **34**:578–579; *J. Bact.*, **79**:615–616; *Radiation Res.*, **13**:854–856 (1960).

Moyed, H. S. 1961. *J. Biol. Chem.*, **236**:2261–2267.

Newton, B. A. 1955. *J. Gen. Microbiol.*, **12**:226–236.

*Newton, B. A. 1958. Surface-active Bactericides. In, VIII Symp. Soc. Gen. Microbiol., Cambridge University Press, pp. 62–93.

Perri, G. C.; Kaplan, L.; and Stock, C. C. 1959. *Nature*, **183**:116–117.

Pollard, E., and Barrett, N. 1959. *Radiation Res.*, **11**:781–790; Pollard, E., and Vogler, C. *Ibid.* **15**:109–117 (1961).

Porath, J. 1960. *Biochim. Biophys. Acta* **39**:193–207.

Postgate, J. R. 1956. *J. Gen. Microbiol.*, **14**:545–572.

Powers, E. L. 1961. *J. Cell. Comp. Physiol.*, **58**:Suppl. 13–25.

Powers, E. L.; Webb, R. B.; and Kalata, B. F. 1960. *Proc. Nat. Acad. Sci.*, **46**:984–993; Webb, R. B.; Powers, E. L.; and Ehret, C. F. *Radiation Res.*, **12**:682–693.

Rabinowitz, J. C. 1960. In, The Enzymes (ed. Boyer, Lardy, and Myrback) 2nd. ed. New York, Academic Press.

Rabinowitz, J. C., and Price, W. E., Jr. 1956–1958. *J. Biol. Chem.*, **222**:537–554; *Fed. Proc.*, **17**:293 (1958).

Raoul, Y., and Marney, C. 1948. *Compt. rend. Acad. sci.*, **227**:1280–1282.

Ravel, J., and Shive, J. W. 1955. *Arch. Biochem. Biophys.*, **54**:341–348.

*Richmond, M. H. 1962. The Effect of Amino Acid Analogues on Growth and Protein Synthesis. *Bact. Revs.*, **26**:398–420.

Roblin, R. O., Jr.; Lampen, J. O.; English, J. P.; Cole, Q. P.; and Vaughan, J. R. 1945. *J. Am. Chem. Soc.*, **67**:290–294.

Rogers, E. F.; Leanza, W. J.; Becker, H. J.; Matzuk, A. R.; O'Neill, R. C.; Basso, A. J.; Stein, G. A.; Solotorovsky, M.; Gregory, F. J.; and Pfister, K., 3rd. 1952. *Science*, **116**:253–254.

Romani, R. J., and Tappel, A. L. 1959. *Arch. Biochem. Biophys.*, **79**:323–329.

Rook, J. J., and Bruckman, H. W. L. 1953. *Ant. v. Leeuwenhoek*, **19**:354–362.

Rose, F. L., and Swain, G. 1956. *J. Chem. Soc.*, pp. 4422–4425.

Rubbo, S. D., and Gillespie, J. M. 1940. *Nature*, **146**:838–839.

Rupert, C. S 1960. *J. Gen. Physiol.*, **43**:473–495.

Rupert, C. S. 1961. *J. Cell Comp. Physiol.*, **58**:Suppl. 1, 57–68.

Rupert, C. S.; Goodgal, S. H.; and Herriott, R. M. 1958. *J. Gen. Physiol.*, **41**:451–471.

Salton, M. R. J. 1951. *J. Gen. Microbiol.*, **5**:391–404.

Schubert, J., and Markley, J. F. 1963. *Nature*, **197**:399–400.

Schulman, J. H., and Armstrong, W. McD. 1949. Soc. chim. phys. and Faraday Soc., papers Bordeaux Meeting, pp. 273–279. London, Butterworths.

Setlow, R. B., and Setlow, J. K. 1962. *Proc. Nat. Acad. Sci.*, **48**:1250–1257; cf. *Nature*, **197**:560–562 (1963).

Seuderling, Y. 1933. (Acta Soc. Med. Fennicae) Duodecim **A16**:1–119; from *Chem. Abstr.*, **29**:2992 (1935).

Shafa, F., and Salton, M. R. J. 1960. *J. Gen. Microbiol.*, **23**:137–141.

Siegel, S.; Baum, L. H.; Skolnik, S.; and Flournoy, J. M. 1960. *J. Chem. Phys.*, **32**:1249–1256.

Stapleton, G. E.; Billen, D.; and Hollaender, A. 1952. *J. Bact.*, **63**:805–809.

Stapleton, G. E., and Engel, M. S. 1960. *J. Bact.*, **80**:544–551.

Stearn, A. E., and Stearn, E. W. 1924. *J. Bact.*, **9**:491–510.

Smith, J. D., and Matthews, R. E. F. 1957. *Biochem. J.*, **66**:323–333.

Stuy, J. H. 1955. *Biochim. Biophys. Acta*, **17**:206–211.

Stuy, J. H. 1956. *Ant. v. Leeuwenhoek*, **22**:337–349.

Stuy, J. H. 1959. *J. Bact.*, **78**:49–58.

Sussman, A. S., and Lowry, R. J. 1955–1956. *J. Bact.*, **70**:675–685; *Arch. Biochem. Biophys.*, **62**:113–124 (1956).

Tatum, E. L. 1946. *Cold Spring Harbor Symp. Quant. Biol.*, **11**:278–284.

Tréfouél, J.; Tréfouél, Mme. J.; Nitti, F.; and Bovet, D. 1935. *Compt. rend. Soc. biol.*, **120**:756–758.

Wacker, A.; Dellweg, H.; and Weinblum, D. 1961. *Angew. Chem.*, **73**:64–65.

Warren, L.; Flaks, J. G.; and Buchanan, J. M. 1957. *J. Biol. Chem.*, **229**:627–640.

Weiss, J. 1959. *Internat. J. Applied Rad.*, **6**:52–58.

Wolf, B., and Hotchkiss, R. D. 1963. *Biochemistry*, **2**:145–150.

Woods, D. D. 1940. *Brit. J. Exp. Path.*, **21**:74–90.

*Woolley, D. W. 1946. Biological Antagonisms between Structurally Related Compounds. *Adv. in Enzymol.*, **6**:129–146; cf. also Harvey Lectures for 1945–1946, pp. 189–215.

*Woolley, D. W. 1952. A Study of Antimetabolites. New York, Wiley and Sons. 269 pp.

Wyss, O.; Clark, J. B.; Haas, F.; and Stone, W. S. 1948. *J. Bact.*, **56**:51–57.

Yamaha, G., and Abe, S. 1934. *Sci. Reports Tokio Bunrika Daigaku*, **B1**:221–229.

Zalokar, M. 1948. *Proc. Nat. Acad. Sci.*, **34**:32–36.

Zelle, M. R.; Ogg, J. E.; and Hollaender, A. 1958. *J. Bact.*, **75**:190–198.

The Inhibition of Growth: Antibiotics

The Lord created medicines out of the earth and he that is wise shall not abhor them.

THE BOOK OF BEN SIRACH (APOCRYPHA)

Infectious disease as a practical problem is conquered, but it will remain endlessly interesting to go on searching out the how and why of that conquest.

SIR F. MACFARLANE BURNET (1961)

1. INTRODUCTION AND EARLY EXPERIMENTS

Those growth inhibitors or bactericidal agents that are formed by living organisms, as opposed to synthetic chemicals or salts, and that are active in very low concentrations, are called *antibiotics*. It is recognized that no clear line can be drawn between the synthetic and natural groups; phenol is, in the last analysis, a biological product (being obtained from coal tar), while chloramphenicol is at the moment being synthesized on a large scale. Thus the term *antibiotic* cannot be too rigidly defined.

"Antagonism" of one microorganism by another has been noticed from early times, and Bryson (1962) records that as early as 1885 Cornil and Babes wrote: "If the study of the mutual antagonism of bacteria were sufficiently far advanced a disease caused by one bacterium could probably be treated by another." E. Duchesne, in a Lyon thesis of 1897, found that a Penicillium reduced the virulence of *E. coli* and *Salmonella* when injected into an animal with them, and concluded: "In pursuing the study and facts of biological antagonism between molds and bacteria one may arrive perhaps at . . . other facts . . . applicable to prophylactic hygiene and to therapy." Several instances of microbial antagonism were studied before the recent great development of antibiotics began. One arose from the discovery that the damping-off fungus, *Rhizoctonia solani*, which kills many seedlings, is itself killed by a common soil organism, *Gliocladium fimbriatum*. This led to the isolation of Gliotoxin (Weindling and Emerson, 1936; Dutcher *et al.*, 1945), the first natural antibiotic to be prepared pure.

Some of the other cases involved deliberate efforts to develop antagonistic organisms or antibiotics, using masses of bacteria as substrate. From such cultures Dubos (1939) isolated a sporeformer, *Bac. brevis*, which inhibited the growth of pneumococci by means of a soluble excretion product. Higher concentrations of the substance actually lysed the cocci. From the culture medium two bactericidal substances, gramicidin and tyrocidin, were isolated (see sec. 7). These early experiments are well reviewed by Waksman (1943) and by Florey *et al.*, (1949).

2. PENICILLIN

The first really effective antibiotic was nearly overlooked. In 1928 Fleming, in studying variation in Staphylococcus "noticed that around a large colony of a contaminating mould the staphylococcus colonies became transparent and were obviously undergoing lysis" (Fleming, 1929). The organism was later identified as *Penicillium notatum* Westling and was found to inhibit streptococci also. Extracts were prepared, and the substance named penicillin. Yet, although Fleming called attention to its potential value "in the treatment of pyogenic infections," medical men showed no interest. It was only when Florey and co-workers at Oxford showed that infected mice could be protected from death by injections of the crude penicillin that clinical trials began to be made. Finally, the war needs stimulated an international project to isolate and purify the active material (see Raper, 1952, or Fleming, 1956, for review).

Many Penicillia other than the original organism produce penicillin. One of the early high-yielding strains belonged to another species, *Pen. chrysogenum*, and besides many other members of this variable group, 12 other species of Penicillium and seven of Aspergillus produce penicillin. Penicillin is also formed by the almost unrelated Trichophyton and by *Malbranchea pulchella*. The strains used for commercial production represent selected mutants, produced by x-ray and ultraviolet treatment from a naturally occurring, high-yielding variant. Many laboratories cooperated in irradiating the cultures and screening the mutants for high-yielding strains.

The Penicillia are grown in liquid culture in a current of sterile air in an acid glucose medium. After a few days of vigorous growth, when the glucose is exhausted, there is added another carbohydrate, such as lactose, which is less rapidly assimilated, and the medium made less acid (*ca. p*H 7). This results in very slow further growth and rapid excretion of penicillin. A complication is that some organisms produce the enzyme penicillinase, which inactivatives penicillin by partial hydrolysis to penicilloic acid (see below). This makes it necessary to harvest the cultures at an optimal time and calls for strict control of the process throughout. Alkali causes the same hydrolysis.

Chemical purification of the antibiotic (see Florey *et al.*, 1949) led, after many difficulties, to the establishment of structure I on p. 802 for penicillin, where R may represent aryl or alkyl groups. The most commonly occurring R groups are benzyl and *p*-hydroxybenzyl, pentenyl, amyl, and heptyl. The resulting different penicillins are listed in Table XXV–1. All are active, but different organisms or media produce different mixtures.

TABLE XXV–I. The Penicillins

(Modified from Lester Smith, 1948)

Nomenclature		R groups	UNITS*/MG	
			M. aureus	*Bac. subtilis*
USA	Great Britain			
X	III	$-CH_2-C_6H_4OH(p)$	900	1450
G	II	$-CH_2-C_6H_5$	1700*	1700*
F	I	$-CH_2 \cdot CH = CH \cdot CH_2CH_3$	1640	1100
Flavicidin		$-CH_2 \cdot CH_2 \cdot CH = CHCH_3$	1400	1000
Dihydro-F	IV	$-CH_2CH_2CH_2CH_2CH_3$	1610	1010
K		$-(CH_2)_6CH_3$	2400	750

* The international unit is defined as the activity of 0.6 µg of a standard penicillin G sodium salt, tested against a standard strain of *M. aureus* for 4.5 hours at 37° C. The international standard, which thus contains 1667 units per milligram, was originally thought to be pure penicillin G, but is now known to have 0.9 per cent impurity. Pure penicillin G would thus have about 1700 units per milligram.

The related *Cephalosporin C*, produced by a species of the imperfect fungus *Cephalosporium*, has a 6-membered thiolactam ring, and the R group is α-aminoadipyl (Abraham and Newton, 1956). When α-aminoadipic acid is added to the medium, it is incorporated into the R group; cystine similarly goes into the ring (Trown *et al.*, 1963).

After the structures were elucidated, and it became clear that penicillin G (R = benzyl) was of particular value as an antibiotic, Moyer suggested that an attempt be made to increase the yield of this compound by providing the fungus with phenylacetic acid. It was indeed found that the total yield of penicillin could thus be increased, and also that cultures producing a high proportion of penicillin K could be made to yield largely penicillin G instead. In current practice, phenylethylamine or phenylacetic acid esters are used (Tabenkin *et al.*, 1952). Many other "biosynthetic" penicillins have been made in the same way; e.g., adipic acid yields carboxy-*n*-butyl penicillin, which has about the same activity against gram-negative forms but much less than penicillin G against gram-positives. Other constituents of the media that favor high penicillin yields are less closely related to its structure; amino acids tend to increase the yield, but cysteine, which is clearly part of the molecule, has little effect (Cook and Brown, 1950). Plant extracts such as corn-steep liquor or pea extract are mainly used for medium, and synthetic penicillin is not economically practical.

In the last few years many new penicillins have been made by hydrolyzing off the benzoyl group from ordinary penicillin G and treating with acyl chlorides to introduce new R groups (see Batchelor *et al.*, 1959). The hydrolysis of the amide linkage uses *penicillin amidase* from several organisms, including *Str. lavendulae*, and was first found to occur spontaneously in penicillin manufacture. Some of the resulting "semi-synthetic" penicillins are fairly resistant to penicillinase (Novick, 1962), and others are absorbed more rapidly than any of the natural penicillins. Some other more complex derivatives are resistant to acid hydrolysis (Doyle *et al.*, 1961).

A development of the work on penicillin was the discovery in *Pen. notatum* of an enzyme oxidizing glucose, called *notatin* or glucose oxidase (Coulthard *et al.*, 1945). It is also formed by *Pen. resticulosum* and other species and has been crystallized from *Pen. amagasakiensis* (Kusai *et al.*, 1960). This enzyme is a flavoprotein containing FAD, which is reduced by the substrate and reoxidized by oxygen; the glucose is converted to gluconic acid:

$$
\begin{array}{c}
\underset{\displaystyle \text{C}\!-\!\!-\!\!-\!\text{O}}{\overset{\displaystyle H \diagdown \quad \diagup OH}{|}} \\
\text{HCOH} \\
\text{HOCH} \\
\text{HCOH} \\
\text{HC}\!-\!\!\!\rule{0pt}{1pt} \\
\text{CH}_2\text{OH}
\end{array}
\quad + \text{H}_2\text{O} + \text{N} \rightarrow
\begin{array}{c}
\underset{\displaystyle \text{C}\!-\!\text{OH}}{\overset{\displaystyle O}{\|}} \\
\text{HCOH} \\
\text{HOCH} \\
\text{HCOH} \\
\text{HCOH} \\
\text{CH}_2\text{OH}
\end{array}
\quad + \text{NH}_2
$$

$$
\text{NH}_2 + \tfrac{1}{2}\,\text{O}_2 \rightarrow \text{N} + \text{H}_2\text{O}_2
$$

(N = notatin)

The accumulation of H_2O_2 might inhibit the growth of the Penicillium, as it does in the case of lactic bacteria (p. 236); however, since the Penicillia contain catalase, the H_2O_2 is either decomposed or used to oxidize alcohol. Because of this enzyme, *Pen. notatum*, which produces alcohol from sugars, forms during its growth a mixture of alcohol, acetaldehyde, and gluconic acid.

Another related discovery is the enzyme penicillinase, which is formed adaptively, especially by *Bac. cereus* (Chap. XX). It occurs in three forms, one extracellular, one internal but readily washed out, and one tightly bound (Pollock, 1956; Sheinin, 1959). In many organisms this enzyme is the basis for penicillin resistance (sec. 10). Fortunately, it can be assayed with great sensitivity (Novick, 1962). Its action is to open the 4-membered ring, as shown below:

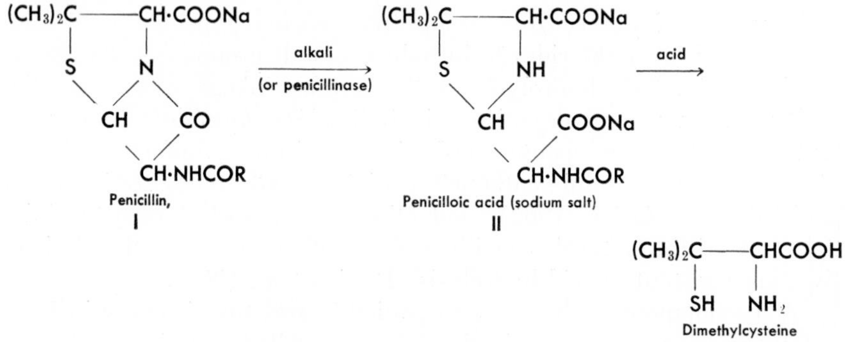

$$(CH_3)_2C\!-\!-\!-\!CH\cdot COONa$$

with S, N, CH, CO, CH·NHCOR

Penicillin, I

alkali (or penicillinase) →

$$(CH_3)_2C\!-\!-\!-\!CH\cdot COONa$$

with S, NH, CH, COONa, CH·NHCOR

Penicilloic acid (sodium salt) II

acid →

$$(CH_3)_2C\!-\!-\!-\!CHCOOH$$

with SH, NH$_2$

Dimethylcysteine III

Penicillin is remarkably nontoxic to man and other mammals, the LD_{50} (i.e., the dose killing 50 per cent of the test animals) being as high as 1 to 2 gm per kilogram body weight. As an antibiotic it is especially effective against cocci, both gram-positive and gram-negative, including pneumococci, streptococci, meningococci, and gonococci; it is also very effective against the clostridia of gas gangrene and against *Bac. anthracis*. Most important from a social viewpoint is its effectiveness against the Treponemas of syphilis and yaws. Thus, both the major venereal diseases (gonorrhea and syphilis) are brought under control for the first time. In the South Pacific penicillin has brought down the incidence of yaws from some 15 per cent of the population to under 1 per cent by 1960.

Penicillin acts mainly against organisms that are actively growing and not merely surviving. This fact has been put to use for isolating nutritional mutants (Davis, 1949), which fail to form some metabolite and therefore require it in the medium. If a culture containing a few such mutants is grown on minimal medium, all the unchanged cells will start to grow, and if penicillin is now added, the growing cells will be killed and only the mutants will survive. (The dosage of penicillin must be carefully graded.) Penicillinase can then be added to destroy the penicillin, and the residual cells will then grow. The basis for this action is discussed in section 10.

3. METHODS OF ASSAY

A. Chemical Methods

When an antibiotic is available in pure form, and its structure is at least partially known, the amount of it can be determined by chemical methods based on its reactive groups. For instance, the lactam ring of penicillin, I, can be hydrolyzed with alkali to sodium penicilloate, II, and the amount of base consumed can then be determined by backtitrating. Or the penicilloic acid formed on hydrolysis can be broken down further with acid to yield dimethylcysteine, III, which can be determined polarographically or by the ninhydrin reaction for amino acids. There are other possibilities also (Lester Smith, 1948). For streptomycin similar methods are possible, e.g., the very reactive CO group can be converted to a fluorescent hydrazone (Boxer and Jelinek, 1947). Tetracyclines can be determined by their ultraviolet absorption (Hiscox, 1951) or better by the fluorescence of their complexes with calcium and barbiturate (Kohn, 1961a).

The most specific methods, however, are those based on antibiotic power. These, of course, can be used with impure preparations at every stage from the first crude extracts onward. Three types of procedure are possible, as follows. (The first two have also been used with the synthetic substances discussed in the preceding chapter.)

B. All-or-none Growth Method

Tubes of nutrient broth are seeded with a standard small inoculum of a susceptible organism and serial dilutions of the antibiotic added. The tubes are incubated and examined. The lowest concentration necessary to inhibit growth completely is taken as end point, and the amount of antibiotic determined by comparison with similar dilutions of a known standard substance. For penicillin, *M. aureus*, incubated 16 hours at 37° C, is used. An advantage of this method is that the volumes used can be quite small.

C. Turbidimetric Method

Here again tubes of broth are seeded with a small inoculum, but the time course of growth is followed with a turbidimeter or colorimeter (Fig. XXV–1A). In this curve, using penicillin, the higher concentrations cause autolysis after four hours, as shown by decreasing density. A plot of the turbidity or optical density $\left(\log \dfrac{I_o}{I} \right)$ at a fixed time against concentration is a curve (Fig. XXV–1B); the same plotted against log

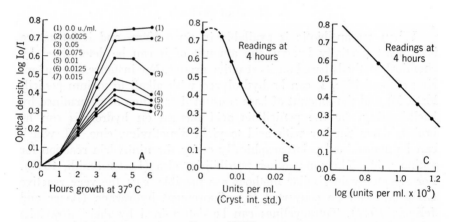

FIGURE XXV-1

A. Growth of *M. pyogenes* var. *aureus* in broth containing graded concentrations of pure penicillin.

B. Growth at four hours from A plotted directly against concentration of penicillin.

C. The same data plotted against the log of the penicillin concentration.

(From C. G. Pope, *The Analyst*, **73**:247–250, 1948. With acknowledgment to the Society of Public Analysts and Other Analytical Chemists.)

concentration usually gives a straight line (Fig. XXV–1C), from which the concentration needed for 50 per cent inhibition is easily read off.

D. Diffusion Methods

These methods are the ones most particularly associated with antibiotics. A plate of solid medium, inoculated in bulk with test organisms, is treated in spots with the solution and then incubated. As the substance diffuses out into the agar, it inhibits growth throughout a zone surrounding the place of application. The radius of the zone is a measure of the amount or concentration of the antibiotic. If the antibiotic applied is small in amount, the radius of the inhibited zone is proportional to its *amount*. This is true of a small drop of solution, and also, roughly, with small filter-paper circles, soaked in the solution. However, if a relatively large volume of solution is used, the radius of the zone is proportional to the *concentration*, or more nearly to the logarithm of the concentration, of the antibiotic in it. This is the case with the classical "Oxford cup" method, in which small glass cylinders, their ends warmed in the flame, are placed on the agar and filled with 1 to 2 ml of the test liquid (Fig. XXV–2). When this method is used

FIGURE XXV-2

The Oxford cup method. The cylinders are 8 mm in diameter. In this picture a large stainless steel plate is used instead of an ordinary Petri dish. All ten vials in one row contain the same penicillin concentration; four concentrations shown (the highest in the front row). (From G. W. Beadle, H. K. Mitchell, and D. Bonner, *J. Bact.*, **49:** 101–104, 1945.)

with penicillin, *Bac. subtilis* is used, since bulk inoculation of agar has to be done at 48° C, a temperature that may damage a coccus (Foster and Woodruff, 1944–1946).

The original Oxford unit of penicillin was established by the cup assay. It was defined as that amount of penicillin which, under the standard conditions, using "*Staph.*" *aureus*, gave an inhibition zone of diameter 24 mm. With the later antibiotics, less importance has been attached to "units" since the actual weights of purified substances have been available.

4. STREPTOMYCIN AND ITS CONGENERS

A systematic study of the antibiotics produced by the *Streptomycetaceae*, begun by Waksman[1] and co-workers at Rutgers University about the beginning of World War II, has led to the discovery of many valuable antibiotics. Over 400 of them have been isolated, and about 30 of these have found use in medicine. In addition, Bryson (1962) lists 70 more, from Aburamycin to Virocidin, all but one formed by Streptomyces species, and mostly discovered since 1957. Waksman (1952) noted that about 20 per cent of all Actinomycetes isolated from soil had *some* depressing effect on the growth of other microorganisms.

The first two compounds obtained, *actinomycin*, from *Str. antibioticus*, and *streptothricin*, from *Str. lavendulae*, were bactericidal in vitro but were too toxic to be useful in medicine; however, *actinomycin* is now being tried for inhibiting the growth of tumors (sec. 7). The third, *streptomycin*, obtained from *Str. griseus*, was extremely powerful and was relatively nontoxic (Schatz *et al.*, 1944). It is a characteristic of penicillin that it affects principally the gram-positive organisms, but streptomycin is active against both gram-negative and gram-positive bacteria, which gives it wider clinical application. In particular, it strongly inhibits *Mycob. tuberculosis*, which is unaffected by penicillin. Many tuberculosis patients have been more or less cured by streptomycin, but some forms of the disease are resistant, and tuberculosis still ranks with malaria as the world's major infectious disease.

Among other human diseases susceptible to streptomycin is tularemia, caused by an organism resembling the Pasteurella of plague. This disease is completely controlled by streptomycin if administered soon enough after infection (Chapman *et al.*, 1949). With monkeys, treatment beginning 48 hours after a heavy infection caused complete recovery, while controls all died in four to six days. Diseases caused by the coli-aerogenes bacteria, including one type of bacterial pneumonia (*"Klebsiella"*), are also susceptible to streptomycin.

A serious difficulty with streptomycin treatment, which holds to some extent for all antibiotics, is that continued treatment with the drug may lead to the appearance of streptomycin-resistant strains, by selection (see sec. 10). Such selection may take place very quickly in culture media containing the antibiotic, since the difference in growth rate between the sensitive culture and the resistant mutant is so very great. Some of the resistant mutants encountered among

[1] Waksman received the Nobel prize for this work.

pathogens are just as virulent as the original culture and grow at about the same rate. For this reason they become established as a permanent part of the population (Davis, 1952), with the result that diseases treated by antibiotics tend to become steadily less amenable to the treatment. The ultimate in the development of resistance is selection of a strain that actually requires streptomycin for growth (p. 824). To some extent the development of resistant strains of *Mycob. tuberculosis* is prevented by administering *p*-aminosalicylic acid, or isonicotinic hydrazide, between the streptomycin injections, for these inhibit growth also (see Long and Ferrebee, 1950), and the chance that the double mutation will appear, giving resistance to both compounds, is slight.

From its first production on a small scale in 1946, the manufacture of streptomycin has increased very rapidly. Thousands of tons a month are now produced in the United States, and large factories operate in England, Japan, Denmark, Germany, etc., as well. Steel tanks, aerated with sterile air, are used as vessels, and the medium is usually a soybean extract with the addition of dextrose, $CaCO_3$, and a vitamin concentrate from cereal grains, such as "distiller's solubles" or cornsteep liquor (see Ledingham, 1953). The yield of the original *Str. griseus* culture was found to decrease with time, but mutant strains have been produced by irradiating with ultraviolet and x-rays, and by treating with "nitrogen mustard." However, the yields have been increased in this way only by a factor of about eight (Dulaney, 1953).

A serious difficulty in streptomycin production is the development of bacteriophage ("actinophage") attacking *Str. griseus*. Phage-resistant strains have been developed, but, unfortunately, these usually produce lower yields of antibiotic. An actinophage is shown in Figure II–25.

The chemistry of streptomycin has been completely elucidated (Brink and Folkers, 1950). It contains three moieties:

Streptidine, an inositol derivative with two guanidine substituents
Streptose, a methyl pentose of unusual branched structure
Streptosamine, which is N-methyl-L-2-glucosamine

These three structures are linked by ether bonds (see formula IV).

Such curious complexity led to the comment (Kluyver, 1952) that: "It can most aptly be described as the product of an organic chemist just before his admittance to a lunatic asylum. The structures of each of the three moieties of the molecule are equally irrational and the mere idea that nature has thought fit to combine these elements to form a molecule with remarkably specific action tends to depress the most modest among biologists." While it is true that the structure is highly unusual, still, it does suggest some possible bases for growth inhibition. First, the two guanidine groups recall the powerful antimalarial activity of diguanidine compounds like Paludrine (p. 765), and indeed

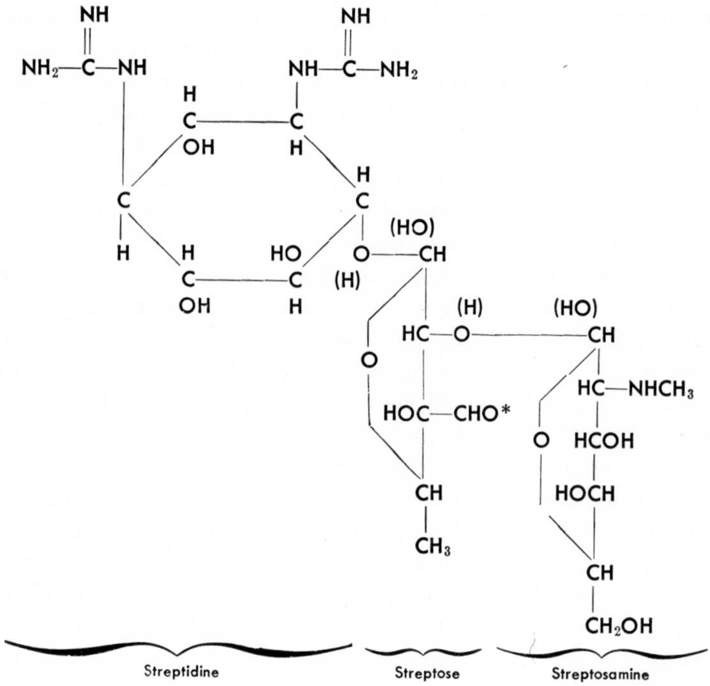

Streptidine   Streptose   Streptosamine

IV

Streptomycin A

The atoms in parentheses are inserted on hydrolysis. The group marked * is reduced to —CH₂OH in dihydrostreptomycin.

when both these groups are hydrolyzed off by alkali, the product is antibiotically inactive. When one is removed, about 10 per cent of the activity remains (Schaffner, 1961). Second, the inositol structure in streptidine reminds us that many organisms require inositol for growth. Inhibition by streptomycin is even partly reversed by adding streptidine (Hancock, 1960). Third, streptosamine resembles the L-isomer of the glucosamine and N-acetyl glucosamine in cell walls (p. 112), and there is some evidence that streptomycin acts on the cell wall, although this is still uncertain (sec. 11).

As to the biosynthesis of streptomycin, the streptosamine portion is formed from glucose, since C^{14} in the 1 and 6 positions in glucose added to the medium is found in high yield in the same positions in the streptosamine (Silverman and Rieder, 1960). How the D-configuration is completely inverted to the L- remains unknown. The inositol ring in streptidine is derived from myoinositol, which enhances production of the antibiotic and decreases the incorporation of C^{14}-glucose into the streptidine (Majumdar and Kutzner, 1962). The guanidine groups apparently come from CO_2, which suggests that they are formed from arginine (Hunter *et al.*, 1954), and added arginine does sometimes increase the yield. The streptose is probably derived from rhamnose, which is found in *Str. griseus* extracts as a nucleotide, thymidinediphosphate-rhamnose (Baddiley *et al.*, 1961).

Streptomycin may also occur in three modifications. One is a mannoside, called streptomycin B; this can be hydrolyzed by a mannosidase. Another, hydroxystreptomycin, is produced by *Str. griseocarneus;* its general properties are similar to those of streptomycin. Third, much of the streptomycin used in medicine is in the form of the dihydro derivative, in which the aldehyde group of streptose is reduced; this has somewhat less toxicity, but its activity, at least in tuberculosis, is undiminished (Brink and Folkers, 1950). Its activity in vitro against *M. aureus* is the same as that of streptomycin and of the mannoside (Hancock, 1960).

Related to streptomycin is the mixture of three substances formed by *Str. fradiae* 3535 and called *neomycin.* One of these has the formula V (Swart *et al.*, 1949); like streptomycin, it is active against both gram-positive and gram-negative bacteria (Waksman and Lechevalier, 1962), but it has not been used clinically because of toxicity to the kidneys. It is formed in much larger amounts than streptomycin, yields of up to 8 gm per liter being obtained industrially on a rich medium (Upjohn, 1958). Kanamycin is similar (Umezawa *et al.*, 1958).

V

Streptothricin also occurs usually in a mixture, being conjugated with various numbers of molecules of the nonprotein-forming amino acid, beta-lysine. Streptothricin itself contains D-gulosamine and the base, streptolidine, making it of similar structure to streptomycin.

The Actinomycins are peptides and will be taken up below.

5. CHLOROMYCETIN[2] OR CHLORAMPHENICOL

This antibiotic is produced by an organism obtained originally from Venezuelan soil (Smith *et al.*, 1948), and hence called *Strepto-*

[2] Although this name is often used, it is actually a registered trade-mark of Parke, Davis and Company.

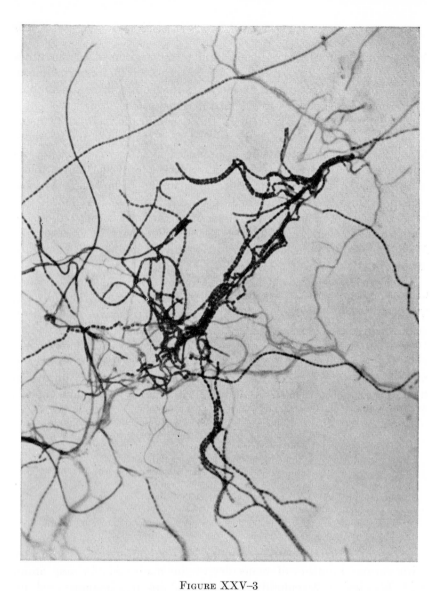

FIGURE XXV–3

Streptomyces venezuelae, gram stain, 1500 ×. (Prepared by Dr. M. L. Littman, Armed Forces Inst. of Pathol. From S. A. Waksman, *The Actinomycetes*, 1950. By courtesy of Chronica Botanica Co.)

myces venezuelae (Fig. XXV–3). The composition is relatively simple (formula VI), and is remarkable for containing a nitro group and two

$$NO_2-\!\!\!\langle\!\!\!\bigcirc\!\!\!\rangle\!\!\!-\overset{*}{C}HOH\cdot\overset{*}{C}H\cdot NHCOCHCl_2$$
$$|$$
$$CH_2OH$$

VI

The starred carbon atoms are optically active

Cl atoms, both very rare in natural products (Bartz, 1948). Indeed, only one other natural nitro compound, β-nitropropionic acid, is known; large yields of this have been isolated from *Pen. atrovenetum* (Raistrick and Stössl, 1958), and it occurs in higher plants too. The two asymmetric carbon atoms of chloramphenicol give rise to four optically active isomers, of which only the $D(-)$*threo*-isomer is highly active. A racemic mixture is readily synthesized, so that the chloramphenicol now used is being made synthetically. It is remarkably stable, resisting nine hours' boiling in neutral solution (Gillissen, 1950) and hence very useful in surgical work.

Many gram-negative organisms are sensitive to chloramphenicol, including the Enterobacteriaceae. It is also used against gonococci and spirochetes, where these are resistant to penicillin. A special value is its action against rickettsiae, including those causing Rocky Mountain spotted fever, scrub typhus, Q fever, and typhus. However, it has recently come into disfavor for clinical use, due to a very slowly appearing anemia.

6. THE TETRACYCLINES

The great effectiveness of streptomycin led, in the late 1940's and 1950's, to a systematic search of soils from all over the world for new species of Streptomyces with antibiotic properties. Several hundred growth-inhibiting compounds have been purified from the resulting cultures; many had only very weak activity, and many turned out to be identical with streptomycin or other known antibiotics. Of the few that are really effective the tetracyclines are outstanding.

Chlortetracycline or Aureomycin, isolated from *Str. aureofaciens* (Duggar *et al.*, 1948), and oxytetracycline or Terramycin from *Str. rimosus* (Sobin *et al.*, 1950) are chemically very similar. Their tetracyclic structures (Stephens *et al.*, 1952) are formulas VII and VIII. Both are produced on well-aerated media, of which corn or soy beans are the main constituent. Both are highly active against gram-negative rods and of very low toxicity to animals. Aureomycin particularly is very rapidly absorbed, circulated, and excreted, and hence is fully

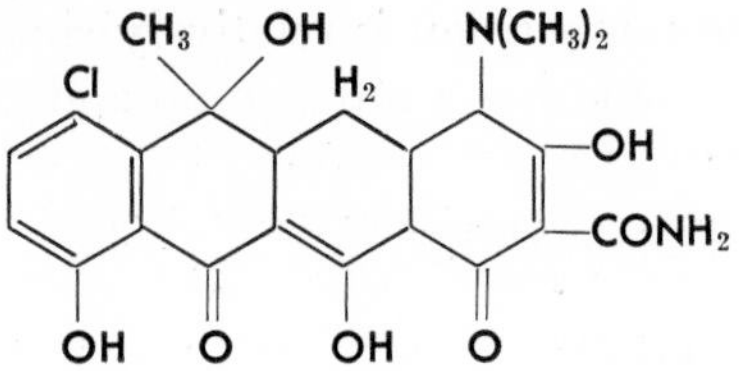

VII
chlortetracycline
(Aureomycin)

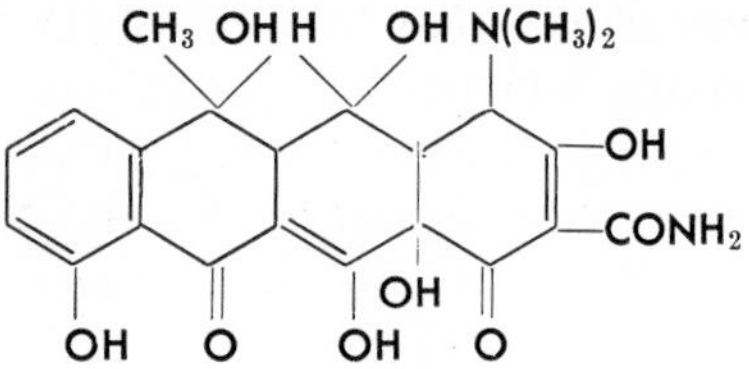

VIII
tetracycline
(Terramycin)

effective when taken orally; gastrointestinal, urinary, and peritoneal infections are readily susceptible to it. Both act to some extent against the "micromicroorganisms," including those of virus pneumonia, influenza, and some Rickettsiae. Terramycin is usually accompanied by a second antibiotic, rimocidin, which inhibits many fungi.

The tetracyclines are so closely related that the same organism often produces both. With NH_4Cl in the medium, *Str. aureofaciens* makes a mixture that is 90 to 95 per cent chlortetracycline, but if —SH compounds are added, the chlorination is inhibited and tetracycline results (Goodman *et al.*, 1959).

7. THE PEPTIDE ANTIBIOTICS

Many sporeformers excrete polypeptides which are powerful antibiotics. The most active organisms are *Bac. brevis*, *Bac. licheniformis* (pp. 412, 419), *Bac. subtilis*, and *Bac. polymyxa* (Chap. XV). Some streptomycetes also form active peptides, especially *Str. antibioticus*, *Str. parvullus*, and *Str. chrysomallus*. These produce the Actinomycins.

Tyrothricin is the mixture of antibiotics produced by *Bac. brevis*, which was the organism that developed when pneumococcus cells were used as an enrichment substrate (Dubos, 1939, cf. p. 799). It contains mainly *tyrocidin* and *gramicidin*, both of which have been crystallized (sée Hotchkiss, 1944). Gramicidin varies in composition; a Russian preparation, gramicidin S, contains only 10 amino acids, two each of valine, ornithine, leucine, D-phenylalanine, and proline, linked in a closed cycle,[3] IX:

```
L-val—L-orn—L-leu—D-phe
 |                    |
L-pro                L-pro
 |                    |
D-phe—L-leu—L-orn—L-val
```
IX

[3] These abbreviations, consisting of the first three (or four) letters of each amino acid name, are now generally used in peptide chemistry (cf. Chap. XX).

Other gramicidins contain a few more amino acids in the ring, including D-leucine.

Both gramicidin and tyrocidin cause kidney damage and are too toxic for internal use but are often applied to bandages and dressings.

Bacitracin is an unfortunate name, derived from "*Bac. subtilis* Tracy" (Johnson *et al.*, 1945). This organism has also been called *Bac. licheniformis* and is undoubtedly related to the true *Bac. subtilis* Cohn, although distinguished from it by the ability to grow anaerobically in the presence of nitrate (cf. Chap. X, sec. 2). Other strains of *Bac. subtilis* produce *subtilin* (Jansen and Hirschmann, 1944), *bacillin* (Foster and Woodruff, 1946), and *mycobacillin* (Majumdar and Bose, 1960). All these are mainly active against gram-positive bacteria and fungi. Like gramicidin, they are polypeptides, and one of them, bacitracin A, has the structure X (Porath, 1953–1954):

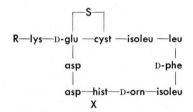

(The amino acids are all L- unless otherwise indicated). Several other preparations differ in detail (Lockhart and Abraham, 1956).

In general they are too toxic for internal use. However, bacitracin is sometimes used on infections resistant to other antibiotics where the treatment can be closely observed and is also used superficially for "sterilization" of the skin and of the intestines prior to surgery (Raper, 1952). Since bacitracin has the same effect on farm animals as the other antibiotics (sec. 8), it is being used in fair quantities as a feed supplement.

Polymyxin and *Aerosporin* are polypeptides produced by *Bac. polymyxa* (Chap. XV), another name for which is *Bac. aerosporus*. These comprise a group of at least five polypeptides, each produced singly by a different strain. *Circulin*, produced by *Bac. circulans*, is very closely related.

The polymyxins are highly active against gram-negative bacteria, but again toxicity to the kidney has so far limited their use in internal medicine. They have been used, however, in diseases of farm animals and in human patients with infections resistant to streptomycin. The chemical composition of polymyxin B (Biserte and Dautrevaux, 1957) is that of a cyclic octapeptide with a long side-chain, XI (di-ab =

L-diaminobutyric acid):

```
di-ab—di-ab—thre—di-ab
 |                |
leu —phe —di-ab —di-ab—thre—di-ab—6-methyloctanoic acid
                  XI
```

Circulin and *polypeptin* have the same C_9-acid in the side-chain, circulin A being XII (Koffler and Kobayashi, 1960);

```
di-ab—di-ab—isoleu—leu—di-ab
 |                        |
thre—di-ab—thre—di-ab—di-ab—6-methyloctanoic acid
                  XII
```

Colimycin, produced by *Bac. colistinus*, is another cyclic decapeptide with five molecules of diaminobutyric acid in the ring, and a similar side-chain. Polymyxin A contains D-leucine as well, while polymyxin D has both D-leucine and serine. All are highly bacteri*cidal* rather than bacterio*static*. Because of the diaminobutyric acid, they are all strongly basic, as are tyrocidin, gramicidin, and subtilin also. This basic character makes their action comparable with that of basic detergents and dyes (Chap. XXIV, sec. 2 and 3); when the free amino groups are substituted or acylated, the bactericidal activity disappears (see Newton, 1958). Not only the basic groups but also the cyclic structure is important, since a straight-chain peptide with the same amino-acid sequence as gramicidin S has less than one-tenth its activity (Erlanger *et al.*, 1954).

The *Actinomycins* are a group of yellow and red compounds containing the tricyclic phenoxazine ring plus two cyclic peptides, e.g., XIII (Sar = sarcosine):

XIII
Actinomycin IV (= D)

Six others are known in which the amino acids between threonine and sarcosine are different (Brockmann, 1960; Johnson, 1960). Since the amino acid, sarcosine, is not a protein constituent, it is missing from most media; by adding it, the yield of actinomycins can be increased (Katz and Goss, 1959). Similarly L-valine also increases the yield, but its isomer, D-valine, decreases it (Katz et al., 1961).

These compounds are produced by a group of 15 or more streptomycetes whose taxonomy and characteristics are rather confused (Woodruff and Waksman, 1960). They act 100 to 1000 times more strongly on gram-positive than on gram-negative bacteria, but are clinically unusable because of their great toxicity. Now, however, they are of renewed interest because they are more toxic to tumors than to normal tissue (Hackmann, 1952–1960). This is particularly true of Actinomycin IV or D, formed by Str. parvullus (Brockmann, 1960). As yet, the actinomycins are the only antibiotics used to treat cancer (see the review of Leiter, 1962).

The role of cyclic peptides is evidently very wide, since penicillin itself is in reality a cyclic dipeptide, comprising valine and serine, with the C_5-C_7 side-chain. The cyclic anhydride of serine amide $O·CH_2·CHNH_2$ (Cycloserine or oxamycin) has very similar properties

$$\underset{NH——CO}{O·CH_2·CHNH_2}$$

(Ciak and Hahn, 1959; see below). It seems almost certain that all these compounds act by interfering with the laying down of the cell-wall peptide.

8. SECONDARY EFFECTS OF ANTIBIOTIC FEEDING

The powerful action of tetracyclines against gram-negative rods, coupled with their great ease of absorption and excretion, often results in almost complete sterilization of the intestine. In man, bacteria sometimes almost disappear from the feces. Other antibiotics have similar, though less striking, effects. Occasionally the sterilized feces become infected with the yeast Candida albicans, which is pathogenic and causes serious secondary infections.

In farm animals, on the other hand, the secondary effects of feeding antibiotics are of great value. It was the feeding of vitamin concentrates that led to this discovery. Since some Actinomycetes produce vitamin B_{12} in large amounts, vitamin concentrates were made from the antibiotic fermentation wastes and fed to cattle, but it was soon noticed that the resulting growth promotion was greater than that due to the vitamin B_{12} alone. The amount of tetracycline needed for maximum growth promotion is about 10 gm per ton of feed, for chicks, turkeys, and pigs (see Raper, 1952). This is about 1000 times the B_{12} requirement, which is only 4 to 8 mg per ton. The young animals grow more rapidly and are freer from disease. Other antibiotics, especially penicillin and bacitracin, have similar effects. All are being used in farm feeds. The great penetrability of chlortetracycline has the odd result that when fed to hens, it can increase the resistance of the eggs to Rickettsiae.

It seems hardly likely that the action results from the inhibition of intestinal bacteria, since penicillin is not very active against these, and because the effective concentrations are too low. More probably the antibiotics act by preventing low-level infections (e.g., by Clostridia) which are ordinarily scarcely detected, although they decrease growth.

A danger of this whole development is that animals fed antibiotics may develop highly resistant strains of intestinal bacteria. This has been proven in one case, where the strain of *E. coli* from turkeys fed on streptomycin was 1000 times as resistant to streptomycin as is normal (Starr and Reynolds, 1951). The spread of antibiotic-resistant pathogens is obviously undesirable. The use of antibiotics in medicine has raised similar problems in the appearance of resistant strains of human pathogens, antibiotic-resistant cocci being now particularly troublesome in hospitals (see Verwey, 1959).

9. MISCELLANY

With so many effective compounds stopping the growth of bacteria, it is not surprising that many treated patients contract infections with fungi. This is particularly the case in the intestines where normally bacteria reign supreme (Chap. XIV, sec. 1). As a result, pathogenic fungi have recently become a serious pest, and a search has been made for antifungal substances. These should eventually have great agricultural use against fungal diseases of crops.

The most effective antifungals so far found are a group of unsaturated large molecules called polyene macrolides. They contain amino sugars and *p*-aminophenyl residues. *Nystatin*, with 46 C atoms and four double bonds, inhibits growth of many fungi and some algae and prevents glycolysis by yeast (Sutton *et al.*, 1961). The group with seven double bonds, including *candidin* ($C_{46}H_{75}NO_{17}$, Vining and Taber, 1956), *candicidin, perimycin, trichomycin,* and *amphotericin,* is more potent, particularly on *Candida albicans,* one of the principal pathogens. The growth of this fungus is inhibited at 0.5 mg antibiotic per liter, or less (trichomycin at 0.03 mg per liter), while most bacteria are scarcely affected at all (Hosoya *et al.*, 1952). Because the polyenes are rather insoluble in water, they have been made soluble by N-acetylation, but this lowers the activity by 5 to 10 times (Lechevalier *et al.*, 1961). These compounds may prove very useful.

Three other water-insoluble types are of interest. The first is the *Oligomycin* group, formed by *Str. diastatochromogenes* (Masamine *et al.*, 1958). Three of these have formulas $C_{24}H_{40}O_6$, $C_{22}H_{36}O_6$, and $C_{28}H_{46}O_6$, and are neutral unsaturated alcohols. They are active against several skin fungi, as well as the fungi causing oak wilt and Dutch elm disease. Second is the peculiar compound *Elaiomycin*, from *Str. hepaticus*, which is effective only against mammalian *Mycob. tuberculosis*. It is an oily nitrogen oxide (Stevens *et al.*, 1958):

$$n-C_6H_{13}CH\!:\!CH\cdot N\!:\!N\cdot CH(CH_2OCH_3)CHOHCH_3$$
$$\downarrow$$
$$O$$

Third is another nitrogenous compound, *Micrococcin*, $C_{25}H_{28}O_6N_6S_3$, soluble neither in water nor in alcohol (Heatley *et al.*, 1951, 1952). It can be given intravenously as fine particles which persist in the body

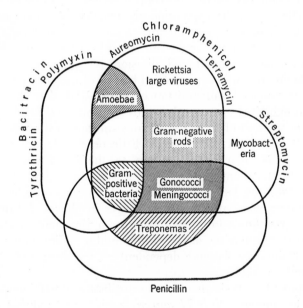

FIGURE XXV–4

Diagram of the "domains" of the action of the principal antibiotics. (Modified from K. B. Raper, *Scientific American*, April, 1952. By courtesy of *Scientific American*, New York.)

for months. Although it inhibits many bacteria, including *Mycob. tuberculosis*, it is ineffective against experimental tuberculosis.

Netropsin, from *Str. netropsis*, is a different type of compound, since it appears to be a purine derivative and thus may be comparable with the synthetic purine antagonists in Chapter XXIV (Waller *et al.*, 1957). Although the growth inhibition it causes is not reversed by adding purines, it can be completely reversed in *E. coli* by adding a mixture of 18 amino acids (Zygmunt, 1961); thus it may interfere with the amination process.

Chemical aspects of many other antibiotics are treated by Woodward (1957), and biological aspects by Bryson (1962).

In Figure XXV–4 the actions of the principal antibiotics on different organisms are presented as a series of overlapping areas. This figure may help to keep in mind the multitude of individual data.

10. DEVELOPMENT OF RESISTANCE

When a bacterium is grown in a series of subcultures in the presence of gradually increasing concentrations of antibiotic, the most resistant cells among the population are selected, and a resistant strain is built up. These strains commonly have characteristically changed morphology, or staining, or become highly filamentous, as though growth can take place but cell division is inhibited. Resistance of bacilli to Actinomycin is accompanied by loss of the ability to sporulate. The phenomenon of "drug resistance" is not limited to the antibiotics but is often exhibited against other growth inhibitors. Figure XXV–5*A* shows the adaptation of *E. coli* to various substances through successive transfers. It is evident that there is little or no adaptation to $HgCl_2$, phenol, or KCN, marked adaptation to the dyes, and very rapid adaptation to streptomycin; in other words, the organism can adapt to some substances but not to others. As a very similar example, *Aerobacter aerogenes*, after 100 subcultures in phenol, did not develop the slightest resistance to phenol, whereas a very few transfers made it resistant to proflavine or to sulfonamides (Hinshelwood, 1949). Resistant strains may become dependent on the drug, especially with streptomycin (p. 824).

Development of resistance to one antibiotic is not independent of resistance to another. With *M. aureus*, resistance to almost any antibiotic confers some resistance to streptomycin, but not to penicillin or tetracycline; resistance to tetracycline confers resistance to subtilin (McVeigh and Hobdy, 1952). Strains of *E. coli* resistant to strep-

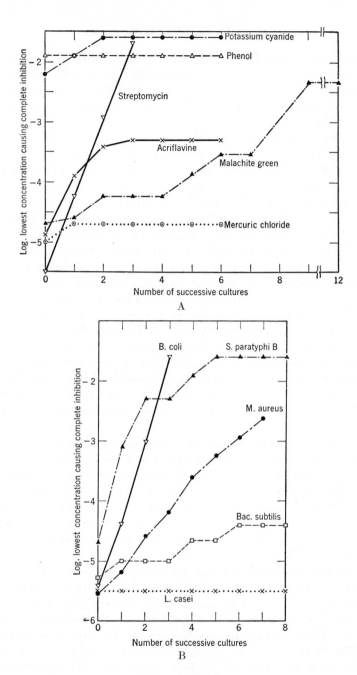

FIGURE XXV-5

A. The course of acquisition of resistance of *E. coli* to streptomycin and some chemical inhibitors.

B. The course of acquisition of resistance to streptomycin by various bacteria.

(From T. Yanagita, T. Sasa, Y. Morimura, T. Uemura, and S. Fukuda, 1951. *J. Antibiotics* [Japan] 1–C; Studies Tokugawa Inst. 6, No. 3, 5 pp.)

tothricin and neomycin are resistant to streptomycin, but not vice versa, while strains resistant to polymyxin and circulin are resistant to neomycin too (Szybalski and Bryson, 1952). Some strains very highly resistant to chloramphenicol are resistant to tetracyclines (Brock, 1961).

It is important to note that the development of resistance does not require the antibiotic (or other growth-inhibiting agent) to be present. The only effect of the antibiotic is as selecting agent. The situation is exactly comparable to that of the phage-resistant mutants (p. 676). This important conclusion has been established in several ways, perhaps most neatly by "replica plating" (Lederberg and Lederberg, 1952). An agar plate bearing a number of colonies is pressed with a piece of fine velveteen; the "pile" acts like several thousand inoculating needles, and when pressed on a new agar plate containing antibiotic, it transfers to the plate separate inocula from each of the colonies. Of these, only the resistant colonies grow. Thus, transfers can be made from all the individual colonies in the parent plate without ever exposing them to the antibiotic, and it is clear that some of these colonies are already resistant. That indeed they *all* are, i.e., that truly adaptive drug resistance is excluded, is not proven by this method, but was later shown by testing a large number of small samples from liquid cultures (Cavalli-Sforza and Lederberg, 1956). Using streptomycin and chloramphenicol, this more laborious method demonstrated that *all* the resistant mutants had arisen before exposure to the drugs. Only with penicillin (see below) is resistance truly inducible.

The degree to which drug resistance is developed depends both on the drug and on the organism; for streptomycin the gram-negative rods (with the exception of *Sh. dysenteriae*) develop much greater drug resistance than most of the gram-positive organisms (see Fig. XXV–5B). From *E. coli* strain K12, mutants have been isolated, by periodic transfer to higher concentrations, that resist chloramphenicol at 1000 mg per liter (see Brock, 1961).

Resistance to antibiotics can be transferred from one strain to another (1) by sexuality, as in *E. coli*, (2) by transduction, as in Salmonella and *M. aureus*, and (3) by transforming factors. Such resistance is one of the most convenient genetic "markers" to work with (see Chap. XXI). In one bacterium, *M. aureus*, resistance to penicillin, to streptomycin, to chlortetracycline, and to novobiocin can all be transduced (Ritz and Baldwin, 1958; Morse, 1959; Pattee and Baldwin, 1961).

In the special case of penicillin, resistance can be due to hydrolysis of the drug by penicillinase. The transduced resistance is of this type. Formation of penicillinase is readily induced by brief exposure to penicillin (p. 670) or indeed to some of the "semi-synthetic" penicillins (Novick, 1962); it is then excreted into the medium, probably by some enzymatic system in or near the cell wall (Pollock, 1961). Streptomycin resistance in a few cases was traced to a decreased uptake; this occurs also in absence of air (Hancock, 1960).

11. MODE OF ACTION

The gross site of action of penicillin (but not its exact mechanism) is now understood; it *prevents formation of the cell wall*. When rod-shaped cells are placed in penicillin broth, they become spheres and then lyse (Bonifas, 1954); if the broth contains 0.3 M sucrose plus penicillin, they are slowly converted to stable spheres (Lederberg, 1956–1957). Dividing cells swell first at the place where the septum is forming; this delicate crosswall is thus the most susceptible point. (For the same reason some organisms fail to form cross-walls in penicillin broth and grow into long filaments.) When the sucrose broth containing the spheres is diluted, they burst at once. The spheres are evidently *protoplasts* like those produced by lysozyme (see p. 110), which have their membrane intact but no wall. However, in *E. coli* and *Aerob. cloacae* the spheres can gradually revert to normal cells, so that it is believed that some primordium of the wall remains, and they are termed *spheroplasts* (see, e.g., Hugo and Russell, 1960–1961). As a rule, they cannot divide, but they can be infected by phages, which grow in them normally.

Earlier studies (Gale, 1949) showed that penicillin-resistant strains of *M. aureus* have lost the ability to accumulate amino acids from the medium. The most resistant strains also become gram-negative, which indicates a change in wall structure. Park and his co-workers (1952, 1957) also found that a few minutes' exposure to penicillin causes *M. aureus* to excrete complex bases, containing uridine and acetyl amino sugars. Evidently the amino sugar was that which *could not be laid down as wall* and hence was excreted (in combined form) instead. The wall mucopeptide (Chap. III, sec. 1) must therefore be the site of penicillin action. More direct proof is given by an isolated and washed cell-wall preparation from *M. aureus*, which has been shown to incorporate C^{14} glycine, alanine, lysine, or glutamate, the four main amino acids of the wall mucopeptide (Mandelstam and Rogers, 1959). This incorporation is drastically inhibited by penicillin. Since penicillin does not affect protein synthesis by these cells, its action is evidently quite specifically exerted on the wall substance. Molecular models strongly suggest that penicillin binds to the wall at

the same site as the N-acetyl-muramic acid (p. 114) (Collins and Richmond, 1962). The N atom common to the two rings of penicillin falls
on the O atom of the propionic sidechain in muramic acid, the two
carboxyls (which have the same dissociation constants) exactly coincide, and the C:O of the amide bond in penicillin falls on the C:O of
the acetyl group of muramic acid. Thus penicillin may well prevent
the insertion of acetylmuramic acid into the wall. It is no wonder that
its action on gram-negative cells is weaker, because their walls have a
very different composition.

D-*cycloserine* has similar action, converting *E. coli* to spheroplasts
and causing uridine nucleotides to accumulate. One of these differs
from the compound formed in presence of penicillin in not containing
two D-alanine residues, and added D-alanine prevents accumulation
of this and other nucleotides. Strominger (1962), therefore, concludes
that D-cycloserine competes with D-alanine and prevents it from being
laid down in the wall peptide.

Chloramphenicol has a quite different action. If *M. aureus* is fed
C^{14}-amino acids in presence of chloramphenicol they are taken up
but not incorporated into protein (Gale and Folkes, 1953). Similarly
in *E. coli*, protein synthesis is stopped completely by 10 mg of the
drug per liter of medium (Wisseman *et al.*, 1954). It thus stops
synthesis of all enzymes, even including the β-galactosidase formed
in cell-free preparations (Novelli *et al.*, 1961). Chloramphenicol has
no effect on the incorporation of glycine into the adenine and guanine
of nucleic acids, and indeed the RNA content, at least of the ribosomes,
may even be increased, because they contain less protein (Dagley and
Sykes, 1960). Neither is the attachment of amino acids to soluble
RNA much affected; it may also be increased. Chloramphenicol must
therefore inhibit the *final* polymerization step in protein synthesis
(Lacks and Gros, 1960), i.e., the transfer of aminoacyl RNA to the
ribosomes. As a result of this, the particles come to contain less and
less protein, and hence the RNA becomes less and less stable (Dagley
et al., 1962). Apparently most of the ribosomal RNA is normally
stabilized by protein, and if not, then its nucleotides are excreted.

Puromycin has a similar effect, interfering with the transfer
from soluble RNA to protein (Yarmolinsky and de la Haba, 1959).
In cell-free preparations from *E. coli*, it clearly prevents the condensation of amino acids to proteins on the ribosomes (Nathans and Lipmann, 1961) and appears to cause the release from the ribosome
surface of protein material that is being synthesized (Morris *et al.*,
1962). In *Ps. fluorescens*, where it also stops protein synthesis, it
does not affect the formation of the RNA.

The role of the *tetracyclines* is unclear, but they bind strongly to metal cations and thus to the metals bound by proteins or DNA (Kohn, 1961b). In bacilli they inhibit sporulation, preventing uptake of Ca and hence formation of calcium dipicolinate (Brock, 1962; Vinter, 1962). The metal-bound tetracycline is probably held firmly at some crucial site on the cell membrane.

The action of the peptide antibiotics has been foreshadowed in Chapter XXIV by the similarity between the basic dyes and polymyxin. Briefly, polymyxin E causes *Ps. fluorescens* cells to leak pentose and phosphate out into the medium; it also allows a dye, ordinarily not taken up, to enter and combine with protein, producing a fluorescence which occurs only together with protein (Newton, 1953–1954). Polyvalent cations, which decrease permeability, protect the cells against polymyxin. Gramicidin inhibits the uptake of phosphate by *M. aureus*, which also suggests action at the membrane (Hotchkiss, 1944). These basic peptides thus probably attach to the membrane and so prevent the incorporation of its normal constituents, making it too permeable as a result.

The polyenes, which act mainly as antifungals, have very similar action, since many of them strongly inhibit phosphate uptake by *Candida albicans* and other fungi (Henis and Grossowicz, 1960). Nystatin causes K^+ to leak out from yeast cells too (Sutton *et al.*, 1961).

Quite different is the action of *Mitomycin C*, produced by *Str. caespitosus;* this drug was found by Japanese workers (e.g., Mizutani *et al.*, 1959) to inhibit the synthesis of DNA. Curiously, infection with bacteriophage reinstates the DNA synthesis, but the resulting phage particles are not infective (Sekiguchi and Tagaki, 1960), so perhaps their DNA has been modified. A transforming DNA of *Bac. subtilis* was 90 per cent inactivated in about an hour (Nakata *et al.*, 1961). The basis for the action seems to lie in the stimulation of DNA hydrolysis in the cell, since the drug does not itself affect DNA or DNA-ase in vitro.

In contrast to these rather well-defined actions, the role of *streptomycin* remains unclear. *Too many* effects seem to have been observed:

(1) Streptomycin-resistant strains of *E. coli* and *M. aureus* oxidize pyruvate only to acetate and seem unable to condense it with oxalacetate to form citrate (Umbreit, 1949, 1953; Oginsky, 1953). Similar accumulation of acetate occurs in more sensitive strains in presence of the drug. Other strains *require* pyruvate or acetate, although hematin will substitute, being perhaps used to form an oxidizing enzyme system (Jensen, 1953). The rates of oxidation of succinate, lactate, pyruvate, and glucose are all decreased, in both gram-positive

and gram-negative forms (Jackson, 1958; Hancock, 1961). All these facts might mean that an oxidizing step, or perhaps the "condensing enzyme" (p. 245, Fig. V–14), is the target of streptomycin's attack.

(2) A quite different result is that uptake of amino acids by Salmonella is prevented, and cells growing on an ammonium medium are resistant to the drug (Ørskov, 1960).

(3) Incorporation of C^{14}-tyrosine into protein is prevented in extracts of a Mycobacterium, while resistant strains of this bacterium showed no such effect (Erdös and Ullmann, 1959–1960).

(4) Resistant strains contain more RNA than sensitive strains— in *M. aureus*, 100 per cent more, and in *E. coli* some 20 per cent more (Beljanski, 1952). Strains that *require* streptomycin also have increased RNA content, which streptomycin lowers to the normal level (Spotts and Stanier, 1961).

These last three phenomena suggest interference with some stage of protein formation, probably the reaction between amino acids and RNA; however, the fifth set of data points to an entirely different locus of action.

(5) Labeled streptomycin is rapidly adsorbed by both sensitive and resistant strains of *E. coli*, reaching completion in one minute, both at $0°$ C and at $37°$ C (Anand *et al.*, 1960). From this physical fixation, which almost certainly occurs on the wall, the streptomycin can be eluted by buffer solutions, i.e., it is held in "ionic linkages," probably by its strongly basic guanidine groups and the phosphate groups in the wall. But after 10 minutes the sensitive cells begin a further major uptake which is slow and prevented by chloramphenicol. Apparently now the streptomycin held on the wall or membrane has damaged its permeability control, and this allows the secondary entry of more streptomycin. Addition of toluene (known to damage cell membranes) causes a similar secondary uptake. Thus, the action would be exerted by opening the cell membrane, perhaps like the action of polymyxin and other basic peptides. Correspondingly, streptomycin is found to cause the excretion of nucleotides and of amino acids.

How all these observations can be unified is not clear. It is remarkable how easily resistance to streptomycin appears in cells cultured in its presence, and still more remarkable how often such resistant types become *dependent* on streptomycin for normal growth. Such dependence suggests that the cell so readily modifies itself, to accommodate the change caused by streptomycin, that the modification is at least as good as the original form. Spotts and Stanier (1961) suggested that the streptomycin that penetrates into the cell combines with the ribosomes, making them unable to react with the messenger-

RNA (p. 652, Fig. XX–2) and therefore unable to form proteins. (Probably it would substitute for a normal ribosome constituent.) However, a slight modification in the ribosomes can reduce their affinity for the drug, making them *resistant*. But this also makes them less able to react with the RNA. Now the structure can be further modified to *accept the streptomycin as part of it;* thus, the ribosome can function again, and the cells are now *dependent* on streptomycin. So the drug must have considerable similarity to the structure of the ribosome surface, and this, it may be suggested, gives it similarity to the membrane structure too. Along some such lines the multiple effects observed may be explained.

12. CONCLUSION

The discovery and development of antibiotics have brought a revolution in medical practice. In the 1880's (Chap. I) the discovery and culture of the principal pathogenic bacteria led to a revolution in the idea of disease, but the advantage to the sick patient came only slowly, through asepsis, public health measures, and the development of immunology. In the period since 1930, the antibiotic revolution has brought much more immediate results, since it has given us, not the cause, but the cure.

Unfortunately the antibiotics have not taught us much about the natural interactions between microbes. The simple facts that *Pen. notatum*, producing penicillin, is less common than *Pen. italicum* which forms no antibiotic, while *Str. griseus* was unknown until recently, suggest that antibiotics play little part in natural selection, since otherwise the antibiotic-producing organisms would long ago have become dominant in a competitive world. Indeed, Waksman (1961) points out that Streptomycetes live in the soil, where antibiotics are probably not produced, and where they would in any event be quite unstable.

The antibiotics have taught us something about research, however. The vitamin analogues, dyes, sulfonamides, etc., described in Chapter XXIV, were developments from what was already known about enzymes and growth factors; they represented an application and perfection of basic knowledge already in hand. The antibiotics, by contrast, were quite new compounds acting in unknown ways. Penicillin and streptomycin are of such curious structures that they would virtually never have been found by routine testing of synthetic compounds. Correspondingly, they have proven very much more valuable in medicine than the previously known inhibitors, and in microbiology they are helping to make comprehensible many and varied aspects of the life of bacteria. Truly, the persistent following up of a new biological lead "opens unknown doors" much more effectively than the refinement of methods and ideas already in existence.

REFERENCES

Abraham, E. P., and Newton, G. G. F. 1956. *Biochem. J.*, **62**:651–658, 658–665; **63**:628–634.

Anand, N., and Davis, B. D. 1960. *Nature*, **185**:22–23; Anand, N.; Davis, B. D.; and Armitage, A. K. *Ibid.*, **185**:23–24.

Baddiley, J.; Blumsom, N. L.; diGirolamo, A.; and diGirolamo, M. 1961. *Biochim. Biophys. Acta*, **50**:391–393; Blumsom, N. L., and Baddiley, J. *Biochem. J.*, **81**: 114–124.

Bartz, Q. R. 1948. *J. Biol. Chem.*, **172**:445–450.

Batchelor, F. R.; Doyle, F. P.; Nayler, J. H. C.; and Rolinson, G. N. 1959. *Nature*, **183**:257–258.

Beadle, G. W.; Mitchell, H. K.; and Bonner, D. 1945. *J. Bact.*, **49**:101–104.

Beljanski, M. 1952. *Ann. Inst. Pasteur*, **83**:80–101.

Biserte, G., and Dautrevaux, M. 1957. *Bull. Soc. Chim. Biol.* (Paris), **39**:795–812.

Bonifas, V. 1954. *Schweitz. Zeit. allgem. Path u. Bakt.*, **17**:525–535.

Boxer, G. E., and Jelinek, V. C. 1947. *J. Biol. Chem.*, **170**:491–500.

*Brink, N. G., and Folkers, K. 1950. Some Aspects of Streptomycin and Other Streptomyces Antibiotics. *Adv. in Enzymol.*, **10**:145–166.

*Brock, T. D. 1961. Chloramphenicol. *Bact. Revs.*, **25**:32–48.

Brock, T. D. 1962. *Nature*, **195**:309.

Brockmann, H. 1960. *Ann. New York Acad. Sci.*, **89**:323–335, and literature there cited.

*Bryson, V. 1962. Antibiotics: Practical and Experimental Aspects. In, *Survey Biol. Prog.*, **IV**:345–440.

Cavalli-Sforza, R., and Lederberg, J. 1956. *Genetics*, **41**:367–381.

Chapman, S. S.; Downs, C. M.; Coriell, L. L.; and Kowal, S. F. 1949. *J. Inf. Dis.*, **85**:25–38; Chapman, S. S.; Coriell, L. L.; and Kowal, S. F. *J. Inf. Dis.*, **85**:39–44; Chapman, S. S.; Coriell, L. L.; and Nelson, W. E. *J. Inf. Dis.*, **85**:45–61.

Ciak, J., and Hahn, F. E. 1959. *Antibiotics and Chemother.*, **9**:47–54.

Collins, J. F., and Richmond, M. H. 1962. *Nature*, **195**:142–143.

Cook, R. P., and Brown, M. 1950. *Proc. Roy. Soc. Edinburgh*, **64B**:137–171.

Coulthard, C. E.; Michaelis, R.; Short, W. F.; Sykes, G.; Skrimshire, G. E.; Standfast, A. B.; Birkinshaw, J. H.; and Raistrick, H. 1945. *Biochem. J.*, **39**:24–36.

Dagley, S., and Sykes, J. 1960. *Biochem. J.*, **74**:11P–12P.

Dagley, S.; White, A. E.; Wild, D. G.; & Sykes, J. 1962. *Nature* **194**:25–27.

Davis, B. D. 1949. *Proc. Nat. Acad. Sci.*, **35**:1–10.

Davis, B. D. 1952. *Pub. Health Reports*, **67**:376–379.

Demerec, M. 1951. *Genetics*, **36**:585–597.

Doyle, F. P.; Long, A. A. W.; Nayler, J. H. C.; and Stove, E. R. 1961. *Nature*, **192**: 1183–1184.

Dubos, R. J. 1939. *Proc. Soc. Exp. Biol. Med.*, **40**:311.

Duggar, B. M., and many others. 1948. *Ann. New York Acad. Sci.*, **51**:177–340.

Dulaney, E. L. 1953. *Mycologia*, **45**:481–487.

Dutcher, J. D.; Johnson, J. R.; and Bruce, W. F. 1945. *J. Am. Chem. Soc.*, **67**:1735–1745.

Erdös, T., and Ullman, A. 1959–1960. *Nature*, **183**:618–619 (1959); **185**:100 (1960).

Erlanger, B. F.; Sachs, H.; and Brand, E. 1954. *J. Am. Chem. Soc.*, **76**:1806–1810.

Fleming, A. 1929. *Brit. J. Exp. Path.*, **10**:226–236.

Fleming, A. (obituary notice for). 1956. *J. Gen. Microbiol.*, **14**:1–13.

*Florey, H. W.; Chain, E.; Heatley, N. G.; Jennings, M. A.; Sanders, A. G.; Abraham, E. P.; and Florey, M. E. 1949. Antibiotics. Oxford Univ. Press. 1774 pp.

Foster, J. W., and Woodruff, H. B. 1944–1946. *J. Bact.*, **47**:43–58; **51**:363–369 (1946).

Gale, E. F. 1949. The Action of Penicillin on the Assimilation and Utilization of Amino Acids by Gram-positive Bacteria. In, Selective Toxicity and Antibiotics (3rd Symp. Soc. Exp. Biol.), pp. 233–242; Cambridge, University Press; New York, Academic Press.

Gale, E. F., and Folkes, J. P. 1953. *Biochem. J.*, **53**:493–498.

Gillissen, G. 1950. *Zentr. Bakt.* I orig., **156**:138–143.

Goodman, J. J.; Matrishin, M.; Young, R. W.; and McCormick, J. R. D. 1959. *J. Bact.*, **78**:492–499.

Hackmann, C. 1952–1960. *Zeit. f. Krebsforschung*, **58**:607–613 (1952); *Strahlenther*, **90**:296–300 (1953); *Ann. New York Acad. Sci.*, **89**:361–367 (1960); cf. Schulte G., *Zeit. f. Krebsforschung*, **58**:500–503 (1952).

Hancock, R. 1960–1961. *J. Gen. Microbiol.*, **23**:179–196; **25**:429–440 (1961).

Heatley, N. G., and Doery, H. M. 1951. *Biochem. J.*, **50**:247–253; Heatley, N. G.; Gowans, J. L.; Florey, H. W.; and Sanders, A. G. 1952. *Brit. J. Exp. Path.*, **33**:105–122.

Henis, Y., and Grossowicz, N. 1960. *J. Gen. Microbiol.*, **23**:345–355.

Hinshelwood, C. N. 1949. In, Selective Toxicity and Antibiotics (3rd Symp. Soc. Exp. Biol.), pp. 243–252, Cambridge, University Press; New York, Academic Press.

Hiscox, D. J. 1951. *J. Am. Pharm. Assoc.*, **40**:237–240.

Hosoya, S.; Komatsu, N.; Soeda, M.; and Sonoda, Y. 1952. *J. Antibiotics* (Japan), **5**:564–568; *Jap. J. Exptl. Med.*, **22**:505–509.

*Hotchkiss, R. D. 1944. Gramicidin, Tyrocidin, Tyrothricin. *Adv. in Enzymol.*, **4**:153–199.

Hugo, W. B., and Russell, A. D. 1960, 1961. *J. Bact.*, **80**:436–440; **82**:411–418 (1961).

Hunter, G. D.; Herbert, M.; and Hockenhull, D. J. D. 1954–1955. *Biochem. J.*, **58**:249–254; Hunter, G. D., and Hockenhull, D. J. D. *Ibid.*, **59**:268–272 (1955).

Jackson, F. L. 1958. *Nature*, **181**:281–282.

Jansen, E. F., and Hirschmann, D. J. 1944. *Arch. Biochem.*, **4**:297–309.

Jensen, J., and Thofern, E., 1953. *Z. Natuforsch.*, **8b**:599–603, 604–607, 697: **9b**:596–600.

Johnson, A. W. 1960. *Ann. New York Acad. Sci.*, **89**:336–341.

Johnson, B. A.; Anker, H.; and Meleney, F. L. 1945. *Science*, **102**:376–377.

Katz, E., and Goss, W. A. 1959. *Biochem. J.*, **73**:458–465.

Katz, E.; Waldron, C. R.; and Meloni, M. L. 1961. *J. Bact.*, **82**:600–608.

Kluyver, A. J. 1952. *Chemistry and Industry*, pp. 136–145.

Koffler, H., and Kobayashi, T. 1960. *Abstr. Comm. 4th Int. Congr. Biochem.* (Vienna, 1958), sec. 1, pp. 63 and 64.

Kohn, K. W. 1961a. *Anal. Chem.*, **33**:862–866.

Kohn, K. W. 1961b. *Nature*, **191**:1156.

Kusai, K.; Sekuzu, I.; Hagihara, B.; Okunuki, K.; Yamauchi, S.; and Nakai, M. 1960. *Biochem. Biophys. Acta*, **40**:555–557.

Lacks, S., and Gros, F. 1960. *J. Mol. Biol.*, **1**:301–320.

Lechevalier, H.; Borowski, E.; Lampen, J. O.; and Schaffner, C. P. 1961. *Antibiotics and Chemotherapy,* 11:640–647.

Lederberg, J. 1956–1957. *Proc. Nat. Acad. Sci.,* 42:574–577; *J. Bact.,* 73:144 (1957).

Lederberg, J., and Lederberg, E. M. 1952. *J. Bact.,* 63:399–406.

*Ledingham, G. A. 1953. Industrial Fermentations. *Ann. Rev. Microbiol.,* 7:433–460.

Leiter, J. 1962. *Cancer Res.* (Suppl.) 22, Pt. 2: 1–155.

Lester Smith, E. 1948. In, Symposium on Methods of Penicillin Assay. *The Analyst,* 73:197–216, 244–257.

Lockhart, I. M., and Abraham, E. P. 1956. *Biochem. J.,* 62:645–651.

Long, E. R., and Ferrebee, B. A. 1950. *Pub. Health Reps.,* 65:1421–1451.

McVeigh, I., and Hobdy, C. J. 1952. *Am. J. Botany,* 39:352–359.

Majumdar, S. K., and Bose, S. K. 1960. *Arch. Biochem. Biophys.,* 90:154–158.

Majumdar, S. K., and Kutzner, H. J. 1962. *Applied Microbiol.,* 10:157–168; *Science,* 135:734.

Mandelstam, J., and Rogers, H. J. 1959. *Biochem. J.,* 72:654–662.

Masamine, S.; Sehgal, J. M.; van Tamalen, E. E.; Strong, F. M.; and Peterson, W. H. 1958. *J. Am. Chem. Soc.,* 80:6092–6095.

Mizutani, H.; Abe, M.; and Mizuno, D. 1959. *Jap. J. Med. Sci. and Biol.,* 12:453–461.

Morris, A.; Favelukes, S.; Arlinghaus, R.; and Schweet, R. 1962. *Biochem. Biophys. Res. Comms.,* pp. 326–330.

Morse, M. L. 1959. *Proc. Nat. Acad. Sci.,* 45:722–727.

Nakata, Y.; Nakata, K.; and Sakamoto, Y. 1961. *Biochem. Biophys. Res. Comms.,* 6:339–343.

Nathans, D., and Lipmann, F. 1961. *Proc. Nat. Acad. Sci.,* 47:497–504.

Newton, B. A. 1953–1954. *J. Gen. Microbiol.,* 9:54–64; 10:491–499.

*Newton, B. A. 1958. Surface-active Bactericides. In, VIII Symp. Soc. Gen. Microbiol., pp. 62–93. Cambridge University Press.

Novelli, G. D.; Kameyama, T.; and Eisenstadt, J. M. 1961. *J. Cell. Comp. Physiol.,* 58:Suppl. 225–244.

Novick, R. P. 1962. *Biochem. J.,* 83:229–235, 236–240.

Oginsky, E. L. 1953. In, Symp. on Mode of Action of Antibiotics. *Bact. Revs.,* 17:37–41.

Ørskov, F. and I. 1960. *Nature,* 188:75–76.

Park, J. T. 1952, 1957. *J. Biol. Chem.,* 194:877–884, 885–895, 897–904; Park, J. T., and Strominger, J. L. *Science,* 125:99–101 (1957).

Pattee, P. A., and Baldwin, J. N. 1961. *J. Bact.,* 82:875–881.

Pollock, M. R. 1956. *J. Gen. Microbiol.,* 15:154–169.

Pollock, M. R. 1961. *J. Gen. Microbiol.,* 26:239–253, 267–276; Kushner, D. J., and Pollock, M. R. *Ibid.,* 26:255–265.

Porath, J. 1953–1954. *Nature,* 172:871; *Acta Chem. Scand.,* 8:1813–1826 (1954).

Raistrick, I., and Stössl, A. 1958. *Biochem. J.,* 68:647–653.

*Raper, K. B. 1952. A Decade of Antibiotics in America. Presidential address, Mycol. Soc. of Amer., *Mycologia,* 44:1–59.

Ritz, H. L., and Baldwin, J. N. 1958. *Bact. Proc.,* 58th. Mtg., p. 40.

Schaffner, C. P. 1961. *Ann. Report Inst. Microbiol. Rutgers Univ.,* pp. 27–30.

Schatz, A.; Bugie, E.; and Waksman, S. A. 1944. *Proc. Soc. Exp. Biol. and Med.,* 55:66–69.

Sekiguchi, M., and Tagaki, Y. 1960. *Biochem. Biophys. Acta,* 41:434–443.

Sheinin, R. 1959. *J. Gen. Microbiol.,* 21:124–134.

Silverman, M., and Rieder, S. V. 1960. *J. Biol. Chem.,* 235:1251–1254.

Smith, R. M.; Joslin, D. A.; Gruhzit, O. M.; McLean, W. Jr.; Penner, M. A.; and Ehrlich, J. 1948. *J. Bact.,* 55:425–448.

Sobin, B. A.; Finlay, A. C.; and Kane, J. H. 1950 (July 18). Terramycin and Its Production. U. S. Patent No. 2,516,080.

Spotts, C. R., and Stanier, R. Y. 1961. *Nature*, **192**:633–637.

Starr, M. P., and Reynolds, D. M. 1951. *Am. J. Pub. Health*, **41**:1375–1380.

Stephens, C. R.; Conover, L. H.; Hochstein, F. A.; Regna, P. P.; Pilgrim, F. J.; Brunings, K. J.; and Woodward, R. B. 1952. *J. Am. Chem. Soc.*, **75**:4976–4977.

Stevens, C. L.; Gillis, B. T.; French, J. C.; and Haskell, T. H. 1958. *J. Am. Chem. Soc.*, **80**:6088–6092.

Strominger, J. L. 1962. *Fed. Proc.*, **21**:134–143.

Sutton, D. D.; Arnow, P. M.; and Lampen, J. O. 1961. *Proc. Soc. Exp. Biol. and Med.*, **106**:170–175.

Swart, E. A.; Hutchison, D.; and Waksman, S. A. 1949. *Arch. Biochem.*, **24**:92–103.

Szybalski, W., and Bryson, V. 1952. *J. Bact.*, **64**:489–499.

Tabenkin, B.; Lehr, H.; Wayman, A. C.; and Goldberg, M. W. 1952. *Arch. Biochem. Biophys.*, **38**:43–48.

Trown, P. W.; Smith, B.; and Abraham, E. P. 1963. *Biochem. J.*, **86**:284–291.

Umbreit, W. W. 1949. *J. Biol. Chem.*, **177**:703–714.

Umbreit, W. W. 1953. *J. Bact.*, **66**:74–81; *J. Cell. Comp. Physiol.*, **41**:Suppl. 39–66.

Umezawa, H., and many participants. 1958. *Ann. N. Y. Acad. Sci.*, **76**:17–408.

Upjohn, C. O. 1958. Brit. Patent 788972 (Feb. 9, 1958); *Chem. Abstr.*, **52**:9526.

*Verwey, W. F. 1959. Newer Antibiotics. In, *Ann. Rev. Microbiol.*, **13**:177–190.

Vining, L. C., and Taber, W. A. 1956. *Canad. J. Chem.*, **34**:1163–1167.

Vinter, V. 1962. *Nature*, **196**:1336–1337.

*Waksman, S. A. 1943. Antagonistic Relations of Microorganisms. *Bact. Revs.*, **5**:231–291.

*Waksman, S. A. 1950. The Actinomycetes. Waltham, Mass., Chronica Botanica Co.

Waksman, S. A. 1952. The Actinomycetes and Their Antibiotics. Nieuwland Lectures, Vol. 6. Indiana, Univ. of Notre Dame.

Waksman, S. A. 1961. The Role of Antibiotics in Nature. In, *Perspectives in Biol. and Med.*, **4**:271–287.

Waksman, S. A., and Lechevalier, H. 1962. The Actinomycetes, Vol. 3. Baltimore, Williams and Wilkins Co.

Waller, C. W.; Wolf, C. E.; Stein, W. J.; and Hutchings, B. L. 1957. *J. Am. Chem. Soc.*, **79**:1265–1268.

Weindling, R., and Emerson, O. H. 1936. *Phytopathol.*, **26**:1068–1070.

Wisseman, C. L.; Smadel, J. E.; Hahn, F. E.; and Hopps, H. E. 1954. *J. Bact.*, **67**: 662–673.

*Woodruff, H. B., and Waksman, S. A. 1960. *Ann. New York Acad. Sci.*, **89**:287–298.

Woodward, R. B. 1957. *Angew. Chem.*, **69**:50–58.

Yanagita, T.; Sasa, T.; Morimura, Y.; Uemura, T.; and Fukuda, S. 1951. *J. Antibiotics* (Japan), **1-C**. *Studies Tokugawa Inst.*, **6**: No. 3, 5 pp.

Yarmolinsky, M. B., and de la Haba, G. L. 1959. *Proc. Nat. Acad. Sci.*, **45**:1721–1729.

Zygmunt, W. A. 1961. *Biochem. Biophys. Res. Comms.*, **6**:324–326.

CHAPTER XXVI

The Evolution of Bacteria

Out of the litter of muds and gravels that make the soil of the world we have picked some traces of the past of our race and the past of life. In our observatories and laboratories we have gleaned some hints of its future. We have a vision of the opening of the story, but the first pages we cannot read.

H. G. WELLS: *The Undying Fire*

One of the most fascinating aspects of the study of any group of organisms is its evolutionary history. In the vertebrates and in the higher plants, evolution has been largely deduced from the fossil forms, and by comparison of the details of anatomical structure. The first of these methods is unavailable for bacteria. It is true that bog iron ore shows spiral structures ascribed to the action of ancient Gallionellae or related iron-depositing bacteria, but this is too isolated a case to be very useful, and, besides, the iron oxide is an excretion and not exactly a part of a fossil bacterium. As to anatomy, there is beginning to be assembled a good deal of knowledge about the bacterial cell and its structure (see Chap. III), but much of this is at the chemical level and in any event its value for comparative study is still quite limited. The few anatomical points which help to place the bacteria in regard to other organisms are:

(1) The small size of the cell
(2) The mode of division, i.e., by transverse fission
(3) The simple structure of the nucleus, with no visible membrane
(4) The noncellulosic cell wall, with acetyl-glucosamine prominent
(5) The flagella

Features (1), (2), and (3) emphasize relationship with the blue-green algae and (4) with the fungi. So many unicellular organisms have flagella that the interpretation of (5) is doubtful. The flagellum of an alga like Euglena is so thick and complex, consisting of many strands associated in a kind of rope, that its similarity to those of the bacteria is uncertain (Houwink, 1951). The absence of flagella in either the Myxobacteria or the blue-green algae suggests that the gulf separating these from the Eubacteria may be greater than appears. The same conclusion can be drawn from the absence of the rigid cell wall in the Myxobacteria and Spirochetes.

1. THE EVOLUTION OF LIFE IN GENERAL

Our interpretation of the evolution of bacteria must depend largely on how we visualize the evolution of organisms in general. Huxley regarded the chemo-autotrophic bacteria as primitive because they produced their kind from inorganic substrates only. Yet they require a complex outfit of enzymes to do this, and most of them, being aerobes, require oxygen-consuming enzymes as well.

The more recent view of evolution, adumbrated by Benjamin Moore in 1912 and worked out in detail by Oparin (1957), is that organic matter was first formed by purely chemical reactions, promoted by the high-intensity radiation which was then reaching the earth. The needed concentration of materials at local spots may have taken place, as Bernal (1951) has suggested, by adsorption at the surface of colloidal particles. The simple organic materials thus produced would have been relatively stable because of the absence of micro-organisms to attack them, and so would have gradually given rise to molecules of greater complexity. Thus, it was only over long periods of time that the first proteins, and thence the first enzymes, were gradually synthesized. It follows that the first organism would have been a heterotroph, metabolizing—perhaps very slowly—the organic compounds that surrounded it.[1] Furthermore, there is some reason to believe that, as the earth cooled down, the large bulk of the oxygen became combined as metallic oxides, carbonates, and sulfates, so that the atmosphere contained little or no oxygen. Our present 20 per cent of oxygen, on this view, arose largely as a product of photosynthesis, although loss of H_2 to the highest atmosphere layers (Miller and Urey, 1959) also played a part. Thus, the first organisms were probably anaerobes.[2]

[1] It would probably not have been recognizable to us as an organism. Since many biochemical reactions are catalyzed, although not very actively, by metallic ions, it is probable that its metabolism may have gone on without the aid of enzymes.

[2] The idea that atmospheric oxygen arose from photosynthesis has as corollary that, for every O_2 molecule formed, a carbon atom must have been converted to organic matter: $CO_2 + H_2O \rightarrow (CH_2O) + O_2$. This can be roughly tested by comparing the

The reality of these ideas has been greatly strengthened by experiments in which an electric discharge is passed through a mixture of CO_2, NH_3, and H_2, and the gases circulated through water; several organic acids and amino acids, especially glycine and α- and β-alanine, and some guanidine derivatives were produced (Miller, 1953–1957; Miller and Urey, 1959; Heyns *et al.*, 1959). Using x-rays, the number of products is enriched by the occurrence of direct carboxylation, because CO_2 combines with ethanol to form lactic acid, with methanol to form glycollic acid, and with acetic acid to form malonic acid (Scholes *et al.*, 1960). These reactions, which involve free radicals, are prevented by O_2 and therefore could only have occurred in the primeval anaerobiosis. CO_2 solutions alone can produce formaldehyde and formic acid when subjected to high intensity UV or γ-rays (Getoff, 1962). The simultaneous presence of glycine and organic acids is important because it could have readily given rise to *porphyrins*, by the pathway given on page 743, since the initial condensation to porphyrinogen occurs spontaneously and *anaerobically*. Hence the porphyrin nucleus of the photosynthetic pigments may well have arisen very early in chemical evolution. How optical activity entered into all the products remains a mystery.

Purines also appear early on the evolutionary ladder, since electron bombardment of CH_4, NH_3, H_2, and H_2O gave rise to HCN and to adenine (Palm and Calvin, 1962); indeed cyanide is an important intermediate because NH_4CN solutions on simple standing produce adenine (Oró and Kimball, 1961).

If we accept this broad picture, some interesting consequences ensue. With limited amounts of organic matter, selection would enormously favor organisms capable of synthesizing complex substances from simple ones, and especially would favor any kind of photosynthesis, however primitive. Photosynthesis probably came when the supply of organic matter was at its lowest ebb, and it will have first replenished, then enormously increased the supply. The photo-

earth's organic carbon with its atmospheric oxygen. Most of the organic carbon is in sedimentary rocks, and the best estimate of it is about 6×10^{20} gm atoms (see Rubey, 1951). The oxygen now free in the atmosphere totals between 2.5 and 4×10^{19} gm mol. In addition, however, oxygen fixed as sulfate in the ocean and in rocks is estimated at another 15×10^{19} gm mol., and another 4×10^{19} gm mol. has been used in oxidizing ferrous to ferric (Rubey, 1951). Bearing in mind also that some of the earth's carbonate may have been oxidized from more reduced forms like CO and CH_4, thus fixing some of the oxygen which had been freed, it appears that the oxygen which has been set free may total close to 3×10^{20} gm mol. The uncertainties are such that this figure must be considered in good agreement with that for the organic carbon. This helps to make acceptable the view that the early conditions on the earth were more or less anaerobic.

synthetic bacteria are anaerobic; the green algae and higher forms are aerobic. However, some algae, although normally aerobic, can carry out photosynthesis anaerobically ("photoreduction") using hydrogen. This suggests that the development of the chlorophylls resulted in a sequence of organisms first using photosynthesis primarily to increase their supply of synthetic energy, then to convert CO_2 to organic matter, and only later to dispense with oxygen acceptors and thus to produce free oxygen. The characteristic of aerobes is to possess the cytochrome system, which consists of hemin derivatives chemically related to chlorophyll. Since cytochromes play a part in all photosynthesis, including that of the anaerobes (Chap. XXIII), and are present too in the anaerobe Desulfovibrio, they have probably undergone a *parallel evolution* in their electron acceptors, first functioning with chlorophylls and sulfate and only much later with oxygen itself. Thus, the colorless aerobes, able to produce energy by consuming oxygen, could have appeared on earth only after photosynthesis had produced quantities of *both* organic matter *and* oxygen for them to live on (cf. DeLey in Symposium, 1962).

Another point in this connection has been made in Chapter V. The path of oxidation of hexose sugars may sometimes lead directly from hexose via phosphogluconic acid, but in very many organisms it leads from pyruvic acid; in other words, it leads from a product of fermentation. This supports the concept that aerobiosis is a later development, superimposed on fermentation.

2. THE EVOLUTION AND CLASSIFICATION OF THE BACTERIA

With this as a working outline, the evolution of the bacteria can be considered. The first true organism contained, within some kind of membrane, (1) enzymes to ferment organic compounds, (2) apparatus (presumably the high-energy phosphate system) to transfer some of the energy to synthetic reactions and to the uptake of more organic matter, and (3) systems to channel the syntheses not only to organic matter in general but specifically to the formation of more enzymes. This last constitutes a problem, since present-day organisms need nucleic acids to synthesize protein; yet proteins (enzymes) are required to form nucleic acids. Perhaps, in the beginning, enzymes were synthesized directly from amino acids by proteinases, as in Chapter XX, section 1. The nucleic acids could then have come only later, and still later that "division of labor" (Lanham, 1952) whereby the DNA achieved the trick of self-duplication, while the RNA's became effective as the machine for protein synthesis (see Hoagland, 1960). The development of even the simplest true organism (as defined today) would have been very slow.

The first would have been a colorless anaerobe, doubtless of the simplest morphology, and from it would have arisen the following improvements:

(1) Motility, enabling a wider survey of food supplies

(2) Spore formation, enabling survival through drought

(3) Gradual increase of synthetic powers, enabling the use of simpler substrates

(4) Varied morphology, apparently in itself of little evolutionary value, but leading to larger size, and hence to multicellular types

(5) Photosynthesis, a major step forward, increasing the amount of organic matter on the earth, and eventually giving rise, as a second photosynthetic line (Stanier and van Niel, 1941) to cells producing oxygen in photosynthesis, i.e., the blue-green and higher algae

(6) Aerobiosis, including chemosynthetic autotrophy as well as heterotrophy of various kinds

Except that (5) should precede (6), these developments need not have occurred in the order shown.

The proposed increase in synthetic powers (3) would of course occur by single steps (Horowitz, 1945). Exhaustion of a particular organic compound in the primordial substrate would selectively favor appearance of a mutant able to synthesize it from a simpler precursor. This process endlessly repeated would lead step by step to the development of the present chains of single-enzyme reactions, as exemplified by the arginine or histidine series (pp. 325, 664) controlled by closely linked genes. The final step in this increase in synthetic powers is the synthesis of organic matter from inorganic, but this requires the introduction of a major energy source, supplied either by oxidation or by light (as in [5] and [6]).

On the other hand, the development of *control* systems like feedback inhibition and enzyme repression must have come later, through the evolutionary pressure caused by competition. Cells with such control over the formation of their chemical contents and their enzymes obviously have an evolutionary advantage because they can develop faster or more economically on a given substrate than cells without such control. Besides, they maintain a balance between those constituents like the amino acids (or purines) that are needed in fixed relative amounts to synthesize specific polymers.

The requirement of "simplest morphology" would make the primitive form a coccus. This agrees with the fact that very few cocci have either spores or flagella. The anaerobic cocci, like Veillonella and Ruminococcus with their propionic-type fermentations, or Methanococcus with its great ability to reduce CO_2, would then be close to the primitive type, although very likely not themselves of primitive origin. Lactic streptococci probably do not belong here but with the lactic rods.

It is probable that the rigid cell wall of the Eubacteria is not a primitive character. If the primitive organism had no rigid cell wall, it might well have given rise to two lines, one becoming the Eubacteria and the other the Myxobacteria. However, the Myxobacteria are all rods in the vegetative form.

The most "advanced" cocci, equipped with flagella and spores (Sporosarcina), are aerobic and may therefore have developed later than the photosynthetic lines.

The bacteria have been pictured as developing along five main lines (Kluyver and van Niel, 1936; Stanier and van Niel, 1941; see Fig. XXVI–1). These comprise (1) cocci; (2) the photosynthetic bacteria, which parallel lines (1) and (3); (3) polarly flagellated forms; (4) the largely nonmotile gram-positive rods; (5) peritrichously flagellated rods, developing spores later. This scheme, like all such schemes, is highly tentative. There are several difficulties. In the first line spores appear independently from those in the fifth line, in which spores and gram-positivity appear at the same time. In the second line photosynthesis appears independently from that in the blue-green algae. Here, too, it is perhaps unfortunate that the anaerobic photo-autotrophs, probably appearing early in evolution, should be placed so closely parallel to the chemo-autotrophs (morphologically Pseudo-monads), which are highly aerobic and likely to have occurred late in time. The bacterium and bacillus group (fifth line) is highly heterogeneous and also does not bring in the anaerobic forms first. However, it does begin with gram-negative and end with gram-positive forms.[3] The fourth line is morphologically very satisfactory, but there are motile streptococci and Corynebacteria, the latter having *polar* flagella (Ferguson Wood, 1950). Even the Actinomycetaceae can form motile cells (Chap. II, sec. 4), which suggests that flagella arose more than once. However, a favorable feature is that both this and the third line become aerobic as they become advanced; in the Corynebacteria,

---

[3] The gram-staining system, apparently connected with the ability to accumulate solutes (p. 821), would not be a really primitive character but would have its main value only when conditions of severe competition developed. It is clearly an *addition*, since it is so easily lost again. Thus the gram-negative cocci would fall early on line 1 or 5 (cf. p. 839).

C. diphtheriae and *C. acnes* are fermentative and the rest aerobic, so that this group is at the border line of aerobiosis. Although Pseudomonas is aerobic, it forms unsaturated acids by the chemical mechanism used by anaerobes (Bloch *et al.*, 1962), which suggests close anaerobic relatives.

In Figure XXVI–1 the primitive coccus is shown as giving rise to the Myxobacteria, but it is also possible (Stanier and van Niel, 1941)

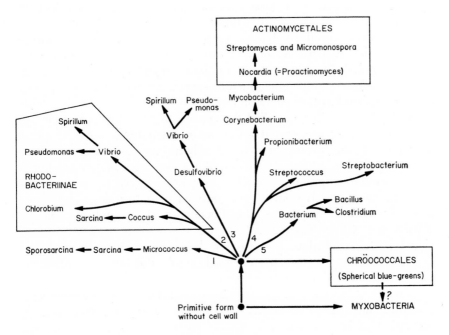

Figure XXVI–1

Modification of a diagram originally suggested by Stanier and van Niel (1941) to show the evolution of principal groups of bacteria and their near relatives. (By courtesy of the Williams and Wilkins Co., Baltimore, Md.)

that the Myxobacteria arose from the blue-green algae by loss of chlorophyll, just as Beggiatoa and other sulfur bacteria are generally considered to have done. The presence of creeping motility and absence of flagella in both groups suggest a relationship.

Bisset (1955) points out that since peritrichously flagellate cells swim less actively than polar ones and can swarm over moist surfaces (Chap. II, sec. 2), they may constitute the first steps in the "adaptation of a fundamentally aquatic organism to a terrestrial environment." The polar types would be the more primitive, and it is noted that motile stages in the Caulobacteria and the Chlamydobacteria are also polarly flagellate. In Figure XXVI-1, the polar and peritrichous groups are well separated, which suggests that the two kinds of flagella arose independently; also, the blue-greens branched off before flagella appeared. If anaerobic life and polar flagella were both primitive, it is perhaps significant that the *polar anaerobes* are not in evidence now. In other words, perhaps they were *lost in evolution*. The only polarly flagellated anaerobes existing now are in the photosynthetic group.

After adaptation to a terrestrial life, the next logical development would be that of aerial structures—stalked fruiting bodies in the Myxobacteria, aerial hyphae and conidia in the Streptomycetaceae, and air-resistant spores in the Bacillaceae (Bisset, 1955). These adaptations to aerial life obviously arose independently. But independent multiple origin of organelles, such as spores, flagella, or photosynthetic structures, is difficult to avoid on any present scheme (cf. Bisset, 1952).

Other workers have applied the criteria of (1) specific compounds, (2) nutritional requirements, (3) toxin formation, and (4) phage susceptibility to the evolutionary problem (see Cowan *et al.*, 1955, and Symposium, 1962). As to (1), the appearance of hemoglobin in three unrelated groups, namely, vertebrates, yeasts, and legume nodules, does not give one much confidence in the idea. The second proves useful, however, in the Rhodobacteriinae and also in the Bacillaceae, where the general characters correlate well with nutritional patterns (Knight and Proom, 1950). The third has value in the Clostridia and the fourth in several groups. But these are taxonomic characters rather than guides to evolution.

Two new biochemical approaches to evolution and taxonomic relationships have recently become available. The first concerns the formation of lysine, which in all the bacteria studied (as well as in the green algae and higher plants) proceeds via the same intermediate, namely, diaminopimelic acid. The C-1 of alanine and the C-3 and -4 of aspartate are readily incorporated into lysine, but C-1 of acetate not at all (Vogel, 1959). The Ascomycetes, Basidiomycetes, and the green Euglenidae form lysine by another route, in which C-1 of acetate is used. The Phycomycetes are divided between the two (Vogel, 1960–1961). This suggests that the fungi are not derived from the bacteria through the Actinomycetes, but rather form a separate line, arising independently from some of the Chytrids, a group which mycologists have long felt to be near the origin of the fungi.

The second approach, more general, rests on the base composition of the DNA's isolated from bacteria. First determined chemically by Chargaff and his associates (1950), and more recently by indirect, physical methods, the base composition shows striking relationship to the taxonomy. Figures assembled by Belozersky and Spirin (1960) and Sueoka (1961) show the following percentages of guanine and cytosine:

	Per cent
Streptomyces (3 spp.)	74
Micromonospora	72
Pseudomonas (3 spp., 8 strains)	63–67
Azotobacter (3 spp., 6 strains)	55–57.5
Aerob. aerogenes (6 strains)	55–59
Erwinia (7 spp.)	52–54
Salmonella (7 spp., 10 strains)	49–54
E. coli (10 strains)	50–53
Bacillus (3 spp., 11 strains)	34–46
Streptococcus (3 spp., 5 strains)	34–39
Clostridium (4 spp., 5 strains)	27–32

Each genus falls within a narrow range, and the interrelations (e.g., of the Enterobacteriaceae or the Actinomycetes) are obvious. *Aerobac. macerans* with $G + C = 50$ per cent is separated from other bacilli; the Sarcinae with 69 to 74 per cent seem more related to the Actinomycetes than to the Streptococci, and Neisseria with 50 per cent falls with the gram-negative rods, rather than with the gram-positive cocci.

Within closer groups the relations hold good too, for *Bac. subtilis* with 43 per cent $G + C$ will undergo genetic transformation only with bacilli having 42.5 to 44 per cent, not, e.g., with *Bac. laterosporus* having 40 per cent (Marmur *et al.*, 1963). Isolated DNA's can also form hybrid helices together *in vitro* if very closely related, e.g., *Bac. subtilis* and *Bac. natto*, both 43 per cent (Schildkraut *et al.*, 1961); *E. coli* strain B hybridizes partially with Shigella and in one case with *E. freundii*, but not with Salmonella. This method may well help to give bacterial taxonomy a much firmer basis.

A point which may have evolutionary significance concerns the fixation of nitrogen. If combined nitrogen became as scarce as carbon compounds after the initial organisms had depleted the supply, then nitrogen fixation would have been an important character at the time when the synthesis of organic compounds was being developed. The ability to fix nitrogen (Chap. IX) is, suggestively, limited to the bacteria and, alone among the algae, to the lowliest group—the blue-greens. In the bacteria it is present in most of the anaerobes, both the clostridia and the photosynthetic forms, which we have given reasons for believing to be relatively primitive. The possible relationship between Azotobacter and certain members of the blue-green algae also fits in well with this idea. Only the peculiar case of nitrogen fixation by symbionts remains out of place, but until we understand just what are the relative contributions of legume and Rhizobium, this is only to be expected. It was suggested above that Pseudomonas, although aerobic, has close kinship with anaerobes, and the marked ability to fix nitrogen in this group supports that point.

It has often been suggested that viruses represent primitive organisms. But it is clear that the property of carrying out metabolism is more primitive than that of self-reproduction. It is true that self-reproduction is the property most commonly associated with the idea of "organism," and that its development gave an almost infinite selective advantage to the organism that achieved it. But the metabolism (probably fermentative) must have come first. Besides, the viruses are not "self"-reproducing, but require the services of a more advanced form for reproduction. Therefore, it seems more likely that they represent a quite different, and later, line of development.

Some workers believe that phylogenetic lines should be the basis for the working classification of the bacteria. It is evident from the above, however, that such a "natural" classification will come only slowly. In the Bergey system some presumably "natural" relationships are used, along with many artificial ones. The system has been extensively criticized, especially by Rahn (1937), Stanier and van Niel (1941), van Niel (1946), and Ferguson Wood (1950). Its excessive division into so-called genera and species, some separated only by differences that could be due to a single enzyme (cf. p. 501 ff.), led Wood to remark: "It is obvious that this work will have very limited value until . . . all genera and species are pruned to a bare minimum." As far back as 1764 Linnaeus wrote: "A multitude of genera is a burden on the memory, to be lightened by system."

A practical difficulty in use of the manual is that organisms are constantly being reassigned, new genera created, and old ones dropped. While this is perhaps inevitable, as the field develops, it makes for a certain amount of confusion. Wald (1952) complained, in connection with similar practices in the taxonomy of vertebrates:

> The most important thing about a name, after all, is that it remain attached to the thing it designates. One wishes that once a name had come into common use for an organism, it could be stabilized for the use of busy persons who want nothing but that each animal have a name.

A broader criticism is directed at the whole policy of developing a taxonomy like that of higher plants. Van Niel (1946) argued that any attempt to set out groups of real taxonomic significance should be abandoned, and bacteriologists instead should "set themselves the task of developing a large number of keys, each one aimed at the segregation of particular groups on the basis of some salient character." Such groups could be quite artificial, such as "red-colored bacteria," or "bacteria capable of decomposing cellulose," and would be purely for purposes of determination. This series of keys would enable all bacteria to be determined and would bring out interrelationships of many new sorts. Sneath (1957) has proposed instead to compare pairs of organisms by supplying all possible recorded characters to a computer, which calculates a "similarity-value," S. The nearer S approaches 100, the more closely the two organisms are considered to be related. The characters used have to be qualitative, i.e., $+$ or $-$. Two organisms that have a recent common ancestor will necessarily have a high S-value, which gives the system some value for phylogeny (Floodgate, 1962) and may help in the problem of distinguishing important from unimportant characters. Such fresh approaches may prove useful, but they do not afford much insight into the relationships.

The difficult problems of bacterial classification are too complex to be discussed here, and it seems likely that a phylogenetic system will be a long time coming (see Cowan et al., 1955, and Symposium, 1962).

The many physiological and ecological types described in this book, and the striking differences between the bacteria and the other orders, make one wonder whether bacteriology has as yet done any more than scratch the surface of the subject. That properties so totally different as chemosynthetic autotrophy, methane formation, and transduction should all be strictly limited to the bacteria is remarkable. Perhaps for many physiologists this represents the fascination of the bacteria, that although they are so complexly interrelated, yet they comprise modes of life more varied than all the other plant types together. They offer an outstanding example of the evolutionary success that attends upon versatility. Perhaps it is because of this very versatility that, although they have been so intensively studied, they remain so profoundly unknown.

REFERENCES

Belozersky, A. N., and Spirin, A. S. 1960. In, The Nucleic Acids, 3:147–185, New York, Academic Press.

Bernal, J. D. 1951. The Physical Basis of Life. 80 pp. London, Routledge and Kegan Paul, pp. 33–37.

Bisset, K. A. 1952. Bacteria. Edinburgh, Livingstone and Co.

Bisset, K. A. 1955. J. Gen. Microbiol., 12:325–329.

Bloch, K.; Baronowsky, P.; Goldfine, H.; Lennarz, W. J.; Light, R.; Norris, A. T.; and Scheuerbrandt, G. 1962. Federation Proc., 20:921–927.

Chargaff, E. 1950. Experientia, 6:201–209; J. Cell. Comp. Physiol., 38:supp., 41–59.

Cowan, S. T., and 21 others. 1955. The Principles of Microbial Classification. J. Gen. Microbiol., 12:325–386.

Ferguson Wood, E. J. 1950. Proc. Linn. Soc., N.S. Wales, 75 (Pts. 3–4):158–166.

Floodgate, G. D. 1962. Bact. Revs., 26:277–291.

Getoff, N. 1962. *Z. Naturforsch.*, **17b**:87–90, 751–757.

Heyns, K.; Walter, W.; and Meyer, E. 1959. *Naturwiss.*, **46**:667–668.

*Hoagland, M. B. 1960. The Relationships of Nucleic Acid and Protein Synthesis as Revealed by Studies in Cell-free Systems. In, The Nucleic Acids, ed. Chargaff and Davidson, **3**:349–408. New York, Academic Press.

Horowitz, N. H. 1945. *Proc. Nat. Acad. Sci.*, **31**:153–157.

Houwink, A. L. 1951. *Proc. Kon. Akad. Wetensch.*, Amsterdam, Ser. C, **54**:132–137.

Kluyver, A. J., and van Niel, C. B. 1936. Prospects for a Natural System of Classification of Bacteria. *Zentr. Bakt.* II, **94**:369–403.

Knight, B. C. J. G., and Proom, H. 1950. *J. Gen. Microbiol.*, **4**:508–538.

Lanham, U. N. 1952. Oparin's Hypothesis and the Evolution of Nucleoproteins. *Amer. Naturalist*, **86**:213–218.

*Marmur, J.; Seaman, E.; and Levine, J. 1963. *J. Bact.*, **85**:461–467; Marmur, J.; Falkow, S.; and Mandel, M. *Ann. Revs. Microbiol.*, **17**:(in press) (356 refs.).

Miller, S. L. 1953–1957. *Science*, **117**:528–529; *J. Am. Chem. Soc.*, **77**:2351–2361 (1955); *Biochim. Biophys. Acta*, **23**:480–489 (1957).

Miller, S. L., and Urey, H. C. 1959. *Science*, **130**:245–251.

*van Niel, C. B. 1946. The Classification and Natural Relationships of Bacteria. *Cold Spring Harbor Symp. Quant. Biol.*, **11**:285–301.

Oparin, A. I. 1957. The Origin of Life on the Earth, 3rd ed. London, Oliver and Boyd. Cf. also The Origin of Life on the Earth, Proc. 1st Symp. Moscow, 1957, ed. F. Clark and R. Synge. London, Pergamon Press, 1959.

Oró, J., and Kimball, A. P. 1961. *Arch. Biochem. Biophys.*, **94**:217–227.

Palm, C., and Calvin, M. 1962. *J. Am. Chem. Soc.*, **84**:2115–2121.

Rahn, O. 1937. *Zentr. Bakt.* II, **78**:1–21.

*Rubey, W. W. 1951. Geologic History of Sea Water. *Bull. Geol. Soc. Am.*, **62**:1111–1147.

Schildkraut, C.; Marmur, J.; and Doty, P. 1961. *J. Mol. Biol.*, **3**:595–617.

Scholes, G.; Simic, M.; and Weiss, J. J. 1960. *Nature*, **188**:1019–1020.

Sneath, P. H. A. 1957. *J. Gen. Microbiol.*, **17**:184–200, 201–226.

Stanier, R. Y., and van Niel, C. B. 1941. The Main Outlines of Bacterial Classification. *J. Bact.*, **42**:437–466.

Sueoka, N. 1961. *J. Mol. Biol.*, **3**:31–40, cf. also Marmur *et al.* (1963).

Symposium on Microbial Classification, 1962. XII Symp. Soc. Gen. Microbiol., ed. Ainsworth and Sneath. Cambridge, Univ. Press.

Vogel, H. J. 1959. *Biochim. Biophys. Acta*, **34**:282–283; *Proc. Nat. Acad. Sci.*, **45**:1717–1721.

Vogel, H. J. 1960–1961. *Biochim. Biophys. Acta*, **41**:172–173; *Nature*, **189**:1026–1027 (1961).

Wald, G. 1952. Biochemical Evolution. In, Modern Trends in Physiology and Biochemistry. New York, Academic Press, p. 339.

Figures in italics refer to the bibliographies at the ends of the chapters. When the page listed does not actually show the author's name, it is placed in parentheses.